W9-CBP-328

PRINCIPLES OF DIGITAL COMMUNICATION AND CODING

McGraw-Hill Series in Electrical Engineering

Consulting Editor
Stephen W. Director, *Carnegie-Mellon University*

Networks and Systems
Communications and Information Theory
Control Theory
Electronics and Electronic Circuits
Power and Energy
Electromagnetics
Computer Engineering and Switching Theory
Introductory and Survey
Radio, Television, Radar, and Antennas

Previous Consulting Editors

Ronald M. Bracewell, Colin Cherry, James F. Gibbons, Willis W. Harman, Hubert Heffner, Edward W. Herold, John G. Linvill, Simon Ramo, Ronald A. Rohrer, Anthony E. Siegman, Charles Susskind, Frederick E. Terman, John G. Truxal, Ernst Weber, and John R. Whinnery

Communications and Information Theory

Consulting Editor
Stephen W. Director, *Carnegie-Mellon University*

Abramson: *Information Theory and Coding*
Angelakos and Everhart: *Microwave Communications*
Antoniou: *Digital Filters: Analysis and Design*
Bennett: *Introduction to Signal Transmission*
Berlekamp: *Algebraic Coding Theory*
Carlson: *Communications Systems*
Davenport: *Probability and Random Processes: An Introduction for Applied Scientists and Engineers*
Davenport and Root: *Introduction to Random Signals and Noise*
Drake: *Fundamentals of Applied Probability Theory*
Gold and Rader: *Digital Processing of Signals*
Guiasu: *Information Theory with New Applications*
Hancock: *An Introduction to Principles of Communication Theory*
Melsa and Cohn: *Decision and Estimation Theory*
Papoulis: *Probability, Random Variables, and Stochastic Processes*
Papoulis: *Signal Analysis*
Schwartz: *Information Transmission, Modulation, and Noise*
Schwartz, Bennett, and Stein: *Communication Systems and Techniques*
Schwartz and Shaw: *Signal Processing*
Shooman: *Probabilistic Reliability: An Engineering Approach*
Taub and Schilling: *Principles of Communication Systems*
Viterbi: *Principles of Coherent Communication*
Viterbi and Omura: *Principles of Digital Communication and Coding*

PRINCIPLES OF DIGITAL COMMUNICATION AND CODING

Andrew J. Viterbi
LINKABIT Corporation

Jim K. Omura
University of California, Los Angeles

McGraw-Hill Book Company

New York St. Louis San Francisco Auckland Bogotá Düsseldorf
Johannesburg London Madrid Mexico Montreal New Delhi
Panama Paris São Paulo Singapore Sydney Tokyo Toronto

PRINCIPLES OF DIGITAL COMMUNICATION AND CODING

1234567890 FGRFGR 7832109

This book was set in Times Roman.
The editors were Frank J. Cerra and J. W. Maisel;
the cover was designed by Albert M. Cetta;
the production supervisor was Charles Hess.
The drawings were done by Santype Ltd.
Fairfield Graphics was printer and binder.

Library of Congress Cataloging in Publication Data

Viterbi, Andrew J
Principles of digital communication and coding.
(McGraw-Hill electrical engineering series: Communications and information theory section)
Includes bibliographical references and index.
1. Digital communications. 2. Coding theory.
I. Omura, Jim K., joint author. II. Title.
III. Series.
TK5103.7.V57 621.38 78-13951
ISBN 0-07-067516-3

CONTENTS

* May be omitted without loss of continuity.

PREFACE

Digital communication is a much used term with many shades of meaning, widely varying and strongly dependent on the user's role and requirements. This book is directed to the communication theory student and to the designer of the channel, link, terminal, modem, or network used to transmit and receive digital messages. Within this community, digital communication theory has come to signify the body of knowledge and techniques which deal with the two-faceted problem of (1) minimizing the number of bits which must be transmitted over the communication channel so as to provide a given printed, audio, or visual record within a predetermined fidelity requirement (called *source coding*); and (2) ensuring that bits transmitted over the channel are received correctly despite the effects of interference of various types and origins (called *channel coding*). The foundations of the theory which provides the solution to this twofold problem were laid by Claude Shannon in one remarkable series of papers in 1948. In the intervening decades, the evolution and application of this so-called information theory have had ever-expanding influence on the practical implementation of digital communication systems, although their widespread application has required the evolution of electronic-device and system technology to a point which was hardly conceivable in 1948. This progress was accelerated by the development of the large-scale integrated-circuit building block and the economic incentive of communication satellite applications.

We have not attempted in this book to cover peripheral topics related to digital communication theory when they involve a major deviation from the basic concepts and techniques which lead to the solution of this fundamental problem. For this reason, constructive algebraic techniques, though valuable for developing code structures and important theoretical results of broad interest, are specifically avoided in this book. Similarly, the peripheral, though practically important, problems of carrier phase and frequency tracking, and time synchronization are not treated here. These have been covered adequately elsewhere. On the other hand, the equally practical subject of intersymbol interference in digital communication, which is fundamentally similar to the problem of convolutional coding, is covered and new insights are developed through connections with the mainstream topics of the text.

This book was developed over approximately a dozen years of teaching a sequence of graduate courses at the University of California, Los Angeles, and later at the University of California, San Diego, with partial notes being distributed over the past few years. Our goal in the resulting manuscript has been to provide the most direct routes to achieve an understanding of this field for a variety of goals and needs. All readers require some fundamental background in probability and random processes and preferably their application to communication problems; one year's exposure to any of a variety of engineering or mathematics courses provides this background and the resulting maturity required to start.

Given this preliminary knowledge, there are numerous approaches to utilization of this text to achieve various individual goals, as illustrated graphically by the prerequisite structure of Fig. P-1. A semester or quarter course for the beginning graduate student may involve only Part One, consisting of the first three chapters (omitting starred sections) which provide, respectively, the fundamental concepts and parameters of sources and channels, a thorough treatment of channel models based on physical requirements, and an undiluted initiation into the evaluation of code capabilities based on ensemble averages. The advanced student or

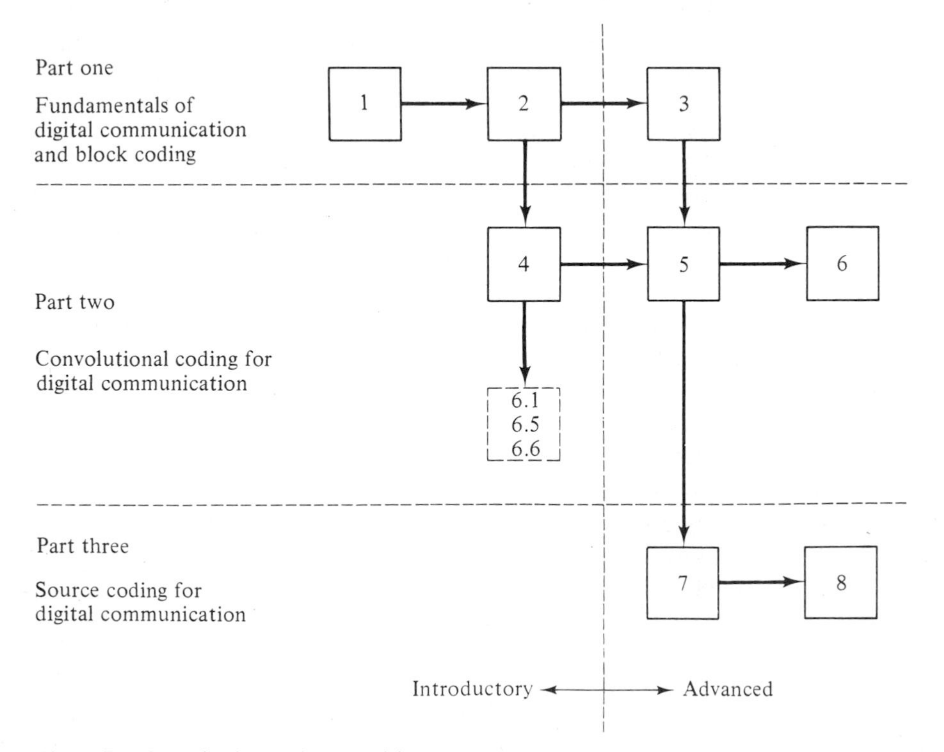

Figure P.1 Organization and prerequisite structure.

specialist can then proceed with Part Two, an equally detailed exposition of convolutional coding and decoding. These techniques are most effective in exploiting the capabilities of the channel toward approaching virtually error-free communications. It is possible in a one-year course to cover Part Three as well, which demonstrates how optimal source coding techniques are derived essentially as the duals of the channel coding techniques of Parts One and Two.

The applications-oriented engineer or student can obtain an understanding of channel coding for physical channels by tackling only Chapters 2, 4, and about half of 6. Avoiding the intricacies of ensemble-average arguments, the reader can learn how to code for noisy channels without making the additional effort to understand the complete theory.

At the opposite extreme, students with some background in digital communications can be guided through the channel-coding material in Chapters 3 through 6 in a one-semester or one-quarter course, and advanced students, who already have channel-coding background, can cover Part Three on source coding in a course of similar duration. Numerous problems are provided to furnish examples, to expand on the material or indicate related results, and occasionally to guide the reader through the steps of lengthy alternate proofs and derivations.

Aside from the obvious dependence of any course in this field on Shannon's work, two important textbooks have had notable effect on the development and organization of this book. These are Wozencraft and Jacobs [1965], which first emphasized the physical characteristics of digital communication channels as a basis for the development of coding theory fundamentals, and Gallager [1968], which is the most complete and expert treatment of this field to date.

Collaboration with numerous university colleagues and students helped establish the framework for this book. But the academic viewpoint has been tempered in the book by the authors' extensive involvement with industrial applications. A particularly strong influence has been the close association of the first author with the design team at LINKABIT Corporation, led by I. M. Jacobs, J. A. Heller, A. R. Cohen, and K. S. Gilhousen, which first implemented high-speed reliable versions of all the convolutional decoding techniques treated in this book. The final manuscript also reflects the thorough and complete reviews and critiques of the entire text by J. L. Massey, many of whose suggested improvements have been incorporated to the considerable benefit of the prospective reader.

Finally, those discouraged by the seemingly lengthy and arduous route to a thorough understanding of communication theory might well recall the ancient words attributed to Lao Tzu of twenty-five centuries ago: "The longest journey starts with but a single step."

Andrew J. Viterbi
Jim K. Omura

PART ONE

FUNDAMENTALS OF DIGITAL COMMUNICATION AND BLOCK CODING

CHAPTER
ONE

DIGITAL COMMUNICATION SYSTEMS: FUNDAMENTAL CONCEPTS AND PARAMETERS

In the field of communication system engineering, the second half of the twentieth century is destined to be recognized as the era of the evolution of digital communication, as indeed the first half was the era of the evolution of radio communication to the point of reliable transmission of messages, speech, and television, mostly in analog form.

The development of digital communication was given impetus by three prime driving needs:

1. Greatly increased demands for data transmission of every form, from computer data banks to remote-entry data terminals for a variety of applications, with ever-increasing accuracy requirements
2. Rapid evolution of synchronous artificial satellite relays which facilitate worldwide communications at very high data rates, but whose launch costs, and consequent power and bandwidth limitations, impose a significant economic incentive on the efficient use of the channel resources
3. Data communication networks which must simultaneously service many different users with a variety of rates and requirements, in which simple and efficient multiplexing of data and multiple access of channels is a primary economic concern

These requirements and the solid-state electronic technology needed to support the development of efficient, flexible, and error-free digital communication

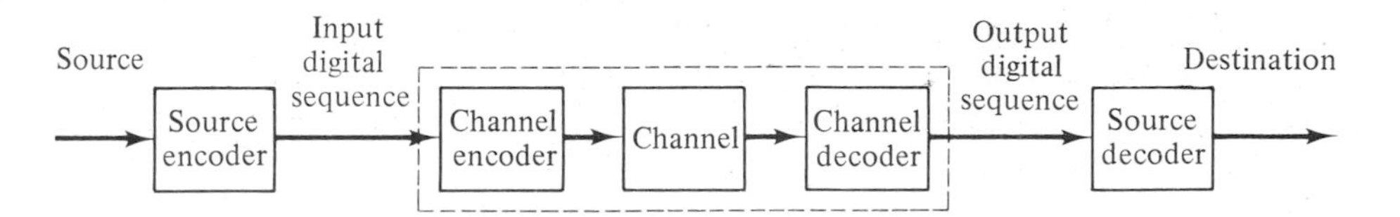

Figure 1.1 Basic model of a digital communication system.

systems evolved simultaneously and in parallel throughout the third quarter of this century, but the theoretical foundations were laid just before mid-century by the celebrated "Mathematical Theory of Communication" papers of C. E. Shannon [1948]. With unique intuition, Shannon perceived that the goals of approaching error-free digital communication on noisy channels and of maximally efficient conversion of analog signals to digital form were dual facets of the same problem, that they share a common framework and virtually a common solution. For the most part, this solution is presented in the original Shannon papers. The refinement, embellishment, and reduction to practical form of the theory occupied many researchers for the next two decades in efforts which paralleled in time the technology development required to implement the techniques and algorithms which the theory dictated.

The dual problem formulated and solved by Shannon is best described in terms of the block diagram of Fig. 1.1. The source is modeled as a random generator of data or a stochastic signal to be transmitted. The source encoder performs a mapping from the source output into a digital sequence (usually binary). If the source itself generates a digital output, the encoder mapping can be one-to-one. Ignore for the moment the channel with its encoder and decoder (within the dashed contour in Fig. 1.1) and replace it by a direct connection called a *noiseless channel.* Then if the source encoder mapping is one-to-one, the source decoder can simply perform the inverse mapping and thus deliver to the destination the same data as was generated by the source. The purpose of the source encoder–decoder pair is then to reduce the source output to a minimal representation. The measure of the "data compression" achieved is the rate in symbols (usually binary) required per unit time to fully represent and, ultimately at the source decoder, to reconstitute the source output sequence. This minimum rate at which the stochastic digital source sequence can be transmitted over a noiseless channel and reconstructed perfectly is related to a basic parameter of stochastic sources called *entropy.*

When the source is analog, it cannot be represented perfectly by a digital sequence because the source output sequence takes on values from an uncountably infinite set, and thus obviously cannot be mapped one-to-one into a discrete set, i.e., a digital alphabet.[1] The best that can be done in mapping the source into a digital sequence is to tolerate some distortion at the destination after

[1] The simplest example of an analog source encoder is an analog-to-digital converter, also called a quantizer, for which the source decoder is a digital-to-analog converter.

the source decoder operation which now only approximates the inverse mapping. In this case, the distortion (appropriately defined) is set at a fixed maximum, and the goal is to minimize the rate—again defined in digital symbols per unit time—subject to the distortion limit. The solution to this problem requires the generalization of the entropy parameter of the source to a quantity called the *rate distortion function*. This function of distortion represents the minimum rate at which the source output can be transmitted over a noiseless channel and still be reconstructed within the given distortion.

The dual to this first problem is the accurate transmission of the digital (source encoder output) sequence over a noisy channel. Considering now only the blocks within the dashed contour in Fig. 1.1, the noisy channel is to be regarded as a random mapping of its input defined over a given discrete set (digital alphabet) into an output defined over an arbitrary set which is not necessarily the same as the input set. In fact, for most physical channels the output space is often continuous (uncountable) although discrete channel models are also commonly considered.

The goal of the channel encoder and decoder is to map the input digital sequence into a channel input sequence and conversely the channel output sequence into an output digital sequence such that the effect of the channel noise is minimized—that is, such that the number of discrepancies (errors) between the output and input digital sequences is minimized. The approach is to introduce redundancy in the channel encoder and to use this redundancy at the decoder to reconstitute the input sequence as accurately as possible. Thus in a simplistic sense the channel coding is dual to the source coding in that the latter eliminates or reduces redundancy while the former introduces it for the purpose of minimizing errors. As will be shown to the reader who completes this book, this duality can be established in a much more quantitative and precise sense. Without further evolution of the concepts at this point, we can state the single most remarkable conclusion of the Shannon channel coding theory: namely, that with sufficient but finite redundancy properly introduced at the channel encoder, it is possible for the channel decoder to reconstitute the input sequence to any degree of accuracy desired. The measure of redundancy introduced is established by the rate of digital symbols per unit time input to the channel encoder and output from the channel decoder. This rate, which is the same as the rate at the source encoder output and source decoder input, must be less than the rate of transmission over the noisy channel because of the redundancy introduced. Shannon's main result here is that provided the input rate to the channel encoder is less than a given value established by the *channel capacity* (a basic parameter of the channel which is a function of the random mapping distribution which defines the channel), there exist encoding and decoding operations which asymptotically for arbitrarily long sequences can lead to *error-free* reconstruction of the input sequence.

As an immediate consequence of the source coding and channel coding theories, it follows that if the minimum rate at which a digital source sequence can be uniquely represented by the source encoder is less than the maximum rate for which the channel output can be reconstructed error-free by the channel decoder then the system of Fig. 1.1 can transfer digital data with arbitrarily high accuracy from source to destination. For analog sources the same holds, but only within a predetermined (tolerable) distortion which determines the source encoder's minimum rate, provided this rate is less than the channel maximum rate mentioned above.

This text aims to present quantitatively these fundamental concepts of digital communication system theory and to demonstrate their applicability to existing channels and sources.

In this first chapter, two of the basic parameters, source entropy and channel capacity, are defined and a start is made toward establishing their significance. Entropy is shown to be the key parameter in the noiseless source coding theorem, proved in Sec. 1.1. The similar role of the capacity parameter for channels is partially established by the proof in Sec. 1.3 of the converse to the channel coding theorem, which establishes that for no rate greater than the maximum determined by capacity can error-free reconstruction be effected by any channel encoder–decoder pair. The full significance of capacity is established only in the next two chapters. Chap. 2 defines and derives the models of the channels of greatest interest to the communication system designer and introduces the rudimentary concepts of channel encoding and decoding. In Chap. 3 the proof of the channel coding theorem is completed in terms of a particular class of channel codes called block codes, and thus the full significance of capacity is established.

However, while the theoretical capabilities and limitations of channel coding are well established by the end of Chap. 3, their practical applicability and manner of implementation is not yet clear. This situation is for the most part remedied by Chap. 4 which describes a more practical and powerful class of codes, called convolutional codes, for which the channel encoding operation is performed by a digital linear filter, and for which the channel decoding operation arises in a natural manner from the simple properties of the code. Chap. 5 establishes further properties and limitations of these codes and compares them with those of block codes established in Chap. 3. Then Chap. 6 explores an alternative decoding procedure, called sequential decoding, which permits under some circumstances and with some limitations the use of extremely powerful convolutional codes.

Finally Chap. 7 returns to the source coding problem, considering analog sources for the first time and developing the fundamentals of rate distortion theory for memoryless sources. Both block and convolutional source coding techniques are treated and thereby the somewhat remarkable duality between channel and source coding problems and solutions is established. Chap. 8 extends the concepts of Chap. 7 to sources with memory and presents more advanced topics in rate distortion theory.

Shannon's mathematical theory of communication almost from the outset became known as *information theory*. While indeed one aspect of the theory is to define information and establish its significance in practical engineering terms, the main contribution of the theory has been in establishing the ultimate capabilities and limitations of digital communication systems. Nevertheless, a natural starting point is the quantitative definition of information as required by the communication engineer. This will lead us in Sec. 1.1 to the definition of entropy and the development of its key role as the basic parameter of digital source coding.

1.1 SOURCES, ENTROPY, AND THE NOISELESS CODING THEOREM

"The weather today in Los Angeles is sunny with moderate amounts of smog" is a news event that, though not surprising, contains some information, since our previous uncertainty about the weather in Los Angeles is now resolved. On the other hand, the news event, "Today there was a devastating earthquake in California which leveled much of downtown Los Angeles," is more unexpected and certainly contains more information than the first report. But what is information? What is meant by the "information" contained in the above two events? Certainly if we are formally to define a quantitative measure of information contained in such events, this measure should have some intuitive properties such as:

1. Information contained in events ought to be defined in terms of some measure of the uncertainty of the events.
2. Less certain events ought to contain more information than more certain events.

In addition, assuming that weather conditions and earthquakes are unrelated events, if we were informed of both news events we would expect that the total amount of information in the two news events be the sum of the information contained in each. Hence we have a third desired property:

3. The information of unrelated events taken as a single event should equal the sum of the information of the unrelated events.

A natural measure of the uncertainty of an event α is the probability of α denoted $P(\alpha)$. The formal term for "unrelatedness" is independence; two events α and β are said to be independent if

$$P(\alpha \cap \beta) = P(\alpha)P(\beta) \tag{1.1.1}$$

Once we agree to define the information of an event α in terms of the probability of α, the properties (2) and (3) will be satisfied if the information in event α is defined as

$$I(\alpha) \equiv -\log P(\alpha) \tag{1.1.2}$$

from which it follows that, if α and β are independent, $I(\alpha \cap \beta) = -\log P(\alpha)P(\beta) = -\log P(\alpha) - \log P(\beta) = I(\alpha) + I(\beta)$. The base of the logarithm merely specifies the scaling and hence the unit of information we wish to use. This definition of information appears naturally from the intuitive properties proposed above, but what good is such a definition of information? Although we would not expect such a simple definition to be particularly useful in quantifying most of the complex exchanges of information, we shall demonstrate that this definition is not only appropriate but also a central concept in digital communication.

Our main concern is the transmission and processing of information in which the information source and the communication channel are represented by probabilistic models. Sources of information, for example, are defined in terms of probabilistic models which emit events or random variables. We begin by defining the simplest type of information source.

Definition A *discrete memoryless source* (*DMS*) is characterized by its output, the random variable u, which takes on letters from a finite alphabet $\mathscr{U} = \{a_1, a_2, \ldots, a_A\}$ with probabilities

$$P(a_k) \qquad k = 1, 2, \ldots, A \tag{1.1.3}$$

Each unit of time, say every T_s seconds, the source emits a random variable which is independent of all preceding and succeeding source outputs.

According to our definition of information, if at any time the output of our DMS is $u = a_k$ which situation we shall label as event α_k, then that output contains

$$I(\alpha_k) = -\log P(a_k) \tag{1.1.4}$$

units of information. If we use natural logarithms, then our units are called "*nats*"; and if we use logarithms to the base 2, our units are called "*bits*." Clearly, the two units differ merely by the scale factor ln 2. We shall use "log" to mean logarithm to the base 2 and "ln" to denote natural logarithm. The average amount of information per source output is simply[2]

$$\begin{aligned} H(\mathscr{U}) &= \sum_{k=1}^{A} P(a_k) I(\alpha_k) \\ &= \sum_{u} P(u) \log \frac{1}{P(u)} \end{aligned} \tag{1.1.5}$$

$H(\mathscr{U})$ is called the *entropy* of the DMS. Here we take $(0) \log (0) = \lim_{\epsilon \to 0} \epsilon \log \epsilon = 0$.

To establish the operational significance of entropy we require the fundamental inequality

$$\ln x \leq x - 1 \tag{1.1.6}$$

[2] Throughout this book we shall write a variable below the summation sign to mean summation over the entire range of the variable (i.e., all possible values which the variable can assume). When the summation is over only a subset of all the possible values, then the subset will also be shown under the summation.

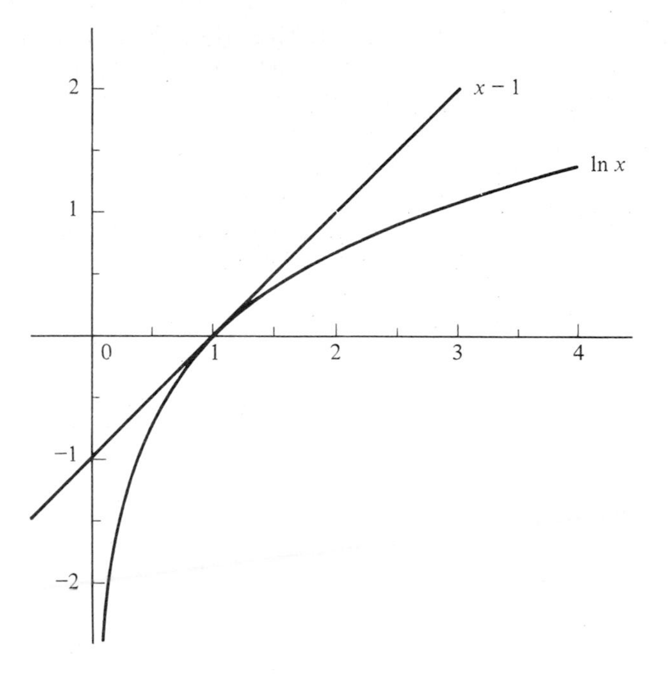

Figure 1.2 Sketch of the functions ln x and $x - 1$.

which can be verified by noting that the function $f(x) = \ln x - (x - 1)$ has a unique maximum value of 0 at $x = 1$. In Fig. 1.2 we sketch ln x and $x - 1$. For any two probability distributions $P(\cdot)$ and $Q(\cdot)$ on the alphabet $\mathscr{U}$, it follows from this inequality that

$$\begin{aligned}\sum_u P(u) \log \frac{Q(u)}{P(u)} &= (\ln 2)^{-1} \sum_u P(u) \ln \frac{Q(u)}{P(u)} \\ &\leq (\ln 2)^{-1} \sum_u P(u) \left[\frac{Q(u)}{P(u)} - 1\right] \\ &= 0 \end{aligned} \tag{1.1.7}$$

which establishes the inequality

$$\sum_u P(u) \log \frac{1}{P(u)} \leq \sum_u P(u) \log \frac{1}{Q(u)} \tag{1.1.8}$$

with equality if and only if $Q(u) = P(u)$ for all $u \in \mathscr{U}$.

Inequalities (1.1.6) and (1.1.8) are among the most commonly used inequalities in information theory. Choosing $Q(u) = 1/A$ for all $u \in \{a_1, a_2, \ldots, a_A\}$ in (1.1.8), for example, shows that sources with equiprobable output symbols have the greatest entropy. That is,

$$0 \leq H(\mathscr{U}) \leq \log A \tag{1.1.9}$$

with equality if and only if $P(u) = 1/A$ for all $u \in \mathscr{U} = \{a_1, a_2, \ldots, a_A\}$.

Example (Binary memoryless source) For a DMS with alphabet $\mathscr{U} = \{0, 1\}$ with probability $P(0) = p$ and $P(1) = 1 - p$ we have entropy

$$\begin{aligned} H(\mathscr{U}) &= p \log \frac{1}{p} + (1 - p) \log \frac{1}{1 - p} \quad \text{bits} \\ &\equiv \mathscr{H}(p) \end{aligned}$$

where $\mathscr{H}(p)$ is called the binary entropy function. Here $\mathscr{H}(p) \leq 1$ with equality if and only if $p = \frac{1}{2}$. When $p = \frac{1}{2}$, we call this source a *binary symmetric source* (*BSS*). Each output of a BSS contains 1 bit of information.

Suppose we next let $\mathbf{u} = (u_1, u_2, \ldots, u_N)$ be the DMS output random sequence of length N. The random variables $u_1, u_2, \ldots, u_N$ are independent and identically distributed; hence the probability distribution of $\mathbf{u}$ is given by[3]

$$P_N(\mathbf{u}) = \prod_{n=1}^{N} P(u_n) \tag{1.1.10}$$

where $P(\cdot)$ is the given source output distribution. Note that for source output sequences $\mathbf{u} = (u_1, u_2, \ldots, u_N) \in \mathscr{U}_N$ of length N, we can define the average amount of information per source output sequence as

$$H(\mathscr{U}_N) = \sum_{\mathbf{u}} P_N(\mathbf{u}) \log \frac{1}{P_N(\mathbf{u})} \tag{1.1.11}$$

As expected, since the source is memoryless, we get

$$\begin{aligned} H(\mathscr{U}_N) &= \sum_{\mathbf{u}} P_N(\mathbf{u}) \log \frac{1}{\prod_{n=1}^{N} P(u_n)} \\ &= \sum_{\mathbf{u}} P_N(\mathbf{u}) \left(\sum_{n=1}^{N} \log \frac{1}{P(u_n)} \right) \\ &= \sum_{n=1}^{N} \left(\sum_{\mathbf{u}} P_N(\mathbf{u}) \log \frac{1}{P(u_n)} \right) \\ &= \sum_{n=1}^{N} \left(\sum_{u_n} P(u_n) \log \frac{1}{P(u_n)} \right) \\ &= NH(\mathscr{U}) \end{aligned} \tag{1.1.12}$$

which shows that the total average information in a sequence of independent outputs is the sum of the average information in each output in the sequence.

[3] We adopt the notation that a subscript on a density or distribution function indicates the dimensionality of the random vector; however, in the case of a one-dimensional random variable, no subscript is used. Similar subscript notation is used for alphabets to indicate Cartesian products.

If the N outputs are not independent, the equality (1.1.12) becomes only an upper bound. To obtain this more general result, let

$$Q_N(\mathbf{u}) \equiv \prod_{n=1}^{N} P(u_n) \qquad \text{where} \qquad P(u_n) = \sum_{u_1} \cdots \sum_{\substack{u_i \\ i \neq n}} \cdots \sum_{u_N} P_N(\mathbf{u}) \tag{1.1.13}$$

is the first-order probability[4] of output u_n and $Q_N(\mathbf{u}) \neq P_N(\mathbf{u})$ unless the variables are independent. Then it follows from (1.1.8) that

$$\begin{aligned} H(\mathscr{U}_N) &= \sum_{\mathbf{u}} P_N(\mathbf{u}) \log \frac{1}{P_N(\mathbf{u})} \\ &\leq \sum_{\mathbf{u}} P_N(\mathbf{u}) \log \frac{1}{Q_N(\mathbf{u})} \\ &= \sum_{\mathbf{u}} P_N(\mathbf{u}) \log \frac{1}{\prod_{n=1}^{N} P(u_n)} \\ &= NH(\mathscr{U}) \end{aligned}$$

where the last step follows exactly as in the derivation of (1.1.12). Hence

$$H(\mathscr{U}_N) \leq NH(\mathscr{U}) \tag{1.1.14}$$

with equality if and only if the source outputs $u_1, u_2, \ldots, u_N$ are independent; i.e., the random variables $u_1, u_2, \ldots, u_N$ are the outputs of a memoryless source.

In many applications, the outputs of an information source are either transmitted to some destination or stored in a computer. In either case, it is convenient to represent the source outputs by binary symbols. It is imperative that this be done in such a way that the original source outputs can be recovered from the binary symbols. Naturally, we would like to use as few binary symbols per source output as possible. Shannon's first theorem, called the *noiseless source coding theorem*, shows that the average number of binary symbols per source output can be made to approach the entropy of the source and no less. This rather surprising result gives the notion of entropy of a source its operational significance. We now prove this theorem for the DMS.

Let $\mathbf{u} = (u_1, u_2, \ldots, u_N)$ be a DMS output random sequence of length N and $\mathbf{x} = (\mathbf{x}_1, \mathbf{x}_2, \ldots, \mathbf{x}_{l_N})$ be the corresponding binary sequence of length $l_N(\mathbf{u})$ representing the source sequence $\mathbf{u}$. For fixed N, the set of all A^N binary sequences (codewords) corresponding to all the source sequences of length N is called a *code*. Since codeword lengths can be different, in order to be able to recover the original

[4] We assume here that this distribution is the same for each output and that

$$H(\mathscr{U}) = -\sum_{u} P(u) \log P(u)$$

For generalizations see Prob. 1.2.

source sequence from the binary symbols we require that no two distinct finite sequences of codewords form the same overall binary sequence. Such codes are called *uniquely decodable.* A sufficient condition for a code to be uniquely decodable is the property that no codeword of length l is identical to the first l binary symbols of another codeword of length greater than or equal to l. That is, no codeword is a *prefix* of another codeword. This is clearly a sufficient condition, for given the binary sequence we can always uniquely determine the end of a codeword and no two codewords are the same. Uniquely decodable codes with this prefix property have the practical advantage of being "instantaneously decodable"; that is, each codeword can be decoded as soon as the last symbol of the codeword is received.

Example Suppose $\mathcal{U} = \{a, b, c\}$. Consider the following codes for sequences of length $N = 1$.

$\mathcal{U}$	Code 1	Code 2	Code 3
a	0	00	1
b	1	01	10
c	01	10	100

Code 1 is not uniquely decodable since the binary sequence 0101 can be due to source sequences *abab, abc, cc,* or *cab.* Code 2 is uniquely decodable since all codewords are the same length and distinct. Code 3 is also uniquely decodable since "1" always marks the beginning of a codeword and codewords are distinct. For $N = 2$ suppose we have a code

$\mathcal{U}_2$	Code 4
aa	000
ab	001
ac	010
ba	011
bb	1000
bc	1001
ca	1010
cb	1011
cc	1100

This code for source sequences of length 2 in $\mathcal{U}_2$ is uniquely decodable since all sequences are unique and the first symbol tells us the codeword length. A first "0" tells us the codeword is of length 3 while a first "1" will tell us the codeword is of length 4. Furthermore this code has the property that no codeword is a prefix of another. That is, all codewords are distinct and no codeword of length 3 can be the first 3 binary symbols of a codeword of length 4.

We now proceed to state and prove the noiseless source coding theorem in its simplest form. This theorem will serve to establish the operational significance of entropy.

Theorem 1.1.1: Noiseless coding theorem for discrete memoryless sources Given a DMS with alphabet $\mathscr{U}$ and entropy $H(\mathscr{U})$, for source sequences of length $N (N = 1, 2, \ldots,)$ there exists a uniquely decodable binary code consisting of binary sequences (codewords) of lengths $l_N(\mathbf{u})$ for $\mathbf{u} \in \mathscr{U}_{\mathbf{N}}$ such that the average length of the codewords is bounded by

$$\langle L_N \rangle \equiv \sum_{\mathbf{u}} P_N(\mathbf{u}) l_N(\mathbf{u})$$

$$\leq N[H(\mathscr{U}) + o(N)] \tag{1.1.15}$$

where $o(N)$ is a term which becomes vanishingly small as N approaches infinity. Conversely, *no such code exists* for which

$$\langle L_N \rangle < NH(\mathscr{U})$$

The direct half of the theorem, as expressed by (1.1.15) is proved by constructing a uniquely decodable code which achieves the average length bound. There are several such techniques, the earliest being that of Shannon [1948] (see Prob. 1.6), and the one producing an optimal code, i.e., the one which minimizes the average length for any value of N, being that of Huffman [1952]. We present here yet another technique which, while less efficient than these standard techniques, not only proves the theorem very directly, but also serves to illustrate an interesting property of the DMS, shared by a much wider class of sources, called the *asymptotic equipartition property* (AEP). We develop this by means of the following:

Lemma 1.1.1 For any $\epsilon > 0$, consider a DMS with alphabet $\mathscr{U}$, entropy $H = H(\mathscr{U})$, and the subset of all source sequences of length N defined by

$$S(N, \epsilon) = \{\mathbf{u}: 2^{-N[H+\epsilon]} \leq P_N(\mathbf{u}) \leq 2^{-N[H-\epsilon]}\} \tag{1.1.16}$$

Then all the source sequences in $S(N, \epsilon)$ can be uniquely represented by binary codewords of fixed length L_N where

$$N[H(\mathscr{U}) + \epsilon] \leq L_N < N(H(\mathscr{U}) + \epsilon) + 1 \tag{1.1.17}$$

Furthermore

$$\Pr\{\mathbf{u} \notin S(N, \epsilon)\} \leq \frac{\sigma^2}{N\epsilon^2} \tag{1.1.18}$$

where

$$\sigma^2 = \sum_{u} [-\log P(u) - H(\mathscr{U})]^2 P(u)$$

Note that all source sequences in the set $S(N, \epsilon)$ are nearly equiprobable, deviating from the value $2^{-NH(\mathscr{U})}$ by a factor no greater than $2^{N\epsilon}$.

PROOF Since $S(N, \epsilon)$ is a subset of $\mathscr{U}_N$, the set of sequences of length N, we have the inequality

$$\begin{aligned} 1 &= \sum_{\mathbf{u}} P_N(\mathbf{u}) \\ &\geq \sum_{\mathbf{u} \in S(N, \epsilon)} P_N(\mathbf{u}) \end{aligned} \tag{1.1.19}$$

Since by definition $P_N(\mathbf{u}) \geq 2^{-N[H+\epsilon]}$ for every $\mathbf{u} \in S(N, \epsilon)$, this becomes

$$\begin{aligned} 1 &\geq \sum_{\mathbf{u} \in S(N, \epsilon)} 2^{-N[H+\epsilon]} \\ &= 2^{-N[H+\epsilon]} \,|S(N, \epsilon)| \end{aligned} \tag{1.1.20}$$

where $|S(N, \epsilon)|$ is the number of distinct sequences in $S(N, \epsilon)$. This gives us the bound

$$|S(N, \epsilon)| \leq 2^{N[H+\epsilon]} \tag{1.1.21}$$

This bound, of course, is generally not an integer, let alone a power of 2. However, we may bracket it between powers of 2 by choosing the integer L_N such that

$$2^{L_N - 1} < 2^{N[H+\epsilon]} \leq 2^{L_N} \tag{1.1.22}$$

Since there are 2^{L_N} distinct binary sequences of length L_N, we can represent uniquely all source sequences belonging to $S(N, \epsilon)$ with binary sequences of length L_N which satisfies (1.1.17).

Turning now to the probability of the set $\overline{S(N, \epsilon)}$, the complementary set of $S(N, \epsilon)$, which consists of all sequences not represented in this manner, let

$$\begin{aligned} F_N &\equiv \Pr\{\mathbf{u} \in \overline{S(N, \epsilon)}\} \\ &= \sum_{\mathbf{u} \in \overline{S(N, \epsilon)}} P_N(\mathrm{u}) \end{aligned} \tag{1.1.23}$$

From the definition (1.1.16) of $S(N, \epsilon)$, we have

$$\begin{aligned} S(N, \epsilon) &= \{\mathbf{u}\colon -N[H+\epsilon] \leq \log P_N(\mathbf{u}) \leq -N[H-\epsilon]\} \\ &= \left\{\mathbf{u}\colon -NH - N\epsilon \leq \log \prod_{n=1}^{N} P(u_n) \leq -NH + N\epsilon\right\} \\ &= \left\{\mathbf{u}\colon -N\epsilon \leq \sum_{n=1}^{N} \log P(u_n) + NH \leq N\epsilon\right\} \\ &= \left\{\mathbf{u}\colon \left| -\frac{1}{N} \sum_{n=1}^{N} \log P(u_n) - H \right| \leq \epsilon\right\} \end{aligned} \tag{1.1.24}$$

Hence the complementary set is,

$$\overline{S(N, \epsilon)} = \left\{\mathbf{u}\colon \left| -\frac{1}{N} \sum_{n=1}^{N} \log P(u_n) - H \right| > \epsilon\right\} \tag{1.1.25}$$

The random variables

$$z_n \equiv -\log P(u_n) \qquad n = 1, 2, \ldots, N \tag{1.1.26}$$

are independent identically distributed random variables with expected value

$$\begin{aligned} \bar{z} &= E[z] \\ &= -\sum_{k=1}^{A} P(a_k) \log P(a_k) \\ &= H(\mathscr{U}) \end{aligned} \tag{1.1.27}$$

and a finite variance which we denote as

$$\sigma^2 = \text{var}\,[z]$$

From the well-known Chebyshev inequality (see Prob. 1.4) it follows that for the sum of N such random variables

$$\Pr\left\{\mathbf{z}: \left| \frac{1}{N} \sum_{n=1}^{N} z_n - \bar{z} \right| > \epsilon \right\} \le \frac{\sigma^2}{N\epsilon^2} \tag{1.1.28}$$

Hence for F_N we have

$$\begin{aligned} F_N &= \sum_{\mathbf{u} \in \overline{S(N,\,\epsilon)}} P_N(\mathbf{u}) \\ &= \Pr\left\{\mathbf{u}: \left| -\frac{1}{N} \sum_{n=1}^{N} \log P(u_n) - H \right| > \epsilon \right\} \\ &\le \frac{\sigma^2}{N\epsilon^2} \end{aligned} \tag{1.1.29}$$

Thus F_N, the probability of occurrence of any source sequence not encoded by a binary sequence of length L_N, becomes vanishingly small as N approaches infinity. Indeed, using the tighter Chernoff bound (see Prob. 1.5) we can show that F_N decreases exponentially with N. The property that source output sequences belong to $S(N, \epsilon)$ with probability approaching 1 as N increases to infinity is called the *asymptotic equipartition property*.

PROOF OF THEOREM 1.1.1 Using the results of Lemma 1.1.1, suppose we add one more binary symbol to each of the binary representatives of the sequences in $S(N, \epsilon)$ by preceding these binary representatives with a "0." While this increases the binary sequence lengths from L_N to $L_N + 1$, it has a vanishingly small influence for asymptotically large N. Then using (1.1.17) we have that all sequences in $S(N, \epsilon)$ are represented uniquely with binary sequences of length $1 + L_N < N[H + \epsilon] + 2$ bits. For all other sequences in $\overline{S(N, \epsilon)}$, suppose these are represented by a sequence of length $1 + L'_N$ where the first binary symbol is always "1" and the remaining L'_N symbols uniquely represent each sequence in $\overline{S(N, \epsilon)}$. This is certainly possible if L'_N satisfies

$$2^{L'_N - 1} < A^N \leq 2^{L'_N}$$

or

$$N \log A \leq L'_N < N \log A + 1 \tag{1.1.30}$$

since this is enough to represent uniquely all sequences in $\mathscr{U}_N$.

We now have a unique binary representation or codeword for each output sequence of length N. This code is the same type as Code 4 in the example. It is uniquely decodable since the first bit specifies the length ("0" means length $1 + L_N$ and "1" means length $1 + L'_N$) of the codeword and the remaining bits uniquely specify the source sequence of length N. If the first bit is a "0" we examine the next L_N bits which establish uniquely a source sequence in $S(N, \epsilon)$ while if the first bit is a "1" we examine the next L'_N bits which establish uniquely a source sequence in $\overline{S(N, \epsilon)}$. Each codeword is a unique binary sequence and there is never any uncertainty as to when a codeword sequence begins and ends. No codeword is a prefix of another. The encoder just described is illustrated in Fig. 1.3.

We have thus developed a uniquely decodable code with two possible codeword lengths, L_N and L'_N. The average length of codewords is thus

$$\begin{aligned}\langle L_N \rangle &= (1 + L_N) \Pr\{\mathbf{u} \in S(N, \epsilon)\} + (1 + L'_N) \Pr\{\mathbf{u} \in \overline{S(N, \epsilon)}\} \\ &\leq 1 + L_N + L'_N F_N \end{aligned} \tag{1.1.31}$$

and it follows from (1.1.17), (1.1.18), and (1.1.30) that

$$\begin{aligned}\langle L_N \rangle &< 1 + N[H(\mathscr{U}) + \epsilon] + 1 + [N \log A + 1] \frac{\sigma^2}{N\epsilon^2} \\ &= N\left[H(\mathscr{U}) + \epsilon + \frac{2}{N} + \left(\log A + \frac{1}{N}\right)\frac{\sigma^2}{N\epsilon^2}\right]\end{aligned}$$

or

$$\frac{\langle L_N \rangle}{N} < H(\mathscr{U}) + \epsilon + \frac{2}{N} + \left(\log A + \frac{1}{N}\right)\frac{\sigma^2}{N\epsilon^2} \tag{1.1.32}$$

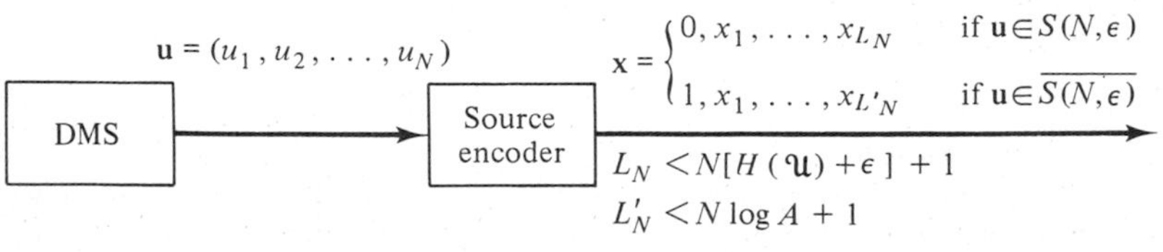

Figure 1.3 Noiseless source encoder.

Choosing $\epsilon = N^{-1/3}$, this yields,

$$\frac{\langle L_N \rangle}{N} < H(\mathcal{U}) + 2N^{-1} + [(\log A + N^{-1})\sigma^2 + 1]N^{-1/3}$$

$$= H(\mathcal{U}) + o(N) \tag{1.1.33}$$

which establishes the direct half of the theorem.

Before proceeding with the converse half of the theorem, we note that by virtue of the asymptotic equipartition property, for large N nearly all codewords can be made of equal length, slightly larger than $NH(\mathcal{U})$, and only two lengths of codewords are required.[5] For small N, a large variety of codeword lengths becomes more desirable. In fact, just as we have chosen here the length L_N to be approximately equal to the negative logarithm (base 2) of the almost common probability of the output sequence of length N where N is large, so it is desirable (and nearly optimal) to make the codeword lengths proportional to the logarithms of the source sequence probabilities when N is small. In the latter case, individual source sequence probabilities are not generally close together and hence many codeword lengths are required to achieve small average length. The techniques for choosing these so as to produce a uniquely decodable code are several (Shannon [1948], Huffman [1952]) and they have been amply described in many texts. The techniques are not prerequisites to any of the material presented in this book and thus they will not be included in this introductory chapter on fundamental parameters (see, however, Prob. 1.6).

To prove the converse, we must keep in mind that in general we may have a large variety of codeword lengths. Thus for source sequence $\mathbf{u} \in \mathcal{U}_N$ we have a codeword $\mathbf{x}(\mathbf{u})$ which represents $\mathbf{u}$ and has length denoted $l_N(\mathbf{u})$. The lengths of the codewords may be arbitrary. However, the resulting code must be uniquely decodable. For an arbitrary uniquely decodable code we establish a lower bound on $\langle L_N \rangle$.

Consider the identity

$$\left(\sum_{\mathbf{u}} 2^{-l_N(\mathbf{u})}\right)^M = \left(\sum_{\mathbf{u}_1} 2^{-l_N(\mathbf{u}_1)}\right)\left(\sum_{\mathbf{u}_2} 2^{-l_N(\mathbf{u}_2)}\right)\cdots\left(\sum_{\mathbf{u}_M} 2^{-l_N(\mathbf{u}_M)}\right)$$

$$= \sum_{\mathbf{u}_1}\sum_{\mathbf{u}_2}\cdots\sum_{\mathbf{u}_M} 2^{-[l_N(\mathbf{u}_1)+l_N(\mathbf{u}_2)+\cdots+l_N(\mathbf{u}_M)]} \tag{1.1.34}$$

where each sum on both sides of the equation is over the entire space $\mathcal{U}_N$. If we let A_k be the number of sequences of M successive codewords having a

[5] If errors occurring with probability F_N could be tolerated, all codewords could be made of equal length. While this may seem unacceptable, we shall find in the next chapter that in transmission over a noisy channel some errors are inevitable; hence if we can make F_N smaller than the probability of transmission errors, this may be a reasonable approach.

total length of k binary symbols, (1.1.34) can be expressed as

$$\left(\sum_{\mathbf{u}} 2^{-l_N(\mathbf{u})}\right)^M = \sum_{k=1}^{Ml_N^*} A_k 2^{-k} \tag{1.1.35}$$

where $l_N^* = \max_{\mathbf{u}} l_N(\mathbf{u})$. But in order for the source sequences to be recoverable from the binary sequences we must have

$$A_k \leq 2^k \qquad k = 1, 2, \ldots, Ml_N^* \tag{1.1.36}$$

Otherwise two or more sequences of M successive codewords will give the same binary sequence, violating our uniqueness requirement. Using this bound for A_k, we have

$$\left(\sum_{\mathbf{u}} 2^{-l_N(\mathbf{u})}\right)^M \leq \sum_{k=1}^{Ml_N^*} 1 = Ml_N^* \tag{1.1.37}$$

for all integers M. Clearly this can be satisfied for all M if and only if

$$\sum_{\mathbf{u}} 2^{-l_N(\mathbf{u})} \leq 1 \tag{1.1.38}$$

for the left side of (1.1.37) behaves exponentially in M while the right side grows only linearly with M. This inequality is known as the *Kraft-McMillan inequality* (Kraft [1949], McMillan [1956]).

If we were now to use the general variable length source encoder whose code lengths must satisfy (1.1.38) we would have an average of

$$\langle L_N \rangle = \sum_{\mathbf{u}} P_N(\mathbf{u}) l_N(\mathbf{u}) \tag{1.1.39}$$

binary symbols per source sequence. Defining on $\mathbf{u} \in \mathscr{U}_N$ the distribution

$$Q_N(\mathbf{u}) = \frac{2^{-l_N(\mathbf{u})}}{\sum_{\mathbf{u}'} 2^{-l_N(\mathbf{u}')}} \tag{1.1.40}$$

we have from inequality (1.1.8) and (1.1.12)

$$\begin{aligned}
NH(\mathscr{U}) &= \sum_{\mathbf{u}} P_N(\mathbf{u}) \log \frac{1}{P_N(\mathbf{u})} \\
&\leq \sum_{\mathbf{u}} P_N(\mathbf{u}) \log \frac{1}{Q_N(\mathbf{u})} \\
&= \sum_{\mathbf{u}} P_N(\mathbf{u}) \log \left\{ \frac{\sum_{\mathbf{u}'} 2^{-l_N(\mathbf{u}')}}{2^{-l_N(\mathbf{u})}} \right\} \\
&= \sum_{\mathbf{u}} P_N(\mathbf{u}) \log \left(\sum_{\mathbf{u}'} 2^{-l_N(\mathbf{u}')} \right) + \sum_{\mathbf{u}} P_N(\mathbf{u}) l_N(\mathbf{u}) \\
&= \langle L_N \rangle + \log \left(\sum_{\mathbf{u}'} 2^{-l_N(\mathbf{u}')} \right)
\end{aligned} \tag{1.1.41}$$

Since the Kraft-McMillan inequality (1.1.38) guarantees that the second term is not positive we have

$$NH(\mathscr{U}) \leq \langle L_N \rangle \tag{1.1.42}$$

This bound applies for any sequence length N and it follows that any source code for which the source sequence can be recovered from the binary sequence (uniquely decodable) requires at least an average of $H(\mathscr{U})$ bits per source symbol.

This completes the proof of Theorem 1.1.1 and we have thus shown that it is possible to source encode a DMS with an average number of binary symbols per source symbol arbitrarily close to its entropy and that it is impossible to have a lower average. This is a special case of the *noiseless source coding theorem* of information theory which applies for arbitrary discrete alphabet stationary ergodic sources and arbitrary finite code alphabets (see Prob. 1.3) and gives the notion of entropy its operational significance. If we were to relax the requirement that the source sequence be recoverable from the binary-code sequence and replaced it by some average distortion requirement, then of course, we could use fewer than $H(\mathscr{U})$ bits per source symbol. This generalization to source encoding with a distortion measure is called rate distortion theory. This theory, which was first presented by Shannon in 1948 and developed further by him in 1959, is the subject of Chap. 7 and Chap. 8.

Another important consequence of the theorem is the asymptotic equality of the probability of source sequences as N becomes large. If we treat these sequences of length N as messages to be transmitted, even without considering their efficient binary representation, we have shown that the "typical" messages are asymptotically equiprobable, a useful property in subsequent chapters where we treat means of accurately transmitting messages over noisy channels.

1.2 MUTUAL INFORMATION AND CHANNEL CAPACITY

Shannon demonstrated how information can be reliably transmitted over a noisy communication channel by considering first a measure of the amount of information about the transmitted message contained in the observed output of the channel. To do this he defined the notion of mutual information between events α and β denoted $I(\alpha; \beta)$ *which is the information provided about the event* α *by the occurrence of the event* β. As before the probabilities $P(\alpha)$, $P(\beta)$, and $P(\alpha \cap \beta)$ are assumed as given parameters of the model. Clearly to be consistent with our previous definition of information we must have two boundary condition properties:

1. If α and β are independent events ($P(\alpha \cap \beta) = P(\alpha)P(\beta)$), then the occurrence of β would provide no information about α. That is, $I(\alpha; \beta) = 0$.

2. If the occurrence of β indicates that α has definitely occurred ($P(\alpha \mid \beta) = 1$), then the occurrence of β provides us with all the information regarding α. That is, $I(\alpha; \beta) = I(\alpha) = \log [1/P(\alpha)]$.

These two boundary condition properties are satisfied if the mutual information between events α and β is defined as

$$I(\alpha; \beta) \equiv \log \frac{P(\alpha \mid \beta)}{P(\alpha)}$$

$$= \log \frac{P(\alpha \cap \beta)}{P(\alpha)P(\beta)} \tag{1.2.1}$$

Note that this definition is symmetric in the two events since $I(\alpha; \beta) = I(\beta; \alpha)$. Also mutual information is a generalization of the earlier definition of the information of an event α since $I(\alpha) = \log [1/P(\alpha)] = I(\alpha; \alpha)$. Hence $I(\alpha)$ is sometimes referred to as the self-information of the event α. Note that although $I(\alpha)$ is always nonnegative, mutual information $I(\alpha; \beta)$ can assume negative values. For example, if $P(\alpha \mid \beta) < P(\alpha)$ then $I(\alpha; \beta) < 0$ and we see that observing β makes α seem less likely than it was a priori before the observation.

We are primarily interested in the mutual information between inputs and outputs of a communication channel. Virtually all the channels treated throughout this book will be reduced to discrete-time channels which may be regarded as a random mapping of the random variable x_n, the channel input, to the variable y_n, the channel output, at integer-valued time n. Generally these random variables will be either discrete random variables or absolutely continuous random variables. While only the former usually apply to practical systems, the latter also merit consideration in that they represent the limiting case of the discrete model. We start with discrete channels where the input and output random variables are discrete random variables. Generalizations to continuous random variables or a combination of a discrete input random variable and a continuous output random variable is usually trivial and requires simply changing probability distributions to probability densities and summations to integrals. In Chap. 2 we shall see how these various channels appear in practice when we have additive white Gaussian noise disturbance in the channel. Here we begin by formally defining discrete memoryless channels.

Definition A *discrete memoryless channel* (*DMC*) is characterized by a discrete input alphabet $\mathscr{X}$, a discrete output alphabet $\mathscr{Y}$, and a set of conditional probabilities for outputs given each of the inputs. We denote the given conditional probabilities[6] by $p(y \mid x)$ for $y \in \mathscr{Y}$ and $x \in \mathscr{X}$. Each output letter of the channel depends only on the corresponding input so that for an input se-

[6] Throughout the book we use lowercase letters for both probability distributions and probability densities associated with channel input and output random variables.

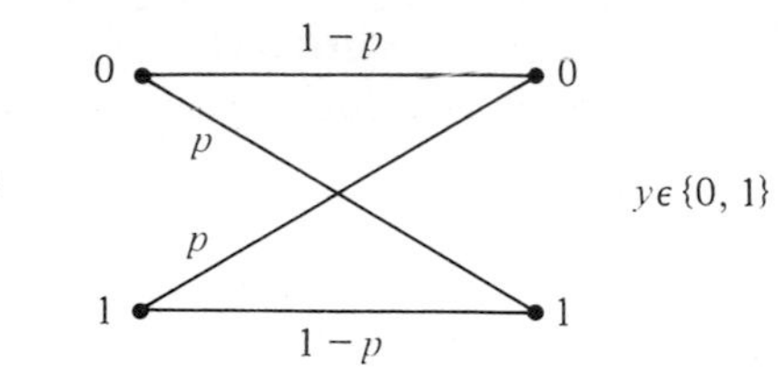

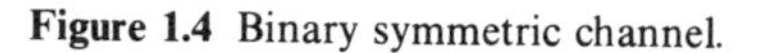
Figure 1.4 Binary symmetric channel.

quence of length N, denoted $\mathbf{x} = (x_1, x_2, \ldots, x_N)$, the conditional probability of a corresponding output sequence, denoted $\mathbf{y} = (y_1, y_2, \ldots, y_N)$, may be expressed as[7]

$$p_N(\mathbf{y} \mid \mathbf{x}) = \prod_{n=1}^{N} p(y_n \mid x_n) \tag{1.2.2}$$

This is the memoryless condition of the definition. We define next the most common type of DMC.

Definition A *binary symmetric channel* (*BSC*) is a DMC with $\mathcal{X} = \mathcal{Y} = \{0, 1\}$ and conditional probabilities of the form

$$\begin{aligned} p(1 \mid 0) &= p(0 \mid 1) = p \\ p(0 \mid 0) &= p(1 \mid 1) = 1 - p \end{aligned} \tag{1.2.3}$$

This is represented by the diagram of Fig. 1.4.

We can easily generalize our definition of DMC to channels with alphabets that are not discrete. A common example is the additive Gaussian noise channel which we define next.

Definition The memoryless discrete-input *additive Gaussian noise channel* is a memoryless channel with discrete input alphabet $\mathcal{X} = \{a_1, a_2, \ldots, a_Q\}$, output alphabet $\mathcal{Y} = (-\infty, \infty)$ and conditional probability density

$$p(y \mid a_k) = \frac{1}{\sqrt{2\pi\sigma^2}} e^{-(y - a_k)^2/2\sigma^2} \quad \text{for all } y \in \mathcal{Y} \tag{1.2.4}$$

where $k = 1, 2, \ldots, Q$.

This is represented by the diagram of Fig. 1.5 where n is a Gaussian random variable with zero mean and variance σ^2. For this case, memoryless again means

[7] This definition is appropriate when and only when feedback is excluded; that is, when the transmitter has no knowledge of what was received. In general, we would require $p(y_n \mid x_1, \ldots, x_n, y_1, \ldots, y_{n-1}) = p(y_n \mid x_n)$ for all n.

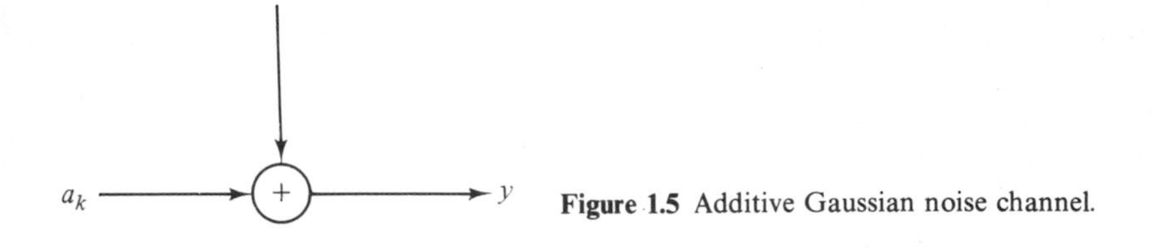

Figure 1.5 Additive Gaussian noise channel.

that for any input sequence **x** of length N and any corresponding output sequence **y** we have

$$p_N(\mathbf{y} \mid \mathbf{x}) = \prod_{n=1}^{N} p(y_n \mid x_n) \tag{1.2.2}$$

for all N. These and other channels will be discussed further in Chap. 2. In this chapter we examine only discrete memoryless channels.

Consider a DMC with input alphabet $\mathscr{X}$, output alphabet $\mathscr{Y}$ and conditional probabilities $p(y \mid x)$ for $y \in \mathscr{Y}$, $x \in \mathscr{X}$. Suppose, in addition, that input letters occur with probability $q(x)$ for $x \in \mathscr{X}$. We can then regard the input to the channel as a random variable and the output as a random variable. If we observe the output y then the amount of information this provides about the input x is the mutual information

$$\begin{aligned} I(x; y) &= \log \frac{p(y \mid x)}{p(y)} \\ &= \log \frac{q(x \mid y)}{q(x)} \end{aligned} \tag{1.2.5}$$

where

$$p(y) = \sum_x p(y \mid x) q(x) \tag{1.2.6}$$

As with sources, we are primarily interested in the average amount of information that the output of the channel provides about the input. Thus we define the *average mutual information* between inputs and outputs of the DMC as[8]

$$\begin{aligned} I(\mathscr{X}; \mathscr{Y}) &= E[I(x; y)] \\ &= \sum_y \sum_x p(y \mid x) q(x) \log \frac{p(y \mid x)}{\sum_{x'} p(y \mid x') q(x')} \end{aligned} \tag{1.2.7}$$

The average mutual information $I(\mathscr{X}; \mathscr{Y})$ is defined in terms of the given channel conditional probabilities and the input probability which is independent of the

[8] Actually the definition is not restricted to channel inputs and outputs. It is the appropriate definition for the average mutual information between an arbitrary pair of random variables. For absolutely continuous random variables we replace summations and probabilities by integrals and density functions.

DMC. We can then maximize $I(\mathscr{X};\mathscr{Y})$ with respect to the input probability distribution $\mathbf{q} = \{q(x) : x \in \mathscr{X}\}$.

Definition The *channel capacity* of a DMC is the maximum average mutual information, where the maximization is over all possible input probability distributions. That is,

$$C \equiv \max_{\mathbf{q}} I(\mathscr{X};\mathscr{Y}) \tag{1.2.8}$$

Example (BSC) By symmetry the capacity for the BSC with crossover probability p, as shown in Fig. 1.4, is achieved with channel input probability $q(0) = q(1) = \frac{1}{2}$. Hence

$$\begin{aligned} C &= I(\mathscr{X};\mathscr{Y})\Big|_{q(0)=q(1)=1/2} \\ &= 1 - p \log \frac{1}{p} - (1-p) \log \frac{1}{1-p} \\ &= 1 - \mathscr{H}(p) \text{ bits/symbol} \end{aligned}$$

As expected when $p = \frac{1}{2}$ we have $\mathscr{H}(\frac{1}{2}) = 1$ and $C = 0$. With $p = 0$ we get $\mathscr{H}(0) = 0$ and $C = 1$ bit which is exactly the information in each channel input. Note that we also have $C = 1$ when $p = 1$ since from the output symbol, which is the complement of the input binary symbol, we can uniquely determine the input symbol. By extending this argument, it follows that $C(p) = C(1 - p)$.

Note that channel capacity is defined only in terms of given channel characteristics. Even though these are assumed given, performing the maximization to find channel capacity is generally difficult. Maximization or minimization of functions over probability distributions can often be evaluated with the aid of the Kuhn-Tucker theorem (see App. 3B). In Chap. 3 we shall find necessary and sufficient conditions on the input probability assignment that achieves capacity as well as for the maximization of other functions that arise in the analysis of digital communication systems. (In App. 3C we also give a simple computational algorithm for evaluating capacity.) We shall see that, like the entropy parameter for a source, the capacity for a channel has operational significance, related directly to limitations on the reliable transmission of information through the channel. First, however, we examine some properties of average mutual information, which will be useful later.

Lemma 1.2.1

$$0 \le I(\mathscr{X};\mathscr{Y}) \le \sum_y \sum_x p(y|x)q(x) \log \frac{p(y|x)}{\hat{p}(y)} \tag{1.2.9}$$

where $\hat{p}(\cdot)$ is any probability distribution. Equality is achieved in the upper bound if and only if $\hat{p}(y) = p(y) \equiv \sum_x q(x)p(y|x)$ for all $y \in \mathscr{Y}$. $I(\mathscr{X};\mathscr{Y}) = 0$ if and only if the output random variable is independent of the input random variable.

PROOF[9] The lower bound is found by using the inequality $\ln x \le x - 1$ as follows:

$$\begin{aligned}
-I(\mathscr{X};\mathscr{Y}) &= \sum_y \sum_x p(y|x)q(x) \log \frac{p(y)}{p(y|x)} \\
&= (\ln 2)^{-1} \sum_y \sum_x p(y|x)q(x) \ln \frac{p(y)}{p(y|x)} \\
&\le (\ln 2)^{-1} \sum_y \sum_x p(y|x)q(x) \left[\frac{p(y)}{p(y|x)} - 1\right] \\
&= (\ln 2)^{-1} \left\{\sum_y \sum_x p(y)q(x) - \sum_y \sum_x p(y|x)q(x)\right\} \\
&= 0
\end{aligned} \tag{1.2.10}$$

with equality to zero if and only if $p(y|x) = p(y)$ for all y and x.

The upper bound to $I(\mathscr{X};\mathscr{Y})$ follows from the form

$$I(\mathscr{X};\mathscr{Y}) = \sum_y p(y) \log \frac{1}{p(y)} - \sum_y \sum_x p(y|x)q(x) \log \frac{1}{p(y|x)} \tag{1.2.11}$$

It follows from (1.1.8) that

$$\sum_y p(y) \log \frac{1}{p(y)} \le \sum_y p(y) \log \frac{1}{\hat{p}(y)}$$

with equality if and only if $\hat{p}(y) = p(y)$ for all $y \in \mathscr{Y}$. Substituting this inequality for the first term of (1.2.11) yields the desired result.

Consider a sequence of input random variables of length N denoted $\mathbf{x} = (x_1, x_2, \ldots, x_N)$. Let the probability of the input sequence be given by $q_N(\mathbf{x})$ for $\mathbf{x} \in \mathscr{X}_N$ and let the resulting marginal probability of x_n be $q^{(n)}(x)$ for $x \in \mathscr{X}$ where $n = 1, 2, \ldots, N$. That is

$$q^{(n)}(x_n) = \sum_{x_1} \cdots \sum_{\substack{x_i \\ (i \ne n)}} \cdots \sum_{x_N} q_N(\mathbf{x})$$

for each n. The average mutual information between input sequences of length N and the corresponding output sequences of length N is

$$I(\mathscr{X}_N;\mathscr{Y}_N) = \sum_{\mathbf{y}} \sum_{\mathbf{x}} p_N(\mathbf{y}|\mathbf{x})q_N(\mathbf{x}) \log \frac{p_N(\mathbf{y}|\mathbf{x})}{p_N(\mathbf{y})} \tag{1.2.12}$$

where $p_N(\mathbf{y}) = \sum_{\mathbf{x}} p_N(\mathbf{y}|\mathbf{x})q_N(\mathbf{x})$.

[9] Although the properties given here hold for any logarithm base we shall prove properties for base 2. Generalization to any base is trivial.

Since the channel is memoryless, the average mutual information between x_n and the corresponding output y_n is

$$I^{(n)}(\mathscr{X};\mathscr{Y}) = \sum_y \sum_x p(y|x)q^{(n)}(x) \log \frac{p(y|x)}{p^{(n)}(y)} \tag{1.2.13}$$

where $p^{(n)}(y) = \sum_x p(y|x)q^{(n)}(x)$ and $n = 1, 2, \ldots, N$. We then have

Lemma 1.2.2

$$I(\mathscr{X}_N;\mathscr{Y}_N) \le \sum_{n=1}^{N} I^{(n)}(\mathscr{X};\mathscr{Y}) \le NC \tag{1.2.14}$$

where equality is achieved in the lower inequality when (but not only when) $x_1, x_2, \ldots, x_N$ are independent random variables and in the upper inequality when and only when each independent input random variable has the probability distribution that achieves channel capacity.

PROOF From Lemma 1.2.1 we have

$$I(\mathscr{X}_N;\mathscr{Y}_N) \le \sum_{\mathbf{y}} \sum_{\mathbf{x}} p_N(\mathbf{y}|\mathbf{x})q_N(\mathbf{x}) \log \frac{p_N(\mathbf{y}|\mathbf{x})}{\hat{p}_N(\mathbf{y})} \tag{1.2.15}$$

for any probability distribution $\hat{p}_N(\cdot)$. Now choose

$$\hat{p}_N(\mathbf{y}) = \prod_{n=1}^{N} p^{(n)}(y_n) \tag{1.2.16}$$

Then since

$$\frac{p_N(\mathbf{y}|\mathbf{x})}{\hat{p}_N(\mathbf{y})} = \prod_{n=1}^{N} \frac{p(y_n|x_n)}{p^{(n)}(y_n)} \tag{1.2.17}$$

we have

$$\begin{aligned} I(\mathscr{X}_N;\mathscr{Y}_N) &\le \sum_{\mathbf{y}} \sum_{\mathbf{x}} p_N(\mathbf{y}|\mathbf{x})q_N(\mathbf{x}) \left\{ \sum_{n=1}^{N} \log \frac{p(y_n|x_n)}{p^{(n)}(y_n)} \right\} \\ &= \sum_{n=1}^{N} \sum_y \sum_x p(y|x)q^{(n)}(x) \log \frac{p(y|x)}{p^{(n)}(y)} \\ &= \sum_{n=1}^{N} I^{(n)}(\mathscr{X};\mathscr{Y}) \end{aligned} \tag{1.2.18}$$

with equality if and only if $\hat{p}_N(\mathbf{y}) = p_N(\mathbf{y})$ for all $\mathbf{y} \in \mathscr{Y}_N$. Equality is thus achieved when the output random variables $y_1, y_2, \ldots, y_N$ are independent. Since the channel is memoryless, this certainly happens if the input random variables $x_1, x_2, \ldots, x_N$ are independent. The upper inequality follows trivially since $I^{(n)}(\mathscr{X};\mathscr{Y}) \le C$ with equality, according to (1.2.8), when and only when the input probability distribution $q^{(n)}(\cdot)$ achieves the maximum average mutual information.

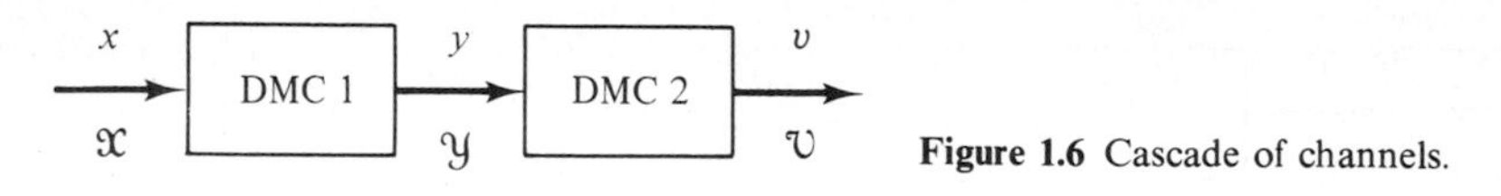

Figure 1.6 Cascade of channels.

Lemma 1.2.3 Consider three random variables x, y, v which have joint probability $p(x, y, v)$ for $x \in \mathscr{X}$, $y \in \mathscr{Y}$, $v \in \mathscr{V}$. Let average mutual information be defined for each pair of random variables, $I(\mathscr{X}; \mathscr{Y})$, $I(\mathscr{X}; \mathscr{V})$, and $I(\mathscr{Y}; \mathscr{V})$. Assume, as shown in Fig. 1.6, that x is an input random variable to one channel with output y which in turn becomes the input to a second channel with output random variable v. Assume further that, as implied by Fig. 1.6,

$$p(v \mid x, y) = p(v \mid y) \tag{1.2.19}$$

which means that x influences v only through y. Then $I(\mathscr{X}; \mathscr{Y})$, $I(\mathscr{X}; \mathscr{V})$, and $I(\mathscr{Y}; \mathscr{V})$ are related by inequalities

$$I(\mathscr{X}; \mathscr{V}) \le I(\mathscr{X}; \mathscr{Y}) \tag{1.2.20}$$

and

$$I(\mathscr{X}; \mathscr{V}) \le I(\mathscr{Y}; \mathscr{V}) \tag{1.2.21}$$

PROOF

$$\begin{aligned} I(\mathscr{X}; \mathscr{V}) - I(\mathscr{X}; \mathscr{Y}) &= \sum_v \sum_x p(x, v) \log \frac{p(v \mid x)}{p(v)} - \sum_y \sum_x p(x, y) \log \frac{p(y \mid x)}{p(y)} \\ &= \sum_v \sum_y \sum_x p(x, y, v) \log \frac{p(v \mid x)p(y)}{p(v)p(y \mid x)} \\ &= (\ln 2)^{-1} \sum_v \sum_y \sum_x p(x, y, v) \ln \frac{p(v \mid x)p(y)}{p(v)p(y \mid x)} \\ &\le (\ln 2)^{-1} \sum_v \sum_y \sum_x p(x, y, v) \left[\frac{p(v \mid x)p(y)}{p(v)p(y \mid x)} - 1\right] \end{aligned} \tag{1.2.22}$$

where we have again used $\ln x \le x - 1$. Note further that by Bayes' rule

$$\begin{aligned} \frac{p(x, y, v)p(v \mid x)p(y)}{p(v)p(y \mid x)} &= \frac{p(x, y, v)p(x, v)p(y)}{p(v)p(x, y)} \\ &= \frac{p(v \mid x, y)p(x, v)p(y)}{p(v)} \\ &= p(v \mid x, y)p(x \mid v)p(y) \\ &= p(v \mid y)p(x \mid v)p(y) \end{aligned} \tag{1.2.23}$$

Figure 1.7 Data processing system.

where in the last equality we used the hypothesis (1.2.19). Hence combining (1.2.22) and (1.2.23)

$$I(\mathscr{X};\mathscr{V}) - I(\mathscr{X};\mathscr{Y}) \le (\ln 2)^{-1}\left\{\left[\sum_v \sum_y \sum_x p(v\,|\,y)p(x\,|\,v)p(y)\right] - 1\right\}$$
$$= (\ln 2)^{-1}\left\{\left[\sum_v \sum_y p(v\,|\,y)p(y)\right] - 1\right\}$$
$$= 0 \tag{1.2.24}$$

The second inequality follows from a similar argument.

Lemma 1.2.3 can be generalized easily to various length sequences in a cascade of devices. A special case of the second DMC in Fig. 1.6 is a deterministic device, that maps input y into output v deterministically. Next consider Fig. 1.7 where we assume that $\mathbf{u}$ is a sequence of length L of random variables with probability $p_L(\mathbf{u})$ for $\mathbf{u} \in \mathscr{U}_L$ which generates the inputs to a deterministic device called an encoder whose output sequence $\mathbf{x}$ is of length N. The sequence $\mathbf{x}$ is then the input to the DMC for which, by definition

$$p_N(\mathbf{y}\,|\,\mathbf{x}) = \prod_{n=1}^{N} p(y_n\,|\,x_n) \qquad \text{for any } \mathbf{x} \in \mathscr{X}_N \quad \text{and} \quad \mathbf{y} \in \mathscr{Y}_N$$

Finally $\mathbf{y}$ is the input to a deterministic device called a decoder whose output is $\mathbf{v}$, a sequence of length L. The encoder can be assumed to operate on the entire L length sequence $\mathbf{u}$ to generate the N length output sequence $\mathbf{x}$. Similarly the decoder can be assumed to operate on the entire N length sequence $\mathbf{y}$ to output the L length sequence $\mathbf{v}$. Regarding sequences as single inputs and outputs we have from Lemma 1.2.3 the inequalities

$$I(\mathscr{U}_L;\mathscr{V}_L) \le I(\mathscr{U}_L;\mathscr{Y}_N) \tag{1.2.25}$$

and

$$I(\mathscr{U}_L;\mathscr{Y}_N) \le I(\mathscr{X}_N;\mathscr{Y}_N) \tag{1.2.26}$$

Combining these we obtain the data-processing theorem:

Theorem 1.2.1: Data-processing theorem For the system of Fig. 1.7

$$I(\mathscr{U}_L;\mathscr{V}_L) \le I(\mathscr{X}_N;\mathscr{Y}_N) \tag{1.2.27}$$

This result assumes that each sequence influences subsequent sequences as shown in Fig. 1.7. That is $\mathbf{u}$ influences $\mathbf{v}$ only through $\mathbf{x}$, which in turn influences $\mathbf{v}$ only through $\mathbf{y}$ so that $p_L(\mathbf{v} \mid \mathbf{u}, \mathbf{x}, \mathbf{y}) = p_L(\mathbf{v} \mid \mathbf{y})$ where $\mathbf{y} \in \mathscr{Y}_N$ and $\mathbf{v} \in \mathscr{V}_L$. Also, from Lemma 1.2.2, we obtain the result that for the system of Fig. 1.7

$$I(\mathscr{U}_L; \mathscr{V}_L) \le NC \tag{1.2.28}$$

where C is the channel capacity of the DMC.

The above properties of average mutual information follow easily from simple inequalities and definitions. Even though mutual information can be negative-valued, the average mutual information cannot be negative. Furthermore, the average mutual information between outputs and inputs of a DMC is nonnegative and becomes zero only when the outputs are independent of the inputs. Thus it is not surprising to find that by cascading more devices between inputs and outputs the average mutual information decreases, for the insertion of each additional device weakens the dependence between input and output. Other properties of average mutual information are given in App. 1A. Although these properties of average mutual information are discussed in terms of "channels" they apply to more general situations. For example, the "data-processing theorem" applies even when the encoder, channel, and decoder in Fig. 1.7 are replaced by arbitrary "data processors."

To show the significance of the definition of mutual information, average mutual information, and channel capacity, we examine the problem of sending the outputs of a source over a communication channel. We shall show that if the entropy of the source is greater than the capacity of the channel, then the communication system cannot operate with arbitrarily small error no matter how complex the coding system. This negative result is called the converse to the coding theorem.

1.3 THE CONVERSE TO THE CODING THEOREM

Let us now examine the problem of sending the outputs of a discrete memoryless source (DMS) to a destination through a communication channel modeled as a discrete memoryless channel (DMC). Specifically, consider the block diagram of Fig. 1.8 where the DMS alphabet is $\mathscr{U} = \{a_1, a_2, \ldots, a_A\}$, with probability distribution $P(\cdot)$ and entropy $H(\mathscr{U})$. We assume that source outputs occur once every T_s seconds so that the DMS average information output rate is $H(\mathscr{U})/T_s$ bits per second, when $H(\mathscr{U})$ is measured in bits per output. The destination accepts letters belonging to the same alphabet, $\mathscr{V} = \mathscr{U}$, at the same source rate of one symbol every T_s seconds.

The DMC has input alphabet $\mathscr{X}$, output alphabet $\mathscr{Y}$, and conditional probabilities $p(y \mid x)$ for $y \in \mathscr{Y}$, $x \in \mathscr{X}$. It also has a channel capacity of C bits per channel use, when mutual information is measured in bits. We assume that the channel is used once every T_c seconds.

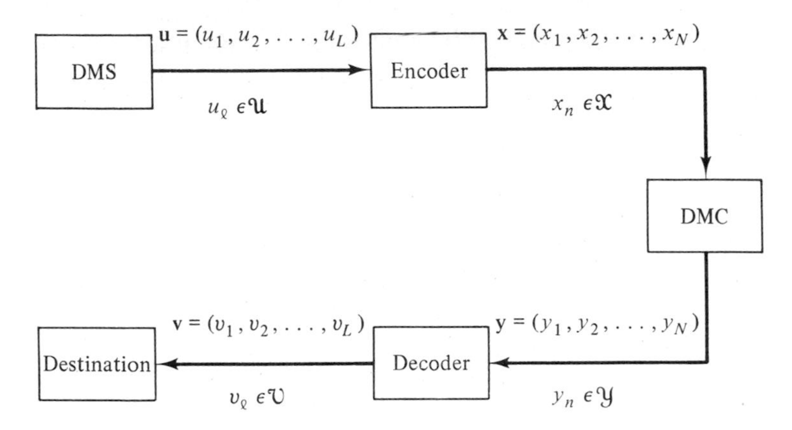

Figure 1.8 A communication system.

We are now dealing with a DMS that outputs a symbol once every T_s seconds and a DMC that can be used once every T_c seconds. Without compromising notation, we can continue to label source outputs and channel inputs with integer indices. We merely adopt the convention that the source output u_l occurs at time lT_s and x_n is the channel input at time $nT_c + T_d$ where T_d is the encoding delay.

We assume that the DMS and DMC are given and are not under our control. The encoder and decoder, on the other hand, can be designed in any way we please. In particular, the encoder takes source symbols and outputs channel input symbols while the decoder takes channel output symbols and outputs symbols belonging to the source alphabet $\mathscr{V} = \mathscr{U}$. Suppose now we wish to send to the destination L source output symbols, **u**. The encoder then sends N channel input symbols, **x**, over the channel where we assume that

$$LT_s = NT_c \tag{1.3.1}$$

Each channel input symbol can depend on the L source symbols, **u**, in any way desired. Similarly the decoder takes the N channel output symbols **y**, and outputs a sequence of L destination symbols, **v**. Again each destination symbol can depend on the N channel output symbols, **y**, in any way desired. The channel is memoryless so that for each time $nT_c + T_d$ the channel output symbol y_n depends only on the corresponding channel input symbol x_n.

In any communication system of this type we would like to achieve very small error probabilities. In particular, we are interested in the probability of error for each source letter, as defined by

$$\begin{aligned} P_{e,l} &\equiv \Pr\{v_l \neq u_l\} \\ &= \sum_{u} \sum_{v \neq u} P^{(l)}(u, v) \end{aligned} \tag{1.3.2}$$

for $l = 1, 2, \ldots, L$. Here $P^{(l)}(u, v)$ is the joint probability distribution of v_l and u_l. $P_{e,l}$ is the probability that the lth source output u_l is decoded incorrectly by the destination. The average per digit error probability, $\langle P_e \rangle$, over the L source outputs is defined as

$$\langle P_e \rangle \equiv \frac{1}{L} \sum_{l=1}^{L} P_{e,l} \tag{1.3.3}$$

For most digital communication systems $\langle P_e \rangle$ is the appropriate performance criterion for evaluating the system. If $\langle P_e \rangle$ can be made arbitrarily small we have a reliable communication system. We proceed to show that if the source entropy is greater than channel capacity, reliable communication is impossible. This result is known as the *converse to the coding theorem.*

We begin by considering the difference between the entropy of the source sequence, $H(\mathscr{U}_L)$, and the average mutual information between the source sequence and the destination sequence, $I(\mathscr{U}_L; \mathscr{V}_L)$. From the definitions and Bayes' rule, it follows that

$$\begin{aligned} H(\mathscr{U}_L) - I(\mathscr{U}_L; \mathscr{V}_L) &= \sum_{\mathbf{u}} P_L(\mathbf{u}) \log \frac{1}{P_L(\mathbf{u})} - \sum_{\mathbf{u}} \sum_{\mathbf{v}} P_L(\mathbf{u}, \mathbf{v}) \log \frac{P_L(\mathbf{u} \mid \mathbf{v})}{P_L(\mathbf{u})} \\ &= \sum_{\mathbf{u}} \sum_{\mathbf{v}} P_L(\mathbf{u}, \mathbf{v}) \log \frac{1}{P_L(\mathbf{u} \mid \mathbf{v})} \\ &= \sum_{\mathbf{v}} P_L(\mathbf{v}) \left\{ \sum_{\mathbf{u}} P_L(\mathbf{u} \mid \mathbf{v}) \log \frac{1}{P_L(\mathbf{u} \mid \mathbf{v})} \right\} \end{aligned} \tag{1.3.4}$$

Next we apply the inequality (1.1.8) to get the bound

$$\sum_{\mathbf{u}} P_L(\mathbf{u} \mid \mathbf{v}) \log \frac{1}{P_L(\mathbf{u} \mid \mathbf{v})} \leq \sum_{\mathbf{u}} P_L(\mathbf{u} \mid \mathbf{v}) \log \frac{1}{\hat{P}_L(\mathbf{u} \mid \mathbf{v})} \tag{1.3.5}$$

for any conditional probability $\hat{P}_L(\mathbf{u} \mid \mathbf{v})$. Let us now choose

$$\hat{P}_L(\mathbf{u} \mid \mathbf{v}) = \prod_{l=1}^{L} P^{(l)}(u_l \mid v_l) \tag{1.3.6}$$

where

$$P^{(l)}(u_l \mid v_l) = \frac{P^{(l)}(u_l, v_l)}{P^{(l)}(v_l)} \tag{1.3.7}$$

and

$$P^{(l)}(v_l) = \sum_{u} P^{(l)}(u, v_l) \tag{1.3.8}$$

This choice in (1.3.4) and (1.3.5) yields the bound

$$H(\mathscr{U}_L) - I(\mathscr{U}_L; \mathscr{V}_L) \le \sum_{\mathbf{v}} P_L(\mathbf{v}) \left\{ \sum_{\mathbf{u}} P_L(\mathbf{u}|\mathbf{v}) \log \frac{1}{\prod_{l=1}^{L} P^{(l)}(u_l|v_l)} \right\}$$

$$= \sum_{\mathbf{v}} \sum_{\mathbf{u}} P_L(\mathbf{u}, \mathbf{v}) \left\{ \sum_{l=1}^{L} \log \frac{1}{P^{(l)}(u_l|v_l)} \right\}$$

$$= \sum_{l=1}^{L} \left\{ \sum_{u} \sum_{v} P^{(l)}(u, v) \log \frac{1}{P^{(l)}(u|v)} \right\}$$

$$= \sum_{l=1}^{L} \left\{ \sum_{u} \sum_{v \ne u} P^{(l)}(u, v) \log \frac{1}{P^{(l)}(u|v)} \right.$$

$$\left. + \sum_{v} P^{(l)}(v, v) \log \frac{1}{P^{(l)}(v|v)} \right\} \tag{1.3.9}$$

We now consider the two parts in this bound separately using again the fundamental inequality $\ln x \le x - 1$ and the relationship

$$P_{e,l} = \sum_{u} \sum_{v \ne u} P^{(l)}(u, v) \tag{1.3.2}$$

from which it readily follows that

$$1 - P_{e,l} = \sum_{v} \sum_{u=v} P^{(l)}(u, v)$$

$$= \sum_{v} P^{(l)}(v, v) \tag{1.3.10}$$

We bound the first term in the brace in (1.3.9) as follows using (1.3.2):

$$\sum_{u} \sum_{v \ne u} P^{(l)}(u, v) \log \frac{1}{P^{(l)}(u|v)}$$

$$= \sum_{u} \sum_{v \ne u} P^{(l)}(u, v) \log \left(\frac{1}{P^{(l)}(u|v)} \frac{(A-1)P_{e,l}}{(A-1)P_{e,l}} \right)$$

$$= \sum_{u} \sum_{v \ne u} P^{(l)}(u, v) \log \frac{P_{e,l}}{(A-1)P^{(l)}(u|v)}$$

$$+ \sum_{u} \sum_{v \ne u} P^{(l)}(u, v) \log \frac{A-1}{P_{e,l}}$$

$$= (\ln 2)^{-1} \sum_{u} \sum_{v \ne u} P^{(l)}(u, v) \ln \frac{P_{e,l}}{(A-1)P^{(l)}(u|v)}$$

$$+ P_{e,l} \log \frac{A-1}{P_{e,l}}$$

$$\leq (\ln 2)^{-1} \sum_u \sum_{v \neq u} P^{(l)}(u, v) \left[\frac{P_{e,l}}{(A-1)P^{(l)}(u|v)} - 1 \right]$$

$$+ P_{e,l} \log \frac{A-1}{P_{e,l}}$$

$$= (\ln 2)^{-1} \left[\sum_u \sum_{v \neq u} P^{(l)}(v) \frac{P_{e,l}}{A-1} - \sum_u \sum_{v \neq u} P^{(l)}(u, v) \right]$$

$$+ P_{e,l} \log \frac{A-1}{P_{e,l}}$$

$$= (\ln 2)^{-1} \left\{ \sum_v \sum_{u \neq v} P^{(l)}(v) \frac{P_{e,l}}{A-1} - P_{e,l} \right\}$$

$$+ P_{e,l} \log \frac{A-1}{P_{e,l}}$$

$$= P_{e,l} \log \frac{A-1}{P_{e,l}} \tag{1.3.11}$$

The second term is bounded in a similar manner as follows using (1.3.10):

$$\sum_v P^{(l)}(v, v) \log \frac{1}{P^{(l)}(v|v)} = \sum_v P^{(l)}(v, v) \log \left(\frac{1}{P^{(l)}(v|v)} \frac{1 - P_{e,l}}{1 - P_{e,l}} \right)$$

$$= \sum_v P^{(l)}(v, v) \log \frac{1 - P_{e,l}}{P^{(l)}(v|v)}$$

$$+ \sum_v P^{(l)}(v, v) \log \frac{1}{1 - P_{e,l}}$$

$$= (\ln 2)^{-1} \sum_v P^{(l)}(v, v) \ln \frac{1 - P_{e,l}}{P^{(l)}(v|v)}$$

$$+ (1 - P_{e,l}) \log \frac{1}{1 - P_{e,l}}$$

$$\leq (\ln 2)^{-1} \sum_v P^{(l)}(v, v) \left[\frac{1 - P_{e,l}}{P^{(l)}(v|v)} - 1 \right]$$

$$+ (1 - P_{e,l}) \log \frac{1}{1 - P_{e,l}}$$

$$= (\ln 2)^{-1} \left\{ \sum_v P^{(l)}(v)(1 - P_{e,l}) - \sum_v P^{(l)}(v, v) \right\}$$

$$+ (1 - P_{e,l}) \log \frac{1}{1 - P_{e,l}}$$

$$= (1 - P_{e,l}) \log \frac{1}{1 - P_{e,l}} \tag{1.3.12}$$

Recalling from Sec. 1.1 the definition of the binary entropy function

$$\mathscr{H}(p) \equiv p \log \frac{1}{p} + (1-p) \log \frac{1}{1-p} \tag{1.3.13}$$

and the definition (1.3.3) of $\langle P_e \rangle$ and using the bounds (1.3.11) and (1.3.12) in (1.3.9), we obtain

$$\begin{aligned} H(\mathscr{U}_L) - I(\mathscr{U}_L; \mathscr{V}_L) &\le \sum_{l=1}^{L} \left\{ P_{e,l} \log \frac{A-1}{P_{e,l}} + (1 - P_{e,l}) \log \frac{1}{1 - P_{e,l}} \right\} \\ &= L\langle P_e \rangle \log (A-1) + \sum_{l=1}^{L} \mathscr{H}(P_{e,l}) \end{aligned} \tag{1.3.14}$$

The next to final form of the desired inequality follows from the observation that from (1.1.8) we have

$$\begin{aligned} &P_{e,l} \log \frac{1}{P_{e,l}} + (1 - P_{e,l}) \log \frac{1}{1 - P_{e,l}} \\ &\qquad \le P_{e,l} \log \frac{1}{\langle P_e \rangle} + (1 - P_{e,l}) \log \frac{1}{1 - \langle P_e \rangle} \end{aligned} \tag{1.3.15}$$

so that

$$\begin{aligned} \sum_{l=1}^{L} \mathscr{H}(P_{e,l}) &\le \sum_{l=1}^{L} \left\{ P_{e,l} \log \frac{1}{\langle P_e \rangle} + (1 - P_{e,l}) \log \frac{1}{1 - \langle P_e \rangle} \right\} \\ &= L\mathscr{H}(\langle P_e \rangle) \end{aligned} \tag{1.3.16}$$

Hence

$$H(\mathscr{U}_L) - I(\mathscr{U}_L; \mathscr{V}_L) \le L\langle P_e \rangle \log (A-1) + L\mathscr{H}(\langle P_e \rangle) \tag{1.3.17}$$

Since the source is memoryless, from (1.1.12) we have

$$H(\mathscr{U}_L) = LH(\mathscr{U}) \tag{1.3.18}$$

Furthermore, Theorem 1.2.1, Lemma 1.2.2, and (1.3.1) give us

$$I(\mathscr{U}_L; \mathscr{V}_L) \le I(\mathscr{X}_N; \mathscr{Y}_N) \le NC = \frac{T_s}{T_c} LC \tag{1.3.19}$$

Using (1.3.18) and (1.3.19) in (1.3.17) yields the desired bound

$$\begin{aligned} H(\mathscr{U}) - \frac{T_s}{T_c} C &\le \frac{H(\mathscr{U}_L) - I(\mathscr{U}_L; \mathscr{V}_L)}{L} \\ &\le \langle P_e \rangle \log (A-1) + \mathscr{H}(\langle P_e \rangle) \end{aligned} \tag{1.3.20}$$

For convenience in using the upper bound of (1.3.20), we define

$$F(\langle P_e \rangle) \equiv \langle P_e \rangle \log (A-1) + \mathscr{H}(\langle P_e \rangle)$$

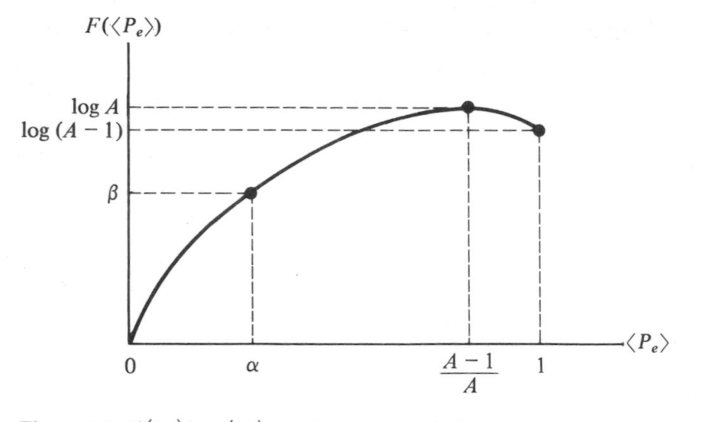

Figure 1.9 $F(\langle P_e \rangle) = \langle P_e \rangle \log (A-1) + \mathscr{H}(P_e)$.

According to (1.3.20), if the source entropy of $H(\mathscr{U})/T_s$ bits per second is greater than the channel capacity of C/T_c bits per second, then $F(\langle P_e \rangle) = \langle P_e \rangle \log (A-1) + \mathscr{H}(\langle P_e \rangle)$ is greater than the constant $\beta = H(\mathscr{U}) - (T_s/T_c)C > 0$. Figure 1.9 shows $F(\langle P_e \rangle)$ as a function of $\langle P_e \rangle$. From this it is clear that if $\beta > 0$ then there exists some $\alpha > 0$ such that $\langle P_e \rangle \geq \alpha$. Note that this holds regardless of the source sequence length L, and hence yields the following form of the converse theorem due to Fano [1952].

Theorem 1.3.1 (Converse to the Coding Theorem) If the entropy per second, $H(\mathscr{U})/T_s$, of the source is greater than the channel capacity per second, C/T_c, then there exists a constant $\alpha > 0$ such that $\langle P_e \rangle \geq \alpha$ for all sequence lengths.

The converse to the coding theorem shows that it is impossible for a communication system to operate with arbitrarily small average error probability when the information rate of the source is greater than channel capacity. We shall see in subsequent chapters that if the information rate is less than channel capacity, then there are ways to achieve arbitrarily small average error probability. These results give the concepts of mutual information and particularly channel capacity their operational significance.

1.4 SUMMARY AND BIBLIOGRAPHICAL NOTES

In this introductory chapter we have presented the basic concepts of information and its more general form, mutual information. We have shown that for a discrete memoryless source the average amount of information per source output, called entropy, represents the theoretical limit on the minimum average number of binary symbols per source output necessary to represent source-output sequences. This result generalizes to discrete stationary ergodic sources (see Prob. 1.3) and more general code alphabets. Next we defined discrete memoryless channels which serve as models for many real noisy communication channels. The maximum average mutual information of a discrete memoryless channel, called channel capacity, represents the theoretical limit on the rate of information that can be reliably transmitted over the channel. In this introductory chapter we have proved for discrete memoryless channels the negative part of this result, commonly called the *converse to the coding theorem*. This result generalizes easily to all memoryless channels.

The theoretical foundations of digital communication were laid by C. E. Shannon [1948]. Most of the concepts of this chapter are found in greater generality in this original work. Other similar treatments can be found in Fano [1961], Abramson [1963], Gallager [1968], and Jelinek [1968*a*]. The books of Feinstein [1958], Wolfowitz [1961], and Ash [1965] may appeal to those who prefer mathematics to engineering applications.

APPENDIX 1A CONVEX FUNCTIONS

In this chapter we defined two fundamental parameters of information theory: $H(\mathscr{U})$, the entropy of an information source, and $I(\mathscr{X}; \mathscr{Y})$, the average mutual information between the inputs and outputs of a communication channel. These are two examples of a more general class of functions which have the property known as convexity. In this section we briefly examine convex functions and some of their properties. These results will be useful throughout the rest of this book.

Definition A real-valued function $f(\cdot)$ of a real number is defined to be convex $\cap$ over an interval $\mathscr{I}$ if, for all $x_1 \in \mathscr{I}$, $x_2 \in \mathscr{I}$, and θ, $0 < \theta < 1$, the function satisfies

$$\theta f(x_1) + (1-\theta) f(x_2) \le f[\theta x_1 + (1-\theta)x_2] \tag{1A.1}$$

If the inequality in (1A.1) is reversed for all such x_1, x_2, and θ then $f(\cdot)$ is called convex $\cup$. When (1A.1) or its converse is a strict inequality whenever $x_1 \neq x_2$ then we call $f(\cdot)$ strictly convex $\cap$ or strictly convex $\cup$.

In Fig. 1A.1 we sketch a typical convex $\cap$ function for fixed x_1 and x_2 as a function of θ. From this it is clear why the $\cap$ (cap) notation is used here.[10] Similar comments apply to convex $\cup$ (cup) functions. In fact since a convex $\cup$ function is the negative of a convex $\cap$ function, we need only examine the properties of convex $\cap$ functions. Commonly encountered convex $\cap$ functions are $\ln x$ and x^ρ $(0 < \rho \le 1)$ for the interval $\mathscr{I} = (0, \infty)$. Convex $\cup$ functions include

[10] In the mathematical literature a convex $\cap$ function is called concave and a convex $\cup$ function convex. Gallager [1968] introduced the notation used here to avoid the usual confusion associated with the names concave and convex.

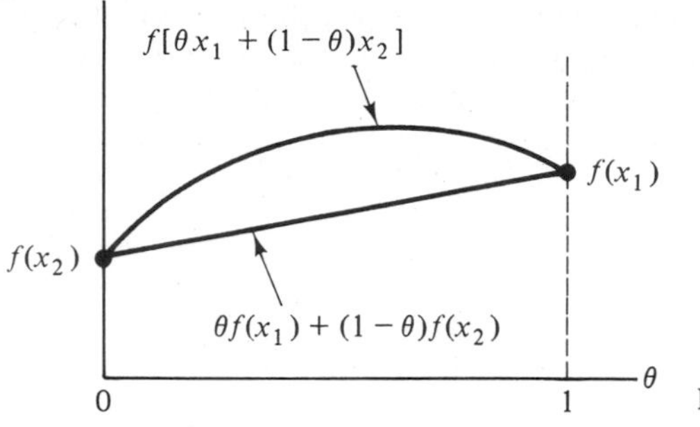

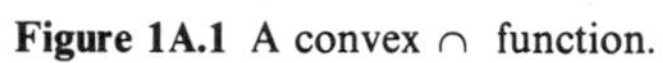
Figure 1A.1 A convex $\cap$ function.

$-\ln x$ and x^ρ $(\rho \geq 1)$ for $\mathscr{I} = (0, \infty)$. Functions that are both convex $\cup$ and convex $\cap$ are linear functions of the form $ax + b$.

Sometimes with more complex functions it is difficult to tell whether or not a function is convex $\cap$. A useful test is given next.

Lemma 1A.1 Suppose $f(\cdot)$ is a real-valued function with derivatives $f'(\cdot)$ and $f''(\cdot)$ defined on an interval $\mathscr{I}$. Then $f(\cdot)$ is a convex $\cap$ function over interval $\mathscr{I}$ if and only if

$$f''(x) \leq 0 \qquad \text{for all } x \in \mathscr{I} \tag{1A.2}$$

PROOF Let x_1, x_2, and γ be any set of points in $\mathscr{I}$. Integrating $f''(\cdot)$ twice, we have

$$\begin{aligned}\int_\gamma^{x_1} \int_\gamma^\beta f''(\alpha)\, d\alpha\, d\beta &= \int_\gamma^{x_1} [f'(\beta) - f'(\gamma)]\, d\beta \\ &= f(x_1) - f(\gamma) - f'(\gamma)[x_1 - \gamma]\end{aligned} \tag{1A.3}$$

and

$$\int_\gamma^{x_2} \int_\gamma^\beta f''(\alpha)\, d\alpha\, d\beta = f(x_2) - f(\gamma) - f'(\gamma)[x_2 - \gamma] \tag{1A.4}$$

For any $\theta \in (0, 1)$ we combine these equations to obtain,

$$\begin{aligned}&\theta f(x_1) + (1-\theta)f(x_2) - f(\gamma) - f'(\gamma)[\theta x_1 + (1-\theta)x_2 - \gamma] \\ &\quad = \theta \int_\gamma^{x_1} \int_\gamma^\beta f''(\alpha)\, d\alpha\, d\beta + (1-\theta) \int_\gamma^{x_2} \int_\gamma^\beta f''(\alpha)\, d\alpha\, d\beta\end{aligned} \tag{1A.5}$$

Now choosing $\gamma = \theta x_1 + (1-\theta)x_2$ we see from (1A.5) that

$$\theta f(x_1) + (1-\theta)f(x_2) \leq f[\theta x_1 + (1-\theta)x_2]$$

for all x_1 and x_2 in $\mathscr{I}$ and $\theta \in (0, 1)$ if and only if (1A.2) is true.

We proceed to define convex functions of several variables, but first we need to define a convex region in a real vector space. Let $\mathscr{R}_N$ be the set of N-dimensional real vectors. We define a region $\mathscr{I}_N \subset \mathscr{R}_N$ to be a *convex region* if for each vector $\mathbf{x}_1 \in \mathscr{I}_N$ and each vector $\mathbf{x}_2 \in \mathscr{I}_N$, the vector $\theta\mathbf{x}_1 + (1-\theta)\mathbf{x}_2$ is in $\mathscr{I}_N$ for all $\theta \in (0, 1)$. This means that for a convex region all points connecting any two points in the region also belong to the region. The convex region most often encountered in this book is $\mathscr{P}_N$, the set of probability vectors. Formally,

$$\mathscr{P}_N = \left\{\mathbf{x}\colon x_n \geq 0,\ n = 1, 2, \ldots, N;\ \sum_{n=1}^{N} x_n = 1\right\} \tag{1A.6}$$

Definition A real-valued function $f(\cdot)$ of vectors of dimension N is defined to be convex $\cap$ over a convex region $\mathscr{I}_N$ if, for all $\mathbf{x}_1 \in \mathscr{I}_N$, $\mathbf{x}_2 \in \mathscr{I}_N$, and θ, $0 < \theta < 1$, the function satisfies

$$\theta f(\mathbf{x}_1) + (1-\theta)f(\mathbf{x}_2) \leq f[\theta\mathbf{x}_1 + (1-\theta)\mathbf{x}_2] \tag{1A.7}$$

If we have a strict inequality whenever $\mathbf{x}_1 \neq \mathbf{x}_2$ then $f(\cdot)$ is called strictly convex $\cap$. The function is convex $\cup$ if the inequality is reversed.

For convex $\cap$ functions of vectors we have two important properties:

1. If $f_1(\mathbf{x}), f_2(\mathbf{x}), \ldots, f_L(\mathbf{x})$ are convex $\cap$ functions and if $c_1, c_2, \ldots, c_L$ are positive numbers, then

$$\sum_{l=1}^{L} c_l f_l(\mathbf{x}) \tag{1A.8}$$

   is convex $\cap$ with strict convexity if any of the $\{f_l(\mathbf{x})\}$ are strictly convex $\cap$. This follows immediately from the definition given in (1A.7).
2. Let $\mathbf{x}$ be a random vector of dimension N and let $f(\mathbf{x})$ be any convex $\cap$ function of vectors of dimension N. Then

$$E[f(\mathbf{x})] \leq f(E[\mathbf{x}]) \tag{1A.9}$$

   where $E[\cdot]$ is the expectation. This very useful inequality, known as the Jensen inequality, is proved in App. 1B.

The entropy function

$$H(\mathbf{x}) = \sum_{n=1}^{N} x_n \ln \frac{1}{x_n} \tag{1A.10}$$

is a convex $\cap$ function over $\mathscr{P}_N$ defined by (1A.6). To see this let

$$f_n(\mathbf{x}) = x_n \ln \frac{1}{x_n} \qquad \text{for} \quad n = 1, 2, \ldots, N$$

By using Lemma 1A.1 we see that each $f_n(\mathbf{x})$ is convex $\cap$. Then by property 1 we have that $H(\mathbf{x}) = \sum_{n=1}^{N} f_n(\mathbf{x})$ is also convex $\cap$. Another proof can be obtained directly from inequality (1.1.8). (See Prob. 1.12.)

Finally suppose we consider a DMC with input alphabet $\mathscr{X}$, output alphabet $\mathscr{Y}$, and transition probabilities $p(y|x)$ for $x \in \mathscr{X}$, $y \in \mathscr{Y}$. For an input probability distribution $q(x)$ for $x \in \mathscr{X}$, we defined average mutual information as

$$I(\mathscr{X}; \mathscr{Y}) = \sum_y \sum_x p(y|x)q(x) \log \frac{p(y|x)}{\sum_{x'} p(y|x')q(x')} \tag{1.2.7}$$

To emphasize the dependence of $I(\mathscr{X}; \mathscr{Y})$ on the transition probabilities represented by $\mathbf{P}$ and the input probability distribution represented by $\mathbf{q}$ we write this as

$$I(\mathscr{X}; \mathscr{Y}) = I(\mathbf{q}; \mathbf{P}) \tag{1A.11}$$

Lemma 1A.2 $I(\mathscr{X}; \mathscr{Y})$ for fixed channel transition probabilities is a convex $\cap$ function over the input probability space, and for fixed input probability distribution a convex $\cup$ function over the channel transition probability space. That is

$$\theta I(\mathbf{q}^{(1)}; \mathbf{P}) + (1-\theta)I(\mathbf{q}^{(2)}; \mathbf{P}) \le I(\theta\mathbf{q}^{(1)} + (1-\theta)\mathbf{q}^{(2)}; \mathbf{P}) \tag{1A.12}$$

where $\theta\mathbf{q}^{(1)} + (1-\theta)\mathbf{q}^{(2)}$ represents the probability distribution $\theta q^{(1)}(x) + (1-\theta)q^{(2)}(x)$, $x \in \mathscr{X}$, for any input probability distributions $\mathbf{q}^{(1)}$ and $\mathbf{q}^{(2)}$ and for all $\theta \in (0, 1)$

$$\theta I(\mathbf{q}; \mathbf{P}^{(1)}) + (1-\theta)I(\mathbf{q}; \mathbf{P}^{(2)}) \ge I(\mathbf{q}; \theta\mathbf{P}^{(1)} + (1-\theta)\mathbf{P}^{(2)}) \tag{1A.13}$$

where $\theta\mathbf{P}^{(1)} + (1-\theta)\mathbf{P}^{(2)}$ represents the transition probabilities $\theta p^{(1)}(y|x) + (1-\theta)p^{(2)}(y|x)$ for $y \in \mathscr{Y}$; $x \in \mathscr{X}$ for any transition probabilities $\mathbf{P}^{(1)}$ and $\mathbf{P}^{(2)}$ and for all $\theta \in (0, 1)$. $\mathbf{P}$ in (1A.12) represents any transition probabilities and $\mathbf{q}$ in (1A.13) represents any input probability distribution.

PROOF For any given $\mathbf{P}$ and $\mathbf{q}$ let us denote by $\mathbf{p}$ the output distribution

$$p(y) = \sum_x p(y|x)q(x) \qquad y \in \mathscr{Y} \tag{1A.14}$$

For fixed $\mathbf{P}$ it should be clear that when input distributions $\mathbf{q}^{(1)}$ and $\mathbf{q}^{(2)}$ result in output distributions $\mathbf{p}^{(1)}$ and $\mathbf{p}^{(2)}$ respectively, then the input distribution $\theta\mathbf{q}^{(1)} + (1-\theta)\mathbf{q}^{(2)}$ results in the output distribution $\theta\mathbf{p}^{(1)} + (1-\theta)\mathbf{p}^{(2)}$. Now note that

$$I(\mathbf{q}; \mathbf{P}) = \sum_x q(x) \sum_y p(y|x) \log p(y|x) + H(\mathbf{p}) \tag{1A.15}$$

where $H(\mathbf{p})$ is the entropy of the output alphabet. The first term in (1A.15) is linear in $\mathbf{q}$ and therefore convex $\cap$ in $\mathbf{q}$. The second term is convex $\cap$ in $\mathbf{p}$, as established by the argument following (1A.10). But since $\mathbf{p}$ is linear in $\mathbf{q}$ this means that it is also convex $\cap$ in $\mathbf{q}$. By property 1 we see that $I(\mathbf{q}; \mathbf{P})$ is convex $\cap$ in $\mathbf{q}$ for fixed $\mathbf{P}$. This proves (1A.12).

To prove (1A.13), let

$$p^{(\theta)}(y \mid x) = \theta p^{(1)}(y \mid x) + (1 - \theta)p^{(2)}(y \mid x) \qquad y \in \mathscr{Y} \text{ and } x \in \mathscr{X}$$

and

$$p^{(\theta)}(y) = \sum_x p^{(\theta)}(y \mid x)q(x) \qquad y \in \mathscr{Y}$$

Then

$$\begin{aligned}
(\ln 2)I(\mathbf{q}; \theta\mathbf{P}^{(1)} &+ (1-\theta)\mathbf{P}^{(2)} \\
&= \sum_y \sum_x q(x)p^{(\theta)}(y \mid x) \ln \frac{p^{(\theta)}(y \mid x)}{p^{(\theta)}(y)} \\
&= \theta \sum_y \sum_x q(x)p^{(1)}(y \mid x) \ln \frac{p^{(\theta)}(y \mid x)}{p^{(\theta)}(y)} \\
&\quad + (1-\theta) \sum_y \sum_x q(x)p^{(2)}(y \mid x) \ln \frac{p^{(\theta)}(y \mid x)}{p^{(\theta)}(y)}
\end{aligned} \tag{1A.16}$$

Next using the inequality $\ln x \le x - 1$ we have

$$\begin{aligned}
\sum_y \sum_x & q(x)p^{(1)}(y \mid x) \ln \frac{p^{(\theta)}(y \mid x)}{p^{(\theta)}(y)} \\
&= \sum_y \sum_x q(x)p^{(1)}(y \mid x) \left[\ln \frac{p^{(1)}(y \mid x)}{p^{(1)}(y)} + \ln \frac{p^{(\theta)}(y \mid x)p^{(1)}(y)}{p^{(\theta)}(y)p^{(1)}(y \mid x)} \right] \\
&\le \sum_y \sum_x q(x)p^{(1)}(y \mid x) \left[\ln \frac{p^{(1)}(y \mid x)}{p^{(1)}(y)} + \left(\frac{p^{(\theta)}(y \mid x)p^{(1)}(y)}{p^{(\theta)}(y)p^{(1)}(y \mid x)} - 1 \right) \right] \\
&= (\ln 2)I(\mathbf{q}; \mathbf{P}^{(1)}) + \sum_y \sum_x q(x)p^{(1)}(y \mid x) \left(\frac{p^{(\theta)}(y \mid x)p^{(1)}(y)}{p^{(\theta)}(y)p^{(1)}(y \mid x)} - 1 \right) \\
&= (\ln 2)I(\mathbf{q}; \mathbf{P}^{(1)})
\end{aligned} \tag{1A.17}$$

since the second term sums to zero. Similarly

$$\sum_y \sum_x q(x)p^{(2)}(y \mid x) \ln \frac{p^{(\theta)}(y \mid x)}{p^{(\theta)}(y)} \le (\ln 2)I(\mathbf{q}; \mathbf{P}^{(2)}) \tag{1A.18}$$

Using (1A.17) and (1A.18) in (1A.16) we have the desired result (1A.13).

We have shown here that the fundamental parameters, entropy and average mutual information, have certain convexity properties. In subsequent chapters we shall encounter other important parameters of information theory that also have convexity properties.

APPENDIX 1B JENSEN INEQUALITY FOR CONVEX FUNCTIONS

Lemma Let $f(\cdot)$ be a convex $\cap$ real-valued function defined on the real line. Let x be a random variable with finite expectation. Then

$$E[f(x)] \leq f(E[x])$$

For convex $\cup$ functions, the inequality is reversed.

PROOF We first prove this for a discrete finite sample space. The definition of a convex function is most concisely stated as the property that any line segment connecting two points $(x_1, f(x_1))$ and $(x_2, f(x_2))$ must lie below the function over the interval $x_1 < x < x_2$ (see Figure 1B.1). Consider first the distribution p_1, $p_2 = 1 - p_1$ for a binary-valued random variable. Then it follows from the definition of the line that the point $(p_1 x_1 + p_2 x_2, p_1 f(x_1) + p_2 f(x_2))$ lies on the line and hence must lie directly below the point $(p_1 x_1 + p_2 x_2, f(p_1 x_1 + p_2 x_2))$ on the function. It follows that

$$p_1 f(x_1) + p_2 f(x_2) \leq f(p_1 x_1 + p_2 x_2) \tag{1B.1}$$

Now extending to a three-point distribution, p_1, p_2, p_3 where $p_1 + p_2 + p_3 = 1$,

$$\begin{aligned} p_1 f(x_1) &+ p_2 f(x_2) + p_3 f(x_3) \\ &= (p_1 + p_2)\left[\frac{p_1}{p_1 + p_2} f(x_1) + \frac{p_2}{p_1 + p_2} f(x_2)\right] + p_3 f(x_3) \\ &\leq (p_1 + p_2) f\left(\frac{p_1}{p_1 + p_2} x_1 + \frac{p_2}{p_1 + p_2} x_2\right) + p_3 f(x_3) \end{aligned} \tag{1B.2}$$

where we have used (1B.1) recognizing that the coefficients $p_1/(p_1 + p_2)$ and $p_2/(p_1 + p_2)$ constitute a binary distribution defined at the points x_1 and x_2.

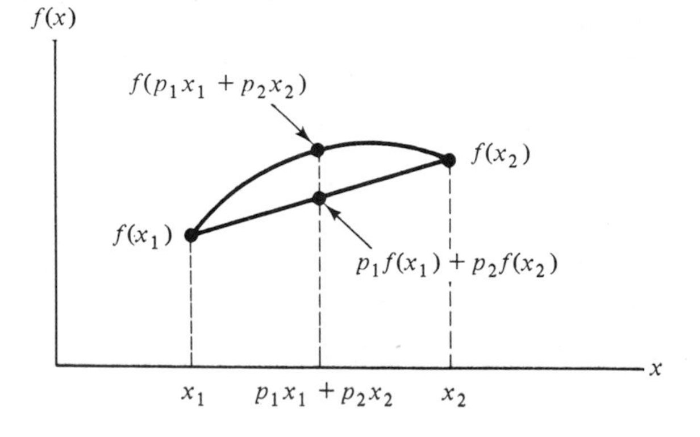

Figure 1B.1 Convex $\cap$ function.

Again using (1B.1) on the binary distribution $(p_1 + p_2)$ and p_3 defined at the points $\xi \equiv (p_1 x_1 + p_2 x_2)/(p_1 + p_2)$ and x_3, we have

$$(p_1 + p_2) f(\xi) + p_3 f(x_3) \le f[(p_1 + p_2)\xi + p_3 x_3] \tag{1B.3}$$

Substituting for ξ and combining (1B.2) and (1B.3), we obtain

$$p_1 f(x_1) + p_2 f(x_2) + p_3 f(x_3) \le f(p_1 x_1 + p_2 x_2 + p_3 x_3) \tag{1B.4}$$

We proceed to extend by induction to a finite distribution of order n. Suppose that for a distribution of order $n - 1$

$$\sum_{i=1}^{n-1} p_i f(x_i) \le f\left(\sum_{i=1}^{n-1} p_i x_i\right) \tag{1B.5}$$

Then for order n

$$\sum_{j=1}^{n} p_j f(x_j) = \sum_{i=1}^{n-1} p_i \frac{\sum_{j=1}^{n-1} p_j f(x_j)}{\sum_{i=1}^{n-1} p_i} + p_n f(x_n)$$

$$\le \sum_{i=1}^{n-1} p_i f(\xi) + p_n f(x_n) \tag{1B.6}$$

where

$$\xi \equiv \sum_{j=1}^{n-1} p_j x_j \bigg/ \sum_{i=1}^{n-1} p_i$$

and where we used (1B.5) and the fact that $p_j / \sum_{i=1}^{n-1} p_i$, for $j = 1, 2, \ldots, (n - 1)$, constitutes an $(n - 1)$-point distribution. Now applying (1B.1) on the binary distribution $\sum_{i=1}^{n-1} p_i$ and p_n, it follows that

$$\sum_{i=1}^{n-1} p_i f(\xi) + p_n f(x_n) \le f\left(\sum_{i=1}^{n-1} p_i \xi + p_n x_n\right) \tag{1B.7}$$

Finally, combining (1B.6) and (1B.7), we have

$$\sum_{j=1}^{n} p_j f(x_j) \le f\left(\sum_{j=1}^{n} p_j x_j\right) \tag{1B.8}$$

or $E[f(x)] \le f(E[x])$, as was to be shown.

Extension to any infinite discrete sample space is direct as is extension to any distribution function $P(\cdot)$ for which the Stieltjes integral $\int f(x)\, dP(x)$ exists. For such cases (1B.8) becomes

$$\int f(x)\, dP(x) \le f\left(\int x\, dP(x)\right) \tag{1B.9}$$

Inequalities (1B.8) and (1B.9) can be expressed generically as

$$E[f(x)] \leq f(E[x])$$

where $f(x)$ is a convex $\cap$ function. If $f(x)$ is convex $\cup$, it immediately follows that all inequalities are reversed.

PROBLEMS

1.1 Examples of entropy

(*a*) For a DMS with $A = 2$ output letters $\mathcal{U} = \{a_1, a_2\}$ and $P(a_1) = p$, show by direct differentiation that the entropy

$$H(\mathcal{U}) = \mathcal{H}(p) \equiv p \log \frac{1}{p} + (1 - p) \log \frac{1}{1 - p}$$

is maximized when $p = \frac{1}{2}$.

(*b*) For the binary source in (*a*) consider sequences of two outputs as a single source output of an extended source with alphabet $\mathcal{U}_2 = \{(a_1, a_1), (a_1, a_2), (a_2, a_1), (a_2, a_2)\}$. Show directly that $H(\mathcal{U}_2) = 2H(\mathcal{U})$.

(*c*) Consider the drawing of a card (with replacement) from a deck of 52 playing cards as a DMS. What is the entropy of a randomly selected card? Suppose suits are ignored so that the output space is now $\mathcal{U} = \{A, 2, 3, 4, 5, 6, 7, 8, 9, 10, J, Q, K\}$. What is the entropy of a randomly selected card now? What if $\mathcal{U} = \{\text{face card, not a face card}\}$?

(*d*) What is the entropy of the output of the toss of a fair die? Suppose the die is biased so that the probability of any face is proportional to the number of dots; now what is the entropy?

1.2 Given a sequence of discrete random variables $u_1, u_2, \ldots, u_N$ with alphabets $\mathcal{U}^{(1)}, \mathcal{U}^{(2)}, \ldots, \mathcal{U}^{(N)}$ and a joint probability $P_N(\mathbf{u})$ for $\mathbf{u} \in \mathcal{U}^{(1)} \times \mathcal{U}^{(2)} \times \cdots \times \mathcal{U}^{(N)}$. Its entropy is

$$H(\mathcal{U}^{(1)}\mathcal{U}^{(2)} \ldots \mathcal{U}^{(N)}) = \sum_{\mathbf{u}} P_N(\mathbf{u}) \log \frac{1}{P_N(\mathbf{u})}$$

Show that

$$H(\mathcal{U}^{(1)}\mathcal{U}^{(2)} \cdots \mathcal{U}^{(N)}) \leq \sum_{n=1}^{N} H(\mathcal{U}^{(n)})$$

with equality if and only if the random variables are independent. Here $H(\mathcal{U}^{(n)})$ is the entropy of the nth random variable.

1.3 For an arbitrary stationary ergodic source define entropy as

$$\hat{H}(\mathcal{U}) = \lim_{N \to \infty} \frac{H(\mathcal{U}_N)}{N}$$

where

$$H(\mathcal{U}_N) = \sum_{\mathbf{u}} P_N(\mathbf{u}) \log \frac{1}{P_N(\mathbf{u})}$$

The asymptotic equipartition property of stationary ergodic sources gives

$$\lim_{N \to \infty} F_N = 0$$

for any $\epsilon > 0$, where $F_N = \Pr\left\{\mathbf{u}: \left| -\frac{1}{N} \log P_N(\mathbf{u}) - \hat{H} \right| > \epsilon\right\}$.

(*a*) Show that

$$\frac{H(\mathcal{U}_n)}{n} \le \frac{H(\mathcal{U}_k)}{k} \qquad \text{for} \quad k \le n$$

(*b*) Prove the noiseless source coding theorem assuming that

$$\lim_{N \to \infty} F_N = 0$$

1.4 (Chebyshev Inequality and the Weak Law of Large Numbers)

(*a*) Show that for a random variable x with mean m and variance σ^2, $\Pr\{|x - m| \ge \epsilon\} \le \sigma^2/\epsilon^2$ for any $\epsilon > 0$.

(*b*) Let $z_1, z_2, \ldots, z_N$ be independent identically distributed random variables with mean $\bar{z}$ and variance σ^2. Show that for any $\epsilon > 0$

$$\Pr\left\{\mathbf{z} : \frac{1}{N}\sum_{n=1}^{N} z_n \ge \bar{z} + \epsilon\right\} \le \frac{\sigma^2}{N\epsilon^2}$$

and

$$\Pr\left\{\mathbf{z} : \left|\frac{1}{N}\sum_{n=1}^{N} z_n - \bar{z}\right| \ge \epsilon\right\} \le \frac{\sigma^2}{N\epsilon^2}$$

Hint: Lower bound the variance of x by reducing the region of integration.

1.5 (Chernoff Bound) Show that F_N defined in (1.1.23) decreases at least exponentially with N by the following steps:

(*a*) Define $\overline{S(N, \epsilon)_+} = \{\mathbf{u} : (1/N) \log P_N(\mathbf{u}) - H > \epsilon\}$.

(*b*) For z_n defined in (1.1.26), note that for $\mathbf{u} \in \overline{S(N, \epsilon)_+}$

$$\sum_{n=1}^{N} z_n - N(H + \epsilon) \ge 0$$

Hence for any $s \ge 0$ show that

$$\begin{aligned} F_N^+ &= \sum_{\mathbf{u} \in \overline{S(N,\epsilon)_+}} P_N(\mathbf{u}) \\ &\le E\left[2^{s\left[\sum_{n=1}^{N} z_n - N(H+\epsilon)\right]}\right] \\ &= 2^{-NG(s)} \end{aligned}$$

where

$$\begin{aligned} G(s) &= s[H + \epsilon] - \log E[2^{sz}] \\ &= s[H + \epsilon] - \log\left\{\sum_{k=1}^{A} P(a_k)^{1-s}\right\} \end{aligned}$$

Hint: $1 \le \exp s[\sum_{n=1}^{N} z_n - N(H + \epsilon)]$ for $\mathbf{u} \in \overline{S(N, \epsilon)_+}$.

(*c*) By examining the first two derivatives of $G(s)$ show that for some $s^* \ge 0$ we have

$$F_N^+ \le 2^{-NG(s^*)}$$

where $G(s^*) > 0$.

(*d*) Do the same for

$$\overline{S(N, \epsilon)_-} = \{\mathbf{u} : (1/N) \log P_N(\mathbf{u}) - H < -\epsilon\}$$

then combine with the result of (*c*) to get the desired bound.

1.6 Assume a DMS with alphabet $\mathscr{U} = \{a_1, a_2, \ldots, a_A\}$ and probability $P(u)$ for $u \in \mathscr{U}$.

(*a*) For each $u \in \mathscr{U}$ pick a binary codeword of length $l(u)$ which satisfies

$$\log \frac{1}{P(u)} \leq l(u) < \log \frac{1}{P(u)} + 1$$

Show that the average length

$$\langle L \rangle = \sum_u P(u) l(u)$$

satisfies

$$H(\mathscr{U}) < \langle L \rangle < H(\mathscr{U}) + 1$$

(*b*) Repeat (*a*) for source sequences of length N and obtain A^N binary codewords of lengths $\{l(\mathbf{u}) : \mathbf{u} \in \mathscr{U}_N\}$ with average length

$$\langle L_N \rangle = \sum_{\mathbf{u}} P_N(\mathbf{u}) l(\mathbf{u})$$

which satisfies

$$NH(\mathscr{U}) \leq \langle L_N \rangle < NH(\mathscr{U}) + 1$$

(*c*) Show that the code words in (*a*) and (*b*) can be chosen such that no codeword of length l is identical to the first l bits of a codeword of length greater than or equal to l. That is, no codeword is a prefix of another. Such a set of distinct codewords has the uniquely decodable property that no two different codeword sequences can form the same binary sequence. Hence with these codes the source outputs can be uniquely determined from the binary-code sequence.

1.7 Show that

(*a*)
$$I(\mathscr{X}; \mathscr{Y}) \leq H(\mathscr{X})$$

and

$$I(\mathscr{X}; \mathscr{Y}) \leq H(\mathscr{Y})$$

where $I(\mathscr{X}; \mathscr{Y})$ is defined by (1.2.7) and

$$H(\mathscr{X}) = \sum_x q(x) \log \frac{1}{q(x)}$$

$$H(\mathscr{Y}) = \sum_y p(y) \log \frac{1}{p(y)}$$

(*b*)
$$H(\mathscr{X}; \mathscr{Y}) = H(\mathscr{Y}) + H(\mathscr{X} \mid \mathscr{Y})$$

where

$$H(\mathscr{X}; \mathscr{Y}) = \sum_x \sum_y p(x, y) \log \frac{1}{p(x, y)}$$

$$H(\mathscr{X} \mid \mathscr{Y}) = \sum_x \sum_y p(x, y) \log \frac{1}{q(x \mid y)}$$

1.8 Find the average mutual information between inputs and outputs of the following DMCs. Then find their capacities.

(*a*) The binary erasure channel (BEC) of Fig. P1.8*a*

(*b*) The Z channel of Fig. P1.8*b*

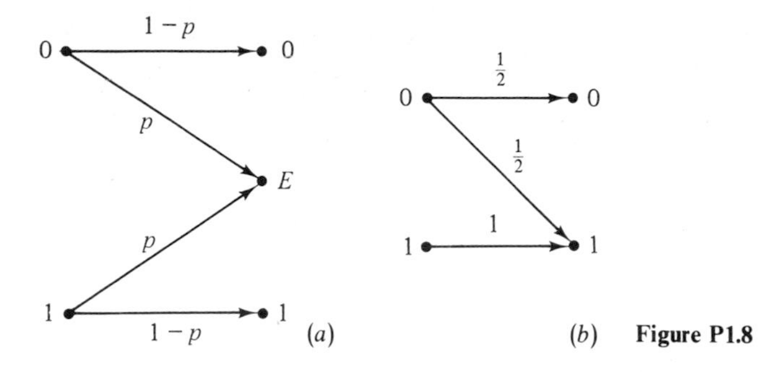

Figure P1.8

1.9 For the BEC given in Prob. 1.8(a) suppose that the encoder can observe the outputs of the channel and constructs a variable length code as follows:

When the information symbol (assume a zero-memory binary-symmetric information source) is a "0," then the encoder keeps sending 0s across the channel until an unerased output is achieved. If the information symbol is a "1," then the encoder keeps sending 1s until an unerased output is achieved. For each information symbol the number of channel symbols used is a random variable.

Compute the average codeword length for each information bit. What is the rate of this encoding scheme measured in information bits per channel use? What is the information bit error probability?

1.10 There are two biased coins in a box. The first coin when flipped will produce a "head" with probability $\frac{3}{4}$ while the second coin will produce a "head" with probability $\frac{1}{4}$. A coin is randomly selected from the box and flipped.

(a) If a head appears how much information does this provide about the first coin being selected? The second coin?

(b) What is the average mutual information provided about the coin selected when the outcome of a flip of a randomly selected coin is observed?

1.11 There are 13 coins of which 12 are known to have equal weight. The remaining coin is either the same weight or heavier or lighter than the other coins. The objective is to find the odd coin, if any, after the coins are mixed and determine whether the odd coin is heavy or light by using a balance and a known standard coin.

(a) Show by considering the information provided that it is impossible to guarantee solving the problem in two uses of the balance. Similarly show that it might be possible always to solve the problem in three weighings.

(b) By trying to maximize the average information provided by the three weighings, give a weighing strategy that works.

(c) Show that three weighings are not enough without the standard coin.

1.12 For a finite alphabet $\mathscr{U}$ consider the three distributions $P_1(u)$, $P_2(u)$, and $P_\lambda(u) = \lambda P_1(u) + (1 - \lambda)P_2(u)$ for all $u \in \mathscr{U}$ and $\lambda \in (0, 1)$. Let $H_1(\mathscr{U})$, $H_2(\mathscr{U})$, and $H_\lambda(\mathscr{U})$, be the corresponding entropies. Using inequality (1.1.8) show that

$$\lambda H_1(\mathscr{U}) + (1 - \lambda)H_2(\mathscr{U}) \le H_\lambda(\mathscr{U})$$

1.13 Let y be an absolutely continuous random variable with probability density function $p(y)$, $y \in \mathscr{Y}$ where

$$\int_{-\infty}^{\infty} yp(y)\, dy = 0 \qquad \text{and} \qquad \int_{-\infty}^{\infty} y^2 p(y)\, dy = \sigma_y^2$$

Using a version of (1.1.8) show that

$$\int_{-\infty}^{\infty} p(y) \log \frac{1}{p(y)}\, dy \le \tfrac{1}{2} \log (2\pi e \sigma_y^2)$$

with equality when y is a Gaussian random variable. Use this to find the maximum mutual information,

$I(\mathscr{X};\mathscr{Y})$ for the additive Gaussian noise channel of Fig. 1.5 where we maximize over the input probability density function $q(x)$, $x \in \mathscr{X}$ subject to

$$\int_{-\infty}^{\infty} xq(x)\,dx = 0 \qquad \text{and} \qquad \int_{-\infty}^{\infty} x^2 q(x)\,dx = \mathscr{E}$$

1.14 Use the source encoder discussed in Prob. 1.6(*b*) to show that in the limit of large N the combination of source and source encoder approximates (in the sense that H_N, defined below, approaches 1 as $N \to \infty$) a binary-symmetric source. Do this by the following steps.

(*a*) If source sequence $\mathbf{u} \in \mathscr{U}_N$ is mapped into codeword $\mathbf{x}(\mathbf{u})$ of length $l(\mathbf{u})$ then the encoder output has normalized information of

$$\frac{-\log P_N(\mathbf{u})}{l(\mathbf{u})} \qquad \text{bits/binary symbol}$$

The average information per binary symbol out of the source encoder is then

$$H_N = \sum_{\mathbf{u}} P_N(\mathbf{u})\left(\frac{-\log P_N(\mathbf{u})}{l(\mathbf{u})}\right)$$

Show that

$$1 + \frac{1}{N \log P(u^*)} \le H_N \le 1 \qquad \text{where} \qquad P(u^*) = \max_{u \in \mathscr{U}} P(u)$$

(*b*) Next show that the binary-symmetric source (BSS) is the only binary source that has $H_N = 1$ for all N.

1.15 Use the source encoder described in the proof of Theorem 1.1.1 (see Fig. 1.3) to show that in the limit of large N the combination of source and source encoder becomes a binary-symmetric source in the sense that $H_N \to 1$ as $N \to \infty$.

CHAPTER
TWO
CHANNEL MODELS AND BLOCK CODING

2.1 BLOCK-CODED DIGITAL COMMUNICATION ON THE ADDITIVE GAUSSIAN NOISE CHANNEL

The most general digital communication system to be treated in this chapter and the next is that shown in Fig. 2.1. The input digital data is usually binary, but may have been encoded into any alphabet of $q \geq 2$ symbols. The incoming data which arrives at the rate of one symbol every T_s seconds is stored in an input register until a *block* of K data symbols[1] has been accumulated. This block is then presented to the channel encoder, as one of M possible messages, denoted H_1, H_2, ..., H_M where $M = q^K$ and q is the size of the data alphabet. The combination of encoder and modulator performs a mapping from a set of M messages, $\{H_m\}$, onto a set of M finite-energy signals, $\{x_m(t)\}$, of finite duration $T = KT_s$.

While the encoder–modulator would appear thus to perform a single indivisible function, it can in fact be divided into separate discrete-time and continuous-time operations. The justification for this separation lies in the *Gram-Schmidt orthogonalization* procedure which permits the representation of any M finite-energy time functions as linear combinations of $N \leq M$ orthonormal *basis functions*. That is, over the finite interval $0 \leq t \leq T$ the M finite-energy signals $x_1(t)$, $x_2(t)$, ..., $x_M(t)$, representing the M block messages H_1, H_2, ..., H_M respectively, can be expressed as (see App. 2.A)

$$x_m(t) = \sum_{n=1}^{N} x_{mn} \phi_n(t) \qquad m = 1, 2, \ldots, M \tag{2.1.1}$$

[1] When the data alphabet is binary, these are generally called bits, whether or not they correspond to bits of information in the sense of Sec. 1.1.

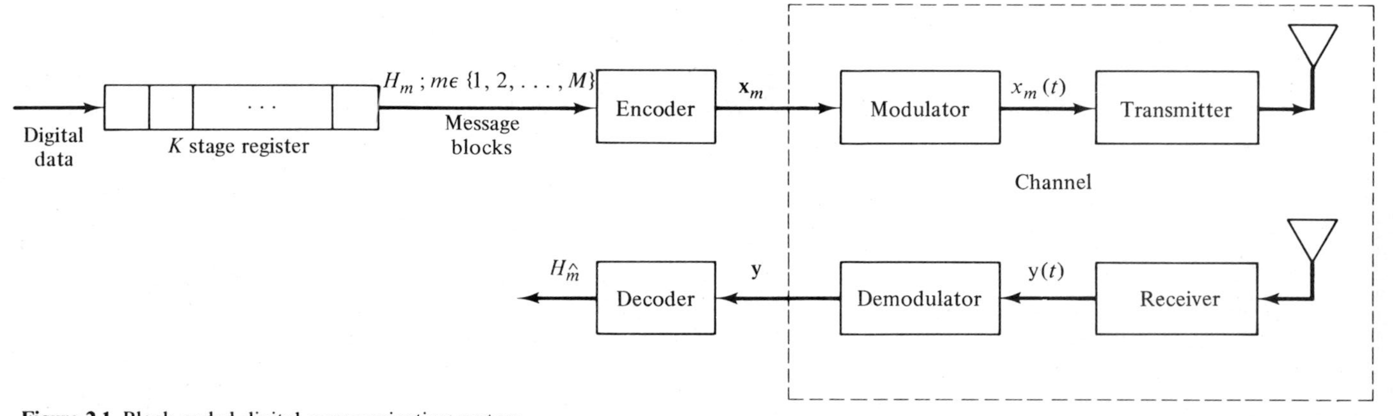

Figure 2.1 Block-coded digital communication system.

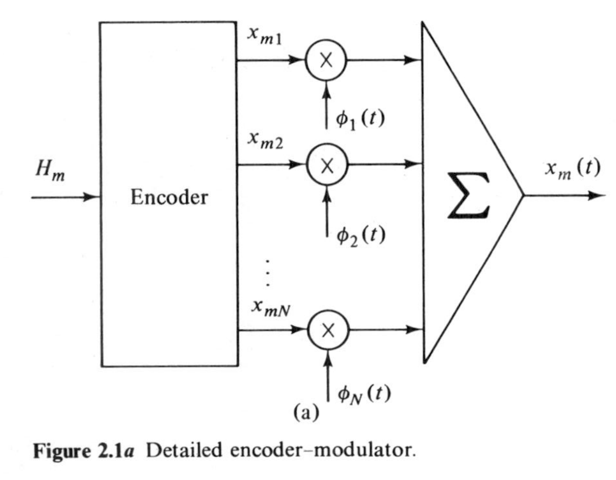

Figure 2.1*a* Detailed encoder–modulator.

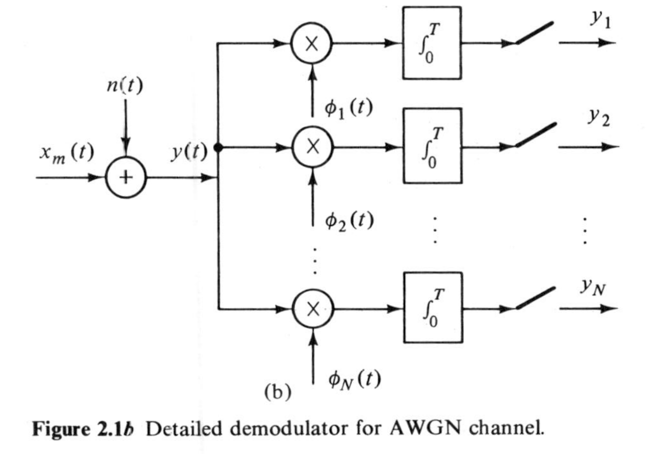

Figure 2.1*b* Detailed demodulator for AWGN channel.

where for each m and n

$$x_{mn} = \int_0^T x_m(t)\phi_n(t)\,dt$$

and the basis functions $\{\phi_1(t), \phi_2(t), \ldots, \phi_N(t)\}$ are orthonormal:

$$\int_0^T \phi_k(t)\phi_j(t)\,dt = \delta_{kj} \equiv \begin{cases} 1 & \text{if } k = j \\ 0 & \text{if } k \neq j \end{cases} \tag{2.1.2}$$

and $N \leq M$. In fact, $N = M$ if and only if the signals are linearly independent. A consequence of this representation is that the signal energies can be expressed as square norms of the vectors

$$\mathbf{x}_m = (x_{m1}, x_{m2}, \ldots, x_{mN}) \qquad m = 1, 2, \ldots, M$$

for it follows from (2.1.2) that for each m

$$\begin{aligned}
\mathscr{E}_m &\equiv \int_0^T [x_m(t)]^2\,dt \\
&= \int_0^T \left[\sum_{n=1}^N x_{mn}\phi_n(t)\right]^2 dt \\
&= \sum_{n=1}^N \sum_{j=1}^N x_{mn}x_{mj} \int_0^T \phi_n\phi_j(t)\,dt \\
&= \sum_{n=1}^N [x_{mn}]^2 \\
&= \|\mathbf{x}_m\|^2
\end{aligned} \tag{2.1.3}$$

The representation (2.1.1) suggests the general implementation of encoder and modulator shown in Fig. 2.1*a*. Thus the encoder becomes a mapping from a discrete set of M messages to a vector of $N \leq M$ real numbers. The most general modulator consists of N amplitude modulators [waveform $\phi_n(t)$ modulated by amplitudes x_{mn} for $n = 1, 2, \ldots, N$] followed by a summer. In fact, this most general form is considerably simplified, as will be discussed in Sec. 2.7, when the amplitudes $\{x_{mn}\}$ are constrained to be elements of a finite alphabet so that strictly digital encoders can be used, and when the basis functions $\{\phi_n(t)\}$ are chosen to be disjoint time-orthogonal (i.e., functions which take on nonzero values on disjoint time intervals) only a single time-shared modulator need be implemented.

The transmitter and receiver of the general system of Fig. 2.1, together with the propagation medium, may be regarded as a random mapping from the finite set of transmitted waveforms $\{x_m(t)\}$ to the received random process $y(t)$. All sorts of distortions including fading, multipath, intersymbol interference, nonlinear distortion, and additive noise may be inflicted upon the signal by the propagation medium and the electromagnetic componentry before it emerges from the receiver. At this point the only disturbance that we will consider is additive white

Gaussian noise, both to establish a minimally complex model for our starting point, and also because this model is in fact very accurate for an important class of communication systems. In Secs. 2.6 and 2.12 we shall consider the influence of some of the other forms of disturbance just mentioned.

The *additive white Gaussian noise* (*AWGN*) *channel* is modeled simply with a summing junction, as shown in Fig. 2.1*b*. For an input $x_m(t)$, the output[2] is

$$y(t) = x_m(t) + n(t) \qquad 0 \le t \le T \tag{2.1.4}$$

where $n(t)$ is a stationary random process whose power is spread uniformly over a bandwidth much wider than the signal bandwidth; hence it is modeled as a process with a uniform arbitrarily wide spectral density, or, equivalently, with covariance function

$$R(\tau) = (N_0/2)\,\delta(\tau) \tag{2.1.5}$$

where $\delta(\cdot)$ is the Dirac delta function and N_0 is the one-sided noise power spectral density.[3]

The demodulator–decoder can be regarded in general as a mapping from the received process $y(t)$ to a decision on the state of the original message $H_{\hat{m}}$. But, for this specific channel model, the demodulator–decoder can also be decomposed into two separate functions which are essentially the duals of those performed by the encoder–modulator. Consider first projecting the random process $y(t)$ onto each of the modulator's *basis* functions, thus generating the N integral inner products

$$y_n = \int_0^T y(t)\phi_n(t)\,dt \qquad n = 1, 2, \ldots, N \tag{2.1.6}$$

This can be performed by the system of Fig. 2.1*b*. We define also

$$n_n \equiv \int_0^T n(t)\phi_n(t)\,dt \qquad n = 1, 2, \ldots, N \tag{2.1.7}$$

and hence it follows from (2.1.1) and (2.1.4) that

$$y_n = x_{mn} + n_n \qquad n = 1, 2, \ldots, N \tag{2.1.8}$$

Now consider the process

$$\tilde{y}(t) = y(t) - \sum_{n=1}^{N} y_n\phi_n(t) \tag{2.1.9}$$

[2] Although the propagation medium naturally attenuates the signal, we may ignore this effect by conceptually amplifying both signal and noise to the normalized pretransmission level.

[3] This means that, in response to this noise input, an ideal bandpass filter of bandwidth 1 Hz would produce an output power of N_0 watts.

Given that $x_m(t)$ is the transmitted signal, it follows from (2.1.9) and (2.1.1) that this process can be written as

$$\tilde{y}(t) = x_m(t) + n(t) - \sum_{n=1}^{N} (x_{mn} + n_n)\phi_n(t)$$

$$= n(t) - \sum_{n=1}^{N} n_n \phi_n(t) \equiv \tilde{n}(t) \qquad (2.1.10)$$

which depends only on the noise process. Thus we may represent the original process as

$$y(t) = \sum_{n=1}^{N} y_n \phi_n(t) + \tilde{y}(t) = \sum_{n=1}^{N} y_n \phi_n(t) + \tilde{n}(t) \qquad (2.1.11)$$

Now, as will be elaborated upon in Sec. 2.2, any statistical decision regarding the transmitted message is based on the a priori probabilities of the messages and on the conditional probabilities (densities or distributions) of the measurements performed on $y(t)$, generally called the *observables*. Suppose, for the moment, that we take as the observables only the N projections $\{y_n\}$ defined by (2.1.6). Because $y(t)$, defined by (2.1.4), is a Gaussian process, the observables are Gaussian variables with means depending only on the corresponding signal components, since

$$E(y_n | \mathbf{x}_m) = \int_0^T x_m(t)\phi_n(t)\,dt$$

$$= x_{mn} \qquad n = 1, 2, \ldots, N \qquad (2.1.12)$$

and with variances equal to $N_o/2$, since for any n

$$\text{var}\,[y_n | \mathbf{x}_m] = E[(y_n - x_{mn})^2 | \mathbf{x}_m]$$

$$= E[n_n^2]$$

$$= E\left[\int_0^T \int_0^T n(t)n(u)\phi_n(t)\phi_n(u)\,dt\,du\right]$$

$$= (N_o/2) \int_0^T \int_0^T \delta(t-u)\phi_n(t)\phi_n(u)\,dt\,du$$

$$= (N_o/2) \int_0^T \phi_n^2(t)\,dt$$

$$= N_o/2 \qquad (2.1.13)$$

Similarly, it follows that these observables are mutually uncorrelated since, for $n \neq l$,

$$\begin{aligned}
\operatorname{cov}[y_n, y_l \mid \mathbf{x}_m] &= E[n_n n_l] \\
&= E\left[\int_0^T \int_0^T n(t)n(u)\phi_n(t)\phi_l(u)\,dt\,du\right] \\
&= (N_o/2)\int_0^T \phi_n(t)\phi_l(t)\,dt \\
&= 0
\end{aligned} \tag{2.1.14}$$

which, since the variables are Gaussian, implies that they are also independent. Then defining the vector of N observables

$$\mathbf{y} = (y_1, y_2, \ldots, y_N)$$

whose components are independent Gaussian variables with means given by (2.1.12) and variances $N_o/2$, it follows that the conditional probability density of $\mathbf{y}$ given the signal vector $\mathbf{x}_m$ (or equivalently, given that message H_m was sent) is

$$\begin{aligned}
p_N(\mathbf{y} \mid \mathbf{x}_m) &= \prod_{n=1}^{N} p(y_n \mid x_{mn}) \\
&= \prod_{n=1}^{N} \frac{e^{-[y_n - x_{mn}]^2/N_o}}{\sqrt{\pi N_o}}
\end{aligned} \tag{2.1.15}$$

Returning to the representation (2.1.11) of $y(t)$, while it is clear that the vector of observables $\mathbf{y} = (y_1, y_2, \ldots, y_N)$ completely characterizes the terms of the summation, there remains the term $\tilde{n}(t)$, defined by (2.1.10), which depends only on the noise and not at all on the signals. Furthermore, since the noise has zero mean, $\tilde{n}(t)$ is a zero-mean Gaussian process. Finally, $\tilde{n}(t)$, and hence any observable derived therefrom, is independent of all the observables $\{y_n\}$ because

$$\begin{aligned}
E[\tilde{n}(t)y_j] &= E\left[\tilde{n}(t)\int_0^T y(u)\phi_j(u)\,du\right] \\
&= E\left[\left(n(t) - \sum_{n=1}^{N} n_n \phi_n(t)\right)(x_{mj} + n_j)\right] \\
&= E\left[n(t)\int_0^T n(u)\phi_j(u)\,du\right] - \sum_{n=1}^{N} E(n_n n_j)\phi_n(t) \\
&= (N_o/2)\phi_j(t) - (N_o/2)\phi_j(t) \\
&= 0 \qquad\qquad j = 1, 2, \ldots, N
\end{aligned}$$

Thus, since any observable based on $\tilde{n}(t)$ is independent of the observables $\{y_n\}$ and of the transmitted signal $\mathbf{x}_m$, it should be clear that such an observable is irrelevant to the decision of which message was transmitted. More explicitly, if $\tilde{\mathbf{n}}$ is

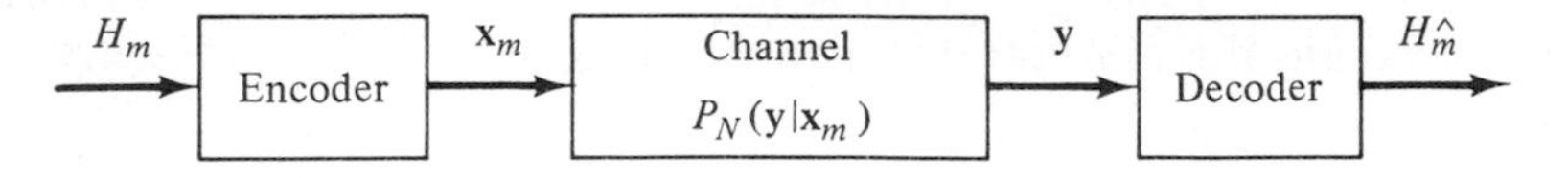

Figure 2.2 General memoryless channel.

any vector of N' observables based only on $\tilde{n}(t)$, then it follows from the above that the joint conditional probability density is

$$p_{N+N'}(\mathbf{y}, \tilde{\mathbf{n}} \,|\, \mathbf{x}_m) = p_N(\mathbf{y} \,|\, \mathbf{x}_m) p_{N'}(\tilde{\mathbf{n}})$$

Since the term $p_{N'}(\tilde{\mathbf{n}})$ enters into all the conditional densities (for $m = 1, 2, \ldots, M$) in identically the same way, it is useless in making the decision.

Hence, we conclude finally that the components of the original observable vector $\mathbf{y}$ are the only data based on $y(t)$ useful for the decision and thus represent *sufficient statistics*. Therefore the demodulator can be implemented as shown in Fig. 2.1*b*. The time-continuous process is thus reduced by the demodulator to the N-dimensional random vector $\mathbf{y}$ which then constitutes the input to the decoder whose structure we shall study in the next section. We may summarize the results of this section by noting that, for the AWGN channel, by using the general but explicit forms of modulators and demodulators of Figs. 2.1*a* and 2.1*b*, we can N-dimensional random vector $\mathbf{y}$ which then constitutes the input to the decoder model of Fig. 2.2 where the channel is in effect a random mapping defined by the conditional probability density

$$p_N(\mathbf{y} \,|\, \mathbf{x}_m) = \prod_{n=1}^{N} p(y_n \,|\, x_{mn}) \tag{2.1.16}$$

While this result has only been shown to characterize an AWGN channel, many other channels can be characterized in this way. Any channel whose conditional (or transition) probability density (or distribution) satisfies (2.1.16) is called a *memoryless* channel. We shall discuss a class of memoryless channels derived from the AWGN channel in Sec. 2.8, and give more elaborate examples in Sec. 2.12.

2.2 MINIMUM ERROR PROBABILITY AND MAXIMUM LIKELIHOOD DECODER

There remain the problems of characterizing more explicitly the encoder and decoder. Both will occupy the better part of this book. The principles and optimal design of the decoder are more easily developed, although its implementation is usually more complex than that of the encoder. The goal of the decoder is to perform a mapping from the vector $\mathbf{y}$ to a decision $H_{\hat{m}}$ on the message transmitted. Such a decision must be based on some desirable criterion of performance. The most reasonable, as well as the most convenient, criterion for this decision is to minimize the probability of error of the decision. Suppose that, when the vector $\mathbf{y}$ takes on some particular value (a real vector), we make the decision $H_{\hat{m}} = H_m$.

The probability of an error in this decision, which we denote by $P_E(H_m; \mathbf{y})$, is just

$$P_E(H_m; \mathbf{y}) = \Pr(H_m \text{ not sent} \mid \mathbf{y}) = 1 - \Pr(H_m \text{ sent} \mid \mathbf{y}) \tag{2.2.1}$$

Now, since our criterion is to minimize the error probability in mapping each given $\mathbf{y}$ into a decision, it follows that the optimum decision rule is

$$H_{\hat{m}} = H_m \qquad \text{if } \Pr(H_m \text{ sent} \mid \mathbf{y}) \geq \Pr(H_{m'} \text{ sent} \mid \mathbf{y}) \qquad \text{for all } m' \neq m \tag{2.2.2}$$

If m satisfies inequality (2.2.2) but equality holds for one or more values of m', we may choose any of these m' as the decision and achieve the same error probability.

Condition (2.2.1), which is completely general for any channel (memoryless or not), can be expressed more explicitly in terms of the prior probabilities of the messages

$$\pi_m \equiv \Pr(H_m \text{ sent}) \qquad m = 1, 2, \ldots, M \tag{2.2.3}$$

and in terms of the conditional probabilities of $\mathbf{y}$ given each H_m (usually called the *likelihood functions*[4])

$$p_N(\mathbf{y} \mid H_m) = p_N(\mathbf{y} \mid \mathbf{x}_m) \qquad m = 1, 2, \ldots, M \tag{2.2.4}$$

This last relation follows from the fact that the mapping from H_m to $\mathbf{x}_m$, which is the coding operation, is deterministic and one-to-one. These likelihood functions, which are in fact the channel characterization (Fig. 2.2), are also called the *channel transition probabilities*. Applying Bayes' rule to (2.2.2), using (2.2.3) and (2.2.4), and for the moment ignoring ties, we conclude that, to minimize error probability, the optimum decision is

$$H_{\hat{m}} = H_m \qquad \text{if } \frac{\pi_m p_N(\mathbf{y} \mid \mathbf{x}_m)}{p_N(\mathbf{y})} > \frac{\pi_{m'} p_N(\mathbf{y} \mid \mathbf{x}_{m'})}{p_N(\mathbf{y})} \qquad \text{for all } m' \neq m \tag{2.2.5}$$

Since the denominator $p_N(\mathbf{y})$, the unconditional probability (density) of $\mathbf{y}$, is independent of m, it can be ignored. Also, since it is usually more convenient to perform summations than multiplications, and since if $A > B > 0$ then $\ln A > \ln B$, we rewrite (2.2.5) as

$$H_{\hat{m}} = H_m \qquad \text{if } \ln \pi_m + \ln p_N(\mathbf{y} \mid \mathbf{x}_m) > \ln \pi_{m'} + \ln p_N(\mathbf{y} \mid \mathbf{x}_{m'}) \qquad \text{for all } m' \neq m \tag{2.2.6}$$

For a *memoryless* channel as defined by (2.1.16), this decision simplifies further to

$$H_{\hat{m}} = H_m$$

if

$$\ln \pi_m + \sum_{n=1}^{N} \ln p(y_n \mid x_{mn}) > \ln \pi_{m'} + \sum_{n=1}^{N} \ln p(y_n \mid x_{m'n}) \qquad \text{for all } m' \neq m \tag{2.2.7}$$

[4] $p_N(\cdot)$ is a density function if $\mathbf{y}$ is a vector of continuous random variables, and is a distribution if $\mathbf{y}$ is a vector of discrete random variables.

Another useful interpretation of the above, consistent with our original view of the decoder as a mapping, is that the decision rule (2.2.6) or (2.2.7) defines a partition of the N-dimensional space of all observable vectors $\mathbf{y}$ into regions Λ_1, $\Lambda_2, \ldots, \Lambda_M$ where

$$\Lambda_m \equiv \{\mathbf{y} : \ln \pi_m + \ln p_N(\mathbf{y}|\mathbf{x}_m) > \ln \pi_{m'} + \ln p_N(\mathbf{y}|\mathbf{x}_{m'})\} \qquad \text{for all } m' \neq m\} \tag{2.2.8}$$

As is clear from their definition, these regions must be disjoint, i.e.,

$$\Lambda_k \cap \Lambda_j = \varnothing \qquad \text{for all } k \neq j \tag{2.2.9}$$

Then the decision rule can indeed be considered as the mapping from $\mathbf{y}$ to $H_{\hat{m}}$ such that

$$\text{if} \qquad \mathbf{y} \in \Lambda_m \qquad \text{then} \qquad H_{\hat{m}}(\mathbf{y}) = H_m \tag{2.2.10}$$

Aside from the boundaries between regions, it is also clear from definition (2.2.8) that the regions Λ_m cover the entire space of observable vectors $\mathbf{y}$. We shall adopt the convention that all ties will be resolved at random. That is, the boundary region between Λ_m and $\Lambda_{m'}$, consisting of all $\mathbf{y}$ for which (2.2.8) becomes an equality, will be resolved a priori by the flip of a fair coin; the outcome of such a flip does not alter the ultimate error probability since, for $\mathbf{y}$ on the boundary, (2.2.2) is satisfied with equality. It then follows that the union of the regions covers the entire N-dimensional observation space $\mathscr{Y}_N$; that is

$$\bigcup_{m=1}^{M} \Lambda_m = \mathscr{Y}_N \tag{2.2.11}$$

The above concept can best be demonstrated by examining again the AWGN channel defined by (2.1.15). Since the channel is memoryless, we have, using (2.1.16) and (2.1.3) and the boundary convention[5]

$$\begin{aligned}
\Lambda_m &= \left\{\mathbf{y}: \ln\left(\frac{\pi_m}{\pi_{m'}}\right) + \sum_{n=1}^{N} \ln\left[\frac{p(y_n|x_{mn})}{p(y_n|x_{m'n})}\right] \geq 0 \qquad \text{for all } m' \neq m\right\} \\
&= \left\{\mathbf{y}: \ln\left(\frac{\pi_m}{\pi_{m'}}\right) - \frac{1}{N_0}\|\mathbf{y} - \mathbf{x}_m\|^2 + \frac{1}{N_0}\|\mathbf{y} - \mathbf{x}_{m'}\|^2 \geq 0 \qquad \text{for all } m' \neq m\right\} \\
&= \left\{\mathbf{y}: \ln\left(\frac{\pi_m}{\pi_{m'}}\right) + \frac{1}{N_o}\left(\sum_{n=1}^{N} 2[x_{mn} - x_{m'n}]y_n \right.\right. \\
&\qquad \left.\left. - \sum_{n=1}^{N} [x_{mn}]^2 + \sum_{n=1}^{N} [x_{m'n}]^2\right) \geq 0 \qquad \text{for all } m' \neq m\right\} \\
&= \left\{\mathbf{y}: \frac{2}{N_0}(\mathbf{x}_m - \mathbf{x}_{m'}, \mathbf{y}) - \frac{(\mathscr{E}_m - \mathscr{E}_{m'})}{N_0} + \ln\left(\frac{\pi_m}{\pi_{m'}}\right) \geq 0 \qquad \text{for all } m' \neq m\right\}
\end{aligned} \tag{2.2.12}$$

[5] We denote the inner product $\sum_{n=1}^{N} a_n b_n$ of vectors $\mathbf{a} = (a_1, a_2, \ldots, a_N)$ and $\mathbf{b} = (b_1, b_2, \ldots, b_N)$ by $(\mathbf{a}, \mathbf{b})$.

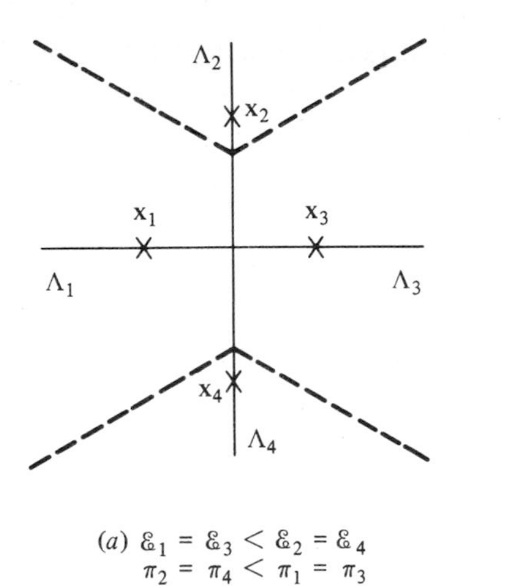

(a) $\mathcal{E}_1 = \mathcal{E}_3 < \mathcal{E}_2 = \mathcal{E}_4$
$\pi_2 = \pi_4 < \pi_1 = \pi_3$

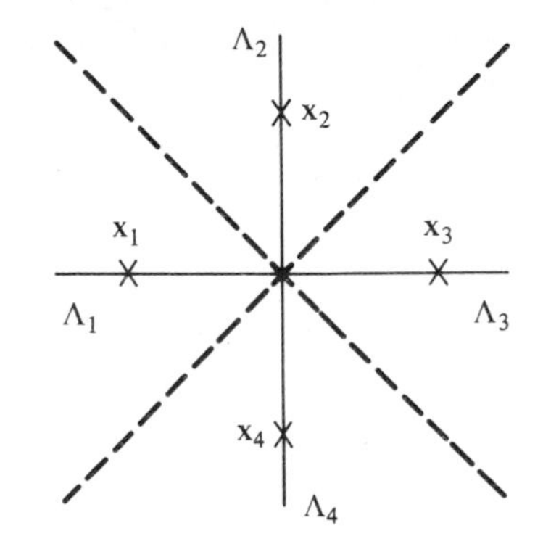

(b) $\mathcal{E}_m = \mathcal{E}, \pi_m = \frac{1}{4} \quad m = 1, 2, 3, 4$

Figure 2.3 Signal sets and decision regions.

Note also that, by virtue of (2.1.1) and (2.1.6)

$$(\mathbf{x}_m - \mathbf{x}_{m'}, \mathbf{y}) = \int_0^T [x_m(t) - x_{m'}(t)]y(t)\, dt$$

while

$$\mathcal{E}_m = \int_0^T x_m^2(t)\, dt$$

Thus it follows from (2.2.12) that for the AWGN channel the decision regions are regions of the N-dimensional real vector space, bounded by linear [$(N - 1)$-dimensional hyperplane] boundaries. Figure 2.3*a* and *b* gives two examples of decision regions for $M = 4$ signals in $N = 2$ dimensions, the first with unequal energies and prior probabilities, and the second with equal energies and prior probabilities, i.e., with $\mathcal{E}_m = \mathcal{E}$ and $\pi_m = 1/M$ for all m. Decision regions for more elaborate signal sets are treated in Probs. 2.1 and 2.2. We note also from this result and (2.2.12) that the decision rule, and hence the decoder, for the AWGN can be implemented as shown in Fig. 2.4, where the M multipliers each multiply the N observables by N signal component values and the products are successively added to form the inner products. When the prior probabilities and energies are all equal, the additional summing junctions can be eliminated. Examples of decoders for other channels will be given in Secs. 2.8 and 2.12.

In most cases of interest, the message a priori probabilities are all equal; that is,

$$\pi_m = \frac{1}{M} \qquad m = 1, 2, \ldots, M \tag{2.2.13}$$

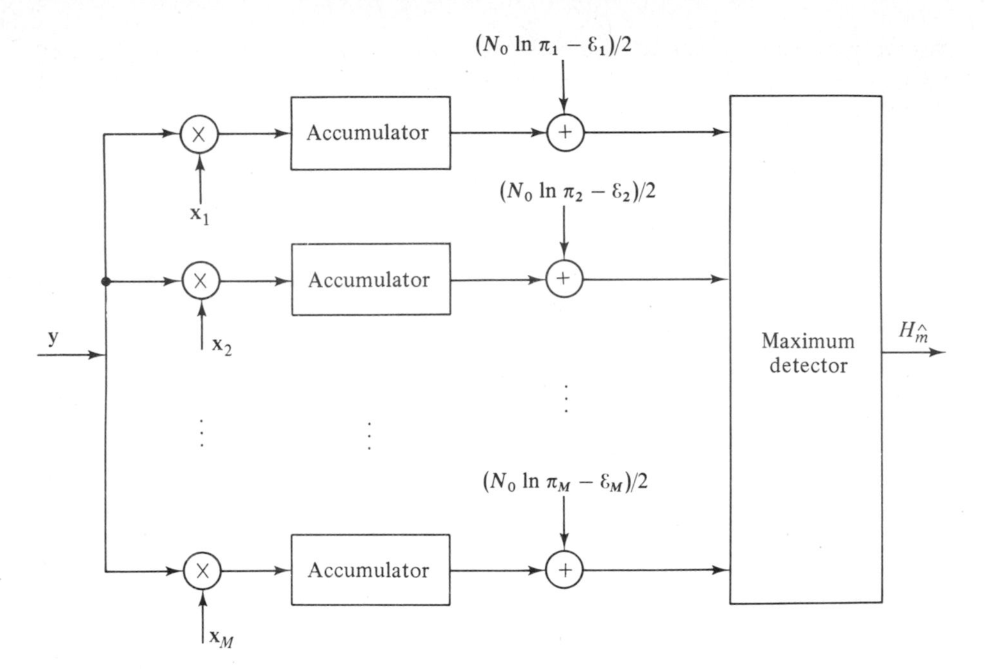

Figure 2.4 An implementation of decoder for AWGN channel.

As was discussed in Chap. 1, this is in fact the situation when the original data source has been efficiently encoded into equiprobable sequences of data symbols. In this case, the factors π_m and $\pi_{m'}$ can be eliminated in (2.2.5) through (2.2.8) and (2.2.12). The decision rule and corresponding decoder are then referred to as *maximum likelihood.* The maximum likelihood decoder depends only on the channel, and is often robust in the sense that it gives the same or nearly the same error probability for each message regardless of the true message a priori probabilities. From a practical design point of view, this is important because different users may have different message a priori probabilities. Henceforth, in the text we shall assume only equiprobable messages[6] and thus the maximum likelihood decoder will be optimum. Unequal prior probability cases will be treated in the problems. For a memoryless channel, the logarithm of the likelihood function (2.2.4) is commonly called the *metric;* thus a maximum likelihood decoder computes the metrics for each possible signal vector, compares them, and decides in favor of the maximum.

2.3 ERROR PROBABILITY AND A SIMPLE UPPER BOUND

Having established the optimum decoder to minimize error probability for any given set of observables, we now wish to determine its performance as a function of the signal set. Given that message H_m (signal vector $\mathbf{x}_m$) was sent and a given

[6] Note that for the AWGN channel, unequal prior probabilities requires only inclusion of the additive term in (2.2.12).

observation vector $\mathbf{y}$ was received, an error will occur if $\mathbf{y}$ is not in Λ_m (denoted $\mathbf{y} \notin \Lambda_m$ or $\mathbf{y} \in \overline{\Lambda_m}$). Since $\mathbf{y}$ is a random vector, the probability of error when $\mathbf{x}_m$ is sent is then

$$\begin{aligned} P_{E_m} &= \Pr\{\mathbf{y} \in \overline{\Lambda_m} \,|\, \mathbf{x}_m) \\ &= 1 - \Pr\{\mathbf{y} \in \Lambda_m \,|\, \mathbf{x}_m\} \\ &= \sum_{\mathbf{y} \in \overline{\Lambda_m}} p_N(\mathbf{y} \,|\, \mathbf{x}_m) \end{aligned} \tag{2.3.1}$$

We use the symbol $\sum$ to denote summation or integration over a subspace of the observation space. Thus, for continuous channels (such as the AWGN channel) with N-dimensional observation vectors, $\sum$ represents an N-dimensional integration and $p_N(\cdot)$ is a density function. On the other hand, for discrete channels where both the $\mathbf{x}_m$ and $\mathbf{y}$ vector components are elements of a finite symbol alphabet, $\sum$ represents an N-fold summation and $p_N(\cdot)$ represents a discrete distribution.

The overall error probability is then the average of the message error probabilities

$$\begin{aligned} P_E &= \sum_{m=1}^{M} \pi_m P_{E_m} \\ &= (1/M) \sum_{m=1}^{M} P_{E_m} \end{aligned} \tag{2.3.2}$$

Although the calculation of P_E by (2.3.2) is conceptually straightforward, it is computationally impractical in all but a few special cases (see, e.g., Probs. 2.4 and 2.5). On the other hand, simple upper bounds on P_E are available which in some cases give very tight approximations. When these fail, a more elaborate upper bound, derived in the next section, gives tight results for virtually all cases of practical interest.

A simple upper bound on P_E is obtained by examining the complements $\overline{\Lambda_m}$ of decision regions. By definition (2.2.8) with $\pi_m = 1/M$ for all m, $\overline{\Lambda_m}$ can be written as[7]

$$\begin{aligned} \overline{\Lambda_m} &= \{\mathbf{y}\colon \ln p_N(\mathbf{y} \,|\, \mathbf{x}_{m'}) \geq \ln p_N(\mathbf{y} \,|\, \mathbf{x}_m) \qquad \text{for some } m' \neq m\} \\ &= \bigcup_{m' \neq m} \{\mathbf{y}\colon \ln p_N(\mathbf{y} \,|\, \mathbf{x}_{m'}) \geq \ln p_N(\mathbf{y} \,|\, \mathbf{x}_m)\} \\ &= \bigcup_{m' \neq m} \Lambda_{mm'} \end{aligned} \tag{2.3.3}$$

where

$$\Lambda_{mm'} \equiv \left\{\mathbf{y}\colon \ln \frac{p_N(\mathbf{y} \,|\, \mathbf{x}_{m'})}{P_N(\mathbf{y}_m \,|\, \mathbf{x}_m)} \geq 0\right\}$$

[7] We take for the moment the pessimistic view that all ties are resolved in favor of the other message, thus at worst increasing the error probability. We note, however, that for continuous channels such as the AWGN, the boundaries do not contribute measurably to the error probability.

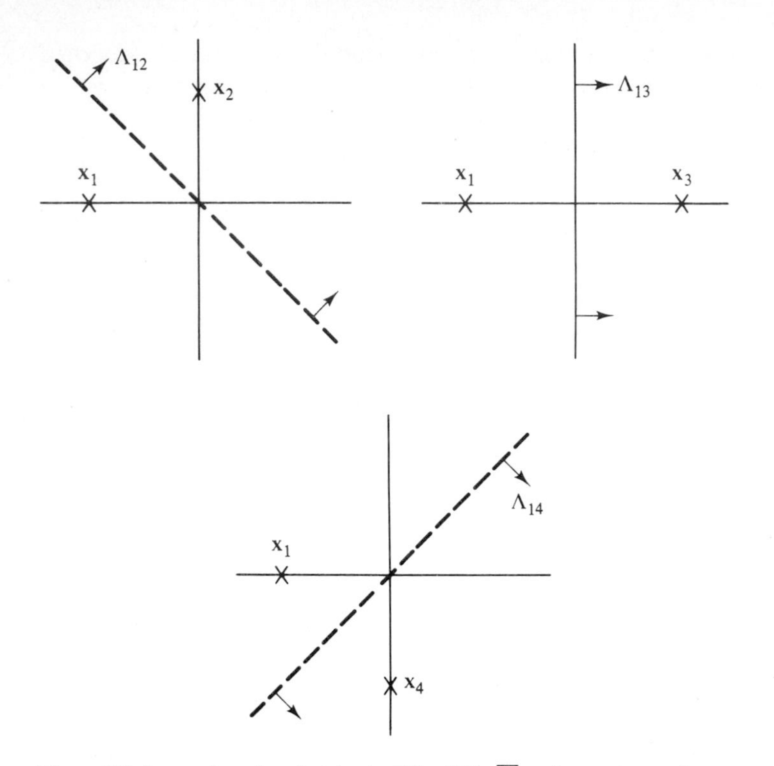

Figure 2.5 Λ_{1m} regions for signal set of Fig. 2.3*b*. $\overline{\Lambda_1} = \Lambda_{12} \cup \Lambda_{13} \cup \Lambda_{14}$.

Note that each of the terms $\Lambda_{mm'}$ of the union is actually the decision region for $\mathbf{x}_{m'}$ when there are only the two signals (messages) $\mathbf{x}_m$ and $\mathbf{x}_{m'}$. An example based on the signal set of Fig. 2.3*b* is shown in Fig. 2.5. Using (2.3.3) in (2.3.1), we find from the axioms of probability that

$$\begin{aligned} P_{E_m} &= \Pr\{\mathbf{y} \in \overline{\Lambda_m} \mid \mathbf{x}_m\} \\ &= \Pr\left\{\mathbf{y} \in \bigcup_{m' \neq m} \Lambda_{mm'} \,\middle|\, \mathbf{x}_m\right\} \\ &\leq \sum_{m' \neq m} \Pr\{\mathbf{y} \in \Lambda_{mm'} \mid \mathbf{x}_m\} \\ &= \sum_{m' \neq m} \Pr\left\{\ln \frac{p_N(\mathbf{y} \mid \mathbf{x}_{m'})}{p_N(\mathbf{y} \mid \mathbf{x}_m)} \geq 0 \,\middle|\, \mathbf{x}_m\right\} \\ &= \sum_{m' \neq m} P_E(m \to m') \end{aligned} \tag{2.3.4}$$

where $P_E(m \to m')$ denotes the pairwise error probability when $\mathbf{x}_m$ is sent and $\mathbf{x}_{m'}$ is the *only* alternative. We note that the inequality (2.3.4) becomes an equality[8]

[8] Also, for some trivial channels, $P_E(m \to m') \neq 0$ for at most one $m' \neq m$, thus obviously satisfying (2.3.4) as an equality.

whenever the regions $\Lambda_{mm'}$ are *disjoint*, which occurs only in the trivial case where $M = 2$. For obvious reasons the bound of (2.3.4) is called a *union bound.*

For the AWGN channel, the terms of the union bound can be calculated exactly, by using (2.2.12) with $\pi_m = \pi_{m'}$. This gives

$$P_E(m \to m') = \Pr\left\{Z_{mm'} \le \frac{(\mathscr{E}_m - \mathscr{E}_{m'})}{N_o} \,\middle|\, \mathbf{x}_m\right\} \tag{2.3.5}$$

where

$$\begin{aligned} Z_{mm'} &\equiv \frac{2}{N_o} \sum_{n=1}^{N} (x_{mn} - x_{m'n}) y_n \\ &= \frac{2}{N_o} (\mathbf{x}_m - \mathbf{x}_{m'}, \mathbf{y}) \end{aligned}$$

But, since $\mathbf{x}_m$ was sent

$$y_n = x_{mn} + n_n \tag{2.3.6}$$

for each n is a Gaussian random variable with mean x_{mn} and variance $N_o/2$. Also, as was shown in (2.1.14), y_n and y_l are independent for all $n \ne l$. Hence, since $Z_{mm'}$ is a linear combination of independent Gaussian variables, it must be itself Gaussian; using (2.1.3) and (2.3.6), we find its mean

$$\begin{aligned} E(Z_{mm'} \mid \mathbf{x}_m) &= \frac{2}{N_o} \sum_{n=1}^{N} (x_{mn} - x_{m'n}) E(y_n \mid x_{mn}) \\ &= \frac{2}{N_o} [\mathscr{E}_m - (\mathbf{x}_{m'}, \mathbf{x}_m)] \\ &\equiv \mu_z \end{aligned} \tag{2.3.7}$$

and its variance

$$\begin{aligned} \text{var}\,(Z_{mm'} \mid \mathbf{x}_m) &= \frac{4}{N_o^2} \sum_{n=1}^{N} [x_{mn} - x_{m'n}]^2 \,\text{var}\,(y_n \mid x_{mn}) \\ &= \frac{2}{N_o} \|\mathbf{x}_m - \mathbf{x}_{m'}\|^2 \equiv \sigma_z^2 \end{aligned} \tag{2.3.8}$$

Thus

$$\begin{aligned} P_E(m \to m') &= \int_{-\infty}^{-(\mathscr{E}_{m'} - \mathscr{E}_m)/N_o} \frac{e^{-(Z_{mm'} - \mu_z)^2/(2\sigma_z^2)}}{\sqrt{2\pi}\,\sigma_z} \, dZ_{mm'} \\ &= \int_{-\infty}^{-\beta} e^{-x^2/2} \frac{dx}{\sqrt{2\pi}} \end{aligned}$$

where

$$\begin{aligned}\beta &= \frac{[(\mathscr{E}_{m'} - \mathscr{E}_m)/N_o] + \mu_z}{\sigma_z} \\ &= \frac{\dfrac{1}{N_o}[\mathscr{E}_{m'} + \mathscr{E}_m - 2(\mathbf{x}_{m'}, \mathbf{x}_m)]}{\sqrt{\dfrac{2}{N_o}}\|\mathbf{x}_m - \mathbf{x}_{m'}\|} \\ &= \frac{\|\mathbf{x}_m - \mathbf{x}_{m'}\|}{\sqrt{2N_o}} \end{aligned} \tag{2.3.9}$$

This leads finally to the simple expression

$$P_E(m \to m') = Q\left(\frac{\|\mathbf{x}_m - \mathbf{x}_{m'}\|}{\sqrt{2N_o}}\right) \tag{2.3.10}$$

where $Q(\cdot)$ is the Gaussian integral function

$$Q(\beta) \equiv \int_{-\infty}^{-\beta} e^{-x^2/2} \frac{dx}{\sqrt{2\pi}} = \int_{\beta}^{\infty} e^{-x^2/2} \frac{dx}{\sqrt{2\pi}} \tag{2.3.11}$$

Returning to the error probability bound (2.3.4), we now derive a weaker but completely general bound on $P_E(m \to m')$. It follows immediately from (2.3.4) and (2.3.3) that

$$\begin{aligned}P_E(m \to m') &= \Pr\{\mathbf{y} \in \Lambda_{mm'} \mid \mathbf{x}_m\} \\ &= \sum_{\mathbf{y} \in \Lambda_{mm'}} p_N(\mathbf{y} \mid \mathbf{x}_m)\end{aligned}$$

where

$$\Lambda_{mm'} = \left\{\mathbf{y}\colon \frac{p_N(\mathbf{y} \mid \mathbf{x}_{m'})}{p_N(\mathbf{y} \mid \mathbf{x}_m)} \geq 1\right\} \subset \mathscr{Y}_N \tag{2.3.12}$$

and $\mathscr{Y}_N$ is the entire observation space. We may express this alternatively as

$$P_E(m \to m') = \sum_{\mathbf{y}} f(\mathbf{y}) p_N(\mathbf{y} \mid \mathbf{x}_m) \tag{2.3.13}$$

where

$$f(\mathbf{y}) = \begin{cases} 1 & \text{for all } \mathbf{y} \in \Lambda_{mm'} \\ 0 & \text{for all } \mathbf{y} \notin \Lambda_{mm'} \end{cases}$$

But we may easily bound $f(\mathbf{y})$ by

$$f(\mathbf{y}) = \begin{cases} 1 \leq \sqrt{\dfrac{p_N(\mathbf{y} \mid \mathbf{x}_{m'})}{p_N(\mathbf{y} \mid \mathbf{x}_m)}} & \text{for all } \mathbf{y} \in \Lambda_{mm'} \\ 0 \leq \sqrt{\dfrac{p_N(\mathbf{y} \mid \mathbf{x}_{m'})}{p_N(\mathbf{y} \mid \mathbf{x}_m)}} & \text{for all } \mathbf{y} \notin \Lambda_{mm'} \end{cases} \tag{2.3.14}$$

where the upper branch bound follows from (2.3.12), while the lower branch bound follows trivially. Then since the factors in the summands of (2.3.13) are everywhere nonnegative, we may replace $f(\mathbf{y})$ by its bound (2.3.14) and obtain

$$P_E(m \to m') \leq \sum_{\mathbf{y}} \sqrt{p_N(\mathbf{y}|\mathbf{x}_{m'})p_N(\mathbf{y}|\mathbf{x}_m)} \tag{2.3.15}$$

The expression (2.3.15) is called the *Bhattacharyya bound*, and its negative logarithm the *Bhattacharyya distance*. It is a special case of the *Chernoff bound* which will be derived in the next chapter (see also Prob. 2.10).

Combining the union bound (2.3.4) with the general Bhattacharyya bound (2.3.15), we obtain finally a bound on the error probability for the mth message

$$\begin{aligned} P_{E_m} &\leq \sum_{m' \neq m} P_E(m \to m') \\ &\leq \sum_{\mathbf{y}} \sum_{m' \neq m} \sqrt{p_N(\mathbf{y}|\mathbf{x}_{m'})p_N(\mathbf{y}|\mathbf{x}_m)} \end{aligned} \tag{2.3.16}$$

The interchange of summations is always valid because at least the sum over m' is over a finite set. Equation (2.3.16) will be shown to be a special case of the more elaborate bound derived in the next section.

To assess the tightness of the Bhattacharyya bound and to gain some intuition, we again consider the AWGN channel and substitute the likelihood functions of (2.1.15) into (2.3.15). Then, since $\mathcal{Y}_N$ is a space of real vectors, we obtain

$$\begin{aligned} P_E(m \to m') &\leq \frac{1}{(\pi N_o)^{N/2}} \int_{-\infty}^{\infty} \cdots \int_{-\infty}^{\infty} \exp\left\{-\frac{1}{2N_o}[\|\mathbf{y} - \mathbf{x}_{m'}\|^2 + \|\mathbf{y} - \mathbf{x}_m\|^2]\right\} d\mathbf{y} \\ &= \exp\{-\|\mathbf{x}_m - \mathbf{x}_{m'}\|^2/4N_o\} \end{aligned} \tag{2.3.17}$$

Comparing the bound (2.3.17) with the exact expression (2.3.10), we find that we have replaced $Q(\beta)$ by $\exp(-\beta^2/2)$. But it is well known (see Wozencraft and Jacobs [1965]) that

$$\left(1 - \frac{1}{\beta^2}\right)\frac{e^{-\beta^2/2}}{\sqrt{2\pi}\,\beta} < Q(\beta) < \frac{e^{-\beta^2/2}}{\sqrt{2\pi}\,\beta} \tag{2.3.18}$$

Thus, for large arguments, the bound (2.3.17) is reasonably tight. Note also that the negative logarithm of (2.3.17) is proportional to the square of the distance between signals. To carry this one step further and evaluate the tightness of the union bound, we consider the special case of M equal-energy M-dimensional signals, each with a unique nonzero component

$$x_{mn} = \sqrt{\mathcal{E}}\,\delta_{mn} = \begin{cases} 0 & \text{if } n \neq m \\ \sqrt{\mathcal{E}} & \text{if } n = m \end{cases}$$

(This is a special case of an orthogonal signal set and will be considered further in Sec. 2.5.) Then (2.3.17) becomes

$$P_E(m \to m') \leq e^{-\mathcal{E}/(2N_o)} \qquad \text{for all } m' \neq m$$

and consequently (2.3.16) yields the union bound

$$P_{E_m} \le (M-1)e^{-\mathscr{E}/(2N_o)} \qquad m = 1, 2, \ldots, M \tag{2.3.19}$$

Thus this bound is useless when $M \ge \exp(\mathscr{E}/2N_o)$. In the next section, we derive a bound which is useful over a considerably extended range.

2.4 A TIGHTER UPPER BOUND ON ERROR PROBABILITY

When the union bound fails to give useful results, a more refined technique will invariably yield an improved bound which is tight over a significantly wider range. Returning to the original general expression (2.3.1), we begin by defining the subset of the observation space

$$\tilde{\Lambda}_m \equiv \left\{ \mathbf{y}: \sum_{m' \ne m} \left[\frac{p_N(\mathbf{y} \mid \mathbf{x}_{m'})}{p_N(\mathbf{y} \mid \mathbf{x}_m)} \right]^\lambda \ge 1 \right\} \qquad \lambda > 0 \tag{2.4.1}$$

which contains the region of summation $\overline{\Lambda_m}$. For if $\pi_m = 1/M$ for all m, then, by the definition (2.2.8) we have for any $\mathbf{y} \in \overline{\Lambda_m}$

$$\frac{p_N(\mathbf{y} \mid \mathbf{x}_{m''})}{p_N(\mathbf{y} \mid \mathbf{x}_m)} \ge 1 \qquad \text{for some } m'' \ne m \tag{2.4.2}$$

Moreover, since $\lambda > 0$, raising both sides of the inequality (2.4.2) to the λth power does not alter the inequality, and summing over all $m' \ne m$ will include the m'' term for which (2.4.2) holds, in addition to other nonnegative terms. Hence (2.4.2) implies

$$\sum_{m' \ne m} \left[\frac{p_N(\mathbf{y} \mid \mathbf{x}_{m'})}{p_N(\mathbf{y} \mid \mathbf{x}_m)} \right]^\lambda \ge 1 \qquad \text{for all } \mathbf{y} \in \overline{\Lambda_m} \tag{2.4.3}$$

It then follows from (2.4.1) and (2.4.3) that every $\mathbf{y} \in \overline{\Lambda_m}$ is also in $\tilde{\Lambda}_m$, and consequently that

$$\overline{\Lambda_m} \subseteq \tilde{\Lambda}_m \tag{2.4.4}$$

Thus, since the summand in (2.3.1) is always nonnegative, by enlarging the domain of summation of (2.3.1) we obtain the bound

$$P_{E_m} \le \sum_{\mathbf{y} \in \tilde{\Lambda}_m} p_N(\mathbf{y} \mid \mathbf{x}_m) = \sum_{\mathbf{y}} f(\mathbf{y}) p_N(\mathbf{y} \mid \mathbf{x}_m)$$

where

$$f(\mathbf{y}) = \begin{cases} 1 & \text{if } \mathbf{y} \in \tilde{\Lambda}_m \\ 0 & \text{if } \mathbf{y} \notin \tilde{\Lambda}_m \end{cases} \tag{2.4.5}$$

Furthermore, we have

$$f(\mathbf{y}) \le \left\{ \sum_{m' \ne m} \left[\frac{p_N(\mathbf{y} \mid \mathbf{x}_{m'})}{p_N(\mathbf{y} \mid \mathbf{x}_m)} \right]^\lambda \right\}^\rho \qquad \text{for all } \mathbf{y} \in \mathscr{Y}_N,\ \rho > 0,\ \lambda > 0 \tag{2.4.6}$$

for it follows from the definition (2.4.1) that, if $\mathbf{y} \in \tilde{\Lambda}_m$, the right side of (2.4.6) is greater than 1, while, if $\mathbf{y} \notin \tilde{\Lambda}_m$, the right side is at least greater than 0.

Substituting the bound (2.4.6) for $f(\mathbf{y})$ in (2.4.5) yields

$$P_{E_m} \leq \sum_{\mathbf{y}} [p_N(\mathbf{y} \mid \mathbf{x}_m)]^{1-\lambda\rho} \left\{ \sum_{m' \neq m} [p_N(\mathbf{y} \mid \mathbf{x}_{m'})]^{\lambda} \right\}^{\rho} \qquad \lambda > 0, \rho > 0 \qquad (2.4.7)$$

Since λ and ρ are arbitrary positive numbers, we may choose $\lambda = 1/(1 + \rho)$ and thus obtain

$$P_{E_m} \leq \sum_{\mathbf{y}} [p_N(\mathbf{y} \mid \mathbf{x}_m)]^{1/(1+\rho)} \left\{ \sum_{m' \neq m} [p_N(\mathbf{y} \mid \mathbf{x}_{m'})]^{1/(1+\rho)} \right\}^{\rho} \qquad \rho > 0 \qquad (2.4.8)$$

This bound, which is due to R. G. Gallager [1965], is much less intuitive than the union bound. However, it is clear that the union bound (2.3.16) is the special case of this bound obtained by setting $\rho = 1$ in (2.4.8). To what extent the Gallager bound is more powerful than the union bound will be demonstrated by the example of the next section.

2.5 EQUAL-ENERGY ORTHOGONAL SIGNALS ON THE AWGN CHANNEL

To test the results of the preceding section on a specific signal set and channel, we consider the most simply described and represented signal set on the AWGN channel. This is the set of equal-energy orthogonal signals defined by the relations

$$\int_0^T x_m(t)x_n(t)\,dt = \mathscr{E}\delta_{mn} = \begin{cases} \mathscr{E} & \text{if } m = n \\ 0 & \text{if } m \neq n \end{cases} \qquad m, n = 1, 2, \ldots, M \quad (2.5.1)$$

In the next section, we shall consider several examples of orthogonal signal sets. Since the signals are already orthogonal, the orthonormal basis functions are most conveniently chosen as

$$\phi_m(t) = \frac{1}{\sqrt{\mathscr{E}}} x_m(t) \qquad m = 1, 2, \ldots, M \qquad (2.5.2)$$

which clearly satisfies (2.1.2). Then the signal vector components become simply

$$x_{mn} = \sqrt{\mathscr{E}}\,\delta_{mn} \qquad m, n = 1, 2, \ldots, M \qquad (2.5.3)$$

and consequently the likelihood function for the AWGN channel given in (2.1.15) becomes, with $N = M$,

$$\begin{aligned} p_M(\mathbf{y} \mid \mathbf{x}_m) &= \frac{\exp[-(y_m - \sqrt{\mathscr{E}})^2/N_o]}{\sqrt{\pi N_o}} \prod_{n \neq m} \frac{\exp(-y_n^2/N_o)}{\sqrt{\pi N_o}} \\ &= \exp\left[\frac{-\mathscr{E} + 2\sqrt{\mathscr{E}}\, y_m}{N_o}\right] \frac{\exp\left(-\sum_{n=1}^{M} y_n^2/N_o\right)}{(\pi N_o)^{M/2}} \qquad m = 1, 2, \ldots, M \end{aligned}$$

(2.5.4)

Substituting into (2.4.8), we obtain after a few manipulations, for every m

$$P_{E_m} \le e^{-\mathscr{E}/N_o} \int_{-\infty}^{\infty} \cdots \int_{-\infty}^{\infty} \prod_{n=1}^{M} \frac{e^{-y_n^2/N_o}}{\sqrt{\pi N_o}}$$

$$\exp\left[\frac{2\sqrt{\mathscr{E}}\, y_m}{N_o(1+\rho)}\right] \left\{ \sum_{m' \ne m} \exp\left[\frac{2\sqrt{\mathscr{E}}\, y_{m'}}{N_o(1+\rho)}\right] \right\}^{\rho} d\mathbf{y}$$

Letting $z_n = y_n/(\sqrt{N_o/2})$, this becomes

$$P_{E_m} \le e^{-\mathscr{E}/N_o} \int_{-\infty}^{\infty} \cdots \int_{-\infty}^{\infty} \prod_{n=1}^{M} \frac{e^{-z_n^2/2}}{\sqrt{2\pi}}\, g(z_m) \left[\sum_{m' \ne m} g(z_{m'}) \right]^{\rho} d\mathbf{z} \qquad \rho \ge 0 \tag{2.5.5}$$

where

$$g(z) \equiv \exp\left(\sqrt{\frac{2\mathscr{E}}{N_o}} \frac{z}{1+\rho} \right) \tag{2.5.6}$$

Since the M-fold product in (2.5.5) is the density function of M independent normalized (zero mean, unit variance) Gaussian variables, (2.5.5) can be expressed as

$$P_{E_m} \le e^{-\mathscr{E}/N_o} E[g(z_m)] E\left[\left(\sum_{m' \ne m} g(z_{m'}) \right)^{\rho} \right] \qquad \rho \ge 0 \tag{2.5.7}$$

where the expectation is with respect to the independent normalized Gaussian variables $z_1, z_2, \ldots, z_M$. Then the expectation of (2.5.6) is readily determined to be

$$E[g(z)] = \int_{-\infty}^{\infty} \frac{e^{-z^2/2}}{\sqrt{2\pi}} \exp\left(\sqrt{\frac{2\mathscr{E}}{N_o}} \frac{z}{1+\rho} \right) dz$$

$$= \exp\left(\frac{\mathscr{E}}{N_o(1+\rho)^2} \right) \tag{2.5.8}$$

The second expectation in (2.5.7) cannot be evaluated in closed form. But it can be upper bounded simply, provided we restrict the parameter ρ to lie in the unit interval. For, by the Jensen inequality derived in App. 1B, we have for a convex $\cap$ function $f(\cdot)$ of a random variable ξ

$$E[f(\xi)] \le f(E[\xi]) \tag{2.5.9}$$

Now letting

$$\xi = \sum_{m' \ne m} g(z_{m'}) \qquad \text{and} \qquad f(\xi) = \xi^{\rho}$$

which is a convex $\cap$ function provided $0 \le \rho \le 1$, we obtain from (2.5.9)

$$E\left[\left(\sum_{m' \ne m} g(z_{m'}) \right)^{\rho} \right] \le \left(E\left[\sum_{m' \ne m} g(z_{m'}) \right] \right)^{\rho}$$

$$= (M-1)^{\rho} (E[g(z)])^{\rho} \qquad 0 \le \rho \le 1 \tag{2.5.10}$$

where the equality follows because all the random variables $z_{m'}$ are identically distributed. Thus (2.5.7) becomes

$$P_{E_m} \leq (M-1)^{\rho}\, e^{-\mathscr{E}/N_o}(E[g(z)])^{1+\rho} \tag{2.5.11}$$

This bound holds uniformly for all m and hence is also a bound on P_E. Finally substituting (2.5.8) into (2.5.11), we obtain

$$P_E \leq (M-1)^{\rho} \exp\left[-\frac{\mathscr{E}}{N_o}\left(\frac{\rho}{1+\rho}\right)\right] \qquad 0 \leq \rho \leq 1 \tag{2.5.12}$$

Clearly, (2.5.12) is a generalization of the union-Bhattacharyya bound (2.3.19), to which it reduces when $\rho = 1$.

Before proceeding to optimize this bound with respect to ρ, it is convenient to define the signal-to-noise parameter

$$\begin{aligned} C_T &\equiv \frac{\mathscr{E}/N_o}{T} \\ &= \frac{S}{N_o} \end{aligned} \tag{2.5.13}$$

where S is the signal power or energy per second, and to define the rate[9] parameter

$$R_T \equiv (\ln M)/T = (\ln q)/T_s \text{ nats/s} \tag{2.5.14}$$

as is appropriate since we assumed that the source emits one of q equally likely symbols once every T_s seconds. Then trivially bounding $(M-1)$ by M, we can express (2.5.12) in terms of (2.5.13) and (2.5.14) as

$$P_E < \exp\{-T[E_o(\rho) - \rho R_T]\}$$

where

$$E_o(\rho) = \frac{\rho C_T}{1+\rho} \qquad 0 \leq \rho \leq 1 \tag{2.5.15}$$

The tightest upper bound of this form is obtained by maximizing the negative exponent of (2.5.15) with respect to ρ on the unit interval. But, for positive ρ, this negative exponent is a convex $\cap$ function, as shown in Fig. 2.6, with maximum at $\rho = \sqrt{C_T/R_T} - 1$. Thus for $\frac{1}{4} \leq R_T/C_T \leq 1$, this maximum occurs within the unit interval; but, for $R_T/C_T < \frac{1}{4}$, the maximum occurs at $\rho > 1$ and consequently the negative exponent increases monotonically on the unit interval; hence, in the latter case, the tightest bound results when $\rho = 1$. Substituting these values of ρ into (2.5.15), we obtain

$$P_E < e^{-TE(R_T)} \tag{2.5.16}$$

[9] This is a scaling of the binary data rate for which the logarithm is usually taken to the base 2 and the dimensions are in bits per second.

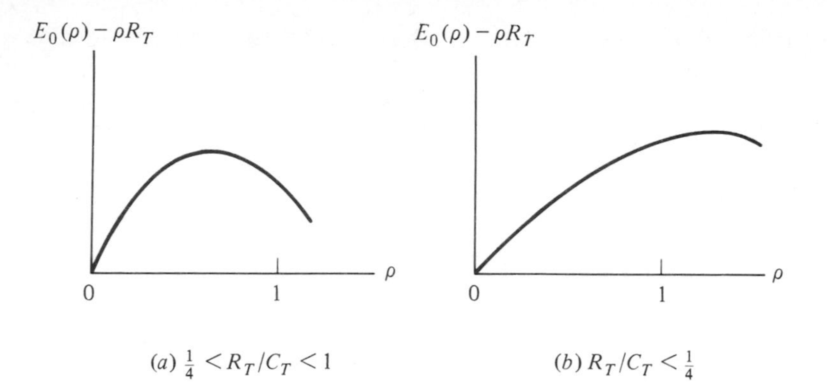

Figure 2.6 Negative exponent of upper bound (2.5.15).

where

$$E(R_T) = \begin{cases} \frac{1}{2}C_T - R_T & 0 \le R_T/C_T \le \frac{1}{4} \\ (\sqrt{C_T} - \sqrt{R_T})^2 & \frac{1}{4} \le R_T/C_T \le 1 \end{cases}$$

For $R_T > C_T$, the bound is useless and in fact, as will be discussed in the next chapter, in this region, $P_E \to 1$ as T and M approach infinity.

The bound (2.5.16) was first obtained in a somewhat more elaborate form by R. M. Fano [1961]. The negative exponent $E(R_T)$, sometimes called the *reliability function*, is shown in Fig. 2.7. Note that the union-Bhattacharyya bound (2.3.19), corresponding to (2.5.12) with $\rho = 1$, would produce the straight-line exponent shown dashed in the figure. Thus the Gallager bound dominates the union bound everywhere but at low rates, a property we shall find true for much more general channels and signal sets.

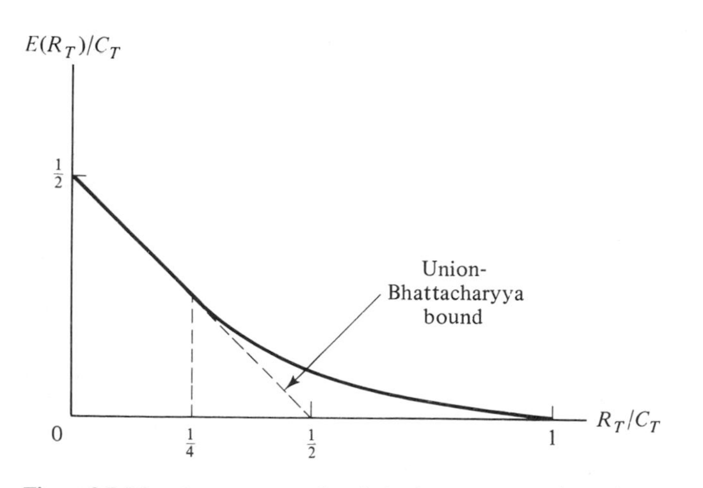

Figure 2.7 Negative exponent of optimized upper bound (2.5.16).

Another choice of parameters, more physically oriented than those in (2.5.13) and (2.5.14), involves the received energy per information bit. This is defined in terms of the system of Fig. 2.1 where $q = 2$, as the energy per signal normalized by the number of bits transmitted per signal, that is,

$$\mathscr{E}_b \equiv \mathscr{E}/K = \frac{\mathscr{E}}{\log_2 M} \tag{2.5.17}$$

Comparing with (2.5.13) and (2.5.14), we see that

$$\frac{C_T}{R_T} = \frac{\mathscr{E}_b}{N_o \ln 2} \tag{2.5.18}$$

$\mathscr{E}_b/N_o$ is called the *bit energy-to-noise density* ratio. Thus, (2.5.16) and (2.5.18) together imply that, with orthogonal signals, P_E decreases exponentially with T for all $\mathscr{E}_b/N_o > \ln 2$.

Ultimately, the most important consequence of (2.5.16) is that, by letting T, and hence M, become asymptotically large, we can make P_E become arbitrarily small for all transmission rates $R_T < C_T$ (or in this case, for all $\mathscr{E}_b/N_o > \ln 2$). Again, this is a fundamental result applicable to all channels. However, making T very large may be prohibitive in system complexity. In fact, as will be shown in the next section, this is always the case for orthogonal signals. The major part of this book deals with the problem of finding signal sets, or codes, and decoding techniques for which system complexity remains manageable as T and M increase.

2.6 BANDWIDTH CONSTRAINTS, INTERSYMBOL INTERFERENCE, AND TRACKING UNCERTAINTY

Up to this point, the only constraint we have imposed on the signal set was the fundamental one of finite energy. Almost as important is the dimensionality constraint imposed by bandwidth requirements. The only limitation on dimensionality discussed thus far was the one inherent in the fact that M signals defined over a T-second interval can be represented using no more than M orthogonal basis functions, or dimensions, as established by the Gram-Schmidt theorem (App. 2A). These orthogonal functions (or signal sets) can take on an infinite multitude of forms. Four of the most common are given in Table 2.1. The orthonormal relation (2.1.2) can be verified in each case. An obvious advantage of the orthonormal set of Example 1 is that, as contrasted with the general modulator and demodulator of Fig. 2.1, only a single modulator and demodulator element need be implemented, for this can be time-shared among the N dimensions, as shown in Fig. 2.8. The observables $\{y_n\}$ then appear serially as sampled outputs of the integrator. These are generated by a device which integrates over each symbol period of duration T/N, is sampled, dumps its contents, and then proceeds to integrate over the next symbol period, etc. The orthonormal set of Example 2 requires two

Table 2.1 Examples of orthonormal signal sets

Name	Function		
1. Time-orthogonal functions	$\phi_n(t) = \begin{cases} \sqrt{\frac{2N}{T}} \sin \omega_0 t & (n-1)T/N \le t < nT/N \\ 0 & \text{otherwise} \end{cases}$		(ω_0 a multiple of $\pi N/T$)
2. Time-orthogonal quadrature-phase functions	$\phi_{2n}(t) = \begin{cases} \sqrt{\frac{2N}{T}} \sin \omega_0 t & (n-1)T/N \le t < nT/N \\ 0 & \text{otherwise} \end{cases}$		
	$\phi_{2n+1}(t) = \begin{cases} \sqrt{\frac{2N}{T}} \cos \omega_0 t & (n-1)T/N \le t < nT/N \\ 0 & \text{otherwise} \end{cases}$		(ω_0 a multiple of $2\pi N/T$)
3. Frequency-orthogonal functions	$\phi_n(t) = \sqrt{\frac{2}{T}} \sin \left[\left(\omega_0 + \frac{\pi n}{T}\right)t\right]$	$0 \le t < T$	(ω_0 a multiple of π/T)
4. Frequency-orthogonal quadrature-phase functions	$\phi_{2n}(t) = \sqrt{\frac{2}{T}} \sin \left[\left(\omega_0 + \frac{2\pi n}{T}\right)t\right]$ $\phi_{2n+1}(t) = \sqrt{\frac{2}{T}} \cos \left[\left(\omega_0 + \frac{2\pi n}{T}\right)t\right]$	$0 \le t < T$	(ω_0 a multiple of $2\pi/T$)

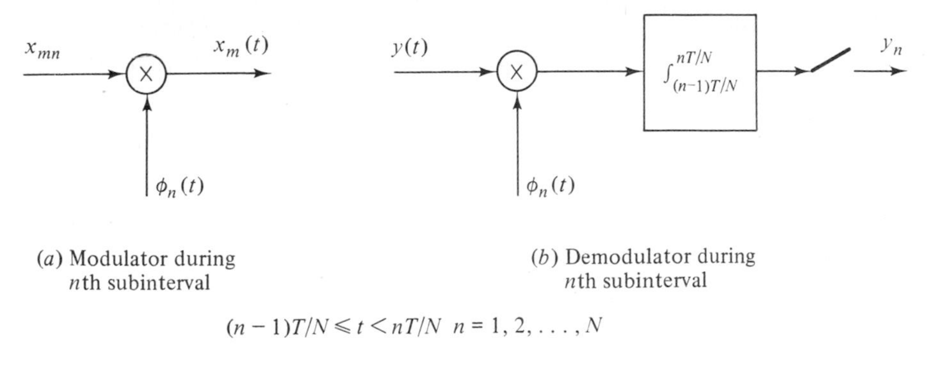

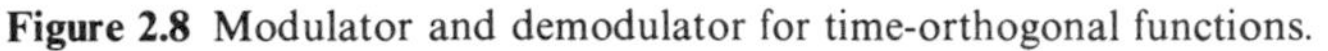

Figure 2.8 Modulator and demodulator for time-orthogonal functions.

modulator–demodulator elements, as shown in Fig. 2.9, which are generally called quadrature modulator–demodulators. On the other hand, 3 and 4 would seem to require a full bank of N demodulating elements.[10]

It is well known that the maximum number of orthogonal dimensions transmittable in time T over a channel of bandwidth W is approximately

$$N \approx 2WT \tag{2.6.1}$$

The approximation comes about because of the freedom in the definition and interpretation of bandwidth. To illustrate, we begin by giving a simplistic interpretation of bandwidth. Suppose all communication channels on all frequency bands are operating on a common time scale and using a common set of orthogonal signals, such as the frequency-orthogonal functions of Example 3. Then, depending on its requirements, a channel would be assigned a given number N of basis functions which are sinusoids at consecutive frequency multiples of π/T

[10] In fact, there exist both analog and digital techniques for implementing the entire bank with a single serial processing device (Darlington [1964], Oppenheim and Schafer [1975]).

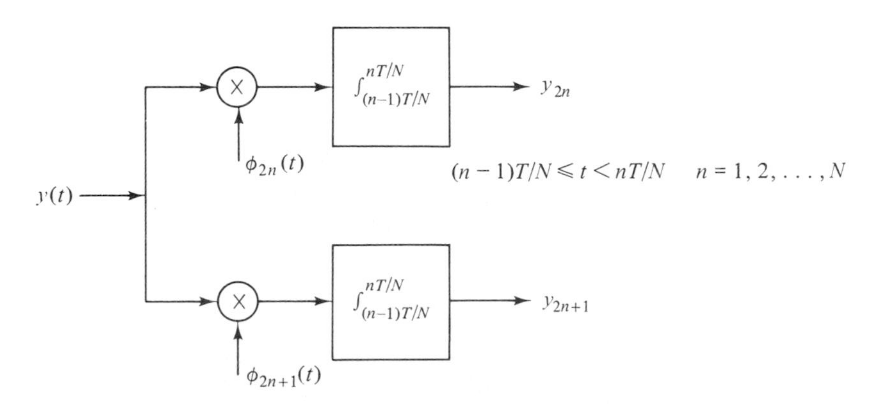

Figure 2.9 Demodulator for time-orthogonal quadrature-phase function.

radians per second. Given that these were processed ideally by the demodulator of Fig. 2.1*b*, all other channels would have no effect on the given channel's performance since the basis functions of the other channels are orthogonal to those assigned to the given channel and consequently would add zero components to the integrator outputs $y_1, y_2, \ldots, y_N$ of the demodulator of Figure 2.1*b*. Now suppose we defined the channel bandwidth occupancy as the minimum frequency separation between the basis functions of the Example 3 signal set times the number of functions utilized by the channel. Then since the former is π/T radians per second or $1/(2T)$ Hz, for a number of dimensions N, the bandwidth occupancy W in Hz is given exactly by (2.6.1). We note also that, if the frequency separation were any less, the functions would not be orthogonal.

The same argument can be made for the time-orthogonal functions of Example 1 provided we take ω_0 to be a multiple of $\pi N/T$. Then it is readily verified that, where the waveforms of any two channels overlap for a time interval T/N, they are orthogonal over this interval and consequently the demodulator of one channel is unaffected by the signals of the other. Thus the separation between channels is exactly $\pi N/T$ radians per second or $N/2T$ Hz, again verifying (2.6.1). In Examples 2 and 4 two phases (sine and cosine) are used for each frequency, but as a result, consecutive frequencies must be spaced twice as far apart; hence the bandwidth occupancy is the same as for 1 and 3.

The weakness in the above arguments, aside from the obvious impossibility of regulating all channels to adopt a common modulation system with identical timing, is that, inherent in the transmitter, receiver, and transmission medium, there is a linear distortion which causes some frequencies to be attenuated more than others. This leads to the necessity of defining bandwidth in terms of the signal spectrum. The spectral density of the transmission just described is actually nonzero for all frequencies, although its envelope decreases in proportion to the frequency separation from ω_0. This, in fact, is a property of all time-limited signals.

On the other hand, we may adopt another simplistic viewpoint, dual to the above, and require that all our signals be strictly bandwidth-limited in the sense that their spectral density is identically zero outside a bandwidth of W Hz. Then, according to the classical sampling theorem, any signal or sequence of signals satisfying this constraint can be represented as

$$x(t) = \sum_{n=-\infty}^{\infty} \frac{\sqrt{2}\sin[\pi W(t - n/W)]}{\pi W(t - n/W)} (a_n \sin \omega_0 t + b_n \cos \omega_0 t) \qquad (2.6.2)$$

This suggests then that any subset of the set of band-limited functions

$$\left.\begin{aligned} \phi_{2n}(t) &= \frac{\sqrt{2W}\sin[\pi W(t - n/W)]}{\pi W(t - n/W)} \sin \omega_0 t \\ \phi_{2n+1}(t) &= \frac{\sqrt{2W}\sin[\pi W(t - n/W)]}{\pi W(t - n/W)} \cos \omega_0 t \end{aligned}\right\} \quad n \text{ any integer} \qquad (2.6.3)$$

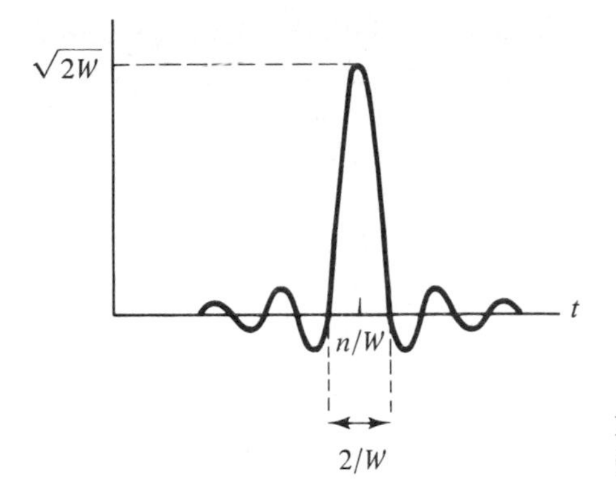

Figure 2.10 Envelope of $\phi_{2n}(t)$ and $\phi_{2n+1}(t)$ of (2.6.3).

can be used as the basis functions for our transmission set. It is readily verified that the functions are orthonormal over the doubly infinite interval, i.e., that

$$\int_{-\infty}^{\infty} \phi_j(t)\phi_k(t)\,dt = \delta_{jk}$$

As shown in Fig. 2.10, the envelope of both $\phi_{2n}(t)$ and $\phi_{2n+1}(t)$ reaches its peak at $t = n/W$ and has nulls at all other multiples of $1/W$ seconds. Furthermore, the functions (2.6.3) can be regarded as the band-limited duals of the time-orthogonal quadrature-phase orthonormal functions of Example 2, where we have exchanged finite time and infinite bandwidth for finite bandwidth and infinite time. Another interesting feature of this set of band-limited basis functions is that the demodulator can be implemented as a pair of ideal bandpass filters (or quadrature multipliers and ideal lowpass filters), sampled every $1/W$ seconds, producing at $t = n/W$ the two observables y_{2n} and y_{2n+1} (see Fig. 2.11; also Prob. 2.6). Thus again it appears that we can transmit in this way $2W$ dimensions per second so that, as $T \to \infty$ where we can ignore the slight excess time-width of the basis functions, (2.6.1) is again satisfied.

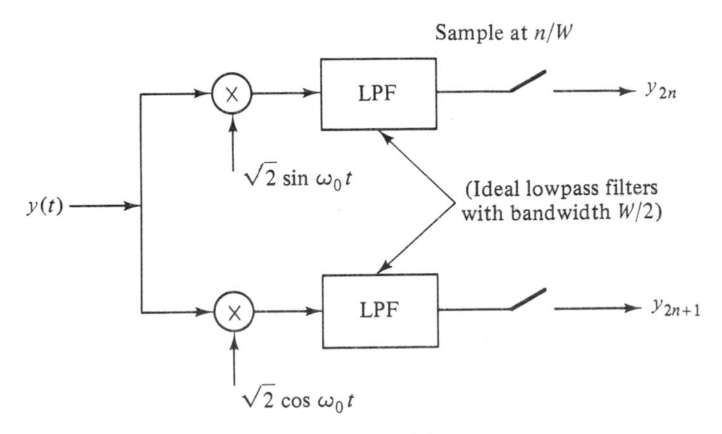

Figure 2.11 Demodulator for functions of Eqs. (2.6.3).

On the basis of (2.6.1) we may draw a conclusion about the practicality of the orthogonal signal set whose performance was analyzed in Sec. 2.5. There we found that the error probability decreases exponentially with the product $TE(R_T)$, but it follows from (2.5.14) that the number of signals, and therefore orthogonal dimensions, is $N = M = e^{TR_T}$. Consequently, according to (2.6.1), we find that, for orthogonal signals,

$$W \approx e^{TR_T}/2T \tag{2.6.4}$$

which implies that, for all $R_T > C_T/4$, the bandwidth grows more rapidly with T than the inverse error probability. This exponential bandwidth growth is a severe handicap to the utilization of such signal sets. We shall find, however, in the next chapter that there exist codes or signal sets whose dimensionality grows only linearly with T and yet which perform nearly as well as the orthogonal set.

The impossibility of generating functions which are both time-limited and band-limited has led to many approaches to a compromise (Slepian and Pollack, [1961], Landau and Pollack [1961, 1962]). In terms of the previous discussions, we may generalize on the time-orthogonal functions of Table 2.1 (Examples 1 and 2) by multiplying all the functions in question by an envelope function $f(t - nT/N)$ with the property that

$$\int_{-\infty}^{\infty} f\left(t - \frac{mT}{N}\right) f\left(t - \frac{nT}{N}\right) dt = \delta_{mn} \tag{2.6.5}$$

to obtain

$$\phi_n(t) = \sqrt{2} f\left(t - \frac{nT}{N}\right) \sin \omega_0 t \qquad n = 1, 2, \ldots \tag{2.6.6}$$

and

$$\left.\begin{aligned} \phi_{2n}(t) &= \sqrt{2} f\left(t - \frac{nT}{N}\right) \sin \omega_0 t \\ \phi_{2n+1}(t) &= \sqrt{2} f\left(t - \frac{nT}{N}\right) \cos \omega_0 t \end{aligned}\right\} \qquad n = 1, 2, \ldots \tag{2.6.7}$$

Equation (2.6.7) includes as a special case the band-limited example of (2.6.3) where the envelope function is taken to be

$$f(t) = \sqrt{W} \frac{\sin \pi W t}{\pi W t} \tag{2.6.8}$$

Typically, however, $f(t)$ is chosen to be time-limited, though not necessarily to T/N seconds, and, though of infinite frequency duration, its spectrum decreases much more rapidly than $1/W$.

The choice of envelope function, also called the *spectrum shaping function*, is not made on the basis of signal spectrum alone. For bandwidth is never an end unto itself; rather, the goal is to minimize interference and linear distortion introduced by the channel. Thus, even if $f(t)$ is the ideal band-limited function of (2.6.8) and the demodulator contains ideal lowpass filters (as shown in Fig. 2.11), the transmitter, transmitting media, and receiver introduce other (non-ideal) linear filtering characteristics which distort the waveform, so that the signal component of the received waveform is no longer exactly $f(t)$. As a result, we no longer have the orthogonality condition (2.6.5) among the signals for successive dimensions and the demodulator output for a given dimension is influenced by the signal component of adjacent dimensions. This phenomenon is called *intersymbol interference*. The degree of this effect depends on the bandwidth of the filters, or linearly distorting elements, in the transmitter, receiver, and medium. Only when the bandwidth of these distorting filters is on the order of that of $f(t)$ does this become a serious problem. In such cases, of which data communication over analog telephone lines is a prime example, spectrum shaping functions are chosen very carefully to minimize the intersymbol interference. Also, with intersymbol interference present, the demodulator of Fig. 2.1*b* is no longer optimum because of the nonorthogonality of signals for successive dimensions. Optimum demodulation for such channels, which has been studied extensively (Lucky, Salz, Weldon [1968], Forney [1972], Omura [1971]), leads to nonindependent observables. In this chapter and the next we shall avoid the problem of intersymbol interference, by assuming a sufficiently wideband channel. In Chap. 4, we return to this issue and treat the problem as a natural extension of decoding techniques developed in that chapter.

Additional sources of imperfection arise because of uncertainties in tracking carrier frequency and phase, and symbol timing. For the time-orthogonal functions (Example 1 of Table 2.1), uncertainty in phase or frequency will cause the demodulator to attenuate the signal component of the output. For example, if the frequency error is $\Delta\omega$ and the phase error is ϕ, the attenuation factor is easily shown to be approximately

$$\frac{\cos\phi \sin(T\Delta\omega/N)}{T\Delta\omega/N}$$

provided we take $T(\Delta\omega)/N \ll 1$ and $T\omega_0/N \gg 1$ (see Prob. 2.7). For time-orthogonal quadrature-phase functions (Example 2 of Table 2.1), the situation is aggravated by the fact that incorrect phase causes intersymbol interference between the two dimensions which share a common frequency. For with a phase error ϕ, the signal component y_{2n} is proportional to $x_{2n}\cos\phi + x_{2n+1}\sin\phi$, while that of y_{2n+1} is proportional to $x_{2n+1}\cos\phi - x_{2n}\sin\phi$ (see Prob. 2.7). Finally, symbol time uncertainty will cause adjacent symbol overlap during presumed symbol times and hence intersymbol interference. The influence of all these imperfections on demodulation and decoding has been treated in the applications literature (Jacobs [1967], Heller and Jacobs [1971]).

2.7 CHANNEL INPUT CONSTRAINTS

The last section treated the causes of performance degradation which arise in the channel, comprising the modulator, transmitter, medium, receiver and demodulator (Fig. 2.1). These imperfections and constraints are inherent in the continuous or analog components of the channel which, as we noted, are not easily controllable. In contrast, we now consider constraints on the channel inputs and outputs imposed by limitations in the encoder and decoder. Such limitations, which may lead to suboptimal operation, are imposed whenever the encoder and decoder are implemented digitally. In most cases, they produce a very small degradation which can be very accurately predicted and controlled.

A digital implementation of the encoder requires that the encoder output symbols $\{x_{mn}\}$ be elements of a finite alphabet. The most common and simplest code alphabet is binary. For an AWGN channel with binary inputs, for any m and n, the choice $x_{mn} = \pm\sqrt{\mathscr{E}_s}$ (where $\mathscr{E}_s$ is the energy per channel symbol) guarantees a constant-energy transmitted signal. The binary choice can be implemented either by amplitude modulation (plus or minus amplitude), or by phase modulation (0° or 180° phases) of any of the basis function sets discussed in the last section. When used with time-orthogonal functions (Table 2.1, Example 1), this is usually referred to as *biphase modulation;* when used with time-orthogonal quadrature-phase functions (Table 2.1, Example 2), this is usually called *quadriphase modulation.* The reason for the latter term is that two successive encoded symbols generate the modulator output signal in the single interval $(n-1)T/N \le t < nT/N$, that is,

$$x_{2n}\phi_{2n}(t) + x_{2n+1}\phi_{2n+1}(t) = \sqrt{2\mathscr{E}_s\frac{N}{T}}\,(\pm \sin \omega_0 t \pm \cos \omega_0 t)$$

$$= 2\sqrt{\mathscr{E}_s\frac{N}{T}}\,\sin(\omega_0 t + \theta_n)$$

where $\theta_n = \pi/4 + k\pi/2$, $k = 0, 1, 2$, or 3.

Note that this results in twice the symbol energy of biphase modulation, but it is spread out over twice the time, since two code symbols are transmitted; hence the signal energy per symbol and consequently the power is the same. We note also that, as shown in Sec. 2.2, the demodulator outputs are the same in both cases, and consequently the performance is identical.[11]

An obvious disadvantage of a binary-code symbol alphabet is that it limits the number of messages which can be transmitted with N dimensions, or channel symbols, to $M \le 2^N$ and hence constrains the transmission rate to $R_T \le (N/T)$ ln 2 nats/s. We may remove this limitation by increasing

[11] Provided of course the phase tracking errors are negligible; otherwise the intersymbol interference from the quadrature component, as discussed in Sec. 2.6, can degrade performance relative to the biphase case.

the code alphabet size to any integer q, although, for efficient digital implementation reasons, q is usually taken to be a power of 2. Then $M \leq q^N$ and $R_T \leq (N/T) \ln q$ nats per second, which can be made as large as desired or as permitted by the channel noise, as we shall find. As an aside, we note that $M = N$ orthogonal signals can always be implemented as biphase-modulated time-orthogonal basis functions, whenever N is a multiple of 4 (see Prob. 2.5 for $N = 2^K$, $K \geq 2$).

For the time-orthogonal waveforms 1 or 2 of Table 2.1, the modulator for q-ary code symbols is commonly implemented as a multiple amplitude modulator. For example, with a four-symbol alphabet, the modulator input symbols might be chosen as $\{a_1, a_2, a_3, a_4\}$. With equiprobable symbols and $a_1 = -a_2 = a$, $a_3 = -a_4 = 3a$, the average symbol energy is $\overline{\mathscr{E}}_s = 5a^2$. Of course, a disadvantage is that the transmitted power is no longer constant. A remedy for this is to use multiphase rather than multiamplitude modulation. This is easily conceived as a generalization of the frequency-orthogonal quadrature-phase basis set of Table 2.1, Example 4. A 16-phase modulation system would transmit a symbol from a 16-symbol alphabet as

$$\sqrt{\frac{2\mathscr{E}_s}{T}} \sin\left(\omega_0 t + \frac{2\pi k}{L}\right) = \sqrt{\frac{2\mathscr{E}_s}{T}} \cos\frac{2\pi k}{L} \sin\omega_0 t + \sqrt{\frac{2\mathscr{E}_s}{T}} \sin\frac{2\pi k}{L} \cos\omega_0 t \qquad 0 \leq t < T$$

where $k = 0, 1, 2, \ldots, 15$ and $L = 16$. We note, however, that this requires two dimensions per symbol so that, in terms of bandwidth or dimensionality, this 16-symbol code alphabet simultaneously modulating two dimensions of a time-orthogonal quadrature-phase system is equivalent to the four-symbol alphabet amplitude modulating one dimension at a time. The signal geometry of the two systems for equal average symbol energy $\overline{\mathscr{E}}_s$ is shown in Fig. 2.12. It is easily

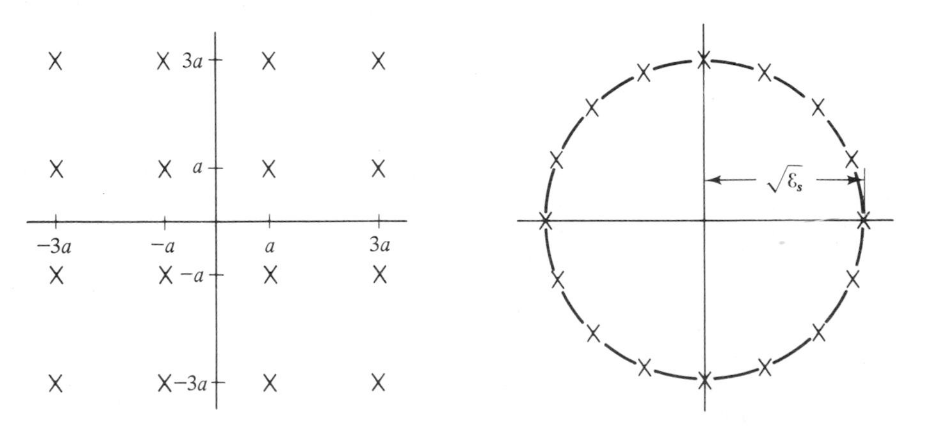

(*a*) Multiamplitude signal set in two dimensions (*b*) Multiphase signal set in two dimensions

Figure 2.12 Two examples of 16 signals in two dimensions.

shown (Prob. 2.8) that, for equal $\overline{\mathscr{E}}_s$, the amplitude modulation system outperforms the phase modulation system, but the latter has the advantage of constant energy. Obviously, we could generalize to signals on a three-dimensional sphere or higher, but for both practical and theoretical reasons to be discussed in the next chapter, this is not profitable.

2.8 CHANNEL OUTPUT QUANTIZATION: DISCRETE MEMORYLESS CHANNELS

We now turn to limitations imposed by the digital implementation of the decoder. Considering first the AWGN optimum decoder (Fig. 2.4), we note the obvious incentive to implement digitally the discrete inner-product calculations $(\mathbf{x}_m, \mathbf{y}) = \sum_{n=1}^{N} x_{mn} y_n$. While the input symbols $\{x_{mn}\}$ are normally elements of a finite set as discussed in the last section, the outputs $\{y_n\}$ are continuous Gaussian variables and consequently must be quantized to a finite number of levels if digital multiplications and additions are to be performed. An example of an eight-level uniform quantizer is shown in Fig. 2.13. Uniform quantizers are most commonly employed, although nonuniform quantization levels may improve performance to a slight degree.

The performance of a quantized, and hence suboptimum, version of the optimum decoder of Fig. 2.4 is difficult to analyze precisely. On the other hand, quantization of the output to one of J levels simply transforms the AWGN channel to a finite-input, finite-output alphabet channel. An example of a biphase modulated AWGN channel with output quantized to eight levels is shown in Fig. 2.14. Denoting the binary input alphabet by $\{a_1, a_2\}$ where $a_1 = -a_2 = \sqrt{\mathscr{E}_s}$ and denoting the output alphabet by $\{b_1, b_2, \ldots, b_8\}$, we can completely describe

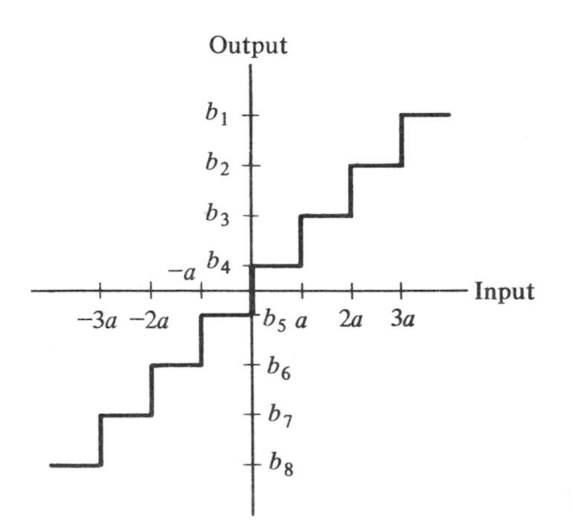

Figure 2.13 Uniform eight-level quantizer.

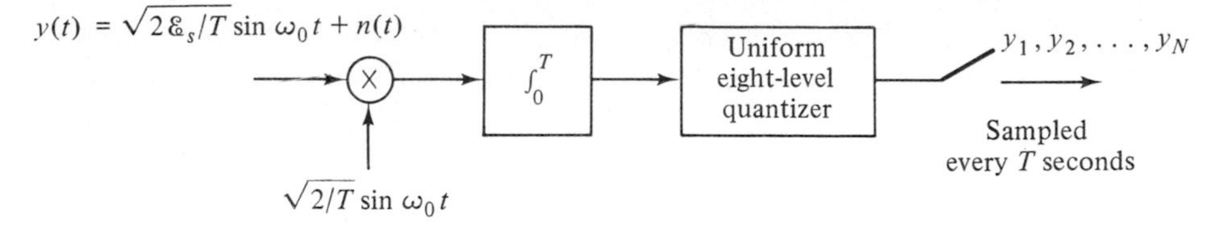

(*a*) Quantized demodulator for binary PSK signals

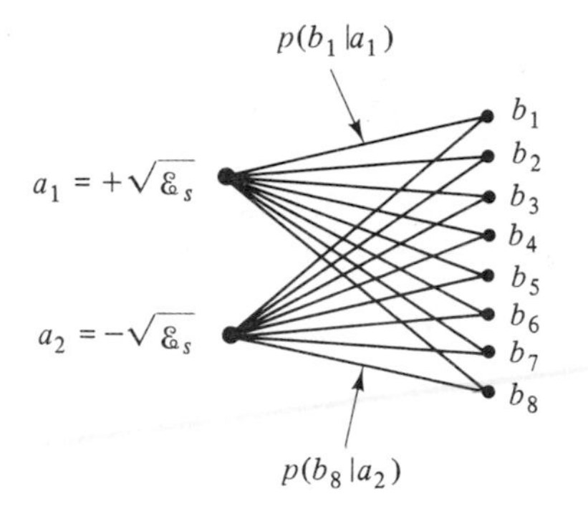

(*b*) Quantized channel model

Figure 2.14 Quantized demodulator and channel model.

the channel by the conditional probabilities or likelihood functions

$$p_N(\mathbf{y} \mid \mathbf{x}_m) = \prod_{n=1}^{N} p(y_n \mid x_{mn}) \qquad m = 1, 2, \ldots, M$$

where for each m and n

$$p(y_n = b_j \mid x_{mn} = a_k) = \frac{1}{\sqrt{\pi N_o}} \int_{z \epsilon B_j} e^{-(z-a_k)^2/N_o}\, dz \qquad \begin{cases} k = 1, 2 \\ j = 1, 2, \ldots, 8 \end{cases} \tag{2.8.1}$$

and B_j is the jth quantization interval. We note that, while a_k can actually be associated with the numerical value of the signal amplitude, b_j is an abstract symbol. Although we could associate with b_j the value of the midpoint of the interval, there is nothing gained by doing this. More significant are the facts that the vector likelihood function can be written as the product of symbol conditional probabilities and that all symbols are identically distributed. In this case, of course, this is just a consequence of the AWGN channel for which individual observables (demodulator outputs prior to quantization) are independent. A channel satisfying these conditions is called *memoryless*, and when its input and output alphabets are finite it is called a *discrete memoryless channel* (DMC) (cf. Sec. 1.2). Other examples of discrete memoryless channels, derived from physical channels other than the AWGN channel, will be treated in Sec. 2.12. Figure 2.14*b* completely describes the DMC just considered in terms of its binary-input, octal-output, conditional probability distribution, sometimes called the *channel transi-*

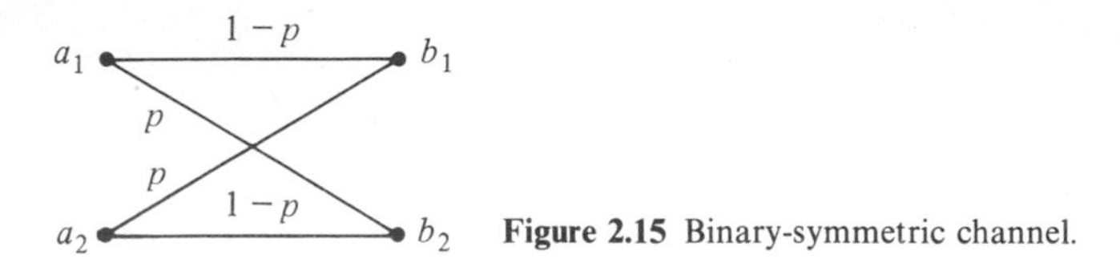

Figure 2.15 Binary-symmetric channel.

tion distribution. Clearly, this distribution, and consequently the decoder performance, depends on the location of the quantization levels, which in turn must depend on the signal level and noise variance. Thus, to implement an effective multilevel quantizer, a demodulator must incorporate automatic gain control (AGC).

The simplest DMC is the one with binary input and output symbols, which may be derived from a binary-input AWGN channel by utilizing a two-level quantizer. The quantizer, whose output is b_1 for nonnegative inputs and b_2 otherwise, is generally called a *hard quantizer* (or *limiter*), in contrast with a multilevel quantizer which is usually called a *soft quantizer*. The resulting hard-quantized output channel is the binary-symmetric channel (BSC). When derived from the AWGN channel, the BSC has the conditional distribution diagram shown in Fig. 2.15 with $p = p\{y = b_2 | x = a_1\} = p\{y = b_1 | x = a_2\}$, generally called the crossover probability, being the same as the symbol error probability for an uncoded digital communication system. The principal advantage of hard quantizing the AWGN channel into a BSC is that no knowledge is needed of the signal energy. In contrast, as commented above, the soft quantizer requires this information and hence must employ AGC. On the other hand, as will be elaborated on in Sec. 2.11 and the next chapter, the hard quantizer considerably degrades performance relative to a properly adjusted soft quantizer.

With quadriphase modulation, demodulated by the system of Fig. 2.9, the same quantization scheme can be used on each of the two streams of observables, resulting in exactly the same channel as with biphase modulation, provided we can ignore the quadrature intersymbol interference discussed in Sec. 2.6. Multi-amplitude modulation can be treated in the same way as two-level modulation. For the case of Q input levels and J-level output quantization, the AWGN channel is reduced to a Q-input, J-output DMC. With Q-phase multiphase modulation employing both quadrature dimensions, as shown in case b of Fig. 2.12, the quantization may be more conveniently implemented in phase rather than amplitude.

Once the AWGN channel has been reduced to a DMC by output quantization, the decoder of Fig. 2.4, or its digital equivalent operating on quantized data, is no longer optimum. Rather, the optimum decoder must implement the decision rule (2.2.7) which is optimum for the resulting memoryless channel. For equiprobable messages, this reduces to the maximum likelihood decoder or decision rule

$$H_{\hat{m}} = H_m \quad \text{if } \sum_{n=1}^{N} [\ln p(y_n | x_{mn}) - \ln p(y_n | x_{m'n})] > 0 \quad \text{for all } m' \neq m \quad (2.8.2)$$

where for each m and n

$$x_{mn} \in \{a_1, a_2, \ldots, a_Q\}$$
$$y_n \in \{b_1, b_2, \ldots, b_J\}$$

For the BSC, (2.8.2) reduces to an even simpler rule. For, as shown in Fig. 2.15, the conditional probability for the nth symbol is p if $y_n \neq x_{mn}$ and is $(1-p)$ if $y_n = x_{mn}$. Suppose that the received vector $\mathbf{y} = (y_1, \ldots, y_N)$ differs from a transmitted vector $\mathbf{x}_m = (x_{m1}, \ldots, x_{mN})$ in exactly d_m positions. The number d_m is then said to be the *Hamming distance* between vectors $\mathbf{x}_m$ and $\mathbf{y}$. The conditional probability of receiving $\mathbf{y}$ given that $\mathbf{x}_m$ was transmitted is

$$p_N(\mathbf{y} \mid \mathbf{x}_m) = \prod_{n=1}^{N} p(y_n \mid x_{mn}) = p^{d_m}(1-p)^{N-d_m} \tag{2.8.3}$$

Note that, because of the symmetry of the channel, this likelihood function does not depend on the particular value of the transmitted symbol, but only on whether or not the channel caused a transition from a_1 to b_2 or from a_2 to b_1. Thus

$$\ln \prod_{n=1}^{N} p(y_n \mid x_{mn}) = \sum_{n=1}^{N} \ln p(y_n \mid x_{mn})$$
$$= N \ln (1-p) - d_m \ln [(1-p)/p] \tag{2.8.4}$$

Substituting (2.8.4) into (2.8.2), we obtain for the BSC the rule

$$H_{\hat{m}} = H_m \qquad \text{if } (d_{m'} - d_m) \ln \left(\frac{1-p}{p}\right) > 0 \qquad \text{for all } m' \neq m$$

Without loss of generality, we may assume $p \leq \frac{1}{2}$ (for if this is not the case, we may make it such by just interchanging the indices on b_1 and b_2). Then the decoding rule becomes

$$H_{\hat{m}} = H_m \qquad \text{if } d_m < d_{m'} \qquad \text{for all } m' \neq m \tag{2.8.5}$$

where d_m is the Hamming distance between $\mathbf{x}_m$ and $\mathbf{y}$. In each case, ties are assumed to be resolved randomly as before.

Hence, we conclude that, for the BSC, the maximum likelihood decoder reduces to a minimum distance decoder wherein the received vector $\mathbf{y}$ is compared with each possible transmitted signal vector and the one closest to $\mathbf{y}$, in the sense of minimum number of differing symbols (Hamming distance), is chosen as the correct transmitted vector. Although this suggests a much simpler mechanization, this rule could be implemented as in Fig. 2.4 if we took $\mathbf{y}$ and $\mathbf{x}_m$ to be binary vectors and $a_1 = b_1 = +1$ and $a_2 = b_2 = -1$.

For discrete memoryless channels other than the BSC, the decoding rule (2.8.2) can be somewhat simplified in many cases (see Prob. 2.9), but usually not to the point of being independent of the transition probabilities as has just been shown for the BSC. Generally, the rule will depend on these probabilities and hence on the energy-to-noise ratios as well as on the quantization scheme used.

This leads to a potential decoder mismatch or suboptimality due to unknown signal levels (incorrect AGC) or noise variance. Also, since the transition probabilities are themselves real numbers, quantization of these is required to implement the rule of (2.8.2) digitally with a resulting minor degradation. As we shall discover in later chapters, some decoders are relatively insensitive to channel statistics, while others degrade rapidly as a function of decoder mismatch. However, it is generally true that, for binary inputs, even with a mismatched decoder, performance of a multilevel (soft) quantized channel decoder is superior to that of a two-level (hard) quantized channel decoder. In performance evaluation of binary-input channels with variable output quantization, we shall generally treat the limiting cases of an AWGN channel without quantization and with hard quantization (BSC) to establish the two limits. Some intermediate cases will also be treated to indicate the rate of approach of multilevel (soft) quantization to the unquantized ideal case.

2.9 LINEAR CODES

Thus far we have devoted considerable attention to all parts of the communication system except the encoder. In its crudest form, encoding can be regarded as a table-look-up operation; each of the M signal vectors $\mathbf{x}_1, \mathbf{x}_2, \ldots, \mathbf{x}_M$ is stored in an N-stage register of a memory bank and, whenever message H_m is to be transmitted, the corresponding signal vector $\mathbf{x}_m$ is read into the modulator. Alternatively, we may label each of the $M = q^K$ messages, as in Fig. 2.1, by a K-vector over a q-ary alphabet. Then the encoding becomes a one-to-one mapping from the set of message vectors $\{\mathbf{u}_m = (u_{m1}, \ldots, u_{mK})\}$ into the set of signal vectors $\{\mathbf{x}_m = (x_{m1}, \ldots, x_{mN})\}$. We shall concern ourselves primarily with binary alphabets; thus initially we take $u_{mn} \in \{0, 1\}$, for all m, n and generalize later to $q > 2$. A particularly convenient mapping to implement is a *linear code*. For binary-input data, a linear code consists simply of a set of modulo-2 linear combinations of the data symbols, which may be implemented as shown in Fig. 2.16. The K-stage register corresponds precisely to the data block register in the general system diagram of Fig. 2.1. The coder then consists of L modulo-2 adders, each of which adds together a subset of the data symbols $u_{m1}, u_{m2}, \ldots, u_{mK}$ to generate one *code symbol* v_{mn} where $n = 1, 2, \ldots, L$ as shown in Fig. 2.16. We shall refer to the vector $\mathbf{v}_m = (v_{m1}, v_{m2}, \ldots, v_{mL})$ as the *code vector*. Modulo-2 addition of binary symbols will be denoted by $\oplus$ and is defined by

$$0 \oplus 1 = 1 \oplus 0 = 1$$

$$0 \oplus 0 = 1 \oplus 1 = 0 \tag{2.9.1}$$

It is readily verified by exhaustive testing that this operation is associative and commutative; that is, if a, b, c are binary symbols (0 or 1), then

$$(a \oplus b) \oplus c = a \oplus (b \oplus c) \tag{2.9.2a}$$

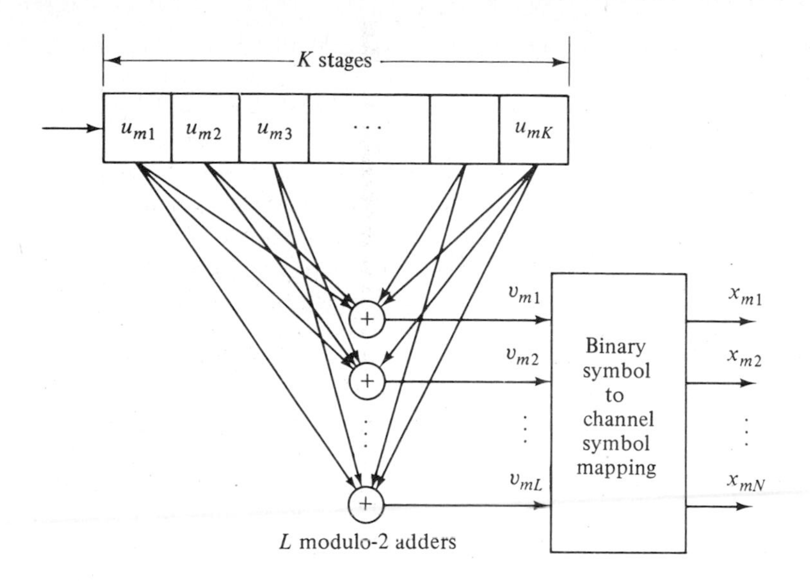

Figure 2.16 Linear block encoder.

and

$$a \oplus b = b \oplus a \tag{2.9.2b}$$

Thus the first stage of the linear coding operation for binary data can be represented by

$$\begin{aligned} v_{m1} &= u_{m1} g_{11} \oplus u_{m2} g_{21} \oplus \cdots \oplus u_{mK} g_{K1} \\ v_{m2} &= u_{m1} g_{12} \oplus u_{m2} g_{22} \oplus \cdots \oplus u_{mK} g_{K2} \\ &\cdots\cdots\cdots\cdots\cdots\cdots\cdots\cdots \\ v_{mL} &= u_{m1} g_{1L} \oplus u_{m2} g_{2L} \oplus \cdots \oplus u_{mK} g_{KL} \end{aligned} \tag{2.9.3}$$

where $g_{kn} \in \{0, 1\}$ for all k, n. The term $u_{mk} g_{kn}$ is an ordinary multiplication, so that u_{mk} enters into the particular combination for v_{mn} if and only if $g_{kn} = 1$. The matrix

$$G = \begin{bmatrix} g_{11} & g_{12} & \cdots & g_{1L} \\ g_{21} & g_{22} & \cdots & g_{2L} \\ \cdots & \cdots & \cdots & \cdots \\ g_{K1} & g_{K2} & \cdots & g_{KL} \end{bmatrix} = \begin{bmatrix} \leftarrow \mathbf{g}_1 \rightarrow \\ \leftarrow \mathbf{g}_2 \rightarrow \\ \vdots \\ \leftarrow \mathbf{g}_K \rightarrow \end{bmatrix} \tag{2.9.4a}$$

is called the *generator matrix* of the linear code and $\{\mathbf{g}_i\}$ are its row vectors. Thus, (2.9.3) can be expressed in vector form as[11]

$$\mathbf{v}_m = \mathbf{u}_m G = \bigoplus\!\!\!\!\sum_{k=1}^{K} u_{mk} \mathbf{g}_k \tag{2.9.4b}$$

[11] $\bigoplus\!\!\!\!\sum$ means modulo-2 addition.

where both $\mathbf{u}_m$ and $\mathbf{v}_m$ are binary row vectors. Note that the set of all possible codewords is the space spanned by the row vectors of G. The rows of G then form a basis with the information bits being the basis coefficients for the codeword. Since the basis vectors are not unique for any linear space, it is clear that there are many generator matrices that give the same set of codewords.

To complete the linear encoding, we must convert the L-dimensional code vector $\mathbf{v}_m$ with elements in $\{0, 1\}$ into the N-dimensional real number signal vector $\mathbf{x}_m = (x_{m1}, x_{m2}, \ldots, x_{mN})$. For the simplest cases of biphase or quadriphase modulation, we need only a one-dimensional mapping

$$\begin{aligned} v_{mn} = 0 &\to x_{mn} = +\sqrt{\mathscr{E}_s} \\ v_{mn} = 1 &\to x_{mn} = -\sqrt{\mathscr{E}_s} \end{aligned} \tag{2.9.5}$$

so that, in fact, $L = N$. For more elaborate modulation schemes, we must take $L > N$. For example, for the four-level amplitude modulation scheme of Fig. 2.12*a* we need to take $L = 2N$. Then the four possible combinations of the pair $(v_{ml}, v_{m,\,l+1})$ (where l is odd) give rise to one of four values for the signal (amplitude) symbol x_{mn} [where $n = (l+1)/2$]. Similarly, for the 16-phase modulation scheme of Fig. 2.12*b*, we must take $L = 4N$ and use four consecutive v-symbols to select one of the 16-phase x-symbols.

Before considering the code or modulation space further, we shall examine an extremely important property of linear codes known as *closure:* namely, the property that the modulo-2 termwise *sum of two code vectors* $\mathbf{v}_m$ and $\mathbf{v}_k$

$$\mathbf{v}_m \oplus \mathbf{v}_k = (v_{m1} \oplus v_{k1}, v_{m2} \oplus v_{k2}, \ldots, v_{mL} \oplus v_{kL})$$

is also a code vector. This is easily shown, for, by applying the associative law to $\mathbf{v}_m = \mathbf{u}_m G$ and $\mathbf{v}_k = \mathbf{u}_k G$, we obtain

$$\begin{aligned} \mathbf{v}_m \oplus \mathbf{v}_k &= \mathbf{u}_m G \oplus \mathbf{u}_k G \\ &= (\mathbf{u}_m \oplus \mathbf{u}_k) G \end{aligned}$$

But since $\mathbf{u}_m$ and $\mathbf{u}_k$ are two K-dimensional data vectors, their modulo-2 sum must also be a data vector, for the 2^K data vectors must coincide with all possible binary vectors of dimension K. Thus, denoting this data vector $\mathbf{u}_m \oplus \mathbf{u}_k \equiv \mathbf{u}_r$, it follows that

$$\begin{aligned} \mathbf{v}_m \oplus \mathbf{v}_k &= \mathbf{u}_r G \\ &= \mathbf{v}_r \end{aligned} \tag{2.9.6}$$

which is, therefore, a code vector. We generally label the data vectors consecutively with the convention that $\mathbf{u}_1 = (0, 0, \ldots, 0) \equiv \mathbf{0}$. It follows from (2.9.4) that also $\mathbf{v}_1 = \mathbf{0}$. The vector $\mathbf{0}$ is called the identity vector since, for any other code vector,

$$\begin{aligned} \mathbf{v}_m \oplus \mathbf{v}_1 &= \mathbf{v}_m \oplus \mathbf{0} \\ &= \mathbf{v}_m \end{aligned} \tag{2.9.7}$$

We note also that as a consequence of (2.9.1)

$$\mathbf{v}_m \oplus \mathbf{v}_m = \mathbf{0} \tag{2.9.8}$$

which means that every vector is its own negative (or additive inverse) under the operation of modulo-2 addition. When a set satisfies the closure property (2.9.6), the identity property (2.9.7), and the inverse property (2.9.8) under an operation which is associative and commutative (2.9.2), it is called an *Abelian group*. Hence linear codes are also called *group codes*. They are also called *parity-check codes*, since the code symbol $v_{mn} = 1$ if the "parity" of the data symbols added to form v_{mn} is odd, and $v_{mn} = 0$ if the parity is even.

An interesting consequence of the closure property is that the set of Hamming distances from a given code vector to the $(M-1)$ other code vectors is the same for all code vectors. To demonstrate this, it is convenient to define first the *Hamming weight* of a binary vector as the number of ones in the vector. The Hamming distance between two vectors $\mathbf{v}_m$ and $\mathbf{v}_{m'}$ is then just the Hamming weight of their modulo-2 termwise sum, denoted $w(\mathbf{v}_m \oplus \mathbf{v}_{m'})$. For example, if

$$\mathbf{v}_m = (0\ 1\ 1\ 0\ 1) \qquad \text{and} \qquad \mathbf{v}_{m'} = (1\ 0\ 1\ 1\ 0)$$

then

$$w(\mathbf{v}_m \oplus \mathbf{v}_{m'}) = w(1\ 1\ 0\ 1\ 1)$$
$$= 4$$

which is clearly the number of differing positions and hence the Hamming distance between the vectors. Now the set of distances of the other code vectors from $\mathbf{v}_1 = \mathbf{0}$ is clearly $\{w(\mathbf{v}_2), w(\mathbf{v}_3), \ldots, w(\mathbf{v}_M)\}$. On the other hand, the set of distances from any code vector $\mathbf{v}_m \neq \mathbf{0}$ to the other code vectors is just $\{w(\mathbf{v}_m \oplus \mathbf{v}_{m'})\text{: all } m' \neq m\}$. But, by the closure property, $\mathbf{v}_{m'} \oplus \mathbf{v}_m$ is some code vector other than $\mathbf{v}_1$. Furthermore, for any two distinct vectors $\mathbf{v}_{m'}, \mathbf{v}_{m''}$ where $m' \neq m$, $m'' \neq m$, and $m' \neq m''$ we have

$$\mathbf{v}_{m'} \oplus \mathbf{v}_m \neq \mathbf{v}_{m''} \oplus \mathbf{v}_m$$

and

$$\mathbf{v}_{m'} \oplus \mathbf{v}_m \neq \mathbf{0} = \mathbf{v}_1$$

Hence, as the index m' varies over all code vectors other than m, the operation $\mathbf{v}_{m'} \oplus \mathbf{v}_m$ generates all $(M-1)$ distinct nonzero code vectors and consequently the entire set except $\mathbf{v}_1$. It follows that

$$\{\mathbf{v}_{m'} \oplus \mathbf{v}_m\text{: all } m' \neq m\} = \{\mathbf{v}_2, \mathbf{v}_3, \ldots, \mathbf{v}_M\} \tag{2.9.9}$$

and thus also that

$$\{w(\mathbf{v}_{m'} \oplus \mathbf{v}_m)\text{: all } m' \neq m\} = \{w(\mathbf{v}_2), w(\mathbf{v}_3) \ldots w(\mathbf{v}_M)\} \tag{2.9.10}$$

which means that the set of distances of all other code vectors from a given code vector $\mathbf{v}_m$ is the same as the set of distances of all code vectors from $\mathbf{v}_1$. Thus, without loss of generality, we may compute just the distances from $\mathbf{v}_1$ or, equivalently, the weights of all the nonzero code vectors.

Another very useful consequence of the closure property of linear codes is that, when these are used on a *input-binary, output-symmetric channel* with maximum likelihood decoding, *the error probability for the* m*th message is the same for all* m; that is,

$$P_{E_m} = P_E \qquad m = 1, 2, \ldots, M \tag{2.9.11}$$

as we next show.

A binary-input symmetric channel, which includes the biphase and quadriphase AWGN channels as well as all symmetrically quantized reductions thereof, can be defined as follows. Let, for each m and n,

$$\begin{aligned} p(y_n \mid x_{mn} = +\sqrt{\mathscr{E}_s}) &= p(y_n \mid v_{mn} = 0) \\ &\equiv p_0(y_n) \\ p(y_n \mid x_{mn} = -\sqrt{\mathscr{E}_s}) &= p(y_n \mid v_{mn} = 1) \\ &\equiv p_1(y_n) \end{aligned} \tag{2.9.12}$$

This binary-input channel is said to be *symmetric* if

$$p_1(y) = p_0(-y) \tag{2.9.13}$$

It is easily verified that the AWGN channel, the BSC,[12] and any other symmetrically quantized AWGN channel all satisfy (2.9.13). To prove the *uniform error property* (2.9.11) for a binary linear code on this class of channels using maximum likelihood decoding, we note, using (2.3.1), (2.3.3), and (2.9.1) that

$$\begin{aligned} P_{E_m} &= \Pr\{\mathbf{y} \in \overline{\Lambda_m} \mid \mathbf{x}_m\} \\ &= \sum_{\mathbf{y} \in \overline{\Lambda_m}} p_N(\mathbf{y} \mid \mathbf{x}_m) \end{aligned}$$

where

$$\begin{aligned} \overline{\Lambda_m} &= \{\mathbf{y}\colon \ln p_N(\mathbf{y} \mid \mathbf{x}_{m'}) \geq \ln p_N(\mathbf{y} \mid \mathbf{x}_m) \text{ for some } m' \neq m\} \\ &= \left\{\mathbf{y}\colon \sum_{\substack{n:\, v_{mn}=0 \\ v_{m'n}=1}} \ln \frac{p(y_n \mid v_{m'n} = 1)}{p(y_n \mid v_{mn} = 0)} \right. \\ &\qquad \left. + \sum_{\substack{n:\, v_{m'n}=0 \\ v_{mn}=1}} \ln \frac{p(y_n \mid v_{m'n} = 0)}{p(y_n \mid v_{mn} = 1)} \geq 0 \text{ for some } m' \neq m \right\} \\ &= \left\{\mathbf{y}\colon \sum_{\substack{n:\, v_{mn}=0 \\ v_{m'n}=1}} \ln \frac{p_0(-y_n)}{p_0(y_n)} \right. \\ &\qquad \left. + \sum_{\substack{n:\, v_{m'n}=0 \\ v_{mn}=1}} \ln \frac{p_0(y_n)}{p_0(-y_n)} \geq 0 \text{ for some } m' \neq m \right\} \end{aligned} \tag{2.9.14a}$$

[12] For the BSC we must use the convention "0" → +1 and "1" → −1 so that $y = +1$ or -1 in order to use the definition (2.9.13) of symmetry.

We have

$$P_{E_m} = \sum_{\mathbf{y} \in \overline{\Lambda_m}} \prod_{n:\, v_{mn}=0} p(y_n | v_{mn} = 0) \prod_{n:\, v_{mn}=1} p(y_n | v_{mn} = 1)$$

$$= \sum_{\mathbf{y} \in \overline{\Lambda_m}} \prod_{n:\, v_{mn}=0} p_0(y_n) \prod_{n:\, v_{mn}=1} p_0(-y_n) \tag{2.9.15a}$$

But if we let

$$z_n = y_n \qquad \text{for all } n \text{ such that } v_{mn} = 0$$

$$z_n = -y_n \qquad \text{for all } n \text{ such that } v_{mn} = 1$$

which is just a change of dummy variables in the summation (or integration), (2.9.15) and (2.9.14) become respectively

$$P_{E_m} = \sum_{\mathbf{z} \in \overline{\Lambda_m}} \prod_{n=1}^{N} p_0(z_n) \tag{2.9.15b}$$

where now

$$\overline{\Lambda_m} \equiv \left\{ \mathbf{z}: \sum_{n:\, v_{m'n} \neq v_{mn}} \ln \frac{p_0(-z_n)}{p_0(z_n)} \geq 0 \text{ for some } m' \neq m \right\} \tag{2.9.14b}$$

But comparing (2.9.14*b*) and (2.9.15*b*) with (2.9.14*a*) and (2.9.15*a*), respectively, with $m = 1$ ($v_{1n} = 0$ for all n) in the latter pair, we find that, because of the symmetry of the linear code (2.9.9) and the random resolution of ties (see Sec. 2.2)

$$P_{E_m} = P_{E_1} \qquad \text{for } m = 1, 2, \ldots, M \tag{2.9.16}$$

Thus not only are all message error probabilities the same, but, in calculating P_E for linear codes on binary-input symmetric channels, we may without loss of generality *assume* always that the all-zeros code vector was transmitted. This greatly reduces the effort and simplifies the computations.

As an example, consider a linearly coded biphase-modulated signal on the AWGN channel. Although computation of the exact error probability is generally prohibitively complicated (except for special cases like the orthogonal or simplex codes; see Probs. 2.4, 2.5), the union upper bound of Sec. 2.3 can easily be calculated if the set of weights of all code vectors is known. For from (2.3.4) and (2.3.10), we obtain that, for the AWGN channel with biphase modulation

$$P_E = P_{E_1} \leq \sum_{k=2}^{M} Q\left(\frac{\|\mathbf{x}_k - \mathbf{x}_1\|}{\sqrt{2N_o}}\right)$$

where $\|\mathbf{x}_k - \mathbf{x}_1\|$ is the Euclidean distance between signal vectors. Now suppose the weight of $\mathbf{v}_k$, which is also its Hamming distance from $\mathbf{v}_1$, is w_k. This means that w_k of the code symbols of $\mathbf{v}_k$ are ones and consequently that w_k of the code symbols of $\mathbf{x}_k$ are $-\sqrt{\mathscr{E}_s}$ (the remainder being $+\sqrt{\mathscr{E}_s}$), and of course all code symbols of $\mathbf{x}_1$ are $+\sqrt{\mathscr{E}_s}$ since $\mathbf{v}_1 = \mathbf{0}$. Thus

$$\|\mathbf{x}_k - \mathbf{x}_1\| = 2\sqrt{\mathscr{E}_s w_k}$$

and, consequently, for the biphase- (or quadriphase-) modulated AWGN channel we have the union bond

$$P_E \leq \sum_{k=2}^{M} Q(\sqrt{(2\mathscr{E}_s/N_o)w_k}) \tag{2.9.17}$$

We may readily generalize (2.9.17) to any binary-input symmetric channel by using the Bhattacharyya bound (2.3.15) in conjunction with the union bound (2.3.4). For memoryless channels, (2.3.15) becomes

$$\begin{aligned} P_E(1 \to k) &\leq \prod_{n=1}^{N} \sum_y \sqrt{p(y \mid v_{kn})p(y \mid v_{1n} = 0)} \\ &= \prod_{n:\, v_{kn}=0} \sum_y \sqrt{p(y \mid v_{kn} = 0)p(y \mid v_{1n} = 0)} \prod_{n:\, v_{kn}=1} \sum_y \sqrt{p(y \mid v_{kn} = 1)p(y \mid v_{1n} = 0)} \\ &= \prod_{n:\, v_{kn} \neq v_{1n}} \sum_y \sqrt{p(y \mid v_{kn} = 1)p(y \mid v_{1n} = 0)} \end{aligned} \tag{2.9.18}$$

where the last step follows since each sum in the first product equals unity. Since $v_{kn} \neq v_{1n}$ in exactly w_k positions we have

$$P_E(1 \to k) \leq \left[\sum_y \sqrt{p_1(y)p_0(y)}\right]^{w_k}$$

and hence from (2.3.4) we find[13] that

$$P_E \leq \sum_{k=2}^{M} \exp\left[w_k \ln \sum_y \sqrt{p_0(y)p_1(y)}\right] \tag{2.9.19}$$

where $-\ln \sum_y \sqrt{p_0(y)p_1(y)}$ is the previously defined Bhattacharyya distance which becomes $\mathscr{E}_s/N_o$ for the AWGN channel [see (2.3.17) and (2.9.17)]. We note also that for the BSC

$$-\ln \sum_y \sqrt{p_0(y)p_1(y)} = -\ln \sqrt{4p(1-p)}$$

where p is the crossover probability. Tighter results for the BSC will be obtained in the next section.

In principle, we could employ the tighter Gallager bound of (2.4.8), but this generally requires more knowledge of the code structure than just the set of distances between code vectors. In fact, even the set of all code vector weights is not easily calculated in general. Often, the only known parameter of a code is the minimum distance between code vectors. Then from (2.9.17) and (2.9.19) we can obtain the much weaker bound for the AWGN channel

$$P_E < (M-1)Q\left\{\sqrt{\left(\frac{2\mathscr{E}_s}{N_o}\right) \min_{k \neq 1} w_k}\right\} \tag{2.9.20}$$

[13] This Bhattacharyya bound is also valid for asymmetric channels, but it is a weaker bound than the Chernoff bound in such cases (see Prob. 2.10).

and for general binary-input channels

$$P_E < (M - 1) \exp \left\{ \min_{k \neq 1} w_k [\ln \sqrt{p_0(y) p_1(y)}] \right\} \tag{2.9.21}$$

A seemingly unsurmountable weakness of this approach to the evaluation of linear codes is that essentially all those long codes which can be elegantly described or constructed with known distances have poor distance properties. A few short codes, such as the Golay code to be treated in Sec. 2.11, are optimum for relatively short block lengths and for some rates, and these are indeed useful to demonstrate some of the advantages of coding. But a few scattered examples of moderately short block codes hardly begin to scratch the surface of the remarkable capabilities of coding, both linear and otherwise. In the next chapter we shall demonstrate most of these capabilities by examining the entire ensemble of codes of a given length and rate, rather than hopelessly searching for the optimum member of this ensemble.

2.10 SYSTEMATIC LINEAR CODES AND OPTIMUM DECODING FOR THE BSC*

In the last section, we defined a linear code as one whose code vectors are generated from the data vectors by the linear mapping

$$\mathbf{v}_m = \mathbf{u}_m G \qquad m = 1, 2, \ldots, M \tag{2.10.1}$$

where G is an arbitrary $K \times L$ matrix of zeros and ones. We now demonstrate that because any useful linear code is a *one-to-one mapping* from the data vectors to the code vectors, it is equivalent to some linear code whose generator matrix is of the form

$$G = \begin{bmatrix} 1 & 0 & 0 & \cdots & 0 & g_{1,K+1} & \cdots & g_{1L} \\ 0 & 1 & 0 & \cdots & 0 & g_{2,K+1} & \cdots & g_{2L} \\ 0 & 0 & 1 & \cdots & 0 & g_{3,K+1} & \cdots & g_{3L} \\ \cdots & \cdots & \cdots & \cdots & \cdots & \cdots & \cdots & \cdots \\ 0 & 0 & 0 & \cdots & 1 & g_{K,K+1} & \cdots & g_{KL} \end{bmatrix} \tag{2.10.2}$$

We note first that a linear code (2.10.1) generated by the matrix (2.10.2) has its first K code symbols identical to the data symbols, that is

$$v_{mn} = u_{mn} \qquad n = 1, 2, \ldots, K \tag{2.10.3a}$$

and the remainder are as before[14] given by

$$v_{mn} = \sum_{k=1}^{K} u_{mk} g_{kn} \qquad n = K+1, K+2, \ldots, L \tag{2.10.3b}$$

* May be omitted without loss of continuity.

[14] $\sum$ means modulo-2 summation.

Such a code, which transmits the original K data symbols unchanged together with $L - K$ "parity-check" symbols is called a *systematic code.*

Any one-to-one linear code is equivalent in performance to a systematic code, as is shown by the following argument. Interchanging any two rows of G or adding together modulo-2 any combination of rows does not alter the set of code vectors generated; it simply relabels them. For, denoting the row vectors of G as $\mathbf{g}_1, \mathbf{g}_2, \ldots, \mathbf{g}_K$, we note that interchanging the two rows $\mathbf{g}_i$ and $\mathbf{g}_j$ changes the original code vectors

$$\mathbf{v}_m = u_{m1}\mathbf{g}_1 \oplus \cdots \oplus u_{mi}\mathbf{g}_i \oplus \cdots \oplus u_{mj}\mathbf{g}_j \oplus \cdots \oplus u_{mK}\mathbf{g}_K$$

into the new code vectors

$$\mathbf{v}'_m = u_{m1}\mathbf{g}_1 \oplus \cdots \oplus u_{mi}\mathbf{g}_j \oplus \cdots \oplus u_{mj}\mathbf{g}_i \oplus \cdots \oplus u_{mK}\mathbf{g}_K$$

But, since u_{mi} and u_{mj} take on all possible combinations of values, the set $\{\mathbf{v}'_m\}$ is identical to the set $\{\mathbf{v}_m\}$ except for relabeling. Similarly, adding row $\mathbf{g}_j$ to row $\mathbf{g}_i$ changes the original set into the new set of code vectors

$$\begin{aligned}\mathbf{v}''_m &= u_{m1}\mathbf{g}_1 \oplus \cdots \oplus u_{mi}(\mathbf{g}_i \oplus \mathbf{g}_j) \oplus \cdots \oplus u_{mj}\mathbf{g}_j \oplus \cdots \oplus u_{mK}\mathbf{g}_K \\ &= \mathbf{v}_m \oplus u_{mi}\mathbf{g}_j\end{aligned}$$

But, since $u_{mi}\mathbf{g}_j$ is itself a code vector, as a consequence of the closure property demonstrated in the last section, adding the same code vector to each of the original code vectors again generates the original set in different order. Hence $\{\mathbf{v}''_m\} = \{\mathbf{v}_m\}$.

To complete the argument, we perform row additions and interchanges on the generator matrix in the following order. Beginning with the first nonzero column j, we take the first row with a one in the jth position, interchange its position with the first row, and add it to all other rows containing ones in the jth position. This ensures that the jth column of the reduced matrix has a one in only the first row. We then proceed to the next nonzero column of the reduced matrix which has a one in any of the last $K - 1$ rows, interchange rows so there is a one in the second row, and add this second row to all rows (including possibly the first) with ones in this position. After K such steps we are left either with K columns, each having a one in a single different row, or with one or more zero rows at the bottom of the matrix; the latter occurs when the original matrix had two or more linearly dependent rows. In the latter case, the reduced generator matrix, and hence also the original G, cannot generate 2^K different code-vectors; hence the mapping is not one-to-one and corresponds, therefore, to a poor code since two or more data vectors produce the same code vector. In the first case, we might need to interchange column vectors in order to arrive at the generator matrix of (2.10.2). This merely results in a reordering of the code symbols.[15]

[15] This does not alter the performance on any binary-input memoryless channel; it might, however, alter performance on a non-binary-input channel, for which each signal dimension depends on more than one code symbol; this is not of interest here.

Thus, whenever the code-generator matrix has linearly independent rows and nonzero columns, the code is *equivalent*, except for relabeling of code vectors and possibly reordering of the columns, to a *systematic* code generated by (2.10.2).

We therefore restrict attention henceforth to systematic linear block codes, and consider, in particular, their use on the BSC. We demonstrated in Sec. 2.8 that maximum likelihood decoding of any binary code transmitted over the BSC is equivalent to minimum distance decoding. That is,

$$H_{\hat{m}} = H_m \qquad \text{if } d_m(\mathbf{y}) < d_{m'}(\mathbf{y}) \qquad \text{for all } m' \neq m \tag{2.10.4}$$

with ties resolved randomly. If we take $y_n \in \{0, 1\}$ and $x_{mn} = v_{mn} \in \{0, 1\}$, the Hamming distance is given by

$$\begin{aligned} d_m(\mathbf{y}) &= w(\mathbf{x}_m \oplus \mathbf{y}) \\ &= w(\mathbf{v}_m \oplus \mathbf{y}) \end{aligned} \tag{2.10.5}$$

Also, since the code and signal symbols are the same here, $L = N$. Thus decoding might be performed by taking the weight of the vector formed by adding modulo-2 the received binary vector $\mathbf{y}$ to each possible code vector and deciding in favor of the message whose code vector results in the lowest weight.

We now demonstrate a simpler table-look-up technique for decoding systematic linear codes on the BSC. Substituting (2.10.3*a*) into the right side of (2.10.3*b*) and adding v_{mn} to both sides of the latter, we obtain

$$0 = \sum_{k=1}^{K} v_{mk} g_{kn} \oplus v_{mn} \qquad n = K+1, K+2, \ldots, L$$

or, in vector form

$$\mathbf{0} = \mathbf{v}_m H^T \tag{2.10.6a}$$

where H^T is the $L \times (L-K)$ matrix

$$H^T = \begin{bmatrix} g_{1,K+1} & \cdots & g_{1,L} \\ g_{2,K+1} & \cdots & g_{2,L} \\ \cdots & \cdots & \cdots \\ g_{K,K+1} & \cdots & g_{K,L} \\ 1 & & \\ & 1 & \mathbf{0} \\ & & \ddots \\ \mathbf{0} & & 1 \end{bmatrix} \tag{2.10.6b}$$

Its transpose, the matrix H, is called the *parity-check matrix*. Thus, from (2.10.6*a*), we see that any code vector multiplied by H^T yields the $\mathbf{0}$ vector; thus the code vectors constitute the null-space of the parity-check matrix. Now consider post-multiplying any received vector $\mathbf{y}$ by H^T. The resulting $(L-K)$-dimensional binary vector is called the *syndrome* of the received vector and is given by

$$\mathbf{s} = \mathbf{y} H^T \tag{2.10.7}$$

This operation can be performed in exactly the same manner as the encoding operation (2.9.3) or (2.9.4), except here we require an L-stage register and $L - K$ modulo-2 adders. Obviously, if no errors are made, $\mathbf{y} = \mathbf{v}_m$ and consequently the syndrome is zero. Now suppose that the BSC causes an arbitrary sequence of errors $\mathbf{e} = (e_1, e_2, \ldots, e_L)$, where we adopt the convention that

$$e_n = \begin{cases} 1 & \text{if an error occurs in the } n\text{th symbol transmission} \\ 0 & \text{if no error occurs in the } n\text{th symbol transmission} \end{cases}$$

Then, if $\mathbf{v}_m$ is transmitted,

$$\mathbf{y} = \mathbf{v}_m \oplus \mathbf{e} \tag{2.10.8}$$

and

$$\mathbf{v}_m \oplus \mathbf{y} = \mathbf{e} \tag{2.10.9}$$

Also, the syndrome is given by

$$\begin{aligned} \mathbf{s} = \mathbf{y}H^T &= (\mathbf{v}_m \oplus \mathbf{e})H^T \\ &= \mathbf{e}H^T \end{aligned} \tag{2.10.10}$$

Now, for a given received vector $\mathbf{y}$ and corresponding syndrome vector $\mathbf{s}$, (2.10.10) will have $M = 2^K$ solutions $\{\mathbf{e}_m = \mathbf{y} \oplus \mathbf{v}_m\}$, one for each possible transmitted vector. However, we have from (2.10.5) that the maximum likelihood (minimum distance) decoder for the BSC chooses the codeword corresponding to the smallest weight vector among the set $\{\mathbf{v}_m \oplus \mathbf{y}\}$. But, according to (2.10.9), for systematic linear codes this indicates that, given the channel output $\mathbf{y}$,

$$H_{\hat{m}} = H_m \qquad \text{if } w(\mathbf{e}_m) < w(\mathbf{e}_{m'}) \qquad \text{for all } m' \neq m \tag{2.10.11}$$

This then suggests the following mechanization of the maximum likelihood decoder for the BSC:

0. Initially, prior to decoding, for each of the 2^{L-K} possible syndromes $\mathbf{s}$ store the minimum weight vector $\mathbf{e}(\mathbf{s})$ which satisfies (2.10.10) in a table of 2^{L-K} L-bit entries.
1. From the L-dimensional received vector $\mathbf{y}$, generate the $(L - K)$-dimensional syndrome $\mathbf{s}$ by the linear operation (2.10.7); this requires an L-stage register and $L - K$ modulo-2 adders.
2. Do a table-look-up in the table of step 0 to obtain $\hat{\mathbf{e}} = \mathbf{e}(\mathbf{s})$ from $\mathbf{s}$.
3. Obtain the most likely code vector by the operation

$$\mathbf{v}_m = \mathbf{y} \oplus \hat{\mathbf{e}}$$

and the first K symbols are the data symbols according to (2.10.3a).

The complexity of this procedure lies in the table containing 2^{L-K} vectors of dimension L; it follows trivially from step 3 that, because the code is systematic, each entry can be reduced to just a K-dimensional vector; that is, it is necessary to store only the errors which occurred in the K data symbols and not those in the $L - K$ parity-check symbols.

As a direct consequence of (2.10.4), (2.10.5), and (2.10.9), it follows that a maximum likelihood decoder for any binary code on the BSC *will decode correctly* if

$$w(\mathbf{e}) < \tfrac{1}{2}d_{\min} \tag{2.10.12}$$

where $d_{\min}$ is the minimum Hamming distance among all pairs of codewords. Letting $\mathbf{y} = \mathbf{x}_{m'}$ in (2.10.5) it follows that

$$d_{\min} = \min_{m' \neq m} w(\mathbf{x}_m \oplus \mathbf{x}_{m'})$$

With the convention that ties are resolved randomly, correct decoding will occur with some nonzero probability when (2.10.12) is an equality. Thus, whenever the number of errors is less than half the minimum distance between code vectors, the decoder will be guaranteed to correct them. (However, this is not an only if condition, unless the code vectors are *sphere-packed*, as will be discussed below.) Nevertheless, (2.10.12) leads to an upper bound on error probability for linear codes on the BSC because, as a consequence of (2.9.11), we have

$$\begin{aligned} P_E &= P_{E_m} \\ &\leq \Pr\{w(\mathbf{e}_m) \geq \tfrac{1}{2}d_{\min}\} \end{aligned} \tag{2.10.13}$$

Then, since $e_n = 1$ with probability p for each $n = 1, 2, \ldots, L$, (2.10.13) is just the binomial sum

$$P_E \leq \begin{cases} \displaystyle\sum_{k=(d_{\min}+1)/2}^{L} \binom{L}{k} p^k (1-p)^{L-k} & d_{\min} \text{ odd} \\[2ex] \displaystyle\sum_{k=d_{\min}/2}^{L} \binom{L}{k} p^k (1-p)^{L-k} & d_{\min} \text{ even} \end{cases} \tag{2.10.14}$$

Codes for which (2.10.14) is exact include the *Hamming single-error correcting codes* which may conventionally be defined in terms of their parity-check matrix. H is the parity-check matrix of an (L, K) Hamming code if its L columns (L rows of H^T) consist of all possible nonzero $L - K$ binary vectors. This implies that for a Hamming code

$$L = 2^{L-K} - 1$$

An example of H^T for a (7, 4) Hamming code is given in Fig. 2.17. Since all rows of H^T are distinct, each of the L unit-weight (single) error vectors has a different nonzero syndrome (corresponding to one row of H^T). There are, in fact, just $2^{L-K} = L + 1$ distinct syndromes, one of which is the zero vector, corresponding to no errors, and the remaining L correspond to the single-error vectors. For note, from step 0 of the syndrome table-look-up decoder, that the minimum weight

$$H^T = \begin{bmatrix} 0 & 1 & 1 \\ 1 & 0 & 1 \\ 1 & 1 & 0 \\ 1 & 1 & 1 \\ 1 & 0 & 0 \\ 0 & 1 & 0 \\ 0 & 0 & 1 \end{bmatrix}$$

Figure 2.17 Transpose of parity-check matrix for (7, 4) Hamming code.

error vector should be used for each syndrome. Since here all the unit-weight error vectors correspond to all the distinct nonzero syndromes, the Hamming codes all correct one error and only one error. This can also be verified by showing that $d_{\min} = 3$ (see Prob. 2.11).

It is instructive to investigate the linear code generated by the H matrix of the Hamming code (which is called its *dual* code)

$$G = H_{\text{Hamming}} \tag{2.10.15}$$

This is a $K \times L$ matrix where

$$L = 2^K - 1$$

and the columns consist of all possible nonzero K-dimensional binary vectors. Figure 2.18 shows the generator matrix of the (7, 3) code, which is the dual of the (7, 4) Hamming code whose transposed parity-check matrix was given in Fig. 2.17. In addition, to its right in Fig. 2.18 we adjoin the all zero column to create an (8, 3) code. We can generalize to a $(2^K, K)$ code whose generator matrix is the transpose of the $(2^K - 1) \times K$ matrix H^T of a Hamming code augmented by an all-zero column, and can show that every nonzero codeword of this augmented code has weight

$$\begin{aligned} w(\mathbf{v}_m) &= L/2 \\ &= 2^{K-1} \qquad \text{for all } m \neq 1 \end{aligned} \tag{2.10.16}$$

For any code vector

$$\mathbf{v}_m = \mathbf{u}_m G = u_{m1}\mathbf{g}_1 \oplus u_{m2}\mathbf{g}_2 \oplus \cdots \oplus u_{mK}\mathbf{g}_K$$

where $\mathbf{g}_k$ is the kth row of G. Also, since the data symbols u_{mk} are zeros and ones, $\mathbf{v}_m$ is the modulo-2 sum of the remaining rows of G, after some subset of the rows has been deleted. But we note that deletion of one row results in a matrix of $L = 2^K$ columns of dimension $K - 1$, where each of the possible 2^{K-1} binary columns appears exactly twice; similarly deletion of j rows results in a matrix of $L = 2^K$ columns of dimension $K - j$ with each of the possible 2^{K-j} columns repeated exactly 2^j times. But in each case, half of these 2^{K-j} columns contain an odd number of ones and the other half an even number. Hence, adding all the

$$G = \left[\begin{array}{ccccccc|c} 0 & 1 & 1 & 1 & 1 & 0 & 0 & 0 \\ 1 & 0 & 1 & 1 & 0 & 1 & 0 & 0 \\ 1 & 1 & 0 & 1 & 0 & 0 & 1 & 0 \end{array}\right]$$

Figure 2.18 Generator matrices for (7, 3) regular simplex and (8, 3) orthogonal codes.

nondeleted rows modulo-2 is equivalent to adding all the nondeleted symbols of the L columns, half of which have even parity and the other half odd. Thus the result is $L/2$ zeros and $L/2$ ones; hence, the desired result (2.10.16).

Equation (2.10.16) also implies, by the closure property (2.9.6), that the Hamming distance between all pairs of codewords is

$$\begin{aligned} w(\mathbf{v}_m \oplus \mathbf{v}_{m'}) &= L/2 \\ &= 2^{K-1} \qquad \text{for all } m' \neq m \end{aligned}$$

Consequently, the biphase-modulated signals generated by such a code (augmented by the additional all-zeros column) are all mutually *orthogonal*, for the normalized inner product for any two binary signals is in general

$$\begin{aligned} \frac{1}{L\mathcal{E}_s} \int_0^T x_m(t) x_{m'}(t)\, dt &= \frac{1}{L\mathcal{E}_s} [L - 2w(\mathbf{v}_m \oplus \mathbf{v}_{m'})]\mathcal{E}_s \\ &= 1 - \frac{2w(\mathbf{v}_m \oplus \mathbf{v}_{m'})}{L} \end{aligned} \tag{2.10.17}$$

For the code under consideration, we thus have

$$\int_0^T x_m(t) x_{m'}(t)\, dt = 0 \qquad \text{for all } m \neq m' \tag{2.10.18}$$

Returning to the original code generated by the $K \times (2^K - 1)$ matrix G of (2.10.15), we note that the weight of each nonzero code vector $\mathbf{v}_m$ is unchanged when the additional all-zeros column (of Fig. 2.18) is deleted. However, the biphase signals derived from the code are no longer orthogonal since now $L = 2^K - 1$. From (2.10.17) we obtain

$$\begin{aligned} \frac{1}{L\mathcal{E}_s} \int_0^T x_m(t) x_{m'}(t)\, dt &= 1 - \frac{2w(\mathbf{v}_m \oplus \mathbf{v}_{m'})}{L} \\ &= 1 - \frac{2^K}{2^K - 1} \\ &= -\frac{1}{2^K - 1} \\ &= -\frac{1}{L} \qquad \text{for all } m \neq m' \end{aligned} \tag{2.10.19}$$

This code is called a *regular simplex* or *transorthogonal* code. It is easily shown (Prob. 2.5) that (2.10.19) corresponds to the minimum average inner product of any equal-energy signal set. We shall discuss the relative performance of the orthogonal and regular simplex signal sets in the next section.

Considerable attention has been devoted, since the earliest days of information theory, to the study of numerous classes of linear block codes, and particularly to algebraic decoding algorithms which are of reasonable complexity and do not require the exponentially growing storage of the syndrome table-look-up approach which we have described. While some very elegant and reasonably powerful linear codes and decoding techniques have been discovered, particularly among the class of "cyclic" codes, these codes fall far short of the performance of the best linear codes, as will be determined in the next chapter. Also, the more readily implementable decoding algorithms, while guaranteeing the correction of a given number of errors per block, are generally suboptimum and restricted to hard quantized channels such as the BSC for binary codes. The last, and probably most important, cause for the limited practical success of linear block codes is the generally far superior capabilities of linear convolutional codes, to be discussed in Chap. 4.

Much of the material in these last two sections can be generalized to non-binary-code alphabets, and specifically to data and code alphabets of size q, where q is either a prime or some power of a prime. For practical storage and implementation purposes, one almost always requires q to be a power of 2. While such generalization is straightforward, it requires the development of some elementary concepts of finite field theory. The limited utility of the results does not seem to warrant their inclusion here. Excellent treatments of algebraic codes over binary as well as nonbinary alphabets are available in Berlekamp [1968], Gallager [1968], Lin [1970], Van Lint [1971], Peterson and Weldon [1972], Blake and Mullin [1976].

2.11 EXAMPLES OF LINEAR BLOCK CODE PERFORMANCE ON THE AWGN CHANNEL AND ITS QUANTIZED REDUCTIONS*

In this section, we consider briefly the performance of the two most commonly used linear block codes for a biphase- (or quadriphase-) modulated AWGN channel, both without and with output quantization. First we consider the classes of orthogonal and regular simplex signals. We found in Sec. 2.5 that the performance of orthogonal signals on the AWGN channel is invariant to the particular waveforms used. Hence, we have the union-Bhattacharyya bound (2.3.19) or the tighter Gallager bound (2.5.12) with $M = 2^K$ and $\mathscr{E} = 2^K \mathscr{E}_s$. One can also readily obtain the exact expression (see Prob. 2.4) which is

$$P_E = 1 - \frac{1}{\sqrt{2\pi}} \int_{-\infty}^{\infty} e^{-x^2/2} \left[1 - Q\left(x + \sqrt{\frac{2\mathscr{E}}{N_o}}\right)\right]^{M-1} dx \tag{2.11.1}$$

This integral has been tabulated for $M = 2^K$ for all K up to 10 (see Viterbi [1966]). It is plotted in Fig. 2.19, for $K = 6$, as a function of $\mathscr{E}_b/N_o$ where $\mathscr{E}_b$ is the energy per transmitted bit, which is related to $\mathscr{E}$ and K by the relation

$$\mathscr{E}_b = \frac{\mathscr{E}}{K} = \frac{2^K \mathscr{E}_s}{K} \tag{2.11.2}$$

* May be omitted without loss of continuity.

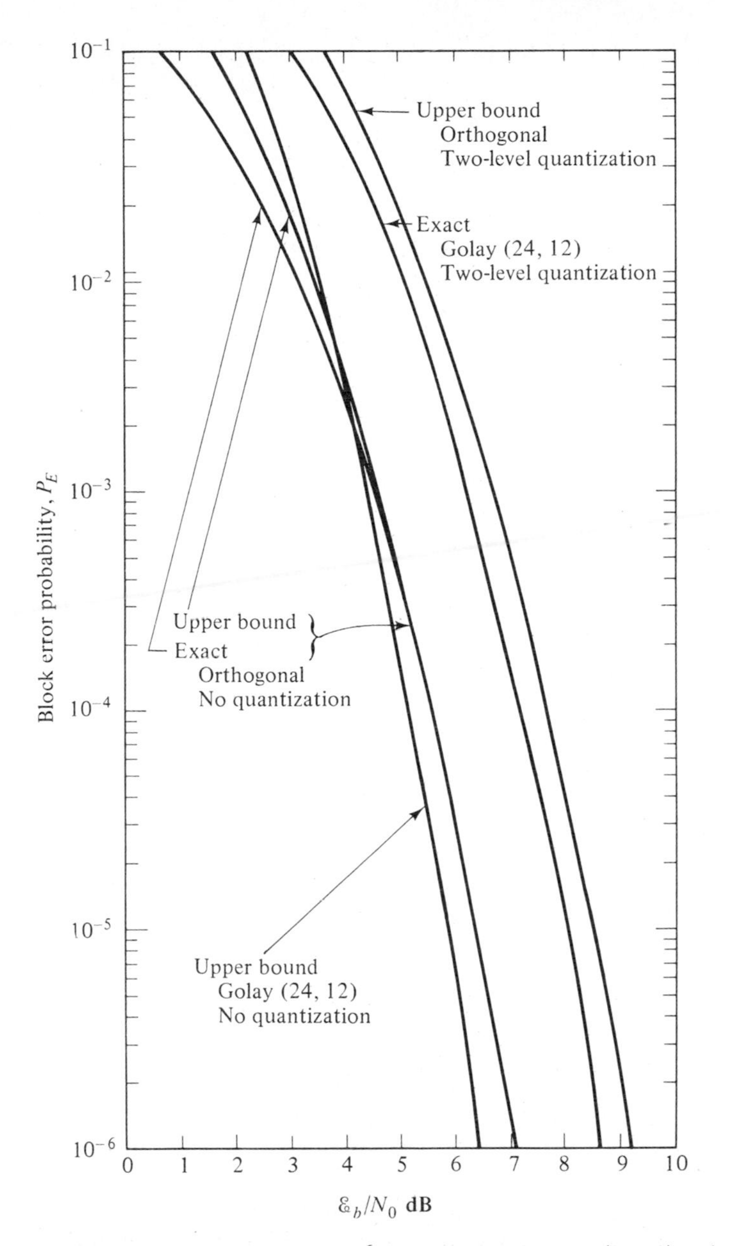

Figure 2.19 Error probability for 2^6 orthogonal and Golay (24, 12) coded signals on the AWGN channel.

The regular simplex signal set performs exactly as well as the orthogonal signal set for, as is evident from Fig. 2.18, one symbol or dimension is identical for all signals in the set; hence, it might as well *not* be transmitted for it does not assist at all in discrimination between signals. However, in so dropping the rightmost symbol from the orthogonal code to obtain the regular simplex code, we are actually reducing the energy per transmitted bit to

$$\mathscr{E}_b' = (2^K - 1)\frac{\mathscr{E}_s}{K} = \mathscr{E}_b(1 - 2^{-K})$$

This means that the error probability curve as a function of $\mathscr{E}_b'/N_o$ of Fig. 2.19 is actually translated to the left by an amount $10 \log_{10} (1 - 2^{-K})$ dB which for $K = 6$ is approximately 0.07 dB. For comparison purposes, the union bound for orthogonal codes, obtained from (2.3.4) and (2.3.10), is also shown.

Now let us consider the limiting case of two-level (hard) quantization so that the AWGN channel is reduced to the BSC. In this case, we have the general bound (2.10.14). For orthogonal codes, however, this bound is very weak. For, while $d_{\min} = 2^{K-1} = L/2$, it is possible to decode correctly in many cases where the number of errors is greater than $L/4$ because of the sparseness of the codewords in the 2^K-dimensional space. In fact, the bound (2.10.14) becomes increasingly poor as K increases (see Prob. 2.12). On the other hand, we may proceed to bound the BSC performance by using the union bound (2.3.4), resolving ties randomly

$$\begin{aligned} P_E &\le \sum_{m'=2}^{2K} \Pr\{w(\mathbf{y} \oplus \mathbf{x}_{m'}) > w(\mathbf{y} \oplus \mathbf{x}_1) \mid \mathbf{x}_1\} \\ &\quad + \tfrac{1}{2} \Pr\{w(\mathbf{y} \oplus \mathbf{x}_{m'}) = w(\mathbf{y} \oplus \mathbf{x}_1) \mid \mathbf{x}_1\} \\ &= (2^K - 1)[\Pr\{\text{more than } 2^{K-2} \text{ errors in } 2^{K-1} \text{ positions}\} \\ &\quad + \tfrac{1}{2} \Pr\{2^{K-2} \text{ errors in } 2^{K-1} \text{ positions}\}] \\ &= (2^K - 1)\left[\sum_{k=(2^{K-2}+1)}^{2^{K-1}} \binom{2^{K-1}}{k} p^k (1-p)^{2^{K-1}-k} \right. \\ &\quad \left. + \frac{1}{2}\binom{2^{K-1}}{2^{K-2}} p^{2^{K-2}} (1-p)^{2^{K-2}} \right] \end{aligned} \tag{2.11.3}$$

where $p = Q(\sqrt{2\mathscr{E}_s/N_o})$. This result is also plotted for $K = 6$ in Fig. 2.19. Again, the performance for regular simplex codes is the same but the transmitted energy is slightly less.

Probably the most famous, and possibly the most useful, linear block codes are the *Golay (23, 12) and (24, 12) codes*, which have minimum distances equal to 7 and 8 respectively. The former is called a *perfect code* which means that all spheres of Hamming radius r around each code vector $\mathbf{v}_m$ (i.e., the sets of all vectors at Hamming distance r from the code vector) are disjoint and every vector $\mathbf{y}$ is at most a distance r from some code vector $\mathbf{v}_m$. The only nontrivial[16] perfect binary codes are the Hamming codes with $r = 1$, and the Golay (23, 12) code with $r = 3$. The (24, 12) code is only quasi-perfect, meaning that all spheres of radius r about each code vector are disjoint, but that every vector $\mathbf{y}$ is at most at distance $r + 1$

[16] Two codewords of odd length that differ in every position form a perfect code and there are many perfect codes with $d_{\min} = 1$.

from some code vector $\mathbf{v}_m$. Here again $r = 3$. It is easy to show that perfect and quasi-perfect codes achieve the minimum error probability for the given values of (L, K). This second code is actually used more often than the first for various reasons including its slightly better performance on the AWGN channel. The Golay codes are among the few linear codes, besides the Hamming and orthogonal classes, for which all the code vector weights are known. These are summarized in Table 2.2. While an exact expression for P_E on the AWGN channel is not obtainable in closed form, given all the code vector weights, we may apply the union bound of (2.9.17) and thus obtain

$$P_E \leq \sum_{w \in W} N_w Q\sqrt{(2\mathscr{E}_s/N_o)w} \tag{2.11.4}$$

where the index set W and the integer N_w are given in Table 2.2. This result is also plotted in Fig. 2.19 and, although it is only a bound, it is reasonably tight as verified by simulation.

On the BSC, for the (24, 12) code, minimum distance decoding always corrects 3 or fewer errors and corrects one-sixth of the weight 4 error vectors. On the other hand, error vectors of weight 5 or more are never corrected, since by the quasi-perfect property, there exists some code vector at a distance no greater than 4 from every received vector $\mathbf{y}$. Similarly for the (23, 12) code all error vectors of weight 3 or less, and only these, are corrected. Hence for the (23, 12) code the expression (2.10.14) holds exactly. For the (24, 12) code we can multiply the first term in (2.10.14) by 5/6 and also obtain an exact result. This result for $p = Q(\sqrt{2\mathscr{E}_s/N_o})$, $L = 24$, $d_{\min} = 8$, $\mathscr{E}_b = 2\mathscr{E}_s$ is plotted in Fig. 2.19.

A potentially disturbing feature of the above results is that in each case we have determined the *block error probability*. But for orthogonal and regular simplex codes, we have used $K = 6$ bits/block while for the Golay code we have $K = 12$ bits/block, and we would expect that the block error probability might be

Table 2.2 Weight of code-vectors in Golay codes (Peterson [1961])

	Number of code-vectors of weight w, N_w	
Weight, w	(23, 12) code	(24, 12) code
0	1	1
7	253	0
8	506	759
11	1288	0
12	1288	2576
15	506	0
16	253	759
23	1	0
24	0	1
Total	4096	4096

influenced by the number of bits transmitted by the block code. We may define *bit error probability* P_b as the expected number of information bit errors per block divided by the total number of information bits transmitted per block. For orthogonal and regular simplex codes, all block errors are equiprobable since all 2^K code vectors are mutually equidistant. Thus, since there are $\binom{K}{k}$ ways in which k out of K bits may be in error and since an error will cause any pattern of errors in the data vector with equal probability $P_E/(2^K - 1)$, it follows that for orthogonal and regular simplex codes over any of the channels considered

$$P_b = \frac{1}{K} \sum_{k=1}^{K} k \binom{K}{k} \frac{P_E}{(2^K - 1)}$$

$$= \frac{2^{K-1}}{2^K - 1} P_E$$

which, for all but very small K, is very nearly

$$P_b \approx P_E/2$$

The evaluation of P_b is not nearly as simple and elegant for other linear block codes and in fact depends on the particular generator matrix chosen. However, for the Golay (24, 12) code with a systematic encoder, we may argue approximately as follows. Block errors will usually (with high probability) cause a choice of an incorrect code vector which is at distance 8 from the correct code vector. This means that one-third of all code symbols are usually in error when a block error is made. But since the code is systematic and half the code symbols are data symbols, the same ratio occurs among the data symbols. Hence, it follows that approximately, $P_b \approx P_E/3$. In general, in any case, we have trivially, $P_b < P_E$ and also the lower bound $P_E/K \le P_b$. Hence the upper bounds on P_E are also valid for P_b, and the comparison of P_E for two codes is nearly as useful as that of P_b even when the block lengths are different.

Comparison in Fig. 2.19 of the performance of each code on the AWGN channel and on its hard quantized reduction, the BSC, indicates that hard quantization causes a degradation of very nearly 2 dB. This result is best explained by using the union-Bhattacharyya bound (2.9.19). By this bound

$$P_E \le \sum_{k=2}^{M} e^{-w_k d} \tag{2.11.5}$$

where

$$d = -\ln \sum_y \sqrt{p_0(y)p_1(y)}$$

is a function of the quantization procedure, while $w_2, w_3, \ldots, w_M$, the weights of the nonzero codewords, are invariant to quantization. As also demonstrated by

(2.3.17), for the AWGN[17] channel

$$d = -\ln \int_{-\infty}^{\infty} \sqrt{p_0(y)p_0(-y)}\, dy$$

$$= -\ln \int_{-\infty}^{\infty} \exp\left[-\left(y - \sqrt{\frac{2\mathscr{E}_s}{N_o}}\right)^2 \Big/ 4\right] \exp\left[-\left(y + \sqrt{\frac{2\mathscr{E}_s}{N_o}}\right)^2 \Big/ 4\right] \frac{dy}{\sqrt{2\pi}}$$

$$= \mathscr{E}_s/N_o \tag{2.11.6}$$

For the BSC on the other hand, we have shown in Sec. 2.9 that

$$d = -\ln \sqrt{4p(1-p)} \tag{2.11.7a}$$

where

$$p = Q(\sqrt{2\mathscr{E}_s/N_o}) \tag{2.11.7b}$$

But in the case of orthogonal codes

$$\mathscr{E}_s/N_o = K2^{-K}\mathscr{E}_b/N_o$$

which is extremely small when $K \gg 1$. Similarly, for any code in which $L \gg K\mathscr{E}_b/N_o$

$$\frac{\mathscr{E}_s}{N_o} = \frac{K}{L}\frac{\mathscr{E}_b}{N_o} \ll 1$$

In such cases (2.11.7*b*) approaches

$$p \approx \frac{1}{2} - \sqrt{\frac{\mathscr{E}_s}{\pi N_o}} \tag{2.11.8}$$

Thus for the BSC with $\mathscr{E}_s/N_o \ll 1$ (or, almost equivalently, $L \gg K$)

$$d \approx -\ln \sqrt{1 - \frac{4\mathscr{E}_s}{\pi N_o}} \approx \frac{2}{\pi}\frac{\mathscr{E}_s}{N_o} \tag{2.11.9}$$

Comparing (2.11.6) and (2.11.9), we see that in order to obtain the same bound (2.11.5), we must increase the energy by a factor $\pi/2$ (2 dB) for the BSC relative to the AWGN channel. Even though (2.11.9) has been shown under the condition that $\mathscr{E}_s/N_o \ll 1$, the approximate 2 dB degradation for two-level quantization seems empirically to hold even when this condition is not met (see, for example, Fig. 2.19). Cases of intermediate quantization are also readily evaluated (see Prob. 2.13) and the resulting d is easily computed. Other measures of quantization loss will also be considered in the next chapter.

[17] For $p_0(y)$, the random variable y can be taken to have mean $\sqrt{\mathscr{E}_s}$ and variance $N_o/2$, or equivalently we may normalize it to have mean $\sqrt{2\mathscr{E}_s/N_o}$ and unit variance. The latter is used in (2.11.6).

Upon initially defining linear block codes in Sec. 2.9, we showed that they could be used in conjunction with multiple-amplitude and multiple-phase modulation by using several code symbols to select each signal symbol (or dimension). However, we have given no examples of performance of such signal sets. One reason is that the uniform error property $P_{E_m} = P_E$ does not generally hold for such cases, making the analysis of a particular code much more complex; another is that the results are much less revealing. On the other hand, in the next chapter we shall develop the technique of ensemble performance evaluation, which is no more difficult for these cases of nonbinary modulation than for biphase (or quadriphase) modulation.

2.12 OTHER MEMORYLESS CHANNELS

Thus far we have concentrated exclusively on the AWGN channel and its quantized reductions, all of which are memoryless channels. These channel models apply most accurately to line-of-sight space and satellite communication. As a result, since such channels have become commonplace, coding to improve error performance in digital communication has been most prevalent in these applications.

2.12.1 Colored Noise

Yet even with the AWGN channel, certain imperfections invariably enter to degrade performance, some of which were discussed in Sec. 2.6. For example, intersymbol interference is caused by linear filtering in the transmitter, channel, or receiver when the "predetection" filters are not sufficiently wideband for the given signal. But receiver filtering also modifies the noise spectral density so that the white noise model is no longer appropriate. The resulting zero-mean noise with nonuniform spectral density is called *colored*. It can be treated in either of two ways. The rigorous theoretical approach is to expand the noise process in a Karhunen-Loève series

$$n(t) = \lim_{N \to \infty} \sum_{n=1}^{N} n_n \phi_n(t)$$

where the $\{\phi_n(t)\}$ are normalized eigenfunctions of the noise covariance function and the $\{n_n\}$ are independent Gaussian variables with zero means and variances equal to the eigenvalues of the noise covariance function (Helstrom [1968], Van Trees [1968]). In particular, if the noise covariance function is positive definite, the eigenfunctions form a complete basis for finite-energy functions so that the signals $\{x_m(t)\}$ can also be represented in terms of their projections on the basis $\{\phi_n(t)\}$. We then have the representation

$$x_m(t) = \lim_{N \to \infty} \sum_{n=1}^{N} x_{mn} \phi_n(t)$$

where

$$x_{mn} = \int_0^T x_m(t)\phi_n(t)\,dt \qquad \begin{cases} n = 1, 2, \ldots, N \\ m = 1, 2, \ldots, M \end{cases}$$

and the channel can be represented as an infinite-dimensional additive vector channel

$$\mathbf{y} = \mathbf{x}_m + \mathbf{n} \qquad \text{when } H_m \text{ is the transmitted message}$$

wherein the individual variances of the noise components differ from dimension to dimension. One can then conceive of coding the signal projections $\{x_{mn}\}$ for this channel model which is memoryless, but not constant since the noise variance varies from dimension to dimension. Such a development has been carried out by Gallager [1968] who obtained the code ensemble average error probability under a constraint on the signal energy. However, no practical channel could be reasonably encoded in this way.

An alternative and more direct, though less rigorous, approach to colored noise, proposed by Bode and Shannon [1950] (see also Wozencraft and Jacobs [1965], Chap. 7) is to "whiten" the noise by passing the received process through a whitening filter, the squared magnitude of whose transfer function is the inverse of the noise spectral density. While this also distorts the signal, it does so in a known manner so that the result is a known, though distorted, signal set in white Gaussian noise which can be treated as before. The weakness of this approach is that it ignores boundary effects for finite-time signals and is hence somewhat imprecise unless the signal symbol durations are long compared to the inverse noise bandwidth. Probably the best approach to this problem is to guarantee that the receiver predetection bandwidth is sufficiently wide, compared to the inverse symbol time, and that the noise spectral density is uniform in the frequency region of interest, so that the white noise model can be applied with reasonable accuracy.

2.12.2 Noncoherent Reception

Another degrading feature, noted briefly in Sec. 2.6, is that of imperfectly known carrier phase, as well as imperfectly known carrier frequency and symbol time. While the latter two parameters must always be estimated with reasonable accuracy, for any digital communication system will degrade intolerably otherwise, it is possible to operate without knowledge of the phase. Referring to Table 2.1 in Sec. 2.6 and to Fig. 2.9, we suppose that we have *only two* frequency-orthogonal signals whose frequency separation is a multiple of $2\pi/T$ radians per second. Note that this is the separation required for quadrature-phase frequency-orthogonal functions; the same separation is necessary when the phase is unknown, for in this event the sine and cosine functions will be indistinguishable upon reception. Thus we have

$$x_m(t) = \sqrt{2\mathscr{E}}\, f(t) \sin(\omega_m t + \phi) \qquad m = 1, 2 \tag{2.12.1}$$

where $f(t)$ is a known *envelope function* of unit norm, ω_m is some multiple of

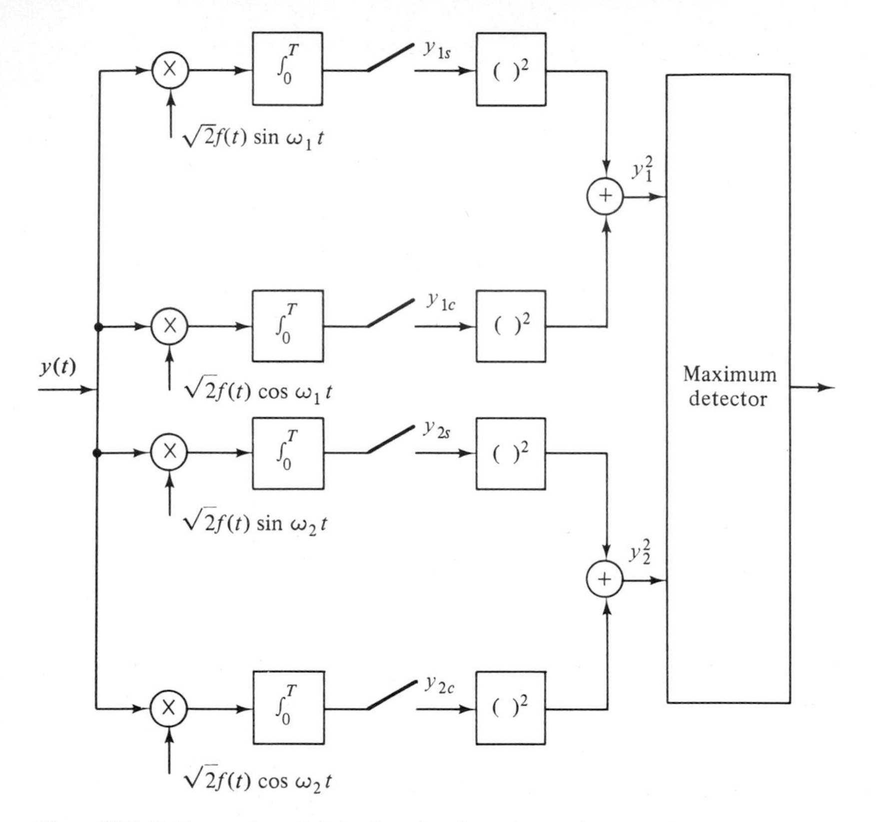

Figure 2.20 Optimum demodulator for noncoherent reception.

$2\pi/T$, $\omega_1 \neq \omega_2$, and ϕ may be taken as a random variable uniformly distributed on the interval 0 to 2π. This is generally called *noncoherent* reception. It is clear that the optimum demodulator (Fig. 2.20) consists of two devices each equivalent to those required by a quadrature-phase signal. When signal $x_1(t)$ is sent, the set of four observables is

$$y_{1s} = \sqrt{\mathscr{E}} \cos \phi + n_{1s} \qquad y_{2s} = n_{2s}$$

$$y_{1c} = \sqrt{\mathscr{E}} \sin \phi + n_{1c} \qquad y_{2c} = n_{2c} \tag{2.12.2}$$

where

$$\left.\begin{aligned} n_{ms} &= \sqrt{2} \int_0^T n(t)f(t) \sin \omega_m t \, dt \\ n_{mc} &= \sqrt{2} \int_0^T n(t)f(t) \cos \omega_m t \, dt \end{aligned}\right\} \quad m = 1, 2$$

all four of which are mutually independent with zero mean and variance $N_o/2$.

The likelihood function, when message 1 is sent and the phase is ϕ, is therefore

$$p_4(y_{1s}, y_{1c}, y_{2s}, y_{2c} | x_1, \phi)$$
$$= \frac{\exp\{-[(y_{1s} - \sqrt{\mathscr{E}}\cos\phi)^2 + (y_{1c} - \sqrt{\mathscr{E}}\sin\phi)^2 + y_{2s}^2 + y_{2c}^2]/N_o\}}{(\pi N_o)^2} \tag{2.12.3}$$

But ϕ is a uniformly distributed random variable and thus the likelihood function of the observables y, given message 1, is just (2.12.3) averaged over ϕ, namely

$$p_4(y_{1s}, y_{1c}, y_{2s}, y_{2c} | x_1)$$
$$= p_2(y_{2s}, y_{2c}) \frac{1}{2\pi} \int_0^{2\pi} p_2(y_{1s}, y_{1c} | x_1, \phi)\, d\phi$$
$$= \frac{1}{(\pi N_o)^2} e^{-y_2{}^2/2} e^{-\mathscr{E}/N_o - y_1{}^2/2}$$
$$\times \int_0^{2\pi} \exp\left[\frac{2\sqrt{\mathscr{E}}}{N_o}[y_{1s}\cos\phi + y_{1c}\sin\phi]\right] \frac{d\phi}{d\pi}$$
$$= \frac{1}{(\pi N_o)^2} e^{-y_2{}^2/2} e^{-(\mathscr{E}/N_o) - (y_1{}^2/2)} I_o\left(\sqrt{\frac{2\mathscr{E}}{N_o}}\, y_1\right) \tag{2.12.4}$$

where

$$y_m^2 \equiv \frac{2}{N_o}(y_{mc}^2 + y_{ms}^2) \tag{2.12.5}$$

and where

$$I_0(x) \equiv \frac{1}{2\pi}\int_0^{2\pi} e^{x\cos(\phi - \gamma)}\, d\phi$$

is the zeroth order modified Bessel function which is a monotonically increasing function of x. By symmetry, it is clear that $p_4(\mathbf{y} | \mathbf{x}_2)$ is the same as $p_4(\mathbf{y} | \mathbf{x}_1)$ with the subscripts 1 and 2 interchanged throughout. Thus the decision rule for two messages is, according to (2.2.7)

$$H_{\hat{m}} = H_1 \qquad \text{if } \ln p_4(\mathbf{y} | \mathbf{x}_1) > \ln p_4(\mathbf{y} | \mathbf{x}_2)$$

or in this case

$$H_{\hat{m}} = H_1 \qquad \text{if } \ln I_0\left(\sqrt{\frac{2\mathscr{E}}{N_o}}\, y_1\right) > \ln I_0\left(\sqrt{\frac{2\mathscr{E}}{N_o}}\, y_2\right)$$

Since I_0 is a monotonically increasing function of its argument, this is equivalent to

$$H_{\hat{m}} = H_1 \qquad \text{if } y_1 > y_2 \tag{2.12.6}$$

Thus the decision depends only on the sum of the squares of the observables, y_1^2 and y_2^2, of each demodulator for each signal (or any monotonic finite function thereof) whose generation from y_{1c}, y_{1s}, y_{2c}, and y_{2s} is as shown in Fig. 2.20. Henceforth then, we may consider y_1 and y_2 to be the observables. It follows from (2.12.4) that these observables are independent, i.e., that

$$p_2(y_1, y_2 | x_1) = p(y_1 | x_1) p(y_2 | x_1)$$

Also from the definition (2.12.5) which is equivalent to a Cartesian-to-polar coordinate transformation, and from the result of (2.12.4), it follows that

$$\begin{aligned} p(y_1 | x_1) &= \pi N_o y_1 p_2(y_{1c}, y_{1s} | x_1) \\ &= y_1 \, e^{-y_1{}^2/2 - \mathscr{E}/N_o} I_0\left(\sqrt{\frac{2\mathscr{E}}{N_o}}\, y_1\right) \\ p(y_2 | x_1) &= \pi N_o y_2 p_2(y_{2c}, y_{2s} | x_1) \\ &= y_2 \, e^{-y_2{}^2/2} \end{aligned} \tag{2.12.7}$$

It is then relatively simple to obtain the error probability for noncoherent demodulation of two frequency-orthogonal signals. For

$$\begin{aligned} P_{E_1} &= \Pr\{y_2 > y_1 | x_1\} = \int_0^\infty p(y_1 | x_1) \int_{y_1}^\infty p(y_2 | x_1) \, dy_2 \, dy_1 \\ &= \int_0^\infty \left[y_1 \, e^{-y_1{}^2/2} \, e^{-\mathscr{E}/N_o} I_0\left(\sqrt{\frac{2\mathscr{E}}{N_o}}\, y_1\right)\right] e^{-y_1{}^2/2} \, dy_1 \\ &= e^{-\mathscr{E}/2N_o} \int_0^\infty y \, e^{-y^2} \, e^{-\mathscr{E}/2N_o} I_0\left(\sqrt{\frac{2\mathscr{E}}{N_o}}\, y\right) dy \\ &= \tfrac{1}{2} \, e^{-\mathscr{E}/2N_o} \end{aligned} \tag{2.12.8}$$

By symmetry,

$$\begin{aligned} P_{E_2} &= P_{E_1} \\ &= P_E \\ &= \tfrac{1}{2} e^{-\mathscr{E}/2N_o} \end{aligned} \tag{2.12.9}$$

Generalization to M frequency-orthogonal signals of the form (2.12.1) is completely straightforward. The demodulator becomes a bank of devices of the type of Fig. 2.20. The error probability can be obtained as an $(M - 1)$-term summation of exponentials (Prob. 2.14) and an asymptotically tight upper bound can be derived which is identical to that for coherent (known phase) reception of M orthogonal signals, given by (2.5.16) (see Prob. 2.15). This result does *not* imply, however, that ignorance of phase does not in general degrade performance. The fact that the performance of noncoherent reception of M orthogonal signals is asymptotically the same as for coherent reception is explained by noting that, as M becomes larger, so does T, and consequently the optimum receiver effectively estimates the phase over a long period T in the process of deciding among the M possible signals. As an example of the opposite extreme, consider a binary coded system of the type treated in the previous section where each binary symbol is transmitted as one of two frequency-orthogonal signals (2.12.1) which are demodulated symbol by symbol, resulting in a BSC with transition probability p given by (2.12.9) with $\mathscr{E} = \mathscr{E}_s$. Now when $\mathscr{E}_s/N_o \ll 1$, the union-Bhattacharyya error bound for such a coded system is the same as (2.11.5) but with the Bhattacharyya distance given by

$$\begin{aligned} d &= -\ln \sqrt{4p(1-p)} \\ &= -\ln \sqrt{2\, e^{-\mathscr{E}_s/2N_o}(1 - \tfrac{1}{2}\, e^{-\mathscr{E}_s/2N_o})} \\ &\approx -\ln \sqrt{(1 - \mathscr{E}_s/2N_o)(1 + \mathscr{E}_s/2N_o)} \\ &\approx \frac{1}{8}\left(\frac{\mathscr{E}_s}{N_o}\right)^2 \end{aligned} \tag{2.12.10}$$

This is clearly a great degradation relative to the coherent case for which $d \approx (2/\pi)\mathscr{E}_s/N_0$ when $\mathscr{E}_s/N_0 \ll 1$. One would suspect initially that a cause of this degradation is that the distance between signals for each symbol is reduced by a factor of 2 by the use of orthogonal signals compared to biphase signals, for the latter are opposite in sign and consequently have $\|\mathbf{s}_1 - \mathbf{s}_2\|^2 = 2\mathscr{E}_s$. There is in fact a technique applicable to noncoherent reception, called differential phase shift keying (see, e.g., Viterbi [1966], Van Trees [1968]) which effectively doubles the energy per symbol and produces the error probability of (2.12.9) with energy doubled. But this is clearly not a sufficient explanation because even if we used double the energy in the noncoherent case, we would merely multiply (2.12.10) by a factor of 4 and this would still be a negligibly small d compared to the coherent case when $\mathscr{E}_s/N_o \ll 1$. The situation is somewhat improved with optimum unquantized decoding, but there is still significant degradation.

There is in fact no justification in a coded system for *not* measuring the phase accurately enough to avoid this major degradation, provided, of course, that the phase varies very slowly relative to the code block length, as assumed here. When the phase varies rapidly, this is usually accompanied by rapidly varying amplitude, and the channel may be characterized as a fading-dispersive medium, the case which we consider next.

2.12.3 Fading-Dispersive Channels

A more serious source of degradation, prevalent in over-the-horizon propagation such as high-frequency ionospheric reflection and tropospheric scatter communication, is the presence of amplitude *fading* as well as rapid phase variations. The model of this phenomenon is usually taken to be a large number of diffuse scatterers or reflectors which move randomly relative to one another, causing the signal to arrive at the receiver as a linear combination of many replicas of the original signal, each attenuated and phase shifted by random amounts. By the central limit theorem, the distribution of the sum of many independent random variables approaches the Gaussian distribution. Hence a sinusoidal signal $\sqrt{2\mathscr{E}}\, f(t) \sin \omega_m t$ will arrive at the receiver as

$$y(t) = \sqrt{2\mathscr{E}}\, f(t)[a(t) \sin \omega_m t + b(t) \cos \omega_m t] + n(t) \qquad 0 \le t \le T \quad (2.12.11)$$

where $a(t)$ and $b(t)$ are independent zero-mean Gaussian processes, with given covariance functions, and where $n(t)$ is AWGN of thermal origin present in the observation. While we might consider more general signal sets, it should be clear that, in view of the random amplitude and phase perturbation by the channel, signals can be distinguished only by frequency. Each received signal, aside from the additive noise $n(t)$, is a Gaussian random process with bandwidth dictated by the propagation medium and determined from the spectral densities of $a(t)$ and $b(t)$. If the frequencies ω_m are spaced sufficiently far apart compared to their bandwidth, the signal random processes will have essentially nonoverlapping spectra and the problem reduces to that of detecting one of M "orthogonal" random processes. Once the observable statistics have been established, the problem is very similar to that of M orthogonal deterministic signals treated in Sec. 2.5, except that the decoding involves quadratic rather than linear operations on the observables (Helstrom [1968], Kennedy [1969], Viterbi [1967c]).

A more realistic model, less wasteful of bandwidth, more amenable to coding, and more representative of practical systems, results from assuming that over short subintervals of T/N seconds the random signal is essentially constant. Then, assuming signal pulses of duration T/N during a given nth subinterval, we have the received signal

$$y(t) = \sqrt{2\mathscr{E}_s}\, f\left(t - \frac{nT}{N}\right)[a \sin \omega_m t + b \cos \omega_m t] + n(t)$$
$$(n-1)T/N \le t < nT/N, \; m = 1, 2 \qquad (2.12.12)$$

where a and b are zero-mean independent Gaussian variables with variance σ^2, ω_m is a multiple of $2\pi N/T$, $\mathscr{E}_s = \mathscr{E}/N$ is the symbol energy, and $f(t)$ with unit norm is as defined in (2.6.5). Defining

$$r = \sqrt{a^2 + b^2} \qquad \phi = \tan^{-1}(b/a) \qquad (2.12.13)$$

we may rewrite (2.12.12) as

$$y(t) = \sqrt{2\mathscr{E}_s}\, r f(t - nT/N) \sin(\omega_m t + \phi) + n(t)$$
$$(n-1)T/N \le t \le nT/N, \; m = 1, 2 \qquad (2.12.14)$$

The statistics of r and ϕ are easily obtained from those of a and b by the transformation[18]

$$p(r, \phi) = J\left(\frac{a, b}{r, \phi}\right)p(a, b)\bigg|_{\substack{a=r\cos\phi \\ b=r\sin\phi}}$$
$$= \left(\frac{1}{2\pi}\right)\left(\frac{r}{\sigma^2} e^{-r^2/2\sigma^2}\right)$$
$$= p(\phi)p(r) \qquad 0 \le \phi \le 2\pi,\ r \ge 0 \tag{2.12.15}$$

Thus, ϕ is uniformly distributed on $[0, 2\pi]$ and r is Rayleigh distributed; hence the term *Rayleigh fading.*

We shall limit attention primarily to a binary input alphabet ($M = 2$) based on two frequency-orthogonal signals, although generalization to a larger set of frequencies is straightforward. Comparing (2.12.14) with (2.12.1), we note that the only difference is the random amplitude in the former. But since the quadrature demodulator of Fig. 2.20 is optimum for a uniformly distributed random phase ϕ and *any* amplitude, it is clear that the fact that the amplitude is a random variable is immaterial. Assuming for the moment that we are merely interested in one symbol (or alternatively that the random variables r and ϕ, or a and b, are constant over the entire T seconds), we may readily evaluate the error probability for the Rayleigh fading binary frequency-orthogonal signals from that for noncoherent detection of fixed amplitude signals. For, if r were known exactly, using the optimum demodulator of Fig. 2.20,[19] we would have error probability for noncoherent reception of (2.12.9) with $\mathscr{E}$ replaced by $\mathscr{E}_s r^2$. Hence

$$P_E(r) = \tfrac{1}{2}e^{-r^2\mathscr{E}_s/2N_o}$$

Now since r is a random variable whose distribution is given by the second factor of (2.12.15), we see that the symbol error probability with Rayleigh fading is

$$P_E = \int_0^\infty p(r)P_E(r)\,dr$$
$$= \frac{1}{2\sigma^2}\int_0^\infty r \exp\left[-\frac{r^2}{2\sigma^2}\left(1 + \frac{\sigma^2\mathscr{E}_s}{N_o}\right)\right]$$
$$= \frac{1}{2(1 + \sigma^2\mathscr{E}_s/N_o)}$$
$$= \frac{1}{2 + \bar{\mathscr{E}}_s/N_0} \tag{2.12.16}$$

[18] For the rectangular-to-polar transformation used here, the Jacobian is

$$J\left(\frac{a, b}{r, \phi}\right) = r$$

[19] The demodulator integrates for T/N second intervals here rather than T seconds as shown in Fig. 2.20.

where we have denoted the average received energy per symbol by

$$\overline{\mathscr{E}}_s \equiv \mathscr{E}_s \int_0^\infty r^2 p(r)\, dr = 2\sigma^2 \mathscr{E}_s \tag{2.12.17}$$

It is quite interesting to note that while phase randomness does not destroy the exponential dependence of P_E on energy-to-noise ratio, amplitude randomness does change it into the much weaker inverse linear dependence.

Let us now consider the demodulation and decoding of multidimensional, or multiple symbol, coded Rayleigh fading signals. The most common form of coding for Rayleigh fading is the trivial repetitive code, using the same signal for all N dimensions, which is generally called *diversity* transmission. Before proceeding with the analysis even in this case, we must impose a fundamental assumption on the communication system: namely, that the random channel amplitude and phase variables are *independent* from symbol to symbol. Several techniques are commonly used to achieve this independence. First, different pairs of frequencies can be used for successive symbols. If the frequency pair for one symbol is widely separated from that of the next few symbols, the necessary independence can usually be acquired, but at the cost of greatly expanded bandwidth. Another approach, space diversity, actually transmits a single symbol, but uses N antennas sufficiently separated spatially that the random phases and amplitudes are independent of one another; then the N observables consist of a combination of N single observables from each antenna–receiver. Of course, spatial diversity corresponds only to the case of trivial repetitive coding. When nontrivial coding is used, particularly when bandwidth must be conserved, a third approach called *time-diversity* is commonly employed. This technique achieves the independence by spacing successive symbols of a given codeword at wide intervals in time, placing in between similarly spaced symbols of other codewords. This technique, illustrated in Fig. 2.21 and discussed further below, is generally called *interleaving*.

Given the independence among symbols, we can consider an N-dimensional signal where each dimension consists of the transmission of one of two binary frequency-orthogonal signals. We then have from the demodulator of Fig. 2.20 (with integration over T/N second intervals) the $2N$ observables $(\mathbf{y}_1, \mathbf{y}_2, \ldots, \mathbf{y}_N) = (y_{11}y_{21}, y_{12}y_{22}, \ldots, y_{1N}y_{2N})$, consisting of N pairs of observations (where y_{1n}, y_{2n} is the pair of observables for the nth symbol), for the two possible transmitted frequencies ω_1 and ω_2.

Again for a fixed amplitude r and a uniformly distributed phase ϕ, we have from (2.12.7) that, for the nth symbol, the observables y_{1n} and y_{2n} are independent with probability density functions

$$p(y_{mn} \mid x_{mn}, r) = y_{mn}\, e^{-y_{mn}^2/2}\, e^{-r^2\mathscr{E}_s/N_o} I_0\left(\sqrt{\frac{2r^2\mathscr{E}_s}{N_o}}\, y_{mn}\right)$$

$$p(y_{m'n} \mid x_{mn}, r) = y_{m'n}\, e^{-y_{m'n}^2/2} \qquad m \text{ and } m' = 1 \text{ or } 2,\ m' \neq m \tag{2.12.18}$$

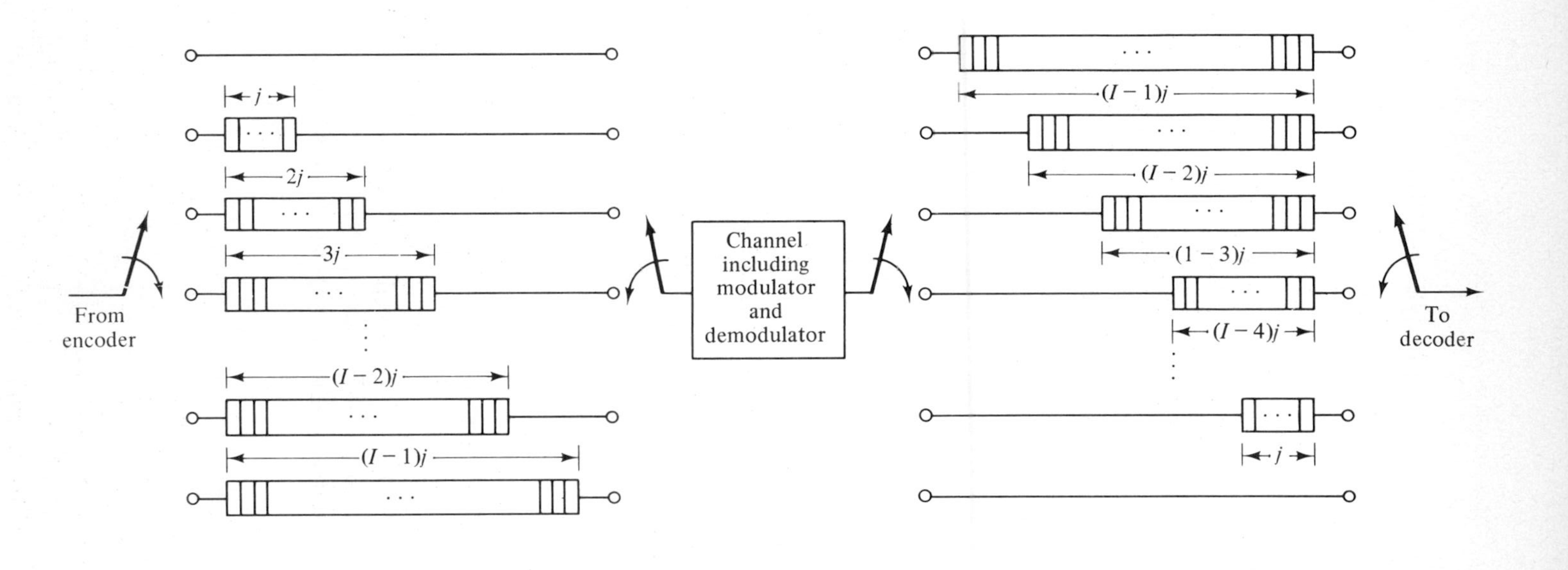

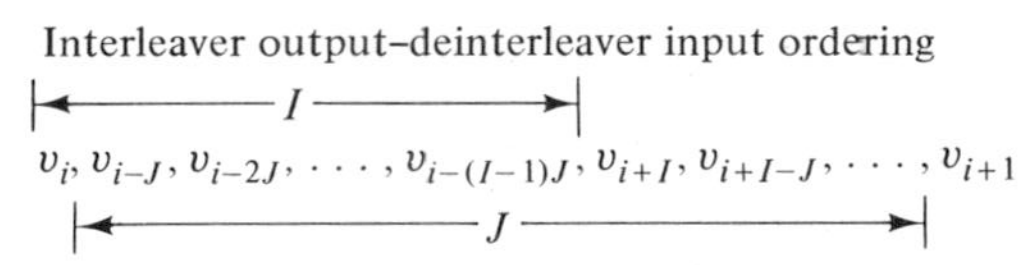

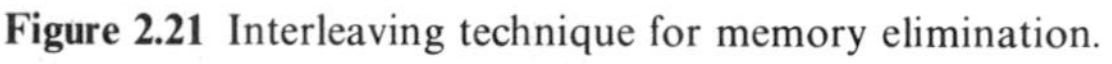

$v_i, v_{i-J}, v_{i-2J}, \ldots, v_{i-(I-1)J}, v_{i+I}, v_{i+I-J}, \ldots, v_{i+1}$
J

Figure 2.21 Interleaving technique for memory elimination.

so that the latter is independent of r. Since r is a Rayleigh distributed variable with parameter σ^2, we have, using (2.12.17)

$$p(y_{mn}|x_{mn}) = \int_0^\infty p(y_{mn}|x_{mn}, r)\left(\frac{r}{\sigma^2}\right) e^{-r^2/2\sigma^2}\, dr$$

$$= y_{mn} e^{-y_{mn}^2/2} \int_0^\infty \frac{r}{\sigma^2} \exp\left[-\frac{r^2}{2\sigma^2}\left(1 + 2\frac{\mathscr{E}_s \sigma^2}{N_o}\right)\right] I_0(\sqrt{2\mathscr{E}_s/N_o}\, y_{mn} r)\, dr$$

$$= y_{mn} e^{-y_{mn}^2/2} \frac{\exp\left[\dfrac{(\bar{\mathscr{E}}_s/N_o) y_{mn}^2}{2(1 + \bar{\mathscr{E}}_s/N_o)}\right]}{1 + \bar{\mathscr{E}}_s/N_o}$$

Hence

$$p(y_{mn}|x_{mn}) = \frac{y_{mn} \exp\left[\dfrac{-y_{mn}^2}{2(1 + \bar{\mathscr{E}}_s/N_o)}\right]}{1 + \bar{\mathscr{E}}_s/N_o}$$

$$p(y_{m'n}|x_{mn}) = y_{m'n} e^{-y_{m'n}^2/2} \qquad m \text{ and } m' = 1 \text{ or } 2,\ m' \neq m \tag{2.12.19}$$

Examining first the case of trivial repetitive coding of two equiprobable messages, we have from (2.2.7) that the optimum decoder for equal prior probabilities and average symbol energies, $\bar{\mathscr{E}}_s$, is

$$H_{\hat{m}} = H_m \qquad \text{if } \sum_{n=1}^{N} \ln \frac{p_2(y_{mn}, y_{m'n}|x_{mn})}{p_2(y_{mn}, y_{m'n}|x_{m'n})} > 0 \qquad \text{for all } m' \neq m$$

which simplifies, according to (2.12.19), to

$$H_{\hat{m}} = H_m \qquad \text{if } \sum_{n=1}^{N} (y_{mn}^2 - y_{m'n}^2) > 0 \qquad \text{for all } m' \neq m \tag{2.12.20}$$

Given that message H_m was sent, we can calculate the error probability by finding the distribution of the sum in (2.12.20), conditioned on $\mathbf{x}_m$, from (2.12.19). It is easily shown (Wozencraft and Jacobs [1965, chap. 7]) that this is a chi-square distribution and that consequently the two-message repetition code error probability is given by

$$P_E = \rho^N \sum_{j=0}^{N-1} \binom{N+j-1}{j} (1-\rho)^j \tag{2.12.21}$$

where

$$\rho \equiv \frac{1}{2 + \bar{\mathscr{E}}_s/N_o} \tag{2.12.22}$$

However, more insight can be drawn from deriving the Bhattacharyya upper bound. From (2.3.15) and (2.12.19), we have

$$\begin{aligned}
P_E &< \sum_{\mathbf{y}} \sqrt{p(\mathbf{y}\,|\,\mathbf{x}_m)p(\mathbf{y}\,|\,\mathbf{x}_{m'})} \\
&= \prod_{n=1}^{N} \iint \sqrt{p(y_{mn}, y_{m'n}\,|\,x_{mn})p(y_{mn}, y_{m'n}\,|\,x_{m'n})}\, dy_{mn}\, dy_{m'n} \\
&= \left\{\int_0^{\infty} \frac{y}{\sqrt{1+\bar{\mathscr{E}}_s/N_o}} \exp\left(-\frac{y^2}{4}\left[\frac{2+\bar{\mathscr{E}}_s/N_o}{1+\bar{\mathscr{E}}_s/N_o}\right]\right) dy\right\}^{2N} \\
&= \left[\frac{4(1+\bar{\mathscr{E}}_s/N_o)}{(2+\bar{\mathscr{E}}_s/N_o)^2}\right]^N \\
&= [4\rho(1-\rho)]^N
\end{aligned} \tag{2.12.23}$$

where ρ is given by (2.12.22). It can be shown (Wozencraft and Jacobs [1965, chap. 7]) that the ratio of the exact expression (2.12.21) to the bound (2.12.23) approaches $[2\sqrt{\pi N}(1-2\rho)]^{-1}$ as $N \to \infty$ so that the bound is asymptotically tight in an exponential sense. Finally, we write the bound as

$$P_E < e^{-Nd} \tag{2.12.24a}$$

where

$$\begin{aligned}
d &= -\ln\,[4\rho(1-\rho)] \\
\rho &= 1/(2+\bar{\mathscr{E}}_s/N_o)
\end{aligned} \tag{2.12.24b}$$

Both the decoding rule (2.12.20) and the error probability bound (2.12.24) can be easily generalized to the case where the symbol energies are not equal (Wozencraft and Jacobs [1965, chap. 7]). A most interesting conclusion can be drawn by comparing (2.12.16) with (2.12.24*a*). Both cases deal with the transmission of a single bit by one of two messages. Suppose the total average received energy is $\bar{\mathscr{E}}$. Then in the first case $\bar{\mathscr{E}}_s = \bar{\mathscr{E}}$ and P_E decreases only inversely with $\bar{\mathscr{E}}/N_o$. In the second case, using the repetitive N-dimensional code, we have $\bar{\mathscr{E}}_s = \bar{\mathscr{E}}/N$ and

$$P_E < e^{-Nd} \tag{2.12.25}$$

where

$$\begin{aligned}
d &= -\ln \frac{1+(\bar{\mathscr{E}}/N_o)/N}{[1+(\bar{\mathscr{E}}/N_o)/2N]^2} \\
&\approx \frac{(\bar{\mathscr{E}}/N_o)^2}{4N^2} \qquad \text{as } N \to \infty
\end{aligned}$$

Clearly then, making N very large degrades performance. However, we can readily show that the maximum of Nd, the exponent of (2.12.25), occurs when

$$N \approx \left(\frac{1}{3}\right)\frac{\bar{\mathscr{E}}}{N_o} \tag{2.12.26}$$

in which case (2.12.25) becomes

$$P_{E_{\text{opt}}} < e^{-0.149\bar{\mathscr{E}}/N_0} \tag{2.12.27}$$

Comparing to the exact expression (2.12.9) for the noncoherent case and ignoring the multiplicative factor of $\frac{1}{2}$ in the latter, we note that fading thus causes a loss of about 5.25 dB in effective energy. More important, we conclude that, while repetitive coding has no effect (either favorable or detrimental) for the coherent AWGN channel, and while it has strictly a detrimental effect when the phase alone is unknown, it can actually improve performance in the case of fading channels provided that the dimensionality is chosen properly, the optimum being given approximately by (2.12.26).

Finally, turning to nontrivial coding, we may again apply the union-Bhattacharyya bound as in Sec. 2.9. Then if a binary linear code is used, since it is obvious from (2.12.19) that the channel is symmetrical, it follows that $P_{E_m} = P_E$ for all m. Then exactly as in (2.9.19) we have

$$P_E \le \sum_{k=2}^{M} e^{-w_k d} \tag{2.12.28}$$

where d is given by (2.12.24*b*) and w_k is the Hamming weight of the kth nonzero codeword.

Of interest also is the effect of quantization. Clearly, the maximum likelihood decoder output (2.12.20) may be quantized by quantizing the decoder symbol output set $\{y_{mn}^2 - y_{m'n}^2\}$ to any number of levels. In the simplest case of hard two-level quantization (positive or negative), this reduces the fading channel to a BSC with crossover probability given by (2.12.16). But this is *exactly* equal to the parameter ρ defined by (2.12.22); and, for the BSC, we found in Sec. 2.9 that the Bhattacharyya distance is

$$d_{\text{BSC}} = -\ln\sqrt{4\rho(1-\rho)} = -\tfrac{1}{2}\ln\left[4\rho(1-\rho)\right] \tag{2.12.29}$$

Thus, comparing with (2.12.24*b*), we find that for the fading channel, hard quantization of the decoder outputs *effectively reduces the Bhattacharyya distance by a factor of 2* (3 dB). This is a more serious degradation than for the AWGN channel, and is a strong argument for "soft" multilevel quantization (Wozencraft and Jacobs [1965, chap. 7]).

2.12.4 Interleaving

With the exception of the AWGN channel, most practical channels exhibit statistical dependence among successive symbol transmissions. This is particularly true of fading channels when the fading varies slowly compared to one symbol time. Such *channels with memory* considerably degrade the performance of codes designed to operate on memoryless channels. The simplest explanation of this is that memory reduces the number of independent degrees of freedom of the transmitted signals. A simple example helps to clarify this point. Suppose a BSC with memory makes errors very rarely, say on the average once every million symbols, but that immediately after any error occurs, the probability of another error is 0.1. Thus, for example, the probability of a burst of three or more errors is one percent of the probability of a single error. Consider coding for this channel using the (7, 4) Hamming single-error correcting code. If this were a memoryless BSC so that errors occurred independently, the probability of error for each four-bit seven-symbol codeword would be reduced by coding from approximately 7×10^{-6} down to approximately 3.5×10^{-11}. On the other hand, for the BSC with memory as just described, the codeword error probability is reduced to only about 6×10^{-7}. Coding techniques for channels with memory have been proposed and demonstrated to be reasonably effective in some cases (Kohlenberg and Forney [1968], Brayer [1971]; see also Secs. 4.9 and 4.10). The greatest problem with coding for such channels is that it is difficult to find accurate statistical models and, even worse, the channel memory statistics are often time-varying. Codes matched to one set of memory parameters will be much less effective for another set of values, as in the simple example above.

One technique which requires no knowledge of channel memory other than its approximate length, and is consequently very robust to changes in memory statistics, is the use of time-diversity, or *interleaving*, which eliminates the effect of memory. Since in all practical cases, memory decreases with time separation, if all the symbols of a given codeword are transmitted at widely spaced intervals and the intervening spaces are filled similarly by symbols of other codewords, the statistical dependence between symbols can be effectively eliminated. This interleaving technique may be implemented using the system shown in Fig. 2.21. Each code symbol out of the encoder is inserted into one of the I tapped shift registers of the interleaver bank. The zeroth element of this bank provides no storage (the symbol is transmitted immediately), while each successive element provides j symbols more storage than the preceding one. The input commutator switches from one register to the next until the $(I - 1)$th after which the commutator returns to the zeroth. I is the minimum channel transmission separation provided for any two code symbols output by the encoder with a separation of less than $J = jI$ symbols. For a block code, J should be made at least equal to the block length. The output commutator feeds to the channel (including the modulator) one code symbol at a time, switching from one register to the next after each symbol, synchronously with the input commutator. When the channel input is not binary, it may be preferable to interleave signal dimensions rather than code symbols. This is achieved, at least conceptually, by making each stage of the registers a storage device for a signal dimension rather than a channel symbol (easily implemented if each dimension contains an integral number of symbols). It is easily verified that, for a natural ordering of input symbols $\ldots, v_i, v_{i+1}, v_{i+2}, \ldots$, the interleaver output sequence and hence the channel transmission ordering is as shown in Fig. 2.21, where it is clear that the minimum separation in channel transmission is at least I for any two code symbols generated by the encoder within a separation of $J - 1$. This is called an (I, J) interleaver.

The deinterleaver, which must invert the action of the interleaver, is clearly just its converse. Observables are fed in with each dimension going to a different shift register. Note, however, that to store the observables digitally, the channel outputs must have been quantized. Hence, the deinterleaver storage must be several times the size of the interleaver storage. For example, if the channel input is binary, we require $J(I - 1)/2$ bits of storage in the interleaver. On the other hand, with eight-level quantization at the channel (demodulator) output, each output dimension contains 3 bits so that the storage required in the deinterleaver is three times as great. We note also that the delay introduced by this interleaving technique is equal to $J(I - 1)$ symbol times.

The system of Fig. 2.21 represents a conceptually simple interleaving technique, and it can be shown to be the minimal implementation of an (I, J) interleaver in the sense of storage requirements and delay (Ramsey [1970]). However, shift registers of varying lengths may be considerably more costly in terms of numbers of required integrated circuits than, for example, a random-access memory with appropriate timing and control to perform the functions of the system of Fig. 2.21, even though the total storage of such a random-access memory will be double that shown in this implementation. The main point to be drawn from this discussion is that channels with memory can be converted into essentially memoryless channels at a cost of only buffer storage and transmission delay. This cost, of course, can become prohibitive if the channel memory is very long compared to the transmission time per symbol.

2.13 BIBLIOGRAPHICAL NOTES AND REFERENCES

The first half of this chapter, through Sec. 2.8, owes much of its organization to the text of Wozencraft and Jacobs [1965], specifically chaps. 4 and 5. This text pioneered in presenting information-theoretic concepts in the framework of practical digital communication systems. We have deviated by presenting in Secs. 2.4 and 2.5 the more sophisticated upper bounds due to Gallager [1965] and Fano [1961] to establish the groundwork for the more elaborate and tighter bounds of successive chapters.

Sections 2.9 and 2.10 are, in part, standard introductory treatments of linear codes. The proof of the uniform error property for linear codes on binary-input, output-symmetric channels is a generalization of a proof of this property for the BSC due to Fano [1961]. The evaluation of error probabilities and bounds for specific linear codes on channels other than the BSC carried out in Secs. 2.9 and 2.11 is scattered throughout the applications literature. Section 2.12 follows for the most part the development of chap. 7 of Wozencraft and Jacobs [1965]. The interleaving technique of Fig. 2.21 is due to Ramsey [1970].

APPENDIX 2A GRAM-SCHMIDT ORTHOGONALIZATION AND SIGNAL REPRESENTATION

Theorem Given M finite-energy functions $\{x_m(t)\}$ defined on $[0, T]$, there exist $N \le M$ unit-energy (normalized) orthogonal functions $\{\phi_n(t)\}$ (that is, for which $\int_0^T \phi_n(t)\phi_k(t)\,dt = \delta_{nk}$) such that

$$x_m(t) = \sum_{n=1}^{N} x_{mn}\phi_n(t) \qquad m = 1, 2, \ldots, M \tag{2.1.1}$$

where for each m and n

$$x_{mn} = \int_0^T x_m(t)\phi_n(t)\,dt$$

Furthermore, $N = M$ if and only if the set $\{x_m(t)\}$ is linearly independent. The $\{\phi_n(t)\}$ are said to form a *basis* for the space generated by the set of functions $\{x_m(t)\}$.

PROOF Let $\mathscr{E}_m \equiv \int_0^T x_m^2(t)\,dt$. Define the first normalized basis function

$$\phi_1(t) \equiv x_1(t)/\sqrt{\mathscr{E}_1} \tag{2A.1}$$

Then clearly

$$\begin{aligned} x_1(t) &= \sqrt{\mathscr{E}_1}\,\phi_1(t) \\ &= x_{11}\phi_1(t) \end{aligned} \tag{2A.2}$$

where $x_{11} = \sqrt{\mathscr{E}_1}$ and $\phi_1(t)$ has unit energy as required. Before proceeding to define the second basis function, define x_{21} as the *projection* of $x_2(t)$ on $\phi_1(t)$, that is

$$x_{21} = \int_0^T x_2(t)\phi_1(t)\,dt \tag{2A.3}$$

Now define

$$\phi_2(t) \equiv \frac{x_2(t) - x_{21}\phi_1(t)}{x_{22}} \tag{2A.4}$$

where

$$\begin{aligned} x_{22} &\equiv \sqrt{\int_0^T x_2^2(t)\,dt - x_{21}^2} \\ &= \sqrt{\mathscr{E}_2 - x_{21}^2} \end{aligned} \tag{2A.5}$$

It then follows from (2A.3) and (2A.4) that

$$\int_0^T \phi_1(t)\phi_2(t)\,dt = 0 \tag{2A.6}$$

and from (2A.4) and (2A.5) that $\phi_2(t)$ has unit energy since

$$\begin{aligned}\int_0^T \phi_2^2(t)\,dt &= \frac{\mathscr{E}_2 - x_{21}^2}{x_{22}^2} \\ &= 1\end{aligned} \tag{2A.7}$$

Also, from (2A.4), we have

$$x_2(t) = x_{21}\phi_1(t) + x_{22}\phi_2(t) \tag{2A.8}$$

and from (2A.6) and (2A.7) it follows that

$$x_{22} = \int_0^T x_2(t)\phi_2(t)\,dt$$

We now proceed to generalize (2A.2) and (2A.8) to the mth function $x_m(t)$, by induction. Suppose that for all $k < m$

$$x_k(t) = \sum_{n=1}^{k} x_{kn}\phi_n(t) \qquad k = 1, 2, \ldots, m-1 \tag{2A.9}$$

where

$$x_{kn} = \int_0^T x_k(t)\phi_n(t)\,dt \tag{2A.10}$$

and where the $\{\phi_n(t), n = 1, 2, \ldots, k\}$ are mutually orthogonal and each has unit energy. Then define

$$x_{mn} \equiv \int_0^T x_m(t)\phi_n(t)\,dt \qquad n = 1, 2, \ldots, m-1 \tag{2A.11}$$

and

$$\phi_m(t) = \frac{x_m(t) - \sum_{n=1}^{m-1} x_{mn}\phi_n(t)}{x_{mm}} \tag{2A.12}$$

where

$$x_{mm} \equiv \sqrt{\mathscr{E}_m - \sum_{n=1}^{m-1} x_{mn}^2} \tag{2A.13}$$

It follows from (2A.11) and (2A.12) that

$$\int_0^T \phi_m(t)\phi_n(t)\,dt = 0 \qquad \text{for all } n < m \tag{2A.14}$$

and from (2A.12) and (2A.13) that $\phi_m(t)$ has unit energy. Reordering (2A.12), we have

$$x_m(t) = \sum_{n=1}^{m} x_{mn}\phi_n(t) \tag{2A.15}$$

and from (2A.14)

$$x_{mm} = \int_0^T x_m(t)\phi_n(t)\,dt \tag{2A.16}$$

It thus follows that, for M finite-energy functions $\{x_m(t)\}$, the representation (2.1.1) is always possible with N no greater than M.

Suppose, however, that a subset of these functions is linearly dependent; i.e., that there exists a set of nonzero real numbers $a_1, a_2, \ldots, a_j$ for which

$$a_1 x_{m_1}(t) + a_2 x_{m_2}(t) + \cdots + a_j x_{m_j}(t) = 0$$

where $m_1 < m_2 < \cdots < m_j$.

In such an event, it follows that $x_{m_j}(t)$ can be expressed as a linear combination of $x_{m_1}(t) \cdots x_{m_{j-1}}(t)$ and thus as a linear combination of the basis functions which generate these previous signal functions. As a result, it is not necessary to generate a new basis function $\phi_{m_j}(t)$ in order to add $x_{m_j}(t)$ to the set of represented functions. In this way, one (or more) basis functions may be omitted and hence $N < M$. It should be clear that a basis function can be thus skipped if and only if the set $\{x_m(t)\}$ is not linearly independent.

PROBLEMS

2.1 (*a*) For the 16-signal set shown in Fig. P2.1*a*, transmitted over the AWGN channel, with equal a priori probabilities, determine the optimum decision regions, and express the exact error probability in terms of the average energy-to-noise density ratio.

(*b*) Repeat for the tilted signal set shown in Fig. P2.1*b*.

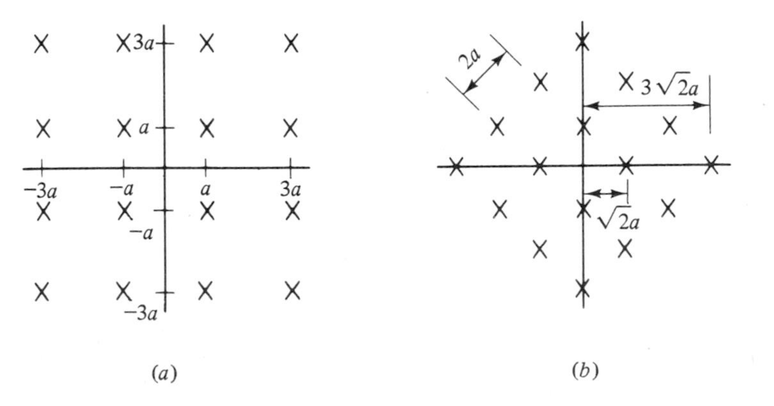

Figure P2.1

2.2 For the seven-signal set shown, transmitted over the AWGN channel, with equal a priori probabilities

(*a*) Determine the optimum decision regions.

(*b*) Show that one can obtain an upper bound on P_{E_m}, $m = 1, 2, \ldots, 7$, and hence on P_E, by calculating the probability that the norm of the two-dimensional noise vector is greater than $\sqrt{\mathscr{E}}/2$, and calculate this bound.

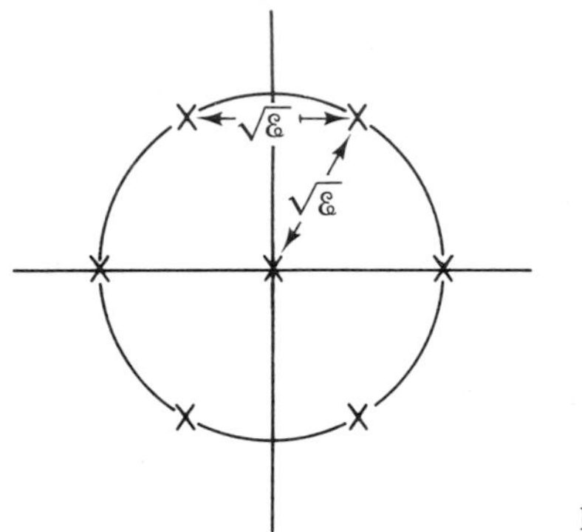

Figure P2.2

2.3 For the signal set of Prob. 2.2, obtain a union bound on P_{E_m} of the form of (2.3.4) for each m. Compare the resulting bound on P_E with that obtained in Prob. 2.2.

2.4 For the orthogonal signal set of M equal-energy signals transmitted over the AWGN channel, first treated in Sec. 2.3

(*a*) Show that the error probability is given exactly by

$$P_E = P_{E_1} = 1 - \Pr\{y_m < y_1 \text{ for all } m \neq 1 \mid \mathbf{x}_1\}$$

where the $\{y_m\}$ are the M observables.

(*b*) From this, derive Eq. (2.11.1).

(*c*) Letting $\mathscr{E} = \mathscr{E}_b \log_2 M$, where $\mathscr{E}_b$ is the energy/bit, show that

$$\lim_{M\to\infty}\left[1 - Q\left(x + \sqrt{\frac{2\mathscr{E}}{N_o}}\right)\right]^{M-1} = \begin{cases} 0 & \text{if } \mathscr{E}_b/N_o < \ln 2 \\ 1 & \text{if } \mathscr{E}_b/N_o > \ln 2 \end{cases}$$

and consequently that $\lim_{M\to\infty} P_E$ is 0 if $\mathscr{E}_b/N_o > \ln 2$ and is 1 if the inequality is reversed.

Hint: Use L'Hospital's rule on the logarithm of the function in question.

2.5 (*a*) Show that, if $M = 2^K$, an orthogonal signal set of M dimensions can be generated for any integer value of K by the following inductive construction. For $K = 1$, let

$$\begin{bmatrix}\mathbf{x}_1\\ \mathbf{x}_2\end{bmatrix} = \sqrt{\frac{\mathscr{E}}{2}}\,H_1 \qquad \text{where } H_1 = \begin{bmatrix}1 & 1\\ 1 & -1\end{bmatrix}$$

Then for any integer $K \geq 2$

$$\begin{bmatrix}\mathbf{x}_1\\ \mathbf{x}_2\\ \vdots\\ \mathbf{x}_{2^K}\end{bmatrix} = \sqrt{\frac{\mathscr{E}}{M}}\,H_K \qquad \text{where } H_K = \begin{bmatrix}H_{K-1} & H_{K-1}\\ H_{K-1} & -H_{K-1}\end{bmatrix}$$

(*b*) Note that, for this construction, the first component of each signal vector is always equal to $+\sqrt{\mathscr{E}/M}$. Consider deleting this component in each vector, thus obtaining a signal set $\{\hat{\mathbf{x}}_j\}$ with $M - 1$ dimensions and normalized inner products among all vectors

$$\frac{1}{\mathscr{E}'}(\hat{\mathbf{x}}_j, \hat{\mathbf{x}}_k) = \frac{-1}{M-1} \qquad \text{for all } j \neq k$$

where $\mathscr{E}' = \mathscr{E}(M-1)/M$, which is the signal energy after deletion of the first component. This new signal set is called a regular simplex signal set.

(*c*) Show that P_E for the regular simplex signal set is identical to that of orthogonal signals as given in Prob. 2.4, but since the energy has been reduced in the simplex case

$$P_E\left[\frac{\mathscr{E}'}{N_o}, -\frac{1}{M-1}\right] = P_E\left[\frac{\mathscr{E}'M}{N_o(M-1)}, 0\right]$$

where the first parameter indicates the energy-to-noise density and the second gives the common normalized inner product among all signal vectors.

(*d*) Show that, for any set of M equal-energy signals, the average normalized inner product

$$\rho_{av} \equiv \frac{1}{\mathscr{E}M(M-1)} \sum\sum_{j \neq k} (\mathbf{x}_j, \mathbf{x}_k) \geq \frac{-1}{M-1}$$

and hence the set generated in (*b*) achieves the minimum.

(*e*) Generalize the argument used in (*c*) to show that, if all normalized inner products are equal to $\rho \geq -1/(M-1)$, then

$$P_E\left[\frac{\mathscr{E}}{N_o}, \rho\right] = P_E\left[\frac{\mathscr{E}(1-\rho)}{N_o}, 0\right]$$

2.6 (*a*) Show that an ideal lowpass filter with transfer function

$$H(\omega) = \begin{cases} \dfrac{1}{W} & \text{if } |\omega| < \pi W \\ 0 & \text{otherwise} \end{cases}$$

has noncausal impulse response

$$h(t) = \frac{\sin \pi W t}{\pi W t}$$

(*b*) Show that, in response to a signal $z(t)$, the response of this lowpass filter at time n/W will be

$$\int_{-\infty}^{\infty} z(t) h\left[\left(\frac{n}{W}\right) - t\right] dt = \int_{-\infty}^{\infty} z(t) \frac{\sin [\pi W(t - n/W)]}{\pi W(t - n/W)} dt$$

(*c*) Show then that the mechanization of Fig. 2.11 is equivalent to that of Fig. 2.9 with finite-time integrators replaced by infinite-time integrators.

2.7 (*a*) Suppose that a signal set utilizes the basis functions of Table 2.1, Example 1, but that at the receiver the frequency and phase are incorrectly known so that the function

$$\phi_n'(t) = \sqrt{2N/T} \sin [(\omega_0 + \Delta\omega)t + \phi] \qquad (n-1)T/N \leq t < nT/N$$

is used. Assuming $\omega_0 T/N \gg 1$ and $\Delta\omega T/N \ll 1$, show that the observables are attenuated approximately by the factor

$$\cos \phi \sin \left(\frac{T\Delta\omega}{N}\right) \Big/ \left(\frac{T\Delta\omega}{N}\right)$$

(*b*) For the basis functions of Table 2.1, Example 2, assume ω_0 is known exactly at the receiver but that the phase is incorrectly assumed to be ϕ. Show that, if $\omega_0 T/N \gg 1$, the signal components of the observables become approximately

$$y_{2n}' = x_{2n} \cos \phi + x_{2n+1} \sin \phi$$

$$y_{2n+1}' = -x_{2n} \sin \phi + x_{2n+1} \cos \phi$$

(*c*) For part (*b*), let $M = 4$ and $N = 2$ (quadriphase transmission). Show how the decision regions are distorted by the incorrect ϕ, and obtain expressions for the resulting error probabilities.

2.8 (*a*) For the signal set of Fig. 2.12*b* transmitted over the AWGN channel, with equal a priori probabilities, determine the optimum decision regions.

(*b*) Show that for all m

$$P < P_{E_m} \leq 2P$$

where $P = Q(\sqrt{2\mathscr{E}_s/N_o}\ \sin(\pi/16))$.

(*c*) Compare this lower bound on P_E with the exact expression for P_E of the signal set of Fig. 2.12*a* (Prob. 2.1), and thus determine which set is superior in performance for equal average energies.

2.9 (*a*) For the binary input AWGN channel with octal output quantization shown in Fig. 2.14 obtain explicit expressions for the transition probabilities

$$p(b_j | a_k) \qquad \begin{cases} k = 1, 2 \\ j = 1, 2, \ldots, 8 \end{cases}$$

(*b*) Give the optimum decision rule in as compact a form as possible.

2.10 (Chernoff Bound)

(*a*) Let z be a random variable such that its distribution (density) $p(\cdot)$ has finite moments of all order. Show that

$$\Pr(z > 0) = \sum_{z>0} p(z) \leq \sum_{z} f(z)p(z) = E\{f(z)\}$$

where

$$f(z) \geq \begin{cases} 1 & z \geq 0 \\ 0 & z < 0 \end{cases}$$

(*b*) Choose $f(z) = e^{\rho z}$, $\rho \geq 0$, and thus show that $\Pr(z > 0) \leq E[e^{\rho z}]$, $\rho \geq 0$.

(*c*) In (2.3.12), let $z(\mathbf{y}|\mathbf{x}_m) = \ln[p_N(\mathbf{y}|\mathbf{x}_{m'})/p_N(\mathbf{y}|\mathbf{x}_m)]$ where $\mathbf{y}$ has distribution (density) $p_N(\mathbf{y}|\mathbf{x}_m)$. Using (*b*), show that

$$P_E(m \to m') \leq E_{\mathbf{y}}[p_N(\mathbf{y}|\mathbf{x}_{m'})/p_N(\mathbf{y}|\mathbf{x}_m)]^\rho = \sum_{\mathbf{y}} p_N(\mathbf{y}|\mathbf{x}_{m'})^\rho p_N(\mathbf{y}|\mathbf{x}_m)^{1-\rho} \qquad \rho \geq 0$$

(*d*) Show that the bound in (*c*) reduces to the Bhattacharyya bound when $\rho = 1/2$.

(*e*) Consider the asymmetric binary "Z" channel specified by

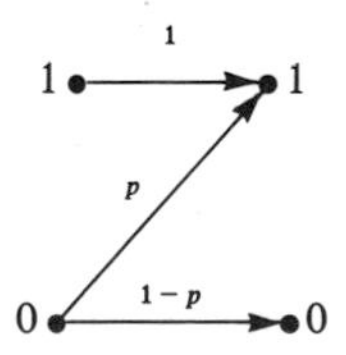

Let $\mathbf{x}_m = 00\ldots0$ and $\mathbf{x}_{m'} = 11\ldots1$ be complementary N-dimensional vectors. Show that the Chernoff bound with ρ optimized yields

$$P_E(m \to m') \leq p^N$$

and show that this is the exact result for maximum likelihood decoding. Compare with the Bhattacharyya bound.

2.11 (*a*) Show that the code whose parity-check matrix is given in Fig. 2.17 has the generator matrix

$$G = \begin{bmatrix} 1 & 0 & 0 & 0 & 0 & 1 & 1 \\ 0 & 1 & 0 & 0 & 1 & 0 & 1 \\ 0 & 0 & 1 & 0 & 1 & 1 & 0 \\ 0 & 0 & 0 & 1 & 1 & 1 & 1 \end{bmatrix}$$

(*b*) Generalize to obtain the form of G for any (L, K) Hamming single-error correcting code where $L = 2^{L-K} - 1$, $L - K \geq 2$.

(*c*) Show that, for all the codes in (*b*), $d_{min} = 3$.

2.12 (*a*) For binary orthogonal codes, show that the expected number of symbol errors η occurring on a BSC defined by hard quantizing an AWGN channel is

$$E(\eta) = Lp = LQ\left\{\sqrt{\frac{2\mathscr{E}_b K}{N_o L}}\right\} \qquad \text{where } L = 2^K$$

and that the variance is var $[\eta] = Lp(1-p)$.

(*b*) For large K and $L = 2^K$, show that

$$E[\eta] = Lp \approx L\left[\frac{1}{2} - \sqrt{\frac{\mathscr{E}_b}{\pi N_o}}(K2^{-K})\right] \approx \frac{L}{2}$$

and that

$$\text{var}[\eta] = Lp(1-p) \approx L/4 \qquad \text{as } K \to \infty$$

(*c*) Since $d_{min} = L/2$ for the codes of (*a*), show that the bound (2.10.14) can be expressed as $P_E \leq \Pr\{\eta \geq L/4\}$.

(*d*) Using (*b*) and the Chebyshev inequality show that

$$\Pr\left\{\left|\eta - \frac{L}{2}\right| \geq \frac{L}{4}\right\} < \frac{4}{L} = 2^{-(K-2)}$$

Thus, $\Pr\{\eta \leq L/4\} \to 0$ as $K \to \infty$ and consequently the bound of (*c*) approaches unity.

2.13 Consider the following normalized four-level quantizer used with the AWGN channel

$$\begin{array}{cccccccc} -2 & | & -1 & | & +1 & | & +2 \\ & -a & & 0 & & a & \end{array} \qquad a \leq \sqrt{\frac{2\mathscr{E}_s}{N_0}} \equiv x$$

(*a*) Show that the resulting binary-input quaternary-output channel is symmetric with transition probabilities

$$p_0(-2) = Q(x+a) = p_1(+2)$$

$$p_0(-1) = Q(x) - Q(x+a) = p_1(+1)$$

$$p_0(+1) = Q(x-a) - Q(x) = p_1(-1)$$

$$p_0(+2) = 1 - Q(x-a) = p_1(-2)$$

(*b*) Evaluate

$$d = -\ln 2[\sqrt{p_0(+2)p_0(-2)} + \sqrt{p_0(+1)p_0(-1)}]$$

and optimize for $\mathscr{E}_s/N_0 = 2$.

2.14 Generalize (2.12.8) to noncoherent detection of M orthogonal signals.

(*a*) Show that

$$P_{E_1} = 1 - \Pr\{y_1 > y_i \text{ for all } i \neq 1 \,|\, x_1\}$$

$$= \int_0^\infty p(y_1|x_1)\left\{1 - \left[\int_0^{y_1} p(y_2|x_1)\,dy_2\right]^{M-1}\right\}dy_1$$

where $p(y_1|x_1)$ and $p(y_2|x_2)$ are given by (2.12.7).

(*b*) Substitute as justified in (*a*) to obtain

$$P_{E_1} = \int_0^\infty p(y_1|x_1)[1 - (1 - e^{-y_1^2/2})^{M-1}]\,dy_1$$

(*c*) Show that the integral in (*b*) reduces to the finite sum

$$P_E = P_{E_1} = e^{-\mathscr{E}/N_o} \sum_{j=2}^{M} \frac{(-1)^j}{M} \binom{M}{j} e^{\mathscr{E}/(jN_o)}$$

2.15 (Continuation and Bound)

(*a*) Show that the term in brackets in Prob. 2.14(*b*) is upper bounded by

$$1 - (1 - e^{-y^2/2})^{M-1} < \min\,[(M-1)e^{-y^2/2}, 1] < [(M-1)e^{-y^2/2}]^\rho \qquad 0 \le \rho \le 1$$

(*b*) Use this to show that

$$P_E < (M-1)^\rho \exp\left[-\frac{\mathscr{E}}{N_o}\left(\frac{\rho}{1+\rho}\right)\right] \qquad 0 \le \rho \le 1$$

which is the same as the bound (2.5.12) for *coherent detection* and leads directly to the exponential bound (2.5.16).

(*c*) Give an intuitive argument for the perhaps unexpected result of (*b*).

2.16 Consider a binary linear block code with $K = 4$, $L = 7$ and generator matrix

$$G = \begin{bmatrix} 1 & 0 & 0 & 0 & 0 & 1 & 1 \\ 1 & 1 & 0 & 0 & 1 & 1 & 0 \\ 0 & 0 & 1 & 0 & 1 & 1 & 0 \\ 0 & 0 & 0 & 1 & 1 & 1 & 1 \end{bmatrix}$$

(*a*) Find a parity-check matrix H for this code.

(*b*) Suppose we use this code over a BSC and the received output is $\mathbf{y} = (1\,1\,0\,1\,1\,1\,1)$. What is the maximum likelihood decision for the transmitted codeword?

(*c*) Repeat (*b*) for $y = (1\,0\,0\,1\,1\,0\,1)$.

(*d*) What is the minimum distance of this code?

2.17 Consider M completely known, orthogonal, time-limited, equal-energy, equally likely signals $x_1(t), \ldots, x_m(t)$ where

$$\int_0^T x_i(t)x_j(t)\,dt = \mathscr{E}\delta_{ij}$$

These signals are used for digital communication over the usual additive white Gaussian noise channel with spectral density $N_o/2$. Consider a receiver that computes

$$\lambda_k = \sqrt{\frac{2}{N_o\mathscr{E}}} \int_0^T y(t)x_k(t)\,dt \qquad k = 1, 2, \ldots, M$$

and decides m_{k*} when $\lambda_{k*} = \max_k \{\lambda_k\}$ provided that $\max_k \{\lambda_k\} \ge \delta$. If $\lambda_k \le \delta$ for all k, then the receiver declares an erasure and does not make any decision. Let $\delta > b = \sqrt{2\mathscr{E}/N_0}$.

(*a*) Find the probability of an erasure.

(*b*) Find the probability of a correct decision.

2.18 Consider detection of a signal of random amplitude in additive white Gaussian noise such that

$$H_0 \qquad y(t) = n(t) \qquad 0 \le t \le T$$

$$H_1 \qquad y(t) = x\phi(t) + n(t) \qquad 0 \le t \le T$$

where

$$E\{n(t)n(t+\tau)\} = \delta(\tau) \qquad \text{and} \qquad \int_0^T \phi^2(t)\,dt = 1$$

and x is a Gaussian random variable with zero mean and unit variance. What is the minimum average error probability when both hypothesis H_0 and H_1 have a priori probability of $\frac{1}{2}$?

2.19 Consider the three signals

$$x_k(t) = \begin{cases} \sqrt{\dfrac{2\mathscr{E}}{T}} \cos\left(2\pi \dfrac{t}{T} + \dfrac{2}{3}\pi k\right) & 0 \le t \le T \\ 0 & \text{elsewhere} \end{cases}$$

$$k = 0, 1, 2$$

to be used to send one of three messages over an additive white Gaussian noise channel of spectral density $N_o/2$.

(*a*) When the messages are equally likely, show that the minimum probability of error is given by

$$P_E = \int_{-\infty}^{\infty} \frac{1}{\sqrt{2\pi}} e^{-\alpha^2/2} \left\{ 1 - \left[1 - Q\left(\alpha + \sqrt{\frac{3\mathscr{E}}{N_o}} \right) \right]^2 \right\} d\alpha$$

(*b*) Find the minimum probability of error when the a priori probabilities are

$$\pi_0 = \Pr\{m_0 \text{ is sent}\} = \tfrac{1}{2}$$
$$\pi_1 = \Pr\{m_1 \text{ is sent}\} = \tfrac{1}{2}$$
$$\pi_2 = \Pr\{m_2 \text{ is sent}\} = 0$$

(*c*) Find the minimum probability of error when

$$\pi_0 = 0 \qquad \pi_1 = \tfrac{1}{4} \qquad \pi_2 = \tfrac{3}{4}$$

2.20 Consider the detection of two *equally likely* signals in additive colored Gaussian noise where

$$E[n(t)n(s)] = \phi(t, s)$$

$$\begin{aligned} H_1 \quad & y(t) = x_1(t) + n(t) \\ H_2 \quad & y(t) = x_2(t) + n(t) \end{aligned} \qquad 0 \le t \le T$$

Suppose that the functions $\psi_1, \psi_2, \ldots, \psi_m$ and the constants $\sigma_1^2, \sigma_2^2, \ldots, \sigma_m^2$ satisfy the equation

$$\int_0^T \phi(t, s)\psi_k(s)\, ds = \sigma_k^2 \psi_k(t) \qquad 0 \le t \le T \qquad k = 1, 2, \ldots, m$$

where

$$\int_0^T \psi_i(t)\psi_j(t)\, dt = \delta_{ij}$$

Suppose that the signals are

$$x_1(t) = \sum_{k=1}^{m} \sqrt{\mathscr{E}_k}\, \psi_k(t)$$

$$x_2(t) = -x_1(t) = -\sum_{k=1}^{m} \sqrt{\mathscr{E}_k}\, \psi_k(t)$$

and let

$$y_k = \int_0^T y(t)\psi_k(t)\, dt \qquad k = 1, 2, \ldots, m$$

(*a*) Show that the minimum-probability-of-error decision rule is

$$\text{if } \sum_{k=1}^{m} y_k \left(\frac{\sqrt{\mathscr{E}_k}}{\sigma_k^2}\right) > 0 \qquad \text{choose } H_1$$

$$\text{Otherwise} \qquad \text{choose } H_2$$

(*b*) Using the optimum decision rule, find an exact expression in terms of $Q(\cdot)$ for the error probability as a function of $\sigma_1^2, \sigma_2^2, \ldots, \sigma_m^2$ and $\mathscr{E}_1, \mathscr{E}_2, \ldots, \mathscr{E}_m$. Check your answer for the special case where

$$\sigma_k^2 = \frac{N_o}{2} \qquad k = 1, 2, \ldots, m$$

with $\mathscr{E} = \mathscr{E}_1 + \mathscr{E}_2 + \cdots + \mathscr{E}_m$ denoting the total signal energy.

2.21 [Staggered (Offset) QPSK and Minimum Shift Keying (MSK)]
Consider the signal set generated by binary modulation ($x_k = \pm 1$ for each k) of the basis vectors

$$\phi_{2n}(t) = \begin{cases} \sqrt{\dfrac{2}{\tau}}\, f[t - (n - \frac{1}{2})\tau] \sin \omega_0 t & (n-1)\tau \le t < n\tau \\ 0 & \text{otherwise} \end{cases}$$

$$\phi_{2n+1}(t) = \begin{cases} \sqrt{\dfrac{2}{\tau}}\, f(t - n\tau) \cos \omega_0 t & (n - \frac{1}{2})\tau \le t < (n + \frac{1}{2})\tau \\ 0 & \text{otherwise} \end{cases}$$

$$\tau = \frac{T}{N} \qquad \omega_0 \text{ is a multiple of } 2\pi/\tau$$

(*a*) [Staggered (Offset) QPSK (SQPSK)]
Let

$$f(t) = \begin{cases} 1 & -\tau/2 \le t < \tau/2 \\ 0 & \text{otherwise} \end{cases}$$

Show that the performance with optimum demodulation is the same as for QPSK, and that the spectral density of the modulation sequence $A \sum_k x_k \phi_k(t)$ for a random binary sequence $\{x_k\}$ is the same as for QPSK:

$$S(\omega) = \tfrac{1}{2}[S_L(\omega - \omega_0) + S_L(\omega + \omega_0)]$$

where

$$S_L(\omega) = A^2 \left(\frac{\sin \omega\tau}{\omega\tau}\right)^2$$

(*b*) Comparing (*a*) with Prob. 2.7(*b*), show that the cross-channel interference effect of the phase error ϕ is reduced relative to ordinary QPSK.

(*c*) [Minimum Shift Keying (MSK)]
Let

$$f(t) = \begin{cases} \sqrt{2} \cos \dfrac{\pi t}{\tau} & -\tau/2 \le t < \tau/2 \\ 0 & \text{otherwise} \end{cases}$$

Show that the performance is the same as for QPSK and SQPSK with optimum demodulation.

(*d*) For MSK, show that for random binary modulation in the interval $(n - \frac{1}{2})\tau \le t < n\tau/2$

the signal can be expressed as

$$x_{2n}\phi_{2n}(t) + x_{2n+1}\phi_{2n+1}(t) = \pm(2/\sqrt{\tau})\cos[(\omega_0 \pm \pi/\tau)t]$$

which amounts to continuous phase frequency shift keying.

(*e*) Show that the spectral density of MSK can be expressed in the form given in (*a*) but with

$$S_L(\omega) = A^2\left(\frac{2\pi}{\tau}\right)^2\left[\frac{\cos(\omega\tau/2)}{\omega^2 - (\pi/\tau)^2}\right]^2$$

which decreases for large frequencies as ω^{-4} rather than ω^{-2} as is the case for QPSK and SQPSK.

CHAPTER

THREE

BLOCK CODE ENSEMBLE PERFORMANCE ANALYSIS

3.1 CODE ENSEMBLE AVERAGE ERROR PROBABILITY: UPPER BOUND

In Chap. 2 we made only modest progress in evaluating the error performance of specific coded signal sets. Since exact expressions for error probability involve multidimensional integrals which are generally prohibitively complex to calculate, we developed tight upper bounds, such as the union-Bhattacharyya bound (2.3.16) and the Gallager bound (2.4.8), which are applicable to any signal set. Nevertheless, evaluation of these error bounds for a *specific* signal set, other than a few cases such as those treated in Sec. 2.11, is essentially prohibitive, and particularly so as the size of the signal set, M, and the dimensionality, N, become large. It follows that, given the difficulty in analyzing specific signal sets, the search for the optimum for a given M and N is generally futile.

Actually, the exit from this impasse was clearly indicated by Shannon [1948], who first employed the central technique of information theory now referred to, not very appropriately, as "random coding." The basis of this technique is very simple: given that the calculation of the error probabilities for a particular set of M signal (or code) vectors of dimension N is not feasible, consider instead the average error probability over the ensemble of all possible sets of M signals with dimensionality N. A tight upper bound on this average over the entire ensemble turns out to be amazingly simple to calculate. Obviously at least one signal set must have an error probability which is no greater than the ensemble average; hence the ensemble average is an upper bound on the error probability for the optimum signal set (or code) of M signals of dimensionality N. Surprisingly, for most rates this upper bound is asymptotically tight, as we shall demonstrate by calculating lower bounds in the latter half of this chapter.

To begin the derivation of this ensemble upper bound, consider a specific code or signal set[1] of M signal vectors $\mathbf{x}_1, \mathbf{x}_2, \ldots, \mathbf{x}_M$, each of dimension N. Suppose there are Q possible channel inputs so that $x_{mn} \in \mathscr{X} = \{a_1, a_2, \ldots, a_Q\}$, and $m = 1, 2, \ldots, M$; $n = 1, 2, \ldots, N$. As discussed in Sec. 2.7, these inputs may be taken as amplitudes, phases, vectors, or just as abstract quantities. In any case, this ensures that there are in all exactly Q^{MN} possible distinct signal sets with the given parameters, some of which are naturally absurd such as those for which $\mathbf{x}_i = \mathbf{x}_j$ for some $i \neq j$. Nevertheless, if $P_{E_m}(\mathbf{x}_1, \mathbf{x}_2, \ldots, \mathbf{x}_M)$ is the error probability for the mth message with a given signal set, the average error probability for the mth message over the ensemble of all possible Q^{MN} signal sets is

$$\overline{P_{E_m}} = \frac{1}{Q^{NM}} \sum_{\mathbf{x}_1} \sum_{\mathbf{x}_2} \cdots \sum_{\mathbf{x}_M} P_{E_m}(\mathbf{x}_1, \mathbf{x}_2, \ldots, \mathbf{x}_M) \qquad m = 1, 2, \ldots, M \qquad (3.1.1)$$

where each of the M summations runs over all Q^N possible N-dimensional Q-ary vectors from $\mathbf{x} = (a_1, a_1, \ldots, a_1)$ to $\mathbf{x} = (a_Q, \ldots, a_Q)$. Hence the M-dimensional sum runs over all possible Q^{MN} signal sets and we divide by this number to obtain the ensemble average.

For the sake of later generalization, we rewrite (3.1.1) as

$$\overline{P_{E_m}} = \sum_{\mathbf{x}_1} \sum_{\mathbf{x}_2} \cdots \sum_{\mathbf{x}_M} q_N(\mathbf{x}_1) q_N(\mathbf{x}_2) \ldots q_N(\mathbf{x}_M) P_{E_m}(\mathbf{x}_1, \mathbf{x}_2, \ldots, \mathbf{x}_M)$$

$$m = 1, 2, \ldots, M \qquad (3.1.2)$$

where $q_N(\mathbf{x})$ will be taken as any distribution over $\mathscr{X}_N$; for now, however, we continue with the uniform weighting of (3.1.1) and take

$$q_N(\mathbf{x}_m) = \frac{1}{Q^N} \qquad m = 1, 2, \ldots, M \qquad (3.1.3)$$

In Sec. 2.4 we derived an upper bound on P_{E_m} for any specific signal set, namely

$$P_{E_m}(\mathbf{x}_1, \mathbf{x}_2, \ldots, \mathbf{x}_M) < \sum_{\mathbf{y}} p_N(\mathbf{y} \mid \mathbf{x}_m)^{1/(1+\rho)} \left[\sum_{m' \neq m} p_N(\mathbf{y} \mid \mathbf{x}_{m'})^{1/(1+\rho)} \right]^{\rho} \qquad \rho \geq 0$$

$$(3.1.4)$$

This Gallager bound is more general than the union-Bhattacharyya bound of Sec. 2.3 to which it reduces for $\rho = 1$. Initially, for the sake of manipulative simplicity, we consider only $m = 1$. Then inserting (3.1.4) into (3.1.2) and changing

[1] Throughout this chapter we shall use the pairs of terms code and signal set, and code vector and signal vector, interchangeably.

the order of the summations, we obtain as the upper bound on ensemble error probability when message 1 is sent

$$\overline{P_{E_1}} < \sum_{\mathbf{y}} \sum_{\mathbf{x}_1} q_N(\mathbf{x}_1) p_N(\mathbf{y} \mid \mathbf{x}_1)^{1/(1+\rho)} \left\{ \sum_{\mathbf{x}_2} \sum_{\mathbf{x}_3} \cdots \sum_{\mathbf{x}_M} q_N(\mathbf{x}_2) q_N(\mathbf{x}_3) \cdots q_N(\mathbf{x}_M) \times \left[\sum_{m'=2}^{M} p_N(\mathbf{y} \mid \mathbf{x}_{m'})^{1/(1+\rho)} \right]^{\rho} \right\} \qquad \rho \geq 0 \quad (3.1.5)$$

To proceed further, we must restrict the arbitrary parameter ρ to lie in the unit interval $0 \leq \rho \leq 1$. Then limiting attention to the term in braces in (3.1.5) and defining

$$f_N(\mathbf{x}_2, \ldots, \mathbf{x}_M) \equiv \sum_{m'=2}^{M} p_N(\mathbf{y} \mid \mathbf{x}_{m'})^{1/(1+\rho)} \qquad 0 \leq \rho \leq 1 \qquad (3.1.6)$$

we have from the Jensen inequality (App. 1B)

$$\sum_{\mathbf{x}_2} \sum_{\mathbf{x}_3} \cdots \sum_{\mathbf{x}_M} q_N(\mathbf{x}_2) q_N(\mathbf{x}_3) \ldots q_N(\mathbf{x}_M) [f_N(\mathbf{x}_2, \ldots, \mathbf{x}_M)]^{\rho}$$
$$\leq \left[\sum_{\mathbf{x}_2} \sum_{\mathbf{x}_3} \cdots \sum_{\mathbf{x}_M} q_N(\mathbf{x}_2) q_N(\mathbf{x}_3) \ldots q_N(\mathbf{x}_M) f_N(\mathbf{x}_2, \ldots, \mathbf{x}_M) \right]^{\rho} \qquad (3.1.7)$$

since f_N^{ρ} is a convex $\cap$ function of f for all $\mathbf{x}$ when $0 \leq \rho \leq 1$. Here $q_N(\mathbf{x}) \geq 0$ and

$$\sum_{\mathbf{x}} q_N(\mathbf{x}) = 1 \qquad (3.1.8)$$

Next, using (3.1.6), we can evaluate the right side of (3.1.7) exactly to be

$$\left[\sum_{\mathbf{x}_2} \cdots \sum_{\mathbf{x}_M} q_N(\mathbf{x}_2) \cdots q_N(\mathbf{x}_M) f_N(\mathbf{x}_2 \cdots \mathbf{x}_M) \right]^{\rho}$$
$$= \left[\sum_{\mathbf{x}_2} \cdots \sum_{\mathbf{x}_M} q_N(\mathbf{x}_2) \cdots q_N(\mathbf{x}_M) \sum_{m'=2}^{M} p_N(\mathbf{y} \mid \mathbf{x}_{m'})^{1/(1+\rho)} \right]^{\rho}$$
$$= \left[\sum_{m'=2}^{M} \sum_{\mathbf{x}_{m'}} q_N(\mathbf{x}_{m'}) p_N(\mathbf{y} \mid \mathbf{x}_{m'})^{1/(1+\rho)} \right]^{\rho}$$
$$= \left[(M-1) \sum_{\mathbf{x}} q_N(\mathbf{x}) p_N(\mathbf{y} \mid \mathbf{x})^{1/(1+\rho)} \right]^{\rho} \qquad (3.1.9)$$

where the last step follows from the fact that each vector $\mathbf{x}_{m'}$ is summed over the same space $\mathscr{X}_N$. Combining (3.1.5) through (3.1.7) and (3.1.9) and recognizing that, since the factors of the summand of (3.1.5) are nonnegative, upper bounding any of them results in an upper bound on the sum, we have

$$\overline{P_{E_1}} < (M-1)^{\rho} \sum_{\mathbf{y}} \sum_{\mathbf{x}_1} q_N(\mathbf{x}_1) p_N(\mathbf{y} \mid \mathbf{x}_1)^{1/(1+\rho)} \left[\sum_{\mathbf{x}} q_N(\mathbf{x}) p_N(\mathbf{y} \mid \mathbf{x})^{1/(1+\rho)} \right]^{\rho}$$
$$= (M-1)^{\rho} \sum_{\mathbf{y}} \left[\sum_{\mathbf{x}} q_N(\mathbf{x}) p_N(\mathbf{y} \mid \mathbf{x})^{1/(1+\rho)} \right]^{1+\rho} \qquad 0 \leq \rho \leq 1 \qquad (3.1.10)$$

Now if, for any $m \neq 1$, we were to interchange the indices 1 and m throughout the above derivation from (3.1.5) on, we would arrive at the same bound which is consequently independent of m. Thus, trivially over-bounding $M - 1$ by M, we obtain finally the following upper bound on the ensemble average error probability when any message m is sent

$$\overline{P_{E_m}} < M^\rho \sum_{\mathbf{y}} \left[\sum_{\mathbf{x}} q_N(\mathbf{x}) p_N(\mathbf{y} \mid \mathbf{x})^{1/(1+\rho)} \right]^{1+\rho} \qquad 0 \le \rho \le 1 \qquad m = 1, 2, \ldots, M \tag{3.1.11}$$

This bound is valid for any discrete (Q-ary) input and *discrete or continuous output* channel, provided in the latter case we replace the summation over $\mathcal{Y}_N$ by an N-dimensional integral and take $p_N(\cdot)$ to be a density function. It is also noteworthy that the steps followed in deriving (3.1.11) are formally similar to those involved in the derivation of P_E for orthogonal signals over the AWGN channel in Sec. 2.5. This similarity will become even more striking in the next section.

Note, however, that we have *not* yet restricted the channel to be *memoryless*. If we so restrict it, we have

$$p_N(\mathbf{y} \mid \mathbf{x}) = \prod_{n=1}^{N} p(y_n \mid x_n) \tag{3.1.12}$$

If we also restrict $q_N(\mathbf{x})$ to be a product distribution

$$q_N(\mathbf{x}) = \prod_{n=1}^{N} q(x_n) \tag{3.1.13}$$

[which is trivially true for the special case (3.1.3) in which $q(x) \equiv 1/Q$] then upon inserting (3.1.12) and (3.1.13) in (3.1.11), we have for a *memoryless channel* that

$$\begin{aligned}
\overline{P_{E_m}} &< M^\rho \sum_{y_1} \sum_{y_2} \cdots \sum_{y_N} \left[\sum_{x_1} \sum_{x_2} \cdots \sum_{x_N} q(x_1) p(y_1 \mid x_1)^{1/(1+\rho)} \cdots \right. \\
&\qquad \left. \times\, q(x_N) p(y_N \mid x_N)^{1/(1+\rho)} \right]^{1+\rho} \\
&= M^\rho \left\{ \sum_{y_1} \left[\sum_{x_1} q(x_1) p(y_1 \mid x_1)^{1/(1+\rho)} \right]^{1+\rho} \right\} \cdots \\
&\qquad \times \left\{ \sum_{y_N} \left[\sum_{x_N} q(x_N) p(y_N \mid x_N)^{1/(1+\rho)} \right]^{1+\rho} \right\} \\
&= M^\rho \left\{ \sum_{y} \left[\sum_{x} q(x) p(y \mid x)^{1/(1+\rho)} \right]^{1+\rho} \right\}^N \qquad 0 \le \rho \le 1
\end{aligned} \tag{3.1.14}$$

where $p(y|x)$ is the symbol transition probability (density). [In the special case (3.1.3), $q(x) = 1/Q$ for all $x \in \mathcal{X}$.]

Before proceeding to evaluate the consequences of the elegantly simple result (3.1.14), let us generalize it slightly. We began in (3.1.1) and (3.1.2) by taking a uniform average over the entire ensemble of possible coded signal sets. However, for some signal sets and for some channels, it will develop that certain choices are preferable to others. In evaluating an average where the ultimate goal is to bound the performance of the best member of the ensemble, it is logical that, based on some side information or intuition, we might wish to weigh certain sets of signal vectors (or certain signal vectors, or certain symbols or components of signal vectors) more heavily than others. An appropriate, though banal, example would be to use the average test score of a class of students to lower bound the score of the best student. However, if an instructor's experience is that red-haired, green-eyed students generally perform above average and green-haired, red-eyed students perform below average, he may choose to use a weighted average which weighs the score of any student from the first group most heavily, that of any student from the second group least heavily, and that of any other student somewhere between the two extremes. The only constraint is that the sum of the (nonnegative) weights be unity or, equivalently, that the vector of weights be a distribution vector. If the instructor's bias is justified, this weighted average will then be a tighter lower bound on the performance of the best student than the original uniform average, but it will *always* be a valid lower bound regardless of the validity of bias.

We can easily achieve such a priori biasing from (3.1.2) on by allowing $q_N(\mathbf{x})$ to be any distribution on the Q^N possible signal vectors. Thus (3.1.2) may be regarded as a weighted ensemble average where the weighting of the signal sets, which are members of the ensemble, are given by the product measure $\prod_{m=1}^{M} q_N(\mathbf{x}_m)$. The same may be said of all subsequent ensemble averages through (3.1.11). For a memoryless channel, defined by (3.1.12), we further restrict this arbitrary weighting to be of the form (3.1.13) which corresponds to weighting each component of each codeword independently according to $q(x)$. For many classes of channels, including all binary-input, output-symmetric channels, a nonuniform weighting does not reduce the bound on the ensemble average error probability. For others such as the Z channel (Prob. 3.1), there is a marked improvement at some rates. And clearly, if by nonuniform weighting of the members of the ensemble we manage to reduce this average, then the best signal set must perform better than this newly reduced average. The advantage of nonuniform weighting depends generally on the skewness of the channel.

We may express (3.1.14) alternatively in terms of the data rate per dimension

$$R \equiv \frac{\ln M}{N} \text{ nats/dimension} \tag{3.1.15}$$

which is of course related to the rate R_T in nats per second defined in Sec. 2.5 by

$$\begin{aligned} R &= R_T(T/N) \\ &\approx R_T/2W \end{aligned} \tag{3.1.16}$$

Thus, since $M = e^{NR}$, we obtain for *memoryless channels*

$$\overline{P_{E_m}} < e^{-N[E_o(\rho,\, \mathbf{q}) - \rho R]} \qquad 0 \le \rho \le 1 \tag{3.1.17}$$

where[2]

$$E_o(\rho, \mathbf{q}) \equiv -\ln \sum_y \left[\sum_x q(x)p(y \mid x)^{1/1+\rho} \right]^{1+\rho} \tag{3.1.18}$$

and where $\mathbf{q} = \{q(a_1), q(a_2), \ldots, q(a_Q)\}$ is an arbitrary distribution vector; that is, $\mathbf{q}$ is an arbitrary vector over the finite space $\mathcal{X} = \{a_1, a_2, \ldots, a_Q\}$ with the properties

$$q(x) \geq 0 \qquad \text{for every } x \in \mathcal{X}$$

and

$$\sum_x q(x) = 1 \tag{3.1.19}$$

We observe finally that, since (3.1.17) is an error probability bound for any message sent, it must also be a bound on the ensemble average of the overall error probability P_E *no matter what the message prior probabilities may be*, provided the maximum likelihood decision rule is used. Also, since ρ is arbitrary within the unit interval and $\mathbf{q}$ is an arbitrary distribution vector subject to the constraints (3.1.19), we may optimize these parameters to yield the tightest upper bound. This is achieved, of course, by maximizing the negative exponent of (3.1.17) with the result that the average error probability over the ensemble of all possible signal sets for a Q-ary input memoryless channel may be bounded by

$$\overline{P_E} < e^{-NE(R)} \tag{3.1.20}$$

where

$$E(R) = \max_{\mathbf{q}} \max_{0 \leq \rho \leq 1} [E_o(\rho, \mathbf{q}) - \rho R]$$

$E_o(\rho, \mathbf{q})$ is given by (3.1.18) and $\mathbf{q}$ is a distribution vector subject to the constraints (3.1.19). It obviously follows that *at least one signal set in the ensemble must have P_E no greater than this ensemble average bound.*

We leave the detailed discussion of this remarkably simple result to the next section where we utilize it to prove Shannon's channel coding theorem.

3.2 THE CHANNEL CODING THEOREM AND ERROR EXPONENT PROPERTIES FOR MEMORYLESS CHANNELS

The key to assessing the value of the bound on the ensemble average error probability given by (3.1.20) lies in determining the properties of the function $E_o(\rho, \mathbf{q})$ given by (3.1.18). The important properties of this function that depend only on the memoryless channel statistics $\{p(y|x)\}$ and the arbitrary input weighting distribution $q(\cdot)$ are summarized in the following.

[2] The function $E_o(\rho, \mathbf{q})$ appears in other bounds as well. It was first defined by Gallager [1965] and is referred to as the Gallager function.

Lemma 3.2.1 (Gallager [1965]) Let

$$E_o(\rho, \mathbf{q}) = -\ln \sum_y \left[\sum_x q(x) p(y \mid x)^{1/(1+\rho)} \right]^{1+\rho} \tag{3.2.1}$$

where $q(\cdot)$ is a probability distribution over the finite space $\mathscr{X} = \{a_1, a_2, \ldots, a_Q\}$, and suppose that[3]

$$I(\mathbf{q}) \equiv \left. \frac{\partial E_o(\rho, \mathbf{q})}{\partial \rho} \right|_{\rho=0}$$

$$= \sum_y \sum_x q(x) p(y \mid x) \ln \left[\frac{p(y \mid x)}{\sum_{x'} q(x') p(y \mid x')} \right] \neq 0 \tag{3.2.2}$$

is nonzero. Then the function $E_o(\rho, \mathbf{q})$ has the following properties:

$$\begin{aligned} E_o(\rho, \mathbf{q}) &\geq 0 \qquad \rho \geq 0 \\ E_o(\rho, \mathbf{q}) &\leq 0 \qquad -1 < \rho \leq 0 \end{aligned} \tag{3.2.3}$$

with equality in either case if and only if $\rho = 0$; and

$$\frac{\partial E_o(\rho, \mathbf{q})}{\partial \rho} > 0 \qquad \rho > -1 \tag{3.2.4}$$

$$\frac{\partial^2 E_o(\rho, \mathbf{q})}{\partial \rho^2} \leq 0 \qquad \rho > -1 \tag{3.2.5a}$$

with equality in (3.2.5a) if and only if

$$\ln \left[\frac{p(y \mid x)}{\sum_{x'} q(x') p(y \mid x')} \right] = I(\mathbf{q}) \tag{3.2.5b}$$

for all $x \in \mathscr{X}$, $y \in \mathscr{Y}$ such that $q(x)p(y \mid x) > 0$.

In (3.2.2) and (3.2.5b) we find the function $I(\mathbf{q})$, called the *average mutual information* of the channel, first defined in Sec. 1.2[4] where it was shown to be nonnegative. Direct substitution of $\rho = 0$ in (3.2.1) shows that $E_o(0, \mathbf{q}) = 0$ and hence that the inequalities (3.2.3) follow from (3.2.4); the proof of inequalities (3.2.4) and (3.2.5a) is based on certain fundamental inequalities of analysis. Appendix 3A contains these inequalities and gives the proof of (3.2.4) and (3.2.5a).

Thus, in all cases except when the condition (3.2.5b) holds, $E_o(\rho, \mathbf{q})$ is a positive increasing convex $\cap$ function, for positive ρ, with a slope at the origin equal to

[3] $I(\mathbf{q}) \equiv I(\mathscr{X}; \mathscr{Y})$ was first defined in Sec. 1.2. Henceforth, the channel input distribution is used as the argument, in preference to the input and output spaces, because this is the variable over which all results will be optimized.

[4] Note that average mutual information here evolves naturally as a parameter of the error probability bound, while in Sec. 1.2 it was defined in a more abstract framework.

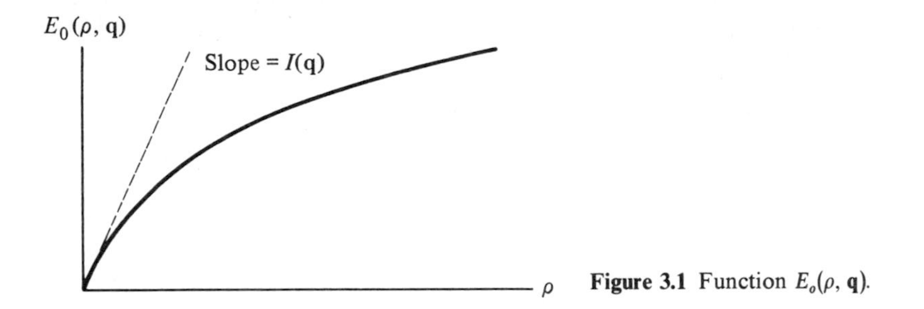

Figure 3.1 Function $E_o(\rho, \mathbf{q})$.

$I(\mathbf{q})$. An example is sketched in Fig. 3.1. On the other hand, if (3.2.5*b*) holds, the second derivative of $E_o(\rho, \mathbf{q})$ with respect to ρ is zero for all ρ, and consequently in this case $E_o(\rho, \mathbf{q}) = \rho I(\mathbf{q})$. While it is possible to construct nontrivial examples of discrete channels for which (3.2.5*b*) holds (see Prob. 3.2), these do not include any case of practical importance.

Then restricting our consideration to the case where (3.2.5*a*) is a strict inequality, we have that, for any particular distribution vector $\mathbf{q}$, the function to be maximized in (3.1.20), $[E_o(\rho, \mathbf{q}) - \rho R]$, is the difference between a convex $\cap$ function and a straight line, and hence must itself be convex $\cap$ for positive ρ as shown in Fig. 3.2. Defining

$$E(R, \mathbf{q}) \equiv \max_{0 \le \rho \le 1} [E_o(\rho, \mathbf{q}) - \rho R] \tag{3.2.6}$$

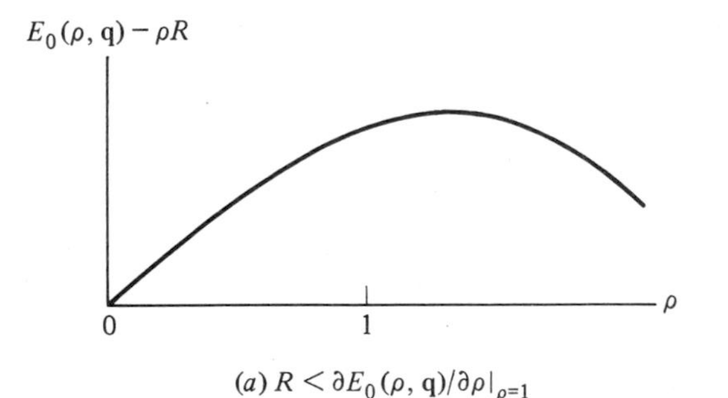

(*a*) $R < \partial E_0(\rho, \mathbf{q})/\partial \rho|_{\rho=1}$

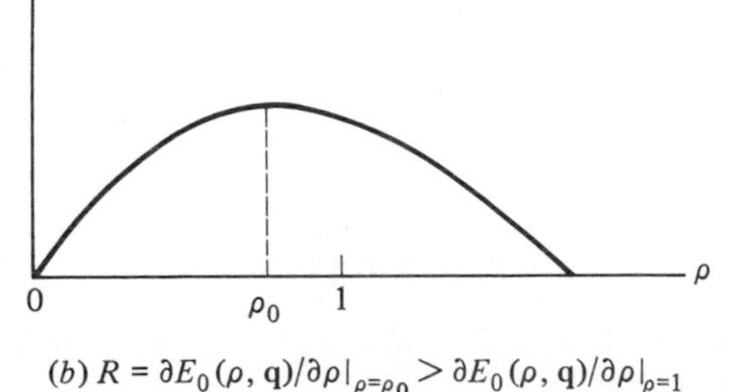

(*b*) $R = \partial E_0(\rho, \mathbf{q})/\partial \rho|_{\rho=\rho_0} > \partial E_0(\rho, \mathbf{q})/\partial \rho|_{\rho=1}$

Figure 3.2 Function $E_o(\rho, \mathbf{q}) - \rho R$.

we note that, as a consequence of Lemma 3.2.1, the exponent has a unique maximum. For small R (Fig. 3.2a), the maximum of $[E_o(\rho, \mathbf{q}) - \rho R]$ occurs for $\rho > 1$ and, consequently, the maximum on the unit interval lies at $\rho = 1$. For larger R (Fig. 3.2b), the maximum occurs at the value of ρ for which $R = \partial E_o(\rho, \mathbf{q})/\partial\rho$. Since the second derivative is strictly negative, the first derivative is a decreasing function of ρ, so that we can express the maximum of (3.2.6) for low rates as

$$E(R, \mathbf{q}) = E_o(1, \mathbf{q}) - R \qquad 0 \le R \le \partial E_o(\rho, \mathbf{q})/\partial\rho \Big|_{\rho=1} \tag{3.2.7}$$

while for higher rates we must use the parametric equations

$$\begin{aligned} E(R, \mathbf{q}) &= E_o(\rho, \mathbf{q}) - \rho\partial E_o(\rho, \mathbf{q})/\partial\rho \\ R &= \partial E_o(\rho, \mathbf{q})/\partial\rho \\ \partial E_o(\rho, \mathbf{q})/\partial\rho \Big|_{\rho=1} &\le R \le \partial E_o(\rho, \mathbf{q})/\partial\rho \Big|_{\rho=0} = I(\mathbf{q}) \end{aligned} \tag{3.2.8}$$

For this higher-rate region, the slope is obtained as the ratio of partial derivatives

$$\begin{aligned} \frac{dE(R, \mathbf{q})}{dR} &= \frac{\partial[E_o(\rho, \mathbf{q}) - \rho\partial E_o(\rho, \mathbf{q})/\partial\rho]/\partial\rho}{\partial R/\partial\rho} \\ &= -\rho \end{aligned} \tag{3.2.9}$$

and the second derivative is

$$\begin{aligned} \frac{d^2E(R, \mathbf{q})}{dR^2} &= \frac{\partial[dE(R, \mathbf{q})/dR]/\partial\rho}{\partial R/\partial\rho} \\ &= \frac{-1}{\partial^2 E_o(\rho, \mathbf{q})/\partial\rho^2} \\ &> 0 \end{aligned} \tag{3.2.10}$$

Hence, while $E(R, \mathbf{q})$ for low rates is linear in R with slope equal to -1, for higher rates it is monotonically decreasing and convex $\cup$. Its slope, which is $-\rho$ $(0 \le \rho \le 1)$, increases from -1 at $R = \partial E_o(\rho, \mathbf{q})/\partial\rho\,|_{\rho=1}$, where it equals the slope of the low-rate linear segment, to 0 at $R = I(\mathbf{q}) = \partial E_o(\rho, \mathbf{q})/\partial\rho\,|_{\rho=0}$, where the function $E(R, \mathbf{q})$ itself goes to zero. A typical $E(R, \mathbf{q})$ function demonstrating these properties is shown in Fig. 3.3a.

For the special class of channels for which condition (3.2.5b) holds so that the second derivative of $E_o(\rho, \mathbf{q})$ is everywhere zero, we have

$$\begin{aligned} E(R, \mathbf{q}) &= \max_{0 \le \rho \le 1} \rho[I(\mathbf{q}) - R] \\ &= I(\mathbf{q}) - R \qquad 0 \le R \le I(\mathbf{q}) \end{aligned} \tag{3.2.11}$$

Thus, as shown in Fig. 3.3b, the curved portion of the typical $E(R, \mathbf{q})$ function disappears and only the linear segment remains.

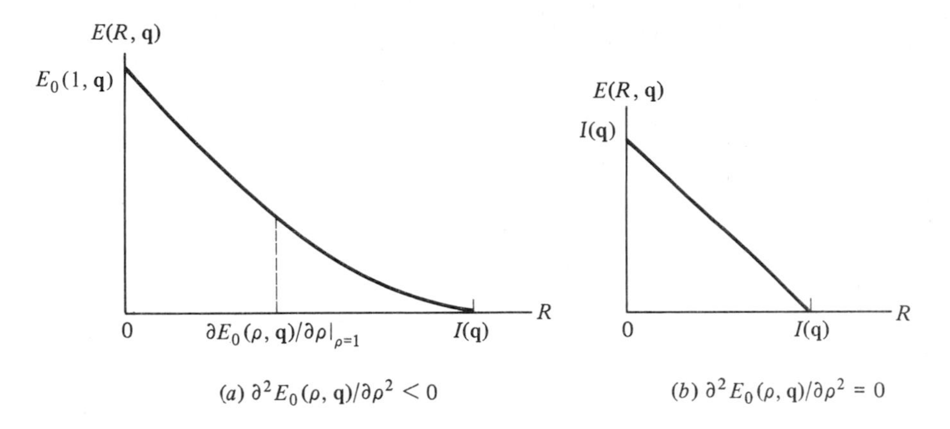

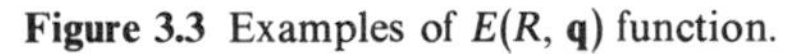

Figure 3.3 Examples of $E(R, \mathbf{q})$ function.

The negative exponent $E(R)$ of (3.1.20) is, of course, obtained from $E(R, \mathbf{q})$ by maximizing over all possible distribution vectors. That is

$$E(R) = \max_{\mathbf{q}} E(R, \mathbf{q}) \tag{3.2.12}$$

where

$$\mathbf{q} = \{q(x): x \in \mathscr{X}\}$$

with the properties

$$q(x) \geq 0 \qquad \text{for all } x \in \mathscr{X}$$

$$\sum_x q(x) = 1$$

Note that, as a consequence of these distribution constraints, the space of allowed $\mathbf{q}$ is a closed convex region. For certain channels, including some of greatest physical interest (see Sec. 3.4), a unique distribution vector $\mathbf{q}$ maximizes $E(R)$ for all rates; for other channels (Prob. 3.3*c*), two or more distributions maximize $E(R)$ over disjoint intervals of R; for still other channels (Prob. 3.5), the maximizing distribution varies continuously with R. Regardless of which of the above situations holds, we have shown that, as a consequence of Gallager's lemma, $E(R, \mathbf{q})$ is a bounded, decreasing, convex $\cup$, positive function of R for all rates R, $0 \leq R < I(\mathbf{q})$. $E(R)$ as defined by (3.2.12) is then the upper envelope of the set of all functions $E(R, \mathbf{q})$ over the space of probability distributions $\mathbf{q}$. It is easily shown that the upper envelope of a set of bounded, decreasing, convex $\cup$, positive functions of R is itself a bounded, decreasing, convex $\cup$, positive function of R. Thus, for all rates R

$$0 \leq R < C \equiv \max_{\mathbf{q}} I(\mathbf{q})$$

$$= \max_{\mathbf{q}} \sum_y \sum_x q(x)p(y \mid x) \ln \left[\frac{p(y \mid x)}{\sum_{x'} q(x')p(y \mid x')} \right] \tag{3.2.13}$$

$E(R)$ is a bounded, decreasing, convex ∪, positive function of R. C is called the channel *capacity*. This then proves the celebrated *channel coding theorem*.

Theorem 3.2.1 (Shannon [1948] et al.[5]) For any discrete-input memoryless channel, there exists an N-symbol code (signal set) of rate R nats per symbol for which the error probability with maximum likelihood decoding is bounded by

$$P_E < e^{-NE(R)} \tag{3.2.14}$$

where $E(R)$, as defined by (3.1.20) and (3.1.18), is a convex ∪, decreasing, positive function of R for $0 \le R < C$, where C is defined by (3.2.13).

Channel capacity was first defined in conjunction with average mutual information in Sec. 1.2. Like the latter, it emerges here naturally as a fundamental parameter of the error bounds—namely, the rate above which the exponential bound is no longer valid. Its significance is increased further by the converse theorem of Sec. 1.3, as well as by that to be proved in Sec. 3.9.

In spite of its unquestionable significance, this coding theorem leaves us with two sources of uneasiness. The first disturbing thought is that, while there exists a signal set or code whose error probability P_E, averaged over all transmitted messages, is bounded by (3.2.14), the message error probability P_{E_m} for some message or signal vector $\mathbf{x}_m$, may be much greater than the bound. While this may indeed be true for some codes, we now show that there always exists a signal set or code in the ensemble for which P_{E_m} is within a factor of 4 of the coding theorem bound for every m.

Corollary For any discrete-input memoryless channel, there exists an N-symbol code of rate R for which maximum likelihood decoding yields

$$P_{E_m} < 4e^{-NE(R)} \qquad 0 \le R < C \qquad m = 1, 2, \ldots, M \tag{3.2.15}$$

PROOF The proof involves applying the channel coding theorem to the ensemble of codes of the same dimensionality but with twice as many messages. Let us assume further, arbitrarily, that the $2M$ messages are all a priori equiprobable. Then from the above theorem, we have that there exists at least one code in the ensemble of codes with $2M$ messages for which

$$\begin{aligned} P_E(2M) &= \frac{1}{2M}\sum_{m=1}^{2M} P_{E_m} \\ &< e^{-NE(\ln(2M)/N)} \end{aligned} \tag{3.2.16}$$

since the rate of this code is $\ln(2M)/N$. Now suppose we discard the M code

[5] Shannon actually proved that $P_E \to 0$ as $N \to \infty$, while the exponential bound was proved in various progressively more explicit forms by Feinstein [1954, 1955], Elias [1955], Wolfowitz [1957], Fano [1961], and Gallager [1965].

(signal) vectors with highest P_{E_m}. This guarantees that the remaining M code vectors have

$$P_{E_m} < 2e^{-NE(\ln(2M)/N)} \tag{3.2.17}$$

for, if this were not so, just the average of the M code vectors with largest error probabilities would exceed the bound (3.2.16). Substituting (3.1.20) for the exponent, we have for rate $\ln(2M)/N$

$$\begin{aligned} P_{E_m} &< 2 \exp\left\{-N \max_{\mathbf{q}} \max_{0 \le \rho \le 1} [E_o(\rho, \mathbf{q}) - \rho(\ln M)/N - \rho(\ln 2)/N]\right\} \\ &\le 2 \exp\left\{-N \max_{\mathbf{q}} \max_{0 \le \rho \le 1} [E_o(\rho, \mathbf{q}) - \rho(\ln M)/N - (\ln 2)/N]\right\} \\ &= 4e^{-NE(R)} \end{aligned} \tag{3.2.18}$$

for each of the M code vectors. (Note that, while the above development was for the code set of $2M$ messages and the corresponding maximum likelihood decision regions, reducing the set to M messages can only reduce P_{E_m} by expanding each decision region.) This proves the corollary.

The second disturbing thought is that, even though a code exists with low error probability, it may be difficult, if not nearly impossible, to find. We may dispel this doubt quickly for ensembles where uniform weighting (that is, $q(x) = 1/Q$ for all $x \in \mathscr{X} = \{a_1, a_2, \ldots, a_Q\}$) is optimum. For in this case *at least half the codes in the ensemble* must have

$$\begin{aligned} P_E &\le 2\overline{P_E} \\ &< 2e^{-NE(R)} \end{aligned}$$

for again, if this were not so, the ensemble average could not be bounded by $\overline{P_E}$ as given by (3.1.20). For nonuniformly weighted ensembles, the argument must include the effect of weighting and reduces essentially to a probabilistic statement. In any case, the practical problem is not solely one of finding codes that yield low P_E, but codes which are easily generated and especially which are *easily decoded*, that yield low P_E. This will be the problem addressed throughout this book.

Before leaving the coding theorem, we dwell a little further on the problem of finding the weighting distribution $\mathbf{q}$ which maximizes the negative exponent of the bound at each rate. To approach this analytically, it is most convenient to rewrite the exponent as

$$E(R) = \max_{0 \le \rho \le 1} \left[-\rho R + \max_{\mathbf{q}} E_o(\rho, \mathbf{q})\right] \tag{3.2.19}$$

Thus we need only maximize $E_o(\rho, \mathbf{q})$ or, equivalently, minimize with respect to $\mathbf{q}$

$$\begin{aligned} e^{-E_o(\rho, \mathbf{q})} &= \sum_y \left(\sum_x q(x) p(y \mid x)^{1/(1+\rho)}\right)^{1+\rho} \\ &= \sum_y \alpha(y, \mathbf{q})^{1+\rho} \end{aligned} \tag{3.2.20}$$

where

$$\alpha(y, \mathbf{q}) \equiv \sum_x q(x)p(y \mid x)^{1/(1+\rho)} \tag{3.2.21}$$

The key to this minimization lies in the following lemma.

Lemma 3.2.2 The quantity $\exp[-E_o(\rho, \mathbf{q})]$ is a convex $\cup$ function on the space of probability distributions $\mathbf{q}$ for all fixed $\rho \geq 0$.

Proof The convexity follows from the fact that $\alpha(y, \mathbf{q})$ is linear in $\mathbf{q}$, while the function $\alpha^{1+\rho}$ is convex $\cup$ in α for all $\rho \geq 0$. Thus, by the definition of convexity (App. 1A), for every $y \in \mathscr{Y}$, $\alpha(y, \mathbf{q})^{1+\rho}$ must be a convex $\cup$ function of $\mathbf{q}$. Finally, the sum of convex $\cup$ functions must also be convex $\cup$; hence the lemma is proved.

Also of interest, although it may be regarded as a byproduct of the maximization of the exponent, is the problem of maximizing $I(\mathbf{q})$ to obtain the channel capacity C. It turns out that this problem is almost equivalent to minimizing $\exp[-E_o(\rho, \mathbf{q})]$ because $I(\mathbf{q})$ has similar properties, summarized in the following.

Lemma 3.2.3 $I(\mathbf{q})$ is a convex $\cap$ function on the space of probability distributions $\mathbf{q}$.

Proof We begin the proof by rewriting the definition (3.2.2) of $I(\mathbf{q})$ as

$$I(\mathbf{q}) = \sum_x q(x) \sum_y p(y \mid x) \ln p(y \mid x)$$

$$+ \sum_y \left\{ \sum_x q(x)p(y \mid x) \ln \left[1 \Big/ \sum_{x'} q(x')p(y \mid x') \right] \right\} \tag{3.2.22}$$

The first term is linear in $\mathbf{q}$; hence it is trivially convex. The second term can be written as

$$\sum_y \beta(y) \ln [1/\beta(y)]$$

where

$$\beta(y) \equiv \sum_x q(x)p(y \mid x)$$

is linear in $q(x)$. But $d^2[\beta \ln (1/\beta)]/d\beta^2 = -1/\beta < 0$ since $\beta > 0$. Hence $\beta \ln (1/\beta)$ is convex $\cap$ in β, and β is linear in $\mathbf{q}$. Thus by the same argument as for the previous lemma, $\beta(y)$ is convex $\cap$ in $\mathbf{q}$; and $I(\mathbf{q})$, which is the sum (finite, infinite, or even uncountably infinite) of convex $\cap$ functions, is itself convex $\cap$, thus proving the lemma.

The minimization (maximization) of convex $\cup$ ($\cap$) functions over a space of distributions is treated in App. 3B where necessary and sufficient conditions, due to Kuhn and Tucker [1951], are derived for the minimum (maximum). For application to the problems at hand, the following theorems are proved there.

Theorem 3.2.2: Exponents Necessary and sufficient conditions on the distribution vector $\mathbf{q}$ which minimizes $\exp[-E_o(\rho, \mathbf{q})]$ [or, equivalently, maximizes $E_o(\rho, \mathbf{q})$], for $\rho \geq 0$, are

$$\sum_y p(y|x)^{1/(1+\rho)}\alpha(y, \mathbf{q})^{\rho} \geq \sum_y \alpha(y, \mathbf{q})^{1+\rho} \qquad \text{for all } x \in \mathscr{X} = \{a_1, a_2, \ldots, a_Q\} \tag{3.2.23}$$

where $\alpha(y, \mathbf{q})$ is defined by (3.2.21), with equality for all x for which $q(x) > 0$.

Theorem 3.2.3: Average mutual information Necessary and sufficient conditions on the distribution vector $\mathbf{q}$ which maximizes $I(\mathbf{q})$, to yield C, are

$$\sum_y p(y|x) \ln \left[\frac{p(y|x)}{\sum_{x'} q(x')p(y|x')}\right] \leq C \qquad \text{for all } x \in \mathscr{X} = \{a_1, a_2, \ldots, a_Q\} \tag{3.2.24}$$

with equality for all x for which $q(x) > 0$.

The above theorems do not give explicit formulas for $\min_{\mathbf{q}} \exp[-E_o(\rho, \mathbf{q})]$ and C. However (3.2.23) and (3.2.24) do serve the purpose of verifying or disproving an intuitive guess for the optimizing distribution. As a very simple example, for a binary input ($Q = 2$) output-symmetric channel as defined in Sec. 2.9, these necessary and sufficient conditions verify the intuitive fact that the optimizing distribution in each case is uniform $[q(a_1) = q(a_2) = \frac{1}{2}]$. In the special case where the output space as well as the input space is $\{a_1, a_2, \ldots, a_Q\}$ and where the Q by Q transition matrix $\{p(y|x)\}$ is nonsingular, it can be shown (Prob. 3.4) that the conditions of both theorems are easily satisfied with the inequalities all holding with equality, and explicit formulas may be obtained both for the optimizing $\mathbf{q}$ and for the quantities to be optimized. In general, however, the maximization (minimization) must be performed numerically. This is greatly facilitated by the fact that the functions are convex, which guarantees convergence to a maximum (minimum) for any of a class of steepest ascent (descent) algorithms. Appendix 3C presents an efficient computational algorithm for determining channel capacity. Similar algorithms for computing $E(R)$ have been found by Arimoto [1976] and Lesh [1976].

Even when the optimum $\mathbf{q}$ is known and is the same for all rates, the actual computation of $E_o(\rho, \mathbf{q})$, $E(R)$, and C is by no means simple in general. Usually the simplest parameter to calculate is

$$E_o(1, \mathbf{q}) = -\ln \sum_y \left[\sum_x q(x)\sqrt{p(y|x)}\right]^2 \tag{3.2.25}$$

Since $E(R)$ is a decreasing function of rate, this provides a bound on the exponent. Also, $[E_o(1, \mathbf{q}) - R]$ as given by (3.2.7) is the low-rate exponent when maximized over $\mathbf{q}$. For any binary-input channel, this maximum is readily evaluated, since the optimizing distribution is uniform, and yields

$$E_o(1) \equiv \max_{\mathbf{q}} E_o(1, \mathbf{q})$$
$$= \ln 2 - \ln(1 + Z) \tag{3.2.26}$$

where

$$Z = \sum_y \sqrt{p_0(y)p_1(y)} \tag{3.2.27a}$$

For the special cases of the BSC and AWGN channel,[6] Z is readily calculated to be

$$Z = \sqrt{4p(1-p)} \qquad \text{(BSC)} \tag{3.2.27b}$$
$$Z = e^{-\mathscr{E}_s/N_o} \qquad \text{(AWGN)} \tag{3.2.27c}$$

It follows upon applying the Schwarz inequality (App. 3A) to (3.2.27a) that $0 \le Z \le 1$.

Now suppose the rate is sufficiently low that the linear bound (3.2.7) is appropriate. Then, for a binary-input channel, we have

$$P_E < e^{-N[E_o(1)-R]}$$
$$= Me^{-N[\ln 2 - \ln(1+Z)]} \tag{3.2.28}$$

On the other hand, we showed in Sec. 2.9 that for linear binary block codes used on this class of channels

$$P_E \le \sum_{k=2}^{M} e^{w_k \ln Z} \tag{2.9.19}$$

where $w_2, \ldots, w_M$ are the weights of the nonzero code vectors and Z is given by (3.2.27a). In particular, as was shown in Sec. 2.10, if we restrict $M = N$ [so that $R = (\ln N)/N \to 0$ as $N \to \infty$], then orthogonal codes exist for all $N = 2^K$ with the property that $w_k = N/2$ for all $k \ne 1$. In this case we have the bound

$$P_E < M\, e^{-N(-\frac{1}{2}\ln Z)} \tag{3.2.29}$$

Since in this latter case the rate approaches zero asymptotically with N, it is clear that the bound (3.2.29) should be compared with the ensemble average upper bound (3.2.28) as $(\ln M)/N \to 0$ in both cases. It is easily shown that the negative exponent of (3.2.29) dominates that of (3.2.28), that is

$$-\tfrac{1}{2}\ln Z \ge \ln 2 - \ln(1+Z) \qquad 0 \le Z \le 1 \tag{3.2.30}$$

with equality if and only if $Z = 1$.

The two exponents of (3.2.28) and (3.2.29) are shown in Fig. 3.4. Note from

[6] See (2.11.6) for the definition of $p_0(y)$ for the AWGN channel.

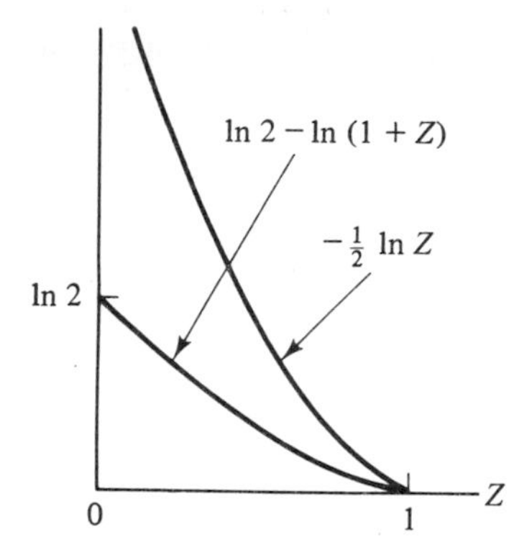

Figure 3.4 Negative exponents of (3.2.28) and (3.2.29).

the examples (3.2.27*b* and *c*) that $Z = 0$ applies to a noiseless channel and that Z grows monotonically with increasing noise, with the channel becoming useless in the limit of $Z = 1$. We note also from the figure that the curves diverge as $Z \rightarrow 0$, while they have the same negative slope at unity.

Now it may not be surprising that a particularly good code (e.g., the orthogonal code) is far better than the ensemble average which includes the effect of some exceedingly bad codes having two or more code vectors which are identical. In fact, however, this discrepancy occurs only at low rates; we shall show in Sec. 3.6 that, for $R > \partial E_o(\rho, \mathbf{q})/\partial \rho \,|_{\rho=1}$ [that is, over the curved portion of the $E(R)$ function], the best code can perform no better asymptotically than the ensemble average. Nevertheless, if at very low rates certain bad codes can cause such a dramatic difference between the ensemble average and the best code, it stands to reason that the ensemble average as such is not a useful bound at these rates. While this might lead the more skeptical to discard the averaging technique at this point, we shall in fact see that, with cleverness, the technique may be modified in such a way as to eliminate the culprits. This modification, called an *expurgated* ensemble average bound, is treated in the next section and shown for the special case of binary-input, output-symmetric channels to yield the exponent of (3.2.29) at asymptotically low rates.

3.3 EXPURGATED ENSEMBLE AVERAGE ERROR PROBABILITY: UPPER BOUND AT LOW RATES

The approach to improving the bound at low rates is to consider a larger ensemble of codes (or signal sets) with the same dimensionality N but having twice as many code vectors, $2M$. If our conjecture in the last section was correct, then the error probability for most codes can be improved considerably by eliminating the particularly bad code vectors. Thus we shall resort to the *expurgation* of the worst half of the code vectors of some appropriate code of the ensemble. The result will be a code with M code vectors of dimensionality N whose average error probability can be shown to be much smaller at low rates than the upper bound given in the channel coding theorem (Theorem 3.2.1).

In developing this expurgated bound, it is convenient to work not with the ensemble average $\overline{P_{E_m}}$, but rather with the ensemble average of a fractional power $\overline{P_{E_m}^s}$, where $0 \le s \le 1$. We obtain such a bound in the form of

Lemma 3.3.1 For the ensemble of codes, defined by a distribution $\mathbf{q}_N(\mathbf{x})$ on $\mathscr{X}_N$ with $\hat{M}$ vectors of N symbols used on a discrete-input channel, the ensemble average of the sth power of the error probability for the mth message, when maximum likelihood decoding is used, is bounded by

$$\overline{P_{E_m}^s} < B \qquad 0 \le s \le 1 \qquad m = 1, 2, \ldots, \hat{M}$$

where

$$B \equiv \hat{M} \sum_{\mathbf{x}} \sum_{\mathbf{x}'} q_N(\mathbf{x}) q_N(\mathbf{x}') \left[\sum_{\mathbf{y}} \sqrt{p_N(\mathbf{y} \mid \mathbf{x}) p_N(\mathbf{y} \mid \mathbf{x}')} \right]^s \tag{3.3.1}$$

Consequently, the sum of these averages over all messages is bounded by

$$\sum_{m=1}^{\hat{M}} \overline{P_{E_m}^s} < \hat{M} B \tag{3.3.2}$$

Proof The derivation of (3.3.1) is along the lines of Sec. 3.1. First of all, since we shall be interested principally in low rates, we use only the union-Bhattacharyya bound, which coincides with the more elaborate Gallager bound at $\rho = 1$. Hence from (3.1.4) we have

$$\begin{aligned} P_{E_m}^s(\mathbf{x}_1, \mathbf{x}_2, \ldots, \mathbf{x}_{\hat{M}}) &< \left[\sum_{\mathbf{y}} \sqrt{p_N(\mathbf{y} \mid \mathbf{x}_m)} \sum_{m' \ne m} \sqrt{p_N(\mathbf{y} \mid \mathbf{x}_{m'})} \right]^s \\ &= \left[\sum_{m' \ne m} \left(\sum_{\mathbf{y}} \sqrt{p_N(\mathbf{y} \mid \mathbf{x}_m) p_N(\mathbf{y} \mid \mathbf{x}_{m'})} \right) \right]^s \end{aligned} \tag{3.3.3}$$

But if we restrict s to lie in the unit interval, we may use the inequality

$$\left[\sum_{m'} a_{m'} \right]^s \le \sum_{m'} a_{m'}^s \qquad 0 < s \le 1 \tag{3.3.4}$$

which follows from the Hölder inequality (App. 3A), to obtain

$$P_{E_m}^s(\mathbf{x}_1 \cdots \mathbf{x}_{\hat{M}}) \le \sum_{m' \ne m} \left[\sum_{\mathbf{y}} \sqrt{p_N(\mathbf{y} \mid \mathbf{x}_m) p_N(\mathbf{y} \mid \mathbf{x}_{m'})} \right]^s \qquad 0 < s \le 1 \tag{3.3.5}$$

Now taking the ensemble average as in Sec. 3.1, we obtain

$$\begin{aligned} \overline{P_{E_m}^s} &= \sum_{\mathbf{x}_1} \cdots \sum_{\mathbf{x}_{\hat{M}}} q_N(\mathbf{x}_1) \cdots q_N(\mathbf{x}_{\hat{M}}) P_{E_m}^s(\mathbf{x}_1 \cdots \mathbf{x}_{\hat{M}}) \\ &\le \sum_{m' \ne m} \sum_{\mathbf{x}_1} \cdots \sum_{\mathbf{x}_{\hat{M}}} q_N(\mathbf{x}_1) \cdots q_N(\mathbf{x}_{\hat{M}}) \left[\sum_{\mathbf{y}} \sqrt{p_N(\mathbf{y} \mid \mathbf{x}_m) p_N(\mathbf{y} \mid \mathbf{x}_{m'})} \right]^s \\ &= (\hat{M} - 1) \sum_{\mathbf{x}} \sum_{\mathbf{x}'} q_N(\mathbf{x}) q_N(\mathbf{x}') \left[\sum_{\mathbf{y}} \sqrt{p_N(\mathbf{y} \mid \mathbf{x}) p_N(\mathbf{y} \mid \mathbf{x}')} \right]^s \end{aligned} \tag{3.3.6}$$

where the last step follows from the facts that each vector $\mathbf{x}_m$ is summed over its entire space and $\sum_{\mathbf{x}_k} q_N(\mathbf{x}_k) = 1$. From this, (3.3.1) follows trivially, as does (3.3.2) since the former is a uniform bound for all messages; hence the lemma.

We now proceed to the key result which will induce us to expurgate half the code vectors of a particular code with $2M$ code vectors to obtain a much better code for M messages.

Lemma 3.3.2 At least one code, in the ensemble of all codes with $2M$ vectors of N symbols, has

$$P_{E_m}^s(\mathbf{x}_1, \ldots, \mathbf{x}_{2M}) < 2B \qquad 0 < s \le 1 \tag{3.3.7}$$

for at least M of its code vectors $\{\mathbf{x}_m\}$, where B is given by Lemma 3.3.1 with $\hat{M} = 2M$.

PROOF The proof is by contradiction and follows easily from Lemma 3.3.1. Suppose Lemma 3.3.2 were *not* true. Then *every code* in the ensemble would have

$$P_{E_k}^s(\mathbf{x}_1, \ldots, \mathbf{x}_{2M}) \ge 2B \tag{3.3.8}$$

for at least $M + 1$ of its code vectors $\{\mathbf{x}_k\}$. But then the sum over all code vectors of the ensemble average of the sth moment would be lower bounded by

$$\begin{aligned}
\sum_{m=1}^{2M} \overline{P_{E_m}^s} &= \sum_{m=1}^{2M} \sum_{\mathbf{x}_1} \sum_{\mathbf{x}_2} \cdots \sum_{\mathbf{x}_{2M}} q_N(\mathbf{x}_1) q_N(\mathbf{x}_2) \cdots q_N(\mathbf{x}_{2M}) P_{E_m}^s(\mathbf{x}_1 \mathbf{x}_2 \cdots \mathbf{x}_{2M}) \\
&= \sum_{\mathbf{x}_1} \sum_{\mathbf{x}_2} \cdots \sum_{\mathbf{x}_{2M}} q_N(\mathbf{x}_1) q_N(\mathbf{x}_2) \cdots q_N(\mathbf{x}_{2M}) \sum_{m=1}^{2M} P_{E_m}^s(\mathbf{x}_1 \mathbf{x}_2 \cdots \mathbf{x}_{2M}) \\
&\ge \sum_{\mathbf{x}_1} \sum_{\mathbf{x}_2} \cdots \sum_{\mathbf{x}_{2M}} q_N(\mathbf{x}_1) q_N(\mathbf{x}_2) \cdots q_N(\mathbf{x}_{2M}) 2B(M+1)
\end{aligned}$$

where the last step follows from the facts that at least $(M + 1)$ terms of the $(2M)$-term sum are lower bounded by (3.3.8), that the remainder of the terms are nonnegative, and that the weighting distribution factors $q_N(\mathbf{x}_1)$, $q_N(\mathbf{x}_2)$, $\ldots, q_N(\mathbf{x}_{2M})$ are nonnegative. Finally, since the sum of the distribution over the entire Q^{2MN} terms of the ensemble is unity, we have

$$\sum_{m=1}^{2M} \overline{P_{E_m}^s} \ge 2MB$$

which is in direct contradiction to (3.3.2) of Lemma 3.3.1 for $\hat{M} = 2M$. The lemma is thus proved by contradiction.

On the basis of this result, we note that if we expurgate (eliminate) the M code vectors with the highest error probability P_{E_m} from the code which satisfies (3.3.7) of Lemma 3.3.2, we are left with a code of only M code vectors of dimension N such that

$$P_{E_m}(\tilde{\mathbf{x}}_1, \tilde{\mathbf{x}}_2, \ldots, \tilde{\mathbf{x}}_M) < (2B)^{1/s} \qquad m = 1, 2, \ldots, M \qquad 0 < s \leq 1 \quad (3.3.9)$$

where we denote the unexpurgated code vectors by $\{\tilde{\mathbf{x}}_m\}$. However, in justifying (3.3.9), we must note that the unexpurgated code vectors will have their error probabilities altered by removal of the expurgated code vectors, but this alteration can only lower the P_{E_m} of the remaining vectors, since removal of some vectors causes the optimum decision regions of the remainder to be expanded. Hence (3.3.9) follows. In combining (3.3.9) with (3.3.1) to obtain the explicit form of the expurgated bound, if we make the further substitution $\rho = 1/s$, where $1 \leq \rho < \infty$, we obtain a result whose form bears a striking similarity to the form of the coding theorem of Sec. 3.2. For we then have that for every message m of the expurgated code,

$$P_{E_m} < (4M)^\rho \left\{ \sum_{\mathbf{x}} \sum_{\mathbf{x}'} q_N(\mathbf{x}) q_N(\mathbf{x}') \left[\sum_{\mathbf{y}} \sqrt{p_N(\mathbf{y} \mid \mathbf{x}) p_N(\mathbf{y} \mid \mathbf{x}')} \right]^{1/\rho} \right\}^\rho \qquad 1 \leq \rho < \infty \tag{3.3.10}$$

If we finally impose the memoryless condition (3.1.12) on the channel,

$$p_N(\mathbf{y} \mid \mathbf{x}) = \prod_{n=1}^{N} p(y_n \mid x_n)$$

and similarly take the distribution to be a product measure,

$$q_N(\mathbf{x}) = \prod_{n=1}^{N} q(x_n)$$

then we obtain by the identical set of steps used in deriving (3.1.14)

$$P_{E_m} < (4M)^\rho \left\{ \sum_{x} \sum_{x'} q(x) q(x') \left[\sum_{y} \sqrt{p(y \mid x) p(y \mid x')} \right]^{1/\rho} \right\}^{N\rho} \qquad 1 \leq \rho < \infty \tag{3.3.11}$$

To obtain the tightest bound, we must minimize with respect to the distribution $q(x)$ and the parameter $\rho \geq 1$. The result can be expressed in exponential form as

Theorem 3.3.1: Expurgated coding theorem (Gallager [1965]) For a discrete-input memoryless channel there exists at least one code of M code vectors of dimension N for which the error probability of each message, when maximum likelihood decoding is used, is bounded by

$$P_{E_m} < e^{-NE_{\text{ex}}(R)} \qquad m = 1, 2, \ldots, M \tag{3.3.12}$$

where

$$E_{\text{ex}}(R) = \max_{\mathbf{q}} \sup_{\rho \geq 1} \left[E_x(\rho, \mathbf{q}) - \rho \left(R + \frac{\ln 4}{N} \right) \right] \tag{3.3.13}$$

$$E_x(\rho, \mathbf{q}) = -\rho \ln \left\{ \sum_{x} \sum_{x'} q(x) q(x') \left[\sum_{y} \sqrt{p(y \mid x) p(y \mid x')} \right]^{1/\rho} \right\} \tag{3.3.14}$$

Note that, since the region of ρ is semi-infinite, the "maximum" over ρ becomes a supremum. One slight inconvenience in the form of this theorem is the appearance of the nuisance term $(\ln 4)/N$ added to the rate. Of course, this term is negligible for most cases of interest. In fact, this term can be made to disappear by an alternative proof (Prob. 3.21); hence we shall ignore it henceforth. In order to assess the significance of this result and the range of rates for which it is useful, we need to establish a few properties of $E_x(\rho, \mathbf{q})$, which are somewhat analogous to those of $E_o(\rho, \mathbf{q})$ discussed in Sec. 3.2. These are summarized as

Theorem 3.3.2 For any discrete-input memoryless channel for which $I(\mathbf{q}) \neq 0$, for all finite $\rho \geq 1$

$$E_x(1, \mathbf{q}) = E_o(1, \mathbf{q}) \tag{3.3.15}$$

$$E_x(\rho, \mathbf{q}) > 0 \tag{3.3.16}$$

$$\frac{\partial E_x(\rho, \mathbf{q})}{\partial \rho} > 0 \tag{3.3.17}$$

$$\frac{\partial^2 E_x(\rho, \mathbf{q})}{\partial \rho^2} \leq 0 \tag{3.3.18}$$

with equality in (3.3.18) if and only if, for every pair of distinct inputs x and x' for which $q(x) > 0$ and $q(x') > 0$, $p(y|x)p(y|x') = 0$ for all y. [If so, $E_x(\rho, \mathbf{q})$ is just a constant multiple of ρ; such a channel is said to be *noiseless*.]

The equality (3.3.15) follows directly from (3.3.14) and (3.2.1) since

$$E_x(1, \mathbf{q}) = -\ln \sum_x \sum_{x'} q(x)q(x') \sum_y \sqrt{p(y|x)p(y|x')}$$

$$= -\ln \sum_y \left[\sum_x q(x)\sqrt{p(y|x)} \right]^2 = E_o(1, \mathbf{q})$$

The remainder of the theorem, consisting of inequalities whose form is identical to those for $E_o(\rho, \mathbf{q})$, is proved in App. 3A.

We note also that $E_x(\rho, \mathbf{q})$ and $E_o(\rho, \mathbf{q})$ are of interest for their corresponding bounds over disjoint intervals of the real line except for the common point $\rho = 1$, where the functions are equal. Figure 3.5 shows a composite graph of the

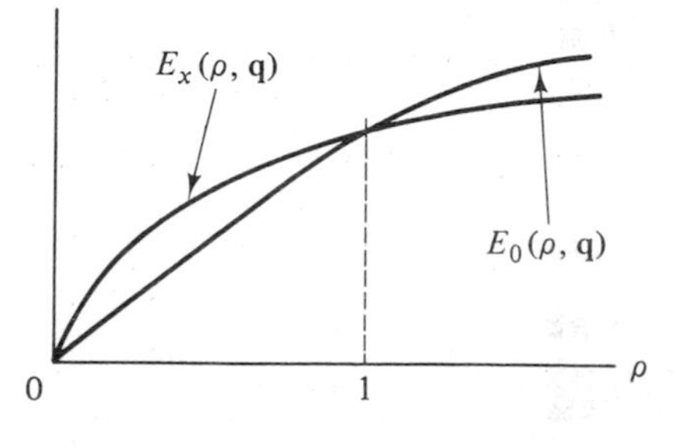

Figure 3.5 $E_o(\rho, \mathbf{q})$ and $E_x(\rho, \mathbf{q})$ for typical channel.

two functions for a typical channel. It can, in fact, be shown (Prob. 3.10) that $\partial E_x(\rho, \mathbf{q})/\partial\rho\,|_{\rho=1} < \partial E_o(\rho, \mathbf{q})/\partial\rho\,|_{\rho=1}$ unless the channel is useless [that is, $C = \max_{\mathbf{q}} I(\mathbf{q}) = 0$]. The maximization of (3.3.13) with respect to ρ is quite similar to that of the ensemble average error exponent in Sec. 3.2. Letting

$$E_{ex}(R, \mathbf{q}) = \sup_{\rho \geq 1} [E_x(\rho, \mathbf{q}) - \rho R] \tag{3.3.19}$$

and taking the channel to be other than noiseless or useless, we have from (3.3.18) that $E_x(\rho, \mathbf{q})$ is strictly convex $\cap$ in ρ, so that the supremum occurs at

$$R = \frac{\partial E_x(\rho, \mathbf{q})}{\partial \rho} \qquad \text{provided } R < \left.\frac{\partial E_x(\rho, \mathbf{q})}{\partial \rho}\right|_{\rho=1} \tag{3.3.20}$$

Then in this region the negative exponent of (3.3.12) for a fixed $\mathbf{q}$ is given by the parametric equations

$$E_{ex}(R, \mathbf{q}) = E_x(\rho, \mathbf{q}) - \rho \frac{\partial E_x(\rho, \mathbf{q})}{\partial \rho}$$

$$R = \frac{\partial E_x(\rho, \mathbf{q})}{\partial \rho} \qquad \lim_{\rho \to \infty} \frac{\partial E_x(\rho, \mathbf{q})}{\partial \rho} < R < \left.\frac{\partial E_x(\rho, \mathbf{q})}{\partial \rho}\right|_{\rho=1} \tag{3.3.21}$$

Also, by exactly the same manipulation as in (3.2.9) and (3.2.10), we have

$$\frac{dE_{ex}(R, \mathbf{q})}{dR} = -\rho \qquad \frac{d^2 E_{ex}(R, \mathbf{q})}{dR^2} > 0 \tag{3.3.22}$$

so that the exponent is convex $\cup$ with negative slope $\rho > 1$ over the region given in (3.3.20). Furthermore, it is tangent to the straight line

$$E_x(1, \mathbf{q}) - R = E_o(1, \mathbf{q}) - R$$

at the point

$$R = \partial E_x(\rho, \mathbf{q})/\partial\rho\,\Big|_{\rho=1} < \partial E_o(\rho, \mathbf{q})/\partial\rho\,\Big|_{\rho=1}$$

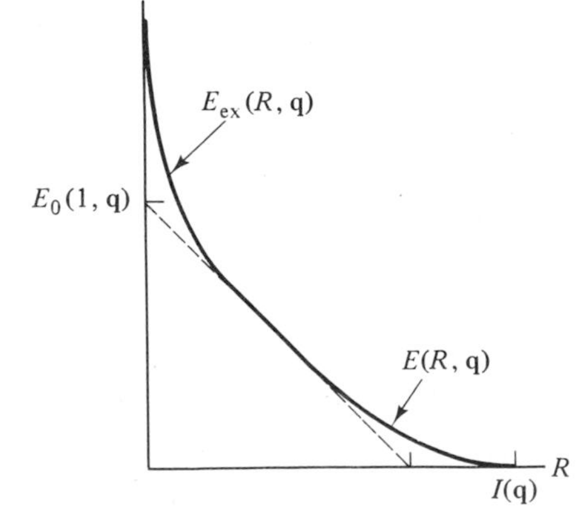

Figure 3.6 Composite exponent function.

The composite of the $E_{ex}(R, \mathbf{q})$ and $E(R, \mathbf{q})$ functions for a typical channel is as shown in Fig. 3.6. For all physical channels, $E_{ex}(R)$ is bounded for all rates as shown, for example, in Fig. 3.6. However, for certain nonphysical but interesting channels (e.g., that in Fig. 3.7), $E_{ex}(R)$ becomes unbounded for sufficiently small but positive rates, and consequently the error probability is exactly zero for certain codes of finite length.

The low-rate behavior of both classes of channels can be determined by examining $E_x(\rho, \mathbf{q})$ and its first derivative in the limit as $\rho \to \infty$. We note that (3.3.21) holds only for rates greater than the limiting value of the derivative. This value is readily determined from the definition (3.3.14), by use of L'Hôpital's rule, to be

$$\begin{aligned} R_x(\infty, \mathbf{q}) &\equiv \lim_{\rho \to \infty} \frac{\partial E_x(\rho, \mathbf{q})}{\partial \rho} \\ &= \lim_{\rho \to \infty} \frac{E_x(\rho, \mathbf{q})}{\rho} \\ &= -\ln \left[\sum_x \sum_{x'} q(x) q(x') \phi(x, x') \right] \end{aligned} \tag{3.3.23}$$

where

$$\phi(x, x') = \begin{cases} 1 & \text{if } \sum_y \sqrt{p(y|x)p(y|x')} \neq 0 \\ 0 & \text{otherwise} \end{cases}$$

Thus

$$R_x(\infty, \mathbf{q}) = 0 \qquad \text{if} \qquad \sum_y \sqrt{p(y|x)p(y|x')} \neq 0 \tag{3.3.24}$$

for *all pairs* of inputs $x, x' \in \mathscr{X}$ while

$$R_x(\infty, \mathbf{q}) > 0 \qquad \text{if} \qquad \sum_y \sqrt{p(y|x)p(y|x')} = 0 \tag{3.3.25}$$

for *some pair* of inputs $x, x' \in \mathscr{X}$ such that $q(x)q(x') \neq 0$. In the latter case, we note also that, since according to (3.3.22) the slope of $E_{ex}(R, \mathbf{q})$ approaches $-\infty$ as

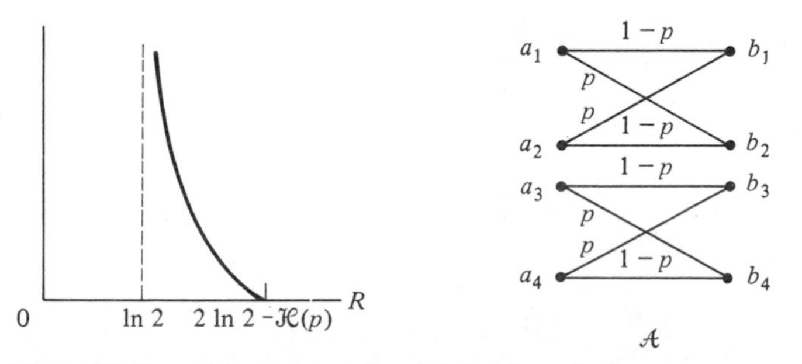

Figure 3.7 Composite exponent function for channel $\mathscr{A}$.

$\rho \to \infty$, the function $E_{ex}(R, \mathbf{q})$ approaches infinity as $R \to R_x(\infty, \mathbf{q}) > 0$ from the right, and is thus infinite for all lower rates. An example of such an exponent and the corresponding channel, which is the disjoint parallel combination of two BSCs, is shown in Fig. 3.7 (Prob. 3.9). The intuitive explanation of this nonphysical result is that if a channel has two distinct inputs which cannot both reach the same output for any particular output, then the exclusive use of these two input symbols will result in error-free communication even without coding.

Returning to the physical situation where $R_x(\infty, \mathbf{q}) = 0$, it is of interest also to determine the value of the zero-rate expurgated exponent. Here, according to (3.3.17) and (3.3.19), and letting $s = 1/\rho$, we have

$$\begin{aligned} E_{ex}(0, \mathbf{q}) &= \sup_{\rho \geq 1} E_x(\rho, \mathbf{q}) \\ &= \lim_{\rho \to \infty} E_x(\rho, \mathbf{q}) \\ &= \lim_{s \to 0} -\frac{1}{s} \ln \sum_x \sum_{x'} q(x)q(x') \left[\sum_y \sqrt{p(y \mid x)p(y \mid x')} \right]^s \end{aligned} \tag{3.3.26}$$

Finally, using L'Hôpital's rule, we have

$$E_{ex}(0) = \max_{\mathbf{q}} \left\{ -\sum_x \sum_{x'} q(x)q(x') \ln \sum_y \sqrt{p(y \mid x)p(y \mid x')} \right\} \tag{3.3.27}$$

The optimization with respect to $\mathbf{q}$ is exceedingly difficult because $E_x(\rho, \mathbf{q})$ is not convex $\cap$ over $\mathbf{q}$ and can have several local maxima.[7] Little is known about the optimum weighting distribution except for a special class of channels (Prob. 3.11) and for *binary-input channels*. In the latter case, it follows easily from (3.3.14) that

$$\begin{aligned} E_x(\rho, \mathbf{q}) &= -\rho \ln \left\{ q^2(a_1) + q^2(a_2) + 2q(a_1)q(a_2) \left[\sum_y \sqrt{p(y \mid a_1)p(y \mid a_2)} \right]^{1/\rho} \right\} \\ &= -\rho \ln \left[1 - 2q(a_1)q(a_2)(1 - Z^{1/\rho}) \right] \end{aligned} \tag{3.3.28}$$

where

$$Z \equiv \sum_y \sqrt{p(y \mid a_1)p(y \mid a_2)}$$

It follows trivially that this is maximized for all ρ by the vector $\mathbf{q} = (\frac{1}{2}, \frac{1}{2})$, and that

$$\max_{\mathbf{q}} E_x(\rho, \mathbf{q}) = -\rho \ln \left(\frac{1 + Z^{1/\rho}}{2} \right) \tag{3.3.29}$$

[7] Furthermore, memoryless channels exist for which the product measure

$$q(\mathbf{x}) = \prod_{n=1}^{N} q(x_n)$$

does not optimize the expurgated exponent (Jelinek [1968*b*]).

Thus, for all binary-input memoryless channels

$$E_{ex}(R) = \sup_{\rho \geq 1} \left[-\rho \ln \left(\frac{1 + Z^{1/\rho}}{2} \right) - \rho R \right] \tag{3.3.30}$$

Furthermore as $R \to 0$, we have, from (3.3.27) with $\mathbf{q} = (\frac{1}{2}, \frac{1}{2})$, that

$$E_{ex}(0) = -\tfrac{1}{2} \ln Z \tag{3.3.31}$$

Note that this is the same as the exponent of (3.2.29) for low-rate orthogonal signals (Z being the same in both cases), which being considerably greater than the ensemble average bound exponent (Fig. 3.4) originally prompted our further investigation of low-rate exponents. Also noteworthy are the facts that the present results are for binary-input channels which *need not* be output-symmetric and, somewhat surprisingly, that the uniform input weighting distribution is optimum for all these channels.

3.4 EXAMPLES: BINARY-INPUT, OUTPUT-SYMMETRIC CHANNELS AND VERY NOISY CHANNELS

The computation of exponential bounds for explicit channels is generally very involved. Except for certain contrived (generally nonphysical) examples (Probs. 3.2, 3.5) and some limiting cases, explicit formulas are not available. Even for the particularly simple, often studied, binary-symmetric channel, the high-rate exponents of both the ensemble average and the expurgated ensemble average bounds can only be obtained in parametric form. These are nevertheless valuable for later comparison.

For the BSC with crossover probability $p < 1/2$, beginning with the ensemble average bound of the coding theorem (Sec. 3.2), we have from (3.2.1)

$$\max_{\mathbf{q}} E_o(\rho, \mathbf{q}) = \rho \ln 2 - (1 + \rho) \ln \left[p^{1/(1+\rho)} + (1 - p)^{1/(1+\rho)} \right] \tag{3.4.1}$$

since the maximizing distribution for this completely symmetrical channel is always the uniform distribution. Upon substituting in (3.2.7) and (3.2.8), after considerable calculation of derivatives and manipulations, letting

$$\mathscr{H}(x) \equiv -x \ln x - (1 - x) \ln (1 - x) \tag{3.4.2}$$

$$T_x(y) \equiv -y \ln x - (1 - y) \ln (1 - x) \tag{3.4.3}$$

which is the line tangent to $\mathscr{H}(x)$ at $y = x$, and letting

$$p_\rho \equiv \frac{p^{1/(1+\rho)}}{p^{1/(1+\rho)} + (1 - p)^{1/(1+\rho)}} \tag{3.4.4}$$

we find for low rates

$$E(R) = \ln 2 - 2 \ln \left(\sqrt{p} + \sqrt{1 - p} \right) - R \qquad 0 \leq R \leq \ln 2 - \mathscr{H}\left(\frac{\sqrt{p}}{\sqrt{p} + \sqrt{1 - p}} \right) \tag{3.4.5}$$

and we find for high rates the parametric equations

$$E(R) = T_p(p_\rho) - \mathscr{H}(p_\rho)$$
$$R = \ln 2 - \mathscr{H}(p_\rho) \qquad 0 < \rho \le 1$$
$$\ln 2 - \mathscr{H}\left(\frac{\sqrt{p}}{\sqrt{p} + \sqrt{1-p}}\right) \le R < \ln 2 - \mathscr{H}(p) \tag{3.4.6}$$

As for the expurgated ensemble average error bound (Sec. 3.3), for the class of binary-input channels[8] (which includes the BSC as the simplest case), we have from (3.3.29)

$$\max_{\mathbf{q}} E_x(\rho, \mathbf{q}) = -\rho \ln \left(\frac{1 + Z^{1/\rho}}{2}\right) \tag{3.4.7}$$

and consequently maximizing (3.3.30) we obtain, after some manipulation, the parametric equations

$$E_{ex}(R) = -\delta \ln Z$$
$$R = \ln 2 - \mathscr{H}(\delta) \qquad 0 \le R < \ln 2 - \mathscr{H}\left(\frac{Z}{1+Z}\right) \tag{3.4.8}$$

where

$$\delta = \frac{Z^{1/\rho}}{1 + Z^{1/\rho}} \tag{3.4.9}$$

For the BSC, as was shown in (3.2.27*b*), $Z = \sqrt{4p(1-p)}$.

The exponent of the exponential upper bounds for any channel is characterized mainly by three parameters:

1. $E(0) = \max_{\mathbf{q}} E_o(1, \mathbf{q})$, the zero-rate ensemble average exponent
2. $E_{ex}(0) = \lim_{\rho\to\infty} \max_{\mathbf{q}} E_x(\rho, \mathbf{q})$, the zero-rate expurgated ensemble average exponent
3. $C = \max_{\mathbf{q}} I(\mathbf{q}) = \lim_{\rho\to 0} \max_{\mathbf{q}} \dfrac{\partial E_o(\rho, \mathbf{q})}{\partial \rho}$, the channel capacity

These are important for two reasons. First, as can be seen in Fig. 3.6 the latter two represent the E-axis and R-axis intercepts of the best upper bounds found, while $E(0)$–R is the "support" line of the bound to which the low-rate and high-rate bounds are both tangent.[9] More important, as we shall find in the next two sections, both $E_{ex}(0)$ and C are similar parameters of the exponent of the lower

[8] Recall that output symmetry is not required for the expurgated bound, because the optimizing distribution is $(\frac{1}{2}, \frac{1}{2})$ for any binary-input channel; this is not the case for the ensemble average bound, however.

[9] For convolutional codes, as we shall discover in Chaps. 5 and 6, $E(0)$ is the most important parameter, especially in connection with sequential decoding.

bound on error probability of the best code, and at least one point of the line $E(0)$–R also lies on the exponent curve for the lower bound.

It is particularly instructive to examine these three parameters for the subclass of binary-input, output-symmetric channels, which includes the binary-input AWGN channel and its symmetrically quantized reductions, the simplest of which is the BSC, as originally described in Sec. 2.8. For this class, all parameters are optimized by the uniform distribution $\mathbf{q} = (\frac{1}{2}, \frac{1}{2})$. The first two parameters are easily expressed in terms of the generic parameter Z [see (3.2.26) and (3.3.31)] as

$$E(0) = \ln 2 - \ln (1 + Z) \tag{3.4.10}$$

$$E_{ex}(0) = -\tfrac{1}{2} \ln Z \tag{3.4.11}$$

where

$$Z = \sum_y \sqrt{p_0(y)p_1(y)} \tag{3.4.12}$$

Capacity is more difficult to calculate but is readily expressed, upon using the fact that $p_1(y) = p_0(-y)$ in (3.2.13), as

$$C = \sum_y p_0(y) \ln p_0(y) - \sum_y p(y) \ln p(y) \tag{3.4.13}$$

where

$$p(y) = \frac{p_0(y) + p_0(-y)}{2} \tag{3.4.14}$$

For the AWGN channel, the first two parameters are characterized by

$$Z = e^{-\mathscr{E}_s/N_o} \qquad \text{(AWGN)} \tag{3.4.15}$$

as was first established in (3.2.27*c*), and the capacity is

$$C = -\tfrac{1}{2} \ln 2\pi e - \int_{-\infty}^{\infty} p(y) \ln p(y)\, dy \qquad \text{(AWGN)}$$

where[10]

$$p_0(y) = \frac{1}{\sqrt{2\pi}} \exp \left[-\left(y - \sqrt{\frac{2\mathscr{E}_s}{N_o}} \right)^2 \Big/ 2 \right] \tag{3.4.16}$$

and $p(y)$ is given by (3.4.14).

For the BSC considered as a two-level quantized reduction of the AWGN channel, we have from (3.2.27*b*) and (3.4.13) or (3.4.6)

$$Z = \sqrt{4p(1-p)} \qquad \text{(BSC)} \tag{3.4.17}$$

$$C = \ln 2 - \mathscr{H}(p) \qquad \text{(BSC)} \tag{3.4.18}$$

where

$$p = Q(\sqrt{2\mathscr{E}_s/N_o})$$

[10] See Eq. (2.11.6).

Intermediate cases of soft quantization require calculation of $p_0(y)$ for $y \in \{b_1, b_2, \ldots, b_J\}$ as a function of $\mathscr{E}_s/N_o$. With symmetric octal quantization, these are determined in (2.8.1). Calculation of Z and C using (3.4.12) and (3.4.13) is straightforward, but tedious and can best be handled numerically. The results for the AWGN channel, BSC, and the binary-input octal-output-quantized channel are shown in Fig. 3.8 where all three parameters, (3.4.10), (3.4.11), and (3.4.13), normalized by $\mathscr{E}_s/N_o$, are plotted as a function of $\mathscr{E}_s/N_o$.

Most noteworthy is the behavior as $\mathscr{E}_s/N_o \to 0$. It appears from the figure that for the AWGN channel

$$C \approx \frac{\mathscr{E}_s}{N_o} \qquad \text{for } \mathscr{E}_s/N_o \ll 1 \qquad \text{(AWGN)} \tag{3.4.19}$$

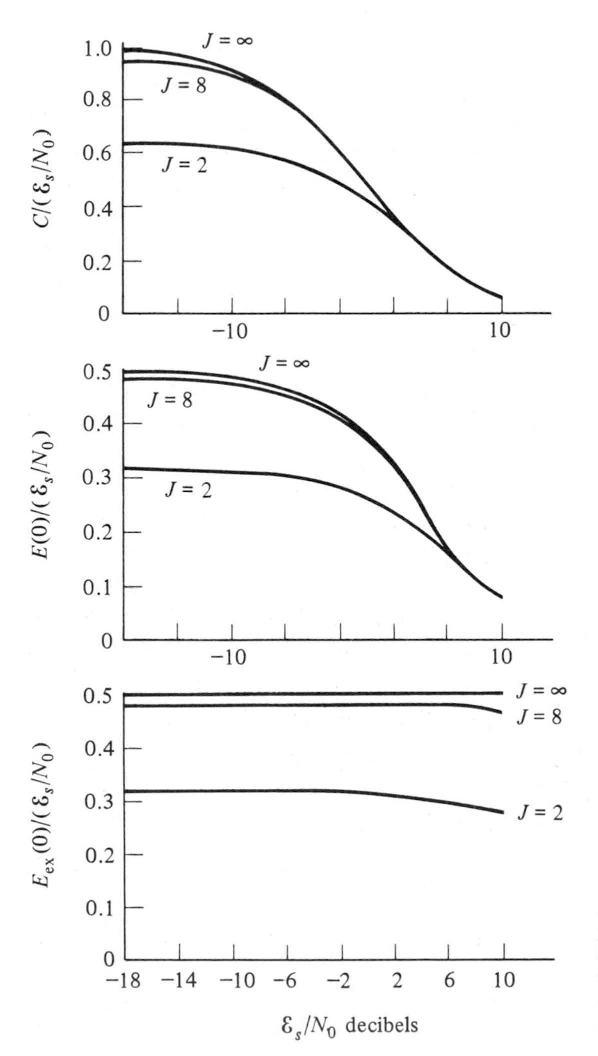

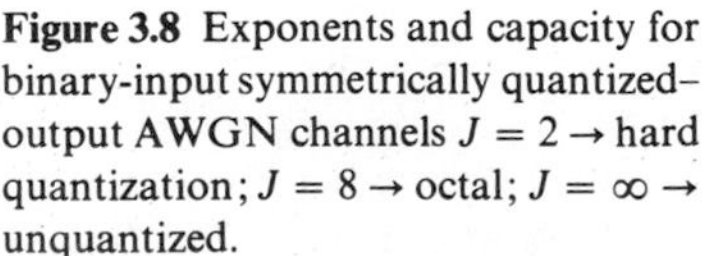
Figure 3.8 Exponents and capacity for binary-input symmetrically quantized-output AWGN channels $J = 2 \to$ hard quantization; $J = 8 \to$ octal; $J = \infty \to$ unquantized.

while for the BSC

$$C \approx \frac{2}{\pi} \frac{\mathscr{E}_s}{N_o} \qquad \text{for } \mathscr{E}_s/N_o \ll 1 \qquad \text{(BSC)} \tag{3.4.20}$$

For the octal channel with uniform quantization and $a = \frac{1}{2}\sqrt{N_o/2}$ (see Fig. 2.13)

$$C \approx 0.95 \frac{\mathscr{E}_s}{N_o} \qquad \text{for } \mathscr{E}_s/N_o \ll 1 \qquad \text{(octal)} \tag{3.4.21}$$

Also of interest is the fact that *for all these channels*

$$E_{\text{ex}}(0) \approx E(0) \approx C/2 \qquad \text{for } \mathscr{E}_s/N_o \ll 1 \tag{3.4.22}$$

Thus, *as the symbol energy-to-noise density ratio becomes very small*, it appears that the expurgated ensemble bound blends into the ensemble bound and both have an E-axis intercept at $C/2$; hard quantization causes a loss of a factor of $2/\pi$ in all parameters, and soft (octal) quantization causes a negligible loss relative to unquantized decoding.

The asymptotic relations (3.4.19), (3.4.20), and (3.4.22) can be easily shown analytically (Prob. 3.12). In each case, letting $\mathscr{E}_s/N_o \to 0$ results in a channel which is an example of a *very noisy channel*. This class of channels is characterized by the property

$$p(y \mid x) = p(y)[1 + \epsilon(x, y)] \qquad \text{all } x, y \tag{3.4.23}$$

where

$$|\epsilon(x, y)| \ll 1$$

and

$$p(y) = \sum_x q(x)p(y \mid x) \tag{3.4.24}$$

Since $q(x)$ is the input weighting distribution used in all bounds, it follows that $p(y)$ is also a distribution, sometimes called the output distribution.[11] Hence

$$1 = \sum_y p(y \mid x) = \sum_y p(y)[1 + \epsilon(x, y)] = 1 + \sum_y p(y)\epsilon(x, y) \tag{3.4.25}$$

and

$$\begin{aligned} p(y) &= \sum_x q(x)p(y \mid x) \\ &= \sum_x q(x)p(y)[1 + \epsilon(x, y)] \\ &= p(y)\left[1 + \sum_x q(x)\epsilon(x, y)\right] \end{aligned} \tag{3.4.26}$$

[11] Note that $p(y)$ is the actual output distribution when the input distribution is $q(x)$; however, the weighting distribution $q(x)$ is only an artifice used to define an ensemble of codes—it says nothing about the actual input distribution when a particular code is used on the channel.

From (3.4.25) we obtain

$$\sum_y p(y)\epsilon(x, y) = 0 \qquad \text{for all } x \in \mathscr{X} \tag{3.4.27}$$

and from (3.4.26)

$$\sum_x q(x)\epsilon(x, y) = 0 \qquad \text{for all } y \text{ for which } p(y) > 0 \tag{3.4.28}$$

Since the optimizing input distribution $q(x) = \frac{1}{2}$ for both inputs, it is easy to verify that, for a BSC with $p = \frac{1}{2}(1 - \epsilon)$ where $|\epsilon| \ll 1$, $p(y) = \frac{1}{2}$ for both outputs and (3.4.23) holds with

$$\epsilon(x, y) = \begin{cases} +\epsilon & \text{for } x = y \\ -\epsilon & \text{for } x \neq y \end{cases}$$

A similar but more elaborate argument (Prob. 3.13) shows that, for $\mathscr{E}_s/N_o \ll 1$, the unquantized AWGN channel satisfies the definition (3.4.23) of very noisy channels, as one would expect. Now using the definition (3.4.23) and the resulting properties (3.4.27) and (3.4.28), we obtain for the basic function of the ensemble bound (3.2.1)

$$E_0(\rho, \mathbf{q}) = -\ln \sum_y \left\{ \sum_x q(x) p(y)^{1/(1+\rho)} [1 + \epsilon(x, y)]^{1/(1+\rho)} \right\}^{1+\rho}$$

Since $|\epsilon| \ll 1$, we may expand $(1 + \epsilon)^{1/(1+\rho)}$ in a Taylor series about $\epsilon = 0$ and drop all terms above quadratic powers. The result is

$$\begin{aligned} E_o(\rho, \mathbf{q}) &\approx -\ln \sum_y p(y) \left\{ \sum_x q(x) \left[1 + \frac{\epsilon(x, y)}{1+\rho} - \frac{\rho\epsilon^2(x, y)}{2(1+\rho)^2} \right] \right\}^{1+\rho} \\ &\approx -\ln \sum_y p(y) \left[1 - \frac{\rho}{2(1+\rho)^2} \sum_x q(x)\epsilon^2(x, y) \right]^{1+\rho} \end{aligned}$$

where the last step follows from (3.4.28). Expanding the result in a Taylor series about $\epsilon = 0$ and again dropping terms above quadratic, we obtain

$$\begin{aligned} E_o(\rho, \mathbf{q}) &\approx -\ln \left[1 - \frac{\rho}{2(1+\rho)} \sum_x \sum_y q(x)p(y)\epsilon^2(x, y) \right] \\ &= \frac{\rho}{2(1+\rho)} \sum_x \sum_y q(x)p(y)\epsilon^2(x, y) \end{aligned} \tag{3.4.29}$$

But for the same class of channels, performing the same operations, we obtain for the channel capacity

$$\begin{aligned} C &= \max_{\mathbf{q}} I(\mathbf{q}) \\ &= \max_{\mathbf{q}} \sum_x \sum_y q(x)p(y)[1 + \epsilon(x, y)] \ln \frac{p(y)[1 + \epsilon(x, y)]}{p(y)} \\ &\approx \max_{\mathbf{q}} \sum_x \sum_y q(x)p(y)[1 + \epsilon(x, y)] \left[\epsilon(x, y) - \frac{\epsilon^2(x, y)}{2} \right] \\ &\approx \max_{\mathbf{q}} \sum_x \sum_y q(x)p(y) \frac{\epsilon^2(x, y)}{2} \end{aligned} \tag{3.4.30}$$

Thus maximizing (3.4.29) over $\mathbf{q}$ and using (3.4.30), we obtain

$$E_o(\rho) = \max_{\mathbf{q}} E_o(\rho, \mathbf{q}) \approx \frac{\rho}{1+\rho} C \tag{3.4.31}$$

For this class of very noisy channels, the ensemble average error bound exponent (3.1.20) thus becomes

$$\begin{aligned} E(R) &= \max_{0 \le \rho \le 1} \left[\max_{\mathbf{q}} E_o(\rho, \mathbf{q}) - \rho R \right] \\ &\approx \max_{0 \le \rho \le 1} \left[\frac{\rho}{1+\rho} C - \rho R \right] \end{aligned} \tag{3.4.32}$$

But this is *identical* to the problem of maximizing the negative exponent of (2.5.15) required to obtain the tightest bound on orthogonal signal sets on the AWGN channel. Thus we employ the same argument that led from (2.5.15) to (2.5.16) to obtain

$$E(R) \approx \begin{cases} \frac{1}{2}C - R & 0 \le R/C \le \frac{1}{4} \\ (\sqrt{C} - \sqrt{R})^2 & \frac{1}{4} \le R/C \le 1 \end{cases} \tag{3.4.33}$$

which is the function shown in Fig. 2.7. We defer comment on this remarkable equivalence until we have also evaluated the expurgated bound exponent. For the class of very noisy channels, we have from (3.3.14)

$$\begin{aligned} E_x(\rho, \mathbf{q}) &= -\rho \ln \sum_x \sum_{x'} q(x)q(x') \left[\sum_y p(y) \sqrt{[1+\epsilon(x, y)][1+\epsilon(x', y)]} \right]^{1/\rho} \\ &\approx -\rho \ln \sum_x \sum_{x'} q(x)q(x') \left\{ \sum_y p(y) \left[1 + \frac{\epsilon(x, y)}{2} - \frac{\epsilon^2(x, y)}{8} \right] \right. \\ &\quad \times \left. \left[1 + \frac{\epsilon(x', y)}{2} - \frac{\epsilon^2(x', y)}{8} \right] \right\}^{1/\rho} \\ &\approx -\rho \ln \sum_x \sum_{x'} q(x)q(x') \\ &\quad \times \left\{ 1 + \sum_y p(y) \left[\frac{\epsilon(x, y)\epsilon(x', y)}{4} - \frac{\epsilon^2(x, y) + \epsilon^2(x', y)}{8} \right] \right\}^{1/\rho} \\ &\approx -\sum_x \sum_{x'} \sum_y q(x)q(x')p(y) \left[\frac{\epsilon(x, y)\epsilon(x', y)}{4} - \frac{\epsilon^2(x, y) + \epsilon^2(x', y)}{8} \right] \end{aligned}$$

Thus finally

$$\begin{aligned} \max_{\mathbf{q}} E_x(\rho, \mathbf{q}) &\approx \max_{\mathbf{q}} \sum_x \sum_y q(x)p(y)\epsilon^2(x, y)/4 \\ &\approx \tfrac{1}{2}C \end{aligned} \tag{3.4.34}$$

and from (3.3.19) we have that the expurgated bound exponent is

$$E_{\text{ex}}(R) = \sup_{\rho \geq 1} \left[\max_{\mathbf{q}} E_x(\rho, \mathbf{q}) - \rho R \right]$$
$$\approx \tfrac{1}{2}C - R \tag{3.4.35}$$

Since this coincides with the straight-line portion of the ensemble average bound (3.4.33), it is clear that expurgation produces no improvement for a very noisy channel. We note also that (3.4.33) and (3.4.35), evaluated at zero rate, confirm the previous limiting result (3.4.22).

We turn now to showing that the coincidence of the results (3.4.33) for very noisy channels with those of (2.5.16) for orthogonal signal sets on the AWGN channel is not so surprising after all. For, while Sec. 2.5 dealt with arbitrary orthogonal signal sets, we found in Sec. 2.10 that a binary orthogonal signal set could be generated from an orthogonal linear code with the number of code vectors equal to the number of symbols N. Now the symbol energy for this signal set is $\mathscr{E}_s = \mathscr{E}/N$ where $\mathscr{E}$ is the energy per signal. Thus no matter how large $\mathscr{E}/N_o$ may be, for large N, $\mathscr{E}_s/N_o$ becomes arbitrarily small; hence the code is operating over a very noisy channel. To complete the parallelism, we note from (2.5.13) and (2.5.14) that

$$C_T = \frac{\mathscr{E}/N_o}{T} = \frac{N}{T}\frac{\mathscr{E}_s}{N_o} = \frac{N}{T}C \tag{3.4.36}$$

while

$$R_T = \frac{\ln M}{T} = \frac{N}{T}\frac{\ln M}{N} = \frac{N}{T}R \tag{3.4.37}$$

Thus (2.5.16) may be rewritten using (3.4.36) and (3.4.37) as

$$P_E < e^{-TE(R_T)} = e^{-NE(R)}$$

where $E(R)$ is given by (3.4.33).

This concludes our treatment of upper bounds on error probability of general block codes. To assess their tightness and consequent usefulness, we must determine corresponding lower bounds on the best signal set (or code) for the given channel and with the given parameters. In the next three sections, we shall discover an amazing degree of similarity between such lower bounds and the upper bounds we have already found, thus demonstrating the value of the latter.

3.5 CHERNOFF BOUNDS AND THE NEYMAN-PEARSON LEMMA

All lower bounds on error probability depend essentially on the following theorem which is a stronger version of the well-known Neyman-Pearson lemma for binary hypothesis testing. After stating the theorem, we shall comment on its uses and applications prior to proceeding with the proof.

Theorem 3.5.1 (Shannon, Gallager, and Berlekamp [1967]). Let $p_N^{(a)}(\mathbf{y})$ and $p_N^{(b)}(\mathbf{y})$ be arbitrary probability distributions (density functions) on the N-dimensional observation space $\mathscr{Y}_N$, and let $\mathscr{Y}_a$ and $\mathscr{Y}_b$ be any two disjoint subspaces of $\mathscr{Y}_N$ with $\overline{\mathscr{Y}}_a$ and $\overline{\mathscr{Y}}_b$ their respective complements. Let there be at least one $\mathbf{y} \in \mathscr{Y}_N$ for which $p_N^{(a)}(\mathbf{y})p_N^{(b)}(\mathbf{y}) \neq 0$. Then for each s, $0 \leq s \leq 1$, *at least one* of the following pair of inequalities must hold

$$P_a \equiv \sum_{\mathbf{y} \in \overline{\mathscr{Y}}_a} p_N^{(a)}(\mathbf{y}) > \tfrac{1}{4} \exp\left[\mu(s) - s\mu'(s) - s\sqrt{2\mu''(s)}\right] \tag{3.5.1}$$

$$P_b \equiv \sum_{\mathbf{y} \in \overline{\mathscr{Y}}_b} p_N^{(b)}(\mathbf{y}) > \tfrac{1}{4} \exp\left[\mu(s) + (1-s)\mu'(s) - (1-s)\sqrt{2\mu''(s)}\right] \tag{3.5.2}$$

where

$$\mu(s) \equiv \ln \sum_{\mathbf{y}} p_N^{(a)}(\mathbf{y})^{1-s} p_N^{(b)}(\mathbf{y})^s \tag{3.5.3}$$

is a nonpositive convex $\cup$ function on the interval $0 \leq s \leq 1$. Furthermore, for the choice

$$\mathscr{Y}_a = \{\mathbf{y}: \ln [p_N^{(b)}(\mathbf{y})/p_N^{(a)}(\mathbf{y})] < \mu'(s)\} = \overline{\mathscr{Y}}_b \tag{3.5.4}$$

then *both* of the following upper bounds hold

$$P_a \leq e^{\mu(s) - s\mu'(s)} \tag{3.5.5}$$

$$P_b \leq e^{\mu(s) + (1-s)\mu'(s)} \tag{3.5.6}$$

These latter two inequalities are known as *Chernoff bounds*. If we associate $\mathscr{Y}_N$ with the observation space for a two-message signal set, $p_N^{(a)}(\mathbf{y})$ and $p_N^{(b)}(\mathbf{y})$ with the likelihood functions of the two signals, and $\mathscr{Y}_a$ and $\mathscr{Y}_b$ with the corresponding decision regions, it follows that P_a and P_b are the error probabilities for the two messages. Thus, this theorem is closely related to the Neyman-Pearson lemma (Neyman and Pearson [1928]) as can best be demonstrated by inspecting the graph of $\mu(s)$, a convex $\cup$ nonpositive function on the unit interval, shown for a typical channel in Fig. 3.9. We note in particular that $\mu(0) = \mu(1) = 0$ if and only if, for every $\mathbf{y} \in \mathscr{Y}_N$, $p_N^{(a)}(\mathbf{y})p_N^{(b)}(\mathbf{y}) \neq 0$, a condition met by most practical channels.[12] We note further that for memoryless channels, since

$$p_N^{(m)}(\mathbf{y}_N) = \prod_{n=1}^{N} p(y_n | x_{mn}) \qquad m = a \text{ or } b$$

[12] However the Z channel described in Probs. 2.10 and 3.17 does not meet this condition; it has $\mu(1) = N \ln p < 0$.

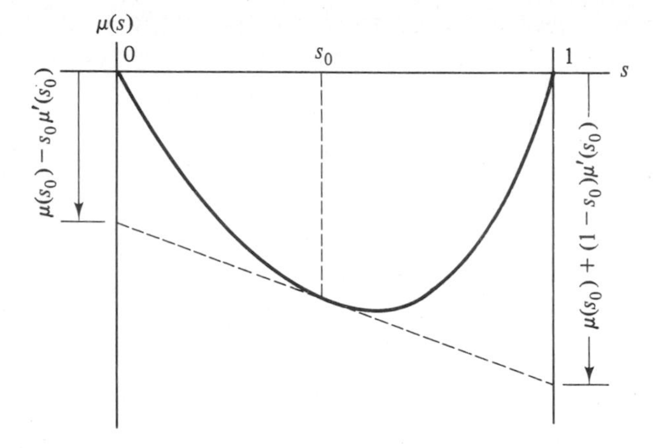

Figure 3.9 Typical $\mu(s)$ and relation between exponents of P_a and P_b.

we have for the two code vectors $\mathbf{x}_a$ and $\mathbf{x}_b$

$$\mu(s) = \sum_{n=1}^{N} \ln \left[\sum_{y_n} p(y_n | x_{an})^{1-s} p(y_n | x_{bn})^s \right] \tag{3.5.7}$$

which grows linearly with N. Consequently, as $N \to \infty$, the square roots in (3.5.1) and (3.5.2) become asymptotically negligible in comparison with the other terms in the exponents. Thus, if we disregard these terms as well as the asymptotically even less significant factors of 1/4, we find that the alternative lower bounds become identical to the upper bounds. Then it follows, as shown in Fig. 3.9, that the line tangent to $\mu(s)$ at some point s_0 will intercept the two vertical lines $s = 0$ and $s = 1$ at negative values of μ exactly equal to the two exponents. It also follows from the statement of the theorem that, fixing the exponent (and hence the asymptotic value) of P_b at $[\mu(s_o) + (1 - s_o)\mu'(s_o)]$ where $s_o \in [0, 1]$, guarantees that the exponent of P_a will be $[\mu(s_o) - s_o \mu'(s_o)]$ and that *no lower* (more negative) *exponent* is possible for P_a. A lower value for the exponent of P_b (or P_a) requires repositioning of the tangent line on this functional "see-saw," with a resulting increase in the value of the other exponent. Thus it should be apparent that the theorem is essentially equivalent to the Neyman-Pearson lemma, although it contains somewhat more detail than the conventional form. The parallel is complete if we note that the subspaces, which make both upper bounds equal asymptotically to the lower bounds and hence the best achievable, are given by (3.5.4). But these correspond to the likelihood ratio rule, which is the optimum according to the Neyman-Pearson lemma, with threshold $\mu'(s)$, which is the slope of the tangent line in Fig. 3.9.

We note finally that, in the two-message case over an N-dimensional memoryless channel, if we require P_a and P_b to be equal, then we must choose s such that $\mu'(s) = 0$ in (3.5.4). Then (3.5.5) and (3.5.6) give identical upper bounds, and

(3.5.1) and (3.5.2) give asymptotically equal lower bounds. We conclude that, if $s = s_o$ where $\mu'(s_o) = 0$, then

$$e^{\mu(s_o) - No(N)} < P_x < e^{\mu(s_o)} \qquad \text{for } x = a \text{ or } b \tag{3.5.8}$$

where[13] $o(N) \to 0$ as $N \to \infty$. With reference to Fig. 3.9, it is clear that this corresponds to the case where the straight line is tangent to the minimum point of $\mu(s)$.

PROOF We now proceed to prove the theorem, beginning by twice differentiating (3.5.3) to obtain

$$\mu'(s) = \frac{\sum_{\mathbf{y}} p_N^{(a)}(\mathbf{y})^{1-s} p_N^{(b)}(\mathbf{y})^s \ln [p_N^{(b)}(\mathbf{y})/p_N^{(a)}(\mathbf{y})]}{\sum_{\mathbf{y}'} p_N^{(a)}(\mathbf{y}')^{1-s} p_N^{(b)}(\mathbf{y}')^s} \tag{3.5.9}$$

$$\mu''(s) = \frac{\sum_{\mathbf{y}} p_N^{(a)}(\mathbf{y})^{1-s} p_N^{(b)}(\mathbf{y})^s \{\ln [p_N^{(b)}(\mathbf{y})/p_N^{(a)}(\mathbf{y})]\}^2}{\sum_{\mathbf{y}'} p_N^{(a)}(\mathbf{y}')^{1-s} p_N^{(b)}(\mathbf{y}')^s} - [\mu'(s)]^2 \tag{3.5.10}$$

Now we denote the log likelihood ratio by

$$D(\mathbf{y}) \equiv \ln [p_N^{(b)}(\mathbf{y})/p_N^{(a)}(\mathbf{y})] \tag{3.5.11}$$

Also, in the interval $0 \le s \le 1$, we define the "tilted" probability density

$$Q_N^{(s)}(\mathbf{y}) \equiv \frac{p_N^{(a)}(\mathbf{y})^{1-s} p_N^{(b)}(\mathbf{y})^s}{\sum_{\mathbf{y}'} p_N^{(a)}(\mathbf{y}')^{1-s} p_N^{(b)}(\mathbf{y}')^s} \qquad 0 \le s \le 1 \tag{3.5.12}$$

As the tilting variable s approaches 0 and 1, $Q_N^{(s)}(\mathbf{y})$ approaches $p_N^{(a)}(\mathbf{y})$ and $p_N^{(b)}(\mathbf{y})$, respectively. Now if we take $\mathbf{y}$ to be a random vector with probability (density) $Q_N^{(s)}(\mathbf{y})$, it is clear from (3.5.9) through (3.5.12) that the random variable $D(\mathbf{y})$ has a mean equal to $\mu'(s)$ and a variance equal to $\mu''(s)$; consequently, $\mu''(s) \ge 0$. Furthermore, it follows from (3.5.3) that $\mu(0) \le 0$ and $\mu(1) \le 0$ with equality in either case if and only if, for every $\mathbf{y} \in \mathscr{Y}_N$, $p_N^{(a)}(\mathbf{y}) p_N^{(b)}(\mathbf{y}) \ne 0$. Thus it follows that $\mu(s)$ is a nonpositive convex function in this interval.

Comparing (3.5.3), (3.5.11), and (3.5.12), we see immediately that

$$p_N^{(a)}(\mathbf{y}) = e^{\mu(s) - sD(\mathbf{y})} Q_N^{(s)}(\mathbf{y}) \tag{3.5.13}$$

$$p_N^{(b)}(\mathbf{y}) = e^{\mu(s) + (1-s)D(\mathbf{y})} Q_N^{(s)}(\mathbf{y}) \tag{3.5.14}$$

We can now establish the upper bounds (3.5.5) and (3.5.6). Let the decision regions be chosen according to (3.5.4), corresponding to a likelihood ratio

[13] Here $o(N) \approx 1/\sqrt{N}$.

decision rule with threshold $\mu'(s)$. Then, using (3.5.11), these may be expressed as

$$\begin{aligned}\mathscr{Y}_a &= \{\mathbf{y}: D(\mathbf{y}) < \mu'(s)\} \\ &= \overline{\mathscr{Y}}_b \end{aligned} \tag{3.5.15}$$

from which it follows that

$$-sD(\mathbf{y}) \leq -s\mu'(s) \qquad \text{for all } \mathbf{y} \in \overline{\mathscr{Y}}_a,\ 0 \leq s \leq 1 \tag{3.5.16}$$

and

$$(1-s)D(\mathbf{y}) < (1-s)\mu'(s) \qquad \text{for all } \mathbf{y} \in \overline{\mathscr{Y}}_b,\ 0 \leq s \leq 1 \tag{3.5.17}$$

Consequently, from (3.5.13) and (3.5.14), we have

$$P_a \equiv \sum_{\mathbf{y} \in \overline{\mathscr{Y}}_a} p_N^{(a)}(\mathbf{y}) \leq \exp\,[\mu(s) - s\mu'(s)] \sum_{\mathbf{y} \in \overline{\mathscr{Y}}_a} Q_N^{(s)}(\mathbf{y}) \tag{3.5.18}$$

$$P_b \equiv \sum_{\mathbf{y} \in \overline{\mathscr{Y}}_b} p_N^{(b)}(\mathbf{y}) \leq \exp\,[\mu(s) + (1-s)\mu'(s)] \sum_{\mathbf{y} \in \overline{\mathscr{Y}}_b} Q_N^{(s)}(\mathbf{y}) \tag{3.5.19}$$

and, since $Q_N^{(s)}(\mathbf{y})$ is a probability (density), the sums (integrals) in (3.5.18) and (3.5.19) are bounded by unity, which yields (3.5.5) and (3.5.6).

We now prove the lower bounds of (3.5.1) and (3.5.2) for arbitrary disjoint decision regions. We begin by defining the subspace

$$\mathscr{Y}_s \equiv \{\mathbf{y}: |D(\mathbf{y}) - \mu'(s)| \leq \sqrt{2\mu''(s)}\} \tag{3.5.20}$$

Then, recalling that $\mu'(s)$ and $\mu''(s) > 0$ are respectively the mean and variance of $D(\mathbf{y})$ with respect to the probability density $Q_N^{(s)}(\mathbf{y})$, we see from the Chebychev inequality that

$$\begin{aligned}\sum_{\mathbf{y} \in \overline{\mathscr{Y}}_s} Q_N^{(s)}(\mathbf{y}) &= \Pr\{|D(\mathbf{y}) - E_s[D(\mathbf{y})]| > \sqrt{2\mu''(s)}\} \\ &< \frac{\operatorname{var}_s[D(\mathbf{y})]}{2\mu''(s)} = \frac{1}{2}\end{aligned} \tag{3.5.21}$$

where $E_s[\cdot]$ and $\operatorname{var}_s[\cdot]$ indicate the mean and variance with respect to $Q_N^{(s)}(\cdot)$. Thus

$$\sum_{\mathbf{y} \in \mathscr{Y}_s} Q_N^{(s)}(\mathbf{y}) \geq \tfrac{1}{2}$$

and we may lower bound P_a and P_b by summing over a smaller subspace in each case, as follows.

$$\begin{aligned}P_a &\equiv \sum_{\mathbf{y} \in \overline{\mathscr{Y}}_a} p_N^{(a)}(\mathbf{y}) \\ &\geq \sum_{\mathbf{y} \in \overline{\mathscr{Y}}_a \cap \mathscr{Y}_s} p_N^{(a)}(\mathbf{y})\end{aligned} \tag{3.5.22}$$

$$\begin{aligned}P_b &\equiv \sum_{\mathbf{y} \in \overline{\mathscr{Y}}_b} p_N^{(b)}(\mathbf{y}) \\ &\geq \sum_{\mathbf{y} \in \overline{\mathscr{Y}}_b \cap \mathscr{Y}_s} p_N^{(b)}(\mathbf{y})\end{aligned} \tag{3.5.23}$$

But, for all $\mathbf{y} \in \mathscr{Y}_s$, it follows from (3.5.20) that

$$\mu'(s) - \sqrt{2\mu''(s)} \le D(\mathbf{y}) \le \mu'(s) + \sqrt{2\mu''(s)} \tag{3.5.24}$$

and consequently, from (3.5.13), (3.5.14), and (3.5.24), that for all $\mathbf{y} \in \mathscr{Y}_s$

$$p_N^{(a)}(\mathbf{y}) \ge \exp\left[\mu(s) - s\mu'(s) - s\sqrt{2\mu''(s)}\right] Q_N^{(s)}(\mathbf{y}) \tag{3.5.25}$$

$$p_N^{(b)}(\mathbf{y}) \ge \exp\left[\mu(s) + (1-s)\mu'(s) - (1-s)\sqrt{2\mu''(s)}\right] Q_N^{(s)}(\mathbf{y}) \tag{3.5.26}$$

Then since the regions of summation (integration) for the right sides of (3.5.22) and (3.5.23) are subspaces of $\mathscr{Y}_s$, it follows that

$$P_a \ge \exp\left[\mu(s) - s\mu'(s) - s\sqrt{2\mu''(s)}\right] \sum_{\mathbf{y} \in \overline{\mathscr{Y}}_a \cap \mathscr{Y}_s} Q_N^{(s)}(\mathbf{y}) \tag{3.5.27}$$

$$P_b \ge \exp\left[\mu(s) + (1-s)\mu'(s) - (1-s)\sqrt{2\mu''(s)}\right] \sum_{\mathbf{y} \in \overline{\mathscr{Y}}_b \cap \mathscr{Y}_s} Q_N^{(s)}(\mathbf{y}) \tag{3.5.28}$$

Finally, since $\mathscr{Y}_a$ and $\mathscr{Y}_b$ are disjoint, we have

$$\overline{\mathscr{Y}}_a \cup \overline{\mathscr{Y}}_b = \mathscr{Y}_N$$

Hence, it follows from this and the consequence of (3.5.21) that

$$\sum_{\mathbf{y} \in \overline{\mathscr{Y}}_a \cap \mathscr{Y}_s} Q_N^{(s)}(\mathbf{y}) + \sum_{\mathbf{y} \in \overline{\mathscr{Y}}_b \cap \mathscr{Y}_s} Q_N^{(s)}(\mathbf{y}) = \sum_{\mathbf{y} \in \mathscr{Y}_s} Q_N^{(s)}(\mathbf{y}) \ge \tfrac{1}{2}$$

Thus, at least one of the following inequalities must hold

$$\sum_{\mathbf{y} \in \overline{\mathscr{Y}}_a \cap \mathscr{Y}_s} Q_N^{(s)}(\mathbf{y}) > \tfrac{1}{4} \tag{3.5.29}$$

$$\sum_{\mathbf{y} \in \overline{\mathscr{Y}}_b \cap \mathscr{Y}_s} Q_N^{(s)}(\mathbf{y}) > \tfrac{1}{4} \tag{3.5.30}$$

Combining (3.5.27) through (3.5.30) yields the lower-bound relations (3.5.1) and (3.5.2), and hence the balance of the theorem.

We have already drawn the immediate parallel to binary hypothesis testing. In applying the theorem in the next section to lower-bound code error probabilities, we shall demonstrate its further power relative to M hypotheses. Before proceeding with this more general case, however, we specialize the result to obtain an upper bound on the tail of the distribution of N independent identically distributed random variables y_n. Thus let

$$\eta \equiv \sum_{n=1}^{N} y_n \tag{3.5.31}$$

and

$$p_N^{(a)}(\mathbf{y}) = \prod_{n=1}^{N} p(y_n) \tag{3.5.32}$$

where $p(\cdot)$ is the common probability distribution (density) of all N variables. Let us further define the dummy distribution (density)

$$p_N^{(b)}(\mathbf{y}) \equiv e^{\eta - N\alpha} p_N^{(a)}(\mathbf{y}) \tag{3.5.33}$$

where α is a constant chosen to properly normalize its sum over $\mathcal{Y}_N$ to unity. This will allow us to apply the previous theorem since

$$\ln [p_N^{(b)}(\mathbf{y})/p_N^{(a)}(\mathbf{y})] = \eta - N\alpha \tag{3.5.34}$$

Consequently (3.5.4) reduces to

$$\mathcal{Y}_a = \{\mathbf{y}: \eta < \mu'(s) + N\alpha\} \tag{3.5.35}$$

and (3.5.5) reduces to

$$\begin{aligned} P_a &\equiv \sum_{\mathbf{y} \in \mathcal{Y}_a} p_N^{(a)}(\mathbf{y}) \\ &= \Pr\{\mathbf{y}: \eta \geq \mu'(s) + N\alpha\} \\ &\leq e^{\mu(s) - s\mu'(s)} \end{aligned} \tag{3.5.36}$$

where, as follows from (3.5.31) and (3.5.33)

$$\begin{aligned} \mu(s) &= \ln \sum_{\mathbf{y}} p_N^{(a)}(\mathbf{y})\, e^{(\eta - N\alpha)s} \\ &= N \ln \left[\sum_y p(y)\, e^{sy}\right] - N\alpha s \end{aligned} \tag{3.5.37}$$

Thus, if we let

$$\begin{aligned} \theta &\equiv \mu'(s) + N\alpha \\ &\equiv \gamma'(s) \end{aligned}$$

we obtain from (3.5.36) as an upper bound on the tail of the distribution of η

$$\Pr\{\eta \geq \theta\} \leq e^{\gamma(s) - s\gamma'(s)} \tag{3.5.38}$$

where $\gamma'(s) = \theta$ and

$$\gamma(s) = N \ln \sum_y p(y)\, e^{sy} \qquad 0 \leq s \leq 1$$

This is also a Chernoff bound and, as one would suspect, can be derived more directly than from the above theorem (see Probs. 2.10 and 3.18). Furthermore, by arguments very similar to those used in the proof of the theorem, the bound (3.5.38) can be shown to be asymptotically tight (Gallager [1968]).

3.6 SPHERE-PACKING LOWER BOUNDS

Theorem 3.5.1 provides the tools for obtaining lower bounds for any discrete-input memoryless channel. Its application in the general proof, however, involves an intellectual *tour-de-force*, for which the reader is best directed to the original work (Shannon, Gallager, and Berlekamp [1967]).[14] We shall content ourselves to state the general result at the end of this section. On the other hand, the flavor, style, elegance, and even the major details of the general lower-bound proof are brought out simply and clearly by the derivation of lower bounds for two special, but important, cases: the unconstrained bandwidth AWGN channel with equal-energy signals, and the BSC. We proceed to consider them in this order, and then return to a discussion of the general result.

3.6.1 Unconstrained Bandwidth AWGN Channel with Equal-Energy Signals

Let each of the M signals have duration T seconds and equal energy $\mathscr{E}$, while the additive white Gaussian noise has one-sided spectral density N_o W/Hz. By lack of bandwidth constraints, we mean that no limitations are placed on the signal dimensionality N or, equivalently, on $W \approx N/2T$ as discussed in Sec. 2.6. However, as we found in Sec. 2.1, any set of M finite-energy signals can be represented using at most M dimensions. Thus unconstrained bandwidth means simply that we do not restrict N to be any less than M. In Sec. 2.1, we found that the likelihood function for the mth signal-vector sent over this channel is

$$p_N(\mathbf{y} \mid \mathbf{x}_m) = \prod_{n=1}^{N} \frac{e^{-(y_n - x_{mn})^2/N_o}}{\sqrt{\pi N_o}} \tag{2.1.15}$$

where

$$\|\mathbf{x}_m\|^2 = \sum_{n=1}^{N} x_{mn}^2 = \mathscr{E} \tag{3.6.1}$$

We express this more conveniently for our present purpose as

$$p_N(\mathbf{y} \mid \mathbf{x}_m) = \exp\left[\left(-\mathscr{E} + 2\sum_{n=1}^{N} y_n x_{mn}\right)\Big/ N_o\right] \prod_{n=1}^{N} \frac{e^{-y_n^2/N_o}}{\sqrt{\pi N_o}} \tag{3.6.2}$$

Our immediate goal is to lower-bound

$$P_{E_m} = \int \cdots \int_{\mathbf{y} \in \bar{\Lambda}_m} p_N(\mathbf{y} \mid \mathbf{x}_m)\, d\mathbf{y} \tag{3.6.3}$$

for the maximum likelihood decision region Λ_m given by

$$\Lambda_m = \{\mathbf{y}\colon p_N(\mathbf{y} \mid \mathbf{x}_m) > p_N(\mathbf{y} \mid \mathbf{x}_{m'}) \text{ for all } m' \neq m\} \tag{3.6.4}$$

with boundary points resolved arbitrarily. We have at our disposal Theorem 3.5.1.

[14] Or the more recent and somewhat more direct approach of Blahut [1974] and Omura [1975] (see Probs. 3.22 and 3.24).

Clearly, we wish to associate $p_N(\mathbf{y} \mid \mathbf{x}_m)$ and Λ_m with one inequality in this theorem, but the choice of the other appears to be an enigma. We proceed, just as in the last example of the previous section [(3.5.31) through (3.5.38)], by choosing the other to be a convenient "dummy" probability density; namely

$$p_N(\mathbf{y}) \equiv \prod_{n=1}^{N} \frac{e^{-y_n^2/N_o}}{\sqrt{\pi N_o}} \tag{3.6.5}$$

and we let

$$p_N^{(a)}(\mathbf{y}) = p_N(\mathbf{y}) \qquad p_N^{(b)}(\mathbf{y}) = p_N(\mathbf{y} \mid \mathbf{x}_m)$$

while

$$\mathscr{Y}_a = \overline{\Lambda_m} = \overline{\mathscr{Y}_b} \tag{3.6.6}$$

We have then met the conditions and hypotheses of Theorem 3.5.1 and may therefore apply (3.5.1) through (3.5.3) to conclude that, for each transmitted signal vector $\mathbf{x}_m$, *at least one* of the following pair of inequalities must hold.

$$\psi_m \equiv \int \underset{\mathbf{y} \in \Lambda_m}{\cdots} \int p_N(\mathbf{y})\, d\mathbf{y} > \tfrac{1}{4} \exp\left[\mu(s) - s\mu'(s) - s\sqrt{2\mu''(s)}\right] \tag{3.6.7}$$

$$\begin{aligned} P_{E_m} &= \int \underset{\mathbf{y} \in \overline{\Lambda}_m}{\cdots} \int p_N(\mathbf{y} \mid \mathbf{x}_m)\, d\mathbf{y} \\ &> \tfrac{1}{4} \exp\left[\mu(s) + (1-s)\mu'(s) - (1-s)\sqrt{2\mu''(s)}\right] \end{aligned} \tag{3.6.8}$$

where

$$\mu(s) = \ln \int_{-\infty}^{\infty} \cdots \int_{-\infty}^{\infty} p_N(\mathbf{y})^{1-s} p_N(\mathbf{y} \mid \mathbf{x}_m)^s \, d\mathbf{y} \qquad 0 \le s \le 1 \tag{3.6.9}$$

Substitution of (3.6.2) and (3.6.5) in (3.6.9), using (3.6.1), yields

$$\begin{aligned} \mu(s) &= \ln \exp\left[-\frac{s(1-s)\sum_{n=1}^{N} x_{mn}^2}{N_o}\right] \int \cdots \int \frac{\exp\left\{-\sum_{n=1}^{N} [y_n - x_{mn}s]^2/N_o\right\}}{(\pi N_o)^{N/2}}\, d\mathbf{y} \\ &= -\frac{\mathscr{E}}{N_o} s(1-s) \end{aligned} \tag{3.6.10}$$

Thus $\mu(s)$ is invariant to the signal vector's orientation and depends only on its energy. To determine the significance of the auxiliary variable ψ_m of (3.6.7), we sum over all messages m. Since the optimum decision regions (3.6.4) are disjoint and their union covers the entire N-space, we obtain

$$\sum_{m=1}^{M} \psi_m = \sum_{m=1}^{M} \int \underset{\mathbf{y} \in \Lambda_m}{\cdots} \int p_N(\mathbf{y})\, d\mathbf{y} = \int_{-\infty}^{\infty} \cdots \int_{-\infty}^{\infty} p_N(\mathbf{y})\, d\mathbf{y} = 1 \tag{3.6.11}$$

Hence, for at least one message $\tilde{m}$, we must have

$$\psi_{\tilde{m}} \le 1/M \tag{3.6.12}$$

for otherwise the summation (3.6.11) would exceed unity. It follows therefore that, for this message $\tilde{m}$, $\psi_{\tilde{m}}$ may be upper-bounded by $1/M$. Consequently, letting

$$P_{E_{\max}} \equiv \max_m P_{E_m} \tag{3.6.13}$$

we conclude from (3.6.12), (3.6.13), and (3.6.7) through (3.6.10) that *at least one* of the following pair of inequalities must hold.

$$1/M \geq \psi_{\tilde{m}} > \tfrac{1}{4} \exp\left[\mu(s) - s\mu'(s) - s\sqrt{2\mu''(s)}\right] \tag{3.6.14}$$

$$P_{E_{\max}} \geq P_{E_{\tilde{m}}} > \tfrac{1}{4} \exp\left[\mu(s) + (1-s)\mu'(s) - (1-s)\sqrt{2\mu''(s)}\right] \tag{3.6.15}$$

where

$$\begin{aligned} \mu(s) &= -\frac{\mathscr{E}}{N_o} s(1-s) \\ &\equiv -TC_T s(1-s) \end{aligned} \tag{3.6.16}$$

Consequently

$$\mu'(s) = -TC_T(1-2s) \tag{3.6.17}$$

$$\mu''(s) = 2TC_T \tag{3.6.18}$$

In the last three equations, we employed the notation of Sec. 2.5, namely

$$C_T \equiv (\mathscr{E}/N_o)/T \tag{2.5.13}$$

We shall also use the rate parameter defined there, namely

$$R_T = \frac{\ln M}{T} \text{ nats/s} \tag{2.5.14}$$

Upon use of (3.6.16) through (3.6.18), (2.5.13), and (2.5.14), the lower bounds (3.6.14) and (3.6.15) become the alternative bounds[15]

$$\begin{aligned} R_T &< T^{-1}\left[TC_T s^2 + 2s\sqrt{TC_T} + \ln 4\right] \\ &= C_T s^2 + o(T) \end{aligned} \tag{3.6.19}$$

and

$$\begin{aligned} P_{E_{\max}} &> \exp\{-[TC_T(1-s)^2 + 2(1-s)\sqrt{TC_T} + \ln 4]\} \\ &= \exp\{-T[C_T(1-s)^2 + o(T)]\} \end{aligned} \tag{3.6.20}$$

Since at least one of this last pair of inequalities must hold, we choose $s = s_o$ such that

$$R_T = C_T s_o^2 + o(T) \tag{3.6.21}$$

where

$$0 \leq R_T \leq C_T$$

[15] Here $o(T) \approx 1/\sqrt{T}$.

or equivalently

$$s_o = \sqrt{[R_T - o(T)]/C_T}$$

where

$$0 \leq s_o \leq 1$$

Then (3.6.19) is not satisfied; consequently (3.6.20) must be satisfied with $s = s_o$ yielding finally

$$\begin{aligned} P_{E_{\max}} &> \exp\{-T[C_T(1-s_o)^2 + o(T)]\} \\ &= \exp\{-T[(\sqrt{C_T} - \sqrt{R_T - o(T)})^2 + o(T)]\} \\ &= \exp\{-T[(\sqrt{C_T} - \sqrt{R_T})^2 + o(T)]\} \end{aligned} \tag{3.6.22}$$

While (3.6.22) lower-bounds the probability of error for the worst case, we actually desire to bound the average error probability

$$P_E(M) \equiv (1/M) \sum_{m=1}^{M} P_{E_m} \tag{3.6.23}$$

Now suppose we have the best code of $M/2$ signals. From (3.6.22), we see that the maximum error probability among this set of signals is lower-bounded by

$$P_{E_{\max}}(M/2) > \exp\{-T[(\sqrt{C_T} - \sqrt{R'_T})^2 + o(T)]\} \tag{3.6.24}$$

where

$$\begin{aligned} R'_T &= \frac{\ln(M/2)}{T} \\ &= R_T - o(T) \end{aligned}$$

Thus R'_T can be replaced by R_T in (3.6.24). On the other hand, for the best code of M signals, at least $M/2$ of its code vectors have

$$P_{E_m} \leq 2P_E(M) \tag{3.6.25}$$

But this subset can be regarded as a code for $M/2$ signals. Hence, the error probability for the worst signal in this case must be lower-bounded by (3.6.24) which pertains to the best code of $M/2$ signals. As a result, we have

$$\begin{aligned} P_E(M) &\geq \tfrac{1}{2} P_{E_{\max}}(M/2) \\ &> \exp\{-T[E_{sp}(R_T) + o(T)]\} \end{aligned} \tag{3.6.26}$$

where

$$E_{sp}(R_T) = (\sqrt{C_T} - \sqrt{R_T})^2 \qquad 0 \leq R_T \leq C_T$$

Amazingly enough, for the range of rates $C_T/4 \leq R_T \leq C_T$, this lower bound agrees asymptotically with the upper bound for orthogonal signals of (2.5.16). For lower rates, the upper bound and this lower bound diverge. However, in the next two sections, we shall determine tighter lower bounds for low rates that agree with (2.5.16) also for $0 \leq R_T \leq C_T/4$.

One minor consequence of these results then is that they establish that orthogonal signals are asymptotically optimum (as T and $M \to \infty$) for the unconstrained AWGN channel. (Regular simplex signal sets are always better, but asymptotically they are indistinguishable from orthogonal sets.) More importantly, we have demonstrated in a special case a very powerful technique for obtaining asymptotically tight lower bounds at all but low rates. This bound is called the *sphere-packing bound* for essentially historical reasons, based on the classical proof for this example and the next example (Fano [1961]). (See Probs. 3.22 and 3.24 for another proof of the sphere-packing bound.)

3.6.2 Binary-Symmetric Channel

We now turn to the application of Theorem 3.5.1 to the classically most often considered channel, the BSC, repeating essentially the arguments used for the AWGN channel but with different justification. In Sec. 2.8, we showed that the likelihood function for this channel is

$$p_N(\mathbf{y} \mid \mathbf{x}_m) = p^{d_m}(1-p)^{N-d_m} \tag{2.8.3}$$

where $d_m = w(\mathbf{y} \oplus \mathbf{x}_m)$ is the Hamming distance between the channel input and output binary vectors. For the dummy distribution, we pick in this case the uniform distribution

$$p_N(\mathbf{y}) = 2^{-N} \qquad \text{for all } \mathbf{y} \in \mathscr{Y}_N \tag{3.6.27}$$

Here we identify[16] $p_N(\mathbf{y})$ with $p_N^{(a)}(\mathbf{y})$ and $p_N(\mathbf{y}|\mathbf{x}_m)$ with $p_N^{(b)}(\mathbf{y})$, and consequently also identify $\overline{\Lambda_m}$ with $\mathscr{Y}_a$ and Λ_m with $\mathscr{Y}_b$. Since these quantities meet the conditions of Theorem 3.5.1, we can then apply (3.5.1) and (3.5.2) to assert that, for message m, at least one of the following pair of inequalities must hold:

$$\psi_m \equiv \sum_{\mathbf{y} \in \Lambda_m} 2^{-N} > \tfrac{1}{4} \exp\left[\mu(s) - s\mu'(s) - s\sqrt{2\mu''(s)}\right] \tag{3.6.28}$$

$$\begin{aligned} P_{E_m} &\equiv \sum_{\mathbf{y} \in \overline{\Lambda_m}} p^{d_m}(1-p)^{N-d_m} \\ &> \tfrac{1}{4} \exp\left[\mu(s) + (1-s)\mu'(s) - (1-s)\sqrt{2\mu''(s)}\right] \end{aligned} \tag{3.6.29}$$

where

$$\mu(s) = \ln \sum_{\mathbf{y}} 2^{-N(1-s)}\left[p^{d_m}(1-p)^{N-d_m}\right]^s \qquad 0 \leq s \leq 1 \tag{3.6.30}$$

and $d_m = w(\mathbf{y} \oplus \mathbf{x}_m)$. But, since $\mathbf{x}_m$ is some N-dimensional binary vector and $\mathbf{y}$ runs over the set of all such vectors, it is clear that there exists exactly one vector $\mathbf{y}$ (namely, $\mathbf{x}_m$) for which $d_m = 0$, N vectors $\mathbf{y}$ for which $d_m = 1$ (at Hamming distance

[16] It is actually immaterial whether this or the opposite association is chosen. In the latter case, we would have to define $s = \rho/(1+\rho)$ instead of (3.6.39).

1 from $\mathbf{x}_m$), $\binom{N}{2}$ vectors $\mathbf{y}$ for which $d_m = 2$, and generally $\binom{N}{k}$ vectors $\mathbf{y}$ for which $d_m = k$ $(0 \le k \le N)$. Thus (3.6.30) may be written and summed as

$$\begin{aligned}\mu(s) &= \ln \sum_{k=0}^{N} \binom{N}{k}[p^k(1-p)^{N-k}]^s 2^{-N(1-s)} \\ &= N\{\ln [(1-p)^s + p^s] - (1-s) \ln 2\} \end{aligned} \tag{3.6.31}$$

To identify ψ_m, we again recognize that the Λ_m are disjoint decision regions whose union covers the total space $\mathscr{Y}_N$. Hence, summing over all messages, we have

$$\begin{aligned}\sum_{m=1}^{M} \psi_m &= \sum_{m=1}^{M} \sum_{\mathbf{y} \in \Lambda_m} 2^{-N} \\ &= \sum_{\mathbf{y}} 2^{-N} = 1\end{aligned}$$

and hence for some $\tilde{m}$

$$\psi_{\tilde{m}} \le 1/M \tag{3.6.32}$$

From (3.6.28) and (3.6.29) we have the two alternative inequalities for some message $\tilde{m}$

$$1/M \ge \psi_{\tilde{m}} > \tfrac{1}{4} \exp [\mu(s) - s\mu'(s) - s\sqrt{2\mu''(s)}] \tag{3.6.33}$$

$$P_{E_{\max}} \ge P_{E_{\tilde{m}}} > \tfrac{1}{4} \exp [\mu(s) + (1-s)\mu'(s) - (1-s)\sqrt{2\mu''(s)}] \tag{3.6.34}$$

where from (3.6.31) we have

$$\mu(s) - s\mu'(s) = N\{-\ln 2 + \ln [(1-p)^s + p^s] - s\delta(s)\} \tag{3.6.35}$$

$$\mu(s) + (1-s)\mu'(s) = N\{\ln [(1-p)^s + p^s] + (1-s)\,\delta(s)\} \tag{3.6.36}$$

where

$$\delta(s) = \frac{(1-p)^s \ln (1-p) + p^s \ln p}{(1-p)^s + p^s} \tag{3.6.37}$$

and[17]

$$\sqrt{2\mu''(s)} = N\, o(N) \tag{3.6.38}$$

Finally, if we make the substitution

$$s = \frac{1}{1+\rho} \qquad 0 \le \rho < \infty \tag{3.6.39}$$

we find that (3.6.35) and (3.6.36) become, after some algebraic manipulation,

$$\mu(s) - s\mu'(s)\Big|_{s=1/(1+\rho)} = -NE_o'(\rho) \tag{3.6.40}$$

$$\mu(s) + (1-s)\mu'(s)\Big|_{s=1/(1+\rho)} = -N[E_o(\rho) - \rho E_o'(\rho)] \tag{3.6.41}$$

[17] Here $o(N) \approx 1/\sqrt{N}$.

where

$$E_o(\rho) = \rho \ln 2 - (1 + \rho) \ln \left[(1 - p)^{1/(1+\rho)} + p^{1/(1+\rho)}\right]$$

Note that this is identical to Eq. (3.4.1) which represents the basic exponent function for the BSC with input weighting distribution optimized at $\mathbf{q} = (\frac{1}{2}, \frac{1}{2})$.

We may now conclude the argument by defining the rate in nats per binary-channel symbol as

$$R = (\ln M)/N \text{ nats/symbol} \tag{3.6.42}$$

and choosing $\rho = \rho^*$ positive. Consequently $s^* = 1/(1 + \rho^*) \in [0, 1]$ is the appropriate value such that

$$\begin{aligned} R &= (\ln M)/N \\ &= (-1/N) \ln e^{\mu(s^*) - s^*\mu'(s^*) - No(N)} \\ &= E_o'(\rho^*) + o(N) \end{aligned} \tag{3.6.43}$$

where we have used (3.6.40). This then satisfies (3.6.33) with equality and consequently requires that (3.6.34) must be an inequality. Thus, using (3.6.41), we have

$$\begin{aligned} P_{E_{\max}} &> e^{\mu(s^*) + (1 - s^*)\mu'(s^*) - No(N)} \\ &= e^{-N[E_o(\rho^*) - \rho^* E_o'(\rho^*) + o(N)]} \qquad 0 \le \rho^* < \infty \end{aligned} \tag{3.6.44}$$

By exactly the same argument which led to (3.6.26), we then have

$$\begin{aligned} P_E(M) &\ge \tfrac{1}{2} P_{E_{\max}}(M/2) \\ &> e^{-N[E_{sp}(R) + o(N)]} \end{aligned} \tag{3.6.45}$$

where $E_{sp}(R)$ is defined by the parametric equations

$$\begin{aligned} E_{sp}(R) &= E_o(\rho^*) - \rho^* E_o'(\rho^*) \qquad 0 \le \rho^* < \infty \\ R &= E_o'(\rho^*) \qquad 0 \le R < C \end{aligned} \tag{3.6.46}$$

The limits of R are established from the properties of $E_o(\rho)$ (Sec. 3.2); namely, the facts that $E_o(\rho)$ is a convex $\cap$ monotonically increasing function and that $\lim_{\rho \to 0} E_o'(\rho) = C$ and $\lim_{\rho \to 0} E_o(\rho) = 0$. But (3.6.46) is then identical to the upper bound $E(R)$ of (3.2.8) for the higher-rate region, $E_o'(1) \le R < C$, for the BSC for which the latter is optimized for all rates by the choice $\mathbf{q} = (\frac{1}{2}, \frac{1}{2})$. For lower rates, $0 \le R \le E_o'(1)$, the lower-bound exponent $E_{sp}(R)$ continues to grow faster than linearly since the function is convex $\cup$, while the upper-bound exponent $E(R)$ grows only linearly (see Fig. 3.10). The gap between the upper and lower bounds at low rates will be reduced in the next two sections.

By analogy to (3.2.6), (3.2.8), and (3.2.12), it follows also that the lower-bound exponent (3.6.46) can be written as

$$E_{sp}(R) = \max_{\mathbf{q}} \sup_{\rho \ge 0} \left[E_o(\rho, \mathbf{q}) - \rho R\right] \tag{3.6.47}$$

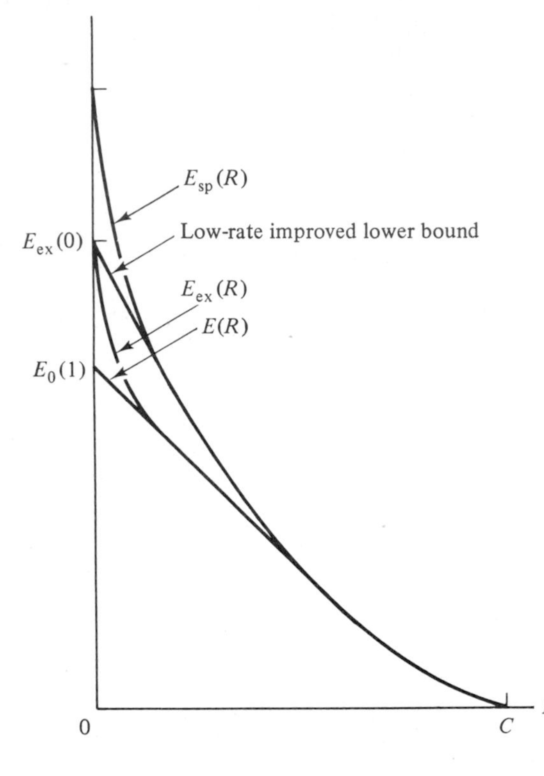

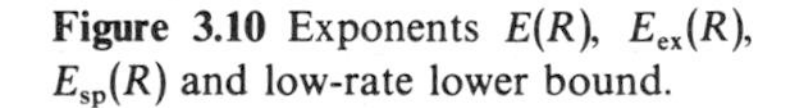

Figure 3.10 Exponents $E(R)$, $E_{ex}(R)$, $E_{sp}(R)$ and low-rate lower bound.

Thus the construction from the $E_o(\rho, \mathbf{q})$ function (see Figs. 3.1 and 3.2) is the same as for the upper bound but, rather than terminating at $\rho = 1$ for $R = E_o'(1)$ (see Fig. 3.3*a*), it continues on for all ρ and hence approaches $R = 0$. This also explains why the bounds diverge for rates below $R = E_o'(1)$.

We have thus obtained almost the same result for the BSC as we had previously for the AWGN channel; namely, that the lower bound is asymptotically the same as the upper bound (and identical in exponent) for all rates above some critical medium rate. The results for both of the above special cases can be obtained in a more intuitive, classical manner using a so-called sphere-packing argument (see, e.g., Gallager [1968]). We have chosen this less intuitive approach for two reasons: first, it augments and illustrates the power of Theorem 3.5.1, the strong version of the Neyman-Pearson lemma; second, it demonstrates the key steps in the proof for any discrete-input memoryless channel. By these same basic arguments, augmented by other somewhat more involved and sophisticated steps,[18] the following general sphere-packing lower bound has been proved.

[18] The simplicity of the proofs for the BSC and AWGN channel is due to the considerable input and output symmetry of these channels. Without this natural symmetry, one must impose the formalism of "fixed composition codes," whose justification and eventual removal obscures the basic elegance of the above technique.

Theorem 3.6.1 (Shannon, Gallager, Berlekamp [1967]) For any discrete memoryless channel, the best code of M vectors [rate $R = (\ln M)/N$] has

$$P_E(M) > e^{-N[E_{sp}(R) + o(N)]}$$

where $E_{sp}(R)$ is given by the parametric equations (3.6.46) and $E_o(\rho)$ is identical to the function defined for the upper bound on P_E for the given channel.

3.7 ZERO-RATE LOWER BOUNDS

As we have just noted, the upper and lower bounds, which agree asymptotically for $R > E'_o(1)$, diverge below this rate and are farthest apart at $R = 0$. We now remedy this situation by deriving new zero-rate lower bounds for the AWGN channel and for all binary-input, output-symmetric channels, which agree asymptotically with the least upper bound in each case at zero rate. This consequently guarantees that the expurgated upper bound is asymptotically exact at zero rate. The low-rate problem is treated in the next section.

3.7.1 Unconstrained Bandwidth AWGN Channel with Equal-Energy Signals

The principal parameter utilized in low-rate bounds is the minimum distance between signal vectors. For M real signal vectors of equal energy in an arbitrary number of dimensions, we upper-bound this minimum distance by first upper-bounding the average distance between distinct vectors.[19]

$$\begin{aligned}
(d^2)_{av} &\equiv \frac{1}{M(M-1)} \sum_i \sum_j \|\mathbf{x}_i - \mathbf{x}_j\|^2 \\
&= \frac{1}{M(M-1)} \sum_i \sum_j \{\|\mathbf{x}_i\|^2 + \|\mathbf{x}_j\|^2 - 2(\mathbf{x}_i, \mathbf{x}_j)\} \\
&= \frac{2M}{M-1}\mathscr{E} - \frac{2M}{M-1} \cdot \frac{1}{M^2} \sum_i \sum_j (\mathbf{x}_i, \mathbf{x}_j) \\
&= \frac{2M}{M-1}\mathscr{E} - \frac{2M}{M-1} \left\| \frac{1}{M} \sum_i \mathbf{x}_i \right\|^2 \\
&\leq \frac{2M}{M-1}\mathscr{E}
\end{aligned}$$

with equality if and only if the centroid $\frac{1}{M}\sum_m \mathbf{x}_m = \mathbf{0}$.

[19] The average involves only those terms for which $i \neq j$; hence the denominator is the number of such terms. However, in the summation we include the $i = j$ terms since they are all zero.

Consequently

$$d_{\min} = \left[\min_{i \neq j} \|\mathbf{x}_i - \mathbf{x}_j\|^2\right]^{\frac{1}{2}} \leq (d^2)_{\mathrm{av}}^{1/2} \leq \sqrt{2\mathscr{E}M/(M-1)} \qquad (3.7.1)$$

Equality holds in (3.7.1) if and only if the signal set is the regular simplex defined by (2.10.19).

We now apply this result to lower-bounding the error probability for any such signal set on the AWGN channel. It is reasonable to expect that the greatest contribution to this error probability will be that resulting from the closest signal pair. Arbitrarily designating these two signals as $\mathbf{x}_1$ and $\mathbf{x}_2$, we have

$$P_{E_{\max}} \geq P_{E_1} \geq P_E(1 \to 2) \qquad (3.7.2)$$

where the notation for the right-hand inequality is that of (2.3.4) and denotes the pairwise error probability when only the two signals $\mathbf{x}_1$ and $\mathbf{x}_2$ are possible and the former is transmitted. This inequality follows from the fact that eliminating all signals but $\mathbf{x}_1$ and $\mathbf{x}_2$ from the signal set allows us to expand both decision regions and thus obtain a lower error probability. Further, in Sec. 2.3 [Eq. (2.3.10)], we determined this error probability to be

$$\begin{aligned} P_E(1 \to 2) &= Q(\|\mathbf{x}_1 - \mathbf{x}_2\|/\sqrt{2N_o}) \\ &= Q(d_{\min}/\sqrt{2N_o}) \\ &\geq Q(\sqrt{\mathscr{E}M/N_o(M-1)}) \end{aligned} \qquad (3.7.3)$$

where the last inequality follows from (3.7.1) and the fact that the function $Q(x)$ is monotonically decreasing in x. Finally, from (3.7.2) and the classical bounds for the error function given in (2.3.18), we have

$$P_{E_{\max}} \geq e^{-\mathscr{E}/2N_o + o(T)} \qquad (3.7.4)$$

where $o(T)$ goes to zero as T goes to infinity. Thus, using the same argument which led to (3.6.26) and the same notation as (2.5.13), we have[20]

$$\begin{aligned} P_E(M) &\geq \tfrac{1}{2} P_{E_{\max}}(M/2) \\ &\geq e^{-T[C_T/2 + o(T)]} \end{aligned} \qquad (3.7.5)$$

While this lower bound on P_E for the best code is independent of rate, it agrees asymptotically with (2.5.16), the upper bound (for orthogonal signals), only at $R_T = 0$. Also, at high rates, it is clearly looser (smaller) than the sphere-packing bound (3.6.26). In fact, in the next section, we shall discuss a low-rate bound which begins with this result and improves on it for all rates $0 < R_T \leq C_T/4$.

[20] This form could also have been obtained from (3.5.8).

3.7.2 Binary-Input, Output-Symmetric Channels

The zero-rate lower bound is as easily obtained for this more general class as for the BSC. The first step again is to upper-bound the minimum distance among code-vectors. Unsurprisingly, the argument is somewhat reminiscent of the above for the Gaussian channel. We summarize it in the following lemma due to Plotkin [1951].

Lemma 3.7.1: Plotkin bound For any binary code of M code vectors of dimension N, the normalized minimum distance between code vectors is upper-bounded by

$$\frac{d_{\min}}{N} \leq \frac{M}{2(M-1)} \tag{3.7.6}$$

PROOF We begin by listing all binary code vectors in an $M \times N$ array

$$\begin{array}{cccc} x_{11} & x_{12} & \cdots & x_{1N} \\ \cdots & \cdots & \cdots & \cdots \\ x_{i1} & x_{i2} & \cdots & x_{iN} \\ \cdots & \cdots & \cdots & \cdots \\ x_{j1} & x_{j2} & \cdots & x_{jN} \\ \cdots & \cdots & \cdots & \cdots \\ x_{M1} & x_{M2} & \cdots & x_{MN} \end{array}$$

Let $d(\mathbf{x}_i, \mathbf{x}_j) \equiv w(\mathbf{x}_i \oplus \mathbf{x}_j)$ be the Hamming distance between $\mathbf{x}_i$ and $\mathbf{x}_j$, and consider the sum over all pairwise Hamming distances (thus counting each nondiagonal term twice and not bothering to eliminate the case $i = j$ since it contributes 0 to the sum)

$$\sum_{i=1}^{M} \sum_{j=1}^{M} d(\mathbf{x}_i, \mathbf{x}_j) = \sum_{n=1}^{N} \sum_{i=1}^{M} \sum_{j=1}^{M} d(x_{in}, x_{jn}) \tag{3.7.7}$$

where

$$d(x_{in}, x_{jn}) = w(x_{in} \oplus x_{jn}) = \begin{cases} 0 & \text{if } x_{in} = x_{jn} \\ 1 & \text{otherwise} \end{cases}$$

Let $\nu(n)$ be the number of zeros in the nth column. Clearly for any good code, $\nu(n) < M$; for otherwise that column could be omitted without decreasing $d_{\min}$. Then, for each column n, there is an m for which $x_{mn} = 1$. Thus there are $\nu(n)$ values of m' for which $x_{m'n} = 0$ and hence for which $x_{m'n} \neq x_{mn}$. Consequently

$$\sum_{m'=1}^{M} d(x_{mn}, x_{m'n}) = \nu(n)$$

Furthermore, by the same assumption, there are $M - v(n)$ values of m for which $x_{mn} = 1$. Thus

$$\sum_{m:\, x_{mn}=1} \sum_{m'=1}^{M} d(x_{mn}, x_{m'n}) = [M - v(n)]v(n) \tag{3.7.8}$$

At the same time there are $v(n)$ values of m for which $x_{mn} = 0$, and consequently $M - v(n)$ values of m' for which $x_{m'n} = 1$. Thus

$$\sum_{m:\, x_{mn}=0} \sum_{m'=1}^{M} d(x_{mn}, x_{m'n}) = v(n)[M - v(n)] \tag{3.7.9}$$

Adding (3.7.8) and (3.7.9), we obtain

$$\sum_{m=1}^{M} \sum_{m'=1}^{M} d(x_{mn}, x_{m'n}) = 2v(n)[M - v(n)]$$

$$\leq \frac{M^2}{2} \tag{3.7.10}$$

since the factor $v(M - v)$ is maximized by $v = M/2$. Substituting in (3.7.7), we obtain

$$\sum_{m=1}^{M} \sum_{m'=1}^{M} d(\mathbf{x}_m, \mathbf{x}_{m'}) = \sum_{n=1}^{N} 2v(n)[M - v(n)]$$

$$\leq \frac{NM^2}{2} \tag{3.7.11}$$

But, since $d(\mathbf{x}_m, \mathbf{x}_m) = 0$ trivially for all diagonal terms, letting

$$d_{\min} \equiv \min_{m \neq m'} d(\mathbf{x}_m, \mathbf{x}_{m'})$$

be the minimum of the nondiagonal terms, we have

$$\sum_{m=1}^{M} \sum_{m'=1}^{M} d(\mathbf{x}_m, \mathbf{x}_{m'}) = \sum_{m=1}^{M} \sum_{m' \neq m} d(\mathbf{x}_m, \mathbf{x}_{m'})$$

$$\geq M(M - 1)\, d_{\min} \tag{3.7.12}$$

Combining the inequalities (3.7.11) and (3.7.12) we obtain

$$d_{\min} \leq \frac{N}{2}\left(\frac{M}{M - 1}\right)$$

which is just (3.7.6) and hence proves the lemma.

We now proceed just as for the AWGN channel. Denoting by $\mathbf{x}_1$ and $\mathbf{x}_2$ two code vectors at minimum distance, we use (3.7.2) again

$$P_{E_{\max}} \geq P_{E_1} \geq P_E(1 \to 2) \tag{3.7.2}$$

with the same justification as before. But in Sec. 3.5 we showed that the two-message error probability is bounded by (3.5.8)

$$P_E(1 \to 2) = P_E(2 \to 1) \qquad (3.5.8)$$
$$> e^{\mu(s_0) - No(N)}$$

where

$$\mu(s) = \ln \sum_{\mathbf{y}} p(\mathbf{y}|\mathbf{x}_1)^{1-s} p(\mathbf{y}|\mathbf{x}_2)^s \qquad (3.7.13)$$

and $s_0 \in [0, 1]$ is such that

$$\mu'(s_0) = 0$$

But since the channel is a memoryless binary-input, output-symmetric channel, we have[21]

$$\frac{p(\mathbf{y}|\mathbf{x}_1)}{p(\mathbf{y}|\mathbf{x}_2)} = \prod_{k=1}^{d_{\min}} \frac{p(y_k|x_{1k})}{p(y_k|\overline{x_{1k}})}$$

where k refers to any component for which $x_{1k} \neq x_{2k} = \overline{x_{1k}}$. Suppose that $x_{1k} = 0$ in l of these components and $x_{1k} = 1$ in the remaining $d_{\min} - l$. Then (3.7.13) becomes

$$\mu(s) = \ln \left\{ \sum_y p_0(y) \left[\frac{p_1(y)}{p_0(y)} \right]^s \right\}^l \left\{ \sum_y p_1(y) \left[\frac{p_0(y)}{p_1(y)} \right]^s \right\}^{d_{\min} - l}$$

But for this class of channels, the output space is symmetric [i.e., for every y, there corresponds a $-y$ such that $p_1(y) = p_0(-y)$]. Thus

$$\sum_y p_0(y) \left[\frac{p_0(-y)}{p_0(y)} \right]^s = \sum_{y>0} \left\{ p_0(y) \left[\frac{p_0(-y)}{p_0(y)} \right]^s + p_0(-y) \left[\frac{p_0(y)}{p_0(-y)} \right]^s \right\} + p_0(0)$$
$$= \sum_y p_0(-y) \left[\frac{p_0(y)}{p_0(-y)} \right]^s \qquad (3.7.14)$$

Hence

$$\mu(s) = d_{\min} \ln \sum_y p_0(y)^{1-s} p_0(-y)^s$$
$$= d_{\min} \ln \sum_y p_0(y)^s p_0(-y)^{1-s} = \mu(1-s) \qquad (3.7.15)$$

Since $\mu(s)$ is convex $\cup$, it has a unique minimum in (0, 1). Furthermore, since $\mu(s) = \mu(1-s)$ this minimum must occur at $s_0 = \frac{1}{2}$, and at this point

$$\mu'(\tfrac{1}{2}) = 0 \qquad (3.7.16)$$

[21] To avoid dividing by 0, if $p(y_k|\bar{x}_{1k}) = 0$, we replace it by ϵ. Then we calculate the exponent (3.7.18), which depends only on Z, and finally let $\epsilon \to 0$. The result is that Z is exactly the same as if Z were calculated directly for the original channel with zero transition probability.

Thus choosing $s = s_0 = \frac{1}{2}$, we have from (3.5.8) and (3.7.15)

$$P_E(1 \to 2) > \exp\left\{N\left[(d_{\min}/N) \ln \sum_y \sqrt{p_0(y)p_0(-y)} - o(N)\right]\right\} \tag{3.7.17}$$

Consequently, as in (3.7.5), we have, using (3.7.2),

$$\begin{aligned} P_E(M) &\geq \tfrac{1}{2} P_{E_{\max}}(M/2) \\ &> e^{N[(d_{\min}/N) \ln Z - o(N)]} \end{aligned} \tag{3.7.18}$$

where

$$Z = \sum_y \sqrt{p_0(y)p_0(-y)}$$

Finally from Lemma 3.7.1, letting[22] $M \geq N$ for any fixed rate as N becomes large, we have

$$\frac{d_{\min}}{N} < \frac{1}{2} + o(N)$$

Hence

$$\begin{aligned} P_E(M) &> e^{N[\frac{1}{2} \ln Z - o(N)]} \\ &= e^{-N[E_{ex}(0) + o(N)]} \end{aligned} \tag{3.7.19}$$

where we have used (3.3.31), which is the zero-rate upper-bound exponent.

Once again we have obtained a result which is asymptotically tight at zero rate. This same result has been shown for the entire class of memoryless discrete-input channels (Shannon, Gallager, and Berklekamp [1967]).

3.8 LOW-RATE LOWER BOUNDS*

We have just closed the gap between the asymptotic lower-bound and the upper-bound expressions for zero rate, as well as for rates above $R = E_o'(1)$. We now turn to narrowing the gap for the range $0 < R < E_o'(1)$. This is partially accomplished by the following useful theorem.

Theorem 3.8.1 (Shannon, Gallager, and Berlekamp [1967]) Given two rates $R'' < R'$ for which error bounds on the best code of dimension N are given by

$$P_E(R') > e^{-N[E_{sp}(R') + o(N)]}$$

$$P_E(R'') > e^{-N[E_l(R'') + o(N)]}$$

[22] This restriction is inconsequential since, provided M grows no faster than linearly with N, $R = (\ln M)/N \to 0$ as $N \to \infty$.

* May be omitted without loss of continuity.

where $o(N) \to 0$ as $N \to \infty$, $E_{sp}(R)$ is the sphere-packing bound exponent, and $E_l(R)$ is any tighter low-rate exponent. Then, for the intermediate rate $R = \lambda(R') + (1-\lambda)R''$, $0 \le \lambda \le 1$, the error probability for the best code of dimension N is lower-bounded by

$$P_E(R) > e^{-N[\lambda E_{sp}(R') + (1-\lambda)E_l(R'') + o(N)]} \qquad \text{when } R = \lambda R' + (1-\lambda)R'',\ 0 \le \lambda \le 1 \tag{3.8.1}$$

In other words, if we have a point on the sphere-packing bound exponent and another on any other asymptotic lower-bound exponent, the straight line connecting these points is itself an asymptotic lower-bound exponent for all intermediate rates. In connection with the results of the last two sections, this suggests that we connect the asymptotically tight result at zero rate with the sphere-packing bound by a straight line which intersects the latter at a rate as close to $E_o'(1)$ as possible. This of course, is achieved by drawing a tangent from the zero-rate exponent value to the curve of the sphere-packing bound exponent. The result (see Fig. 3.10) is a bound which is everywhere asymptotically exact for the unconstrained AWGN channel and for the limit of very noisy channels,[23] while for all other channels when $E(0)$ is finite, it is generally reasonably close to the best (expurgated) upper bounds.

The proof of this theorem is best approached by first proving two key lemmas, which are interesting in their own right. The first has to do with *list decoding*, an important concept with numerous ramifications. Suppose that in decoding a code of M vectors of dimension N we were content to output a list of the L messages corresponding to the L highest likelihood functions and declare that an error occurred only if the transmitted message were not on the list. Then naturally the probability of error for list-of-L decoding is lower than for ordinary decoding with a single choice. However, a lower bound, which is identical in form to the sphere-packing lower bound, holds also in this case.

Lemma 3.8.1 For a code of M vectors of dimension[24] N with list-of-L decoding the error probability is lower bounded by

$$P_E(N, M, L) > e^{-N[E_{sp}(\tilde{R}) + o(N)]} \tag{3.8.2}$$

where

$$0 \le \tilde{R} = \frac{\ln (M/L)}{N} < C \tag{3.8.3}$$

PROOF (for binary-input, output-symmetric and AWGN channels) The argument is almost identical to those in Sec. 3.6 with the exception that now the decision regions are enlarged to

$$\Lambda_m = \{\mathbf{y}: p(\mathbf{y} \mid \mathbf{x}_m) > p(\mathbf{y} \mid \mathbf{x}_k) \text{ for all } \mathbf{x}_k \notin \{\mathbf{x}_m, \mathbf{x}_{\mathbf{m}_1}, \mathbf{x}_{\mathbf{m}_2}, \ldots, \mathbf{x}_{\mathbf{m}_{L-1}}\}\}$$

[23] These channels, for which $E_{ex}(0) = E(0) = E_o(1)$, are the only channels for which everywhere asymptotically exact results are known. See also Sec. 3.9.

[24] For the unconstrained AWGN channel, the lemma holds with N replaced by T throughout.

That is, Λ_m is the region over which $p(\mathbf{y} \mid \mathbf{x}_m)$ is among the top L likelihood functions. Consequently, each point $\mathbf{y} \in \mathcal{Y}_N$ (the observation space) must lie in exactly L regions; specifically if $p(\mathbf{y} \mid \mathbf{x}_{m_1}) > \cdots > p(\mathbf{y} \mid \mathbf{x}_{m_L})$ are the L greatest likelihood functions, then $\mathbf{y} \in \Lambda_{m_k}$, $k = 1, 2, \ldots, L$. With this redefinition of Λ_m, the pairs of inequalities (3.6.7), (3.6.8), and (3.6.28), (3.6.29), as well as the forms of $\mu(s)$, (3.6.9) and (3.6.30), appear exactly as before. However, the values of the ψ_m now differ, and this requires changes in (3.6.12) and (3.6.32). For now

$$\begin{aligned}\sum_{m=1}^{M} \psi_m &= \sum_{m=1}^{M} \sum_{\mathbf{y} \in \Lambda_m} p_N(\mathbf{y}) \\ &= L \sum_{\mathbf{y}} p_N(\mathbf{y}) \\ &= L \end{aligned} \tag{3.8.4}$$

since it follows that, if each $\mathbf{y}$ lies in exactly L regions, summing over each of the M regions $\{\Lambda_m\}$ results in counting each point in the space L times. Thus (3.6.12) and (3.6.32) are replaced by

$$\psi_{\tilde{m}} \leq L/M \tag{3.8.5}$$

and the rest of the derivation is identically the same. For binary-input, output-symmetric channels, this means that we replace[25] (3.6.42) by

$$\tilde{R} = \frac{\ln (M/L)}{N}$$

and proceed in exactly the same manner as before, thus obtaining (3.6.45) and (3.6.46) with R replaced by $\tilde{R}$, which are just (3.8.2) and (3.8.3) of this lemma.

The other key lemma relates ordinary decoding with list decoding as an intermediate step.

Lemma 3.8.2 For arbitrary dimensions N_1 and N_2, code size M, and list size L, on a memoryless channel

$$P_E(N_1 + N_2, M) \geq P_E(N_1, M, L) P_E(N_2, L + 1) \tag{3.8.6}$$

where $P_E(N, M, L)$ is the list-of-L average error probability for the best code of length N with M codewords, and $P_E(N', M')$ is the ordinary average error probability for the best code of length N' with M' codewords. The two argument error probabilities apply to ordinary decoding; the three argument probabilities apply to list decoding.

The intuitive basis of this result is that an error will certainly occur for a transmitted code vector of length $N_1 + N_2$ if L other code vectors have higher

[25] For the AWGN channel we replace (2.5.14) by $\tilde{R}_T = \dfrac{\ln (M/L)}{T}$.

likelihood functions over the first N_1 symbols and if any one of these has a higher likelihood function over the last N_2 symbols.

PROOF Let each transmitted code-vector $\mathbf{x}_m$ of dimension $N_1 + N_2$ be separated into a prefix

$$\mathbf{x}'_m = (x_{m1}, x_{m2}, \ldots, x_{mN_1})$$

and a suffix

$$\mathbf{x}''_m = (x_{m,(N_1+1)}, x_{m,(N_1+2)}, \ldots, x_{m,(N_1+N_2)})$$

Similarly let the received vector $\mathbf{y}$ be so separated into an N_1-dimensional prefix $\mathbf{y}'$ and an N_2-dimensional suffix $\mathbf{y}''$. The overall error probability for ordinary decoding is, of course, given by (2.3.1) and (2.3.2) as

$$P_E = \frac{1}{M} \sum_{m=1}^{M} \sum_{\mathbf{y} \in \bar{\Lambda}_m} p_N(\mathbf{y} \mid \mathbf{x}_m) \tag{3.8.7}$$

For each prefix $\mathbf{y}'$ let

$$\Lambda''_m(\mathbf{y}') \equiv \{\mathbf{y}'' : \mathbf{y} = (\mathbf{y}', \mathbf{y}'') \in \Lambda_m\} \tag{3.8.8}$$

be the set of suffixes for which the overall vector $\mathbf{y}$ is in the mth decision region. Then, since the channel is memoryless, we may rewrite (3.8.7) as

$$\begin{aligned} P_E &= \frac{1}{M} \sum_{m=1}^{M} \sum_{\mathbf{y}'} p_{N_1}(\mathbf{y}' \mid \mathbf{x}'_m) \sum_{\mathbf{y}'' \in \overline{\Lambda''_m(\mathbf{y}')}} p_{N_2}(\mathbf{y}'' \mid \mathbf{x}''_m) \\ &= \frac{1}{M} \sum_{m=1}^{M} \sum_{\mathbf{y}'} p_{N_1}(\mathbf{y}' \mid \mathbf{x}'_m) P_{E_m}(\mathbf{y}') \end{aligned} \tag{3.8.9}$$

where $P_{E_m}(\mathbf{y}')$ is the error probability for message m given that the prefix $\mathbf{y}'$ was received.

Let $m_1(\mathbf{y}')$, $m_2(\mathbf{y}')$, $\ldots$, $m_L(\mathbf{y}')$ be the L values of m (the L messages) for which the overall error probabilities, conditioned on the prefix $\mathbf{y}'$ being received, are the smallest. That is

$$P_{E_{m,1}}(\mathbf{y}') \le P_{E_{m,2}}(\mathbf{y}') \le \cdots \le P_{E_{m,L}}(\mathbf{y}') \le P_{E_{m,k}}(\mathbf{y}') \tag{3.8.10}$$

for every $k > L$. Consequently, for every

$$m_k \notin \{m_1(\mathbf{y}'), m_2(\mathbf{y}'), \ldots, m_L(\mathbf{y}')\}$$

it follows that

$$P_{E_{m,k}}(\mathbf{y}') \ge P_E(N_2, L+1) \tag{3.8.11}$$

For suppose on the contrary that

$$P_{E_{m,1}}(\mathbf{y}') \le P_{E_{m,2}}(\mathbf{y}') \le \cdots < P_{E_{m,L}}(\mathbf{y}') \le P_{E_{m,k}}(\mathbf{y}') < P_E(N_2, L+1)$$

Now restrict the code to only the $L+1$ messages $m_1, m_2, \ldots, m_L, m_k$. The decision regions could then be expanded leading to

$$P_{E_{m,j}}(\mathbf{y}', L+1) \leq P_{E_{m,j}}(\mathbf{y}') \qquad j = 1, 2, \ldots, L, k$$

where the left side of the inequality refers to error events for the $L+1$ message code. Combining these two inequalities, we obtain

$$P_{E_{m,j}}(\mathbf{y}', L+1) < P_E(N_2, L+1)$$

which is obviously in contradiction to the fact that $P_E(N_2, L+1)$ is a lower bound for the *best* code of $L+1$ vectors. Thus (3.8.11) must hold and we can lower-bound the inner summation in (3.8.9) by

$$\sum_{\mathbf{y}'' \in \overline{\Lambda''_m(\mathbf{y}')}} p_{N_2}(\mathbf{y}''\,|\,\mathbf{x}''_m) = P_{E_m}(\mathbf{y}')$$

$$\geq \begin{cases} 0 & m \in \{m_1(\mathbf{y}'), m_2(\mathbf{y}'), \ldots, m_L(\mathbf{y}')\} \\ P_E(N_2, L+1) & m = m_k(\mathbf{y}') \text{ where } k > L \end{cases} \tag{3.8.12}$$

Substituting (3.8.12) in (3.8.9) and changing the order of summation, we obtain

$$P_E \geq \frac{1}{M} \sum_{\mathbf{y}'} \sum_{m = m_k(\mathbf{y}') : k > L} p_{N_1}(\mathbf{y}'\,|\,\mathbf{x}'_m) P_E(N_2, L+1) \tag{3.8.13}$$

Finally, consider the prefix symbols $\mathbf{x}'_1, \mathbf{x}'_2, \ldots, \mathbf{x}'_M$ as a code of M vectors of dimension N_1. Then again interchanging the order of summation, we have, using (3.8.10),

$$\frac{1}{M} \sum_{\mathbf{y}'} \sum_{m = m_k(\mathbf{y}') : k > L} p_{N_1}(\mathbf{y}'\,|\,\mathbf{x}'_m) = \frac{1}{M} \sum_{m=1}^{M} \sum_{\mathbf{y}' \in \overline{\Lambda_m'}} p_{N_1}(\mathbf{y}'\,|\,\mathbf{x}'_m) \tag{3.8.14}$$

where $\Lambda'_m \equiv \{\mathbf{y}' : m \in \{m_1(\mathbf{y}'), m_2(\mathbf{y}'), \ldots, m_L(\mathbf{y}')\}\}$.

Hence, the right side of (3.8.14) is just the overall error probability for a list-of-L decoder and consequently is lower-bounded by $P_E(N_1, M, L)$. Substituting this lower bound for (3.8.14) into (3.8.13) we obtain

$$P_E(N_1 + N_2, M) \geq P_E(N_1, M, L) P_E(N_2, L+1) \tag{3.8.6}$$

which thus proves the lemma.

PROOF (of Theorem 3.8.1) Substituting (3.8.2) for $P_E(N_1, M, L)$ and an arbitrary low-rate exponential lower bound for $P_E(N_2, L+1)$ into (3.8.6), we have

$$P_E(N_1 + N_2, M) \geq e^{-N_1[E_{sp}(R') + o(N_1)] - N_2[E_l(R'') + o(N_2)]} \tag{3.8.15}$$

where $o(N_1) \to 0$ and $o(N_2) \to 0$ as $N_1 \to \infty$ and $N_2 \to \infty$, respectively. From (3.8.3), we have

$$R' = \frac{\ln (M/L)}{N_1} \tag{3.8.16}$$

and we let

$$R'' \equiv \frac{\ln L}{N_2} \tag{3.8.17}$$

Defining

$$\begin{aligned} \lambda &= \frac{N_1}{N_1 + N_2} \\ 1 - \lambda &= \frac{N_2}{N_1 + N_2} \end{aligned} \tag{3.8.18}$$

we have, using (3.8.16) through (3.8.18)

$$\begin{aligned} R &\equiv \frac{\ln M}{N_1 + N_2} \\ &= \lambda \frac{\ln (M/L)}{N_1} + (1 - \lambda) \frac{\ln L}{N_2} \\ &= \lambda R' + (1 - \lambda) R'' \end{aligned} \tag{3.8.19}$$

Hence, letting $N = N_1 + N_2$ where both $N_1 \to \infty$ and $N_2 \to \infty$, we obtain from (3.8.15)

$$P_E(R) \geq e^{-N[\lambda E_{sp}(R') + (1-\lambda)E_l(R'') + o(N)]}$$

where

$$R = \lambda R' + (1 - \lambda) R'' \qquad 0 \leq \lambda \leq 1$$

and

$$R'' < R < R'$$

which is just (3.8.1) and hence proves the theorem.

The application of Theorem 3.8.1 involves letting $R'' = 0$ and using the zero-rate bound of Sec. 3.7 for $E_l(0)$. Thus in (3.8.1) we let $R'' = 0$, $R' = R/\lambda$, and $E_l(0) = E_{ex}(0)$ so that

$$\begin{aligned} P_E(R) &> e^{-N[\lambda E_{sp}(R/\lambda) + (1-\lambda)E_{ex}(0) + o(N)]} \\ &= \exp\left(-N\left\{E_{ex}(0) - \left[\frac{E_{ex}(0) - E_{sp}(R_1)}{R_1}\right] R + o(N)\right\}\right) \qquad 0 < \lambda < 1 \end{aligned}$$

where $R_1 = R/\lambda$, and hence

$$0 < R < R_1$$

The best choice of R_1, obviously, is the one for which the line from $E_{ex}(0)$ at $R = 0$ has maximum slope, i.e., the rate at which a tangent line from $E_{ex}(0)$ at $R = 0$ strikes the sphere-packing bound exponent (see Fig. 3.10).

3.9 CONJECTURES AND CONVERSES*

In the preceding three sections, we have found lower bounds on the best code, for given N and M, which agree asymptotically at $R = 0$ and $R \geq E_o'(1)$ with the upper bounds derived in the first half of this chapter by ensemble average arguments. For the low-rate region $0 < R < E_o'(1)$, asymptotically tight results are not available, although the exponents of upper and lower bounds are generally close together and become asymptotically the same in the limit of very noisy channels.

The most likely improvement in the lower bound for this region will come about as a result of an improvement in the upper bound on minimum distance. In the case of binary-input, output-symmetric channels, we found in Sec. 3.7 the lower bound

$$P_E > e^{-N[-(d_{min}/N)\ln Z + o(N)]} \tag{3.7.18}$$

where

$$Z = \sum_y \sqrt{p_0(y)p_0(-y)} \leq 1$$

Thus, an upper bound on d_{min} is needed to complete the error bound. In Sec. 3.7, we derived the Plotkin bound

$$\frac{d_{min}}{N} < \frac{1}{2} + o(N)$$

where $o(N) \to 0$ as $N \to \infty$, which then led to the lower error bound (3.7.19) which is tight at zero rate. But it is intuitively clear that, the higher the rate, the more code vectors are placed in the N-dimensional space and the achievable minimum distance is lower. It is possible to modify the Plotkin bound so as to obtain a form which decreases linearly with rate (see Prob. 3.33), specifically

$$\frac{d_{min}}{N} < \frac{1}{2}[1 - (R/\ln 2)] + o(N) \tag{3.9.1}$$

but this is by no means tight either. A tighter upper bound on d_{min} is due to Elias [1960].[26] Also of interest is the tightest known lower bound on d_{min}; this was derived

* May be omitted without loss of continuity.

[26] An even tighter upper bound has been derived by McEliece, Rodemich, Rumsey, and Welch [1977]. Also, see McEliece and Omura [1977].

by Gilbert [1952] using an essentially constructive argument (see Prob. 3.34). [One can also derive the Gilbert bound[27] by using the expurgated upper bound (3.4.8) and the lower error bound (3.7.18) for the binary-input, output-symmetric channel.] The Gilbert lower and Elias upper bounds on normalized minimum distance for a binary code of N symbols are, respectively,

$$\delta(R) < \frac{d_{\min}}{N} < 2\delta(R)[1 - \delta(R)] + o(N) \tag{3.9.2}$$

where $\delta(R)$ is the function defined by

$$R = \ln 2 - \mathscr{H}(\delta) \qquad 0 \leq \delta \leq \tfrac{1}{2} \tag{3.9.3}$$

The Plotkin and Elias upper bounds and the Gilbert lower bound are all plotted in Fig. 3.11.

It is tempting to conjecture, as have Shannon, Gallager, and Berlekamp [1967], that in fact the Gilbert bound is tight, i.e., that

$$\frac{d_{\min}}{N} = \delta(R) + o(N) \qquad \text{[conjecture]} \tag{3.9.4}$$

where $\delta(R)$ is given by (3.9.3). For then, at least for binary-input, output-symmetric channels, we would have, using (3.7.18) and (3.9.3)

$$P_E > e^{-N[E_l(R) + o(N)]}$$

[27] Also known as the Varshamov-Gilbert bound, in recognition of independent work of Varshamov [1957].

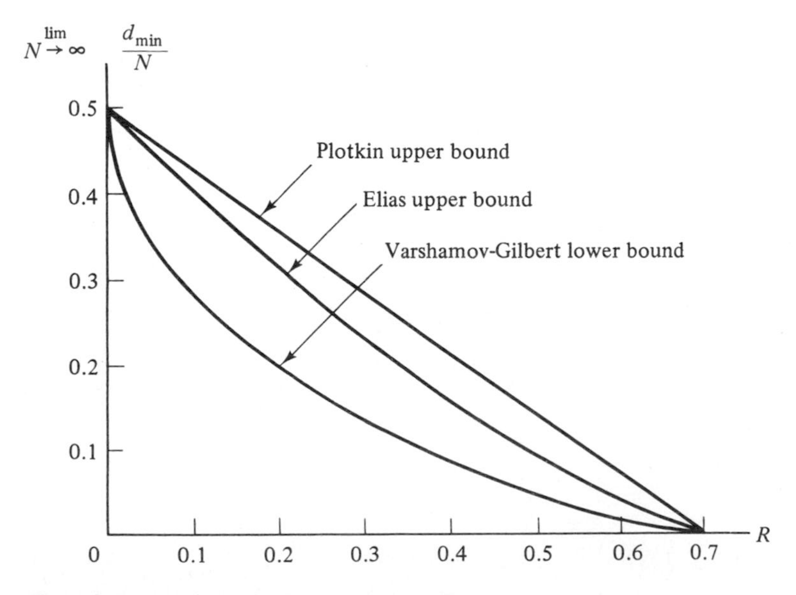

Figure 3.11 Bounds on $d_{\min}/N$.

where

$$E_l(R) = -\delta \ln Z \qquad \text{[conjecture]}$$
$$R = \ln 2 - \mathscr{H}(\delta) \tag{3.9.5}$$

But interestingly enough, this coincides asymptotically with the expurgated bound for these channels derived in Sec. 3.4 [see (3.4.8)] so that

$$E_l(R) = E_{ex}(R) \text{ [conjecture]} \qquad 0 \le R < \ln 2 - \mathscr{H}\left(\frac{Z}{1+Z}\right) \tag{3.9.6}$$

Finally, for rates $\ln 2 - \mathscr{H}[Z/(1+Z)] = E_x'(1) < R < E_o'(1)$, the upper-bound exponent is a line of slope -1, tangent to the curved portions for low and high rates at $E_x'(1)$ and $E_o'(1)$, respectively. Similarly, by Theorem 3.8.1 if the lower bound (3.9.6) holds, we could then connect it at the highest rate $E_x'(1)$ to the sphere-packing bound at $E_o'(1)$ by the same straight line. Thus it appears, at least for the class of binary-input, output-symmetric channels, that the missing link in showing that the best upper bounds are asymptotically tight *everywhere*, is being able to show that the conjecture (3.9.4) on the asymptotic tightness of the Gilbert bound is indeed true. No evidence exists to the contrary, but no real progress toward a proof is evident. Historical precedents demonstrate that when a particular result is proven for the BSC, the proof can ultimately be bent to cover essentially all memoryless channels. Thus, the asymptotic tightness of the Gilbert bound is one of the most important open questions in information theory.

The other gap in the results of this chapter involves the behavior of any of the channels considered at rates above capacity. Since both upper and asymptotic lower-bound exponents approach zero as $R \to C$ from below, it would appear that there is little chance for good performance above C. In fact, for rates above capacity, two very negative statements can be made. These are known as the converses to the coding theorem. The first, more general result due to Fano [1952] was derived and discussed in Sec. 1.3. It shows that, independent of the encoding and decoding technique, the average (per symbol) error probability is bounded away from zero. The second converse, which holds *only for block codes*, is the following stronger result.

Theorem 3.9.1: Strong converse to the coding theorem[28] (Arimoto [1973]) For an arbitrary discrete-input memoryless channel of capacity C and equal a priori message probabilities, the error probability of any block code of dimension N and rate $R > C$ is lower bounded by

$$P_E \ge 1 - e^{-NE_{sc}(R)} \tag{3.9.7}$$

[28] Earlier versions are due to Wolfowitz [1957], who first showed that $\lim_{N\to\infty} P_E = 1$ for $R > C$, and Gallager [1968], who first obtained an exponential form of the bound.

where

$$E_{sc}(R) \equiv \max_{-1<\rho<0} \left[\min_{\mathbf{q}} E_o(\rho, \mathbf{q}) - \rho R \right] > 0 \qquad \text{for } R > C \tag{3.9.8}$$

and $E_o(\rho, \mathbf{q})$ is given in (3.1.18).

{Note that $E_{sc}(R)$ is a dual to the form of $E(R)$ given in Sec. 3.1. The main difference is that the parameter ρ is restricted to the interval $(-1, 0)$.}

Proof We bound the average probability of correct decoding of an arbitrary code by first examining the form

$$\begin{aligned} P_C &= \frac{1}{M} \sum_{m=1}^{M} \sum_{\mathbf{y} \in \Lambda_m} p_N(\mathbf{y} \mid \mathbf{x}_m) \\ &= \frac{1}{M} \sum_{\mathbf{y}} \max_{m} p_N(\mathbf{y} \mid \mathbf{x}_m) \end{aligned} \tag{3.9.9}$$

This follows from the fact that the optimum decision regions are defined as

$$\Lambda_m = \left\{ \mathbf{y}: \max_{m'} p_N(\mathbf{y} \mid \mathbf{x}_{m'}) = p_N(\mathbf{y} \mid \mathbf{x}_m) \right\} \qquad m = 1, 2, \ldots, M \tag{3.9.10}$$

Now for any $\beta > 0$, we have

$$\begin{aligned} \max_{m} p_N(\mathbf{y} \mid \mathbf{x}_m) &= \left(\max_{m} p_N(\mathbf{y} \mid \mathbf{x}_m)^{1/\beta} \right)^{\beta} \\ &\leq \left(\sum_{m=1}^{M} p_N(\mathbf{y} \mid \mathbf{x}_m)^{1/\beta} \right)^{\beta} \end{aligned} \tag{3.9.11}$$

Defining a special probability distribution on codewords, namely

$$q_N(\mathbf{x}) = \begin{cases} \dfrac{1}{M} & \mathbf{x} = \mathbf{x}_m \qquad m = 1, 2, \ldots, M \\ 0 & \text{otherwise} \end{cases} \tag{3.9.12}$$

gives us the relation

$$\begin{aligned} \max_{m} p_N(\mathbf{y} \mid \mathbf{x}_m) &\leq \left(M \sum_{\mathbf{x}} q_N(\mathbf{x}) p_N(\mathbf{y} \mid \mathbf{x})^{1/\beta} \right)^{\beta} \\ &= M^{\beta} \left(\sum_{\mathbf{x}} q_N(\mathbf{x}) p_N(\mathbf{y} \mid \mathbf{x})^{1/\beta} \right)^{\beta} \end{aligned} \tag{3.9.13}$$

Using this in (3.9.9), we have the bound

$$\begin{aligned} P_C &\leq \frac{1}{M^{1-\beta}} \sum_{\mathbf{y}} \left(\sum_{\mathbf{x}} q_N(\mathbf{x}) p_N(\mathbf{y} \mid \mathbf{x})^{1/\beta} \right)^{\beta} \\ &\leq \frac{1}{M^{1-\beta}} \max_{\mathbf{q}_N} \sum_{\mathbf{y}} \left(\sum_{\mathbf{x}} q_N(\mathbf{x}) p_N(\mathbf{y} \mid \mathbf{x})^{1/\beta} \right)^{\beta} \end{aligned} \tag{3.9.14}$$

where the maximization is over *all* distributions $\mathbf{q}_N$ on $\mathscr{X}_N$, not just the special distribution of (3.9.12). Defining the parameter

$$\rho = \beta - 1 \geq -1 \tag{3.9.15}$$

where $\rho = -1$ is taken as the limit as $\rho \to -1$ from above, we have

$$P_C \leq M^\rho \max_{\mathbf{q}_N} \sum_{\mathbf{y}} \left(\sum_{\mathbf{x}} q_N(\mathbf{x}) p_N(\mathbf{y} \mid \mathbf{x})^{1/(1+\rho)} \right)^{1+\rho} \tag{3.9.16}$$

In Lemma 3.2.2, we showed that

$$\sum_{\mathbf{y}} \left(\sum_{\mathbf{x}} q_N(\mathbf{x}) p_N(\mathbf{y} \mid \mathbf{x})^{1/(1+\rho)} \right)^{1+\rho} \tag{3.9.17}$$

is a convex $\cup$ function over the space of distributions $q_N(\cdot)$ on $\mathscr{X}_N$ for $\rho \geq 0$. For $\rho \leq 0$, the same proof of Lemma 3.2.2 shows that (3.9.17) is a convex $\cap$ function over the space of distributions $q_N(\cdot)$ on $\mathscr{X}_N$. We now restrict ρ to the semi-open interval $\rho \in (-1, 0]$. The Kuhn-Tucker theorem (App. 3B) shows that there is a unique maximum of (3.9.17) with respect to distributions on $\mathscr{X}_N$ and that it satisfies the necessary and sufficient conditions

$$\sum_{\mathbf{y}} p_N(\mathbf{y} \mid \mathbf{x})^{1/(1+\rho)} \alpha(\mathbf{y}, \mathbf{q}_N)^\rho \leq \sum_{\mathbf{y}} \alpha(\mathbf{y}, \mathbf{q}_N)^{1+\rho} \tag{3.9.18}$$

where

$$\alpha(\mathbf{y}, \mathbf{q}_N) = \sum_{\mathbf{x}} q_N(\mathbf{x}) p_N(\mathbf{y} \mid \mathbf{x})^{1/(1+\rho)}$$

for all $\mathbf{x} \in \mathscr{X}_N$ with equality when $q_N(\mathbf{x}) > 0$. This maximization is satisfied by a distribution of the form

$$q_N(\mathbf{x}) = \prod_{n=1}^{N} q(x_n) \tag{3.9.19}$$

where $q(\cdot)$ satisfies the necessary and sufficient conditions

$$\sum_{y} p(y \mid x)^{1/(1+\rho)} \alpha(y, \mathbf{q})^\rho \leq \sum_{y} \alpha(y, \mathbf{q})^{1+\rho} \tag{3.9.20}$$

where

$$\alpha(y, \mathbf{q}) = \sum_{x} q(x) p(y \mid x)^{1/(1+\rho)}$$

for all $x \in \mathscr{X}$ with equality when $q(x) > 0$. Hence from (3.9.16), we have

$$\begin{aligned} P_C &\leq M^\rho \max_{\mathbf{q}} \left[\sum_{y} \left(\sum_{x} q(x) p(y \mid x)^{1/(1+\rho)} \right)^{1+\rho} \right]^N \\ &= \exp\left\{ -N \min_{\mathbf{q}} \left[E_o(\rho, \mathbf{q}) - \rho R \right] \right\} \end{aligned} \tag{3.9.21}$$

Minimizing the bound with respect to $\rho \in (-1, 0]$ yields

$$P_C \leq e^{-NE_{sc}(R)} \tag{3.9.22}$$

and hence (3.9.7) when we use $P_E = 1 - P_C$.

For $R > C$ we can show $E_{sc}(R)$ is greater than zero by examining properties for $E_o(\rho, \mathbf{q})$ for $-1 \leq \rho \leq 0$. Using Lemma 3.2.1, which is proved in App. 3A, we have for $-1 \leq \rho \leq 0$

$$E_o(\rho, \mathbf{q}) \leq 0 \tag{3.9.23}$$

with equality if and only if $\rho = 0$. Further, we have

$$\frac{\partial E_o(\rho, \mathbf{q})}{\partial \rho} > 0 \tag{3.9.24}$$

$$\frac{\partial^2 E_o(\rho, \mathbf{q})}{\partial \rho^2} \leq 0 \tag{3.9.25}$$

and

$$I(\mathbf{q}) = \left. \frac{\partial E_o(\rho, \mathbf{q})}{\partial \rho} \right|_{\rho=0} \tag{3.9.26}$$

With these properties, we see that $E_{sc}(R) > 0$ for $R > C$ by using arguments dual to those used in Sec. 3.2 to show that $E(R) > 0$ for $R < C$.

This concludes our discussion of converses as well as our treatment of error bounds for general block codes.

3.10 ENSEMBLE BOUNDS FOR LINEAR CODES*

All the bounds derived so far pertain to the best code over the ensemble of all possible codes of a given size, M, and dimension, N. However, virtually all codes employed in practical applications are members of the much more restricted ensemble of *linear codes*. Clearly the best linear code can be no better than the best code over the wider set of all possible codes. Hence, all the previous lower bounds also apply to linear codes. The problem is that the upper bounds, based on averages over the wider ensemble of all codes, must now be proved over the narrower ensemble of linear codes. It turns out that this task is not nearly as formidable as would initially appear. We shall consider here only binary linear codes and binary-input, output-symmetric channels, but the extension to the codes over any finite field alphabet is straightforward.

A binary linear code of $M = 2^K$ code vectors, as defined in Sec. 2.9, is one in which the code vectors $\{\mathbf{v}_m\}$ are generated by a linear algebraic operation on the data vectors $\{\mathbf{u}_m\}$, the latter being lexicographically associated with all 2^K possible binary vectors from $\mathbf{u}_1 = \mathbf{0}$ to $\mathbf{u}_{2^K} = \mathbf{1}$. We generalize the definition of linear codes

* May be omitted without loss of continuity.

of Sec. 2.9 to one for which the code-vectors contain a constant additive vector $\mathbf{v}_0$, that is

$$\mathbf{x}_m = \mathbf{v}_m = \mathbf{u}_m G \oplus \mathbf{v}_0 \qquad m = 1, 2, \ldots, 2^K \tag{3.10.1}$$

where

$$G = \begin{bmatrix} g_{11} & g_{12} & \cdots & g_{1N} \\ g_{21} & g_{22} & \cdots & g_{2N} \\ \cdots & \cdots & \cdots & \cdots \\ g_{K1} & g_{K2} & \cdots & g_{KN} \end{bmatrix}$$

and

$$\mathbf{v}_0 = (v_{01}, \ldots, v_{0N})$$

are an arbitrary binary matrix and binary vector. We take here $L = N$ and we take the signal vectors $\{\mathbf{x}_m = \mathbf{v}_m\}$ to be the code vectors. The additive vector $\mathbf{v}_0$ is an unnecessary artifice for output-symmetric channels but becomes necessary for the proof in the absence of symmetry. It is clear that the ensemble of all possible binary linear codes contains $2^{(K+1)/N}$ members, corresponding to all distinguishable forms of G and $\mathbf{v}_0$.

The average error probability of the mth message over the ensemble of all possible linear codes is, analogously to (3.1.1)

$$\overline{P_{E_m}} = \frac{1}{2^{(K+1)N}} \sum_{(\mathbf{x}_1, \mathbf{x}_2, \ldots, \mathbf{x}_M) \in \mathscr{L}_{(K+1)N}} \cdots \sum P_{E_m}(\mathbf{x}_1, \ldots, \mathbf{x}_M) \tag{3.10.2}$$

where $\mathscr{L}_{(K+1)N}$ is the space of all possible signal sets generated by (3.10.1). Substituting the error probability bound for a specific signal set (3.1.4), we have for $m = 1$

$$\overline{P_{E_1}} < \sum_{\mathbf{y}} \frac{1}{2^{(K+1)N}} \sum_{(\mathbf{x}_1, \mathbf{x}_2, \ldots, \mathbf{x}_M) \in \mathscr{L}_{(K+1)N}} \cdots \sum p_N(\mathbf{y} \mid \mathbf{x}_1)^{1/(1+\rho)}$$
$$\times \left[\sum_{m'=2}^{M} p_N(\mathbf{y} \mid \mathbf{x}_{m'})^{1/(1+\rho)} \right]^{\rho} \qquad \rho \geq 0 \tag{3.10.3}$$

But

$$\mathbf{x}_1 = \mathbf{v}_1 = \mathbf{0}G + \mathbf{v}_0$$
$$= \mathbf{v}_0$$

and hence can take on any of 2^N values. However, once $\mathbf{x}_1$ is fixed by the choice of $\mathbf{v}_0$, the remaining signal vectors $\mathbf{x}_2, \ldots, \mathbf{x}_M$ jointly can take on just 2^{KN} possible values depending only on the KN binary degrees of freedom of the matrix G. Thus we may express (3.10.3) as

$$\overline{P_{E_1}} < \sum_{\mathbf{y}} \frac{1}{2^N} \sum_{\mathbf{x}_1} p_N(\mathbf{y} \mid \mathbf{x}_1)^{1/(1+\rho)}$$
$$\times \left\{ \frac{1}{2^{KN}} \sum_{(\mathbf{x}_2, \ldots, \mathbf{x}_M) \in \mathscr{L}_{KN}} \cdots \sum \left[\sum_{m'=2}^{M} p_N(\mathbf{y} \mid \mathbf{x}_{m'})^{1/(1+\rho)} \right]^{\rho} \right\} \qquad \rho \geq 0 \tag{3.10.4}$$

where $\mathscr{L}_{KN}$ is the space of all signal sets generated by (3.10.1) when $\mathbf{v}_0$ is fixed. Using the definition (3.1.6) we find, analogously to (3.1.7) and (3.1.9) with $0 \le \rho \le 1$, that the expression in brackets in (3.10.4) becomes

$$
\begin{aligned}
\frac{1}{2^{KN}} & \sum_{(\mathbf{x}_2, \ldots, \mathbf{x}_M) \in \mathscr{L}_{KN}} \cdots \sum [f_N(\mathbf{x}_2, \ldots, \mathbf{x}_M)]^\rho \\
& \le \left[\frac{1}{2^{KN}} \sum_{(\mathbf{x}_2, \ldots, \mathbf{x}_M) \in \mathscr{L}_{KN}} \cdots \sum f_N(\mathbf{x}_2, \ldots, \mathbf{x}_M)\right]^\rho \\
& = \left[\frac{1}{2^{KN}} \sum_{(\mathbf{x}_2, \ldots, \mathbf{x}_M) \in \mathscr{L}_{KN}} \cdots \sum \sum_{m'=2}^{M} p_N(\mathbf{y} \mid \mathbf{x}_{m'})^{1/(1+\rho)}\right]^\rho \\
& = \left[\frac{1}{2^{KN}} \sum_{m'=2}^{M} \sum_{(\mathbf{x}_2, \ldots, \mathbf{x}_M) \in \mathscr{L}_{KN}} \cdots \sum p_N(\mathbf{y} \mid \mathbf{x}_{m'})^{1/(1+\rho)}\right]^\rho
\end{aligned} \tag{3.10.5}
$$

But clearly, for $m' \neq 1$, any given value of $\mathbf{x}_{m'} \in \mathscr{X}_N$ can be obtained by choosing some row vector of the G matrix to be an appropriate distinct function of the remaining row vectors. However, this only leaves $2^{(K-1)N}$ choices for the remaining vectors. Thus

$$
\begin{aligned}
\sum_{(\mathbf{x}_2, \ldots, \mathbf{x}_M) \in \mathscr{L}_{KN}} & \cdots \sum p_N(\mathbf{y} \mid \mathbf{x}_{m'})^{1/(1+\rho)} \\
& = \sum_{(\mathbf{x}_2, \ldots, \mathbf{x}_{m'-1}, \mathbf{x}_{m'+1}, \ldots, \mathbf{x}_M) \in \mathscr{L}_{(K-1)N}} \cdots \sum \sum_{\mathbf{x}_{m'}} p_N(\mathbf{y} \mid \mathbf{x}_{m'})^{1/(1+\rho)} \\
& = 2^{(K-1)N} \sum_{\mathbf{x}} p_N(\mathbf{y} \mid \mathbf{x})^{1/(1+\rho)}
\end{aligned} \tag{3.10.6}
$$

Combining (3.10.4) through (3.10.6), using definition (3.1.6), we obtain

$$
\begin{aligned}
\overline{P_{E_1}} & < \sum_{\mathbf{y}} \sum_{\mathbf{x}_1} \frac{1}{2^N} p_N(\mathbf{y} \mid \mathbf{x}_1)^{1/(1+\rho)} \left[\sum_{m'=2}^{M} \sum_{\mathbf{x}_{m'}} \frac{1}{2^N} p_N(\mathbf{y} \mid \mathbf{x}_{m'})^{1/(1+\rho)}\right]^\rho \\
& = \sum_{\mathbf{y}} \sum_{\mathbf{x}_1} \frac{1}{2^N} p_N(\mathbf{y} \mid \mathbf{x}_1)^{1/(1+\rho)} \left[(M-1) \sum_{\mathbf{x}'} \frac{1}{2^N} p_N(\mathbf{y} \mid \mathbf{x}')^{1/(1+\rho)}\right]^\rho \\
& = (M-1)^\rho \sum_{\mathbf{y}} \left[\sum_{\mathbf{x}} \frac{1}{2^N} p_N(\mathbf{y} \mid \mathbf{x})^{1/(1+\rho)}\right]^{1+\rho} \qquad 0 \le \rho \le 1
\end{aligned} \tag{3.10.7}
$$

which is identical to (3.1.10) with $q_N(\mathbf{x}) = 1/2^N$. Clearly $\overline{P_{E_m}}$ can be identically bounded by interchanging indices m and 1 throughout, and the rest of the ensemble average upper-bound derivation (i.e., the balance of Secs. 3.1 and 3.2) follows identically to that for the wider ensemble of all block codes. Thus all the results of Sec. 3.2 hold for binary linear codes also (with $Q = 2$) when $q(0) = q(1) = \frac{1}{2}$, which holds for output-symmetric channels. As we found in Sec. 3.6, this bound is asymptotically tight for all rates $R \ge E_o'(1)$ for this class of channels.

To improve the *upper bound at low rates*, for the wider ensemble of all block codes we employed an expurgation argument (Sec. 3.3). However, for binary linear codes, the proof of the expurgated bound is easier than the more general proof of Sec. 3.3. Indeed, expurgation of codewords is not necessary. For M binary codewords of a linear code used over any binary-input memoryless channel, we have from (2.3.16) the Bhattacharyya bound for the mth message error probability

$$P_{E_m} \leq \sum_{m' \neq m} \sum_{\mathbf{y}} \sqrt{p_N(\mathbf{y}|\mathbf{x}_m) p_N(\mathbf{y}|\mathbf{x}_{m'})} \tag{2.3.16}$$

For binary code vectors $\mathbf{x}_m$ and $\mathbf{x}_{m'}$, we have

$$\sum_{\mathbf{y}} \sqrt{p_N(\mathbf{y}|\mathbf{x}_m) p_N(\mathbf{y}|\mathbf{x}_{m'})} = \left[\sum_{y} \sqrt{p_0(y)p_1(y)}\right]^{w(\mathbf{x}_m \oplus \mathbf{x}_{m'})} \tag{3.10.8}$$

where $w(\cdot)$ denotes the weight of the vector and here $w(\mathbf{x}_m \oplus \mathbf{x}_{m'})$ equals the number of symbols in which $\mathbf{x}_{m'}$ differs from $\mathbf{x}_m$. Thus

$$P_{E_m} \leq \sum_{m' \neq m} \left[\sum_{y} \sqrt{p_0(y)p_1(y)}\right]^{w(\mathbf{x}_m \oplus \mathbf{x}_{m'})} \tag{3.10.9}$$

For any linear code of the form

$$\mathbf{x}_m = \mathbf{v}_m = \mathbf{u}_m G \oplus \mathbf{v}_0 \tag{3.10.10}$$

we have from[29] (2.9.10), for any m

$$\{w(\mathbf{x}_m \oplus \mathbf{x}_{m'}) \text{ for all } m' \neq m\} = \{w(\mathbf{u}_2 G), w(\mathbf{u}_3 G), \ldots, w(\mathbf{u}_M G)\}$$

Thus

$$P_{E_m} \leq \sum_{m'=2}^{M} \left[\sum_{y} \sqrt{p_0(y)p_1(y)}\right]^{w(\mathbf{u}_{m'} G)} \tag{3.10.11}$$

for $m = 1, 2, \ldots, M$. Since the bound is the same for all codewords, we have

$$P_E \leq \sum_{m=2}^{M} \left[\sum_{y} \sqrt{p_0(y)p_1(y)}\right]^{w(\mathbf{u}_m G)} \tag{3.10.12}$$

Note that this is exactly the form of (2.9.19) but holds for arbitrary binary-input memoryless channels, without the requirement of output symmetry.

Defining

$$Z = \sum_{y} \sqrt{p_0(y)p_1(y)} \tag{3.10.13}$$

and the parameter $0 < s \leq 1$ we have the inequality (App. 3A)

$$\begin{aligned} P_E^s &\leq \left[\sum_{m=2}^{M} Z^{w(\mathbf{u}_m G)}\right]^s \\ &\leq \sum_{m=2}^{M} Z^{s w(\mathbf{u}_m G)} \end{aligned} \tag{3.10.14}$$

[29] We identify $\mathbf{v}_m$ there with $\mathbf{v}_m \oplus \mathbf{v}_0$ here and note that $\mathbf{x}_m \oplus \mathbf{x}_{m'} = (\mathbf{u}_m \oplus \mathbf{u}_{m'})G$.

P_E^s and its bound (3.10.14) depend on the particular code generator G as shown in (3.10.10). We next average P_E^s and its bound over the ensemble of all possible binary linear codes which contain 2^{KN} members, corresponding to all distinguishable forms of G. The average of (3.10.14) over all possible linear codes is

$$\overline{P_E^s} \leq \sum_G \frac{1}{2^{KN}} \sum_{m=2}^{M} Z^{sw(\mathbf{u}_m G)}$$
$$= \sum_{m=2}^{M} \sum_G \frac{1}{2^{KN}} Z^{sw(\mathbf{u}_m G)} \tag{3.10.15}$$

where we sum over the space of all possible generator matrices G. Noting that each generator matrix consists of K rows of dimension N, we can express (3.10.15) in terms of row vectors of the generator matrices as follows.

$$\overline{P_E^s} \leq \sum_{m=2}^{M} \sum_{\mathbf{g}_1} \cdots \sum_{\mathbf{g}_K} \left(\frac{1}{2^N}\right)^K Z^{sw(u_{m1}\mathbf{g}_1 \oplus u_{m2}\mathbf{g}_2 \oplus \cdots \oplus u_{mK}\mathbf{g}_K)} \tag{3.10.16}$$

where now, for each row, we sum over the space of all possible row vectors. In this case, all the row vector spaces are the same N-dimensional binary vector space, $\mathscr{X}_N$. For each $m \neq 1$, we have $\mathbf{u}_m \neq \mathbf{0}$ and hence, in $\mathbf{u}_m G = u_{m1}\mathbf{g}_1 \oplus u_{m2}\mathbf{g}_2 \oplus \cdots \oplus u_{mK}\mathbf{g}_K$, at least one row vector adds into the sum to form $\mathbf{u}_m G$. Varying over all 2^{NK} possible matrices G and taking the sum of the rows $\mathbf{g}_k$, for which $u_{mk} \neq 0$ results in $2^{N(K-1)}$-fold repetition of each of the 2^N possible N-dimensional vectors $\mathbf{x} = \mathbf{u}_m G$. Thus

$$\left(\frac{1}{2^N}\right)^K \sum_{\mathbf{g}_1} \cdots \sum_{\mathbf{g}_K} Z^{sw(u_{m1}\mathbf{g}_1 \oplus u_{m2}\mathbf{g}_2 \oplus \cdots \oplus u_{mK}\mathbf{g}_K)} = \sum_{\mathbf{x}} \frac{1}{2^N} Z^{sw(\mathbf{x})}$$
$$= \sum_{k=0}^{N} \binom{N}{k} \frac{1}{2^N} Z^{sk}$$
$$= \left(\frac{1+Z^s}{2}\right)^N \tag{3.10.17}$$

Combining (3.10.16), (3.10.17), and using $(M-1) < M$ yields

$$\overline{P_E^s} < M\left(\frac{1+Z^s}{2}\right)^N \tag{3.10.18}$$

Hence there exists at least one linear code for which

$$P_E < M^{1/s}\left(\frac{1+Z^s}{2}\right)^{N/s} \qquad 0 < s \leq 1 \tag{3.10.19}$$

or with parameter $1 \leq \rho = 1/s < \infty$

$$P_E < M^\rho\left(\frac{1+Z^{1/\rho}}{2}\right)^{\rho N}$$
$$= e^{-N[E_x(\rho,\, 1/2) - \rho R]} \tag{3.10.20}$$

where

$$E_x(\rho, \tfrac{1}{2}) \equiv -\rho \ln \left[\frac{1 + \left(\sum_y \sqrt{p_0(y)p_1(y)} \right)^{1/\rho}}{2} \right] \tag{3.10.21}$$

Minimizing over $\rho \geq 1$, we have that, for at least one binary linear code

$$P_E \leq e^{-NE_{ex}(R)} \tag{3.10.22}$$

where

$$E_{ex}(R) \equiv \sup_{\rho \geq 1} [E_x(\rho, \tfrac{1}{2}) - \rho R]$$

which corresponds to (3.3.12) and (3.3.13) for this class of channels and is given in parametric form in (3.4.8) with Z given by (3.10.13).

Thus, for linear block codes over output-symmetric channels, we have obtained the ensemble average upper bound of Sec. 3.1, and we have demonstrated that the expurgated error bound of Sec. 3.3 holds regardless of whether or not the channel is output-symmetric. In the next three chapters we shall consider a special class of linear codes which can be conveniently decoded and which achieves performance superior to that of linear block codes.

3.11 BIBLIOGRAPHICAL NOTES AND REFERENCES

The fundamental concepts of this chapter are contained in the original work of Shannon [1948]. The first published presentation of the results in Secs. 3.1 and 3.2 appeared in Fano [1961], as did those of Sec. 3.10 for the ensemble average. The present development of Secs. 3.1 through 3.4 is due to Gallager [1965]. The lower-bound results in Secs. 3.5 through 3.8 follow primarily from Shannon, Gallager, and Berklekamp [1967]. The strong converse in Sec. 3.9 was first proved by Wolfowitz [1957]; the present result is due to Arimoto [1973].

APPENDIX 3A USEFUL INEQUALITIES AND THE PROOFS OF LEMMA 3.2.1 AND THEOREM 3.3.2

3A.1 USEFUL INEQUALITIES (after Gallager [1968], Jelinek [1968])[30]

Throughout this appendix we use real positive parameters $r > 0$, $s > 0$, and $0 < \lambda < 1$. Letting $I = \{1, 2, \ldots, A\}$ be an index set, we define real nonnegative numbers indexed by I

$$a_i \geq 0 \qquad b_i \geq 0 \qquad \text{for } i \in I$$

[30] See also Hardy, Littlewood, Polya [1952].

and probability distributions indexed by I,

$$P_i \geq 0 \qquad Q_i \geq 0 \qquad \text{for } i \in I$$

where

$$\sum_{i=1}^{A} P_i = 1 \qquad \sum_{i=1}^{A} Q_i = 1$$

We proceed to state and prove 11 basic and useful inequalities.

(a) $\ln r \leq r - 1$ with equality iff[31] $r = 1$

PROOF $f(r) = \ln r - (r - 1)$ has derivatives

$$f'(r) = \frac{1}{r} - 1$$

$$f''(r) = -\frac{1}{r^2}$$

Since $f''(r) < 0$, we have a unique maximum at $r = 1$. Hence $f(r) = \ln r - (r - 1) \leq f(1) = 0$ with equality iff $r = 1$.

(b) $\prod_{i=1}^{A} a_i^{P_i} \leq \sum_{i=1}^{A} P_i a_i$ with equality iff

$$a_i = \sum_{j=1}^{A} P_j a_j \qquad \text{for all } i \in I \text{ such that } P_i > 0$$

PROOF From (a) we have

$$\begin{aligned} \ln \prod_{i=1}^{A} a_i^{P_i} - \ln\left(\sum_{i=1}^{A} P_i a_i\right) &= \sum_{i=1}^{A} P_i \ln \frac{a_i}{\sum_{j=1}^{A} P_j a_j} \\ &\leq \sum_{i=1}^{A} P_i \left[\frac{a_i}{\sum_{j=1}^{A} P_j a_j} - 1\right] \\ &= 0 \end{aligned}$$

with equality iff

$$a_i = \sum_{j=1}^{A} P_j a_j \qquad \text{for all } i \in I \text{ such that } P_i > 0$$

[31] Note that iff denotes "if and only if."

(*c*) $\sum_{i=1}^{A} Q_i^{\lambda} P_i^{1-\lambda} \leq 1$ with equality iff $P_i = Q_i$ for all $i \in I$.

PROOF From (*b*) we have for each $i \in I$

$$b_i^{\lambda} a_i^{1-\lambda} \leq \lambda b_i + (1-\lambda) a_i$$

with equality iff $a_i = b_i$. Hence, substituting P_i and Q_i for a_i and b_i and summing over i,

$$\sum_{i=1}^{A} Q_i^{\lambda} P_i^{1-\lambda} \leq \lambda \sum_{i=1}^{A} Q_i + (1-\lambda) \sum_{i=1}^{A} P_i$$

$$= 1$$

with equality iff $P_i = Q_i$ for all $i \in I$.

(*d*) $$\sum_{i=1}^{A} a_i b_i \leq \left(\sum_{i=1}^{A} a_i^{1/\lambda} \right)^{\lambda} \left(\sum_{i=1}^{A} b_i^{1/(1-\lambda)} \right)^{1-\lambda} \qquad \text{(Hölder inequality)}$$

with equality iff, for some c, $a_i^{1-\lambda} = c b_i^{\lambda}$ for all $i \in I$.

PROOF In (*c*), for each $i \in I$, let

$$Q_i = \frac{a_i^{1/\lambda}}{\sum_{j=1}^{A} a_j^{1/\lambda}} \qquad P_i = \frac{b_i^{1/(1-\lambda)}}{\sum_{j=1}^{A} b_i^{1/(1-\lambda)}}$$

The special case $\lambda = \frac{1}{2}$ gives

$$\sum_{i=1}^{A} a_i b_i \leq \left(\sum_{i=1}^{A} a_i^2 \right)^{1/2} \left(\sum_{i=1}^{A} b_i^2 \right)^{1/2} \qquad \text{(Cauchy inequality)}$$

and the integral analog

$$\int a(x) b(x)\, dx \leq \left(\int a^2(x)\, dx \right)^{1/2} \left(\int b^2(x)\, dx \right)^{1/2} \qquad \text{(Schwarz inequality)}$$

(*e*) $$\sum_{i=1}^{A} P_i a_i b_i \leq \left(\sum_{i=1}^{A} P_i a_i^{1/\lambda} \right)^{\lambda} \left(\sum_{i=1}^{A} P_i b_i^{1/(1-\lambda)} \right)^{1-\lambda} \qquad \text{(variant of Hölder inequality)}$$

with equality iff, for some c

$$P_i a_i^{1/\lambda} = c P_i b_i^{1/(1-\lambda)} \qquad \text{for all } i \in I$$

More generally, if the g_i are any nonnegative real numbers indexed by I, then

$$\sum_{i=1}^{A} g_i a_i b_i \leq \left(\sum_{i=1}^{A} g_i a_i^{1/\lambda} \right)^{\lambda} \left(\sum_{i=1}^{A} g_i b_i^{1/(1-\lambda)} \right)^{1-\lambda}$$

PROOF Let $\hat{a}_i = g_i^{\lambda} a_i$ and $\hat{b}_i = g_i^{1-\lambda} b_i$ be used in (d).

(f) $\left(\sum_{i=1}^{A} P_i a_i^{\lambda}\right)^{1/\lambda} \leq \sum_{i=1}^{A} P_i a_i \leq \left(\sum_{i=1}^{A} P_i a_i^{1/\lambda}\right)^{\lambda}$ (Jensen inequality)

with equality iff, for some c, $P_i a_i = cP_i$ for all $i \in I$.

PROOF The upper bound follows from (e) with $b_i = 1$ for all $i \in I$. The lower bound follows from (e) with $\hat{a}_i = a_i^{\lambda}$ and $\hat{b}_i = 1$ for all $i \in I$.

(g) $\left(\sum_{i=1}^{A} a_i^{1/\lambda}\right)^{\lambda} \leq \sum_{i=1}^{A} a_i \leq \left(\sum_{i=1}^{A} a_i^{\lambda}\right)^{1/\lambda}$ with equality iff only one a_i is nonzero.

PROOF Let

$$P_i = \frac{a_i}{\sum_{j=1}^{A} a_j} \qquad \text{for all } i \in I$$

Since $P_i \leq 1$ we have

$$P_i^{1/\lambda} \leq P_i \leq P_i^{\lambda}$$

with equality iff $P_i = 0$ or 1, and thus

$$\sum_{i=1}^{A} P_i^{1/\lambda} \leq \sum_{i=1}^{A} P_i = 1 \leq \sum_{i=1}^{A} P_i^{\lambda}$$

with equality iff only one a_i is nonzero.

Thus

$$\sum_{i=1}^{A} P_i^{1/\lambda} = \frac{\sum_{i=1}^{A} a_i^{1/\lambda}}{\left(\sum_{j=1}^{A} a_j\right)^{1/\lambda}} \leq 1$$

and

$$1 \leq \sum_{i=1}^{A} P_i^{\lambda} = \frac{\sum_{i=1}^{A} a_i^{\lambda}}{\left(\sum_{j=1}^{A} a_j\right)^{\lambda}}$$

(h) $\left(\sum_{i=1}^{A} P_i a_i^{r}\right)^{1/r} \leq \left(\sum_{i=1}^{A} P_i a_i^{s}\right)^{1/s} \qquad 0 < r < s$

with equality iff for some constant c, $P_i a_i = cP_i$ for all $i \in I$.

PROOF Let $\hat{b}_i = 1$, $\hat{a}_i = a_i^r$, and $\lambda = r/s \in (0, 1)$ in (e).

(i) $$\left[\sum_{i=1}^{A} Q_i a_i^{1/(\lambda s + \bar{\lambda} r)}\right]^{\lambda s + \bar{\lambda} r} \le \left[\sum_{i=1}^{A} Q_i a_i^{1/s}\right]^{\lambda s} \left[\sum_{i=1}^{A} Q_i a_i^{1/r}\right]^{\bar{\lambda} r}$$

where $\bar{\lambda} = 1 - \lambda$, with equality iff, for some c

$$c Q_i a_i^{1/s} = Q_i a_i^{1/r} \qquad \text{for all } i \in I$$

PROOF Let

$$\hat{P}_i = Q_i \qquad \hat{a}_i = a_i^{\lambda/(\lambda s + \bar{\lambda} r)} \qquad \hat{b}_i = a_i^{\bar{\lambda}/(\lambda s + \bar{\lambda} r)} \qquad \hat{\lambda} = \frac{\lambda s}{\lambda s + \bar{\lambda} r}$$

in (e).

(j) Let a_{jk} be a set of nonnegative numbers for $1 \le j \le J$ and $1 \le k \le K$. Then

$$\left[\sum_{j=1}^{J} \left(\sum_{k=1}^{K} a_{jk}\right)^{1/\lambda}\right]^{\lambda} \le \sum_{k=1}^{K} \left(\sum_{j=1}^{J} a_{jk}^{1/\lambda}\right)^{\lambda}$$

and

$$\sum_{k=1}^{K} \left(\sum_{j=1}^{J} a_{jk}^{\lambda}\right)^{1/\lambda} \le \left[\sum_{j=1}^{J} \left(\sum_{k=1}^{K} a_{jk}\right)^{\lambda}\right]^{1/\lambda} \qquad \text{(Minkowski inequality)}$$

PROOF Note that

$$\left(\sum_{k=1}^{K} a_{jk}\right)^{1/\lambda} = \left(\sum_{k=1}^{K} a_{jk}\right)\left(\sum_{k=1}^{K} a_{jk}\right)^{(1/\lambda) - 1} = \sum_{k=1}^{K} a_{jk}\left(\sum_{i=1}^{K} a_{ji}\right)^{(1-\lambda)/\lambda}$$

and from (d)

$$\sum_{j=1}^{J} \left(\sum_{k=1}^{K} a_{jk}\right)^{1/\lambda} = \sum_{j=1}^{J} \sum_{k=1}^{K} a_{jk}\left(\sum_{i=1}^{K} a_{ji}\right)^{(1-\lambda)/\lambda}$$
$$= \sum_{k=1}^{K} \left[\sum_{j=1}^{J} a_{jk}\left(\sum_{i=1}^{K} a_{ji}\right)^{(1-\lambda)/\lambda}\right]$$
$$\le \sum_{k=1}^{K} \left(\sum_{j=1}^{J} a_{jk}^{1/\lambda}\right)^{\lambda} \left[\sum_{j=1}^{J} \left(\sum_{i=1}^{K} a_{ji}\right)^{1/\lambda}\right]^{1-\lambda}$$

or, by dividing both sides by the second term on the right, we have

$$\left[\sum_{j=1}^{J} \left(\sum_{k=1}^{K} a_{jk}\right)^{1/\lambda}\right]^{\lambda} \le \sum_{k=1}^{K} \left(\sum_{j=1}^{J} a_{jk}^{1/\lambda}\right)^{\lambda}$$

The second inequality follows from this one with the substitution $\hat{a}_{jk} = a_{jk}^{\lambda}$.

(k) Let a_{jk} be a set of nonnegative numbers for $1 \le j \le J$, $1 \le k \le K$. Then

$$\left[\sum_{j=1}^{J} Q_j \left(\sum_{k=1}^{K} a_{jk}\right)^{1/\lambda}\right]^{\lambda} \le \sum_{k=1}^{K} \left(\sum_{j=1}^{J} Q_j a_{jk}^{1/\lambda}\right)^{\lambda}$$

and

$$\sum_{k=1}^{K} \left(\sum_{j=1}^{J} Q_j a_{jk}^{\lambda}\right)^{1/\lambda} \le \left[\sum_{j=1}^{J} Q_j \left(\sum_{k=1}^{K} a_{jk}\right)^{\lambda}\right]^{1/\lambda} \quad \text{(Variant of Minkowski inequality)}$$

PROOF Let $\hat{a}_{jk} = Q_j^{\lambda} a_{jk}$ in (j) for the first inequality and $\hat{a}_{jk} = Q_j^{1/\lambda} a_{jk}$ in (j) for the second inequality.

3A.2 PROOF OF LEMMA 3.2.1

$$E_o(\rho, \mathbf{q}) = -\ln \sum_y \left[\sum_x q(x) p(y \mid x)^{1/(1+\rho)}\right]^{1+\rho} \tag{3A.1}$$

From inequality (h) we have, for $-1 < \rho_1 < \rho_2$

$$\left[\sum_x q(x) p(y \mid x)^{1/(1+\rho_1)}\right]^{1+\rho_1} \ge \left[\sum_x q(x) p(y \mid x)^{1/(1+\rho_2)}\right]^{1+\rho_2} \tag{3A.2}$$

with equality iff, for some c, $q(x)p(y \mid x) = cq(x)$ for all $x \in \mathscr{X}$. Hence

$$E_o(\rho_1, \mathbf{q}) \le E_o(\rho_2, \mathbf{q}) \tag{3A.3}$$

with equality iff, for every $y \in \mathscr{Y}$, $p(y \mid x)$ is independent of $x \in \mathscr{X}$ for those x for which $q(x) > 0$. But this is impossible since we assumed $I(\mathbf{q}) > 0$ [see property 1 given in (1.2.9)]. Thus $E_o(\rho, \mathbf{q})$ is strictly increasing for $\rho > -1$ and hence

$$\frac{\partial E_o(\rho, \mathbf{q})}{\partial \rho} > 0 \qquad \rho > -1 \tag{3A.4}$$

Also

$$E_o(\rho, \mathbf{q}) \ge E_o(0, \mathbf{q}) = 0 \qquad \rho \ge 0 \tag{3A.5}$$

with equality iff $\rho = 0$. The inequality is reversed for $-1 < \rho \le 0$.

Letting $\lambda \in (0, 1)$, and $\rho_\lambda = \lambda\rho_1 + \bar{\lambda}\rho_2$ (where $\bar{\lambda} = 1 - \lambda$), we have from inequality (i) upon letting $s = 1 + \rho_1$ and $r = 1 + \rho_2$

$$\left[\sum_x q(x) p(y \mid x)^{1/(1+\rho_\lambda)}\right]^{1+\rho_\lambda} \le \left[\sum_x q(x) p(y \mid x)^{1/(1+\rho_1)}\right]^{\lambda(1+\rho_1)} \times \left[\sum_x q(x) p(y \mid x)^{1/(1+\rho_2)}\right]^{\bar{\lambda}(1+\rho_2)} \tag{3A.6}$$

Summing (3A.6) over all $y \in \mathscr{Y}$, we have

$$\sum_y \left[\sum_x q(x)p(y|x)^{1/(1+\rho_\lambda)}\right]^{1+\rho_\lambda} \leq \sum_y \left[\sum_x q(x)p(y|x)^{1/(1+\rho_1)}\right]^{\lambda(1+\rho_1)} \times \left[\sum_x q(x)p(y|x)^{1/(1+\rho_2)}\right]^{\bar{\lambda}(1+\rho_2)} \tag{3A.7}$$

Applying inequality (d) to the right side of (3A.7), we have

$$\sum_y \left[\sum_x q(x)p(y|x)^{1/(1+\rho_\lambda)}\right]^{1+\rho_\lambda} \leq \left\{\sum_y \left[\sum_x q(x)p(y|x)^{1/(1+\rho_1)}\right]^{1+\rho_1}\right\}^{\lambda} \times \left\{\sum_y \left[\sum_x q(x)p(y|x)^{1/(1+\rho_2)}\right]^{1+\rho_2}\right\}^{\bar{\lambda}} \tag{3A.8}$$

Taking $-\ln(\ )$ of both sides of this last equation yields the desired result

$$E_o(\lambda\rho_1 + \bar{\lambda}\rho_2, \mathbf{q}) \geq \lambda E_o(\rho_1, \mathbf{q}) + \bar{\lambda} E_o(\rho_2, \mathbf{q}) \tag{3A.9}$$

This proves that $E_o(\rho, \mathbf{q})$ is convex $\cap$ in ρ for $\rho > -1$ and therefore

$$\frac{\partial^2 E_o(\rho, \mathbf{q})}{\partial \rho^2} \leq 0 \tag{3A.10}$$

Equality is achieved in (3A.9) and (3A.10) iff we had equality in the application of inequalities (i) and (d) that led to (3A.9). Inequality (i) resulted in (3A.6) where for the given y we have equality iff, for some c_y

$$q(x)p(y|x)^{1/(1+\rho_1)} = c_y q(x)p(y|x)^{1/(1+\rho_2)} \qquad \text{for all } x \tag{3A.11}$$

Thus equality holds in (3A.7) iff (3A.11) holds for each y. Inequality (d) used to obtain (3A.8) holds with equality iff, for some c'

$$\left[\sum_x q(x)p(y|x)^{1/(1+\rho_1)}\right]^{1+\rho_1} = c' \left[\sum_x q(x)p(y|x)^{1/(1+\rho_2)}\right]^{1+\rho_2} \qquad \text{for all } y \tag{3A.12}$$

In (3A.12), because of (3A.11), we can factor out $p(y|x) = c_y'' > 0$ to obtain

$$\left[\sum_{x:\, p(y|x)>0} q(x)\right]^{1+\rho_1} = c' \left[\sum_{x:\, p(y|x)>0} q(x)\right]^{1+\rho_2} \qquad \text{for all } y \tag{3A.13}$$

This implies that for some constant α

$$\sum_{x:\, p(y|x)>0} q(x) = \alpha \qquad \text{for all } y \tag{3A.14}$$

Thus, for all x, y such that $q(x)p(y|x) > 0$, we have

$$\frac{\sum_{x'} q(x')p(y|x')}{p(y|x)} = \alpha \tag{3A.15}$$

or as a consequence of definition (3.2.2)

$$\ln \frac{p(y|x)}{\sum_{x} q(x')p(y|x')} = I(\mathbf{q}) \tag{3A.16}$$

3A.3 PROOF OF THEOREM 3.3.2

$$\begin{aligned} E_x(\rho, \mathbf{q}) &= -\rho \ln \sum_{x}\sum_{x'} q(x)q(x')\left[\sum_{y} \sqrt{p(y|x)p(y|x')}\right]^{1/\rho} \\ &= -\ln \left\{\sum_{x}\sum_{x'} q(x)q(x')\left[\sum_{y} \sqrt{p(y|x)p(y|x')}\right]^{1/\rho}\right\}^{\rho} \end{aligned} \tag{3A.17}$$

Let $1 \leq \rho_1 < \rho_2$. From inequality (h), we have

$$\begin{aligned} &\left\{\sum_{x}\sum_{x'} q(x)q(x')\left[\sum_{y} \sqrt{p(y|x)p(y|x')}\right]^{1/\rho_1}\right\}^{\rho_1} \\ &\qquad \geq \left\{\sum_{x}\sum_{x'} q(x)q(x')\left[\sum_{y} \sqrt{p(y|x)p(y|x')}\right]^{1/\rho_2}\right\}^{\rho_2} \end{aligned} \tag{3A.18}$$

with equality iff, for some c

$$\sum_{y} \sqrt{p(y|x)p(y|x')} = c \tag{3A.19}$$

for all x, x' such that $q(x)q(x') > 0$. Hence $E_x(\rho, \mathbf{q})$ is an increasing function of ρ for $\rho \geq 1$.

Let us examine the condition for equality given by (3A.19). For any x such that $q(x) > 0$, we have trivially $q(x)q(x) > 0$ and

$$\begin{aligned} \sum_{y} \sqrt{p(y|x)p(y|x)} &= \sum_{y} p(y|x) \\ &= 1 \\ &= c \end{aligned} \tag{3A.20}$$

Furthermore inequality (c) states that

$$\sum_{y} \sqrt{p(y|x)p(y|x')} \leq 1 \tag{3A.21}$$

with equality iff $p(y|x) = p(y|x')$. Hence equality in (3A.18) is achieved iff

$$p(y|x) = p(y|x')$$

for all y and all x, x' such that $q(x)q(x') > 0$. This is impossible since we assume $I(\mathbf{q}) > 0$. Thus $E_x(\rho, \mathbf{q})$ is strictly increasing with ρ for $\rho \geq 1$

$$\frac{\partial E_x(\rho, \mathbf{q})}{\partial \rho} > 0 \tag{3A.22}$$

and

$$E_x(\rho, \mathbf{q}) \geq E_x(1, \mathbf{q}) > 0 \qquad \text{for } \rho \geq 1 \tag{3A.23}$$

Next, from inequality (*i*), it follows that, for any $\lambda \in (0, 1)$ and $\rho_\lambda = \lambda\rho_1 + \bar{\lambda}\rho_2$, we have

$$\left\{\sum_x \sum_{x'} q(x)q(x')\left[\sum_y \sqrt{p(y|x)p(y|x')}\right]^{1/\rho_\lambda}\right\}^{\rho_\lambda}$$
$$\leq \left\{\sum_x \sum_{x'} q(x)q(x')\left[\sum_y \sqrt{p(y|x)p(y|x')}\right]^{1/\rho_1}\right\}^{\lambda\rho_1}$$
$$\times \left\{\sum_x \sum_{x'} q(x)q(x')\left[\sum_y \sqrt{p(y|x)p(y|x')}\right]^{1/\rho_2}\right\}^{\bar{\lambda}\rho_2} \tag{3A.24}$$

with equality iff, for some c

$$\sum_y \sqrt{p(y|x)p(y|x')} = c \tag{3A.25}$$

for all *nonzero* values of

$$\sum_y \sqrt{p(y|x)p(y|x')} \qquad \text{where } q(x)q(x') > 0$$

From inequality (*c*), we again have that this sum is 1 iff for all y, $p(y|x) = p(y|x')$. The sum is 0 iff, for all y, $p(y|x)p(y|x') = 0$. Thus from (3A.24) we have

$$E_x(\lambda\rho_1 + \bar{\lambda}\rho_2, \mathbf{q}) \geq \lambda E_x(\rho_1, \mathbf{q}) + \bar{\lambda} E_x(\rho_2, \mathbf{q}) \tag{3A.26}$$

or equivalently

$$\frac{\partial^2 E_x(\rho, \mathbf{q})}{\partial \rho^2} \leq 0 \tag{3A.27}$$

with equality iff, for every pair of inputs x and x' for which $q(x)q(x') > 0$, either $p(y|x)p(y|x') = 0$ for all y or $p(y|x) = p(y|x')$ for all y.

APPENDIX 3B KUHN-TUCKER CONDITIONS AND PROOFS OF THEOREMS 3.2.2 AND 3.2.3

3B.1 KUHN-TUCKER CONDITIONS

Theorem (Gallager [1965]—special case of Kuhn and Tucker [1951]) Let $f(\mathbf{q})$ be a continuous convex $\cap$ function of $\mathbf{q} = (q_1, q_2, \ldots, q_Q)$ defined over the region

$$\mathcal{P}_Q = \left\{\mathbf{q}: \sum_{l=1}^{Q} q_l = 1,\ q_k \geq 0,\ k = 1, 2, \ldots, Q\right\}$$

Assume that the partial derivatives $\partial f(\mathbf{q})/\partial q_k$, $k = 1, 2, \ldots, Q$ exist and are continuous, except possibly when $q_k = 0$ (on the boundary of $\mathscr{P}_Q$). Then $f(\mathbf{q})$ has a maximum for some $\mathbf{q}^0 \in \mathscr{P}_Q$ and necessary and sufficient conditions on $\mathbf{q}^0 = (q_1^0, \ldots, q_Q^0)$ to maximize $f(\mathbf{q})$ are that, for some constant λ

$$\left.\frac{\partial f(\mathbf{q})}{\partial q_k}\right|_{\mathbf{q}=\mathbf{q}^0} \leq \lambda \qquad k = 1, 2, \ldots, Q \tag{3B.1}$$

$$\left.\frac{\partial f(\mathbf{q})}{\partial q_k}\right|_{\mathbf{q}=\mathbf{q}^0} = \lambda \qquad \text{for all } k \text{ such that } q_k^0 \neq 0 \tag{3B.2}$$

It is well known that, in real vector spaces without constraints, a convex $\cap$ function either has a unique maximum or, if it possesses more than one maximum, they are all equal, and all points on the line, plane, or hyperplane, connecting these maxima, are also maxima of the function. Also, necessary and sufficient conditions for maxima are that all partial derivatives be zero.

Now, if we impose a linear constraint such as

$$\sum_{k=1}^{Q} q_k = 1$$

then, by the standard technique of Lagrange multipliers, this can be treated as the problem of maximizing

$$f(\mathbf{q}) + \lambda \sum_k q_k$$

which yields then (3B.2), and λ can be obtained from the constraint equation. On the other hand, if the region $\mathscr{P}_Q$ is bounded by hyperplanes ($q_k \geq 0$), we must recognize that a maximum may occur on the boundary, in which case (3B.2) will not hold for that dimension, but it would appear that (3B.1) should (see Fig. 3B.1 for the one-dimensional case). We now proceed to prove (3B.1) and (3B.2).

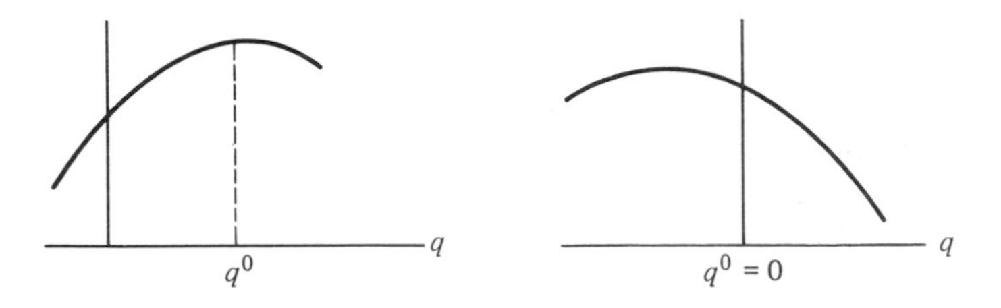

(*a*) Maximum at interior point (3B.2) (*b*) Maximum on boundary (3B.1)

Figure 3B.1 Examples of maxima over regions bounded by hyperplanes.

PROOF *Necessity:* Assume $f(\mathbf{q})$ has a maximum at $\mathbf{q}^0$. Let $\mathbf{q}' = (q'_1, q'_2, \ldots, q'_Q)$ be a distribution vector with $q'_k > 0$ for all k. Since $\mathbf{q}^0$ maximizes $f(\mathbf{q})$, we have, for any $\theta \in (0, 1)$

$$0 \geq f(\theta\mathbf{q}' + (1-\theta)\mathbf{q}^0) - f(\mathbf{q}^0) \tag{3B.3}$$

[*Note:* $\theta\mathbf{q}' + (1-\theta)\mathbf{q}^0$ is interior to $\mathscr{P}_Q$ since $\mathbf{q}'$ is interior to $\mathscr{P}_Q$.] Then consider

$$\frac{df[\theta\mathbf{q}' + (1-\theta)\mathbf{q}^0]}{d\theta} = \sum_{k=1}^{Q} \left.\frac{\partial f(\mathbf{q})}{\partial q_k}\right|_{\mathbf{q}=\theta\mathbf{q}'+(1-\theta)\mathbf{q}^0} (q'_k - q^0_k) \tag{3B.4}$$

Since $\mathbf{q} = \theta\mathbf{q}' + (1-\theta)\mathbf{q}^0$ is interior to $\mathscr{P}_Q$, all partial derivatives exist by the hypothesis of the theorem, and consequently the left side also exists. Obviously

$$\mathbf{q}^0 = \left.\theta\mathbf{q}' + (1-\theta)\mathbf{q}^0\right|_{\theta=0}$$

so that, by the mean value theorem, we have from (3B.3)

$$0 \geq \frac{df[\alpha\mathbf{q}' + (1-\alpha)\mathbf{q}^0]}{d\alpha} \qquad \text{for some } \alpha \in (0, \theta) \tag{3B.5}$$

Using (3B.4) and letting $\theta \to 0$, we obtain

$$0 \geq \lim_{\alpha\to 0} \sum_{k=1}^{Q} \left.\frac{\partial f(\mathbf{q})}{\partial q_k}\right|_{\mathbf{q}=\alpha\mathbf{q}'+(1-\alpha)\mathbf{q}^0} (q'_k - q^0_k)$$

and since the derivatives are continuous by hypothesis

$$0 \geq \sum_{k=1}^{Q} \left.\frac{\partial f(\mathbf{q})}{\partial q_k}\right|_{\mathbf{q}=\mathbf{q}^0} (q'_k - q^0_k) \tag{3B.6}$$

Now, for some $k = k_1$, we must have $q^0_{k_1} \neq 0$. Let k_2 be any other integer from 1 to Q. Now since $\mathbf{q}'$ was an arbitrary point in $\mathscr{P}_Q$, let us choose it such that

$$q'_{k_2} - q^0_{k_2} = q^0_{k_1} - q'_{k_1} = \epsilon > 0 \tag{3B.7}$$

$$q'_k = q^0_k \qquad \text{for all } k \neq k_1 \text{ or } k_2 \tag{3B.8}$$

This is always possible, since $q^0_{k_1} \neq 0$ and (3B.7) and (3B.8) guarantee that $\mathbf{q}'$ so chosen is a distribution vector. Substituting (3B.7) and (3B.8) in (3B.6), we have

$$0 \geq \epsilon \left.\left(\frac{\partial f(\mathbf{q})}{\partial q_{k_2}} - \frac{\partial f(\mathbf{q})}{\partial q_{k_1}}\right)\right|_{\mathbf{q}=\mathbf{q}^0} \tag{3B.9}$$

Now *define*

$$\lambda \equiv \left.\frac{\partial f(\mathbf{q})}{\partial q_{k_1}}\right|_{\mathbf{q}=\mathbf{q}^0} \tag{3B.10}$$

Since $\epsilon > 0$ in (3B.9), it follows that

$$\left.\frac{\partial f(\mathbf{q})}{\partial q_{k2}}\right|_{\mathbf{q}=\mathbf{q}^0} \leq \lambda \tag{3B.11}$$

But, since k_2 is arbitrary, this establishes the *necessity* of (3B.1). Furthermore, if $q^0_{k_2} \neq 0$, we could take $\epsilon < 0$ in (3B.7). This reverses inequality (3B.11), which thus proves the necessity of (3B.2).

Sufficiency: Now given (3B.1) and (3B.2), we show that

$$f(\mathbf{q}^0) \geq f(\mathbf{q}') \qquad \text{for all } \mathbf{q}' \in \mathscr{P}_Q$$

Given (3B.1) and (3B.2), we have

$$\left.\frac{\partial f(\mathbf{q})}{\partial q_k}\right|_{\mathbf{q}=\mathbf{q}^0}(q'_k - q^0_k) \leq \lambda(q'_k - q^0_k)$$

with equality if $q^0_k \neq 0$. Summing over k, we have

$$\sum_{k=1}^{Q} \left.\frac{\partial f(\mathbf{q})}{\partial q_k}\right|_{\mathbf{q}=\mathbf{q}^0}(q'_k - q^0_k) \leq \lambda\left(\sum_{l=1}^{Q} q'_l - \sum_{k=1}^{Q} q^0_k\right) = 0$$

Now (3B.4) yields

$$\left.\frac{df[\theta\mathbf{q}' + (1-\theta)\mathbf{q}^0]}{d\theta}\right|_{\theta=0} = \sum_{k=1}^{Q} \left.\frac{\partial f(\mathbf{q})}{\partial q_k}\right|_{\mathbf{q}=\mathbf{q}^0}(q'_k - q^0_k) \leq 0$$

or equivalently

$$\lim_{\theta\to 0} \frac{f[\theta\mathbf{q}' + (1-\theta)\mathbf{q}^0] - f(\mathbf{q}^0)}{\theta} \leq 0 \tag{3B.12}$$

But, since $f(\mathbf{q})$ is convex $\cap$, the left side of (3B.12) can be replaced by

$$\frac{f[\theta\mathbf{q}' + (1-\theta)\mathbf{q}^0] - f(\mathbf{q}^0)}{\theta} \geq \frac{\theta f(\mathbf{q}') + (1-\theta)f(\mathbf{q}^0) - f(\mathbf{q}^0)}{\theta} = f(\mathbf{q}') - f(\mathbf{q}^0)$$

which proves the sufficiency of (3B.1) and (3B.2).

3B.2 APPLICATION TO $E_o(\rho, \mathbf{q})$ AND $I(\mathbf{q})$

PROOF OF THEOREM 3.2.2 We showed in Lemma 3.2.2 that $e^{-E_o(\rho,\mathbf{q})}$ is convex $\cup$. Thus

$$f(\rho, \mathbf{q}) \equiv -e^{-E_o(\rho,\mathbf{q})} = -\sum_y \alpha(y, \mathbf{q})^{1+\rho}$$

is convex $\cap$, and maximizing $f(\rho, \mathbf{q})$ is equivalent to maximizing $E_o(\rho, \mathbf{q}) = -\ln[-f(\rho, \mathbf{q})]$. Then applying (3B.1) and (3B.2), we have

$$\begin{aligned}\lambda \geq \frac{\partial f(\rho, \mathbf{q})}{\partial q(x)} &= -(1+\rho)\sum_y \alpha(y, \mathbf{q})^{\rho} \frac{\partial \alpha(y, \mathbf{q})}{\partial q(x)} \\ &= -(1+\rho)\sum_y p(y\,|\,x)^{1/(1+\rho)}\alpha(y, \mathbf{q})^{\rho}\end{aligned}$$

since

$$\alpha(y, \mathbf{q}) = \sum_x q(x)p(y|x)^{1/(1+\rho)}$$

Thus

$$\sum_y p(y|x)^{1/(1+\rho)}\alpha(y, \mathbf{q})^\rho \geq \lambda' = \frac{-\lambda}{1+\rho} \qquad \text{for all } x \in \mathscr{X} \tag{3B.13}$$

with equality if $q(x) \neq 0$. Summing over $\mathscr{X}$, after multiplying by $q(x)$ and interchanging the order of summation, we have for the left side of (3B.13)

$$\sum_x q(x) \sum_y p(y|x)^{1/(1+\rho)}\alpha(y, \mathbf{q})^\rho = \sum_y \alpha(y, \mathbf{q})^\rho \sum_x q(x)p(y|x)^{1/(1+\rho)}$$
$$= \alpha(y, \mathbf{q})^{1+\rho}$$

and for the right side

$$\sum_x q(x)\lambda' = \lambda'$$

Thus (3B.13) requires

$$\alpha(y, \mathbf{q})^{1+\rho} = \lambda' \tag{3B.14}$$

[since (3B.13) holds as an equality if $q(x) > 0$ while, if $q(x) = 0$, it did not figure in the sum on either side]. Thus combining (3B.13) and (3B.14), we have

$$\sum_y p(y|x)^{1/(1+\rho)}\alpha(y, \mathbf{q})^\rho \geq \alpha(y, \mathbf{q})^{1+\rho} \qquad \text{for all } x \in \mathscr{X} \tag{3.2.23}$$

with equality for all x such that $q(x) > 0$.

Proof of theorem 3.2.3 In Lemma 3.2.3, we proved that $I(\mathbf{q})$ is convex $\cap$. Thus applying (3B.1) and (3B.2), we have

$$\frac{\partial I(\mathbf{q})}{\partial q(x')} = \frac{\partial}{\partial q(x')}\left[\sum_x \sum_y q(x)p(y|x) \ln p(y|x)\right.$$
$$\left. - \sum_x \sum_y q(x)p(y|x) \ln \sum_{x''} q(x'')p(y|x'')\right]$$
$$= \sum_y p(y|x') \ln \frac{p(y|x')}{\sum_{x''} q(x'')p(y|x'')} - 1$$
$$\leq \lambda \tag{3B.15}$$

Summing over $x' \in \mathscr{X}$, after multiplying by $q(x')$, we have for the left side

$$\sum_{x'} q(x') \sum_y p(y|x') \ln \frac{p(y|x')}{\sum_{x''} q(x'')p(y|x'')} - 1 = I(\mathbf{q}) - 1$$

and for the right side, of course

$$\sum_{x'} q(x')\lambda = \lambda$$

Thus $\lambda = I(\mathbf{q}) - 1$, and consequently (3B.15) becomes

$$\sum_y p(y \mid x) \ln \frac{p(y \mid x)}{\sum_{x'} q(x')p(y \mid x')} \leq I(\mathbf{q}) = C \qquad \text{for all } x \in \mathscr{X} \quad (3.2.2)$$

[since $\mathbf{q}$ maximizes $I(\mathbf{q})$] with equality for all x such that $q(x) > 0$.

APPENDIX 3C COMPUTATIONAL ALGORITHM FOR CAPACITY (Arimoto [1972], Blahut [1972])

We have a DMC with input alphabet $\mathscr{X}$, output alphabet $\mathscr{Y}$, and transition probabilities $p(y \mid x)$ for $x \in \mathscr{X}$, $y \in \mathscr{Y}$. Let $\mathbf{q} = \{q(x): x \in \mathscr{X}\}$ be a probability distribution on $\mathscr{X}$. Then channel capacity is

$$C = \max_{\mathbf{q}} I(\mathbf{q}) \tag{3C.1}$$

where

$$\begin{aligned} I(\mathbf{q}) &= \sum_x \sum_y p(y \mid x) q(x) \ln \frac{p(y \mid x)}{p(y)} \\ &= \sum_x \sum_y p(y \mid x) q(x) \ln \frac{q(x \mid y)}{q(x)} \end{aligned} \tag{3C.2}$$

where

$$q(x \mid y) \equiv \frac{p(y \mid x) q(x)}{p(y)} \tag{3C.3}$$

and

$$p(y) \equiv \sum_x p(y \mid x) q(x) \tag{3C.4}$$

Let $\mathbf{Q} = \{Q(x \mid y): x \in \mathscr{X}, y \in \mathscr{Y}\}$ be any set of conditional probability distributions; then

$$Q(x \mid y) \geq 0 \qquad \text{for all } x, y \tag{3C.5}$$

and

$$\sum_x Q(x \mid y) = 1 \qquad \text{for all } y \tag{3C.6}$$

Let

$$F(\mathbf{q}, \mathbf{Q}) \equiv \sum_x \sum_y p(y \mid x) q(x) \ln \frac{Q(x \mid y)}{q(x)} \tag{3C.7}$$

Lemma For any $\mathbf{Q}$ we have

$$I(\mathbf{q}) \geq F(\mathbf{q}, \mathbf{Q}) \tag{3C.8}$$

with equality iff $Q(x \mid y) = q(x \mid y)$ for all x, y.

PROOF From inequality (1.1.8) we have for any y

$$\sum_x q(x \mid y) \ln \frac{1}{q(x \mid y)} \leq \sum_x q(x \mid y) \ln \frac{1}{Q(x \mid y)} \tag{3C.9}$$

with equality iff $Q(x \mid y) = q(x \mid y)$ for all x. Observing that

$$p(y \mid x) q(x) = q(x \mid y) p(y)$$

we see that (3C.8) follows directly from (3C.9).

This lemma then yields

$$I(\mathbf{q}) = \max_{\mathbf{Q}} F(\mathbf{q}, \mathbf{Q}) \tag{3C.10}$$

where the maximum is achieved by

$$Q(x \mid y) = \frac{p(y \mid x) q(x)}{\sum_{x'} p(y \mid x') q(x')} \qquad \text{for all } x, y \tag{3C.11}$$

Channel capacity can be expressed in the form

$$C = \max_{\mathbf{q}} \max_{\mathbf{Q}} F(\mathbf{q}, \mathbf{Q}) \tag{3C.12}$$

Suppose now we fix $\mathbf{Q}$ and consider the maximization of $F(\mathbf{q}, \mathbf{Q})$ with respect to the input probability distribution $\mathbf{q}$. First we note from (3C.7) that, for fixed $\mathbf{Q}$

$$F(\mathbf{q}, \mathbf{Q}) = \sum_x q(x) \ln \frac{1}{q(x)} + \sum_x \sum_y p(y \mid x) q(x) \ln Q(x \mid y) \tag{3C.13}$$

is a convex $\cap$ function of the set of input distributions $\mathbf{q}$. The Kuhn-Tucker theorem (App. 3B) states that necessary and sufficient conditions on the $\mathbf{q}$ that maximizes $F(\mathbf{q}, \mathbf{Q})$ are

$$\frac{\partial F(\mathbf{q}, \mathbf{Q})}{\partial q(x)} \leq \lambda \qquad \text{for all } x \tag{3C.14}$$

with equality when $q(x) > 0$. λ is chosen to satisfy the equality constraint

$$\sum_x q(x) = 1$$

For $q(x) > 0$, this becomes

$$-1 - \ln q(x) + \sum_y p(y|x) \ln Q(x|y) = \lambda \tag{3C.15}$$

or

$$q(x) = \exp\left\{-1 - \lambda + \sum_y p(y|x) \ln Q(x|y)\right\} \tag{3C.16}$$

Choosing λ to meet the equality constraint

$$\sum_x q(x) = 1$$

we have for $q(x) > 0$

$$q(x) = \frac{\exp\left\{\sum_y p(y|x) \ln Q(x|y)\right\}}{\sum_{x'} \exp\left\{\sum_y p(y|x') \ln Q(x'|y)\right\}} \tag{3C.17}$$

Hence we have (3C.11) for the $\mathbf{Q}$ that maximizes $F(\mathbf{q}, \mathbf{Q})$ for fixed $\mathbf{q}$, and we have (3C.17) for the $\mathbf{q}$ that maximizes $F(\mathbf{q}, \mathbf{Q})$ for fixed $\mathbf{Q}$. Simultaneous satisfaction of (3C.11) and (3C.17) by $\mathbf{q}$ and $\mathbf{Q}$ achieves capacity.

The computation algorithm consists of alternating the application of (3C.11) and (3C.17). For any index $k = 0, 1, 2, \ldots$, let us define

$$Q^{(k)}(x|y) \equiv \frac{p(y|x)q^{(k)}(x)}{\sum_{x'} p(y|x')q^{(k)}(x')} \qquad \text{for all } x, y \tag{3C.18}$$

$$q^{(k+1)}(x) \equiv \frac{\exp\left\{\sum_y p(y|x) \ln Q^{(k)}(x|y)\right\}}{\sum_{x'} \exp\left\{\sum_y p(y|x') \ln Q^{(k)}(x'|y)\right\}} \qquad \text{for all } x \tag{3C.19}$$

and

$$C(k+1) \equiv F(\mathbf{q}^{(k+1)}, \mathbf{Q}^{(k)}) \tag{3C.20}$$

The algorithm is as follows:

Step 1. Pick an initial input probability distribution $\mathbf{q}^{(0)}$ and set $k = 0$. (The uniform distribution will do.)

Step 2. Compute $\mathbf{Q}^{(k)}$ according to (3C.18).
Step 3. Compute $\mathbf{q}^{(k+1)}$ according to (3C.19).
Step 4. Change index k to $k + 1$ and go to Step 2.

To stop the algorithm, merely set some tolerance level $\delta > 0$ and stop when index k first achieves

$$|C(k+1) - C(k)| \leq \delta \tag{3C.21}$$

There remains only the proof that this algorithm converges to the capacity.

Theorem For the above algorithm

$$\lim_{k \to \infty} |C - C(k)| = 0 \tag{3C.22}$$

PROOF Let

$$r^{(k+1)}(x) \equiv \exp\left\{\sum_y p(y|x) \ln Q^{(k)}(x|y)\right\} \qquad k = 0, 1, 2, \ldots \tag{3C.23}$$

so that, from (3C.19)

$$q^{(k+1)}(x) = \frac{r^{(k+1)}(x)}{\sum_{x'} r^{(k+1)}(x')} \tag{3C.24}$$

From (3C.12), we have $C \geq C(k + 1)$ where now

$$\begin{aligned}
C(k+1) &= F(\mathbf{q}^{(k+1)}, \mathbf{Q}^{(k)}) \\
&= \sum_x \sum_y p(y|x) q^{(k+1)}(x) \ln \frac{Q^{(k)}(x|y)}{q^{(k+1)}(x)} \\
&= \sum_x \sum_y p(y|x) q^{(k+1)}(x) \ln \frac{Q^{(k)}(x|y)}{\left(r^{(k+1)}(x) \big/ \sum_{x'} r^{(k+1)}(x')\right)} \\
&= \sum_x q^{(k+1)}(x) \left\{\sum_y p(y|x) \ln Q^{(k)}(x|y)\right. \\
&\qquad \left. - \ln r^{(k+1)}(x) + \ln\left(\sum_{x'} r^{(k+1)}(x')\right)\right\}
\end{aligned} \tag{3C.25}$$

From the definition of $r^{(k+1)}(x)$ in (3C.23), we see that the first two terms cancel giving us

$$C(k+1) = \ln\left(\sum_x r^{(k+1)}(x)\right) \tag{3C.26}$$

Now suppose $\mathbf{q}^*$ achieves capacity so that $C = I(\mathbf{q}^*)$. Consider

$$\sum_x q^*(x) \ln \frac{q^{(k+1)}(x)}{q^{(k)}(x)} = \sum_x q^*(x) \ln \frac{r^{(k+1)}(x)}{q^{(k)}(x)\left(\sum_{x'} r^{(k+1)}(x')\right)}$$

$$= -C(k+1) + \sum_x q^*(x) \ln \frac{1}{q^{(k)}(x)} + \sum_x q^*(x) \ln r^{(k+1)}(x)$$

$$= -C(k+1) + \sum_x \sum_y p(y|x)q^*(x) \ln \frac{1}{q^{(k)}(x)}$$

$$+ \sum_x \sum_y p(y|x)q^*(x) \ln Q^{(k)}(x|y)$$

$$= -C(k+1) + \sum_x \sum_y p(y|x)q^*(x) \ln \frac{Q^{(k)}(x|y)}{q^{(k)}(x)}$$

$$= -C(k+1) + \sum_x \sum_y p(y|x)q^*(x) \ln \frac{p(y|x)p^*(y)}{p^{(k)}(y)p^*(y)}$$

$$= -C(k+1) + C + \sum_y p^*(y) \ln \frac{p^*(y)}{p^{(k)}(y)} \tag{3C.27}$$

where

$$p^*(y) \equiv \sum_x p(y|x)q^*(x)$$

and

$$p^{(k)}(y) \equiv \sum_x p(y|x)q^{(k)}(x)$$

Again using inequality (1.1.8), we have

$$\sum_y p^*(y) \ln \frac{p^*(y)}{p^{(k)}(y)} \geq 0 \tag{3C.28}$$

and, from (3C.27)

$$C - C(k+1) \leq \sum_x q^*(x) \ln \frac{q^{(k+1)}(x)}{q^{(k)}(x)} \tag{3C.29}$$

Noting that $C \geq C(k+1)$ and summing (3C.29) over k from 0 to $N-1$, we have

$$\sum_{k=0}^{N-1} |C - C(k+1)| \leq \sum_x q^*(x) \ln \frac{q^{(N)}(x)}{q^{(0)}(x)} \tag{3C.30}$$

Again from inequality (1.1.8), we have

$$\sum_x q^*(x) \ln q^{(N)}(x) \leq \sum_x q^*(x) \ln q^*(x) \tag{3C.31}$$

and thus

$$\sum_{k=1}^{N} |C - C(k)| \leq \sum_{x} q^*(x) \ln \frac{q^*(x)}{q^{(0)}(x)} \tag{3C.32}$$

The upper bound on (3C.32) is finite and independent of N. Hence $\{|C - C(k)|\}_{k=1}^{\infty}$ is a convergent series, which implies

$$\lim_{k \to \infty} |C - C(k)| = 0 \tag{3C.33}$$

Similar efficient computational algorithms have been developed for the expurgated exponent $E_{ex}(R)$ (Lesh [1976]) given by (3.3.13) and (3.3.14) and for the sphere-packing exponent $E_{sp}(R)$ (Arimoto [1976], Lesh [1976]) given by (3.6.47). Recall that the ensemble average exponent equals the sphere-packing exponents for higher rates and is easy to derive from $E_{sp}(R)$.

PROBLEMS

3.1 Compute $E_o(1, \mathbf{q})$ and $E_o(1) = \max_{\mathbf{q}} E_o(1, \mathbf{q})$ for each of the following channels:

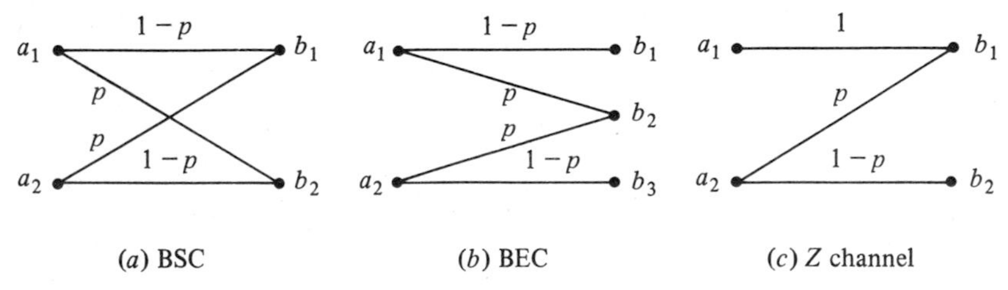

Figure P3.1

3.2 (*a*) Compute $\max_{\mathbf{q}} E_o(\rho, \mathbf{q}) = E_o(\rho)$ and $C \equiv \max_{\mathbf{q}} I(\mathbf{q})$ for the following channels.
(*b*) Compute $E(R)$ for each channel.
Hint: Check conditions (3.2.23) for the obvious intuitive choice of $\mathbf{q}$.

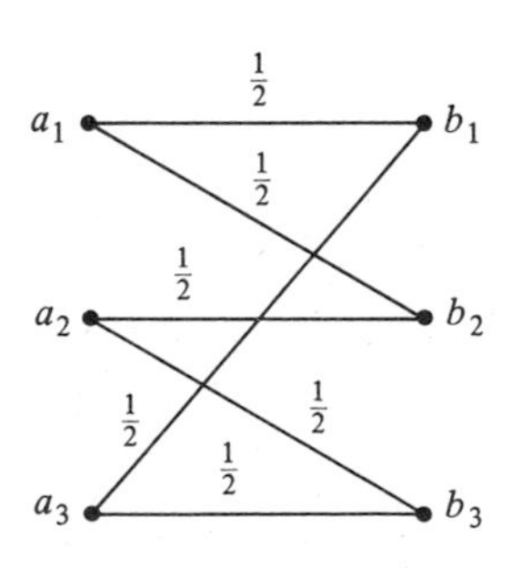

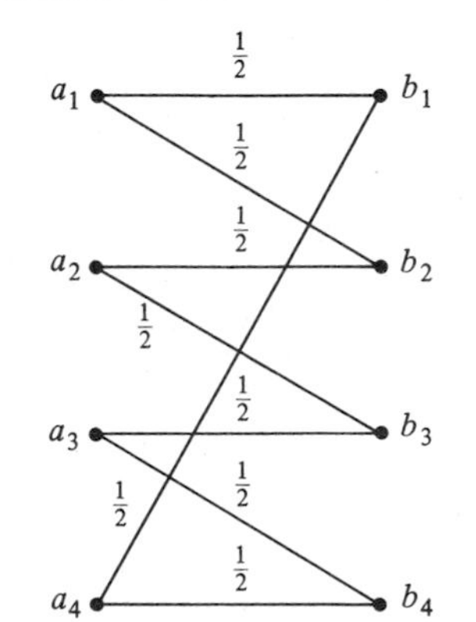

Figure P3.2

3.3 (*a*) Compute $E_o(\rho)$, C, and $E(R)$ for the Q-input, Q-output noiseless channel

$$p(b_k|a_k) = 1 \qquad\qquad i, k = 1, 2, \ldots Q$$
$$p(b_k|a_i) = 0 \qquad \text{for all } k \neq i$$

(*b*) Compute $E_o(\rho)$, $E_o'(\rho)$, $E_o(1)$, and $C = \lim_{\rho \to 0} E_o'(\rho)$ for the Q-input, Q-output channel

$$p(b_k|a_i) = p \qquad \text{for all } i \neq k$$
$$p(b_k|a_k) = \bar{p} \qquad \text{where} \qquad \bar{p} + (Q-1)p = 1$$

Do *not* compute $E(R)$, but sketch it denoting key numerical parameters.

(*c*) Find the optimizing $\mathbf{q}$ and sketch $E(R)$ for the six-input, four-output channel.

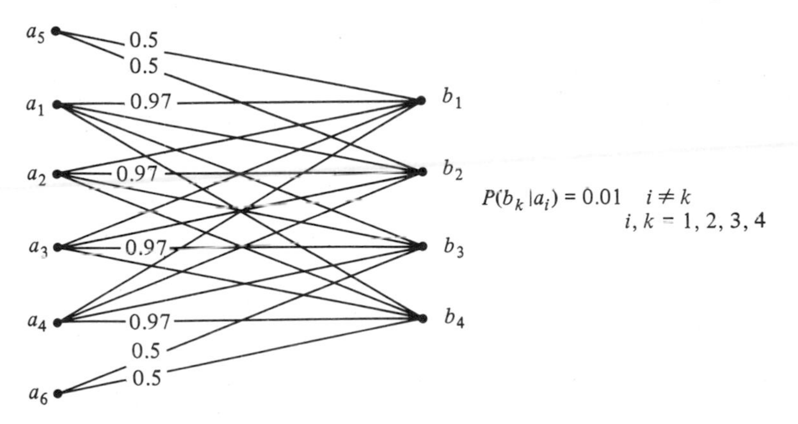

Figure P3.3

Hint: Show that (*c*) can be regarded as the superimposition of (*b*) with $Q = 4$ and (*a*) with $Q = 2$.

3.4 (*a*) Show that, for a Q-input, J-output memoryless channel, the necessary and sufficient condition (3.2.23) on the input distribution $\mathbf{q}$ which maximizes $E_o(\rho, \mathbf{q})$ can be stated in matrix form as follows

$$\boldsymbol{\alpha}^{\rho}[P_{jk}^{1/(1+\rho)}] \geq (\exp[-E_o(\rho)])\mathbf{u} \qquad \text{where} \qquad \boldsymbol{\alpha}^T = [P_{jk}^{1/(1+\rho)}]\mathbf{q}^T$$

with equality for all k for which $q_k \neq 0$, where we have used the notation

$$q_k = q(a_k) \qquad j = 1, 2, \ldots, J$$
$$P_{jk} = p(b_j|a_k) \qquad k = 1, 2, \ldots, Q$$
$$\boldsymbol{\alpha} = (\alpha_1, \alpha_2, \ldots, \alpha_Q) \qquad \boldsymbol{\alpha}^{\rho} = (\alpha_1^{\rho}, \alpha_2^{\rho}, \ldots, \alpha_Q^{\rho})$$
$$\mathbf{u} = \underbrace{(1, 1, \ldots, 1)}_{\leftarrow Q \rightarrow} \qquad E_o(\rho) = \max_{\mathbf{q}} E_o(\rho, \mathbf{q}) \qquad \text{(scalar)}$$

and $\mathbf{X}^T$ is the transpose of $\mathbf{X}$.

(*b*) Under the following conditions

(*i*) $J = Q$

(*ii*) $\det[P_{jk}^{1/(1+\rho)}] \neq 0$

(*iii*) $q_k > 0 \qquad$ for all k

show that

(1) $e^{E_o(\rho)}\boldsymbol{\alpha}^{\rho} = \mathbf{u}[P_{jk}^{1/(1+\rho)}]^{-1} \equiv \boldsymbol{\xi}^{\rho}$

(2) $e^{E_o(\rho)/\rho}\boldsymbol{\alpha}^T = \boldsymbol{\xi}^T$

and consequently

$$\mathbf{q}^T = e^{-E_o(\rho)/\rho}[P_{jk}^{1/(1+\rho)}]^{-1}\boldsymbol{\xi}^T$$

(3) Applying the constraint equation $(\mathbf{u}, \mathbf{q}) = 1$, show that

$$E_o(\rho) = \rho \ln \{\mathbf{u}[P_{jk}^{1/(1+\rho)}]^{-1}\xi^T\}$$

3.5 Apply the results of Prob. 3.4 to obtain, for the channel of Prob. 3.1*c* with $p = \frac{1}{2}$

(*a*) $E_o(\rho) = \rho \ln [1 + (2^{1/(1+\rho)} - 1)^{(1+\rho)/\rho}]$.

(*b*) Find $\mathbf{q}$ in terms of ρ and thus show that the optimizing distribution varies with R. Indicate specifically $\mathbf{q}|_{\rho=0}$ and $\mathbf{q}|_{\rho=1}$.

(*c*) Find C.

(*d*) Sketch $E(R)$.

3.6 For the Q-input, $(Q + 1)$-output "erasure" channel with

$$P(b_k | a_k) = \tfrac{1}{2}$$

$$p(b_{Q+1} | a_k) = \tfrac{1}{2}$$

$$p(b_j | a_k) = 0 \qquad j \neq k \qquad j = 1, 2, \ldots Q \qquad k = 1, 2, \ldots Q$$

(*a*) Determine the maximizing distribution $\mathbf{q}$ for all $\rho \in [0, 1]$.

(*b*) Determine $E_o(\rho)$, $E_o'(\rho)$ and $E(R)$ explicitly and sketch $E(R)$.

3.7 For all three channels of Prob. 3.1, determine

(*a*) $E_x(\rho) = \max_\rho E_x(\rho, \mathbf{q})$

(*b*) $E_x'(\rho)$

(*c*) $E_{ex}(R)$ and sketch

3.8 (*a*) For the channel of Prob. 3.3*a*, determine $E_x(\rho)$ and $E_{ex}(R)$.

(*b*) Repeat for the channels of Prob. 3.2 and discuss the difference in the results of (*i*) and (*ii*).

3.9 For the channel of Fig. 3.7

(*a*) Find the maximizing $\mathbf{q}$, $E_o(\rho)$, and C. Sketch $E(R)$.

(*b*) Find $E_x(\rho, \mathbf{q})$ using the same $\mathbf{q}$ as in (*a*). Sketch $E_{ex}(R, q)$ on the same diagram as (*a*).

3.10 For any distribution $\mathbf{q}$, show that

$$(a) \quad \left.\frac{\partial E_o(\rho, \mathbf{q})}{\partial \rho}\right|_{\rho=1} \leq E_o(\rho, \mathbf{q})\Big|_{\rho=1}$$

$$(b) \quad \left.\frac{\partial E_x(\rho, \mathbf{q})}{\partial \rho}\right|_{\rho=1} \leq \left.\frac{\partial E_o(\rho, \mathbf{q})}{\partial \rho}\right|_{\rho=1} \qquad \text{with equality iff } C = 0$$

3.11 (*a*) Show that if the $Q \times Q$ matrix with elements

$$\alpha_{xx'} = \left[\sum_y \sqrt{p(y|x)p(y|x')}\right]^{1/\rho} \qquad x, x' \in \mathscr{X} = \{a_1 \cdots a_Q\}$$

is nonnegative definite, then the function

$$f(\mathbf{q}) = \sum_x \sum_{x'} q(x)q(x')\left[\sum_y \sqrt{p(y|x)p(y|x')}\right]^{1/\rho}$$

is convex $\cup$ in the probability distribution space of $\mathbf{q}$ (Jelinek [1968*b*]).

(*b*) Obtain necessary and sufficient conditions on $\mathbf{q}$ to minimize f, and consequently maximize $E_x(\rho, \mathbf{q})$, for any channel satisfying (*a*).

3.12 (*a*) For the binary-input AWGN channel and for the BSC derived from it by hard quantization of the channel output symbols, verify (3.4.19) and (3.4.20).

(*b*) Verify Fig. 3.8 (*a*), (*b*), (*c*) in the limit as $\mathscr{E}_s/N_o \to 0$ and $\mathscr{E}_s/N_o \to \infty$.

(*c*) Verify (3.4.21) and obtain curves for the octal output quantized AWGN channel (for the quantizer of Fig. 2.13, let $a = \frac{1}{2}\sqrt{N_o/2}$).

3.13 Show that the AWGN channel with $\mathcal{E}_s/N_o \ll 1$ satisfies the definitions (3.4.23) and (3.4.24) of a very noisy channel.

3.14 (Parallel Channels) (Gallager [1965]) Let the independent memoryless channels 1 and 2 with identical input and output alphabets be used in parallel. That is, for each symbol time, we send a symbol x over channel 1 and simultaneously a symbol z over channel 2.

(*a*) Treating these parallel channels as a single composite channel, show that for the composite

$$E_o(\rho, \mathbf{q}) = E_{o_1}(\rho, \mathbf{q}_1) + E_{o_2}(\rho, \mathbf{q}_2)$$

where the subscripts 1 and 2 refer to the corresponding exponent function for the individual channels and $\mathbf{q} = (\mathbf{q}_1, \mathbf{q}_2)$ is a $2Q$-dimensional vector where $\mathbf{q}_1$ and $\mathbf{q}_2$ are each Q dimensional.

(*b*) Show then that

$$\max_{\mathbf{q}} E_o(\rho, \mathbf{q}) = \max_{\mathbf{q}_1} E_{o_1}(\rho, \mathbf{q}_1) + \max_{\mathbf{q}_2} E_{o_2}(\rho, \mathbf{q}_2)$$

3.15 (Sum Channels) (Gallager [1968]) Suppose we have n independent memoryless channels, possibly with different input and output alphabets. At each symbol time, a symbol is sent over only one of the channels. We call this a sum channel.

Let $\quad E_{o_i}(\rho) \equiv \max_{\mathbf{q}} E_{o_i}(\rho, \mathbf{q}) \qquad$ for the ith channel, $i = 1, 2, \ldots, n$

$\qquad E_o(\rho) \equiv \max_{\mathbf{q}} E_o(\rho, \mathbf{q}) \qquad$ for the sum channel

$\qquad \beta(i) \equiv \Pr\{\text{using } i\text{th channel}\}$

Hence if the weighting vector for the ith channel is $(q_1^{(i)}, \ldots, q_Q^{(i)}) = \mathbf{q}^i$, the sum channel weighting is $\mathbf{q} = (\beta(1)\mathbf{q}^{(1)}, \beta(2)\mathbf{q}^{(2)}, \ldots, \beta(n)\mathbf{q}^{(n)})$.

(*a*) Show that

$$e^{E_o(\rho)/\rho} = \sum_{i=1}^{n} e^{E_{o,i}(\rho)/\rho}$$

and

$$\beta(i) = \frac{e^{E_{o,i}(\rho)/\rho}}{\sum_{i=1}^{n} e^{[E_{o,i}(\rho)/\rho]}}$$

(*b*) Show from this that the sum channel capacity C is related to the individual channel capacities C_i by

$$C = \ln \sum_{i=1}^{n} e^{C_i}$$

(*c*) Apply these results to obtain $E_o(\rho)$ and C for the channel of Fig. 3.7.

3.16 (List Decoding) Suppose the decoder, rather than deciding in favor of a single message m, constructs a list $m_1, m_2, \ldots, m_L$ of the L most likely messages. An error is said to occur in list decoding if the correct message is not in this list.

(*a*) Show that, for a memoryless channel

$$P_{E_m} = \sum_{\mathbf{y} \in \overline{\Lambda_m}} p_N(\mathbf{y} \mid \mathbf{x}_m)$$

where $\overline{\Lambda_m} \equiv \left\{\mathbf{y}: \dfrac{p_N(\mathbf{y} \mid \mathbf{x}_{m_l})}{p_N(\mathbf{y} \mid \mathbf{x}_m)} > 1 \text{ for some set of } L \text{ messages } m_1, m_2, \ldots, m_L \text{ where } m_l \neq m \text{ for all } l.\right\}$

(*b*) Using the techniques of Sec. 2.4, show that

$$\overline{\Lambda}_m \subset \Lambda_m^b \equiv \left\{\mathbf{y}: \sum_{m_1 \neq m} \cdots \sum_{m_L \neq m} \left[\prod_{l=1}^{L} \frac{p_N(\mathbf{y} \mid \mathbf{x}_{m_l})}{p_N(\mathbf{y} \mid \mathbf{x}_m)}\right]^{\lambda} > 1\right\} \qquad \lambda > 0$$

and

$$P_{E_m} < \sum_{\mathbf{y}} p_N(\mathbf{y} \mid \mathbf{x}_m) f_N(\mathbf{y})$$

where

$$f_N(\mathbf{y}) \equiv \left\{ \sum_{m_1 \neq m} \cdots \sum_{m_L \neq m} \prod_{l=1}^{L} \left[\frac{p_N(\mathbf{y} \mid \mathbf{x}_{m_l})}{p_N(\mathbf{y} \mid \mathbf{x}_m)} \right]^{\lambda} \right\}^{\rho} \qquad \rho > 0$$

and thus that, with $\lambda = \dfrac{1}{1 + \rho L}$

$$P_{E_m} < \sum_{\mathbf{y}} p_N(\mathbf{y} \mid \mathbf{x}_m)^{1/(1+\rho L)} \left\{ \sum_{m_1 \neq m} \cdots \sum_{m_L \neq m} \prod_{l=1}^{L} p_N(\mathbf{y} \mid \mathbf{x}_{m_l})^{1/(1+\rho L)} \right\}^{\rho}$$

(*c*) Now applying the techniques of Sec. 3.1, obtain an ensemble average bound

$$\bar{P}_{E_1} < \sum_{\mathbf{y}} \sum_{\mathbf{x}_1} q_N(\mathbf{x}_1) p_N(\mathbf{y} \mid \mathbf{x}_1)^{1/(1+\rho L)} \left\{ \binom{M-1}{L} \left[\sum_{\mathbf{x}} q_N(\mathbf{x}) p_N(\mathbf{y} \mid \mathbf{x})^{1/(1+\rho L)} \right]^{L} \right\}^{\rho}$$

and, since $\binom{M-1}{L} < (M-1)^L$, show that

$$\bar{P}_e < \sum_{\mathbf{y}} \sum_{\mathbf{x}} q_N(\mathbf{x}) p_N(\mathbf{y} \mid \mathbf{x})^{1/(1+\rho L)} \left\{ (M-1) \sum_{\mathbf{x}} q_N(\mathbf{x}) p_N(\mathbf{y} \mid \mathbf{x})^{1/(1+\rho L)} \right\}^{L\rho} \qquad 0 \le \rho \le 1$$

$$< e^{-N[E_o(\tilde{\rho}, \mathbf{q}) - \tilde{\rho} R]}$$

where $\tilde{\rho} \equiv \rho L$ so that $0 \le \tilde{\rho} \le L$.

(*d*) Compare this result, after maximizing with respect to $\mathbf{q}$, with the sphere-packing lower bound.

3.17 Find $\mu(s)$ of (3.5.3) for the two N-symbol code vectors (a, a, ..., a) and (b, b, ..., b) for each of the following channels

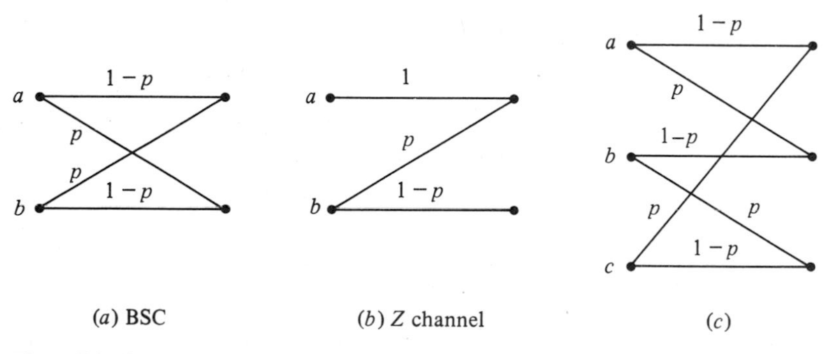

(*a*) BSC (*b*) *Z* channel (*c*)

Figure P3.17

3.18 (Chernoff Upper Bound on the Tail of a Distribution)

(*a*) If η is an arbitrary random variable with finite moments of all orders and θ is a constant, show

$$\Pr\{\eta \ge \theta\} \le E[e^{s(\eta - \theta)}] \qquad s \ge 0$$
$$= e^{\Gamma(s) - s\theta}$$

where

$$\Gamma(s) = \ln \sum_{\eta} e^{s\eta} p(\eta)$$

(*b*) Show that minimizing on s results in

$$\Pr\{\eta \geq \theta\} \leq e^{\Gamma(s) - s\Gamma'(s)}$$

where $\theta = \Gamma'(s) = \dfrac{d\Gamma(s)}{ds}$

Hint: Show first that $\Gamma(s) - s\theta$ is convex ∪ by comparing it to $\mu(s)$ of (3.5.3).

(*c*) Let

$$\eta = \sum_{n=1}^{N} y_n$$

where the y_n's are independent identically distributed random variables. Verify (3.5.38)

$$\Pr\{\eta > \theta\} < e^{N[\gamma(s) - s\gamma'(s)]}$$

where

$$\gamma(s) = \frac{\Gamma(s)}{N} = \ln \sum_y e^{sy} p(y)$$

3.19 (*a*) Apply Prob. 3.18*c* to the binomial distribution by letting

$$\eta = \sum_{n=1}^{N} y_n \text{ where } y_n = \begin{cases} 0 & \text{with probability } 1-p \\ 1 & \text{with probability } p \end{cases}$$

Obtain upper bounds on $\Pr(\eta \geq ND)$ and $\Pr(\eta \leq ND)$:

$$e^{N\mathscr{H}(D)} p^{ND} (1-p)^{N(1-D)} \geq \begin{cases} \Pr(\eta \geq ND), & p < D \\ \Pr(\eta \leq ND), & p > D \end{cases}$$

Hint: For $p > D$, replace η by $N - \eta$, p by $1 - p$, and D by $1 - D$.
Also show that, when $p = \frac{1}{2}$ and $D < \frac{1}{2}$

$$e^{-N[R(D) + o(N)]} \leq \Pr\{\eta \leq ND\} \leq e^{-NR(D)}$$

where

$$R(D) \equiv \ln 2 - \mathscr{H}(D)$$

(*b*) Apply Prob. 3.18*b* to the Gaussian distribution showing that, if η is a zero-mean unit variance Gaussian random variable

$$\Pr\{\eta > \theta\} = Q(\theta) < e^{-\theta^2/2}$$

3.20 Find the sphere-packing bound for all the channels of Probs. 3.2, 3.3, 3.5, and 3.6.

3.21 Alternative proof of the expurgated bound: For any DMC channel, the expurgated bound given by Theorem 3.3.1 can be proven using a sequence of ensemble average arguments rather than expurgating codes from an ensemble as is done in Sec. 3.3.

Begin with a code of block length N and rate $R = (\ln M)/N$ given by $\mathscr{C} = \{\mathbf{x}_1, \mathbf{x}_2, \ldots, \mathbf{x}_M\}$. The Bhattacharyya bound of (2.3.16) gives

$$P_{E_m}(\mathscr{C}) \leq \sum_{m' \neq m} \left[\sum_{\mathbf{y}} \sqrt{p_N(\mathbf{y}|\mathbf{x}_m) p_N(\mathbf{y}|\mathbf{x}_{m'})} \right] \equiv B_m(\mathscr{C})$$

for $m = 1, 2, \ldots, M$.

(*a*) Show that for any $s \in (0, 1]$

$$B_m^s(\mathscr{C}) \le \sum_{m' \ne m} \left[\sum_{\mathbf{y}} \sqrt{p_N(\mathbf{y}|\mathbf{x}_m)p_N(\mathbf{y}|\mathbf{x}_{m'})} \right]^s$$

for $m = 1, 2, \ldots, M$.

(*b*) Consider an ensemble of codewords where any codeword $\mathbf{x}$ is chosen with probability

$$q_N(\mathbf{x}) = \prod_{n=1}^{N} q(x_n)$$

Assume that the $M - 1$ codewords $\{\mathbf{x}_{m'}\}_{m' \ne m}$ are fixed and average $B_m^s(\mathscr{C})$ with respect to codeword $\mathbf{x}_m$ chosen from the above ensemble. Denote this average by $\overline{B_m^s(\mathscr{C})}$ and show that

$$\overline{B_m^s(\mathscr{C})} \le M[\gamma(s, \mathbf{q})]^N$$

where

$$\gamma(s, \mathbf{q}) \equiv \max_{\substack{x' \\ q(x') > 0}} \sum_{x} q(x) \left(\sum_{y} \sqrt{p(y|x)p(y|x')} \right)^s$$

[Here, without loss of essential generality, assume that all codewords in $\mathscr{C}$ satisfy $q_N(\mathbf{x}) > 0$.]

(*c*) Given code $\mathscr{C}$, show that there exists a codeword $\hat{\mathbf{x}}_m$ such that a new code $\mathscr{C}_m$ which is the same as $\mathscr{C}$ with $\mathbf{x}_m$ replaced by $\hat{\mathbf{x}}_m$ satisfies

$$P_{E_m}(\mathscr{C}_m) \le B_m(\mathscr{C}_m) \le M^{1/s}[\gamma(s, \mathbf{q})]^{N/s} \qquad \text{for any } s \in (0, 1]$$

(*d*) Using (*c*), construct a sequence of codes

$$\hat{\mathscr{C}}_0 = \mathscr{C} = \{\mathbf{x}_1, \mathbf{x}_2, \ldots, \mathbf{x}_M\}$$
$$\hat{\mathscr{C}}_1 = \{\hat{\mathbf{x}}_1, \mathbf{x}_2, \mathbf{x}_3, \ldots, \mathbf{x}_M\}$$
$$\hat{\mathscr{C}}_2 = \{\hat{\mathbf{x}}_1, \hat{\mathbf{x}}_2, \mathbf{x}_3, \ldots, \mathbf{x}_M\}$$
$$\vdots$$
$$\hat{\mathscr{C}}_M = \{\hat{\mathbf{x}}_1, \hat{\mathbf{x}}_2, \hat{\mathbf{x}}_3, \ldots, \hat{\mathbf{x}}_M\}$$

such that

$$P_{E_m}(\hat{\mathscr{C}}_m) \le B_m(\hat{\mathscr{C}}_m) \le M^{1/s}[\gamma(s, \mathbf{q})]^{N/s}$$

where

$$B_m(\hat{\mathscr{C}}_m) \equiv \sum_{m'=1}^{m-1} \left[\sum_{\mathbf{y}} \sqrt{p_N(\mathbf{y}|\hat{\mathbf{x}}_m)p_N(\mathbf{y}|\hat{\mathbf{x}}_{m'})} \right] + \sum_{m'=m+1}^{M} \left[\sum_{\mathbf{y}} \sqrt{p_N(\mathbf{y}|\hat{\mathbf{x}}_m)p_N(\mathbf{y}|\mathbf{x}_{m'})} \right]$$

for $m = 1, 2, \ldots, M$.

(*e*) For code $\hat{\mathscr{C}}_M = \{\hat{\mathbf{x}}_1, \hat{\mathbf{x}}_2, \ldots, \hat{\mathbf{x}}_M\}$, show that

$$B_m(\hat{\mathscr{C}}_M) \le B_m(\hat{\mathscr{C}}_m) + \sum_{m'=m+1}^{M} \left[\sum_{\mathbf{y}} \sqrt{p_N(\mathbf{y}|\hat{\mathbf{x}}_m)p_N(\mathbf{y}|\hat{\mathbf{x}}_{m'})} \right]$$

for $m = 1, 2, \ldots, M$.

(*f*) For code $\hat{\mathscr{C}}_M$,

$$P_{E_m}(\hat{\mathscr{C}}_M) \le B_m(\hat{\mathscr{C}}_M)$$

and the average error probability is defined by

$$P_E(\hat{\mathscr{C}}_M) = \frac{1}{M} \sum_{m=1}^{M} P_{E_m}(\hat{\mathscr{C}}_M)$$

Show that for any $s \in (0, 1]$

$$P_E(\hat{\mathscr{C}}_M) \leq 2M^{1/s}[\gamma(s, \mathbf{q})]^{N/s}$$

(*g*) By examining necessary conditions for achieving a minimum, show that, over all probability distributions on $\mathscr{X}$

$$\min_{\mathbf{q}} \sum_{x} \sum_{x'} q(x)q(x')\left(\sum_{y} \sqrt{p(y|x)p(y|x')}\right)^s = \min_{\mathbf{q}} \gamma(s, \mathbf{q})$$

This then proves that, for any distribution $q(\cdot)$ and any $\rho = 1/s \in [1, \infty)$, there exists a code $\mathscr{C}$ of block length N and rate R such that

$$\begin{aligned} P_E(\mathscr{C}) &\leq 2M^{\rho}\left\{\sum_{x} \sum_{x'} q(x)q(x')\left[\sum_{y} \sqrt{p(y|x)p(y|x')}\right]^{1/\rho}\right\}^{N\rho} \\ &= 2e^{-N\{E_x(\rho, \mathbf{q}) - \rho R\}} \end{aligned}$$

where

$$E_x(\rho, \mathbf{q}) = -\rho \ln \left\{\sum_{x} \sum_{x'} q(x)q(x')\left[\sum_{y} \sqrt{p(y|x)p(y|x')}\right]^{1/\rho}\right\}$$

By maximizing the exponent with respect to the distribution $\mathbf{q}$ and the parameter $\rho \in [1, \infty)$, obtain the expurgated bound. Note that this proof does not give the inconvenient term $(\ln 4)/N$ added to the rate R as does that in Theorem 3.3.1.

3.22 Discrimination functions and the sphere-packing bound: The sphere-packing lower bound can be proven for discrete memoryless channels using discrimination functions (see Omura [1975]). Here this approach is demonstrated for the BSC channel with crossover probability p.

Define a "dummy" BSC with crossover probability $\tilde{p}$ and capacity $\tilde{C} = \ln 2 - \mathscr{H}(\tilde{p})$. The discrimination between the actual channel and the dummy channel is defined in terms of channel transition probabilities as

$$\begin{aligned} J(\tilde{p}, p) &\equiv \sum_{y} \tilde{p}(y|x) \ln \frac{\tilde{p}(y|x)}{p(y|x)} \\ &= \tilde{p} \ln \frac{\tilde{p}}{p} + (1 - \tilde{p}) \ln \frac{1 - \tilde{p}}{1 - p} \end{aligned}$$

For any $\gamma > 0$ and any $\mathbf{x} \in \mathscr{X}_N$, define the subset $G_\gamma(\mathbf{x}) \subset \mathscr{Y}_N$ as follows:

$$G_\gamma(\mathbf{x}) \equiv \left\{\mathbf{y}: \frac{1}{N} \ln \frac{\tilde{p}_N(\mathbf{y}|\mathbf{x})}{p_N(\mathbf{y}|\mathbf{x})} - J(\tilde{p}, p) < \gamma\right\}$$

(*a*) For any code $\mathscr{C} = \{\mathbf{x}_1, \mathbf{x}_2, \ldots, \mathbf{x}_M\}$ of block length N and rate $R = (\ln M)/N$, show that

$$\begin{aligned} P_E &= \frac{1}{M} \sum_{m=1}^{M} \sum_{\mathbf{y} \in \overline{\Lambda_m}} p_N(\mathbf{y}|\mathbf{x}_m) \\ &\geq e^{-N\{J(\tilde{p}, p) + \gamma\}} \frac{1}{M} \sum_{m=1}^{M} \sum_{\mathbf{y} \in \overline{\Lambda_m} \cap G_\gamma(\mathbf{x}_m)} \tilde{p}_N(\mathbf{y}|\mathbf{x}_m) \\ &\geq e^{-N\{J(\tilde{p}, p) + \gamma\}}\left\{\tilde{P}_E - \frac{1}{M} \sum_{m=1}^{M} \sum_{\mathbf{y} \in G_\gamma(\mathbf{x}_m)} \tilde{p}_N(\mathbf{y}|\mathbf{x}_m)\right\} \end{aligned}$$

where $\tilde{P}_E$ is the error probability when code $\mathscr{C}$ is used over the dummy BSC.

(*b*) Show that

$$\sum_{\mathbf{y} \in \bar{G}_\gamma(\mathbf{x}_m)} \tilde{p}_N(\mathbf{y} | \mathbf{x}_m) = \tilde{\Pr}\left\{\frac{1}{N} \ln \frac{\tilde{p}_N(\mathbf{y} | \mathbf{x}_m)}{p_N(\mathbf{y} | \mathbf{x}_m)} - J(\tilde{p}, p) \geq \gamma\right\}$$

goes to 0 as $N \to \infty$.

(*c*) Using the converse to the coding theorem for $\tilde{p}$ chosen such that

$$\tilde{C} = \ln 2 - \mathscr{H}(\tilde{p}) < R$$

show that there exists an $\alpha > 0$ such that for N large enough

$$P_E \geq \alpha\, e^{-N\{J(\tilde{p},\, p) + \gamma\}}$$

Since this is true for any $\gamma > 0$ and dummy BSC where $\tilde{C} < R$, define the limiting exponent

$$E_{\text{sp}}(R) \equiv J(\tilde{p}, p)$$

where $\tilde{p}$ satisfies

$$\ln 2 - \mathscr{H}(\tilde{p}) = R$$

and check that this is the sphere-packing exponent for the BSC.

3.23 Consider sending one of two codewords, $\mathbf{x}_1$ or $\mathbf{x}_2$, over a BSC with crossover probability p. Using the method of Prob. 3.22 where $M = 2$ and $\tilde{p} = \frac{1}{2}$, show that for any $\gamma > 0$ and for all N large enough

$$P_E(1 \to 2) \geq \tfrac{1}{2} \exp\left[-w(\mathbf{x}_1 \oplus \mathbf{x}_2)\{-\ln \sqrt{4p(1-p)} + \gamma\}\right]$$

where $w(\mathbf{x}_1 \oplus \mathbf{x}_2)$ is the Hamming distance between the two codewords. [For large N we assume $w(\mathbf{x}_1 \oplus \mathbf{x}_2)$ is also large.]

Hint: Consider only those coordinates where $x_{1n} \neq x_{2n}$, $n = 1, 2, \ldots, N$.

3.24 For the unconstrained AWGN channel, prove the sphere-packing lower bound on P_E for any code $\mathscr{C} = \{\mathbf{x}_1, \mathbf{x}_2, \ldots, \mathbf{x}_M\}$ with

$$\|\mathbf{x}_m\|^2 = \mathscr{E} \qquad m = 1, 2, \ldots, M$$

by following the method of Prob. 3.22. Here use the "dummy" AWGN channel that multiplies all inputs by ρ. That is, for codeword $\mathbf{x} \in \mathscr{X}_N$ the dummy AWGN channel has transition probability density

$$\tilde{p}_N(\mathbf{y}|\mathbf{x}) = \left(\frac{1}{\pi N_o}\right)^{N/2} e^{-\|\mathbf{y} - \rho\mathbf{x}\|^2/N_o}$$

whereas the actual channel has transition probability density

$$p_N(\mathbf{y}|\mathbf{x}) = \left(\frac{1}{\pi N_o}\right)^{N/2} e^{-\|\mathbf{y} - \mathbf{x}\|^2/N_o}$$

3.25 Consider AWGN channels that employ m frequency-orthogonal signals such as in (2.12.1). These are commonly called MFSK signals. Show that, for these M-ary input memoryless channels, the expurgated function $E_x(\rho) = \max_{\mathbf{q}} E_x(\rho, \mathbf{q})$ has the form

$$E_x(\rho) = -\rho \ln \left[\frac{1 + (M-1)Z^{1/\rho}}{M}\right]$$

where

$$Z = \sum_y \sqrt{p(y|x)p(y|x')}$$

for any $x \neq x'$. Find Z for the following cases:

(a) Coherent channel with hard M-ary decision outputs.
(b) Noncoherent channel with hard M-ary decision outputs.
(c) Coherent channel with unquantized output vectors.
(d) Noncoherent channel with unquantized output vectors.

Show that the expurgated exponent $D = E_{\mathrm{ex}}(R)$ satisfies

$$R = \ln M - \mathscr{H}(D/d) - (D/d) \ln (M-1)$$

where $d = -\ln Z$.

3.26 Suppose we have a DMC with transition probabilities $p(y|x)$. The decoder mistakenly assumes that the transition probabilities are $\tilde{p}(y|x)$ and bases the maximum likelihood decision rule on these incorrect transition probabilities. Following Secs. 2.4 and 3.1, derive an ensemble average upper bound to the probability of a decoding error (Stiglitz [1966]).

It should have the form

$$\bar{P}_E \leq \exp\{-N[-\rho R + F(\rho, \mathbf{q}, \mathbf{p}, \tilde{\mathbf{p}}]\} \qquad 0 \leq \rho \leq 1$$

The quantity

$$R_o(\mathbf{p}, \tilde{\mathbf{p}}) = \max_{\mathbf{q}} F(1, \mathbf{q}, \mathbf{p}, \tilde{\mathbf{p}})$$

can be used to examine the loss due to not knowing the actual channel parameters.

3.27 Repeat Prob. 3.25 for the noncoherent fading channels with MSFK signals that are discussed in Sec. 2.12.3.

3.28 Suppose we have a DMC with input alphabet $\mathscr{X}$ containing Q symbols. Let

$$d(x, x') = \ln \sum_y \sqrt{p(y|x)p(y|x')}$$

satisfy the "balanced channel" condition

$$\{d(x, x') : x' \in \mathscr{X}\} = \{d_1, d_2, \ldots, d_Q\}$$

for all $x \in \mathscr{X}$. This shows that the set of *Bhattacharyya distances* from any input x to all other inputs are the same for all $x \in \mathscr{X}$. For these channels, show that the expurgated exponent $D = E_{\mathrm{ex}}(R)$ is given parametrically by

$$D = \frac{\sum_{i=1}^{Q} d_i e^{sd_i}}{\sum_{i=1}^{Q} e^{sd_i}}$$

$$R = sD - \ln \left(\frac{1}{Q} \sum_{i=1}^{Q} e^{sd_i} \right)$$

for $s = -1/\rho \in [-1, 0]$. Give the specific form of these equations for the multiphase signal set of Fig. 2.12*b* used over the AWGN channel.

3.29 Consider a DMC with input alphabet $\mathscr{X}$, output alphabet $\mathscr{Y}$, and transition probabilities $\{p(y|x) : x \in \mathscr{X}, y \in \mathscr{Y}\}$. Given a code $\mathscr{C} = \{\mathbf{x}_1, \mathbf{x}_2, \ldots, \mathbf{x}_M\}$ of block length N and rate $R = (\ln M)/N$, following the proof of Theorem 3.9.1,

(a) Show that the probability of correct decoding is

$$P_C = \frac{1}{M} \sum_{\mathbf{y}} \max_m p_N(\mathbf{y}|\mathbf{x}_m)$$

(Assume all messages are equally likely and that the optimum decision rule is used.)

(*b*) For any $\beta > 0$ show that

$$P_C \leq \frac{1}{M} \sum_{\mathbf{y}} \left(\sum_{m=1}^{M} p_N(\mathbf{y} \mid \mathbf{x}_m)^{1/\beta} \right)^{\beta}$$

(*c*) Consider an ensemble of codes where code $\mathscr{C} = \{\mathbf{x}_1, \mathbf{x}_2, \ldots, \mathbf{x}_M\}$ is selected with probability

$$Q(\mathscr{C}) = \prod_{m=1}^{M} q_N(\mathbf{x}_m)$$

where

$$q_N(\mathbf{x}) = \prod_{n=1}^{N} q(x_n)$$

and $q(\cdot)$ is any distribution on $\mathscr{X}$. For $0 \leq \beta \leq 1$, show that P_C averaged over this code ensemble satisfies

$$\overline{P_C} \leq e^{-N\{E_o(\rho, \mathbf{q}) - \rho R\}} \qquad \text{where} \qquad \rho = \beta - 1 \in [-1, 0]$$

and

$$E_o(\rho, \mathbf{q}) = -\ln \sum_{y} \left(\sum_{x} q(x) p(y \mid x)^{1/(1+\rho)} \right)^{1+\rho}$$

(*d*) Show that, for some distribution $q(\cdot)$ and $\rho \in [-1, 0]$

$$E_o(\rho, \mathbf{q}) - \rho R > 0 \qquad \text{for } R > C$$

Here C is channel capacity for the DMC.

(*e*) From (*d*), it follows that, over the ensemble of codes of block length N and rate R with some distribution $q(\cdot)$, the average probability of correct decoding satisfies

$$\overline{P_C} \leq e^{-NE_{sc}(R)}$$

where

$$E_{sc}(R) = \max_{-1 \leq \rho \leq 0} \{E_o(\rho, \mathbf{q}) - \rho R\} > 0$$

for $R > C$. Compare this result with the strong converse coding theorem in Sec. 3.9. What is the difference between these results? Explain why the above result is not useful.

3.30 Consider the K-input, K-output DMC where

$$P(b_k \mid a_k) = 1 - p \qquad k = 1, 2, \ldots, K$$

$$P(b_{k+1} \mid a_k) = p \qquad k = 1, 2, \ldots, K - 1$$

and

$$P(b_1 \mid a_K) = p \qquad \text{where} \qquad 0 < p < \tfrac{1}{2}$$

(*a*) Find $E_o(\rho) = \max_{\mathbf{q}} E_o(\rho, \mathbf{q})$ and $E_o'(\rho)$.

(*b*) Find channel capacity.

(*c*) Suppose codeword $\mathbf{x}_1$ which has N components gives an output $\mathbf{y}$. We now randomly select $\mathbf{x}_2$ according to the probability

$$q_N(\mathbf{x}_2) = \frac{1}{K^N}$$

What is the probability that $\mathbf{x}_2$ is chosen such that it is *possible* for $\mathbf{x}_2$ also to give output $\mathbf{y}$?

(d) Suppose $\mathbf{x}_2, \mathbf{x}_3, \ldots, \mathbf{x}_M$ are randomly selected as in (*c*). Find a union upper bound for the probability that one or more of the codewords $\mathbf{x}_2, \mathbf{x}_3, \ldots, \mathbf{x}_M$ can give output $\mathbf{y}$.

(*e*) Determine the ensemble average exponent $E(R)$ for the case where $p = \frac{1}{2}$, and compare this with the exponent in the bound obtained in (*d*).

(*f*) Determine $E(R)$ for $p = 0$ and explain why it is finite.

3.31 Consider M signals and an additive white Gaussian noise channel with spectral density $N_o/2$. The signal set is

$$x_i(t) = \sum_{k=1}^{N} x_{ik}\,\phi_k(t) \qquad 0 \le t \le T,\ i = 1, 2, \ldots, M$$

where $\{\phi_k(\cdot)\}_{k=1}^{N}$ is a set of orthonormal functions. Suppose we now randomly select codewords by choosing each x_{ik} independently from the ensemble of random variables with zero mean and variance $\mathscr{E}$.

Using a union of events bound, show that there exists a set of codewords such that the error probability satisfies

$$P_e < M2^{-NC_o}$$

Find C_o when

(*a*) x is a Gaussian random variable.

(*b*) $x = \begin{cases} +\sqrt{\mathscr{E}} & \text{with probability } \frac{1}{2} \\ -\sqrt{\mathscr{E}} & \text{with probability } \frac{1}{2} \end{cases}$

Hint: Assume $x_1(t)$ is sent and bound the error probability by the sum of the two signal error probabilities between $x_1(t)$ and each of the other signals. Then use the bound

$$\int_x^{\infty} \frac{1}{\sqrt{2\pi}} e^{-\alpha^2/2}\, d\alpha < e^{-x^2/2}$$

and average the bound over the ensemble of codewords.

3.32 Consider the four-input, four-output DMC shown.

(*a*) What is the channel capacity?

(*b*) Determine $E_o(\rho) = \max_{\mathbf{q}} E_o(\rho, \mathbf{q})$.

(*c*) Determine and sketch $E(R)$, $E_{ex}(R)$, and $E_{sp}(R)$.

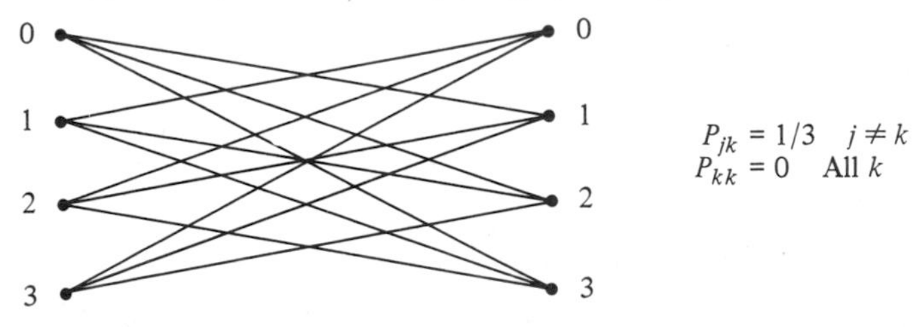

Figure P3.32

3.33 (Improved Plotkin Bound) Assume a systematic binary linear code of $M = 2^K$ code vectors of dimensionality N. Let d_{min} be the minimum distance between code vectors in this code.

(*a*) For any $1 \le j \le K$, consider the 2^j code vectors in the code with the first $K - j$ information bits constrained to be 0. By eliminating these first $K - j$ components in these code vectors, a binary code of 2^j code vectors of dimensionality $N - (K - j)$ is obtained. Use Lemma 3.7.1 to show that

$$d_{min} \le \frac{N - (K - j)}{2}\left(\frac{2^j}{2^j - 1}\right)$$

(*b*) Next, show the improved Plotkin bound

$$\frac{d_{min}}{N} < \frac{1}{2}(1 - R/\ln 2) + o(N)$$

where

$$R = (\ln M)/N$$

(*c*) Show that the improved Plotkin bound is valid for all binary codes of M code vectors of dimensionality N.

3.34 (Gilbert Bound for Binary Codes)

1. List all 2^N possible distinct binary vectors of length N.
2. Choose an arbitrary binary vector from this list and denote it as $\mathbf{x}_1$. Delete from the list $\mathbf{x}_1$ and all other binary vectors of distance $d - 1$ or less from $\mathbf{x}_1$.
3. From the remaining binary vectors on the list arbitrarily pick $\mathbf{x}_2$, then delete from the list $\mathbf{x}_2$ and all other binary vectors that are distance $d - 1$ or less from $\mathbf{x}_2$.
4. Repeat Step 3 for vectors $\mathbf{x}_3, \mathbf{x}_4, \ldots, \mathbf{x}_M$ until the list is empty.

(*a*) Show that the number of binary vectors selected, M, satisfies

$$M \geq \frac{2^N}{\sum_{i=0}^{d-1} \binom{N}{i}}$$

(*b*) Using the Chernoff bound (see Prob. 3.19*a*), show that

$$\sum_{i=0}^{d-1} \binom{N}{i} p^i (1-p)^{N-i} \leq e^{N\mathscr{H}(d/N)} p^d (1-p)^{N-d}$$

and, choosing $p = \frac{1}{2}$, show

$$\sum_{i=0}^{d-1} \binom{N}{i} \leq e^{N\mathscr{H}(d/N)}$$

(*c*) From (*a*) and (*b*), show that, for any rate $R = (\ln M)/N < \ln 2$, there exists a code of minimum distance $d_{\min}$ where

$$\frac{d_{\min}}{N} \geq \delta$$

and δ satisfies $\delta < \frac{1}{2}$ and

$$R = \ln 2 - \mathscr{H}(\delta)$$

This is the Gilbert bound on $d_{\min}$.

(*d*) Rederive the Gilbert bound for large N by using the expurgated upper bound (3.4.8) and the lower error bound (3.7.18) for the binary-input, output-symmetric channel. Furthermore, show that the Gilbert bound holds for linear codes as well by using the expurgated upper error bound derived in Sec. 3.10.

PART TWO

CONVOLUTIONAL CODING AND DIGITAL COMMUNICATION

CHAPTER

FOUR

CONVOLUTIONAL CODES

4.1 INTRODUCTION AND BASIC STRUCTURE

In the two preceding chapters we have treated digital communication over a variety of memoryless channels and the performance enhancement achievable by block coding. Beginning with the most general block codes, we proceeded to impose the linearity condition which endowed the codes with additional structure, thus simplifying both the encoding-decoding procedure and the performance analysis for many channels of interest. Of particular significance is the fact that, for a given block length and code rate, the best linear block code performs about as well as the best block code with the same parameters. This was demonstrated for a few isolated codes and channels in Chap. 2, and more generally by ensemble arguments in Chap. 3.

In the narrowest sense, convolutional codes can be viewed as a special class of linear block codes, but, by taking a more enlightened viewpoint, we shall find that the additional convolutional structure endows a linear code with superior properties which both facilitate decoding and improve performance. We begin with the narrow viewpoint, mainly to establish the connection with previous material, and then gradually widen our horizon. In this chapter and the next, we shall exploit the additional structure to derive a maximum likelihood decoder of reduced complexity and improved performance, first for specific codes and channels and then more generally on an ensemble basis, following essentially the outlines used for block codes in Chaps. 2 and 3. Finally, in Chap. 6, we treat sequential decoding algorithms which reduce decoder complexity at the cost of increased memory and computational speed requirements.

Consider first the linear block code specified by the binary generator matrix

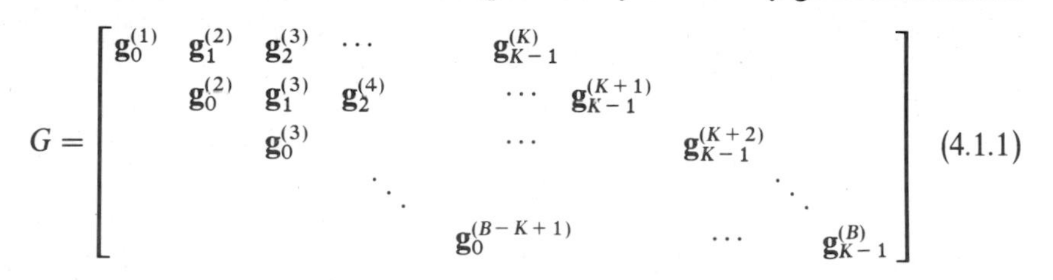

$$G = \begin{bmatrix} \mathbf{g}_0^{(1)} & \mathbf{g}_1^{(2)} & \mathbf{g}_2^{(3)} & \cdots & \mathbf{g}_{K-1}^{(K)} & & & & \\ & \mathbf{g}_0^{(2)} & \mathbf{g}_1^{(3)} & \mathbf{g}_2^{(4)} & \cdots & \mathbf{g}_{K-1}^{(K+1)} & & & \\ & & \mathbf{g}_0^{(3)} & & \cdots & & \mathbf{g}_{K-1}^{(K+2)} & & \\ & & & \ddots & & & & \ddots & \\ & & & & \mathbf{g}_0^{(B-K+1)} & & & \cdots & \mathbf{g}_{K-1}^{(B)} \end{bmatrix} \qquad (4.1.1)$$

where $\mathbf{g}_j^{(i)} = (g_{j1}^{(i)} g_{j2}^{(i)} \cdots g_{jn}^{(i)})$ is an n-dimensional binary vector and blank areas in the matrix G indicate zero values. G describes an $(nB, B - K + 1)$ linear block code which could be implemented, as shown in Fig. 2.16, by a $(B - K + 1)$-stage fixed register and nB modulo-2 adders. A simpler mechanization, particularly since generally $B \gg K$, utilizes a K-stage shift register with n modulo-2 adders and time-varying tap coefficients $g_{jk}^{(i)}$, as shown in Fig. 4.1. The shift register can be viewed either as a register whose contents are shifted one stage to the right as each new bit is shifted in from the left, with the rightmost stage contents being lost, or as a digital delay line in which each delay element stores one bit between arrival times of the input bits. Both representations are shown in Fig. 4.1, with the former shown dotted, the latter being the preferred form.

We note also that in the shift register or delay line implementation the

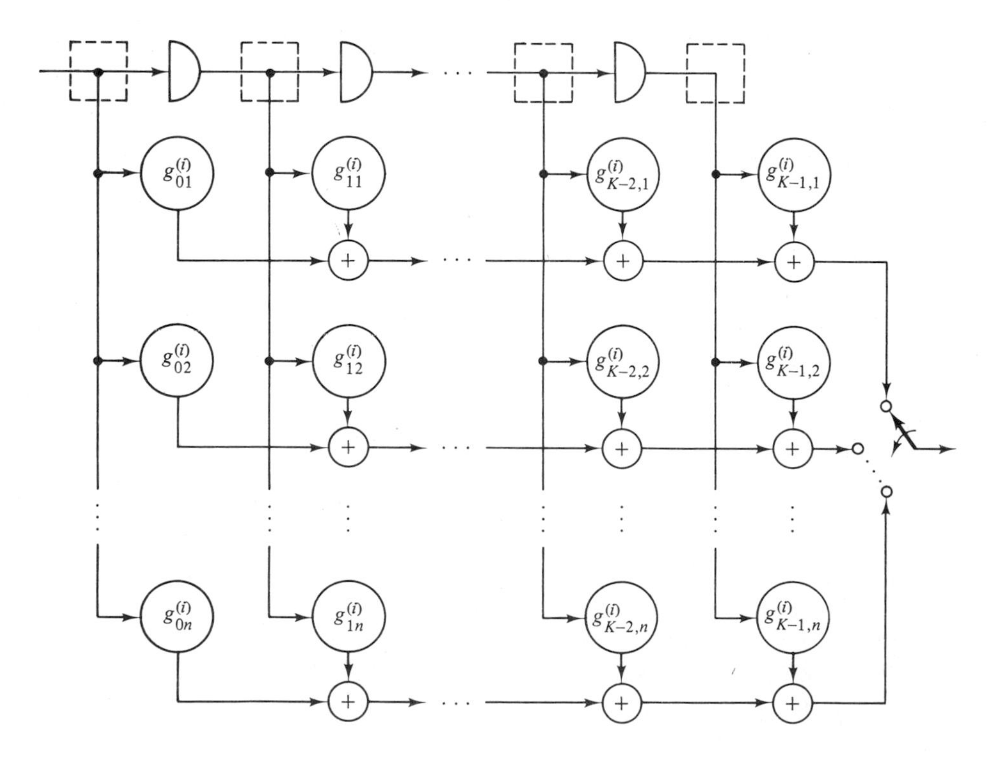

Figure 4.1 A time-varying convolutional encoder: rate $r = 1/n$ bits/channel symbol.

$(B - K + 1)$st (last) bit must be followed by $K - 1$ zeros to clear the register[1] and to produce the last $K - 1$ output branches, which are sometimes called the *tail* of the code.

Thus it appears that the encoder complexity is independent of block length nB, and depends only on the register length K, and the code rate,[2] which, when measured in bits per output symbol, approaches $1/n$ as $B \to \infty$. K is called the *constraint length* of the *convolutional code.* On the basis of the shift register implementation it should also be clear that the greater the ratio B/K, the less the tail "overhead" in the sense that, since the last $K - 1$ input bits are zeros, the tail reduces the code rate in proportion to $(K - 1)/B$.

The term "convolutional" applies to this class of codes because the output symbol sequence $\mathbf{v}$ can be expressed as the convolution of input (bit) sequence $\mathbf{u}$ with the generator sequences. For, since the code is linear, we have

$$\mathbf{v} = \mathbf{u}G$$

and, as a consequence of the form of G of Eq. (4.1.1)

$$\mathbf{v}_i = \sum_{k=\max(1,\, i-K+1)}^{i} u_k \, \mathbf{g}_{i-k}^{(i)} \qquad i = 1, 2, \ldots \tag{4.1.2}$$

where $\mathbf{v}_i = (v_{i1}, v_{i2}, \ldots, v_{in})$ is the n-dimensional coder output just after the ith bit has entered the encoder.

While, for theoretical reasons, in the next chapter we shall be interested in the ensemble of *time-varying* convolutional codes just described, virtually all convolutional codes of practical interest are *time-invariant* (*fixed*). For such codes, the tap coefficients are fixed for all time, and consequently we may delete all superscripts in the matrix (4.1.1) with the result that each row is identical to the preceding row shifted n terms to the right. An example of a fixed convolutional code with constraint length $K = 3$ and code rate $\frac{1}{2}$ is shown in Fig. 4.2a. Here the generator matrix of (4.1.1) has the form

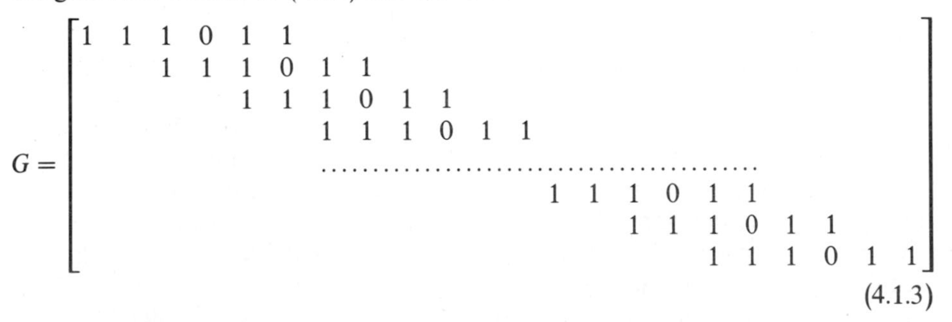

$$G = \begin{bmatrix} 1 & 1 & 1 & 0 & 1 & 1 & & & & & & & & & & & & \\ & & 1 & 1 & 1 & 0 & 1 & 1 & & & & & & & & & & \\ & & & & 1 & 1 & 1 & 0 & 1 & 1 & & & & & & & & \\ & & & & & & 1 & 1 & 1 & 0 & 1 & 1 & & & & & & \\ & & & & & & \cdots & \cdots & \cdots & \cdots & \cdots & \cdots & \cdots & \cdots & \cdots & \cdots & & \\ & & & & & & & & & & & & 1 & 1 & 1 & 0 & 1 & 1 & & & & \\ & & & & & & & & & & & & & & 1 & 1 & 1 & 0 & 1 & 1 & & \\ & & & & & & & & & & & & & & & & 1 & 1 & 1 & 0 & 1 & 1 \end{bmatrix} \tag{4.1.3}$$

[1] This is required to terminate the code. Alternatively, the convolutional code may be regarded as a long block code (with block length nB arbitrarily large) and this termination with $(K - 1)$ zeros clears the encoder register for the next block.

[2] The code rate is actually $[1 - (K - 1)/B]/n$ because of the $(K - 1)$ zeros in the tail. However we generally disregard the rate loss in the tail since it is almost always insignificant, and henceforth the rate shall refer to the asymptotic rate; that is to the ratio of input bits to output symbols, exclusive of the tail ($1/n$ in this case).

The rate of the class of convolutional codes defined in this manner is $1/n$ bits per output symbol.[3] To generalize to any other rational rate less than unity, we must generalize the matrix G of (4.1.1) or its implementation in Fig. 4.1. We may most easily describe higher code rate convolutional codes by specifying that $b > 1$ bits be shifted together in parallel into the encoder every b bit times, and simultaneously that the bits already within the encoder are shifted to the right in blocks of b. Here K is the number of b-tuples in the register so that a total of bK bits influence any given output and consequently bK is now the *constraint length*. In terms of the generator matrix (4.1.1), we may describe a convolutional code of rate b/n by replacing the n-dimensional vector components $\mathbf{g}_j^{(i)}$ with $b \times n$ matrices. The implementation of Fig. 4.1 can best be generalized by providing b parallel delay lines, every stage of each delay line being connected through a tap multiplier to each modulo-2 adder. Examples of fixed convolutional codes of rates $\frac{2}{3}$ and $\frac{3}{4}$ with $K = 2$ are shown in Fig. 4.2*b* and *c*, respectively. The generalization to time-varying convolutional codes of any rate b/n and any constraint length K is immediate.

A fixed convolutional coder may be regarded as a linear time-invariant finite-state machine whose structure can be exhibited with the aid of any one of several diagrams. We shall demonstrate the use and insight provided by such diagrams with the aid of the simple example of Fig. 4.2*a*. It is both traditional in this field and instructive to begin with the tree diagram of Fig. 4.3. On it we may display both input and output sequences of the encoder. Inputs are indicated by the path followed in the diagram, while outputs are indicated by symbols along the tree's branches. An input zero specifies the upper branch of a bifurcation while a one specifies the lower one. Thus, for the encoder of Fig. 4.2*a*, the input sequence 0110 is indicated by moving up at the first branching level, down at the second and third, and again up at the fourth to produce the outputs indicated along the branches traversed: 00, 11, 01, 01. Thus, on the diagram of Fig. 4.3, we may indicate all output sequences corresponding to all 32 possible sequences for the first five input bits.

From the diagram, it also becomes clear that after the first three branches the structure becomes repetitive. In fact, we readily recognize that beyond the third branch the code symbols on branches emanating from the two nodes labeled **a** are identical, and similarly for all the identically labeled pairs of nodes. The reason for this is obvious from examination of the encoder. When the third input bit enters the encoder, the first input bit comes out of the rightmost delay element, and thereafter no longer influences the output code symbols. Consequently, the data sequences $100xy\ldots$ and $000xy\ldots$ generate the same code symbols after the third branch and thus both nodes labeled **a** in the tree diagram can be joined together.

This leads to redrawing the tree diagram as shown in Fig. 4.4. This new figure has been called a *trellis* diagram, since a trellis is a tree-like structure with remerg-

[3] We use small r to denote code rate in bits per output symbol; that is, when we use the logarithm to the base 2 to define rate.

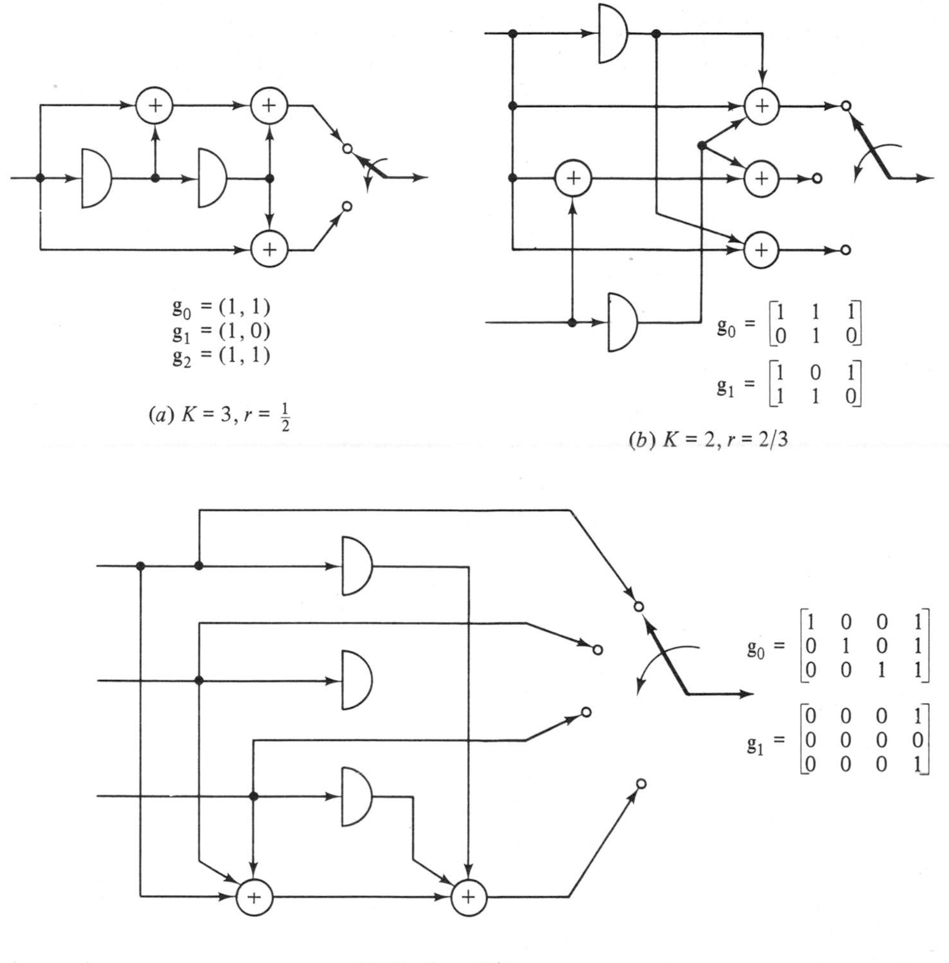

Figure 4.2 Fixed convolutional encoder examples.

ing branches. We adopt the convention here that code branches produced by a "0" input bit are shown as solid lines and code branches produced by a "1" input bit are shown dashed. We note also that, since after $B - K + 1$ input bits the code block (4.1.1) is terminated by inserting $K - 1$ zeros into the encoder, the trellis terminates at an **a** node as shown in Fig. 4.4. The last two branches are then the tail of the code in this case.

The completely repetitive structure of the trellis diagram suggests a further reduction of the representation of the code to the state diagram of Fig. 4.5. The states of the state diagram are labeled according to the nodes of the trellis diagram. However, since the states correspond merely to the last two input bits to the coder, we may use these bits to denote the nodes or states of this diagram.

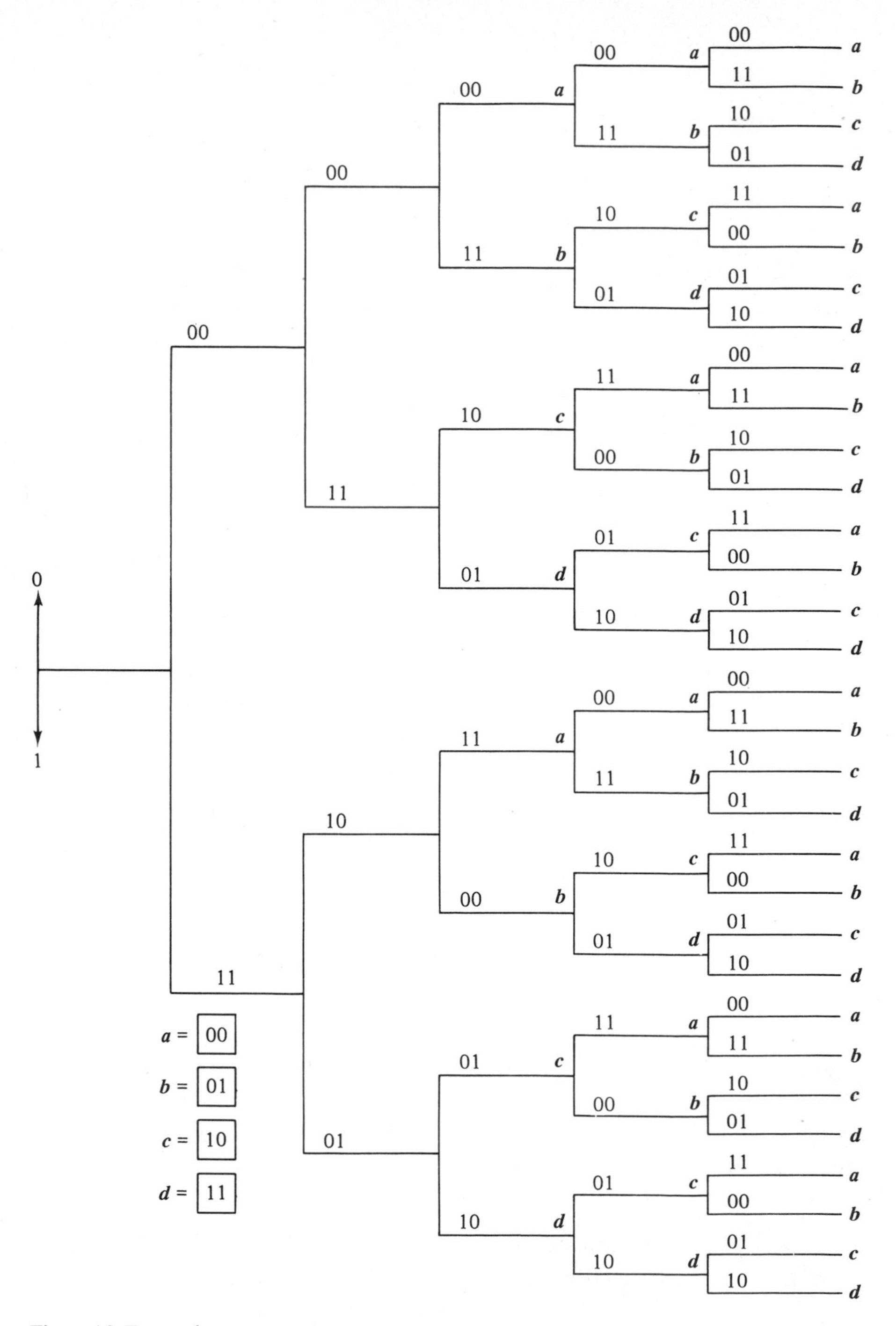

Figure 4.3 Tree-code representation for encoder of Fig. 4.2*a*.

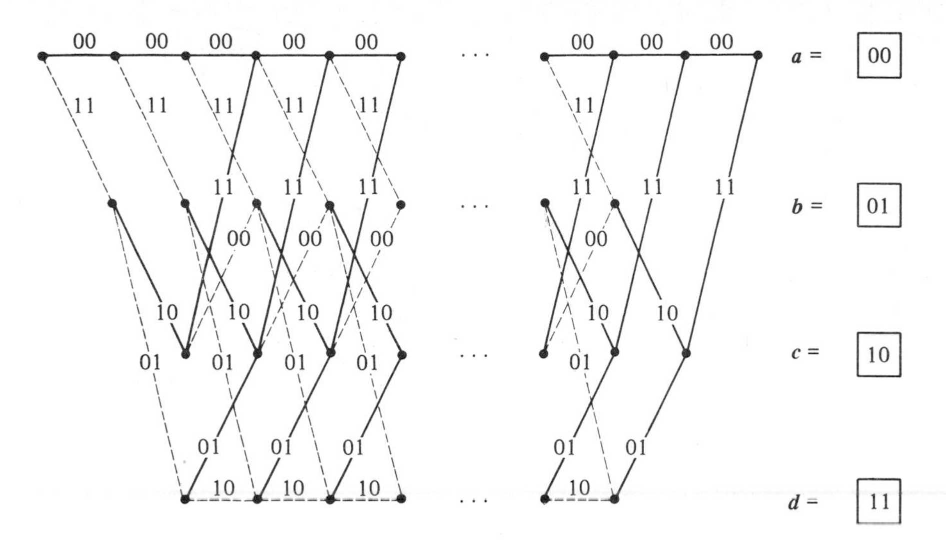

Figure 4.4 Trellis-code representation for encoder of Fig. 4.2*a*.

Throughout the text, we shall adopt this convention of denoting the state of a rate $1/n$ convolutional encoder by the latest $K - 1$ binary symbols in the register with the most recent bit being the last bit in the state.

We observe finally that the state diagram can be drawn directly by observing the finite-state machine properties of the encoder and particularly by observing the fact that a four-state directed graph can be used to represent uniquely the input-output relation of the $K = 3$ stage machine. For the nodes represent the previous two bits, while the present bit is indicated by the transition branch; for example, if the encoder contains 011, this is represented in the diagram by the

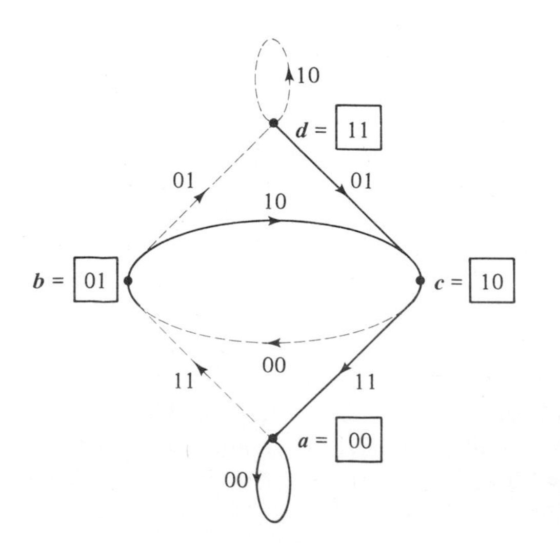

Figure 4.5 State diagram for encoder of Fig. 4.2*a*.

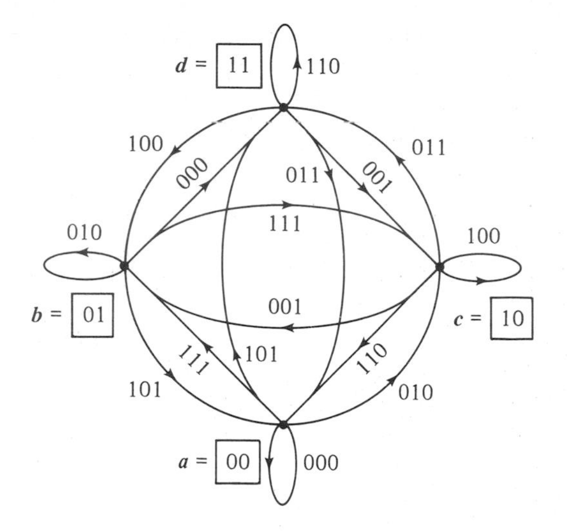

Figure 4.6 State diagram for encoder of Fig. 4.2*b*.

transition from state **b** = 01 to state **d** = 11 and the corresponding branch indicates the code symbol outputs 01.

To generalize to rate b/n convolutional codes, we note simply that the tree diagram will now have 2^b branches emanating from each branching node. However, the effect of the constraint length K is the same as before, and hence, after the first K branches, the paths will begin to remerge in groups of 2^b; more precisely, all paths with $b(K-1)$ identical data bits will merge together, producing a trellis of $2^{b(K-1)}$ states with all branchings and mergings occurring in groups of 2^b branches. Here K represents the number of b-tuples stored in the register. Consequently, the state diagram will also have $2^{b(K-1)}$ states, with each state having 2^b output branches emanating from it and 2^b input branches arriving into it. An example of a state diagram for the rate $\frac{2}{3}$ code of Fig. 4.2*b* is shown in Fig. 4.6. Other examples are treated in the problems.

Up to this point in our treatment of nonblock codes, we have only considered linear codes. Just as linear block codes are a subclass of block codes, convolutional codes are a subclass of a broader class of codes which we call *trellis codes*. Rate b/n trellis encoders also emit n channel symbols each time b source bits enter the register. However, general trellis encoders can produce symbols from any channel input alphabet, and these symbols may be an arbitrary (nonlinear) function of the bK source bits in the encoder register. Since the K-stage register is the same for the general class of trellis codes as for convolutional codes, the tree, trellis, and state diagrams are the same and the trellis encoder output symbols can be associated with branches just as was done previously for the subclass of convolutional codes. It is clear that general trellis codes have the same relationship to general block codes as convolutional codes have to linear block codes.

We have seen here that the tree, trellis, and state diagram descriptions of convolutional and trellis codes are quite different from our earlier description of block codes. How then do we compare block codes with convolutional codes?

Returning to our earlier discussion on the generation of convolutional codes, we see that the parameters bK, the constraint or "memory" length of the encoder, and $r = b/n$, the rate in bits per channel symbol, are common to both block and convolutional encoders. For both cases, the same value of these parameters result in roughly the same encoder complexity. We shall soon see that the complexity of a maximum likelihood decoder for the same bK and r is also roughly the same for block codes and convolutional or trellis codes. Hence, for the purpose of comparing block codes and convolutional codes, we use the parameters bK and r. We shall see that, for the same parameters bK and r, convolutional codes can achieve much smaller error probabilities than block codes.

We began the discussion in this section by viewing convolutional codes as a special case of block codes. By choosing $K = 1$ and $n = N$ in the above, we get a rate b/N block code, and thus paradoxically linear block codes can themselves be considered special cases of convolutional codes, and the broader class of block codes can be considered special cases of trellis codes. It is a matter of taste as to which description is considered more general.

4.2 MAXIMUM LIKELIHOOD DECODER FOR CONVOLUTIONAL CODES—THE VITERBI ALGORITHM

As we have seen, convolutional codes can be regarded as a special class of block codes; hence the maximum likelihood decoder for a convolutional code, as specified by (4.1.1), can be implemented just as described in Chap. 2 for a block code of $B - K + 1$ bits, and will achieve a minimum block error probability for equiprobable data sequences. The difficulty, of course, is that efficient convolutional codes have a very large block length relative to the constraint length K, as discussed in the preceding section; in fact, rarely is B less than several hundred, and often the encoded data consists of the entire message (plus final tail). Since the number of code vectors or code paths through the tree or trellis is $2^{b(B-K+1)}$, a straightforward block maximum likelihood decoder utilizing one decoder element per code vector would appear to be absurdly complex. On the other hand, just as we found that the encoder can be implemented with a complexity which depends on $K - 1$ rather than on B, we shall demonstrate that the decoder complexity need only grow exponentially with $K - 1$ rather than B. For the sake of simple exposition, we begin this discussion by treating the $K = 3$, rate $= 1/2$ code of Fig. 4.2a, and we assume transmission over a binary symmetric channel (BSC). Once the basic concepts are established by this example, the maximum likelihood decoder of minimum complexity can be easily found for any convolutional code and any memoryless channel.

We recall from Sec. 2.8 that, for a BSC which transforms a channel code symbol "0" to "1" or "1" to "0" with probability p, the maximum likelihood decoder reduces to a minimum distance decoder which computes the Hamming distance from the error-corrupted received vector $y_1, y_2, \ldots, y_j, \ldots$ to each possible transmitted code vector $x_1, x_2, \ldots, x_j, \ldots$ and decides in favor of the closest code vector (or its corresponding data vector).

Referring first to the tree diagram code representation of Fig. 4.3, we see that this implies that we should choose that path in the tree whose code sequence differs in the fewest number of symbols from the received sequence. However, recognizing that the transmitted code branches remerge continually, we may equally limit our choice to the possible paths in the trellis diagram of Fig. 4.4. Examination of this diagram indicates that it is unnecessary to consider the entire received sequence of length nB ($n = 2$ in this case) in deciding upon earlier segments of the most likely (minimum distance) transmitted sequence, since we can eliminate segments of nonminimum distance paths when paths merge. In particular, immediately after the third branch we may determine which of the two paths leading to node or state **a** is more likely to have been sent. For example if 010001 is received, then since this sequence is at distance 2 from 000000 while it is at distance 3 from 111011, we may exclude the lower path into node **a**. For, no matter what the subsequent received symbols will be, they will affect the distances only over subsequent branches after these two paths have remerged, and consequently in exactly the same way. The same can be said for pairs of paths merging at the other three nodes, **b**, **c** and **d**, after the third branch. Of the two paths merging at a given node, we shall refer to the minimum distance one as the *survivor*. Thus it is necessary to remember only which was the survivor (or minimum-distance path from the received sequence) at each node, as well as the value of that minimum distance. This is necessary because, at the next node level, we must compare the two branches merging at each node that were survivors at the previous level for possibly different nodes; thus the comparison at node **a** after the fourth branch is among the survivors of comparisons at nodes **a** and **c** after the third branch. For example, if the received sequence over the first four branches is 01000111, the survivor at the third node level for node **a** is 000000 with distance 2 and at node **c** it is 110101, also with distance 2. In going from the third node level to the fourth, the received sequence agrees precisely with the survivor from **c** but has distance 2 from the survivor from **a**. Hence the survivor at node **a** of the fourth level is the data sequence 1100, which produced the code sequence 11010111 which is at (minimum) distance 2 from the received sequence.

In this way, we may proceed through the trellis and, at each step for each state, preserve only one surviving path and its distance from the received sequence; this distance is the metric[4] for this channel. The only difficulty which may arise is the possibility that, in a given comparison between merging paths, the distances or metrics are identical. Then we may simply flip a coin to choose one, as was done for block codewords at equal distances from the received sequence. For even if we preserved both of the equally valid contenders, further received symbols would affect both metrics in exactly the same way and thus not further influence

[4] As defined in Sec. 2.2, the metric is the logarithm of the likelihood function. For the BSC, it is convenient to use the negative of this which is proportional to Hamming distance [see also (4.2.2)].

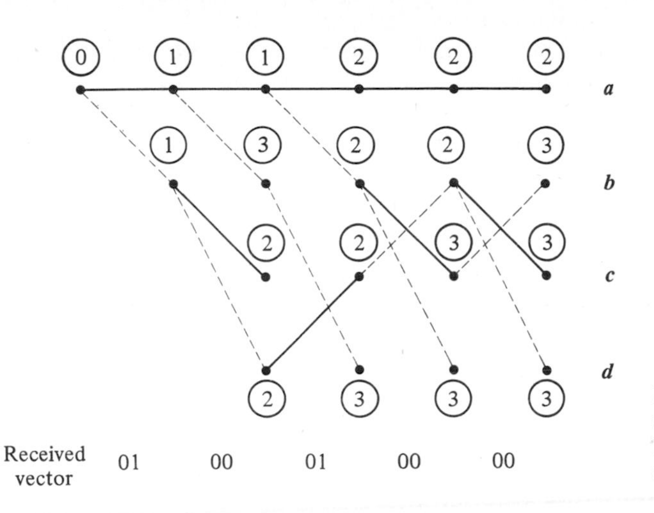

Figure 4.7 Example of decoding for encoder of Fig. 4.2*a* on BSC: decoder state metrics are encircled.

our choice. The decoding algorithm just described was first proposed by Viterbi [1967*a*]; it can perhaps be better appreciated with the aid of Fig. 4.7 which shows the trellis for the code just considered with the accumulated distance and corresponding survivors for the particular received vector 0100010000 ....

It is also evident that, in the final decisions for the complete trellis of Fig. 4.4, the four possible trellis states are reduced to two and then to one in the tail of the code. While at first glance this appears appropriate, practically it is unacceptable because it requires a decoding delay of B as well as the storage, for each state, of path memories (i.e., the sequence of input bits leading to the most likely set of four states at each node level) of length B. We shall demonstrate in Secs. 4.7 and 5.6 that performance is hardly degraded by proper truncation of delay and memory at a few constraint lengths. For the moment, however, we shall ignore this problem and be amply content with the realization that we have reduced the number of decoding elements per data bit (metric calculations) to an exponential growth in $K - 1$ ($2^{K-1} = 4$ in this case) rather than in B.

Another description of the algorithm can be obtained from the state-diagram representation of Fig. 4.5. Suppose we sought that path around the directed state diagram, arriving at node **a** after the kth transition, whose code symbols are at a minimum distance from the received sequence. But clearly this minimum distance path to node **a** at time k can be only one of two candidates: the minimum distance path to node **a** at time $k - 1$ and the minimum distance path to node **c** at time $k - 1$. The comparison is performed by adding the new distance accumulated in the kth transition by each of these paths to their minimum distances (metrics) at time $k - 1$.

It thus appears that the state diagram also represents a system diagram for this decoder. With each node or state, we associate a storage register which remembers the minimum-distance path into the state after each transition, as well as a metric register which remembers its (minimum) distance from the received sequence. Furthermore, comparisons are made at each step between the two paths which lead into each node. Thus, one comparator must also be provided for each state, four in the above example.

Generalization to convolutional codes of any constraint length K and any rational rate b/n is straightforward. The number of states becomes $2^{b(K-1)}$, with each branch again containing n code symbols. The only modification required for $b > 1$ is that due to the fact that 2^b paths now merge at any given level beyond the $(K-1)$st; comparison of distance or metric must be made among 2^b rather than just two paths, and again only one survivor is preserved. Hence the potential path population is reduced by a factor 2^{-b} at each merging level, but it then grows again by the factor 2^b before the next branching level, thus keeping the states constant at $2^{b(K-1)}$.

Generalization to arbitrary memoryless channels is almost as immediate. First, we note that, just as in Sec. 2.9, we may map the branch vectors $v_{i1}, v_{i2}, \ldots, v_{in}$ into nonbinary signal vectors $\mathbf{x}_i$ (of arbitrary dimension up to n) over an arbitrary finite alphabet of, symbols (for example, amplitudes, phases, etc.). The memoryless channel (including the demodulator, see Fig. 2.1) then converts these symbols into noisy output vectors $\mathbf{y}_i$ of dimension up to n. The Viterbi decoder[5] is then based on the metric

$$\prod_{i=1}^{B} p(\mathbf{y}_i \mid \mathbf{x}_{mi})$$

or equivalently its logarithm

$$\ln \prod_{i=1}^{B} p(\mathbf{y}_i \mid \mathbf{x}_{mi}) = \sum_{i=1}^{B} \ln p(\mathbf{y}_i \mid \mathbf{x}_{mi}) \tag{4.2.1}$$

where $\mathbf{x}_{mi}$ is the code-subvector of the mth message sequence for the ith branching level. For the BSC just considered, this reduces to

$$p(\mathbf{y}_i \mid \mathbf{x}_{mi}) = p^{d_{mi}}(1-p)^{n-d_{mi}}$$

where d_{mi} is the distance between the n-dimensional received vector and the code-subvector for the ith branch of the mth path. The logarithm of this metric for a particular path is

$$\sum_{i=1}^{B} \ln p(\mathbf{y}_i \mid \mathbf{x}_{mi}) = \sum_{i=1}^{B} \left[-d_{mi} \ln\left(\frac{1-p}{p}\right) + n \ln(1-p) \right] \tag{4.2.2}$$

Maximizing this metric is equivalent to maximizing

$$\alpha \sum_{i=1}^{B} (-d_{mi}) - \beta$$

[5] While the exact terminology is maximum likelihood decoder using the Viterbi algorithm (VA), it has become common usage to call this simply the Viterbi decoder; we have chosen to adhere to common usage, with apologies by the first author for this breach of modesty.

where α is a positive constant (for $p < \frac{1}{2}$) and β is completely arbitrary. We should choose paths with maximum metric or, equivalently, we should minimize the Hamming distance as we have done. For the binary-input constant energy AWGN channel, on the other hand we have [see (2.1.15)]

$$\sum_{i=1}^{B} \ln p(\mathbf{y}_i | \mathbf{x}_{mi}) = \frac{2}{N_o} \sum_{i=1}^{B} (\mathbf{y}_i, \mathbf{x}_{mi}) - \beta$$

$$= \frac{2}{N_o} \sum_{i=1}^{B} \sum_{j=1}^{n} y_{ij} x_{mij} - \beta \tag{4.2.3}$$

where y_{ij} is the jth symbol of the ith branch, x_{mij} is the jth symbol of the ith branch for the mth possible code path, and β is a constant. Maximizing this metric is equivalent to maximizing the accumulated inner product of the received vector with the signal vector for each path. Comparisons are made exactly as for the BSC, except that the survivor in this case corresponds to the maximum inner product rather than the minimum distance. A similar argument applies to any memoryless channel, based on the accumulated metric given by (4.2.1).

For maximum likelihood decoding of general trellis codes, the Viterbi algorithm proceeds exactly as for convolutional codes. Thus, only the encoder of trellis codes differs essentially from that of convolutional codes as discussed in Sec. 4.1. It would of course be desirable to be able to generate code symbols using the simpler convolutional encoders, if the performance is the same. In Chap. 5, we shall find that in most applications this is in fact the case.

4.3 DISTANCE PROPERTIES OF CONVOLUTIONAL CODES FOR BINARY-INPUT CHANNELS

We found in Chap. 2 that the error probability for linear codes and binary-input channels can be bounded simply by (2.9.19) in terms of the weights of all code vectors, which correspond to the set of distances from any one code vector to all others. Error performance of convolutional codes, which constitute a subclass of linear codes, can similarly be bounded, but with considerably more explicit results as we shall discover below.

The calculation of the set of code path weights, or equivalently the set of distances from the all-zeros path to all paths which have diverged from it, is readily performed with the aid of the code trellis or state diagram. For expository purposes, we again pursue the example of the $K = 3$, $r = \frac{1}{2}$ code of Fig. 4.2*a* whose trellis and state diagram are shown in Figs. 4.4 and 4.5, respectively. We begin by redrawing the trellis in Fig. 4.8, labeling the branches according to their distances from the all-zeros path.

Consider now all paths which merge with the all-zeros for the first time at some arbitrary node j. It is seen from the diagram that, of these paths, there will be just one path at distance 5 from the all-zeros path, and that this path diverged from the latter three branches back. Similarly, there are two at distance 6 from the

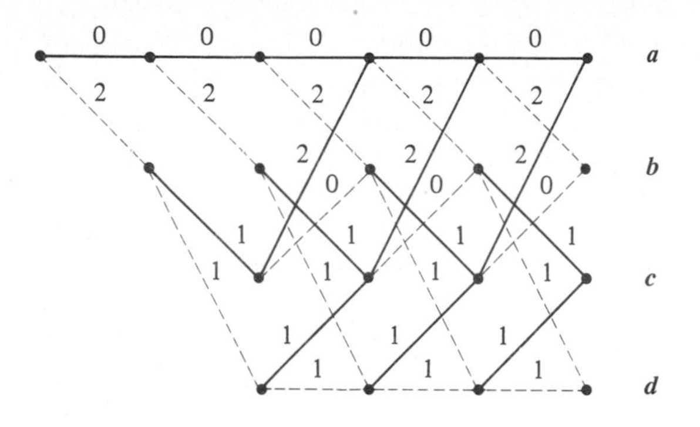

Figure 4.8 Trellis diagram labeled with distances from the all-zeros path.

all-zeros path, one which diverged four branches back and the other which diverged five branches back, and so forth. We note also that the input bits for the distance 5 path are $00 \cdots 0100$, and thus differ in only one input bit from those of the all-zero symbols path (which of course consists of all input zeros) while the input bits for the distance 6 paths are $00 \cdots 001100$ and $00 \cdots 010100$, and thus each differs in 2 input bits from the all-zeros path. The minimum distance, sometimes called the *free* distance, among all paths is thus seen to be 5. This implies that any pair of errors over the BSC can be corrected, for two or fewer errors will cause the received sequence to be at most distance 2 from the transmitted (correct) sequence but it will be at least at distance 3 from any other possible code sequence. It appears that with enough patience the distance of all paths from the all-zeros (or any arbitrary) path can be determined from the trellis diagram.

However, by examining instead the state diagram, we can readily obtain a closed-form expression whose expansion yields all distance information directly. We begin by labeling the branches[6] of the state diagram of Fig. 4.5 either D^2, D, or $D^0 = 1$, where the exponent corresponds to the distance of the particular branch from the corresponding branch of the all-zeros path. Also we split open the node $\mathbf{a} = 00$, since circulation around this self-loop simply corresponds to branches of the all-zeros path, whose distance from itself is obviously zero. The result is Fig. 4.9. Now, as is clear from examination of the trellis diagram, every path which first remerges with state $\mathbf{a} = 00$ at node level j must have at some previous node level (possibly the first) originated at this same state $\mathbf{a} = 00$. All such paths can be traced on the modified state diagram. Adding branch exponents we see that path **a b c a** is at distance 5 from the correct path, paths **a b d c a** and **a b c b c a** are both at distance 6, and so forth, for the *generating functions* of the output sequence weights of these paths are D^5 and D^6, respectively.

Now we may evaluate the generating function of all paths merging with the all-zeros at the jth node level simply by summing the generating functions of all the output sequences of the encoder. This generating function, which can also be

[6] The parameters D, L, and I in this section are abstract terms.

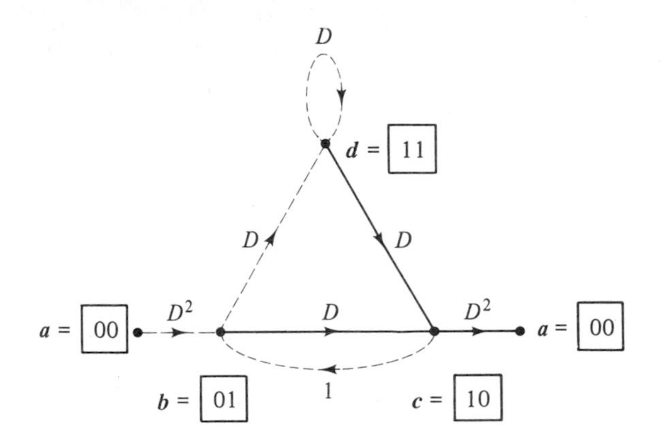

Figure 4.9 State diagram labeled with distances from the all-zeros path.

regarded as the transfer function of a signal-flow graph with unity input, can most directly be computed by simultaneous solution of the state equations obtained from Fig. 4.9

$$\begin{aligned}\xi_b &= D^2 + \xi_c \\ \xi_c &= D\xi_b + D\xi_d \\ \xi_d &= D\xi_b + D\xi_d \\ T(D) &= D^2\xi_c \end{aligned} \tag{4.3.1}$$

where ξ_b, ξ_c, and ξ_d are dummy variables for the partial paths to the intermediate nodes, the input to the **a** node is unity, and the output is the desired generating function $T(D)$. Solution of (4.3.1) for $T(D)$ results in

$$\begin{aligned}T(D) &= \frac{D^5}{1 - 2D} \\ &= D^5 + 2D^6 + 4D^7 + \cdots + 2^k D^{k+5} + \cdots \end{aligned} \tag{4.3.2}$$

This verifies our previous observation, and in fact shows that, among the paths which merge with the all-zeros at a given node, there are 2^k paths at distance $k + 5$ from the all-zeros path.

Of course, (4.3.2) holds for an infinitely long code sequence; if we are dealing with the jth node level, we must truncate the series at some point. This is most easily done by considering the additional information indicated in the modified state diagram of Fig. 4.10. The L terms will be used to determine the length of a given path; since each branch has an L, the exponent of the L factor will be augmented by one every time a branch is passed through. The I term is included only if that branch transition was caused by an input data " 1," corresponding to a dotted branch in the trellis diagram. Rewriting the state equations (4.3.1), including now the factors in I and L shown in Fig. 4.10, and solving for the augmented

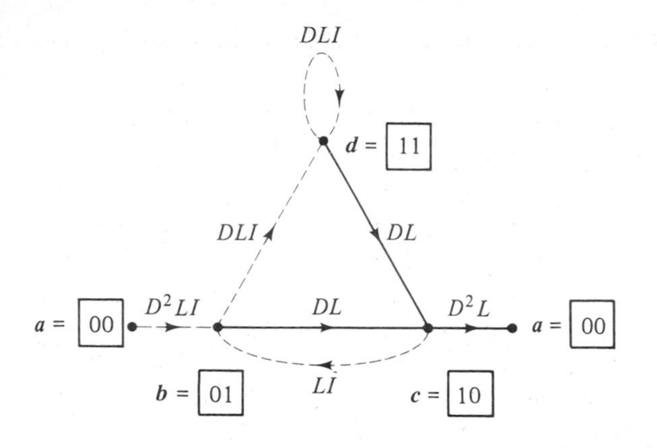

Figure 4.10 State diagram labeled with distance, length, and number of input "1"s.

generating function yields

$$T(D, L, I) = \frac{D^5L^3I}{1 - DL(1 + L)I}$$

$$= D^5L^3I + D^6L^4(1 + L)I^2 + D^7L^5(1 + L)^2I^3$$

$$+ \cdots + D^{5+k}L^{3+k}(1 + L)^kI^{1+k} + \cdots \tag{4.3.3}$$

Thus we have verified that of the two distance 6 paths, one is of length 4 and the other is of length 5, and both differ in two input bits from the all-zeros. Thus, for example, if the all-zeros was the correct path and the noise causes us to choose one of these incorrect paths, two bit errors will be made. Also, of the distance 7 paths, one is of length 5, two are of length 6, and one is of length 7; all four paths correspond to input sequences with three "1"s. If we are interested in the jth node level, clearly we should truncate the series such that no terms of power greater than L^j are included.

We have thus fully determined the properties of all code paths of this simple convolutional code. The same techniques can obviously be applied to any binary-symbol code of arbitrary constraint length and arbitrary rate b/n. However, for $b > 1$, each state equation of the type of (4.3.1) is a relationship among at most $2^b + 1$ node variables. In general, there will be $2^{b(K-1)}$ state variables and as many equations. (For further examples, see Probs. 4.6, 4.17, and 4.18.) In the next two sections we shall demonstrate how the generating function can be used to bound directly the error probability of a Viterbi decoder operating on any convolutional code on a binary-input, memoryless channel.

4.4 PERFORMANCE BOUNDS FOR SPECIFIC CONVOLUTIONAL CODES ON BINARY-INPUT, OUTPUT-SYMMETRIC MEMORYLESS CHANNELS

It should be reasonably evident at this point that the block length nB of a convolutional code is essentially irrelevant, for both the encoder and decoder complexity and operation depend only on the constraint length K, the code rate,

Figure 4.11 Example of error events.

and channel parameters; furthermore, the performance is a function of relative distances among signals, which may be determined from the code state diagram, whose structure and complexity depends strongly on the constraint length but not at all on the block length. Thus it would appear that block error probability is not a reasonable performance measure, particularly when, as is often the case, an entire message is convolutionally encoded as a single block, whereas in block coding the same message would be encoded into many smaller blocks. Ultimately, the most useful measure is *bit error probability* P_b which, as initially defined in Sec. 2.11, is the expected number of bit errors in a given sequence of received bits normalized by the total number of bits in the sequence.

While our ultimate goal is to upper-bound P_b, we consider initially a more readily determined performance measure, the *error probability per node*, which we denote P_e. In Fig. 4.11 we show (as solid lines) two paths through the code trellis. Without loss of essential generality, we take the upper all-zeros path to be correct, and the lower path to be that chosen by the maximum likelihood decoder. For this to occur, the correct path metric increments over the unmerged segments must be lower than those of the incorrect (lower solid line) path shown. We shall refer to these error events as node errors at nodes i, j, and k. On the other hand, the dotted paths which diverge from the correct path at nodes j' and k' may also have higher metric increments than the correct path over the unmerged segments, and yet not be ultimately selected because their accumulated metrics are smaller than those of the lower solid paths. We may conclude from this exposition that a necessary, but not sufficient, condition for a node error to occur at node j is that the metric of an incorrect path diverging from the correct path at this node accumulates higher metric increments than the correct path over the unmerged segment.

We may therefore upper-bound the probability of node error at node j by the probability that any path diverging from the correct path at node j accumulates higher total metric over the unmerged span of the path.

$$P_e(j) \leq \Pr\left[\bigcup_{\mathbf{x}'_j \in \mathscr{X}'(j)} \{\Delta M(\mathbf{x}'_j, \mathbf{x}_j) \geq 0\}\right] \tag{4.4.1}$$

where $\mathbf{x}'_j$ is an incorrect path diverging from the correct path at node j, $\mathscr{X}'(j)$ is the set of all such paths, known as the incorrect subset for node j, $\Delta M(\mathbf{x}'_j, \mathbf{x}_j)$ is the difference between the metric increment of this path and of the correct path $\mathbf{x}_j$ over the unmerged segment.

Employing the union bound, we obtain the more convenient, although looser, form

$$P_e(j) \leq \sum_{\mathbf{x}'_j \in \mathscr{X}'(j)} \Pr\left[\Delta M(\mathbf{x}'_j, \mathbf{x}_j) \geq 0\right] \tag{4.4.2}$$

But each term of this summation is the pairwise error probability for two code vectors over the unmerged segment. For a binary-input channel, this is readily bounded as a function of the distance between code vectors over this segment. For, if the total Hamming distance between code vectors $\mathbf{x}_j$ and $\mathbf{x}'_j$ (over their unmerged segment) is $d(\mathbf{x}'_j, \mathbf{x}_j) = d$, we have from (2.9.19) that, for an output-symmetric channel, the pairwise error probability is bounded by the Bhattacharyya bound

$$P_d \le \exp\left[d \ln \sum_y \sqrt{p_0(y)p_1(y)}\right] \tag{4.4.3}$$

where $p_i(y)$ is the conditional (channel transition) probability of output y given that the input symbol was $i (i = 0, 1)$. Equivalently, we may express this bound in the more convenient form

$$P_d \le Z^d \tag{4.4.4}$$

where

$$Z \equiv \sum_y \sqrt{p_0(y)p_1(y)} \tag{3.4.12}$$

Thus given that there are $a(d)$ incorrect paths which are at Hamming distance d from the correct path over the unmerged segment, we obtain from (4.4.1) through (4.4.4)

$$\begin{aligned} P_e(j) &\le \sum_{d=d_f}^{\infty} \Pr \begin{Bmatrix} \text{error caused by any one of } a(d) \\ \text{incorrect paths at distance } d \end{Bmatrix} \\ &\le \sum_{d=d_f}^{\infty} a(d) P_d \\ &\le \sum_{d=d_f}^{\infty} a(d) Z^d \end{aligned} \tag{4.4.5}$$

where d_f is the minimum distance of any path from the correct path, which we called the free distance in the last section. Clearly (4.4.5) is a union-Bhattacharyya bound similar to those derived for block codes in Chap. 2.

We also found in the last section that the set of all distances from any one path to all other paths could be found from the generating function $T(D)$. For demonstration purposes, let us consider again the code example of Figs. 4.2*a*, 4.4, and 4.5. We found then that

$$\begin{aligned} T(D) = \frac{D^5}{1 - 2D} &= D^5 + 2D^6 + 4D^7 + \cdots + 2^{k-5}D^k + \cdots \\ &= \sum_{d=5}^{\infty} 2^{d-5} D^d \end{aligned}$$

Thus in this case $d_f = 5$ and $a(d) = 2^{d-d_f}$. The same argument can be applied to any binary code whose generating function we can determine by the techniques of the last section. Thus we have in general that

$$T(D) = \sum_{d=d_f}^{\infty} a(d)D^d \tag{4.4.6}$$

and it then follows from (4.4.5) and (4.4.6) that

$$P_e(j) \leq T(D)\Big|_{D=Z} \tag{4.4.7}$$

We note also that this node error probability bound for a fixed convolutional code is the same for all nodes when $B = \infty$ and that this is also an upper bound for finite B.

Turning now to the bit error probability, we note that the expected number of bit errors, caused by any incorrect path which diverges from the correct path at node j, can be bounded by weighting each term of the union bound by the number of bit errors which occur on that incorrect path. Taking the all-zeros data path to be the correct path (without loss of generality on output-symmetric channels), this then corresponds to the number of "1"s in the data sequence over the unmerged segment. Thus the bound on the expected number of bit errors caused by an incorrect path diverging at node j is

$$E[n_b(j)] \leq \sum_{i=1}^{\infty} \sum_{d=d_f}^{\infty} ia(d, i)P_d \leq \sum_{i=1}^{\infty} \sum_{d=d_f}^{\infty} ia(d, i)Z^d \tag{4.4.8}$$

where $a(d, i)$ is the number of paths diverging from the all-zeros path (at node j) at distance d and with i "1"s in its data sequence over the unmerged segment. But the coefficients $a(d, i)$ are also the coefficients of the augmented generating function $T(D, I)$ derived in the last section. For the running example, we have from (4.3.3) (with $L = 1$ since we are not interested in path lengths)

$$T(D, I) = \frac{D^5 I}{1 - 2DI} = D^5 I + 2D^6 I^2 + 4D^7 I^3 + \cdots + 2^{k-5} D^k I^{k-4} + \cdots$$

$$= \sum_{d=5}^{\infty} 2^{d-5} D^d I^{d-4}$$

and hence

$$a(d, i) = \begin{cases} 2^{d-5} & \text{for } i = d - 4,\ d \geq 5 \\ 0 & \text{otherwise} \end{cases}$$

In this case then,

$$E[n_b(j)] \leq \sum_{d=5}^{\infty} (d - 4)2^{d-5} |Z^d = \frac{\partial T(D, I)}{\partial I}\Big|_{I=1,\ D=Z}$$

In general it should be clear that the augmented generating function can be expanded in the form

$$T(D, I) = \sum_{i=1}^{\infty} \sum_{d=d_f}^{\infty} a(d, i) D^d I^i \tag{4.4.9}$$

whose derivative at $I = 1$ is

$$\left. \frac{\partial T(D, I)}{\partial I} \right|_{I=1} = \sum_{i=1}^{\infty} \sum_{d=d_f}^{\infty} i a(d, i) D^d \tag{4.4.10}$$

Consequently, comparing (4.4.8) and (4.4.10), we have

$$E[n_b(j)] \le \left. \frac{\partial T(D, I)}{\partial I} \right|_{I=1,\, D=Z} \tag{4.4.11}$$

This is an upper bound on the expected number of bit errors caused by an incorrect path diverging at any node j.

For a rate $1/n$ code, each node (branch) represents one bit of information into the encoder or decoder. Thus the bit error probability defined as the expected number of bit errors per bit decoded is bounded by

$$P_b(j) = E\{n_b(j)\} \le \left. \frac{\partial T(D, I)}{\partial I} \right|_{I=1,\, D=Z} \tag{4.4.12}$$

as shown in (4.4.11). For a rate b/n code, one branch corresponds to b information bits. Thus in general

$$P_b(j) = \frac{E\{n_b(j)\}}{b} \le \frac{1}{b} \left. \frac{\partial T(D, I)}{\partial I} \right|_{I=1,\, D=Z} \tag{4.4.13}$$

where Z is given by (3.4.12).

4.5 SPECIAL CASES AND EXAMPLES

It is somewhat instructive to consider the BSC and the binary-input AWGN channel, special cases of the channels considered in the last section. Clearly the union-Bhattacharyya bounds apply with [see (2.11.6) and (2.11.7) and (3.4.15) and (3.4.17)]

$$(Z)_{\text{BSC}} = \sqrt{4p(1-p)} \tag{4.5.1}$$

and

$$(Z)_{\text{AWGN}} = e^{-\mathscr{E}_s/N_0} \tag{4.5.2}$$

We note also, as was already observed in Sec. 2.11, that if the AWGN channel is converted to the BSC by hard quantization for $\mathscr{E}_s/N_o \ll 1$, then

$$p \approx \frac{1}{2} - \sqrt{\frac{\mathscr{E}_s}{\pi N_o}}$$

in which case

$$-\ln Z \approx -\ln [\sqrt{1 - 4\mathscr{E}_s/\pi N_o}] \approx -\ln \left[1 - \frac{2}{\pi}\frac{\mathscr{E}_s}{N_o}\right] \approx \frac{(2/\pi)\mathscr{E}_s}{N_o}$$

for a loss of $2/\pi$, or approximately 2 dB, in energy-to-noise ratio.

However, for these two special channels, tighter bounds can be found by obtaining the exact pairwise error probabilities rather than their Bhattacharyya bounds. For the BSC, we recall from (2.10.14) that, for unmerged segments at distance d from the correct path[7]

$$P_d = \begin{cases} \displaystyle\sum_{k=(d+1)/2}^{d} \binom{d}{k} p^k (1-p)^{d-k} & d \text{ odd} \\ \displaystyle\frac{1}{2}\binom{d}{d/2} p^{d/2}(1-p)^{d/2} + \sum_{k=d/2+1}^{d} \binom{d}{k} p^k (1-p)^{d-k} & d \text{ even} \end{cases} \tag{4.5.3}$$

This can be used in the middle expressions of inequalities (4.4.5) and (4.4.8) to obtain tighter results than (4.4.7) and (4.4.12) (see also Prob. 4.10).

Similarly, for the binary-input AWGN channel, we have from (2.3.10) that the pairwise error probability for code vectors at distance d is

$$P_d = Q(\sqrt{2d\mathscr{E}_s/N_o}) \tag{4.5.4}$$

While we may substitute this in the above expressions in place of $Z^d = e^{-d\mathscr{E}_s/N_o}$, a more elegant and useful expression results from noting that (Prob. 4.8)

$$Q(\sqrt{x+y}) \le Q(\sqrt{x})e^{-y/2} \qquad x \ge 0,\ y \ge 0 \tag{4.5.5}$$

Since $d \ge d_f$ we may bound (4.5.4) by

$$P_d \le Q\left(\sqrt{\frac{2d_f\mathscr{E}_s}{N_o}}\right) e^{-(d-d_f)\mathscr{E}_s/N_o} \tag{4.5.6}$$

which is tighter than the Bhattacharyya bound. Substituting in the middle terms of (4.4.5) and (4.4.8), then using (4.4.6) and (4.4.10), we obtain

$$\begin{aligned} P_e &\le Q\left(\sqrt{\frac{2d_f\mathscr{E}_s}{N_o}}\right) e^{d_f\mathscr{E}_s/N_o} \sum_{d=d_f}^{\infty} a(d)\, e^{-d\mathscr{E}_s/N_o} \\ &= Q\left(\sqrt{\frac{2d_f\mathscr{E}_s}{N_o}}\right) e^{d_f\mathscr{E}_s/N_o} T(D)\Big|_{D=e^{-\mathscr{E}_s/N_o}} \end{aligned} \tag{4.5.7}$$

[7] Ties are assumed to be randomly resolved. Note that unlike the block code case for which (2.10.14) holds, all probabilities here are for pairwise errors.

and

$$P_b = \frac{E[n_b(j)]}{b} \le \frac{1}{b} Q\left(\sqrt{\frac{2d_f \mathscr{E}_s}{N_o}}\right) e^{d_f \mathscr{E}_s/N_o} \sum_{i=1}^{\infty} \sum_{d=d_f}^{\infty} i a(d, i) D^d \Bigg|_{D=e^{-\mathscr{E}_s/N_o}}$$
$$= \frac{1}{b} Q\left(\sqrt{\frac{2d_f \mathscr{E}_s}{N_o}}\right) e^{d_f \mathscr{E}_s/N_o} \frac{\partial T(D, I)}{\partial I} \Bigg|_{I=1,\, D=e^{-\mathscr{E}_s/N_o}} \tag{4.5.8}$$

The last bound has been used very effectively to obtain tight upper bounds for the bit error probability on the binary-input AWGN channel for a variety of convolutional codes of constraint lengths less than 10. For, while the computation of $T(D, I)$ for a constraint length K code would appear to involve the analytical solution of $2^{b(K-1)}$ simultaneous algebraic equations (Sec. 4.3), the computation of $T(D, I)$ for fixed values of $D = Z$ and I becomes merely a numerical matrix inversion. Also since $T(D, I)$ is a polynomial in I with nonnegative coefficients and has a nondecreasing first derivative for positive arguments, the derivative at $I = 1$ can be upper-bounded numerically by computing instead the normalized first difference. Thus

$$\frac{\partial T(D, I)}{\partial I}\Bigg|_{I=1,\, D=Z} < \frac{T(Z, 1+\epsilon) - T(Z, 1)}{\epsilon} \qquad \epsilon \ll 1 \tag{4.5.9}$$

Even the numerical matrix inversion involved in calculating $T(D, I)$ for fixed D and I is greatly simplified by the fact that the diagonal terms of the state equations matrix [see (4.3.1) and Probs. 4.17 and 4.18] dominate all other terms in the same row. As a result, the inverse can be computed as a rapidly convergent series of powers of the given matrix (see Prob. 4.18). The results for optimum rate $\frac{1}{2}$ codes[8] of constraint length 3 through 8 are shown in Fig. 4.12. To assess the tightness of these bounds we show also in the figure the results of simulations of the same codes, but with output quantization to eight levels. For the low error probability region ($\mathscr{E}_b/N_o > 5$ dB), it appears that the upper bounds lie slightly below the simulation. The simulations should, in fact, lie above the exact curve because the quantization loss is on the order of 0.25 dB (see Sec. 2.8). This, in fact, appears to be the approximate separation between simulation and upper bounds, attesting to the accuracy of the bounds.

In all codes considered thus far, the generating function sequence

$$T(D) = \sum_{d=d_f}^{\infty} a(d) D^d \tag{4.5.10}$$

was assumed to converge for any value of D less than unity. That this will not always be true is demonstrated by the example of Fig. 4.13. For this code, the self

[8] The codes were selected on the basis of maximum free distance and minimum number of bit errors caused by incorrect paths at the free distance, i.e., minimum $a(d_f, i)$ (Odenwalder [1970]).

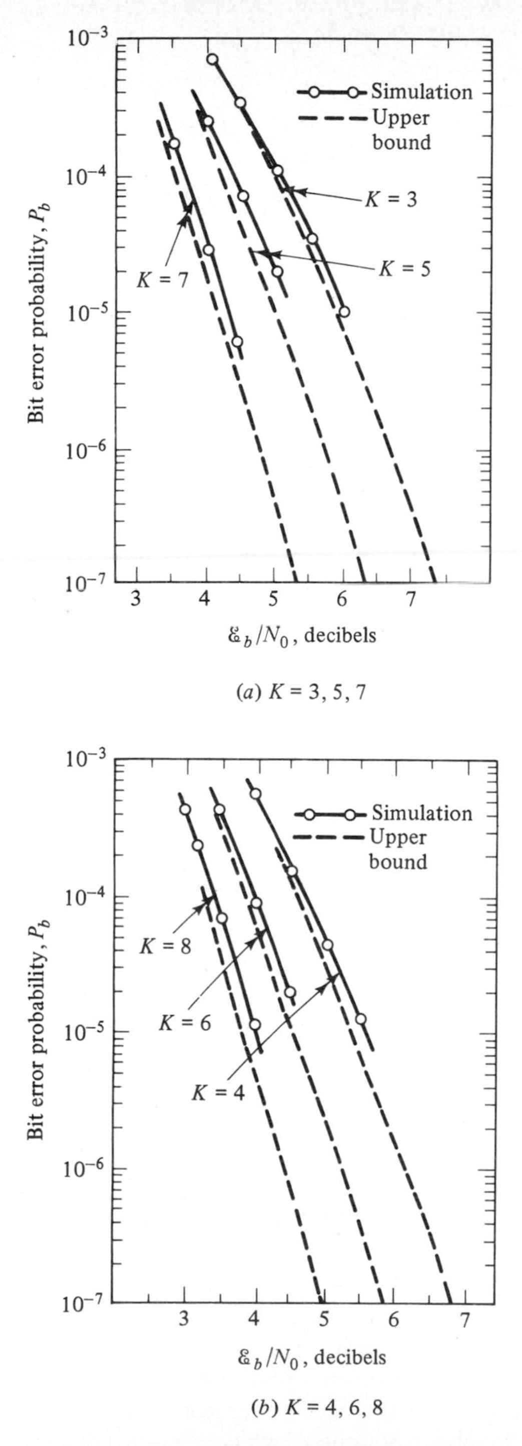

Figure 4.12 P_b as a function of $\mathscr{E}_b/N_o$ for Viterbi decoding of rate $\frac{1}{2}$ codes: simulations with eight-level quantization and 32-bit path memory (solid); upper bounds for unquantized AWGN (dotted). (*Courtesy of Heller and Jacobs* [*1971*].)

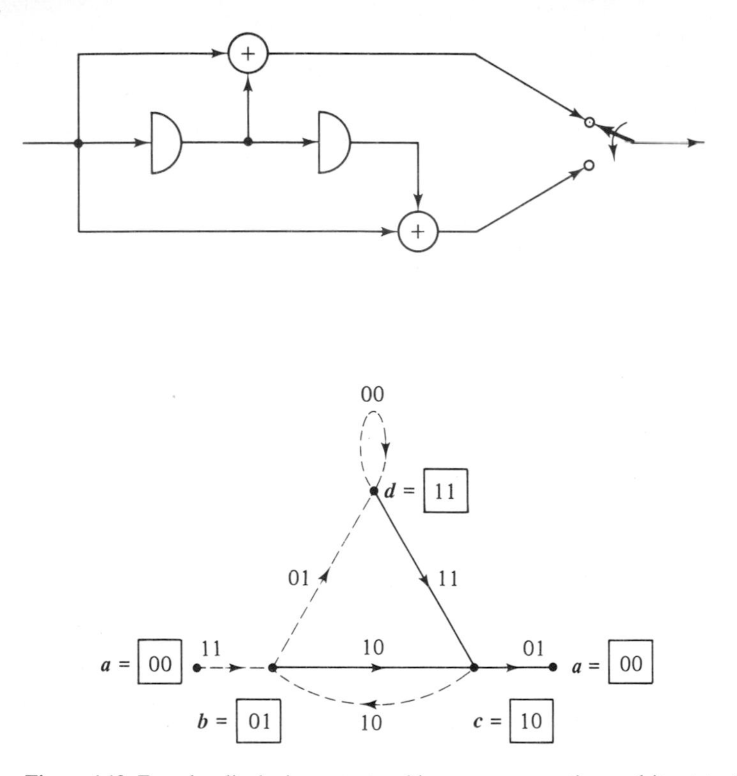

Figure 4.13 Encoder displaying catastrophic error propagation and its state diagram.

loop at state d does not increase distance, so that the path **abddd ... ddca** will be at distance 6 from the correct path no matter how many times it circulates about this self-loop. Thus it is possible on a BSC, for example, for a fixed finite number of channel errors to cause an arbitrarily large number of decoded bit errors. To illustrate in this case, for example, if the correct path is the all-zeros and the BSC produces two errors in the first branch, no errors in the next B branches and two errors in the $(B + 1)$st branch, $B - 1$ decoded bit errors will occur for an arbitrarily large B. For obvious reasons, such a code, for which a finite number of channel errors (or noise) can cause an infinite number of decoded bit errors, is called *catastrophic*.

It is clear from the above example that a convolutional code is catastrophic if and only if, for some directed closed loop in the state diagram, all branches have zero weight; that is, the closed loop path generating function is D^0. An even more useful method to ensure the avoidance of a catastrophic code is to establish necessary and sufficient conditions in terms of the code-generator sequences $\mathbf{g}_i$. For rate $1/n$ codes, Massey and Sain [1968] have obtained such conditions in terms of the code *generator polynomials* which are defined in terms of the generator sequences as[9]

$$g_k(z) = 1 + g_{1,k} z + g_{2,k} z^2 + \cdots + g_{(K-1),k} z^{K-1} \qquad k = 1, 2, \ldots, n$$

In terms of these polynomials, the theorem of Massey and Sain (see Prob. 4.11) states that a fixed convolutional code is catastrophic if and only if all generator polynomials have a common polynomial factor (of degree at least one). Also of interest is the question of the relative fraction of catastrophic codes in the ensemble of all convolutional codes of a given rate and constraint length. Forney [1970] and Rosenberg [1971] have shown that, for a rate $1/n$ code, this fraction is $1/(2^n - 1)$, independent of constraint length (see Prob. 4.12). Hence generally, the search for a good code is not seriously encumbered by the catastrophic codes, which are relatively sparse and easy to distinguish.

One subclass of convolutional codes that are not catastrophic is that of the *systematic convolutional codes*. As with systematic block codes, systematic convo-

[9] In this context, z is taken to be an abstract variable, not a real number. The lowest order coefficient can always be taken as one without loss of optimality or essential generality.

Table 4.1 Maximum free distance of noncatastrophic codes

Rate $r = \frac{1}{2}$

K	Systematic† d_f	Nonsystematic d_f
2	3	3
3	4	5
4	4	6
5	5	7
6	6	8
7	6	10
8	7	10

Rate $r = \frac{1}{3}$

K	Systematic† d_f	Nonsystematic d_f
2	5	5
3	6	8
4	8	10
5	9	12
6	10	13
7	12	15
8	12	16

† With feed-forward logic.

lutional codes have the property that the data symbols are transmitted unchanged among the coded symbols. For a systematic rate b/n convolutional code, in each branch the first b symbols are data symbols followed by $n - b$ parity or coded symbols. The coded symbols are generated just as for nonsystematic codes, and consequently depend on the last Kb data symbols where Kb is the constraint length. Since data symbols appear directly on each branch in the state or trellis diagram, for systematic convolutional codes it is impossible to have a self-loop in which distance to the all-zeros path does not increase, and therefore these codes are not catastrophic.

In Sec. 5.7, we show that systematic feed-forward convolutional codes do not perform as well as nonsystematic convolutional codes.[10] There we show that, for asymptotically large K, the performance of a systematic code of constraint length K is approximately the same as that of a nonsystematic code of constraint length $K(1 - r)$ where $r = b/n$. Thus for rate $r = \frac{1}{2}$ and very large K, systematic codes have about the performance of nonsystematic codes of half the constraint length, while requiring exactly the same optimal decoder complexity.

Another indication of the relative weakness of systematic convolutional codes is shown in the free distance, d_f, which is the exponent of D in the leading term of the generating function $T(D)$. Table 4.1 shows the maximum free distance achievable with binary feed-forward systematic codes and nonsystematic codes that are not catastrophic. We show this for various constraint lengths K and rates r. As indicated by the results of Sec. 5.7, for large K the differences are even greater.

4.6 STRUCTURE OF RATE $1/n$ CODES AND ORTHOGONAL CONVOLUTIONAL CODES

While the weight or distance properties of the paths of a convolutional code naturally depend on the encoder generator sequences, both the unmerged path lengths and the number of "1"s in the data sequence for a particular code path are functions only of the constraint length, K, and rate numerator, b. Thus for example, for any rate $1/n$, constraint length 3 code [see (4.3.3)]

$$T_3(L, I) = \frac{L^3 I}{1 - L(1 + L)I} \tag{4.6.1}$$

To obtain a general formula for the generating function $T_K(L, I)$ of any rate $1/n$ code of constraint length K, we may proceed as follows. Consider the state just prior to the terminal state in the state diagram of a constraint length K code (see Fig. 4.10 for $K = 3$). The $(K - 1)$-dimensional vector for this state is $10 \ldots 0$. Suppose this were the terminal state and that when a path reached this state it was considered absorbed (or remerged) without the possibility to go on to either of the

[10] It can be shown (Forney [1970]) that for any nonsystematic convolutional code, there is an equivalent systematic code in which the parity symbols are generated with linear *feedback* logic.

states $0 \ldots 0$ or $0 \ldots 01$. Then the initial input into the encoder register could be ignored, and we would have a code of constraint length $K - 1$. It follows that the generating function of all paths from the origin to this next-to-terminal state, must be $T_{K-1}(L, I)$. Now, if an additional "0" enters when the encoder is in this state, the terminal state is reached. If, on the other hand, a "1" enters we are effectively back to the situation of initial entry into the state diagram; that is, the "1" takes us to state $00 \ldots 1$ with the branch from $10 \ldots 0$ playing the same role as that from the initial state. This implies that the recursion formula for the generating function $T_K(L, I)$ is

$$T_K(L, I) = LT_{K-1}(L, I) + T_{K-1}(L, I)T_K(L, I) \qquad K \geq 2 \tag{4.6.2}$$

In words, to arrive at the terminal state, since we must first pass through the state $100 \ldots 0$, the first term on the right corresponds to a "0" entering when the encoder is in this state, in which case the terminal state is reached with an addition of one branch length (with data zero); the second term on the right corresponds to an input "1," in which case we may treat the state $100 \ldots 0$ as if it were the initial state and the terminal state can only be reached by following one of the paths of $T_K(L, I)$. From (4.6.2), we immediately obtain

$$T_K(L, I) = \frac{LT_{K-1}(L, I)}{1 - T_{K-1}(L, I)} \qquad K \geq 2 \tag{4.6.3}$$

Trivially, for $K = 1$

$$T_1(L, I) = LI \tag{4.6.4}$$

Then the solution of (4.6.3) is obtained by induction as

$$\begin{aligned} T_K(L, I) &= \frac{IL^K}{1 - IL(1 + L + L^2 + \cdots + L^{K-2})} \\ &= \frac{IL^K(1 - L)}{1 - L[1 + I(1 - L^{K-1})]} \qquad K \geq 2 \end{aligned} \tag{4.6.5}$$

If only the path length structure is of interest, we may restrict attention to

$$T_K(L) \equiv T_K(L, 1) = \frac{L^K(1 - L)}{1 - 2L + L^K} \qquad K \geq 2 \tag{4.6.6}$$

We shall utilize these results in the next chapter when we treat convolutional code ensembles. We conclude this discussion by considering a class of codes whose distance or weight properties are the same for all branches, and consequently whose performance depends only on the path structure. Such a class of codes is the orthogonal, rate 2^{-K} convolutional codes generated by the encoder of Fig. 4.14. The block orthogonal encoder generates one of 2^K orthogonal binary sequences of dimension $n = 2^K$ (as described in Sec. 2.5). Hence the weight of any branch not on the all-zeros data path is exactly $2^{K-1} = n/2$. Thus for this class of

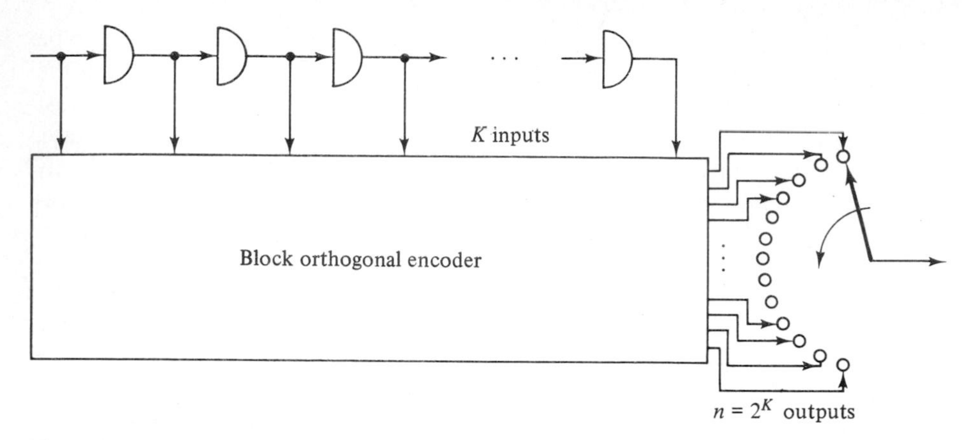

Figure 4.14 Convolutional orthogonal encoder: constraint length K; rate $r = 2^{-K}$.

codes, since each branch has weight $n/2$, $T_K(D, I)$ is obtained from $T_K(L, I)$ by replacing L by $D^{n/2}$ everywhere, and thus

$$T_K(D, I) = \frac{ID^{Kn/2}(1 - D^{n/2})}{1 - D^{n/2}[1 + I(1 - D^{(n/2)(K-1)})]} \tag{4.6.7}$$

$$T_K(D) = \frac{D^{Kn/2}(1 - D^{n/2})}{1 - 2D^{n/2} + D^{Kn/2}} \tag{4.6.8}$$

Consequently, employing (4.4.7) and (4.4.12), we obtain the node and bit error probabilities for the AWGN channel for which $Z = e^{-\mathscr{E}_s/N_o}$ as

$$P_e < T_K(D)\Big|_{D=Z} = \frac{Z^{Kn/2}(1 - Z^{n/2})}{1 - 2Z^{n/2} + Z^{Kn/2}} < \frac{Z^{Kn/2}}{1 - 2Z^{n/2}} \tag{4.6.9}$$

$$P_b < \frac{\partial T_K(D, I)}{\partial I}\Big|_{I=1,\, D=Z} = \frac{Z^{Kn/2}(1 - Z^{n/2})^2}{(1 - 2Z^{n/2} + Z^{Kn/2})^2} < \frac{Z^{Kn/2}}{(1 - 2Z^{n/2})^2} \tag{4.6.10}$$

Recognizing that, since for a rate $1/n$ code there are n code symbols/bit

$$Z^n = e^{-n\mathscr{E}_s/N_o} = e^{-\mathscr{E}_b/N_o}$$

we find

$$P_e < \frac{e^{-K\mathscr{E}_b/2N_o}}{1 - 2e^{-\mathscr{E}_b/2N_o}}$$

$$P_b < \frac{e^{-K\mathscr{E}_b/2N_o}}{(1 - 2e^{-\mathscr{E}_b/2N_o})^2} \qquad \mathscr{E}_b/N_o > 2 \ln 2 \tag{4.6.11}$$

We recall also from Sec. 2.5 [Eqs. (2.5.13) and (2.5.18)] that

$$\mathscr{E}_b/(N_o \ln 2) = C_T/R_T \tag{4.6.12}$$

where R_T, the transmission rate, and C_T, the capacity, are in nats per second and the transmission time per bit is

$$T_b \equiv \ln 2/R_T \qquad \text{s/bit}$$

Thus (4.6.11) becomes

$$P_e < \frac{2^{-KC_T/(2R_T)}}{1 - 2^{1-C_T/(2R_T)}} \tag{4.6.13}$$

$$R_T/C_T < \tfrac{1}{2}$$

$$P_b < \frac{2^{-KC_T/(2R_T)}}{[1 - 2^{1-C_T/(2R_T)}]^2} \tag{4.6.14}$$

For orthogonal block codes we were able to show in Sec. 2.5 that the error probability decreases exponentially with block length for all $R_T < C_T$. We recall, however, that to obtain that result we employed a more refined bounding technique than the union bound; we now use a similar approach for convolutional codes to demonstrate an exponential bound in terms of constraint length for all rates up to capacity.

We begin with node error probability, and recall that an error can occur at node j only if an incorrect path diverging at this node from the correct path has higher metric upon remerging. From the generating function $T_K(L)$ of (4.6.6), we can determine all unmerged path lengths, and from this the totality of diverging paths which remerge again a number of branches ahead. This formula can be somewhat simplified, if we bound (4.6.6), in the sense of counting for every L more paths than actually exist, as follows

$$T_K(L) < \frac{L^K}{1 - 2L} = \sum_{k=0}^{\infty} 2^k L^{K+k} \tag{4.6.15}$$

Thus, of the totality of paths diverging at a given node, there are no more than 2^k incorrect paths which merge after $K + k$ branches; as we shall find, this overestimate of number of paths (by approximately double) has negligible asymptotic effect. Now for an orthogonal convolutional code, all paths which are unmerged from the correct path for $K + k$ branches have code vectors which are orthogonal to it over this entire unmerged segment. The node error probability can be bounded by

$$P_e < \sum_{k=0}^{\infty} \Pi_k \tag{4.6.16}$$

where $$\Pi_k = \Pr \left\{ \begin{array}{l} \text{error caused by any one of no more than } 2^k \\ \text{incorrect paths unmerged over } K + k \text{ branches} \end{array} \right\}$$

This, of course, is a union bound, but rather than summing over all individual path error events, as in Sec. 4.4, we treat as a single event all errors caused by paths unmerged for the same number of branches. Now instead of bounding the probability of these events by a union bound over their members, as was done before, we employ a Gallager bound. In fact, we may apply precisely the derivation of Sec. 2.5, based on the Gallager bound (2.4.8), to the set of up to 2^k incorrect paths, unmerged with, and hence orthogonal to, the correct path over $K + k$ branches. Noting that this argument does not require all code vectors to be mutually orthogonal, but only that each incorrect code vector be pairwise orthogonal to the correct code vector, we thus have from (2.5.12), for orthogonal codes on the AWGN channel

$$\Pi_k \leq 2^{k\rho} \exp\left[-\frac{(K+k)\mathscr{E}_b}{N_o}\left(\frac{\rho}{1+\rho}\right)\right] \qquad 0 \leq \rho \leq 1 \tag{4.6.17}$$

since the energy over this segment is $(K + k)$ times the energy per branch, which equals $\mathscr{E}_b$ for a rate $1/n$ code. Substituting (4.6.17) into (4.6.16), then using (4.6.12) yields

$$P_e < \exp\left[\frac{-K\mathscr{E}_b}{N_o}\left(\frac{\rho}{1+\rho}\right)\right] \sum_{k=0}^{\infty} \exp\left\{-k\rho\left[\frac{\mathscr{E}_b}{N_o(1+\rho)} - \ln 2\right]\right\}$$

$$= \frac{2^{-K(C_T/R_T)\rho/(1+\rho)}}{1 - 2^{\rho\{1-C_T/[R_T(1+\rho)]\}}} \qquad 0 \leq \rho \leq 1 \tag{4.6.18}$$

Clearly if we take $\rho = 1$, we obtain the bound (4.6.13). On the other hand, taking for some $0 < \epsilon \ll 1$

$$\rho = \frac{C_T}{R_T}(1 - \epsilon) - 1 \tag{4.6.19}$$

we have

$$P_e < \frac{2^{-K[(C_T/R_T) - 1/(1-\epsilon)]}}{1 - 2^{-\epsilon[(C_T/R_T) - 1/(1-\epsilon)]}} \qquad C_T/2 \leq R_T \leq C_T(1 - \epsilon) \tag{4.6.20}$$

Thus we have an exponential decrease in K for all $R_T < C_T(1 - \epsilon)$. For asymptotically large K, the denominator becomes insignificant so that we can let $\epsilon \to 0$.

To bound the bit error probability requires little more effort if we recognize that a node error due to an incorrect path which has been unmerged over $K + k$ branches can cause *at most* $k + 1$ bit errors; for in order to merge with the correct path, the last $K - 1$ data bits for the incorrect path must coincide with those of the correct path. It follows then that the bit error probability is bounded by a summation of the form of (4.6.16) with each term weighted by $k + 1$. Thus

$$P_b < \sum_{k=0}^{\infty} (k + 1)\Pi_k$$

Now using (4.6.17), and recognizing that

$$\sum_{k=0}^{\infty} (k + 1)e^{-kx} = \frac{1}{(1 - e^{-x})^2}$$

we have

$$P_b < \exp\left[\frac{-K\mathscr{E}_b}{N_o}\left(\frac{\rho}{1+\rho}\right)\right]\sum_{k=0}^{\infty}(k+1)\exp\left\{-k\rho\left[\frac{\mathscr{E}_b}{N_o(1+\rho)} - \ln 2\right]\right\}$$

$$= \frac{2^{-K(C_T/R_T)\rho/(1+\rho)}}{(1-2^{\rho\{1-C_T/[R_T(1+\rho)]\}})^2} \tag{4.6.21}$$

Finally, applying (4.6.19) we obtain, analogously to (4.6.20)

$$P_b < \frac{2^{-K[(C_T/R_T)-1/(1-\epsilon)]}}{(1-2^{-\epsilon[(C_T/R_T)-1/(1-\epsilon)]})^2} \qquad C_T/2 \le R_T \le C_T(1-\epsilon) \qquad \epsilon \ll 1 \tag{4.6.22}$$

Combining (4.6.13), (4.6.14), (4.6.20), and (4.6.22), we obtain

$$P_e < \frac{2^{-KE_c(R_T)/R_T}}{1-2^{-\delta(R_T)}} \qquad \begin{cases} 0 \le R_T < C_T/(1-\epsilon) \\ T_b = \ln 2/R_T \end{cases}$$

$$P_b < \frac{2^{-KE_c(R_T)/R_T}}{[1-2^{-\delta(R_T)}]^2} \tag{4.6.23}$$

where $\delta(R_T) > 0$ for $\epsilon > 0$ and

$$E_c(R_T) = \begin{cases} C_T/2 & 0 \le R_T < C_T/2 \\ C_T - R_T/(1-\epsilon) & C_T/2 \le R_T \le C_T(1-\epsilon) \end{cases} \tag{4.6.24}$$

Figure 4.15 compares $E_c(R_T)$, the convolutional exponent as $\epsilon \to 0$, with the block exponent $E(R_T)$ of (2.5.16) as a function of R_T/C_T. Comparing the latter with (4.6.23), we note that T for block codes is the time to transmit K bits, as is KT_b for convolutional codes; thus (2.5.16) can be expressed as

$$P_E < 2^{-KE(R_T)/R_T}$$

with $E(R_T)$ as defined there. Hence, as is seen from the comparison of $E_c(R_T)$ and $E(R_T)$ in Fig. 4.15, the convolutional coding exponent clearly dominates the block coding exponent for orthogonal codes.

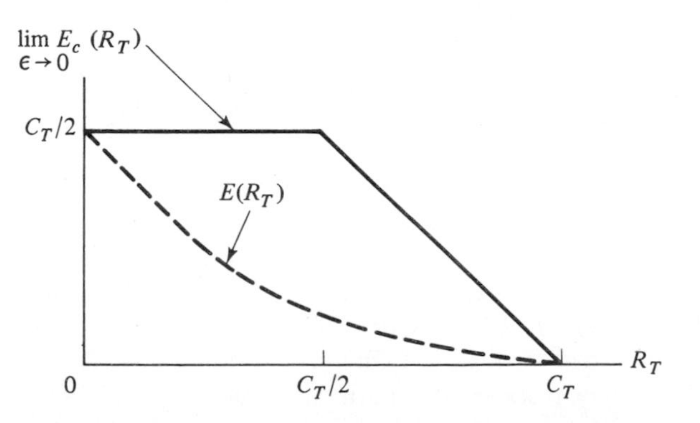

Figure 4.15 Limiting form of $E_c(R_T)$ for orthogonal convolutional codes and comparison with orthogonal block codes.

Comparing decoding complexity, a maximum likelihood block decoder performs 2^K comparisons every K bits or $2^K/K$ comparisons per bit while a Viterbi maximum likelihood convolutional decoder performs 2^{K-1} comparisons per bit; the difference becomes insignificant for large K. On the other hand, the bandwidth expansion of block codes is proportional to $2^K/K$ while it is proportional to 2^{K-1} for convolutional codes, a severe drawback; this, however, is a feature only of orthogonal codes, and in the next chapter we shall show by ensemble arguments that, for the same bandwidth expansion (or code rate), the convolutional code exponent dominates the block exponent in a similar manner for all memoryless channels.

4.7 PATH MEMORY TRUNCATION, METRIC QUANTIZATION, AND CODE SYNCHRONIZATION IN VITERBI DECODERS

In deriving the Viterbi algorithm for maximum likelihood decoding of convolutional codes in Sec. 4.2, we made three impractical assumptions which are, in order of importance, arbitrarily long path memories, arbitrarily accurate metrics, and perfect code synchronization. All three of these requirements can be eliminated with a minimal loss of performance, as we shall now discuss.

As initially described, the algorithm requires that a final decision on the most probable code path be deferred until the end of the code block, or message, when the trellis merges into the single state **0** by insertion of a $b(K-1)$ zero "tail" into the coder register. Thus if the message or block length is $(B-K+1)b$ bits, the decoder must provide a register of this length for each of the $2^{b(K-1)}$ possible states. One obvious remedy to this situation is to limit B to some manageable number, say on the order of 1000 or less, by terminating the "block" with a $b(K-1)$ zero bit tail every $(B-K+1)b$ data bits. This has two disadvantages, however. First, it reduces the efficiency by increasing the effective required $\mathscr{E}_b/N_o$, and the required bandwidth, by a multiplicative factor of $1+[(K-1)/B]$; also it requires interruption of the data bit stream periodically to insert nondata tails, a common drawback of block codes.

These drawbacks can be avoided by simple modification of the basic algorithm. The simplest approach is to recognize that, other than in a catastrophic code, a path which is unmerged from the correct path will accumulate distance from it as an increasing function of the length of the unmerged span. Thus, upon merging, an incorrect path with a very long unmerged span will have very low probability of having higher metric than the correct path since this probability decreases exponentially with distance. Consequently, with very high probability, the best path to each of the $2^{b(K-1)}$ states will have diverged from the correct path only within a reasonably short span, typically a few constraint lengths. Thus without ever inserting tails, we may truncate the path memory to say five constraint lengths, using shift registers of length $5bK$ for each state. As each new set of b bits enters the registers of each state, the b bits which entered $5K$ branch times earlier are eliminated, but as this occurs the decoder makes a final decision on these bits, either by choosing for each set of b bits the oldest shift register contents of the majority of the states, or more simply, by accepting the contents of an arbitrary state, on the grounds that, with high probability, all paths will be identical at this point and before. The analysis of the loss in performance caused by these truncation strategies appears quite difficult, but simulations indicate a minimal loss when path memories are truncated more than five constraint lengths back.

A better, but more complex, truncation strategy is to compare all likelihood functions or metrics after each new branch, not only in groups of 2^b but also among all $2^{b(K-1)}$ surviving paths, to determine the most probable path leaving the given node at the truncation point; then among the $2^{b(K-1)}$ paths, we choose the outputs corresponding to the highest metric (several constraint lengths forward). In a somewhat superior manner, this strategy permits reduction of the memory length to $4bK$ or less in practical situations as has been determined by simulation. In addition, the loss in performance due to truncation with this decision strategy can be analyzed on an ensemble basis, as will be shown in Sec. 5.6 (also see Prob. 4.24).

The second inherent assumption has been that accumulated branch metrics

$$\sum_{i=1}^{B} \ln p(\mathbf{y}_i \mid \mathbf{x}_{mi})$$

can be stored precisely. We note that, other than for the BSC where they simplify to integers, the metrics will be real numbers. For example, on an AWGN channel, they consist of linear combinations of the demodulator outputs for each symbol [see (4.2.3)]. Even if these symbols are quantized to J levels, this does not mean that the metrics are quantized; for as shown in Sec. 2.8 (see Fig. 2.14) the quantized channel is characterized by a transition probability matrix $\{p(b_j \mid a_j)\}$ whose logarithms are real numbers.[11] Nevertheless, it has been found, again by extensive simulation (see Heller and Jacobs [1971]), that for all values of $\mathscr{E}_b/N_o$, for an eight-level quantized AWGN channel with binary (biphase or quadriphase modulated) inputs, use of the definitely *suboptimal* metric

$$\sum_i (\hat{\mathbf{y}}_i, \mathbf{x}_{mi})$$

where the $\hat{\mathbf{y}}_i$ are n-dimensional vectors of *quantized* demodulator outputs with integer values from zero to seven, results in a total performance loss of only 0.25 dB relative to that with unquantized demodulator outputs and unquantized metric (see Fig. 4.12). Another problem arises because, even though we may quantize each branch metric to a reasonable number of bits to be stored, the accumulated metrics will grow linearly with the number of branches decoded. This difficulty is easily avoided by renormalizing the highest metric to zero simply by subtracting an equal amount from each accumulated metric after each branch

[11] See Prob. 4.20 for a bounding technique for a decoder which uses integer metrics.

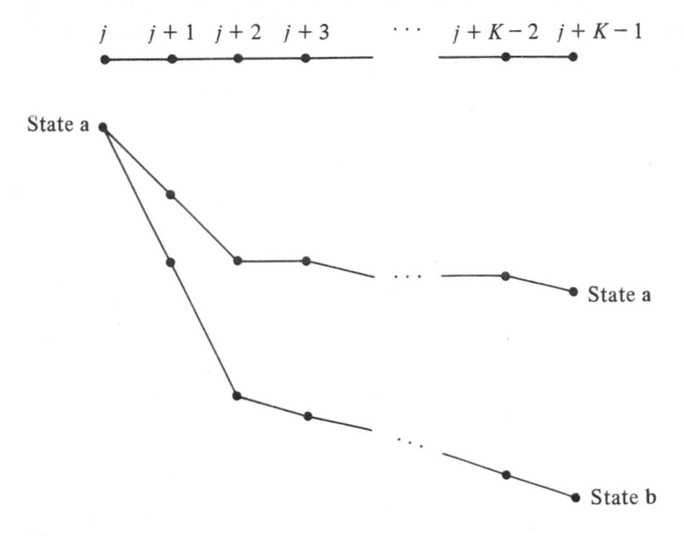

Figure 4.16 Unnormalized metrics for direct paths from state **a** at node j to states **a** and **b** at node $j + K - 1$.

calculation. The maximum spread among all $2^{b(K-1)}$ state metrics is easily bounded as follows. Suppose that the greatest *branch metric* possible is zero and the least is the negative integer $-v$, which we can guarantee by subtracting a constant from all possible branch metrics. For the binary-input, octal-output quantized AWGN channel just discussed with rate $1/n$ coding, $v = 7n$. Then it follows easily that the maximum spread in metrics for a constraint length K, rate b/n code is $(K - 1)v$, for any state can be reached from any other state in at most $K - 1$ transitions. At any node depth $j + K - 1$, consider the highest metric state **a**, without normalization, and any other state **b**. There exists a path (not necessarily the surviving path) which diverged from the path to state **a** at node j and arrives at state **b** at node $j + K - 1$ (see Fig. 4.16). Now since all branch metrics lie between zero and $-v$, the metric change in the path to **a** over the last $K - 1$ branches is nonpositive while the metric change in the path to state **b** must be between zero and $-(K - 1)v$; hence the spread is no greater than $(K - 1)v$. Now if this particular path did not survive, this can only be due to the fact that the surviving path to state **b** has higher metric than this path; hence the spread will be even less. In conclusion then, if we renormalize by adding an integer to bring the highest state metric to zero after each branch calculation, the minimum branch metric is never smaller than $-(K - 1)v$, so we need only provide $\lceil \log (K - 1)v \rceil$ bits of storage for each state metric (where $\lceil x \rceil$ denotes the least integer not less than x).

Finally, we consider the synchronization of a Viterbi decoder. For block codes, it is obvious that, without knowledge of the position of the initial symbol of each received code vector, decoding cannot be performed. Hence block coding systems either incorporate periodic uncoded synchronization sequences which permit the receiver initially to acquire the code synchronization, or they modify the block code so as to cause unsynchronized code vectors to be detected as such. In the first case, the effective data rate is reduced by insertion of the uncoded synchronization sequence, while in the second a relatively complex synchronization system must be provided in the decoder. These difficulties are greatly reduced in convolutional decoders. In an unterminated convolutional code, it would appear that we require both *branch* and *symbol* synchronization. In a binary-input, rate b/n code, symbol synchronization refers to knowledge of which of n successive received symbols initiates a branch; let us assume initially that this has already been acquired. On the other hand, branch synchronization refers to knowledge of which branch in the code path is presently being received. But if symbol synchronization is known, branch synchronization is not required. For suppose that, rather than initiating the decoding operation at the initial node (all-zeros in the encoder) as we have always assumed, we were to begin in the middle of the trellis. The Viterbi algorithm is identical at each node; the only problem would be how to choose the initial values of the $2^{b(K-1)}$ state metrics. In normal decoding when correct decisions are being made, one metric, generally corresponding to the correct path or at least to a path which diverged from it only a few branches back, will be largest; but, when errors are occurring, paths unmerged from the correct path will have the highest metric so that conceivably the correct path might even have the lowest metric at a given node. Yet we have seen that with probability one for all but catastrophic codes, error sequences are of finite length so that, even from the worst condition when the correct path has lowest metric at a given node, the decoder will eventually recover and resume making correct decisions. Thus it is clear that if we start decoding at an arbitrary node with all state metrics set to zero, the decoder performance may initially be poor for several branches but, after at most a few constraint lengths, it will recover in the sense that the correct path metric will begin to dominate, and the data will be decoded correctly in much the same way as the decoder recovers after a span of decoding errors. Analysis of this effect on an ensemble basis is very similar to that of path memory truncation, and is treated in Sec. 5.6.

Thus the only real synchronization problem in Viterbi decoding of convolutional codes is that of symbol synchronization. Here, fortuitously, we have the reverse of the above situation. In a rate b/n code, if the wrong initial symbol out of n possible consecutive symbols is initially assumed, the correct path branch metrics will appear much like those of other paths; thus all path metrics will tend to remain relatively close together with no path emerging with more rapidly growing metric than all the others (see for example Prob. 4.19); this condition can be easily detected and the initial assumption of the initial symbol changed to another of the n possibilities. Thus at most n positions must be searched; even with enough time spent at each position to be able to exclude the incorrect hypotheses with low probability of error, symbol synchronization can be achieved within a few hundred bits when n is on the order of four or less.

4.8 FEEDBACK DECODING*

We have thus far considered only maximum likelihood decoding of convolutional codes, developing and analyzing the Viterbi algorithm which results naturally from the structure of the code. Its major drawback is, of course, that while error probability decreases exponentially with constraint length, the number of code states, and consequently decoder complexity, grows correspondingly. Partially to avoid this difficulty, a number of other decoding algorithms have been proposed, analyzed, and employed in convolutionally coded systems. *Sequential decoding* achieves asymptotically the same error probability as maximum likelihood decoding, but without searching all possible states; in fact, the number of states searched is essentially independent of constraint length, thus rendering possible the use of very large K and resulting in very low error probabilities. This very optimistic picture is clouded by the fact that the number of state metrics actually searched is a random variable with unbounded higher-order moments; this poses some rather subtle difficulties which degrade performance. To do justice to the complex subject of sequential decoding, we must first explore more of the ensemble properties of convolutional codes. This is done in Chap. 5, and then Chap. 6 is devoted to sequential decoding.

Another class of decoding algorithms, known collectively as *feedback decoding*, has received much attention for its simplicity and applicability to interleaved data transmission. The principles of operation of a feedback decoder, or more precisely a *syndrome-feedback decoder*, are best understood in terms of a specific example; Fig. 4.17 shows the ultimately simplest rate $= \frac{1}{2}$ encoder, and its trellis and tree diagrams. Clearly, the free distance is 3, so that, if on a BSC only one error occurs in a sequence of two branches (the constraint length), the error will be corrected by a maximum likelihood (minimum distance) decoder. Now suppose that instead of a true maximum likelihood decoder as described and analyzed earlier, we use instead a truncated-memory decoder which makes a maximum likelihood decision on a given bit or branch based only on a finite number of received branches beyond this point. For the example at hand, suppose the decision for the first bit were based on only the two branches shown on the tree diagram in dotted box A. If the metric at nodes **a** or **b** is greatest, we decide that the first bit was a "0"; while if the metric at nodes **c** or **d** is greatest, we decide in favor of a "1." Specifically, if the sequence received over a BSC is $\mathbf{y} = 100110$, the metric (negative Hamming distance) is -1 at node **c** and less at all other nodes at the third branching level. This decoder will then decide irrevocably that the first transmitted bit was a "1." From this point, only paths in the lower half of the tree are considered. Thus the next decision is among the paths in dotted box B and is based on the metric at the four nodes **e**, **f**, **g**, and **h**. For the given **y**, the metric, based on branches 2 and 3, at nodes **e** and **f** is -1 and at all other nodes it is less. Hence the second bit decision is a "0." Note that the effect on the metric of the

* May be omitted without loss of continuity.

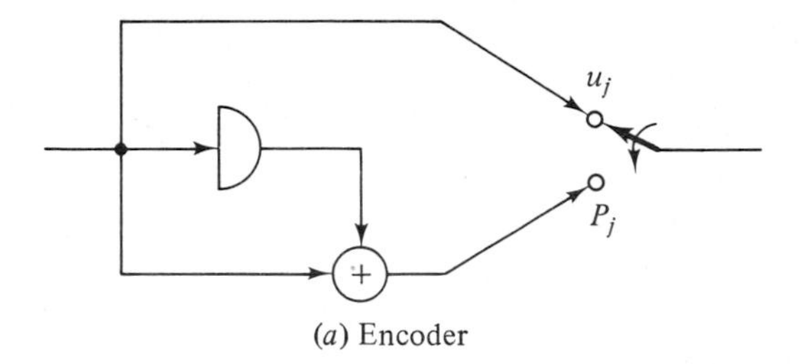

(a) Encoder

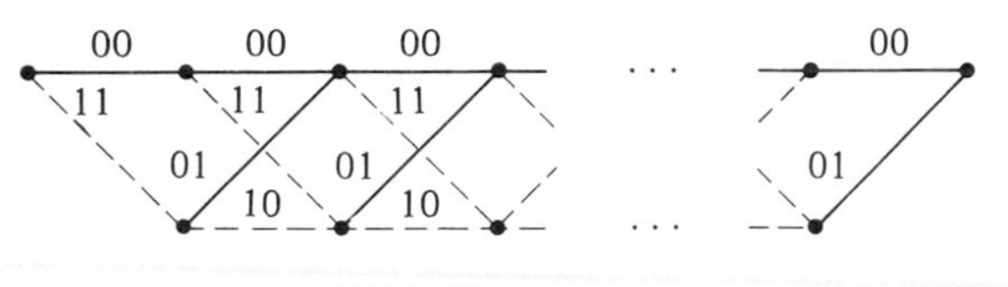

(b) Trellis diagram

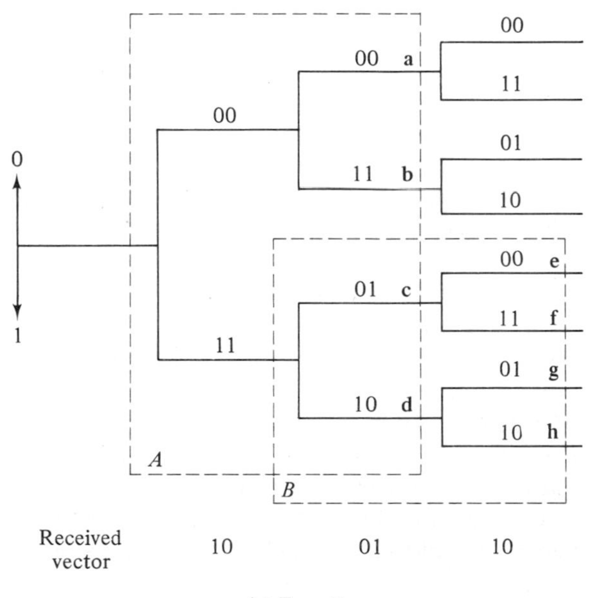

(c) Tree diagram

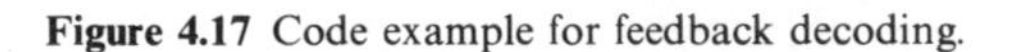

Figure 4.17 Code example for feedback decoding.

first branch could be removed because all paths in B have the same first branch, this having been irrevocably decided in the previous step. The decoder can then proceed in this manner, operating essentially as a "sliding block decoder" on codes of four codewords of 2 branches each. This decoder is also called a *feedback decoder* because the decisions are "fed back" to the decoder in determining the subset of code paths which are to be considered next. On the BSC, in general, it performs nearly as well[12] as the Viterbi decoder in that it corrects all the more probable error patterns, namely all those of weight $(d_f - 1)/2$, where d_f is the free distance of the code. Hence, some (though not necessarily all) of the minimum weight error patterns which cause a decision error with this decoder will also cause decision errors with the Viterbi decoder.[13]

The above example is misleadingly simple in that the memory length, which we henceforth denote by L, needs only to be equal to the constraint length to guarantee that the minimum distance between the correct path and any path which diverges from it will be at least d_f within L branches. Examining the trellis of the rate $= \frac{1}{2}$, $K = 3$ code of Fig. 4.8, for which $d_f = 5$, we find that it takes $L = 6$ branches for *all paths* (unmerged as well as merged) which diverged from the **0** path at the first node to accumulate a weight equal to d_f or greater. In fact, the worst culprit is the path whose data sequence 101010 takes exactly six branches to reach weight $d_f = 5$. This code then guarantees the correction of all two-error patterns in any sequence of 12 code symbols (six branches). To correct three-error patterns, we must have a code for which d_f is at least 7, which with rate $= \frac{1}{2}$ requires $K \geq 5$. The best $K = 5$, $r = \frac{1}{2}$ code requires $L = 12$ for all unmerged incorrect paths to reach weight 7. It turns out, however, that there is a $K = 10$, $r = \frac{1}{2}$ systematic code for which all paths which diverge from **0** reach weight 7 by $L = 11$; hence a feedback decoder for this code with $L = 11$ corrects all three-error patterns in any sequence of 22 symbols. We shall return to the question of systematic codes momentarily.

The fact that this decoder can be regarded as a sliding block decoder can be exploited to simplify its implementation for a BSC. We recall from Sec. 2.10 that a maximum likelihood, or minimum distance, decoder for a systematic block code on a BSC can be efficiently implemented by calculating the syndrome of the received vector, and from this obtaining the most likely error vector by consulting a table which contains the most likely error vector for each syndrome. The simple example under consideration is a systematic code since one of its generators contains only one tap, and hence the information symbols are transmitted

[12] For the special case of the code of Fig. 4.17, Morrissey [1970] has shown that on the BSC the feedback decoder coincides with the Viterbi decoder. However, this is the only case for which this is known to hold.

[13] Note that the Viterbi decoder must also truncate its memory for practical reasons, as discussed in Sec. 4.7, but that if this is done after about five constraint lengths negligible degradation results. In the present discussion, memory is truncated much earlier so that the decoders are generally much more suboptimal, although not in the special case of Fig. 4.17.

unmodified through this tap. The transmitted code vector can be written for convenience as

$$\mathbf{x} = (u_1, u_2, \ldots, u_j, \ldots, p_1, p_2, \ldots, p_j, \ldots)$$

where u_j is the jth information symbol (upper generator in this case) and p_j is the jth parity (lower generator) symbol. This is generated from the data source by the operation

$$\mathbf{x} = \mathbf{u}G$$

where

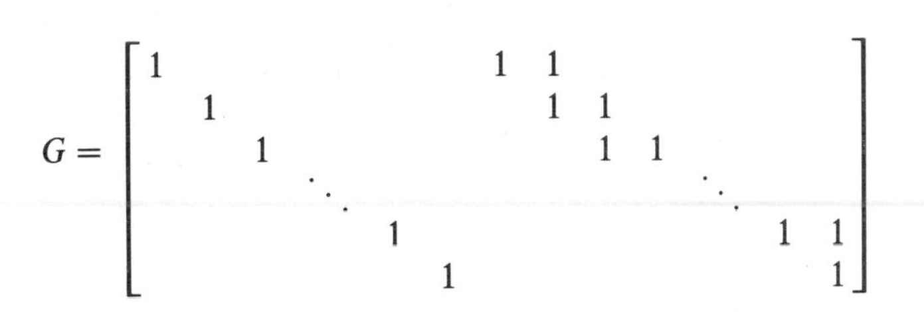

Note that for convenience here we have departed from the convention established in Sec. 4.1 of writing consecutively[14] all the generator outputs for the jth input, choosing rather to partition the vector into two (generally n) subsequences, one for each generator. This then requires that the generator matrix also be partitioned into submatrices, one for each subgenerator sequence. It follows from Sec. 2.10 then that the transpose of the parity-check matrix for this code is

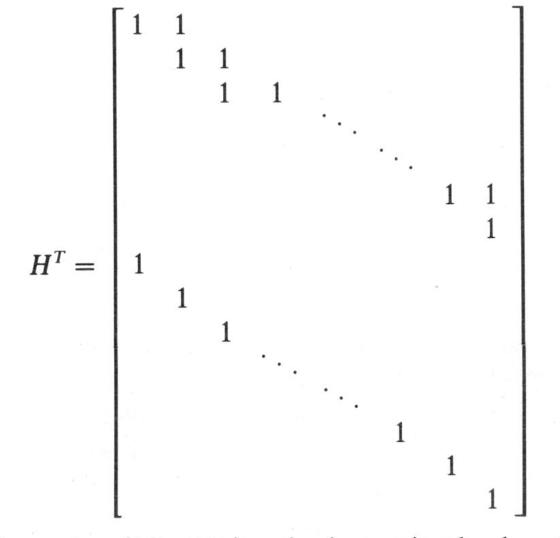

But since each submatrix of the parity check matrix also has the property that each row is shifted from the preceding row by one term, it is clear that the

[14] This is merely a convention and does not alter the fact that p_j is transmitted immediately after u_j and thus that the $\mathbf{u}$ and $\mathbf{p}$ subsequences are interleaved together on transmission.

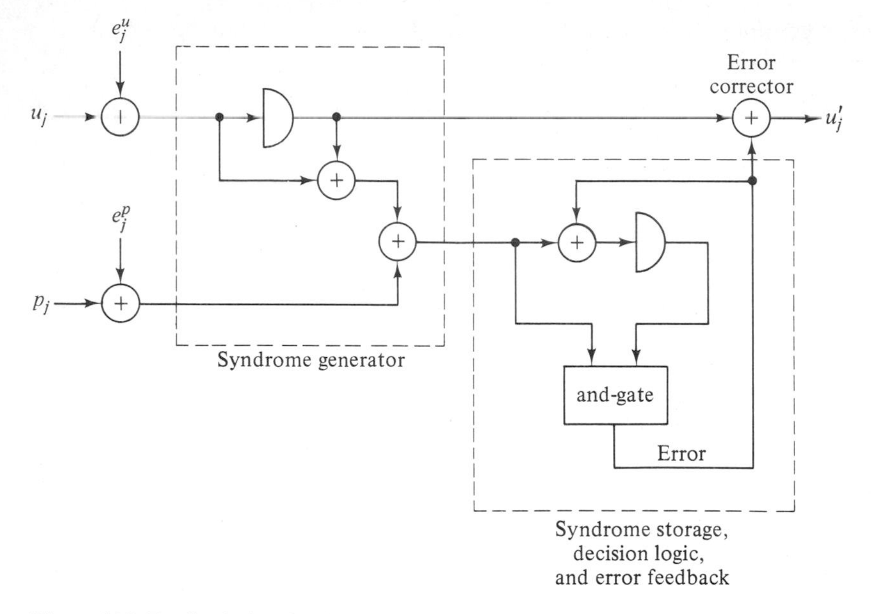

Figure 4.18 Feedback decoder for code of Fig. 4.17.

syndrome

$$\mathbf{s} = \mathbf{y}H^T$$

can be generated by passing the received noise-corrupted information symbols to a single generator sequence convolutional encoder and adding its output to the received noise-corrupted parity symbols. In Fig. 4.18 we show the information and parity symbols as if they were on two separate channels. In fact, a commutator at the encoder output provides for consecutive transmission of u_j and p_j, while a decommutator before the encoder separates the error-corrupted information and parity subsequences. However, since the channel is memoryless, we may treat the interleaved information and parity subsequences as if they were transmitted on separate BSCs with the same error statistics.

Clearly, in the absence of errors, the syndrome is always zero since it is then the sum of two identical sequences. In the presence of errors, "1"s will appear. Returning to the "sliding block" decoding viewpoint, we see that if we preserve L symbols of the syndrome, then this represents the syndrome for a specialized block code corresponding to a segment of the tree over L branches. For the 2^L syndromes of this block code, we could provide a table-look-up corresponding to the most likely (lowest weight) error pattern for each syndrome. But, in fact, the decision at each step of a feedback decoder is only on which half of the tree is more likely. Equivalently, the decision may be on whether the received information symbol corresponding to the first branch was correctly received or had an error in it. This then requires only that the syndrome table store a "0" or "1," the latter corresponding to an error, which can then be added modulo-2 to the correspond-

Table 4.2. Syndrome look-up table for code of Fig. 4.17

Syndrome		Most likely error pattern				Table output
S_1	S_2	Error in u_1	p_1	u_2	p_2	Error in u_1
0	0	0	0	0	0	0
0	1	0	0	1	0	0
1	0	0	1	0	0	0
1	1	1	0	0	0	1

ing information symbol, which itself also had to be stored in an L-stage shift register.

For the code under consideration the syndromes, most likely error sequences, and required output are shown in Table 4.2. Thus in general, the look-up table can be implemented by a read-only memory logic element with L inputs whose single output is used to correct the information bit. In this simple case, as shown in Fig. 4.18, the general logic element may be replaced by an and-gate. There remains, however, one more function to be implemented in this feedback decoder. This is to feed back the decision just made; if the decision was that an error occurred in u_1, this is most easily implemented by adjusting in the decision device for the effect of that error. But the decision device here consists of just the stored syndrome for the past L branches and a time-invariant table. The error in u_1 here produced "1"s in both syndrome stages, but, for the next decision (on u_2) the contents of the rightmost stage is lost and replaced by the contents of the previous stage. Thus to eliminate the effect of the u_1 error, we need only add modulo-2 the decision output to the rightmost stage and store this until the arrival of the next syndrome bit.

As long as no decision errors occur, the decoder continues to operate in this manner, in this case correcting all single errors in any sequence of four symbols. However, if two out of any four consecutive symbols are ever in error, a decision error occurs that may propagate well beyond a single decision error since the error is in fact fed back to affect further decisions. This is called the *error propagation effect*, which is common to some extent to all convolutional decoders. That the error propagation in this case is finite, however, is evident from the fact that, if no channel errors occur in two consecutive branches, both syndrome stages cannot simultaneously contain "1"s; hence, as seen in Table 4.2, no decision error is detected or fed back, thus returning the syndrome register to the all-zeros state and passing the correct information symbols unmolested. The above example for rate $r = \frac{1}{2}$ single-error–correcting codes can be generalized to any rate $(n - 1)/n$ single-error–correcting code (see Prob. 4.13).

Generalization to any systematic convolutional code of any rate b/n is straightforward. For such a code, the information sequence is subdivided into subsequences of length b bits. Each symbol of each length b information subsequence is transmitted and simultaneously inserted into the first stage of b encoder registers, each of which is of length K. The contents of these registers are linearly (modulo-2) combined to generate $(n - b)$ parity symbols after each insertion of the b information symbols. The syndrome generator in the decoder then operates in almost the same way as the encoder. That is, the b error-corrupted information symbols are again encoded as above into $(n - b)$ symbols, which are added to the corresponding error-corrupted parity symbols to form syndrome symbols. Thus for each subsequence of b information symbols, a subsequence of $(n - b)$ syndrome symbols is generated, which, in the absence of errors, would be all zeros. If the truncated maximum likelihood decision is to be based on L branches back, the $(n - b)L$ syndrome bits must be stored and, in general, the syndrome table-look-up must consist of $2^{(n-b)L}$ entries of b bits each. A "1" in any of the b table-look-up outputs indicates an error to be corrected in an information bit and corresponding corrections to be made in the syndrome.

To illustrate a somewhat more powerful code, as well as a further simplification in the decoder which is possible for a limited subclass of convolutional codes, let us consider a two-error-correcting, $r = \frac{1}{2}$ code. As discussed earlier, the nonsystematic $K = 3$, $r = \frac{1}{2}$ code of Fig. 4.2*a* requires a memory of six branches to ensure that all incorrect unmerged paths reach the free distance 5 from the correct path. But the complexity of the feedback decoder depends almost exclusively on the complexity of the syndrome logic and hardly at all on constraint length. Furthermore, for correcting information errors, systematic codes are more natural to work with than nonsystematic ones.[15] In general, with true maximum likelihood decoding whose complexity depends directly and almost exclusively on constraint length, nonsystematic convolutional codes are superior as noted in Sec. 4.5 since they achieve higher free distance for a given K. On the other hand, since a feedback decoder is really a sliding block decoder of block length L branches and, as shown in Sec. 2.10, for every nonsystematic block code there is a systematic block code with equal performance, there appears to be every advantage to using systematic convolutional codes with feedback decoders. The systematic code which may be feedback decoded with a syndrome memory of six branches is shown in Fig. 4.19. It may be verified from the corresponding tree diagram that $d_f = 5$ and that all paths which diverge from the all-zeros at a given

[15] Actually a syndrome can be calculated almost as easily for a nonsystematic code, but errors then must be found in all the received symbols which must then be combined to generate the information symbol.

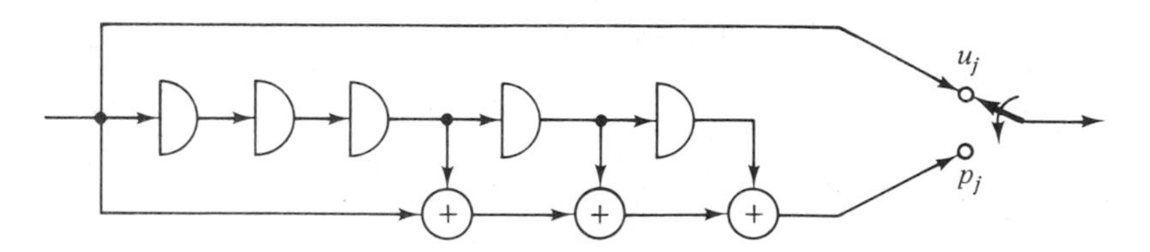

Figure 4.19 Systematic encoder capable of two-error correction ($K = 6$, $r = \frac{1}{2}$).

node are at least at distance 5 from it within six branches. Thus a feedback decoder with a memory of six branches can correct any two symbol errors in any sequence of 12 symbols of this code.

While the general structure of this feedback decoder has already been described, we now demonstrate a considerable simplification on the general syndrome lookup-table procedure that is possible for a limited class of codes of which this is a member. Suppose we denote possible errors in the information and parity symbols on the jth branch by e_j^u and e_j^p, respectively, each of which equals zero if the corresponding symbol is received correctly and equals one if it is in error. Then, since the syndrome symbols are all zero when no errors are made (assuming no previous errors), the first six syndrome symbols, corresponding to as many branches, are (see Fig. 4.20)

$$\begin{aligned} S_1 &= e_1^p \oplus e_1^u \\ S_2 &= e_2^p \oplus e_2^u \\ S_3 &= e_3^p \oplus e_3^u \\ S_4 &= e_4^p \oplus e_4^u \oplus e_1^u \\ S_5 &= e_5^p \oplus e_5^u \oplus e_2^u \oplus e_1^u \\ S_6 &= e_6^p \oplus e_6^u \oplus e_3^u \oplus e_2^u \oplus e_1^u \end{aligned} \tag{4.8.1}$$

Now suppose we consider the set of equations for S_1, S_4, S_6 and the modulo-2 sum $S_2 \oplus S_5$

$$\begin{aligned} S_1 &= e_1^p \oplus e_1^u \\ S_4 &= e_4^p \oplus e_4^u \oplus e_1^u \\ S_2 \oplus S_5 &= e_5^p \oplus e_5^u \oplus e_2^p \oplus e_1^u \\ S_6 &= e_6^p \oplus e_6^u \oplus e_3^u \oplus e_2^u \oplus e_1^u \end{aligned} \tag{4.8.2}$$

These equations have two important properties: (a) each equation contains e_1^u, the error in the first information symbol and (b) no other symbol error occurs in more than one equation. Such a set of equations is said to be *orthogonal* on e_1^u. Hence if u_1 is in error so that $e_1^u = 1$ and no other symbol errors occur in the first six branches, all the syndrome linear combinations of (4.8.2) will equal 1. If any other error occurs alone among the first 12 symbols [or, more precisely, among the 11 of those 12 symbols whose error terms appear in (4.8.2)] only one sum in (4.8.2) will be 1 and the other three will be 0. If $e_1^u = 1$ and any other error occurs among the first 12 symbols, three of the sums are 1 and the other is a 0. Finally, if $e_1^u = 0$ but two other symbols are in error, at most two sums of (4.8.2) will be 1, since each such error term occurs in one equation (possibly both in the same equation). Thus we conclude that $e_1^u = 1$ if and only if three or four of the sums of (4.8.2) equal 1, and $e_1^u = 0$ if less than three of the sums equal 1. This suggests the alternate mechanization of the syndrome table-look-up shown in Fig. 4.20. Aside from the simplification of the general logic element, the remainder of the syndrome-feedback

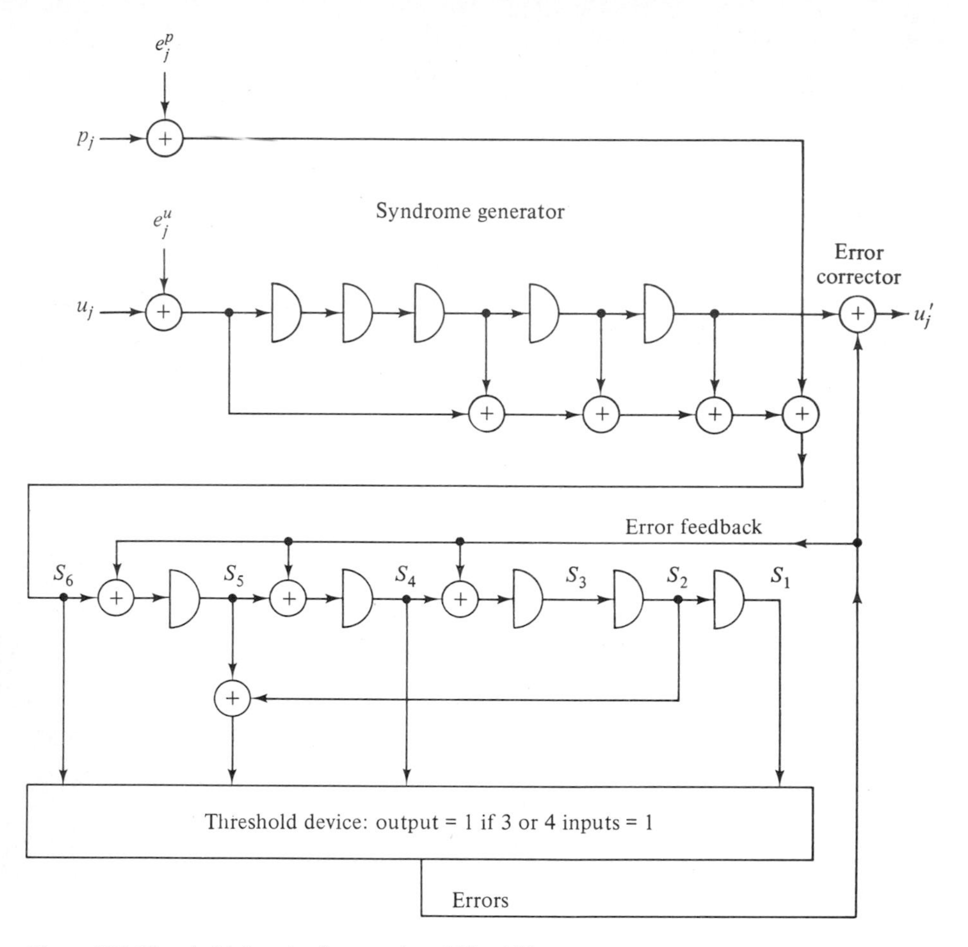

Figure 4.20 Threshold decoder for encoder of Fig. 4.19.

decoder is as previously described. This special form of a feedback decoder is called a *threshold decoder* because of the *threshold* logic (also called *majority logic*) involved in the error decisions. The class of threshold-decodable convolutional codes was first defined and extensively developed by Massey [1963].

Clearly, what has just been described for the first branch applies to all further branches, with a correction to the information symbol u_j performed by adding e_j^u to it. Also wherever $e_j^u = 1$, the effect of the error is canceled by adding, in the appropriate positions of the syndrome register, the parity-check symbols generated by a 1 in the erroneous information symbol. In this way it is clear that any single error or pair of errors in six consecutive branches are corrected. It should be recognized, however, that, since there are 64 possible syndromes and only $1 + \binom{6}{1} + \binom{6}{2} = 22$ error patterns of weight less than or equal to 2, this decoding procedure does not necessarily replace exactly the table-look-up corresponding to the truncated maximum likelihood decoder. That is, while it does guarantee that all error patterns of weight up to $(d_f - 1)/2$ are corrected, there may be some three-error patterns corrected by the table-look-up procedure which are not corrected here. Obviously, not all systematic convolutional codes may be decoded by a threshold decoder. It should be clear from the above example that a code is e-error–correctable by a threshold decoder if and only if $2e$ linear combinations of syndrome symbols can be formed which are orthogonal on one information symbol error. Then the threshold logic declares an error whenever more than e of the linear sums equal 1. It is also clear that our original example of Fig. 4.18 was a threshold decoder for a rate $r = \frac{1}{2}$ code with $e = 1$.

Another difficulty with threshold decoding is that for more than three-error correction, the required syndrome memory length grows very rapidly. As noted previously, there exists a systematic rate $= \frac{1}{2}$ convolutional code (Bussgang [1965]) for which all incorrect paths are at distance 7 from the correct path within $L = 11$ branches, thus affording the possibility of correcting any error pattern of up to three errors in any sequence of 22 symbols. However, it is not orthogonalizable and hence not threshold-decodable. The existence of read-only memories containing 2^{11} bits in a single integrated circuit makes it possible to implement the entire table-look-up function (with an 11-bit input and a single output) quite easily. The shortest L for $r = \frac{1}{2}$, three-error–correcting orthogonalizable convolutional code is 12 affording correction of up to three errors in sequences of length 24 symbols. The situation is much less favorable, however, for a $r = \frac{1}{2}$ four-error–correcting code which requires that all incorrect paths be at distance at least 9 from the correct path. Computer search (Bussgang [1965]) has shown that the minimum value of L is 16. This code is not orthogonalizable and the table-look-up would require a memory of 2^{16} bits. On the other hand, the shortest orthogonalizable, and hence threshold-decodable, four-error–correcting $r = \frac{1}{2}$ code requires $L = 22$. L grows rapidly beyond this point with $L = 36$ for a threshold-decodable five-error–correcting convolutional code. (Lucky, Salz, Weldon, [1968]).

While the feedback decoding, or sliding block decoding, concept can apply to channels other than the BSC, its appeal decreases considerably when the binary operations must be replaced by operations involving more elaborate metrics. Then also, as we have noted, even for the BSC, complexity hardly justifies the procedure for the correction of more than a few errors. On the other hand, one rather important feature of the procedure is that it can be very simply adapted to interleaved operation on channels with memory where bursts of errors are prevalent. While a general interleaver, applicable to any channel, was described in Sec. 2.12, this was external to the encoder and decoder, constituting an interface between the latter and the channel. A somewhat more direct approach to interleaving with convolutional codes is to replace all the single-unit delay elements in the encoder shift register by I-unit delay elements,[16] where I is the degree of inter-

[16] Integrated circuits providing thousands of bits delay-line storage are common.

leaving. As a result, the encoder becomes effectively I serial encoders each operating on one of the subsequences of information symbols $u_i, u_{i+I}, u_{i+2I}, \ldots$ where i is an integer between 1 and I. This technique is called *internal interleaving*. Its main drawback is that the storage required in the decoder is multiplied by I. Thus, for Viterbi decoding, the $2^{b(K-1)}$ state metrics and path memories must be stored for each of the I interleaved codes, making the resulting storage requirements prohibitive, when I is in the hundreds or thousands. A feedback decoder, on the other hand, consists merely of the replica of the encoder, to generate the syndrome, and a syndrome memory shift register. Thus interleaved decoding, corresponding to I serial decoders, can be implemented just as in the encoder by replacing all single-unit delays by I-unit delays both in the syndrome generator and the syndrome memory register, leaving the syndrome table-look-up or threshold logic unchanged. Thus, for degree-I interleaving, a constraint length K, rate b/n, syndrome-memory L code requires $(K-1)b$ I-unit delay elements in the encoder and $[(K-1)b + (L-1)(n-b)]$ I-unit delay elements in the decoder. Such decoders represent a simple approach to effective decoding of bursty channels such as are common in HF ionospheric propagation. Several techniques for embellishing this basic concept by varying the delays between coder and decoder stages have been proposed (Gallager [1968], Kohlenberg and Forney [1968], Peterson and Weldon [1972]) with moderate degrees of improvement.

4.9 INTERSYMBOL INTERFERENCE CHANNELS*

The Viterbi algorithm, originally developed for decoding convolutional codes, has also led somewhat surprisingly to a fundamental result in the optimum demodulation of channels exhibiting *intersymbol interference*. This phenomenon, first discussed in Sec. 2.6, arises whenever a digital signal is passed through a linear channel (or filter) whose transfer function is other than constant over the bandwidth of the signal. The narrower the channel bandwidth, the more severe the intersymbol interference. A general model of a band-limited channel is shown in Fig. 4.21. We first treat only the uncoded case of digital (pulse amplitude or biphase) modulation over an AWGN channel with intersymbol interference. In the next section and in Sec. 5.8, we shall extend our results to the coded case.

The digital signal is characterized by a sequence of impulses,[17] or Dirac delta functions

$$u(t) = \sum_{k=-N}^{N-1} u_k \delta(t - kT) \tag{4.9.1}$$

* Intersymbol interference is treated in Secs. 4.9, 4.10, and 5.8 only. These sections may be omitted without loss of continuity.

[17] If the signal is instead a pulse train, i.e., a sequence of pulses each of duration T and amplitudes $\{u_k\}$, the channel output can still be represented by (4.9.2) with $h(t)$ being the channel impulse response convolved with a single unit amplitude pulse of duration T.

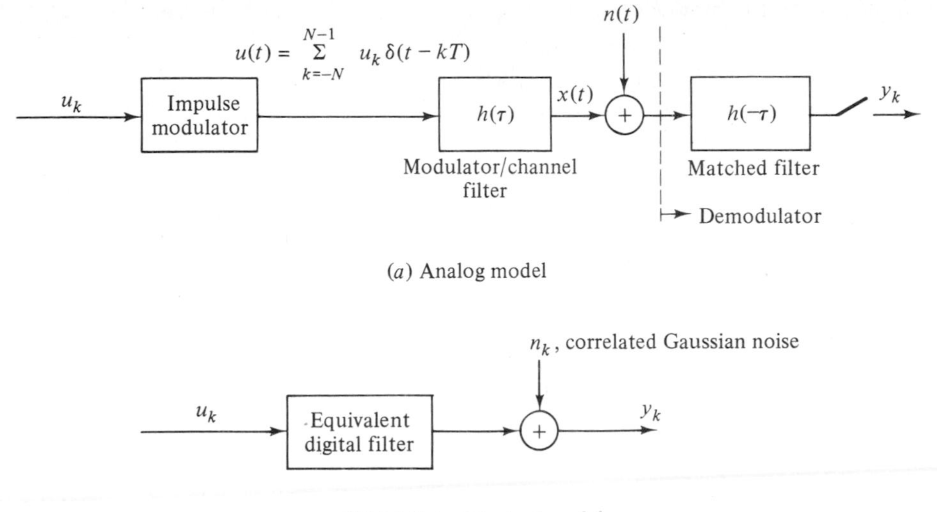

Figure 4.21 Intersymbol interference (band-limited) channel and matched filter demodulator.

where $\{u_k\}$ is a sequence from a finite alphabet, usually binary ($u_k = \pm 1$) in what follows. The total transmission sequence is taken to be of arbitrary length $2N$. Then the first part of the channel, which is characterized by a linear impulse response $h(t)$, has output

$$x(t) = \sum_{k=-N}^{N-1} u_k h(t - kT) \qquad -\infty < t < \infty \tag{4.9.2}$$

The additive noise, $n(t)$, is taken as usual to be white Gaussian noise with spectral density $N_o/2$, and the received signal is denoted, as in Chap. 2, by

$$y(t) = x(t) + n(t) \tag{4.9.3}$$

The decision rule which minimizes the error probability, based on the entire received signal, is as derived in Sec. 2.2:
choose $x_m(t)$, $m = 1, 2, \ldots, M$ if

$$\ln\left(\frac{p(\mathbf{y} \mid \mathbf{x}_m)}{p(\mathbf{y} \mid \mathbf{x}_{m'})}\right) \geq 0 \qquad \text{for all } m' \neq m$$

where $\mathbf{y}$ and $\mathbf{x}_m$ are the coefficients of the Gram-Schmidt orthonormal representation of the functions $y(t)$ and $x_m(t)$. The number, M, of possible sequences $\{\mathbf{x}_m\}$ is bounded by $M \leq Q^{2N}$ where Q is the size of the alphabet of the components x_{mn}. As shown in Sec. 2.2, assuming a priori equiprobable sequences, the log likelihood ratio for m and m' is given by

$$\ln\left(\frac{p(\mathbf{y}\,|\,\mathbf{x}_m)}{p(\mathbf{y}\,|\,\mathbf{x}_{m'})}\right) = -\frac{\|\mathbf{y}-\mathbf{x}_m\|^2 - \|\mathbf{y}-\mathbf{x}_{m'}\|^2}{N_o}$$

$$= \frac{2}{N_o}\int_{-\infty}^{\infty}[x_m(t) - x_{m'}(t)]y(t)\,dt - \frac{1}{N_o}\int_{-\infty}^{\infty}[x_m^2(t) - x_{m'}^2(t)]\,dt \tag{4.9.4}$$

For this case, the integral representation of the log likelihood function is more useful. The infinite limits of the integrals are a consequence of the fact that $h(t)$ is defined over at least the semi-infinite line.

Returning to the representation (4.9.2) of $x(t)$, and letting

$$x_m(t) = \sum_{k=-N}^{N-1} u_{mk}\,h(t-kT) \qquad m = 1, 2, \ldots, M$$

it follows that the maximum likelihood decision rule can be based on

$$\begin{aligned}
\lambda_m &\equiv \frac{2}{N_o}\int_{-\infty}^{\infty} x_m(t)y(t)\,dt - \frac{1}{N_o}\int_{-\infty}^{\infty} x_m^2(t)\,dt \\
&= \frac{2}{N_o}\int_{-\infty}^{\infty}\sum_{k=-N}^{N-1} u_{mk}\,h(t-kT)y(t)\,dt \\
&\quad - \frac{1}{N_o}\int_{-\infty}^{\infty}\sum_{k=-N}^{N-1}\sum_{j=-N}^{N-1} u_{mk}u_{mj}\,h(t-kT)h(t-jT)\,dt \\
&= \frac{2}{N_o}\sum_{k=-N}^{N-1} u_{mk}\,y_k - \frac{1}{N_o}\sum_{k=-N}^{N-1}\sum_{j=-N}^{N-1} u_{mk}u_{mj}\,h_{k-j}
\end{aligned} \tag{4.9.5}$$

where

$$y_k \equiv \int_{-\infty}^{\infty} y(t)h(t-kT)\,dt = \int_{-\infty}^{\infty} y(t)h(t-\tau)\,dt\,\Big|_{\tau=kT} \tag{4.9.6}$$

and

$$\begin{aligned}
h_{k-j} &= \int_{-\infty}^{\infty} h(t-kT)h(t-jT)\,dt \\
&= \int_{-\infty}^{\infty}\frac{1}{2\pi}\,|H(\omega)|^2 e^{-i\omega T(k-j)}\,d\omega = h_{j-k}
\end{aligned} \tag{4.9.7}$$

where $H(\omega)$ is the channel transfer function, which is the Fourier transform of its impulse response. The variables y_k are the observables on which all decisions will be based. Note that it follows from (4.9.6) that these are formed by sampling, at intervals of T seconds, the received waveform $y(t)$ convolved with the function $h(-\tau)$. But this is just the output of the *filter* matched to the channel impulse response $h(\tau)$ when its input is $y(t)$. Thus, the observables are just the outputs of a *matched filter*. The result is similar and reminiscent of that first derived in Secs. 2.1 and 2.2 for maximum likelihood decisions in AWGN, except that here the infinite duration channel impulse response replaces the finite duration signal.

The constants, $\{h_i\}$, which depend only on the channel impulse response are called *intersymbol interference coefficients*. Although, according to (4.9.7), $h_i = h_{-i}$ is potentially nonzero for all i, in practice, for sufficiently large i, $h_i \approx 0$. We shall accept this approximation to limit the dimensionality of the problem. Thus we take

$$h_i \approx 0 \qquad \text{for } i \geq \mathscr{L} \qquad \text{where } \mathscr{L} \ll N \tag{4.9.8}$$

Also, by virtue of the symmetry of the coefficients h_i, the symmetrical quadratic form in (4.9.5) can be written as the sum of the diagonal terms plus twice the upper triangular quadratic form. Thus

$$\begin{aligned} -\frac{1}{N_o}\sum_{k=-N}^{N-1}\sum_{j=-N}^{N-1} u_{mk}u_{mj}h_{k-j} &= -\frac{2}{N_o}\sum_{k=-N}^{N-1}\sum_{j=-N}^{k-1} u_{mk}u_{mj}h_{k-j} - \frac{1}{N_o}\sum_{k=-N}^{N-1} u_{mk}^2 h_o \\ &= -\frac{1}{N_o}\sum_{k=-N}^{N-1} u_{mk}^2 h_o - \frac{2}{N_o}\sum_{k=-N}^{N-1} u_{mk}\sum_{i=1}^{k+N} u_{m,k-i}h_i \end{aligned}$$

Substituting this in (4.9.5) and using (4.9.8), we have

$$\begin{aligned} \lambda_m &= \frac{1}{N_o}\sum_{k=-N}^{N-1}\left(2u_{mk}y_k - u_{mk}^2 h_o - 2u_{mk}\sum_{i=1}^{\mathscr{L}-1} u_{m,k-i}h_i\right) \\ &= \sum_{k=-N}^{N-1} \lambda_{mk}(y_k;\, u_{mk}, u_{m,k-1}, \ldots, u_{m,k-(\mathscr{L}-1)}) \end{aligned} \tag{4.9.9}$$

where we let $u_{mj} = 0$ for $j < -N$, and define

$$N_o\lambda_{mk}(y_k;\, u_{mk}, u_{m,k-1}, \ldots, u_{m,k-(\mathscr{L}-1)}) \equiv 2u_{mk}y_k - u_{mk}^2 h_o - 2u_{mk}\sum_{i=1}^{\mathscr{L}-1} u_{m,k-i}h_i \tag{4.9.10}$$

This expression is reminiscent of the branch metric which establishes the decoding criterion for convolutional codes on a binary-input AWGN channel. The latter, as given by (4.2.3) restated in the present notation, is

$$N_o\lambda_{mk}(\mathbf{y}_k;\, u_{mk}, u_{m,k-1}, \ldots, u_{m,k-(K-1)}) = 2(\mathbf{x}_{mk}, \mathbf{y}_k) - \beta N_o \tag{4.9.11}$$

where

$$\mathbf{y}_k = (y_{k1}, y_{k2}, \ldots, y_{kn})$$

and

$$\mathbf{x}_{mk} = (x_{mk1}, x_{mk2}, \ldots, x_{mkn})$$
$$= \mathbf{x}_{mk}(u_{mk}, u_{m,k-1}, \ldots, u_{m,k-(K-1)})$$

are respectively the n-symbol received vector for the kth branch and the n-symbol code vector for the kth branch of the mth code path, whose inner product properly scaled constitutes the kth branch metric. The last expression for $\mathbf{x}_{mk}$ follows from the observation that the code vector for the kth branch of a constraint K convolutional code depends on the present data symbol and the preceding $K - 1$.

Equation (4.9.10) differs from (4.9.11), the branch metric expression for convolutional codes, in two respects: the "branch" observable is a scalar rather than a vector and the expression is quadratic in the u_{mk}'s rather than linear in the x_{mkj}'s which are algebraic (finite field) functions of the u_{mk}'s. However, in the most important characteristic, namely the dependence on finitely many past data inputs, the expressions are fundamentally the same. This then leads us to the important conclusion that the maximum likelihood demodulation of binary data, transmitted over an AWGN channel with intersymbol interference of finite memory $\mathscr{L}$, can be based on a $2^{\mathscr{L}-1}$ state trellis[18] where the states are determined by the preceding $\mathscr{L} - 1$ data symbols. In other words, to maximize λ_m, it suffices to maximize over all paths through the $2^{\mathscr{L}-1}$ state trellis whose branch metrics are given by (4.9.10). This, of course, is achieved by the Viterbi algorithm (VA) developed in Sec. 4.2, which we restate as follows. Given the $2^{\mathscr{L}-1}$ best paths *through branch* k − 1, denoted by

$$\hat{u}_1 \hat{u}_2 \cdots \hat{u}_{k-\mathscr{L}} u_{k-(\mathscr{L}-1)} \cdots u_{k-1} \qquad \text{where } u_{k-(\mathscr{L}-1)} \cdots u_{k-1}$$

denotes one of the $2^{\mathscr{L}-1}$ binary state vectors and $\hat{u}_1 \cdots \hat{u}_{k-\mathscr{L}}$ are the best path "memories" for that state, and given the corresponding path metrics to that point, $M_{k-1}(u_{k-1} \cdots u_{k-(\mathscr{L}-1)})$, the best paths to each state *through branch* k are determined by the pairwise maximization

$$M_k(u_k, u_{k-1}, \ldots, u_{k-(\mathscr{L}-2)})$$
$$= \max \begin{cases} M_{k-1}(u_{k-1}, u_{k-2}, \ldots, u_{k-(\mathscr{L}-2)}, -1) \\ \qquad + \lambda_k(y_k; u_k, u_{k-1}, \ldots, u_{k-(\mathscr{L}-2)}, -1) \\ M_{k-1}(u_{k-1}, u_{k-2}, \ldots, u_{k-(\mathscr{L}-2)}, +1) \\ \qquad + \lambda_k(y_k; u_k, u_{k-1}, \ldots, u_{k-(\mathscr{L}-2)}, +1) \end{cases} \quad u_k = -1, +1 \tag{4.9.12}$$

If the upper branch of (4.9.12) is the greater, the resulting path memory symbol is $\hat{u}_{k-(\mathscr{L}-1)} = -1$ for the given state; while if the lower is greater, $\hat{u}_{k-(\mathscr{L}-1)} = +1$ for this state.

[18] This generalizes trivially for Q-level data input sequences to a $Q^{\mathscr{L}-1}$ state trellis.

We proceed now to evaluate the performance of this maximum likelihood decision, based on the fact that it is implementable using the VA. Given the correct path due to message m and another path through the trellis corresponding to message m' (or, equivalently, the state diagram), with corresponding metrics[19] λ and λ' for correct and incorrect paths respectively, an error will occur if $\lambda' > \lambda$. The probability that this incorrect path causes an error is given by (2.3.10)

$$P_E(m \to m') = \Pr\{\lambda' > \lambda\}$$
$$= Q\left(\frac{\|\mathbf{x} - \mathbf{x}'\|}{\sqrt{2N_o}}\right) \tag{4.9.13}$$

where from (4.9.2) and (4.9.7) we get

$$\begin{aligned}
\|\mathbf{x} - \mathbf{x}'\|^2 &= \int_{-\infty}^{\infty} (x(t) - x'(t))^2 \, dt \\
&= \int_{-\infty}^{\infty} \left[\sum_{k=-N}^{N-1} (u_k - u'_k) h(t - kT)\right]^2 dt \\
&= \sum_{k=-N}^{N-1} \sum_{j=-N}^{N-1} (u_k - u'_k)(u_j - u'_j) \int_{-\infty}^{\infty} h(t - kT) h(t - jT) \, dt \\
&= \sum_{k=-N}^{N-1} \sum_{j=-N}^{N-1} (u_k - u'_k)(u_j - u'_j) h_{k-j}
\end{aligned} \tag{4.9.14}$$

Again note that $\mathbf{x}$ is a vector of coefficients of the Gram-Schmidt orthonormal expansion of the signal $x(t)$. Defining error signals

$$\epsilon_k \equiv \tfrac{1}{2}(u_k - u'_k) = \begin{cases} 1 & u_k = 1, \; u'_k = -1 \\ 0 & u_k = u'_k \\ -1 & u_k = -1, \; u'_k = 1 \end{cases} \tag{4.9.15}$$

and noting that $h_{k-j} = h_{j-k}$, we rewrite (4.9.14) as

$$\begin{aligned}
\|\mathbf{x} - \mathbf{x}'\|^2 &= 4 \sum_{k=-N}^{N-1} \sum_{j=-N}^{N-1} \epsilon_k \epsilon_j h_{k-j} \\
&= 4 \sum_{k=-N}^{N-1} \left(\epsilon_k^2 h_o + 2 \sum_{j=-N}^{k-1} \epsilon_k \epsilon_j h_{k-j}\right) \\
&= 4 \sum_{k=-N}^{N-1} \left(\epsilon_k^2 h_o + 2 \sum_{i=1}^{k+N} \epsilon_k \epsilon_{k-i} h_i\right) \\
&= 4 \sum_{k=-N}^{N-1} \left(\epsilon_k^2 h_o + 2 \sum_{i=1}^{\mathscr{L}-1} \epsilon_k \epsilon_{k-i} h_i\right)
\end{aligned} \tag{4.9.16}$$

[19] In what follows, we avoid first subscripts m and m' and use instead only a superscript prime to distinguish the incorrect path from the correct path.

Thus for a given error sequence $\boldsymbol{\epsilon} = (\epsilon_{-N}, \epsilon_{-N+1}, \ldots, \epsilon_0, \ldots, \epsilon_{N-1})$, we have the probability of error given by

$$P_E(\boldsymbol{\epsilon}) \equiv \Pr(\lambda' > \lambda)$$
$$= Q\left[\sqrt{\frac{2}{N_o}\sum_{k=-N}^{N-1}\left(\epsilon_k^2 h_o + 2\sum_{i=1}^{\mathscr{L}-1}\epsilon_k\epsilon_{k-i}h_i\right)}\right] \tag{4.9.17}$$

Using the bound $Q(x) < e^{-x^2/2}$ first used in Sec. 2.3, we have

$$P_E(\boldsymbol{\epsilon}) < \exp\left[-\frac{1}{N_o}\sum_{k=-N}^{N-1}\left(h_o\epsilon_k^2 + 2\sum_{i=1}^{\mathscr{L}-1}h_i\epsilon_k\epsilon_{k-i}\right)\right]$$
$$= \prod_{k=-N}^{N-1}\exp\left[-\frac{1}{N_o}\left(h_o\epsilon_k^2 + 2\sum_{i=1}^{\mathscr{L}-1}h_i\epsilon_k\epsilon_{k-i}\right)\right] \tag{4.9.18}$$

We use the notation $P_E(\boldsymbol{\epsilon})$ to indicate that the error probability depends on the differences between the data symbols along the two paths. Note further that the result depends on the *sign* of the differences and their locations. That is, unlike the error probability for linear codes over binary-input, output-symmetric channels, where performance does not depend on the sign of the channel input and hence the uniform error property holds, the situation is complicated here by the fact that the sign of the errors and hence of the data symbols must be accounted for. Of course, either sign is equally likely for each data symbol, and hence the error components for each pair of (correct and incorrect) paths can take on values 0, + 1, and − 1.

Up to this point, we have examined the transmitted binary sequence $\mathbf{u}$ and any other sequence $\mathbf{u}'$. Defining the error sequence

$$\boldsymbol{\epsilon} = \tfrac{1}{2}(\mathbf{u} - \mathbf{u}') \tag{4.9.19}$$

we defined the error probability $P_E(\boldsymbol{\epsilon})$ which is bounded by the expression (4.9.18). We now focus our attention on only those sequences $\mathbf{u}$ and $\mathbf{u}'$ that can cause an error event as shown in Fig. 4.11. Equivalently, we restrict error sequences $\{\boldsymbol{\epsilon}\}$ to those that begin at some fixed time and have no consecutive $\mathscr{L} - 1$ zeros until after the last nonzero component. Define the number of nonzero components of $\boldsymbol{\epsilon}$ as $w(\boldsymbol{\epsilon})$, and note that $\boldsymbol{\epsilon}$ uniquely specifies the source sequence $\mathbf{u}$ in exactly $w(\boldsymbol{\epsilon})$ places. Over the ensemble of all equally likely source sequences, the probability that a source sequence can have the error sequence $\boldsymbol{\epsilon}$ is $2^{-w(\boldsymbol{\epsilon})}$, and thus the probability of an error event occurring at a given node is union bounded by

$$P_E \le \sum_{\boldsymbol{\epsilon}} \frac{1}{2^{w(\boldsymbol{\epsilon})}} P_E(\boldsymbol{\epsilon}) \tag{4.9.20}$$

where the summation is over all error sequences starting at a given node and terminating when the two paths merge. This probability includes averaging over all transmitted sequences. To determine the bit error probability at any given node, we observe that, for any pair of sequences $\mathbf{u}$ and $\mathbf{u}'$ with the resulting error sequence ϵ, the number of bit errors associated with this error event is $w(\epsilon)$. Hence

$$P_b \leq \sum_{\epsilon} \frac{w(\epsilon)}{2^{w(\epsilon)}} P_E(\epsilon) \tag{4.9.21}$$

Using the bound (4.9.18), the bounds on probabilities (4.9.20) and (4.9.21) can be bounded further as

$$P_E \leq \sum_{\epsilon} \prod_{k=-N}^{N-1} \frac{1}{2^{w(\epsilon_k)}} \exp\left[-\frac{1}{N_o}\left(h_o \epsilon_k^2 + 2\sum_{i=1}^{\mathscr{L}-1} h_i \epsilon_k \epsilon_{k-i}\right)\right] \tag{4.9.22}$$

and

$$P_b \leq \sum_{\epsilon} w(\epsilon) \prod_{k=-N}^{N-1} \frac{1}{2^{w(\epsilon_k)}} \exp\left[-\frac{1}{N_o}\left(h_o \epsilon_k^2 + 2\sum_{i=1}^{\mathscr{L}-1} h_i \epsilon_k \epsilon_{k-i}\right)\right] \tag{4.9.23}$$

The evaluation of (4.9.22) and (4.9.23) is facilitated by the use of the *error-state diagram.* The dimensionality of the diagram is $3^{\mathscr{L}-1}$, since each pair of paths at a given node will differ in each state component by 0, + 1, or − 1, with + 1 and − 1 being equally likely. The all-zero error state is the initial and final state, as usual; Figs. 4.22 and 4.23 illustrate the error-state diagram for $\mathscr{L} = 2$ and $\mathscr{L} = 3$. Note that the weighting factors of (4.9.22) are accounted for by preceding the branch transfer function by a factor of $\frac{1}{2}$ if the transition involves a discrepancy (error) between states. If the bit error probability is desired, it is for exactly these transitions that a bit error is made. Hence the factor I should also be inserted on these branches. P_b is then obtained by differentiating the generating function with respect to I and setting $I = 1$, just as in Sec. 4.4 for convolutional codes.

For the case $\mathscr{L} = 2$ of Fig. 4.22, in the complete error-state diagram of Fig. 4.22*d*, the + 1 and − 1 states are equivalent[20] and can be combined into a single state resulting in the simpler error-state diagram of Fig. 4.22*e*. It follows directly from this that

$$T(a_0, a_1, a_2; I) = \frac{a_0 I}{1 - (a_1 + a_2)I/2}$$

$$\left.\frac{\partial T(a_0, a_1, a_2; I)}{\partial I}\right|_{I=1} = \frac{a_0}{[1 - (a_1 + a_2)/2]^2}$$

and

$$P_b < \frac{e^{-h_o/N_o}}{[1 - \frac{1}{2}e^{-h_o/N_o}(e^{2h_1/N_o} + e^{-2h_1/N_o})]^2} \tag{4.9.24}$$

This result is of particular interest since it applies to *duobinary* transmission,

[20] There is no way to distinguish these states by observing branch values.

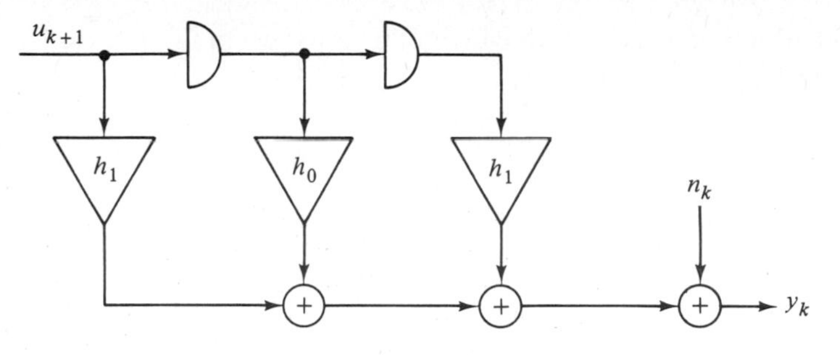

(a) Digital equivalent model for $\mathcal{L} = 2$

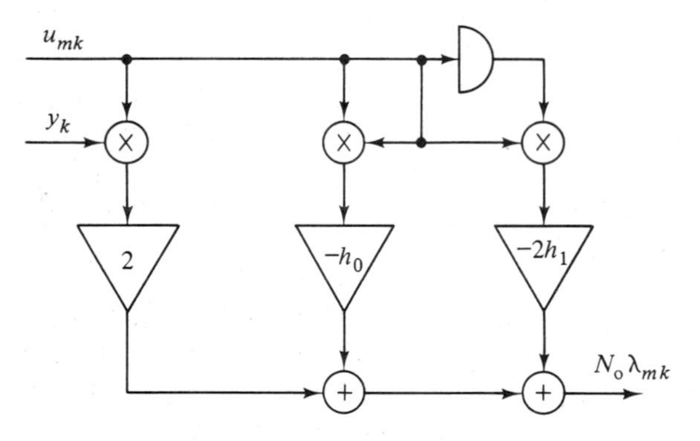

(b) Branch metric generator

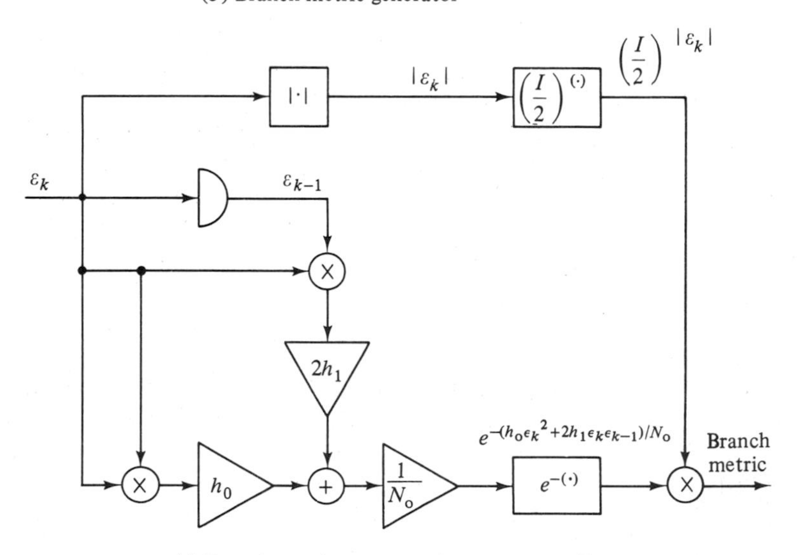

(c) Branch metric generator for error-state diagram

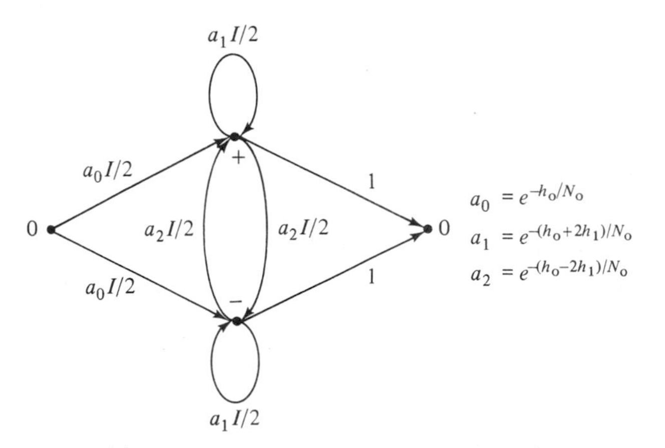

(*d*) Error-state diagram for bit error computation

$$T(a_0, a_1, a_2; I) = \frac{a_0 I}{1-(a_1+a_2)I/2}$$

$$P_b \le \left.\frac{\partial T}{\partial I}\right|_{I=1} = \frac{a_0}{[1-(a_1+a_2)/2]^2}$$

(*e*) Reduced error-state diagram and bit error bound

Figure 4.22 ISI channel example for $\mathscr{L} = 2$.

where each transmitted signal is made a pulse of double width, that is

$$h(\tau) = \begin{cases} \sqrt{\mathscr{E}/2T} & 0 < \tau < 2T \\ 0 & \text{otherwise} \end{cases}$$

For this case, it is easily verified from (4.9.7) that

$$h_o = \mathscr{E}$$
$$h_1 = \mathscr{E}/2$$
$$h_i = 0 \qquad \text{for all } i \ge 2$$

Thus

$$P_b < \frac{e^{-\mathscr{E}/N_o}}{[1-\frac{1}{2}e^{-\mathscr{E}/N_o}(e^{\mathscr{E}/N_o}+e^{-\mathscr{E}/N_o})]^2} = \frac{4e^{-\mathscr{E}/N_o}}{(1-e^{-2\mathscr{E}/N_o})^2}$$

Of particular importance is the fact that the asymptotic exponent is not degraded relative to the case without intersymbol interference.

The error-state diagram shown in Fig. 4.23*d* for the $\mathscr{L} = 3$ case has four equivalent pairs of states which can be combined to form the simpler reduced error-state diagram shown in Fig. 4.23*e*. This type of reduction always occurs so that in general the error-state diagram for intersymbol interference of memory length $\mathscr{L}$ has a reduced error-state diagram of $(3^{\mathscr{L}-1} - 1)/2$ nonzero states.

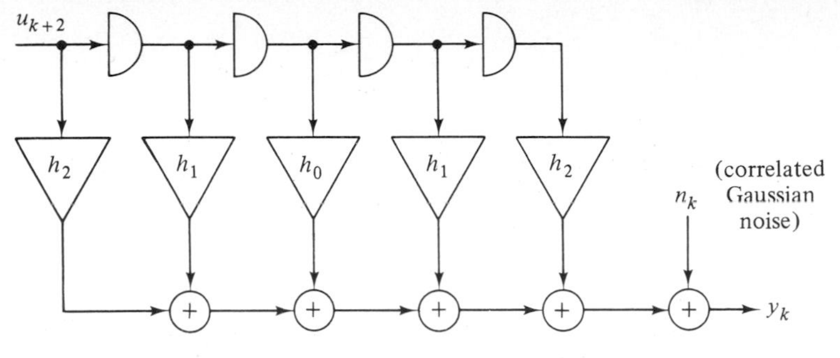

(a) Digital equivalent model for $\mathcal{L} = 3$

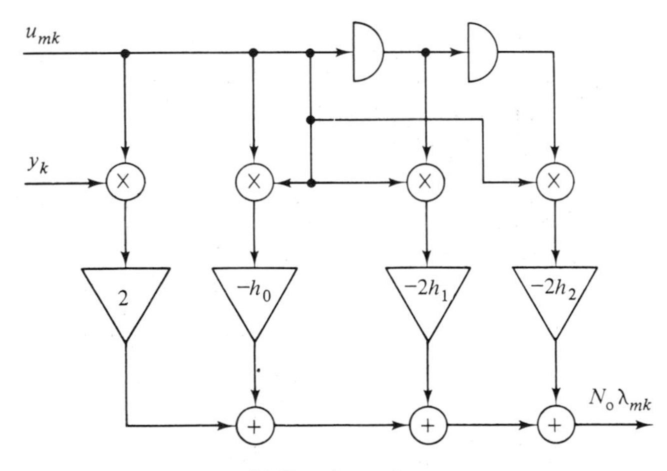

(b) Branch metric generator

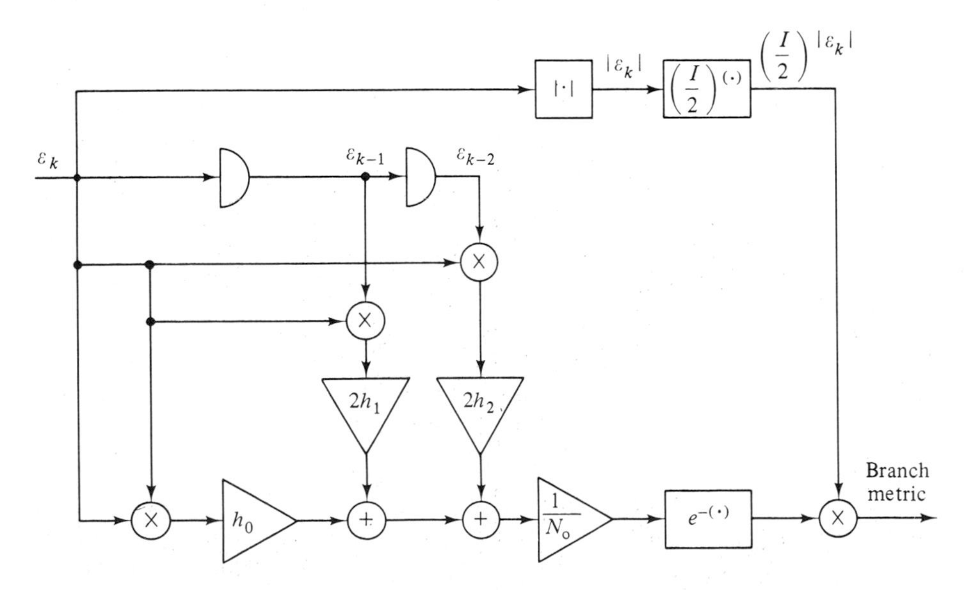

(c) Branch metric generator for error-state diagram

Figure 4.23 ISI channel example for $\mathscr{L} = 3$.

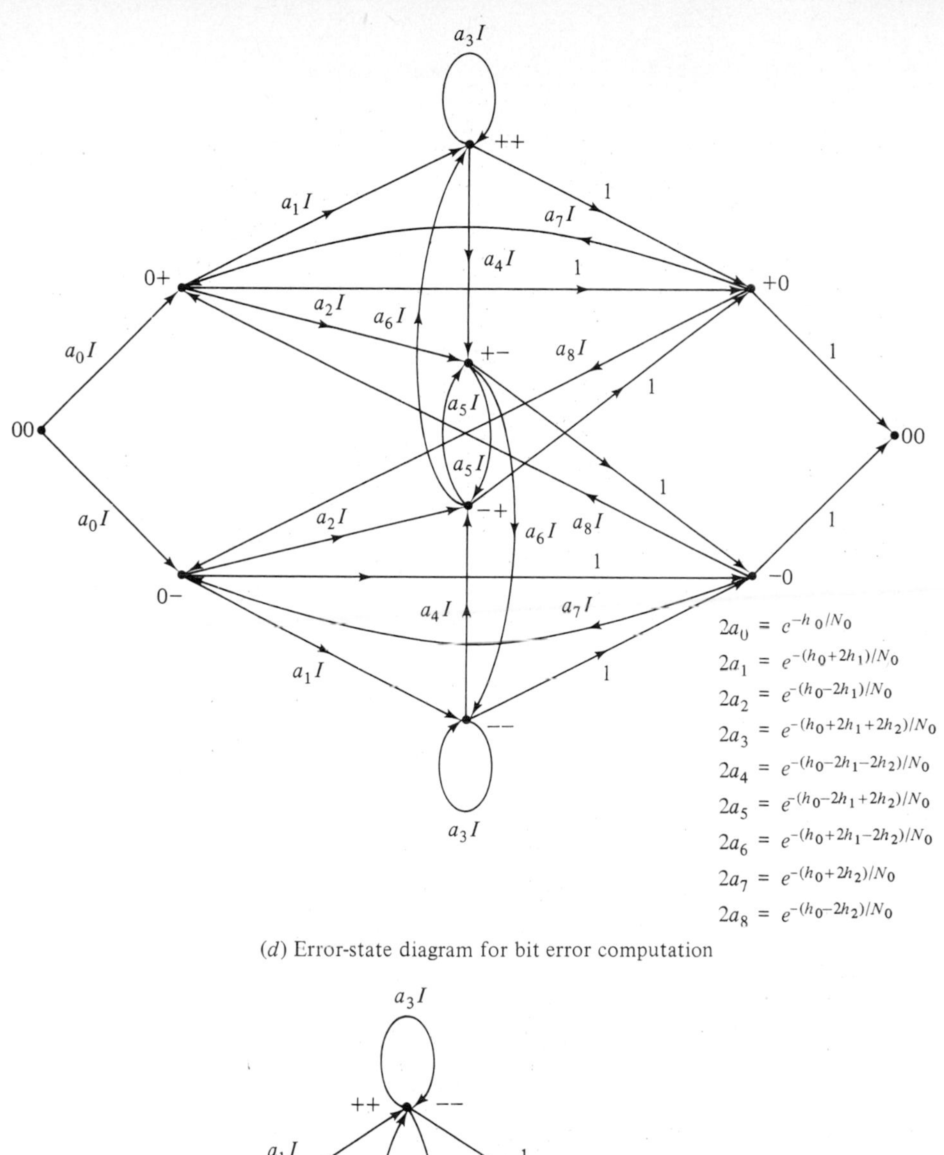

(*d*) Error-state diagram for bit error computation

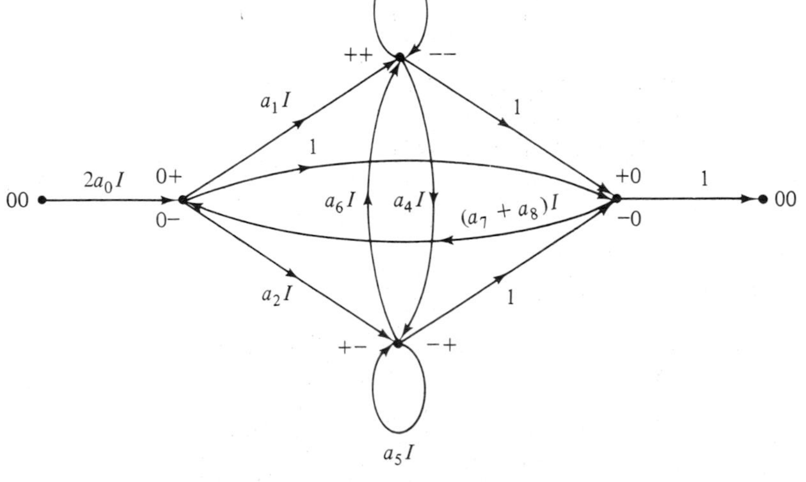

(*e*) Reduced error-state diagram

We have treated here the case of a known modulator/channel filter followed by additive white Gaussian noise. The output of the filter is modeled as some linear weighting of a finite number of data symbols, and it can be viewed as a "real number convolutional code" which we decode with the Viterbi algorithm. Except for the error-state diagrams, there is nothing special about *linear* intersymbol interference channels of this type. Just as the Viterbi algorithm is a maximum likelihood decoding algorithm for arbitrary nonlinear trellis codes, it can also be applied as a maximum likelihood demodulator for data sequences that enter any channel which consists of an arbitrary (possibly nonlinear) but noiseless finite memory part followed by a memoryless noisy part. The noiseless finite memory part of the channel acts like a trellis code which the Viterbi algorithm demodulator decodes in the presence of additive memoryless noise.

4.10 CODING FOR INTERSYMBOL INTERFERENCE CHANNELS*

Considering the commonality in structure of the optimum decoder for convolutional codes and the optimum demodulator for intersymbol interference channels, it is reasonable to expect that a combined demodulator–decoder for coded transmission over intersymbol interference channels would have the same structure as each component. This is readily shown by examining the intersymbol interference channel model of Fig. 4.21 preceded by a convolutional encoder, and the modifications this produces in Eqs. (4.9.2) through (4.9.10).

With coding, the channel output signal, prior to addition of the AWGN, is

$$x(t) = \sum_{k=-Nn}^{Nn-1} x_k h(t - kT) \tag{4.10.1}$$

where x_k is now the kth code symbol and hence, for a constraint length K convolutional code, it depends on K binary data symbols for a rate $1/n$ code, or on K b-dimensional binary data vectors for a rate b/n code. Thus the $2Nn$ code symbols $\{x_k\}$ are generated from the $2N$ data vectors $\mathbf{u}_i$ by the expression

$$x_k = \gamma_{1+k-n\lfloor k/n \rfloor}(\mathbf{u}_{\lfloor k/n \rfloor}, \mathbf{u}_{\lfloor k/n \rfloor - 1}, \ldots, \mathbf{u}_{\lfloor k/n \rfloor - (K-1)}) \qquad -Nn \le k \le Nn - 1 \tag{4.10.2}$$

where $\lfloor v \rfloor$ is the greatest integer not greater than v and $\mathbf{u}_i = \mathbf{0}$ for $i < -N$. For a rate $1/n$ code, the data vectors $\mathbf{u}_i$ become binary scalars and the γ_j function is the scalar projection of the vector formed from the terms of the jth tap sequence of the code ($g_{0j}, g_{1j}, \ldots, g_{K-1,j}$ in Fig. 4.1). For a rate b/n code, the $\mathbf{u}_i$ are b-dimensional binary vectors and the γ_j function is the corresponding matrix operation on the data matrix (e.g., in Fig. 4.2*b* and *c*, this matrix is formed from the jth rows of the matrices $\mathbf{g}_0$ and $\mathbf{g}_1$).

Upon replacing (4.9.2) by (4.10.1) and (4.10.2), the remainder of the derivation

* May be omitted without loss of continuity.

of Sec. 4.9 proceeds as before with u_{mk} replaced by x_{mk}. Thus (4.9.10) becomes, upon dropping the first subscript m for notational simplification

$$N_o\lambda_k(y_k; x_k, x_{k-1}, \ldots, x_{k-(\mathscr{L}-1)}) = 2x_k y_k - x_k^2 h_o - 2x_k \sum_{i=1}^{\mathscr{L}-1} x_{k-i} h_i \quad (4.10.3)$$

But from (4.10.2), we have that x_k depends on

$$\mathbf{u}_{\lfloor k/n \rfloor}, \mathbf{u}_{\lfloor k/n \rfloor - 1}, \ldots, \mathbf{u}_{\lfloor k/n \rfloor - (K-1)}$$

and hence similarly, for $i = 1, 2, \ldots, \mathscr{L} - 1$, x_{k-i} depends on

$$\mathbf{u}_{\lfloor (k-i)/n \rfloor}, \mathbf{u}_{\lfloor (k-i)/n \rfloor - 1}, \ldots, \mathbf{u}_{\lfloor (k-i)/n \rfloor - (K-1)}$$

Thus the kth branch metric of (4.10.3) can be written as the function of the $\lceil (\mathscr{L} - 1)/n \rceil + K$ data vectors

$$\mathbf{u}_{\lfloor k/n \rfloor}, \mathbf{u}_{\lfloor k/n \rfloor - 1}, \ldots, \mathbf{u}_{\lfloor (k-(\mathscr{L}-1))/n \rfloor - (K-1)}$$

(where $\lceil v \rceil$ denotes the least integer not less than v) by substituting (4.10.2) with the appropriate index for each term x_k and x_{k-i} in (4.10.3).

Thus, maximizing (4.10.3) over all possible data paths $\{\mathbf{u}_k\}$ is exactly the same problem as maximizing (4.9.10) for uncoded intersymbol interference channels, or (4.9.11) for coded channels without interference. The only differences are that, for those cases, the state vectors are of dimensions $\mathscr{L} - 1$ and $K - 1$, respectively, while here their dimension is $\lceil (\mathscr{L} - 1)/n \rceil + (K - 1)$, and the functions which define the branch metrics are somewhat more elaborate, being a composite of the previous two.

However, once the branch metrics are formed, the maximizing algorithm is again the VA, exactly as before. Thus, the algorithm is again expressed by (4.9.12) but with $\mathscr{L} - 1$ replaced by $\lceil (\mathscr{L} - 1)/n \rceil + (K - 1)$. We conclude thus that the optimum demodulator–decoder for coded intersymbol interference channels is no more complex, other than for dimensionality, than the corresponding uncoded channel.

Unfortunately, however, the calculation of error probability is greatly complicated here, even though the error probability development in Sec. 4.9, beginning with (4.9.13) and leading to the expression (4.9.18) for $P_E(\boldsymbol{\epsilon})$, can proceed with u_k and u'_k replaced by x_k and x'_k, respectively, and $\epsilon_k \equiv \frac{1}{2}(u_k - u'_k)$ of (4.9.15) through (4.9.18) replaced by

$$\hat{\epsilon}_k \equiv \tfrac{1}{2}(x_k - x'_k) \quad (4.10.4)$$

But the difficulty arises when we attempt to average over all possible error events as in (4.9.20). For, in the uncoded case, all error sequences $\boldsymbol{\epsilon}$ are possible and, given that the data symbol is in error ($\epsilon_k \neq 0$), it is equally likely to be $+1$ or -1. This is not the case for coded transmission. First of all, not all error sequences $\hat{\boldsymbol{\epsilon}}$ are possible; for if the correct and incorrect path code symbols are identical in the kth position, then

$$\hat{\epsilon}_k = \tfrac{1}{2}(x_k - x'_k) = 0$$

a condition dictated by the code. To make matters worse, if $\epsilon_k \neq 0$, it is not necessarily equally likely to be $+1$ or -1; this too depends on the code.

In principle, an expression similar to (4.9.20) can be written in the form

$$P_E \leq \sum_{\substack{\text{all correct} \\ \text{paths}}} \sum_{\substack{\text{all incorrect} \\ \text{paths}}} f(\mathbf{x}, \mathbf{x}') P_E(\hat{\boldsymbol{\epsilon}} = \tfrac{1}{2}(\mathbf{x} - \mathbf{x}')) \tag{4.10.5}$$

where $f(\mathbf{x}, \mathbf{x}')$, the distribution function, is dictated by the code and by the fact that all data sequences $\mathbf{u}$ are equally probable. While this calculation can be carried out with considerable effort in a few very simple cases (Acampora [1976]), it provides little insight into the general problem. Using ensemble average techniques to be developed in Chap. 5, we shall obtain in Sec. 5.8 some rather general and revealing results on the effect of intersymbol interference on the ensemble of time-varying convolutional codes.

Before concluding, however, it is worth noting that some simplification is possible in the branch metric expression whenever $n \geq \mathscr{L} - 1$; for the total memory then becomes

$$\lceil (\mathscr{L} - 1)/n \rceil + (K - 1) = K \qquad n \geq \mathscr{L} - 1 \tag{4.10.6}$$

and the branch metric function given by (4.10.3) with (4.10.2) can be expressed functionally as

$$N_o \lambda_k(y_k; \mathbf{u}_{\lfloor k/n \rfloor}, \mathbf{u}_{\lfloor k/n \rfloor - 1}, \ldots, \mathbf{u}_{\lfloor k/n \rfloor - K}) \tag{4.10.7}$$

Now, while it would appear that the condition $n \geq \mathscr{L} - 1$ is overly restrictive, this is not at all the case. For suppose $\mathscr{L} - 1 = 3$, and the code rate $b/n = 1/2$; without any change in the code implementation, we may treat it as if it were a rate $b/n = 2/4$ code and thus achieve the desired condition for (4.10.6). Of course, the data vectors are now two-dimensional rather than scalar, but all code representations from shift register implementation to state diagram can be redrawn in this way without changing the code symbols generated and consequently the performance in any way. For the code itself (not considering the intersymbol interference channel), the state vector dimensionality is the same as before but the connectivity of the state diagram increases; yet the generating function does not change in any way (see Prob. 4.26), and thus it is clear that all that has changed is the representation.

4.11 BIBLIOGRAPHICAL NOTES AND REFERENCES

The concept of convolutional codes was first advanced by Elias [1955]. The first important decoding algorithm, known as sequential decoding, was introduced by Wozencraft [1957] and refined by Reiffen [1960]. This material, and the later more efficient algorithm due to Fano [1963], led to an important class of decoding techniques which will be treated in Chap. 6. The material in this chapter, while chronologically subsequent to these early developments, is more fundamental and, for tutorial purposes, logically precedes the presentation of sequential decoding algorithms.

Sections 4.2 through 4.6 follow primarily from three papers by Viterbi [1967*a*], [1967*b*], and [1971]. The last is a tutorial exposition which contains most of the approach of Secs. 4.2 through 4.5 and 4.7. The material in Sec. 4.6 appeared in the second of the above papers. The so-called Viterbi algorithm was originally presented in the first paper as "a new probabilistic nonsequential decoding algorithm." The tutorial exposition [1971] appeared after the availability in preliminary form of some most enlightening clarifications by Forney (which later appeared in final form in Forney [1972*b*], [1973], and [1974]); to this work, we owe the concept of the trellis exposition of the decoder. In the same work, Forney also recognized the fact that the VA was a maximum likelihood decoding algorithm for trellis codes. Omura [1969] first observed that the VA could be derived from dynamic programming principles.

The state diagram approach as a compressed trellis and the generating function analysis first appeared in Viterbi [1971]. The first code simulation which led to the recognition of the practical value of the decoding algorithm was performed by Heller [1968]. The code search leading to Table 4.1 was performed by Odenwalder [1970].

Feedback decoding traces its conceptual roots to the threshold decoder of Massey [1963]. Important code search results which revealed properties of convolutional codes necessary for feedback decoding appeared in Bussgang [1965]. The exposition in Sec. 4.8 follows primarily from the work of Heller [1975].

The important realization that maximum likelihood demodulation for intersymbol interference channels can be performed using the VA is due to Forney [1972*a*]. The development of Sec. 4.9 follows this work conceptually, although the derivation is basically that of Acampora [1976]. Section 4.10 on combined demodulation and decoding for intersymbol interference channels follows the work of Omura [1971], Mackechnie [1973], and Acampora [1976].

PROBLEMS

4.1 Draw the code tree, trellis, and state diagram for the $K = 2$, $r = \frac{1}{2}$ code generated by

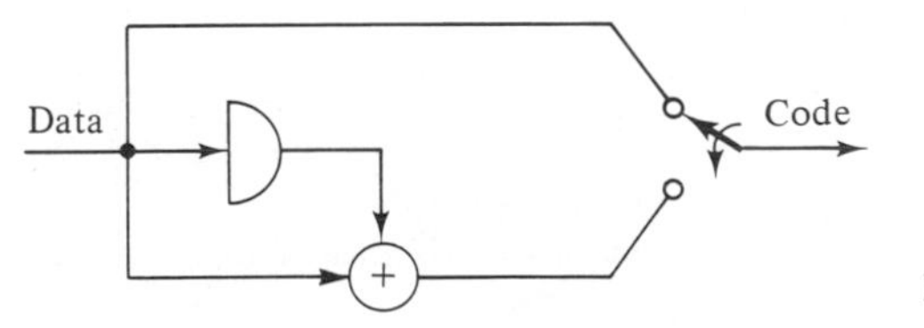

Figure P4.1

4.2 Draw the trellis and state diagram for the $K = 3$, $r = \frac{1}{3}$ code generated by

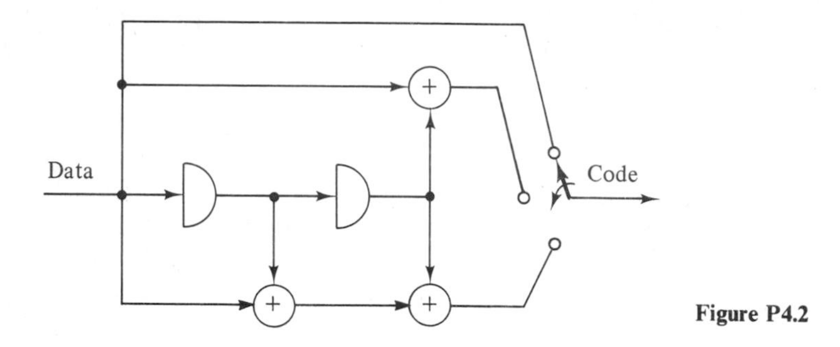

Figure P4.2

4.3 Draw the state diagram for the $K = 4$, $r = \frac{1}{2}$ code generated by

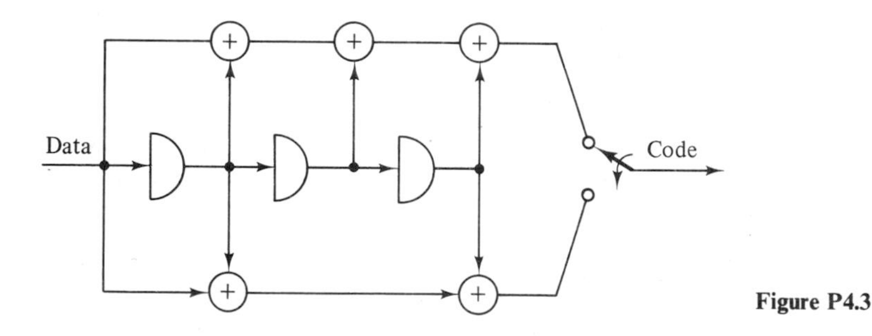

Figure P4.3

4.4 Draw the code tree, trellis, and state diagram for the $K = 2$, $r = \frac{3}{4}$ code of Fig. 4.2*c*.

4.5 Given the $K = 3$, $r = \frac{1}{2}$ code of Fig. 4.4 of the text, suppose the code is used on a BSC and the received sequence for the first eight branches is

00 01 10 00 00 00 10 01

Trace the decisions on a trellis diagram labeling the survivor's Hamming distance metric at each node level. If a tie occurs in the metrics required for a decision, always choose the upper (lower) path.

4.6 (*a*) Solve for the generating function (in D only) of the labeled state diagram of Fig. 4.6 of the text and show that the minimum distance between paths is 3.

(*b*) Repeat for the $K = 2$ code of Prob. 4.1 and show that the minimum distance between paths is 3.

(*c*) Repeat for the $K = 4$ code of Prob. 4.3 and show that the minimum distance between paths is 6.

4.7 Determine the node error probability bounds and the bit error probability bounds for all codes of Prob. 4.6 for a binary-input, output-symmetric channel for which z is known.

4.8 Verify inequality (4.5.5) of the text.

4.9 It is of interest to determine the maximum value of the free distance for any fixed or time-invariant code of a given constraint length and rate. The following sequence of steps leads to an upper bound, nearly achievable for low K, for rate $1/n$ codes. Consider the rate $1/n$ fixed convolutional code whose generator matrix is given by (4.1.1) with all rows shifted versions of the first row.

(*a*) Show that for any binary linear code, if we array the code in a matrix, each of whose rows is a code vector, any column has either all zeros or half zeros and half ones.

(*b*) Consider the set of all finite-length data sequences of length no greater than k. Show that the code generated by these finite-length data sequences has length $(K - 1 + k)$ branches, or $(K - 1 + k)n$ symbols, and show that the average weight (number of "1"s) of all codewords (excluding the all-zeros) is no greater than

$$w_{av}(k) \leq \frac{2^{k-1}(K - 1 + k)n}{2^k - 1}$$

(*c*) Using (*b*) show that the code has minimum distance between paths (free distance) $d_f \leq w_{av}(k)$ for any k.

(*d*) Let k vary over all possible integers and thus show that (Heller [1968])

$$d_f \leq \min_k \frac{2^{k-1}(K - 1 + k)n}{2^k - 1}$$

That is, for small K and $n = 2$, $r = \frac{1}{2}$ this yields

K	Upper bound on d_{free} (integer)	Achievable (noncatastrophic)
2	4†	3
3	5	5
4	6	6
5	8†	7

† Achievable with catastrophic code.

4.10 (Van de Meeberg [1974]) For a BSC where $Z = \sqrt{4p(1 - p)}$ show that (4.4.4) can be replaced by

$$P_d \leq Z^{d+1} \qquad \text{when } d \text{ is odd}$$

This can be shown by examining the decision region *boundary* and the Bhattacharyya bound on decoding error when $d = 2t$ and when $d = 2t - 1$. Using this show that

$$P_e(j) \leq \tfrac{1}{2}[(1 + Z)T(Z) + (1 - Z)T(-Z)]$$

can replace (4.4.7) when we have a BSC.

Hint: First show that for two codewords at odd distance d, the decoding error probability (maximum likelihood) is the *same* as for two codewords at distance $d + 1$.

4.11 Consider a rate $1/n$ fixed binary convolutional code and define the code generator polynomials

$$g_i(z) = 1 + g_{1,i}z + g_{2,i}z^2, \cdots + g_{(K-1),i}z^{K-1} \qquad i = 1, 2, \ldots, n$$

Show that this convolutional code is catastrophic if and only if all the n generator polynomials have a common polynomial factor of degree at least one. Use the fact that for a catastrophic code some infinite-weight information sequence will result in a finite-weight code sequence.

4.12 Use the result of Prob. 4.11 to show that, for rate $1/n$ fixed binary convolutional codes the relative fraction of catastrophic codes in the ensemble of all convolutional codes of a given constraint length is $1/(2^n - 1)$, which is independent of constraint length.

4.13 For any integer n, find a rate $(n - 1)/n$ single-error-correcting code and its feedback decoding implementation, which is a generalization of Figs. 4.17 and 4.18.

4.14 Consider a rate $1/n$ convolutional code with constraint length K. Let $a(l)$ be the number of paths that diverge from the all-zeros path at node j and remerge for the first time at node $j + K + l$.

(*a*) Show that

$$a(l) = \begin{cases} 1 & l = 0 \\ 2^{l-1} & 1 \le l < K \\ \sum_{i=1}^{K-1} a(l-i) & l \ge K \end{cases}$$

(*b*) Directly from (*a*) prove that

$$T_K(L) = \sum_{l=0}^{\infty} a(l)L^{K+l}$$

$$= \frac{L^K(1-L)}{1-2L+L^K}$$

(*c*) Noting that $a(l)$ is the number of binary sequences of length $l-1$ which do not have $K-1$ consecutive "0"s, show that

$$2^{l-1} \ge a(l) \ge 2^{l-1}\{1 - l2^{-(K-1)}\}$$

Hence when $l2^{-(K-1)} \ll 1$, we have the approximation

$$a(l) \approx 2^{l-1}$$

For most codes with large constraint lengths K, this approximation would be valid for all values of l that contribute significantly to error probabilities.

4.15 Given a $K = 3$, $r = \frac{1}{2}$ binary convolutional code with the partially completed state diagram below, find the complete state diagram and sketch a diagram for this encoder.

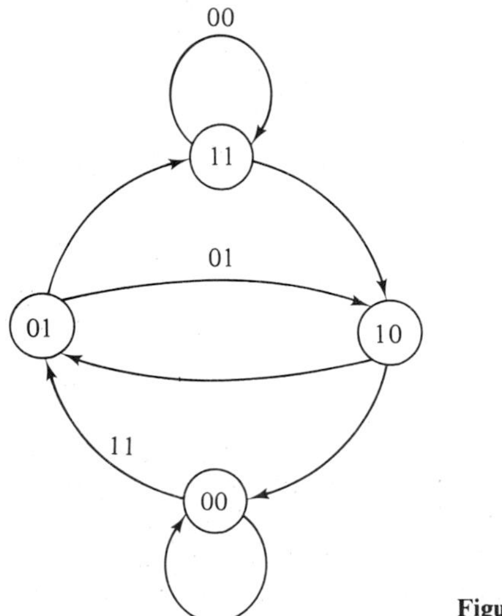

Figure P4.15

4.16 Suppose the $K = 3$, $r = \frac{1}{3}$ convolutional code given in Prob. 4.2 is used over a BSC. Assume that the initial code state is the (00) state. At the output of the BSC, we receive the sequence

$$\mathbf{y} = (101\ 010\ 100\ 110\ 011 \text{ rest all "0"})$$

Find the maximum likelihood path through the trellis and give the decoded information bits. In case of a tie between any two merged paths, choose the upper branch coming into the particular state.

4.17 In Fig. 4.10 let ξ_b, ξ_c, and ξ_d be dummy variables for the partial paths to the intermediate nodes. Let

$$\boldsymbol{\xi} = \begin{bmatrix} \xi_b \\ \xi_c \\ \xi_d \end{bmatrix}$$

and write state equations of the form

$$\boldsymbol{\xi} = \mathbf{A}\boldsymbol{\xi} + \mathbf{b}$$

Find $\mathbf{A}$, a 3×3 matrix, and vector $\mathbf{b}$. $\boldsymbol{\xi}$ can be found by

$$\boldsymbol{\xi} = (\mathbf{I} - \mathbf{A})^{-1}\mathbf{b}$$

where $\mathbf{I}$ is the 3×3 identity matrix. Solve this to find $T(D, L, I)$ and check your answer with (4.3.3).

4.18 In Prob. 4.17 consider the expansion

$$(\mathbf{I} - \mathbf{A})^{-1} = \mathbf{I} + \mathbf{A} + \mathbf{A}^2 + \mathbf{A}^3 + \mathbf{A}^4 + \cdots$$

(*a*) Use the Cayley-Hamilton theorem to show that for $L = 1$ and $I = 1$

$$\mathbf{A}^3 = D\mathbf{A}^2 + D\mathbf{A}$$

Hint: The Cayley-Hamilton theorem states that a matrix $\mathbf{A}$ satisfies its characteristic equation

$$p(\lambda) = |\mathbf{A} - \lambda\mathbf{I}| = 0$$

(*b*) Use (*a*) to find $(\mathbf{I} - \mathbf{A})^{-1}$ by the above expansion, and then find $T(D)$ for Prob. 4.17.
(*c*) Show that terms in $\mathbf{A}^k$ decrease at least as fast as $D^{k/2}$.
(*d*) Repeat (*a*) and (*b*) for arbitrary L and I.

4.19 Given the $K = 3$, $r = \frac{1}{2}$ code of Fig. 4.4 of the text, suppose the code is used on a BSC and the transmitted sequence for the first eight branches is

11 01 01 00 10 11 00

Suppose this sequence is received *error free*, but somehow the first bit is lost and the received sequence is incorrectly synchronized giving the assumed received sequence

10 10 10 01 01 10

This is the same sequence except the first bit is missing and there is now incorrect bit synchronization at the decoder. Trace the decisions on a trellis diagram, labeling the survivor's Hamming distance metric at each node.

Note that, when there is incorrect synchronization, path metrics tend to remain relatively close together. This fact can be used to detect incorrect bit synchronization.

4.20 Suppose that the Viterbi decoder uses only integer branch metrics $j \in \{\pm i_1, \pm i_2, \ldots, \pm i_{J/2}\}$, where J is even, giving rise to a channel with input 0 and 1, transition probabilities $P_0(j)$ with $P_0(j) \geq P_0(-j)$ for $j > 0$, and $P_1(j) = P_0(-j)$. Let

$$\Pi(z) = \sum_{j=-i_{J/2}}^{+i_{J/2}} P_0(z)z^j \qquad \text{and} \qquad A(z) = \sum_{k=-N}^{N} a_k z_k$$

and define

$$\{A(z)\}_- = 1/2a_0 + \sum_{k=-N}^{-1} a_k$$

(*a*) Show that the pairwise error probability for an incorrect path at Hamming distance d from the correct path upon remerging is exactly

$$P_d = \{[\Pi(z)]^d\}_-$$

(*b*) If the code-generating function is $T(D, I)$ and

$$\left.\frac{dT(D, I)}{dI}\right|_{I=1} = \sum_{d=d_f}^{\infty} b(d)D^d$$

show that

$$P_b \le \sum_{d=d_f}^{\infty} b(d)P_d$$

(*c*) In (*a*) show that

$$P_d \le \tfrac{1}{2}\tilde{Z}^d$$

where $\tilde{Z} = \min \Pi(z)$

$$z \le 1$$

and using (*b*) show that

$$P_b \le \frac{1}{2}\left.\frac{dT(D, I)}{dI}\right|_{I=1,\, D=\tilde{Z}}$$

(*d*) For the BSC, show that $\tilde{Z} = Z$.

4.21 For the DMC with input alphabet $\mathscr{X}$, output alphabet $\mathscr{Y}$, and transition probabilities $\{p(y|x)\colon y \in \mathscr{Y}, x \in \mathscr{X}\}$, define the Bhattacharyya distance between any two inputs $x, x' \in \mathscr{X}$ as

$$d(x, x') = -\ln \sum_y \sqrt{p(y|x)p(y|x')}$$

For two sequences $\mathbf{x}, \mathbf{x}' \in \mathscr{X}_N$ define the Bhattacharyya distance as

$$d(\mathbf{x}, \mathbf{x}') = \sum_{n=1}^{N} d(x_n, x'_n)$$

Show that, for any two diverging and remerging paths of a trellis whose Bhattacharyya distance is d, (4.4.3) generalizes to

$$P_d \le e^{-d}$$

and (4.4.5) generalizes to

$$P_e(j) \le \sum_d a(d)e^{-d}$$

where $a(d)$ is the number of paths of Bhattacharyya distance d from the transmitted path. What is necessary to be able to define generating functions that generalize (4.4.7) and (4.4.13)?

4.22 Consider the $r = \frac{1}{3}$ convolutional code of Prob. 4.2. Suppose each time an information bit enters the register, the three code bits are used to transmit one of eight orthogonal signals over the white Gaussian noise channel. At the output of the channel, a hard decision is made as to which one of the eight signals was sent. This results in a DMC with transition probabilities

$$P(y|x) = \begin{cases} 1 - p & y = x \\ p/7 & y \ne x \end{cases}$$

Following the suggested generalization of Prob. 4.21, find the generating function $T(D, I)$ and give the bit error bound of (4.4.13). Repeat this problem when the outputs of the channel are not forced to be hard decisions.

4.23 Show that the bound in (4.6.15) can be made tighter by

$$T_K(L) = \frac{L^K(1-L)}{1-2L+L^K} \le \frac{1}{2} L^K \left[1 + \sum_{k=0}^{\infty} 2^k L^k\right]$$

4.24 In Fig. 4.9 let

$\xi_x(D, t) =$ generating function for all paths that go from state **a** to state **x** in exactly t branches.

$\mathbf{x} = \mathbf{b}, \mathbf{c}, \mathbf{d}$

Let

$$\boldsymbol{\xi}(D, t) = \begin{bmatrix} \xi_b(D, t) \\ \xi_c(D, t) \\ \xi_d(D, t) \end{bmatrix}$$

(*a*) Show that

$$\boldsymbol{\xi}(D, t+1) = \mathbf{A}\boldsymbol{\xi}(D, t)$$

and find **A**.

(*b*) Find

$$\sum_{t=1}^{\infty} \boldsymbol{\xi}(D, t)$$

and show that

$$T(D) = [0 \;\; D^2 \;\; 0] \sum_{t=1}^{\infty} \boldsymbol{\xi}(D, t)$$

(*c*) Suppose we have a BSC with crossover-probability p and in the Viterbi decoder we truncate path memory after τ branches and make a decision by comparing all metrics of surviving paths leaving the given node at the truncation point. Metrics are computed only for the τ branches following the truncation point. Show that the probability of a node error at node j is bounded by

$$P_e(j, \tau) \le [0 \;\; D^2 \;\; 0] \sum_{t=1}^{\tau-1} \boldsymbol{\xi}(D, t) + [1 \;\; 1 \;\; 1]\boldsymbol{\xi}(D, \tau)$$

where $D = \sqrt{4p(1-p)}$. Give an interpretation of each term in the bound. Note that $\boldsymbol{\xi}(D, t)$ is easily found recursively with initial condition

$$\boldsymbol{\xi}(D, 1) = \begin{bmatrix} D^2 \\ 0 \\ 0 \end{bmatrix}$$

(*d*) Obtain a closed-form expression for the bound in (*c*) for $\tau = 7$.
Hint: Use the result of Prob. 4.18(*b*).

4.25 Consider a binary convolutional code, a BSC with parameter p, and a feedback decoder of memory length L. In the usual state diagram of the convolutional code, label distances from the all-zeros path and define

$\xi_x(D, t) =$ generating function for all paths that initially leave the all-zero state and go to state **x** in exactly t branches (return to the all-zeros state is allowed)

(*a*) Show that the probability that the decoded path leaves the correct path at node j, $P_e(j, L)$, is bounded by

$$P_e(j, L) \leq \sum_x \xi_x(D, L)\Big|_{D=\sqrt{4p(1-p)}}$$

where the summation is over all states including the all-zeros state.

(*b*) Evaluate a closed-form expression for the bound in (*a*) for $L = 6$ and a code with the distance-labeled state diagram below:

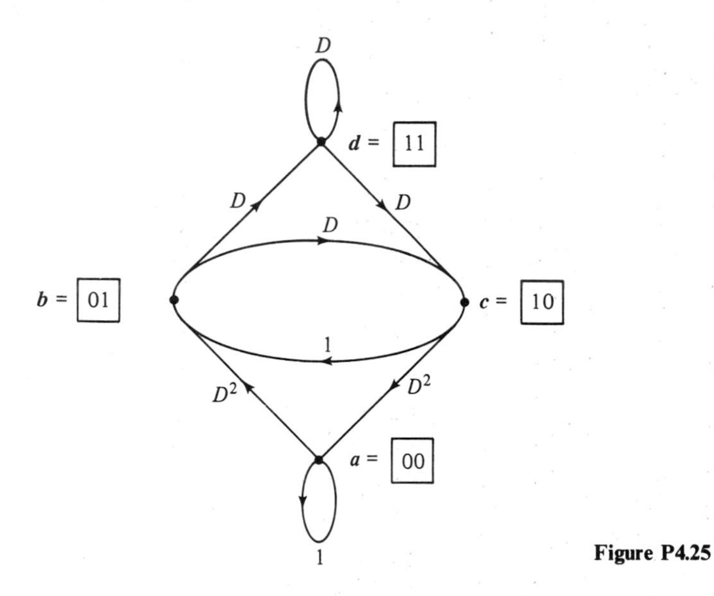

Figure P4.25

Hint: Find a recursive equation for

$$\xi(D, t) = \begin{bmatrix} \xi_a(D, t) \\ \xi_b(D, t) \\ \xi_c(D, t) \\ \xi_d(D, t) \end{bmatrix} \qquad \xi(D, 1) = \begin{bmatrix} 0 \\ D^2 \\ 0 \\ 0 \end{bmatrix}$$

and use the Cayley-Hamilton theorem [see Prob. 4.18(*b*)].

4.26 Treat the $K = 3$, $r = \frac{1}{2}$ code of Fig. 4.2*a* as if it were an $r = \frac{2}{4}$ code; i.e., define a branch as the four symbols generated for every two data bits. Draw the corresponding state diagram and determine $T(D, I)$. From this, compute the upper bound on P_b using (4.4.13) and verify that the result is the same as computed directly from the original state diagram for the $r = \frac{1}{2}$ code.

4.27 Show that the noise components of the matched filter output in Fig. 4.21 have covariance

$$E[n_k n_j] = \frac{N_o}{2} h_{k-j}$$

Instead of the matched filter, assume that the suboptimum "integrate and dump" filter is used. That is, assume that the observables are

$$\tilde{y}_k = \int_{-\infty}^{\infty} y(t)p(t - kT)\, dt \qquad k = -N, -N + 1, \ldots, N - 1$$

where

$$p(t) = \begin{cases} \dfrac{1}{\sqrt{T}} & 0 \le t < T \\ 0 & \text{otherwise} \end{cases}$$

Show that the maximum likelihood demodulator based on observables $\tilde{y}_{-N}, \tilde{y}_{-N+1}, \ldots, \tilde{y}_{N-1}$ is realized with the Viterbi algorithm with the bit error bound analogous to (4.9.23) given by

$$P_b \le \sum_{\epsilon} w(\epsilon) \prod_{k=-N}^{N-1} \frac{1}{2^{w(\epsilon_k)}} \exp\left[-\frac{1}{N_o}\left(\sum_{i=0}^{\mathscr{L}-1} \tilde{h}_i \epsilon_{k-i}\right)^2\right]$$

where

$$\tilde{h}_{k-j} = \int_{-\infty}^{\infty} h(t - jT)p(t - kT)\, dt$$

For $\mathscr{L} = 2$, give the state diagram, determine the transfer function, and find the generating function for the bit error bound in terms of $\tilde{h}_0$ and $\tilde{h}_1$.

4.28 (Whitened Matched Filter, Forney [1972a]) Consider the intersymbol interference example of Fig. 4.22 where $\mathscr{L} = 2$. Suppose the matched filter outputs $\{y_k\}$ are followed by the following digital filter with outputs $\{\tilde{y}_k\}$.

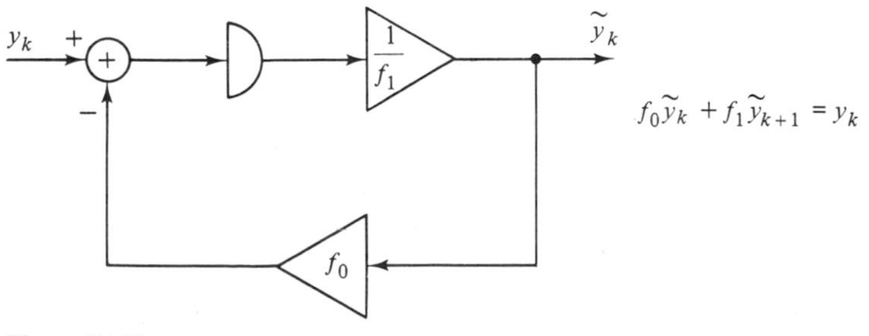

Figure P4.28

Here we choose f_0 and f_1 to satisfy

$$f_0^2 + f_1^2 = h_0$$

$$f_0 f_1 = h_1$$

The matched filter combined with this transversal filter is called a whitened matched filter.

(*a*) Show that the outputs $\{\tilde{y}_k\}$ are given by

$$\tilde{y}_k = f_0 u_k + f_1 u_{k-1} + \tilde{n}_k$$

where

$$E[\tilde{n}_k \tilde{n}_j] = \frac{N_o}{2} \delta_{kj}$$

(*b*) Show that the maximum likelihood demodulator based on observables $\{\tilde{y}_k\}$ is realized with the Viterbi algorithm, and give the error-state diagram for this case.

(*c*) Show that the bit error bound based on the error-state diagram in (*b*) is also given by (4.9.24).

(*d*) Generalize the above results to arbitrary $\mathscr{L}$. First define

$$H(D) = \sum_{i=-(\mathscr{L}-1)}^{\mathscr{L}-1} h_i D^i$$

and show that there exists a polynomial of degree $\mathscr{L} - 1$

$$f(D) = \sum_{i=0}^{\mathscr{L}-1} f_i D^i$$

such that

$$H(D) = f(D) f(D^{-1})$$

Show that the transversal filter with inputs $\{y_k\}$ and outputs $\{\tilde{y}_k\}$ that satisfy the difference equation

$$\sum_{i=0}^{\mathscr{L}-1} f_i \tilde{y}_{k+i} = y_k$$

result in outputs satisfying the form

$$\tilde{y}_k = \sum_{i=0}^{\mathscr{L}-1} f_i u_{k-i} + \tilde{n}_k$$

where

$$E[\tilde{n}_k \tilde{n}_j] = \frac{N_o}{2} \delta_{kj}$$

(*e*) Describe the error-state diagram when using the whitened matched filter in (*d*) and derive the bit error bound

$$P_b \le \sum_{\epsilon} w(\epsilon) \prod_{k=-N}^{N-1} \frac{1}{2^{w(\epsilon_k)}} \exp\left[-\frac{1}{N_o} \left(\sum_{i=0}^{\mathscr{L}-1} f_i \epsilon_{k-i} \right)^2 \right]$$

(*f*) In (*d*), show that

$$\int_{-\infty}^{\infty} (x(t) - x'(t))^2 \, dt = 4 \sum_n \left(\sum_{i=0}^{\mathscr{L}-1} f_i \epsilon_{n-i} \right)^2$$

$$= 4 \sum_n \left(\epsilon_n^2 h_0 + 2 \sum_{k=1}^{\mathscr{L}-1} \epsilon_n \epsilon_{n-k} h_k \right)$$

4.29 (*a*) For the rate $r = 2^{-K}$ orthogonal convolutional encoder shown, consider a noncoherent demodulator on each branch with linear combining so that path metrics are formed as the sums of the branch metrics $z_j(m)$. Using techniques of Secs. 2.12 and 4.6, show that the probability of error caused by an incorrect path merging after J unmerged branches is bounded by

$$P_j = \Pr\left\{ \sum_{j=1}^{J} z_j' > \sum_{j=1}^{J} z_j \right\}$$

$$< \max_{0 \le \rho \le 1} \prod_{j=1}^{J} E[e^{\rho(z_j' - z_j)}]$$

$$= Z^J$$

where

$$Z = \max_{0 \le \rho \le 1} \frac{1}{1 - \rho^2} \exp\left[\left(\frac{-\rho}{1 + \rho} \right) \frac{\mathscr{E}_b}{N_o} \right]$$

(*b*) From this, derive the bound on the bit error probability (Viterbi and Jacobs [1975]).

$$P_b < \frac{Z^K}{(1 - 2Z)^2}$$

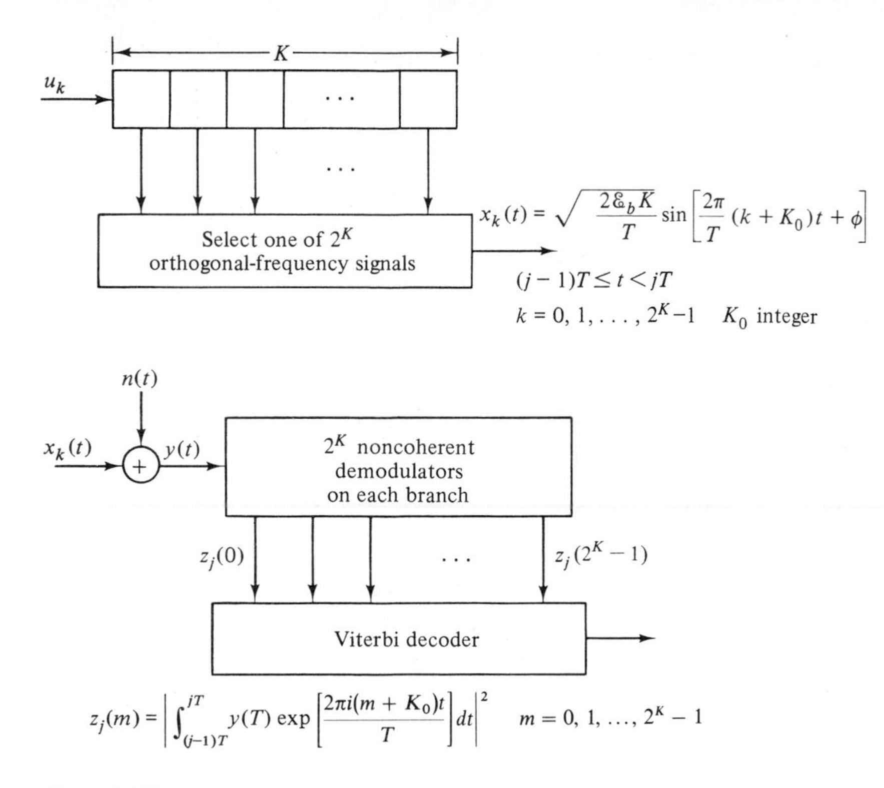

Figure P4.29

4.30 (a) For the same noncoherent channel and demodulator–decoder as in Prob. 4.29, show that the rate $r = \frac{1}{2}$ quaternary code generated by the $K = 5$ encoder shown above yields

$$P_b < Z \frac{1 + Za(Z)}{1 + Zb(Z)}$$

where $a(Z)$ and $b(Z)$ are polynomials in Z with integer coefficients.

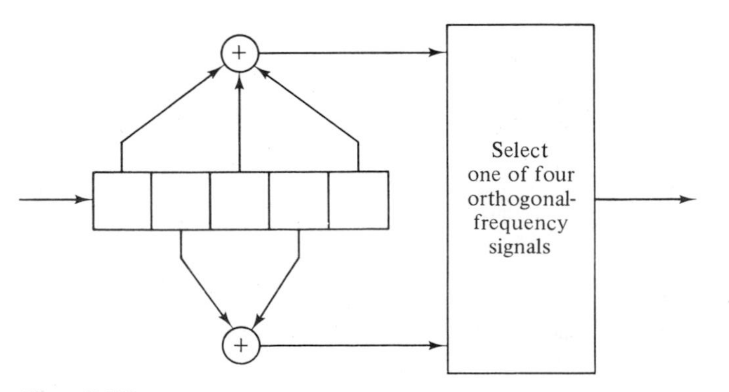

Figure P4.30

(*b*) Generalize the results to a rate $r = 2^{-k}$ code of constraint length $K = 2k + 1$ and a 2^K-ary orthogonal signaling alphabet where k is any integer. This has been called the class of *semiorthogonal* convolutional encoders.

4.31 Suppose the $K = 3$, $r = \frac{1}{2}$ convolutional code shown in Fig. 4.2*a* is used over the intersymbol interference channel with $\mathscr{L} = 2$ shown in Fig. 4.22*a*. Assume the *whitened matched filter* (see Prob. 4.28) so that the discrete model for the system becomes

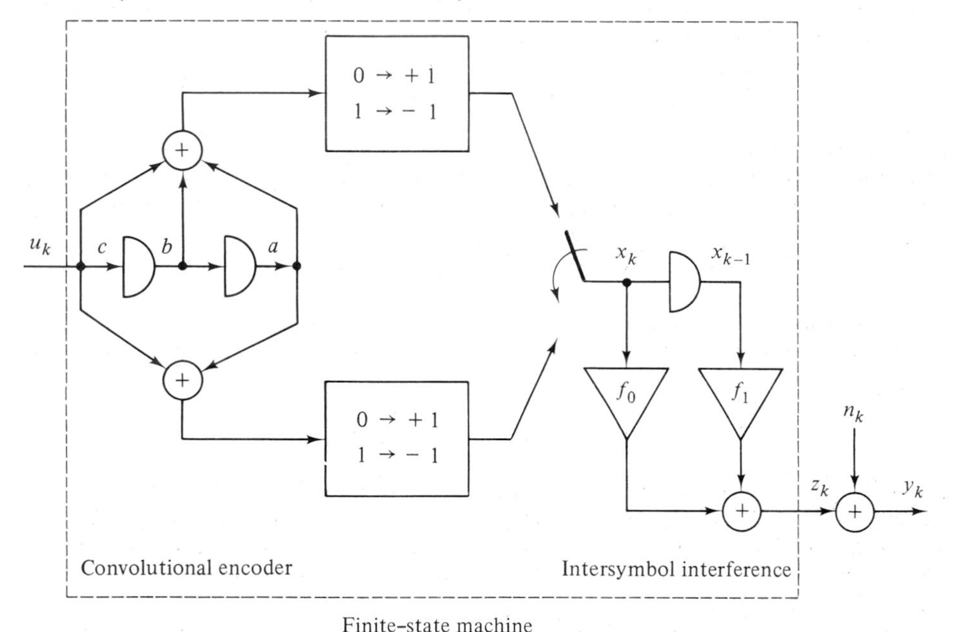

Figure P4.31

Here, the ⊕ in the convolutional encoder is a modulo-2 sum and $\mathbf{u}$ is the binary data sequence with symbols from $\{0, 1\}$. The summer in the intersymbol interference is a real sum. For each binary symbol into the convolutional encoder, two coded symbols from $\{-1, 1\}$ enter the intersymbol interference channel and there are two corresponding outputs of the channel.

(*a*) Regard the combined convolutional encoder and intersymbol interference as a single *finite-state machine* with binary inputs $\{u_k\}$ and pairs of outputs from $\{z_k\}$. Defining the *state* of the system as the binary sequence (a, b, c) shown as the contents of the encoder register, sketch the state diagram for the device with pairs of the outputs (z_k, z_{k+1}) on the branches from state to state.

(*b*) Suppose the transmitted data sequence is $\mathbf{u} = \mathbf{0}$. Consider another data sequence $\mathbf{u}'$ where $u'_k = \delta_{k0}$. That is $u'_0 = 1$ and $u'_k = 0$, $k \neq 0$. What is the pairwise error probability $P_E(\mathbf{u} \to \mathbf{u}')$?

(*c*) Assuming transmitted data sequence $\mathbf{u} = \mathbf{0}$, construct a state diagram which will give a generating function with which we can bound $P_E(\mathbf{u})$ and $P_b(\mathbf{u})$. Express the generating function in terms of vectors and matrices.

4.32 Consider a channel with memory $\mathscr{L} = 2$, input alphabet $\mathscr{X} = \{0, 1\}$, output alphabet $\mathscr{Y} = \{a, b, c, d\}$ which consists of a noiseless memory part followed by a DMC as shown.

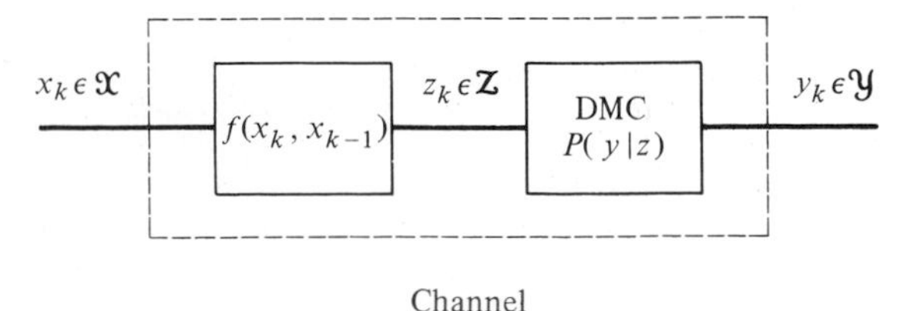

Figure P4.32

Here

$$z_k = f(x_k, x_{k-1}) = \begin{cases} a & x_k = 0, x_{k-1} = 0 \\ b & x_k = 0, x_{k-1} = 1 \\ c & x_k = 1, x_{k-1} = 0 \\ d & x_k = 1, x_{k-1} = 1 \end{cases}$$

$$\mathscr{Z} = \mathscr{Y} = \{a, b, c, d\}$$

and

$$\{P(y \mid z)\} = \begin{array}{c} \\ a \\ b \\ c \\ d \end{array} \begin{array}{c} \begin{array}{cccc} a & b & c & d \end{array} \\ \begin{bmatrix} q^2 & pq & p^2 & pq \\ pq & q^2 & pq & p^2 \\ p^2 & pq & q^2 & pq \\ pq & p^2 & pq & q^2 \end{bmatrix} \end{array} \qquad q = 1 - p > p$$

(*a*) Assume $x_0 = 0$ and equiprobable binary data symbols $x_k (k = 1, 2, \ldots)$ are sent over the channel. For the channel output sequence

$$y_1 = a \qquad y_2 = b \qquad y_3 = c \qquad y_4 = b \qquad y_k = a \qquad k \geq 5$$

determine the maximum likelihood data sequence $\hat{x}_k (k = 1, 2, \ldots)$.

Hint: Consider branch metric $-\left[\log\left(\frac{P(y \mid z)}{q^2}\right)\right] \Big/ \log\left(\frac{q}{p}\right)$.

(*b*) Determine the union-Bhattacharyya bound on $P_b(\mathbf{x})$, the bit error probability when $\mathbf{x} = \mathbf{0}$ is sent.

4.33 (Unknown Intersymbol Interference Channel) For the linear channel of memory $\mathscr{L}$ and the suboptimum "integrate and dump" filter discussed in Prob. 4.27, determine the performance degradation when the Viterbi demodulator is designed under the mistaken impression that the impulse-response is $\widehat{h}(t)$ rather than $\widetilde{h(t)}$, the true channel impulse-response. Here, define

$$\hat{\hat{h}}_{k-j} = \int_{-\infty}^{\infty} \widehat{h}(t - jT)p(t - kT)\,dt$$

and $\widetilde{\tilde{h}_{k-i}}$ as in Prob. 4.27.

(*a*) Show that, if the demodulator is realized with the Viterbi algorithm designed for $\hat{h}(t)$, then the bit error bound is given by

$$P_b \leq \sum_{\mathbf{u}} \sum_{\mathbf{u}' \neq \mathbf{u}}' w(\mathbf{u}, \mathbf{u}') \prod_{k=1}^{\infty} \frac{1}{2} e^{-R_k/4N_o}$$

where $\sum'_{\mathbf{u}' \neq \mathbf{u}}$ is the summation over all incorrect sequences $\mathbf{u}'$ which diverge from the correct sequence $\mathbf{u}$ at some fixed initial time and remerge with it later, $w(\mathbf{u}, \mathbf{u}')$ is the weight of the error sequence between $\mathbf{u}$ and $\mathbf{u}'$, and

$$R_k = \left(\sum_{i=0}^{\mathscr{L}-1} \widehat{h_i(u'_{k-i} - u_{k-i})}\right)^2 + 4 \sum_{i=0}^{\mathscr{L}-1} \sum_{j=0}^{\mathscr{L}-1} \hat{h}_i(\hat{h}_j - \tilde{h}_j)(u'_{k-j} - u_{k-j})u_{k-j}$$

Assume that $h(t)$ and $\hat{h}(t)$ are zero for $t \geq \mathscr{L}T$.

(*b*) For evaluation of the bit error bound using a generating function, we need a state diagram in which each state consists of a pair of states S and S', where S is the correct state and S' is an incorrect state. Initial and final states are states in which $S = S'$. There are $2^{\mathscr{L}-1}$ initial and $2^{\mathscr{L}-1}$ final states. Introduce an initial dummy state and a final dummy state and note that there is probability $2^{-(\mathscr{L}-1)}$ of transition from the initial dummy state to each initial state. For $\mathscr{L} = 2$, consider the *pair state diagram* as shown below and find all transitions and the transfer function. Note that this state diagram can be reduced.

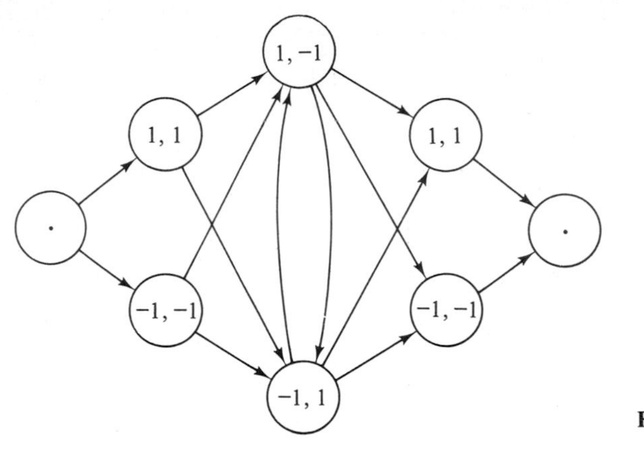

Figure P4.33

(*c*) Show that the bit error bound is given by

$$P_b \leq \frac{\cosh\left(\dfrac{2\hat{\hbar}_0(\tilde{\hat{\hbar}}_1 - \hat{\hbar}_1)}{N_o}\right)\cosh\left(\dfrac{2\hat{\hbar}_1(\tilde{\hat{\hbar}}_0 - \hat{\hbar}_0)}{N_o}\right)\exp\left\{-\dfrac{\hat{\hbar}_0(2\tilde{\hat{\hbar}}_0 - \hat{\hbar}_0) + \hat{\hbar}_1(2\tilde{\hat{\hbar}}_1 - \hat{\hbar}_1)}{N_o}\right\}}{\left[1 - \cosh\left(\dfrac{2(\tilde{\hat{\hbar}}_0\hat{\hbar}_1 + \hat{\hbar}_0\tilde{\hat{\hbar}}_1 - \hat{\hbar}_0\hat{\hbar}_1)}{N_o}\right)\exp\left\{-\dfrac{\hat{\hbar}_0(2\tilde{\hat{\hbar}}_0 - \hat{\hbar}_0) + \hat{\hbar}_1(2\tilde{\hat{\hbar}}_1 - \hat{\hbar}_1)}{N_o}\right\}\right]^2}$$

CHAPTER

FIVE

CONVOLUTIONAL CODE ENSEMBLE PERFORMANCE

5.1 THE CHANNEL CODING THEOREM FOR TIME-VARYING CONVOLUTIONAL CODES

This chapter treats for convolutional codes the same ensemble average error bounds which were studied in Chap. 3 for block codes. However, useful tight bounds can be found only for time-varying convolutional codes, corresponding to the matrix (4.1.1) with $\mathbf{g}_j^{(k)}$ and $\mathbf{g}_j^{(k-l)}$ *not* necessarily equal. (For a fixed convolutional code, each row is a shifted replica of every other row.)

For any convolutional code, we have from (4.4.1) and (4.4.2) that the node error probability at the jth node of a maximum likelihood decoder employing the Viterbi algorithm is bounded by

$$P_e(j) \le \Pr\left\{ \bigcup_{\mathbf{x}_j' \in \mathscr{X}'(j)} [\Delta M(\mathbf{x}_j', \mathbf{x}_j) \ge 0] \right\} \le \sum_{\mathbf{x}_j' \in \mathscr{X}'(j)} \Pr\,[\Delta M(\mathbf{x}_j', \mathbf{x}_j) \ge 0] \quad (5.1.1)$$

where $\mathbf{x}_j'$ is any incorrect path stemming from node j, $\mathscr{X}'(j)$ is the set of all such incorrect paths, $\mathbf{x}_j$ is the correct path after node j, and $\Delta M(\mathbf{x}_j', \mathbf{x}_j)$ is the difference between the metric increment of incorrect path $\mathbf{x}_j'$ and correct path $\mathbf{x}_j$ over the branches of their unmerged span.

For rate $1/n$ (binary-trellis) convolutional codes, we determined in Sec. 4.6 the structure of all paths through the trellis. In particular, the bound (4.6.15) indicated that for a constraint length K code, there are less than 2^k paths which diverge from the correct path at node j and remain unmerged for exactly $K + k$ branches. This conclusion can be arrived at alternatively by the following argument. Without loss of generality, since a convolutional code is linear, we may take the all-zeros path to be the correct path. Then any incorrect path which diverges from the correct path at node j and remains unmerged for $K + k$ branches must have binary data symbols

$$1, u_{j+1}, u_{j+2}, \ldots, u_{j+k-1}, \underbrace{1, 0, 0, \ldots, 0}_{|\leftarrow K-1 \rightarrow|} \tag{5.1.2}$$

where $u_{j+1}, \ldots, u_{j+k-1}$ is any binary vector containing no strings of more than $K - 2$ consecutive zeros. While the exact number of such incorrect paths is best computed by the generating function technique of Sec. 4.6, 2^k is an obvious upper bound on the number of such paths. We shall concentrate on rate $1/n$ codes initially, and later generalize to rate b/n.

Now, as was done for block codes in Chap. 3, we average this error probability bound over all possible codes in the ensemble. We begin by noting that each term of the sum in the rightmost bound of (5.1.1) is a pairwise error probability between the correct path $\mathbf{x}_j$ and the incorrect path $\mathbf{x}'_j$ over the unmerged segment of $K + k$ branches, where $k \geq 0$. Using the Bhattacharyya bound (2.3.15) for each such term, we have

$$\Pr[\Delta M(\mathbf{x}'_j, \mathbf{x}_j) \geq 0] \leq \sum_{\mathbf{y}} \sqrt{p_N(\mathbf{y} \mid \mathbf{x}'_j) p_N(\mathbf{y} \mid \mathbf{x}_j)} \tag{5.1.3}$$

where $N = (K + k)n$ is the number of symbols on the unmerged segment of length $K + k$ branches and $\mathbf{y}$ is the received vector for this unmerged segment.

We must average over all possible values of $\mathbf{x}_j$ and $\mathbf{x}'_j$ in the ensemble of time-varying convolutional codes. Suppose, as for block codes, that the channel input alphabet is Q-ary and that the time-varying convolutional code is generated by the operation (Fig. 5.1)

$$\begin{aligned} \mathbf{v}_i &= \sum_{k=i-K+1}^{i} u_k \, \mathbf{g}_{i-k}^{(i)} \oplus \mathbf{v}_{0,i} \\ \mathbf{x}_i &= \mathscr{L}(\mathbf{v}_i) \end{aligned} \tag{5.1.4}$$

where $\mathbf{g}_0^{(i)}, \mathbf{g}_1^{(i)}, \ldots, \mathbf{g}_{K-1}^{(i)}$ are time-varying binary connection vectors of dimension l; $u_{i-K+1}, u_{i-K+2}, \ldots, u_i$ are binary data symbols; $\mathbf{v}_i$ is the ith binary branch vector with l symbols (where l is a multiple of n) and $\mathbf{v}_{0,i}$ is an arbitrary binary branch vector with the same dimensionality as $\mathbf{v}_i$. Here $\mathbf{v}_{0,i}$ plays the same role as in the linear block code ensemble of Sec. 3.10, and is required for nonbinary and asymmetric binary channels. $\mathscr{L}(\mathbf{v}_i)$ is a memoryless mapping from sequences $\mathbf{v}_i$ to sequences $\mathbf{x}_i$ of n Q-ary symbols ($Q \leq 2^{l/n}$) (see Fig. 5.1 with $b = 1$).

The mapping $\mathscr{L}$ must be chosen carefully, particularly to ensure that the ensemble over which averages will be taken is properly constructed. In the first part of the derivation [through (5.1.9)], we shall deal with uniform weighting on the ensemble, just as was done in the earlier part of Sec. 3.1. Then l and n must be chosen so that $2^l \approx Q^n$, and each binary l-tuple input sequence should be mapped into a unique Q-ary n-tuple output sequence. This can be achieved exactly if Q is a power of 2, and otherwise approximated as closely as desired by choosing l and n

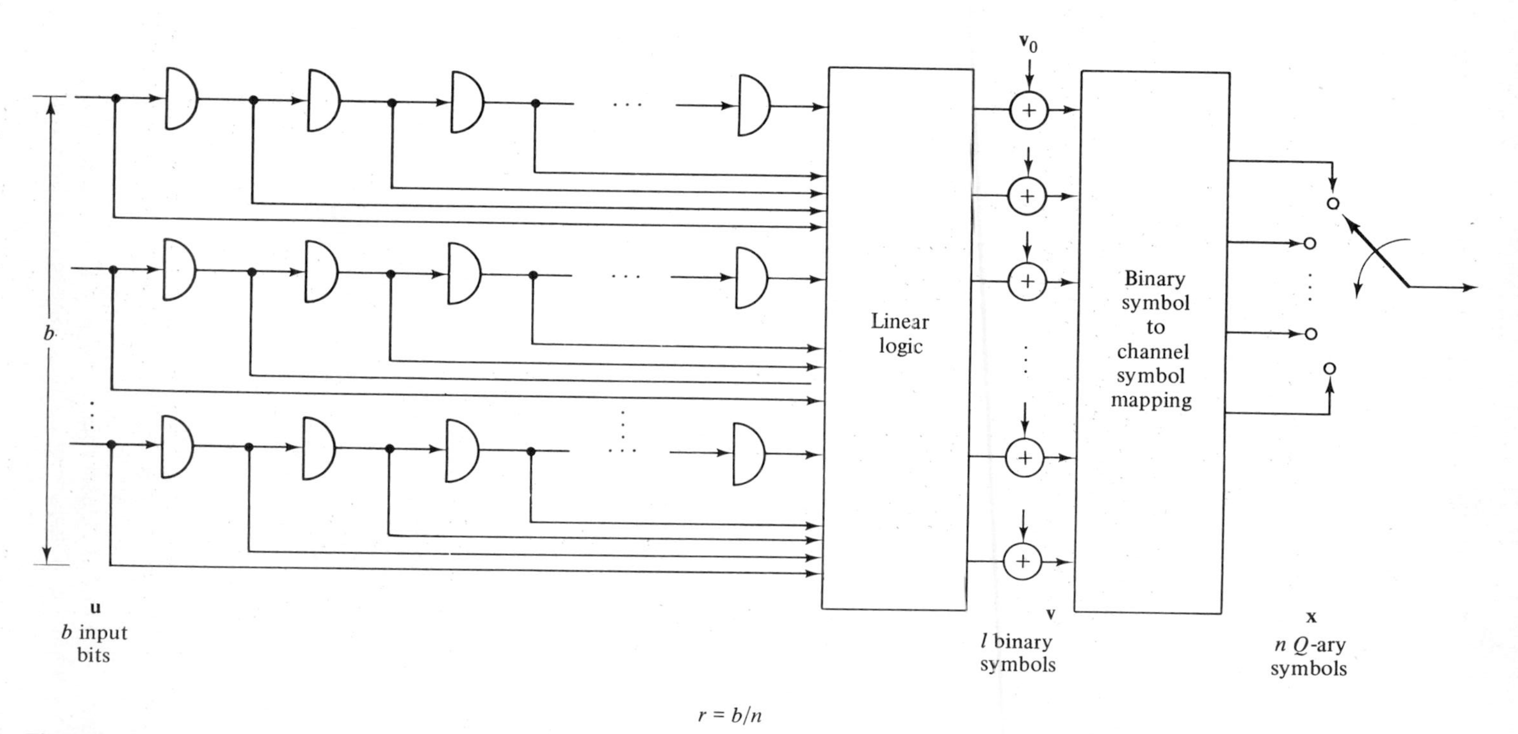

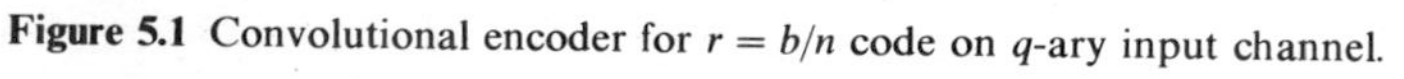

$r = b/n$

Figure 5.1 Convolutional encoder for $r = b/n$ code on q-ary input channel.

sufficiently large. This results in approximately Q^n possible Q-ary sequences with uniform weighting if the original 2^l binary sequences have uniform weighting. We shall consider nonuniform weighting on the Q-ary sequence below.

Now let us consider the correct path and any incorrect path unmerged with it from node j to node $j + K + k$. If we take the correct path to correspond to the all-zeros data (without loss of generality), then its code sequence is $\mathbf{v}_{0,j}$, $\mathbf{v}_{0,j+1}$, $\mathbf{v}_{0,j+2}, \ldots, \mathbf{v}_{0,j+K+k-1}$ and there are $2^{l(K+k)}$ possible binary sequences over the $(K + k)$-branch unmerged span. After mapping this sequence onto the signal vector $\mathbf{x}_0$, we have $Q^{n(K+k)}$ possible Q-ary $\mathbf{x}$ sequences over this span. As for the incorrect path in question, it must correspond to a data vector $\mathbf{u}'_j$ over the unmerged span of the form of (5.1.2) where $u'_{j+1} \cdots u'_{j+k-1}$ contains no strings of more than $K - 2$ consecutive zeros. This implies then that each of the corresponding branch vectors of the form $\mathbf{v}'_i$ is formed by the modulo-2 sum of $\mathbf{v}_{0,i}$ and at least one of the vectors $\mathbf{g}_0^{(i)}, \mathbf{g}_1^{(i)}, \ldots, \mathbf{g}_{K-1}^{(i)}$ [see (5.1.4)]. Thus $\mathbf{v}'_j, \mathbf{v}'_{j+1}, \ldots, \mathbf{v}'_{j+K+k-1}$ can be any one of $2^{l(K+k)}$ possible binary sequences over the $(K + k)$-branch unmerged span, and therefore $\mathbf{x}'_j$ can be any one of $Q^{n(K+k)}$ Q-ary sequences, independent of what the correct sequence $\mathbf{x}_j$ may be. As a result, we may average the bound (5.1.3) over the Q^{2N} [where $N = n(K + k)$] possible correct and incorrect sequences as follows

$$\begin{aligned}
\overline{\Pr[\Delta M(\mathbf{x}'_j, \mathbf{x}_j) \geq 0]} &\equiv \frac{1}{Q^{2N}} \sum_{\mathbf{x}'_j} \sum_{\mathbf{x}_j} \Pr[\Delta M(\mathbf{x}'_j, \mathbf{x}_j) \geq 0] \\
&\leq \sum_{\mathbf{x}'_j} \sum_{\mathbf{x}_j} \frac{1}{Q^{2N}} \sum_{\mathbf{y}} \sqrt{p_N(\mathbf{y} \mid \mathbf{x}'_j) p_N(\mathbf{y} \mid \mathbf{x}_j)} \\
&= \sum_{\mathbf{y}} \sum_{\mathbf{x}'_j} \frac{1}{Q^N} \sqrt{p_N(\mathbf{y} \mid \mathbf{x}'_j)} \sum_{\mathbf{x}_j} \frac{1}{Q^N} \sqrt{p_N(\mathbf{y} \mid \mathbf{x}_j)} \\
&= \sum_{\mathbf{y}} \left[\sum_{\mathbf{x}} \frac{1}{Q^N} \sqrt{p_N(\mathbf{y} \mid \mathbf{x})} \right]^2
\end{aligned}$$

which is clearly independent of the node j.

Also, using the fact that the channel is memoryless and letting $q(x) = 1/Q$ for all x in the channel input alphabet, we obtain

$$\begin{aligned}
\overline{\Pr[\Delta M(\mathbf{x}'_j, \mathbf{x}_j) \geq 0]} &\leq \left\{ \sum_y \left[\sum_x q(x) \sqrt{p(y \mid x)} \right]^2 \right\}^N \\
&= e^{-NR_o(\mathbf{q})}
\end{aligned} \tag{5.1.5}$$

where $N = n(K + k)$ and

$$R_o(\mathbf{q}) \equiv -\ln \sum_y \left[\sum_x q(x) \sqrt{p(y \mid x)} \right]^2 \tag{5.1.6}$$

Finally, inserting (5.1.5) into the ensemble average of (5.1.1) and using 2^k as the upper bound on the number of incorrect paths $\mathbf{x}'_j$ diverging from the correct path at node j and remerging $K + k$ branches later, we obtain a bound on the ensemble average of the node error probability for each node, namely

$$\overline{P_e(j)} < \sum_{k=0}^{\infty} 2^k e^{-n(K+k)R_o(\mathbf{q})}$$

$$= \frac{e^{-KnR_o(\mathbf{q})}}{1 - 2^{-[nR_o(\mathbf{q})/\ln 2 - 1]}} \tag{5.1.7}$$

Since $r = 1/n$ is the rate in bits per channel symbol, to define rate in nats per symbol as for block codes, we let

$$R \equiv r \ln 2$$

$$= (\ln 2)/n \qquad \text{nats/channel symbol} \tag{5.1.8}$$

and thus obtain

$$\overline{P_e(j)} < \frac{2^{-KR_o/R}}{1 - 2^{-(R_o - R)/R}} \qquad 0 < R < R_o(\mathbf{q}) \tag{5.1.9}$$

where $R_o(\mathbf{q})$ is defined in (5.1.6).

Note also that, just as was done for block code ensemble averages in Sec. 3.1, we may impose a nonuniform weighting $q(x)$ on the channel input symbols. To achieve this nonuniform weighting, we must choose the binary to Q-ary mapping of Fig. 5.1 differently from that described after (5.1.4) for uniform weighting. Now let $l = n\lambda$ and let each binary λ-tuple be mapped into a Q-ary symbol. Further let the mapping be chosen such that exactly r_i of the 2^λ binary λ-tuples map into the Q-ary output symbol x_i, where $i = 1, 2, \ldots, Q$, and

$$\sum_{i=1}^{Q} r_i = 2^\lambda = 2^{l/n}$$

Thus by choosing λ, and hence l, sufficiently large, any nonuniform distribution can be approximated arbitrarily closely [by the distribution $(r_i 2^{-\lambda})$] starting with a uniform distribution on the binary l-tuples. Thus, (5.1.9) is valid even when $R_o(\mathbf{q})$ is defined with an almost arbitrary nonuniform $q(x)$.

The bit error probability, defined as the expected number of bit errors per bit decoded, can be bounded by the same argument used in Sec. 4.6 [preceding (4.6.21)]. There we noted that an incorrect path which has been unmerged over $K + k$ branches can cause *at most* $k + 1$ bit errors, for, in order to merge with the correct path, the last $K - 1$ data bits must coincide. Thus it follows, using (5.1.8), that the ensemble average of the expected number of bit errors, caused by a node error which begins at node j, is bounded by

$$\overline{E[n_b(j)]} < \sum_{k=0}^{\infty} (k + 1) 2^k e^{-n(K+k)R_o(\mathbf{q})}$$

$$= \frac{2^{-KR_o(\mathbf{q})/R}}{[1 - 2^{-(R_o(\mathbf{q}) - R)/R}]^2} \qquad 0 < R < R_o(\mathbf{q}) \tag{5.1.10}$$

Comparing $R_o(\mathbf{q})$ as defined in (5.1.6) with the Gallager function $E_o(\rho, \mathbf{q})$ as defined by (3.1.18), we find

$$R_o(\mathbf{q}) = E_o(1, \mathbf{q}) \tag{5.1.11}$$

which is strictly less than capacity C for all physical channels, but may equal capacity in certain degenerate cases as was shown in Sec. 3.2 [see (3.2.11)].

To extend our bounds for rates up to capacity, we must employ a more refined argument than the simple union bound used so far. The technique, based on the Gallager bound, is similar to that used in the latter half of Sec. 4.6. We begin by considering the set of all incorrect paths diverging from the correct path at node j and unmerged for exactly $K + k$ branches, and take the sum over all $k \geq 0$. Thus the node error probability at any node is bounded by

$$P_e(j) < \sum_{k=0}^{\infty} \Pi_k(j) \tag{5.1.12}$$

where

$$\Pi_k(j) = \Pr\begin{Bmatrix} \text{error caused by any one of up to } 2^k \text{ incorrect} \\ \text{paths unmerged from node } j \text{ to node } j + k + K \end{Bmatrix}$$

This, then, is still a union bound, but over larger sets. For $\Pi_k(j)$ for a given code, we can again use the Gallager bound (2.4.8)

$$\Pi_k(j) \leq \sum_{\mathbf{y}} p_N(\mathbf{y}|\mathbf{x}_j)^{1/(1+\rho)} \left\{ \sum_{\hat{\mathbf{x}}_j \in \hat{\mathscr{X}}(j)} p_N(\mathbf{y}|\hat{\mathbf{x}}_j)^{1/(1+\rho)} \right\}^{\rho} \tag{5.1.13}$$

where $N = n(K + k)$, $\hat{\mathscr{X}}(j)$, whose cardinality is no greater than 2^k, is the set of all incorrect paths diverging at node j and remerging $K + k$ branches later and $\hat{\mathbf{x}}_j$ is any member path of this set.

As before we note that $\mathbf{x}_j$, defined by (5.1.4) with $\mathbf{u} = \mathbf{0}$, can be any one of Q^N possible sequences. However the set $\hat{\mathscr{X}}(j)$ is somewhat more restricted. For example, suppose $k = 2$. Then there are just two *compatible*[1] paths in the set $\hat{\mathscr{X}}(j)$ whose data sequences, between node j and node $j + K + 2$, are

$$\underbrace{1\,0\,1\,0\,0\,0 \cdots 0}_{\leftarrow K-1 \rightarrow} \qquad \text{and} \qquad \underbrace{1\,1\,1\,0\,0\,0 \cdots 0}_{\leftarrow K-1 \rightarrow}$$

But obviously over the first branch, after diverging from the correct (all-zeros) path, the two paths in question are still merged and hence their branch symbols $\hat{x}$ are identical for this branch. Yet, even though the cardinality of $\hat{\mathscr{X}}(j)$ is limited, any single path in this set can take on any one of Q^N code sequences, as can be shown by exactly the same argument as before. However, when one path has been chosen, all the others compatible with it are restricted in the choice of their code symbols, to a lesser or greater extent depending on the span over which they are

[1] Compatible refers to those incorrect paths which are unmerged from the correct path in the given number of branches.

merged with already chosen paths. Let us then assign the weight $q_N(\mathbf{x}_j)$ to the $N = (K + k)n$ symbols of the correct path between nodes j and $j + K + k$; $q_N(\mathbf{x}_j)$ equals $1/Q^N$ if we use a uniform weighting. Also, we assign the weight

$$q_{NM}(\hat{\mathbf{x}}_j^{(1)}, \hat{\mathbf{x}}_j^{(2)}, \ldots, \hat{\mathbf{x}}_j^{(M)}) \text{ where } \{\hat{\mathbf{x}}_j^{(i)} : i = 1, 2, \ldots, M\} \equiv \hat{\mathscr{X}}(j)$$

is the set of compatible incorrect paths. For uniform weighting, this weight will just be the inverse of the number of distinct choices for the set of path sequences; in general, $q_{NM}(\cdot)$ has the property that its sum over all distinct possible members of the set $\hat{\mathscr{X}}(j)$ equals unity. In fact, this notation allows us to augment the set $\hat{\mathscr{X}}(j)$ to include all Q^{NM} choices of the M vectors $\hat{\mathbf{x}}_j^{(1)}, \ldots, \hat{\mathbf{x}}_j^{(M)}$, where $M < 2^k$, whether or not they are compatible based on the trellis structure just described, since any inadmissible combination may be eliminated by assigning it zero weight.

Thus, averaging (5.1.13) over the ensemble with the weighting just defined, we have

$$\begin{aligned}\overline{\Pi_k(j)} &= \sum_{\mathbf{x}_j} q_N(\mathbf{x}_j) \sum_{\hat{\mathbf{x}}_j^{(1)}} \cdots \sum_{\hat{\mathbf{x}}_j^{(M)}} q_{NM}(\hat{\mathbf{x}}_j^{(1)}, \hat{\mathbf{x}}_j^{(2)}, \ldots, \hat{\mathbf{x}}_j^{(M)}) \Pi_k(j) \\ &\le \sum_{\mathbf{y}} \sum_{\mathbf{x}_j} q_N(\mathbf{x}_j) p_N(\mathbf{y} \mid \mathbf{x}_j)^{1/(1+\rho)} \sum_{\hat{\mathbf{x}}_j^{(1)}} \cdots \sum_{\hat{\mathbf{x}}_j^{(M)}} q_{NM}(\hat{\mathbf{x}}_j^{(1)}, \hat{\mathbf{x}}_j^{(2)}, \ldots, \hat{\mathbf{x}}_j^{(M)}) \\ &\quad \times \left\{ \sum_{i=1}^{M} [p_N(\mathbf{y} \mid \hat{\mathbf{x}}_j^{(i)})]^{1/(1+\rho)} \right\}^{\rho} \qquad 0 \le \rho \le 1\end{aligned} \tag{5.1.14}$$

Note that the summation on i is now unrestricted, since any inadmissible path combinations are excluded by making $q_{NM}(\cdot)$ zero for that choice of $\hat{\mathbf{x}}_j^{(1)}, \hat{\mathbf{x}}_j^{(2)}, \ldots, \hat{\mathbf{x}}_j^{(M)}$. Then, limiting ρ to the unit interval allows us to use the Jensen inequality (App. 1B) to obtain

$$\begin{aligned}\overline{\Pi_k(j)} &\le \sum_{\mathbf{y}} \sum_{\mathbf{x}_j} q_N(\mathbf{x}_j) p_N(\mathbf{y} \mid \mathbf{x}_j)^{1/(1+\rho)} \\ &\quad \times \left\{ \sum_{i=1}^{M} \sum_{\hat{\mathbf{x}}_j^{(1)}} \cdots \sum_{\hat{\mathbf{x}}_j^{(M)}} q_{NM}(\hat{\mathbf{x}}_j^{(1)}, \hat{\mathbf{x}}_j^{(2)}, \ldots, \hat{\mathbf{x}}_j^{(M)}) p_N(\mathbf{y} \mid \hat{\mathbf{x}}_j^{(i)})^{1/(1+\rho)} \right\}^{\rho} \qquad 0 \le \rho \le 1\end{aligned}$$

Now, for the terms in braces, suppose we consider the ith term of the outer sum and sum over all the internal summations except $\hat{\mathbf{x}}_j^{(i)}$. Since only $q_{NM}(\cdot)$ depends on these $\hat{\mathbf{x}}_j^{(l)} \neq \hat{\mathbf{x}}_j^{(i)}$, we have

$$\begin{aligned}\overline{\Pi_k(j)} &\le \sum_{\mathbf{y}} \sum_{\mathbf{x}_j} q_N(\mathbf{x}_j) p_N(\mathbf{y} \mid \mathbf{x}_j)^{1/(1+\rho)} \\ &\quad \times \left\{ \sum_{i=1}^{M} \sum_{\mathbf{x}_j^{(i)}} q_N(\hat{\mathbf{x}}_j^{(i)}) p_N(\mathbf{y} \mid \hat{\mathbf{x}}_j^{(i)})^{1/(1+\rho)} \right\}^{\rho} \qquad 0 \le \rho \le 1\end{aligned} \tag{5.1.15}$$

The key observation to be made is that, as a result of this last step, we limit consideration to a single incorrect path $\hat{\mathbf{x}}_j^{(i)}$. And, as was discussed previously, even though the choices of the set of path sequences for the entire incorrect set $\hat{\mathscr{X}}(j)$ is limited by trellis constraints, the symbols for any single path may be freely chosen among Q^N possible sequences in the space $\mathscr{X}_N$. Thus the weighting $q_N(\hat{\mathbf{x}}_j^{(i)})$ is the same as $q_N(\mathbf{x}_j)$ for the correct path (both being $1/Q^N$ if uniform weighting is assumed). Hence the bound (5.1.15) can be written as[2]

$$\overline{\Pi_k(j)} < 2^{k\rho} \sum_{\mathbf{y}} \left[\sum_{\mathbf{x}} q_N(\mathbf{x}) p_N(\mathbf{y} \mid \mathbf{x})^{1/(1+\rho)} \right]^{1+\rho}$$

$$= 2^{k\rho} \left\{ \sum_{y} \left[\sum_{x} q(x) p(y \mid x)^{1/(1+\rho)} \right]^{1+\rho} \right\}^N \qquad 0 \le \rho \le 1 \quad (5.1.16)$$

since $M < 2^k$, the channel is memoryless and $q_N(\mathbf{x})$ is a product of N identical one-dimensional weight functions. Since $N = (K + k)n$, this may be written as

$$\overline{\Pi_k(j)} < 2^{k\rho} e^{-(K+k)nE_o(\rho, \mathbf{q})} \qquad (5.1.17)$$

where as was first defined in Sec. 3.1

$$E_o(\rho, \mathbf{q}) \equiv -\ln \sum_{y} \left[\sum_{x} q(x) p(y \mid x)^{1/(1+\rho)} \right]^{1+\rho} \qquad 0 \le \rho \le 1 \quad (3.1.18)$$

Finally, substituting (5.1.17) in the ensemble average of (5.1.12) and using (5.1.8), we obtain as our bound on the ensemble node error probability

$$\overline{P_e(j)} < \sum_{k=0}^{\infty} \overline{\Pi_k(j)}$$

$$< e^{-KnE_o(\rho, \mathbf{q})} \sum_{k=0}^{\infty} 2^{k\rho} e^{-knE_o(\rho, \mathbf{q})}$$

$$= \frac{2^{-KE_o(\rho, \mathbf{q})/R}}{1 - 2^{-\{[E_o(\rho, \mathbf{q})/R] - \rho\}}} \qquad \rho < E_o(\rho, \mathbf{q})/R \qquad (5.1.18)$$

Similarly, the ensemble average of the expected number of bit errors caused by an error at node j is obtained by weighting the kth term in (5.1.18) by $(k + 1)$, since an error caused by an incorrect path unmerged for $K + k$ branches can cause no more than $k + 1$ bit errors. Thus

$$\overline{E[n_b(j)]} < \sum_{k=0}^{\infty} (k + 1)\overline{\Pi_k(j)}$$

$$< e^{-KnE_o(\rho, \mathbf{q})} \sum_{k=0}^{\infty} (k + 1) 2^{k\rho} e^{-knE_o(\rho, \mathbf{q})}$$

$$= \frac{2^{-KE_o(\rho, \mathbf{q})/R}}{[1 - 2^{-\{E_o(\rho, \mathbf{q})/R - \rho\}}]^2} \qquad \rho < E_o(\rho, \mathbf{q})/R \qquad (5.1.19)$$

[2] Here we assume there are $M = 2^k$ such paths. Since this is larger than the actual number of incorrect paths, this gives us a further upper bound on the error probability $\Pi_k(j)$.

There remains only the problem of choosing the parameter ρ and the best weight distribution $\mathbf{q}$. Note also that (5.1.18) and (5.1.19) reduce to (5.1.9) and (5.1.10), respectively, for $\rho = 1$, as follows from the definition (5.1.11).

The function $E_o(\rho, \mathbf{q})$ was first studied in Sec. 3.2 and its basic properties, summarized in Lemma 3.2.1, are that it is a positive increasing convex $\cap$ function for positive ρ, approaching 0 as $\rho \to 0$ with slope $I(\mathbf{q})$ (see Fig. 3.1). Thus to minimize the bounds for asymptotically large K, this suggests that we should choose ρ as large as possible consistent with a positive exponent in the braces of the denominator of (5.1.18) and (5.1.19). Such a choice would be, for small [3] $\epsilon > 0$

$$\rho = \frac{E_o(\rho, \mathbf{q})}{R}(1 - \epsilon) \tag{5.1.20}$$

which reduces the bounds (5.1.18) and (5.1.19) to

$$\overline{P_e(j)} < \frac{2^{-KE_c(R, \mathbf{q})/R}}{1 - 2^{-\epsilon E_c(R, \mathbf{q})/R}} \tag{5.1.21a}$$

$$\overline{E[n_b(j)]} < \frac{2^{-KE_c(R, \mathbf{q})/R}}{[1 - 2^{-\epsilon E_c(R, \mathbf{q})/R}]^2} \tag{5.1.21b}$$

where the exponent $E_c(R, \mathbf{q})$ is established by the parametric equations

$$E_c(R, \mathbf{q}) = E_o(\rho, \mathbf{q}) \qquad 0 \le \rho \le 1$$

$$R = \frac{E_o(\rho, \mathbf{q})}{\rho}(1 - \epsilon) \qquad R_o(\mathbf{q})(1 - \epsilon) \le R \le I(\mathbf{q})(1 - \epsilon) \tag{5.1.22}$$

The construction of Fig. 5.2, based on the properties of $E_o(\rho, \mathbf{q})$, establishes that the exponent $E_c(R, \mathbf{q})$ is positive and that the rate R increases continuously from

$$R = (1 - \epsilon)E_o(1, \mathbf{q}) \equiv (1 - \epsilon)R_o(\mathbf{q})$$

to

$$R = (1 - \epsilon) \lim_{\rho \to 0} [E_o(\rho, \mathbf{q})/\rho] = (1 - \epsilon)I(\mathbf{q})$$

as ρ decreases from 1 to 0. Recall also from Sec. 3.2 that

$$\max_{\mathbf{q}} I(\mathbf{q}) = C$$

which is the channel capacity.

[3] Of course ϵ is any positive number. Even though all our results are functions of ϵ, exponents are plotted for the limiting case of $\epsilon = 0$, for which they are maximized. Strictly, as $\epsilon \to 0$, the multiplying factor approaches ∞, although only algebraically (not exponentially) in $1/\epsilon$.

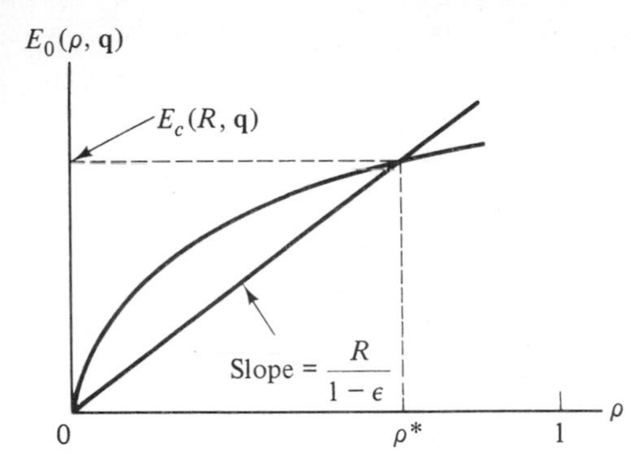

Figure 5.2 Construction for upper bound exponent ($0 < \rho \leq 1$).

Finally we may combine (5.1.9) and (5.1.10) with our present result, with exponents maximized with respect to the weight distribution $\mathbf{q}$. This yields

$$\overline{P_e(j)} < \frac{2^{-KE_c(R)/R}}{1 - 2^{-\epsilon E_c(R)/R}} \tag{5.1.23a}$$

$$\overline{E[n_b(j)]} < \frac{2^{-KE_c(R)/R}}{[1 - 2^{-\epsilon E_c(R)/R}]^2} \tag{5.1.23b}$$

where

$$E_c(R) = R_o = \max_{\mathbf{q}} E_o(1, \mathbf{q}) \qquad \text{for } 0 \leq R \leq R_o(1 - \epsilon) \tag{5.1.24}$$

and

$$E_c(R) = \max_{\mathbf{q}} E_o(\rho, \mathbf{q}) \qquad 0 \leq \rho \leq 1$$

for

$$R = (1 - \epsilon) \max_{\mathbf{q}} [E_o(\rho, \mathbf{q})]/\rho \qquad R_o(1 - \epsilon) \leq R \leq C(1 - \epsilon) \tag{5.1.25}$$

The composite exponent is plotted for a typical memoryless channel in Fig. 5.3. Maximization of $E_o(\rho, \mathbf{q})$ with respect to the weight distribution $\mathbf{q} = \{q(x): x = a_1, a_2, \ldots, a_Q\}$ is performed exactly as in Sec. 3.2 (Theorem 3.2.2). It is clear that, for asymptotically large K, ϵ may be chosen asymptotically small.

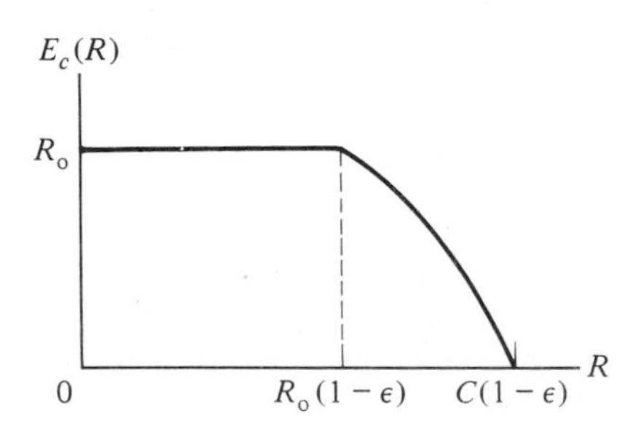

Figure 5.3 $E_c(R)$ for typical memoryless channel.

It remains to generalize this binary trellis (rate $1/n$) coding result to trellises with 2^b branches[4] per node (rate b/n). Such encoders, shown in Fig. 5.1, require effectively b shift registers, each of constraint length K, and the decoder storage and computational complexity grows as $2^{b(K-1)}$. For the present analysis, we need only determine the form of the data sequences for all incorrect paths diverging at node j and remerging with the correct path after an unmerged span of $K + k$ branches, where again, without loss of generality, we may take the correct path to correspond to the all-zeros data sequence. For binary trellises, this was given by (5.1.2). For 2^b-ary trellises, this is generalized to the form

$$\mathbf{u}_j, \mathbf{u}_{j+1}, \mathbf{u}_{j+2}, \ldots, \mathbf{u}_{j+k}, \underbrace{\mathbf{0}, \mathbf{0}, \ldots, \mathbf{0}}_{\leftarrow K-1 \rightarrow} \tag{5.1.26}$$

where all terms are b-dimensional binary vectors representing the b bits input to the encoder register per branch. Now, $\mathbf{u}_j$ and $\mathbf{u}_{j+k}$ can be any of the $2^b - 1$ nonzero b-dimensional binary vectors, since we require that the path diverge from the all-zeros at node j and not remerge before $j + k + K$. And $\mathbf{u}_{j+1}$ through $\mathbf{u}_{j+k-1}$ may each be any b-dimensional binary vector, the only limitation being that no string of $K - 1$ or more consecutive $\mathbf{0}$ vectors may begin before the $(j + k + 1)$st branch, for otherwise remerging with the correct path would occur before node $j + K + k$. Thus there are less than $(2^b - 1)2^{bk}$ possible incorrect paths in the subset $\hat{\mathscr{X}}(j)$ of incorrect paths which diverge at node j and remerge at node $j + K + k$. Hence, all results obtained for rate $1/n$ trellis codes can be generalized to rate b/n by replacing 2^k with $(2^b - 1)2^{bk}$ in expressions (5.1.7), (5.1.9), (4.6.16), (5.1.12), and (5.1.16) through (5.1.19). It suffices to consider only the last two expressions, which represent the most general case. Thus for rate b/n codes

$$\begin{aligned} \overline{P_e(j)} &< \sum_{k=0}^{\infty} \overline{\Pi_k(j)} \\ &< e^{-KnE_o(\rho, \mathbf{q})} \sum_{k=0}^{\infty} [(2^b - 1)2^{bk}]^{\rho} e^{-knE_o(\rho, \mathbf{q})} \\ &< \frac{(2^b - 1)2^{-KbE_o(\rho, \mathbf{q})/R}}{1 - 2^{-b\{[E_o(\rho, \mathbf{q})/R] - \rho\}}} \qquad 0 \le \rho < E_o(\rho, \mathbf{q})/R \le 1 \end{aligned} \tag{5.1.27}$$

where

$$\begin{aligned} R &= r \ln 2 \\ &= (b/n) \ln 2 \qquad \text{nats/channel symbol} \end{aligned} \tag{5.1.28}$$

[4] The mapping function for rate b/n codes is the same as for rate $1/n$ codes—see the description following (5.1.4) and (5.1.9) for uniform and nonuniform weightings. We could even consider trellises with β branches per node, where β is not a power of 2. However, this requires linear encoders with input data in nonbinary form, a very impractical possibility. Also it requires that all linear operations be performed over a finite field of β elements; hence β must be a prime or the power of a prime.

Similarly generalizing (5.1.19) for rate b/n, recognizing that an erroneous branch can cause up to b bit errors, we obtain

$$\overline{E[n_b(j)]} < \sum_{k=0}^{\infty} b(k+1)\,\overline{\Pi_k(j)}$$

$$< e^{-KnE_o(\rho,\mathbf{q})} \sum_{k=0}^{\infty} b(k+1)[(2^b-1)2^{bk}]^{\rho} e^{-knE_o(\rho,\mathbf{q})}$$

$$< \frac{b(2^b-1)2^{-KbE_o(\rho,\mathbf{q})/R}}{(1-2^{-b\{[E_o(\rho,\mathbf{q})/R]-\rho\}})^2} \qquad 0 \le \rho < E_o(\rho,\mathbf{q})/R \le 1 \qquad (5.1.29)$$

Choosing $\rho = 1$ for

$$R \le R_o(1-\epsilon) \qquad (5.1.30a)$$

and

$$\rho = \frac{E_o(\rho,\mathbf{q})}{R}(1-\epsilon) \qquad (5.1.30b)$$

for higher rates, we generalize (5.1.23) and (5.1.24) to rate b/n codes by replacing $E_c(R)$ by $bE_c(R)$ and multiplying both expressions by $2^b - 1$ and the second also by b.

All our results thus far have been for events at a particular node level. However, bit error probability is defined as the expected number of bit errors over the total length of the code, normalized by the number of bits decoded. Thus for an L-branch trellis code of rate b/n, since b bits are decoded per branch

$$P_b = \frac{E[N_b]}{Lb}$$

$$\le \frac{1}{Lb} \sum_{j=1}^{L} E[n_b(j)] \qquad (5.1.31)$$

where N_b is the total number of bit errors in the L-branch code sequence and the inequality follows from the fact that bit error sequences may overlap, as discussed in Sec. 4.4. Consequently, combining (5.1.29), (5.1.30), and (5.1.31) and optimizing with respect to $\mathbf{q}$, we obtain over the entire length of the code

$$\overline{P_b} \le \frac{\overline{LE[n_b(j)]}}{Lb}$$

$$< (2^b-1)\frac{2^{-KbE_c(R)/R}}{[1-2^{-\epsilon bE_c(R)/R}]^2} \qquad \epsilon > 0 \qquad (5.1.32)$$

$$E_c(R) = R_o \qquad 0 \le R \le R_o(1-\epsilon) \qquad (5.1.33)$$

$$\begin{cases} E_c(R) = \max\limits_{\mathbf{q}} E_o(\rho,\mathbf{q}) & 0 \le \rho \le 1 \\ R = (1-\epsilon)\max\limits_{\mathbf{q}} \dfrac{E_o(\rho,\mathbf{q})}{\rho} & R_o(1-\epsilon) \le R \le C(1-\epsilon) \end{cases} \qquad (5.1.34)$$

Since this is an ensemble average over all possible trellis codes of length L branches, we conclude that there must exist at least one code in the ensemble with $P_b \le \overline{P_b}$. Hence we obtain

Theorem 5.1.1: Convolutional channel coding theorem (Viterbi [1967], [1971]) For any discrete-input memoryless channel, there exists a time-varying convolutional code of constraint length K, rate b/n bits per channel symbol, and arbitrary block length, whose bit error probability P_b, resulting from maximum likelihood decoding, is bounded by (5.1.32) through (5.1.34) where ϵ is an arbitrary positive number.

5.2 EXAMPLES: CONVOLUTIONAL CODING EXPONENTS FOR VERY NOISY CHANNELS

As was done in Sec. 3.4 for block codes, we now evaluate the error bound exponents for convolutional codes, for the class of channels for which explicit formulas are most easily obtained. This will provide a direct comparison of the performance of block and convolutional codes. Of course, most of the effort is involved in computing $E_o(\rho)$ and C and the techniques to do this are already available from Sec. 3.4.

For the class of *very noisy channels* defined by (3.4.23), we have that

$$\begin{aligned} E_o(\rho) &= \max_{\mathbf{q}} E_o(\rho, \mathbf{q}) \\ &= \frac{\rho}{1+\rho} C \qquad 0 \le \rho \le 1 \end{aligned} \tag{3.4.31}$$

Substituting this into (5.1.33) and using (5.1.11), we obtain $R_o = C/2$ and hence, for low rates

$$E_c(R) = \frac{C}{2} \qquad 0 \le R \le (1-\epsilon)C/2 \tag{5.2.1a}$$

For higher rates, substituting (3.4.31) into the second parametric equation (5.1.34) and solving for ρ, we obtain

$$\rho = \frac{C(1-\epsilon)}{R} - 1$$

Then substituting this into (3.4.31) and in turn into the first parametric equation (5.1.34), we obtain

$$E_c(R) = C - \frac{R}{1-\epsilon} \qquad (1-\epsilon)C/2 \le R \le (1-\epsilon)C \tag{5.2.1b}$$

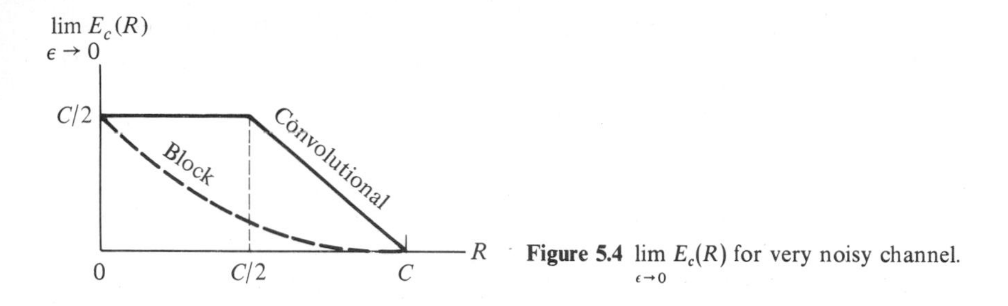

Figure 5.4 $\lim_{\epsilon \to 0} E_c(R)$ for very noisy channel.

Ignoring for the moment the parameter $\epsilon \ll 1$, we plot the composite exponent (5.2.1a) and (5.2.1b) in Fig. 5.4 and compare it with the exponent for block codes on very noisy channels given by (3.4.33). To obtain a meaningful comparison, we must let (for convolutional codes)

$$N_c \equiv Kn = \frac{Kb \ln 2}{R} \tag{5.2.2}$$

For block codes, of course

$$N = \frac{K_B \ln 2}{R} \tag{5.2.3}$$

where K_B is the block length in bits.[5]

With these definitions, the exponents of the bounds on error probability are $N_c E_c(R)$ and $NE(R)$, for convolutional codes and block codes, respectively. We recall from Sec. 4.6 that the relative decoding complexities per bit are

$$\frac{2^{K_B}}{K_B} = \frac{e^{NR}}{K_B} \qquad \text{comparisons/bit} \qquad \text{(block codes)}$$

and, as follows from a direct generalization of previous results to rate b/n convolutional codes

$$\frac{(2^b - 1)(2^{b(K-1)})}{b} < \frac{2^{Kb}}{b} = \frac{e^{N_c R}}{b} \qquad \text{comparisons/bit} \qquad \text{(convolutional codes)}$$

Thus, setting $N = N_c$, we find that, while the exponents diverge considerably, the computational complexity is only slightly greater for convolutional codes. Clearly, by making N_c slightly smaller than N, we may achieve equal complexity, and still maintain a convolutional exponent which is much greater than the block exponent.

[5] Note that this compares encoders with the same "memory" since a convolutional code symbol is determined by Kb information bits and a block code symbol is determined by K_B information bits. Decoder complexity grows roughly exponentially with this memory for both block and convolutional codes.

Also noteworthy is the fact that the exponent of (5.2.1) for very noisy channels is identical to the exponent of (4.6.24) for convolutional orthogonal codes on the AWGN channel, provided we make the obvious substitution

$$\frac{C \text{ nats/symbol}}{R \text{ nats/symbol}} = \frac{C_T \text{ nats/s}}{R_T \text{ nats/s}} \tag{5.2.4}$$

The explanation is the same as that in Sec. 3.4 for block codes.

5.3 EXPURGATED UPPER BOUND FOR BINARY-INPUT, OUTPUT-SYMMETRIC CHANNELS

We have thus demonstrated that the ensemble average convolutional exponent is considerably greater then the corresponding block exponent everywhere except for $R = C$ and $R = 0$. In the former case, both exponents, of course, become zero; while at zero rate

$$E(0) = E_c(0) = R_0 = E_o(1)$$

But, for block codes, we found in Chap. 3, Sec. 3.3 that, by expurgating the ensemble, we could obtain the much tighter upper-bound exponent[6]

$$E_{ex}(0) = \max_{\mathbf{q}} \left[-\sum_x \sum_{x'} q(x)q(x') \ln \sum_y \sqrt{p(y \mid x)p(y \mid x')} \right] \tag{3.3.27}$$

For binary-input channels, this reduces in fact to

$$E_{ex}(0) = -\tfrac{1}{2} \ln Z > \ln 2 - \ln (1 + Z) = E_o(1) \tag{3.3.31}$$

where

$$Z = \sum_y \sqrt{p_0(y)p_1(y)}$$

Thus the convolutional coding exponents, obtained thus far, are weaker than the block exponents at low rates. As already discussed in Sec. 3.10, it is not possible to expurgate code vectors from a linear code without destroying its linearity. With convolutional codes, not only would expurgation destroy linearity, but it would equally damage the essential topological structure of the trellis. However, on the class of binary-input, output-symmetric channels, we found in Sec. 2.9 that for a linear code the error probability is always the same no matter which code vector is transmitted. Hence, for this class of channels, we need not expurgate, since the bound on the bit error probability for any transmitted path is a bound for the entire code (independent of the path transmitted).

[6] For physical channels, this exponent is finite, but for degenerate channels this exponent can be infinite.

The task then is to obtain a tighter bound on P_b at low rates. Consider again node j and the probability that a bit error occurs at this node. A decoding bit error can occur at node j only if, for some k and some i, $0 \le i \le k$, an error event of length $K + k$ began diverging at node $j - i$; that is, if the bit in question lies within an unmerged span corresponding to an error event. Since the event of a bit error is the union of such error events,[7] we have the union bound on the bit error probability at node j

$$P_b(j) \le \sum_{k=0}^{\infty} \sum_{i=0}^{k} \Pi_k(j-i) \tag{5.3.1}$$

where we recall that $\Pi_k(j-i)$ is the probability of an error event caused by one of up to 2^{bk} incorrect paths unmerged from node $j - i$ to node $j - i + k + K$. For any parameter $0 \le s \le 1$, we have (inequality g in App. 3A)

$$P_b^s(j) \le \sum_{k=0}^{\infty} \sum_{i=0}^{k} \Pi_k^s(j-i) \tag{5.3.2}$$

The ensemble average of $P_b^s(j)$ is then

$$\overline{P_b^s(j)} \le \sum_{k=0}^{\infty} \sum_{i=0}^{k} \overline{\Pi_k^s(j-i)} \tag{5.3.3}$$

For low rates, we may use the union-bound argument, which leads to (5.1.10), rather than the Gallager bound, which leads to (5.1.19), to bound $\overline{\pi_k^s(j-i)}$. Thus for a rate b/n code

$$\overline{\Pi_k^s(j-i)} < (2^b - 1)2^{kb}[\Pr\{\Delta M(\mathbf{x}'_{j-i}, \mathbf{x}_{j-i}) \ge 0\}]^s \tag{5.3.4}$$

where $\mathbf{x}_{j-i}$ and $\mathbf{x}'_{j-i}$ are the correct path and an incorrect path unmerged for $K + k$ branches, respectively. Then, by the same steps which led to (5.1.5)

$$\begin{aligned}\overline{\Pi_k^s(j-i)} &< (2^b - 1)2^{kb} \sum_{\mathbf{x}} \sum_{\mathbf{x}'} q_N(\mathbf{x})q_N(\mathbf{x}') \left[\sum_{\mathbf{y}} \sqrt{p_N(\mathbf{y}\,|\,\mathbf{x})p_N(\mathbf{y}\,|\,\mathbf{x}')}\right]^s \\ &= (2^b - 1)2^{kb} \left\{\sum_{x} \sum_{x'} q(x)q(x') \left[\sum_{y} \sqrt{p(y\,|\,x)p(y\,|\,x')}\right]^s\right\}^N \qquad 0 < s \le 1\end{aligned} \tag{5.3.5}$$

where $N = n(K + k)$. Finally, letting $\rho = 1/s$, we obtain

$$\overline{\Pi_k^{1/\rho}(j-i)} < (2^b - 1)2^{kb} e^{-n(K+k)E_x(\rho,\, \mathbf{q})/\rho} \qquad 1 \le \rho < \infty \tag{5.3.6}$$

where, as was first defined in Sec. 3.3,

$$E_x(\rho, \mathbf{q}) = -\rho \ln \sum_{x} \sum_{x'} q(x)q(x') \left[\sum_{y} \sqrt{p(y\,|\,x)p(y\,|\,x')}\right]^{1/\rho} \tag{3.3.14}$$

[7] The argument used here differs from that used previously for bit error probability bounds in this and the last chapter, which was based on the expected number of bit errors per error event. While it leads to the same result for the ensemble average bound of Theorem 5.1.1, it leads here to a tighter form of Theorem 5.3.1 than was previously obtained based on the earlier argument.

Thus substituting (5.3.6) into (5.3.3), we have

$$\overline{P_b^{1/\rho}} \leq \sum_{k=0}^{\infty} \sum_{i=0}^{k} (2^b - 1)2^{kb} e^{-n(K+k)E_x(\rho, \mathbf{q})/\rho}$$

$$= \sum_{k=0}^{\infty} (k+1)(2^b - 1)2^{kb} e^{-n(K+k)E_x(\rho, \mathbf{q})/\rho}$$

$$= \frac{(2^b - 1)2^{-KbE_x(\rho, \mathbf{q})/(\rho R)}}{(1 - 2^{-b[E_x(\rho, \mathbf{q})/(\rho R) - 1]})^2} \qquad 1 \leq \rho < \infty \tag{5.3.7}$$

where $R = (b/n) \ln 2$ nats per channel symbol.

Since for binary-input, output-symmetric channels, P_b is the same for all paths of a given code, (5.3.7) can be regarded as a bound over the ensemble of convolutional codes, or equivalently, over the ensemble of generator matrices (4.1.1). Thus from (5.3.7) we have that for at least one code in the ensemble $P_b^{1/\rho} \leq \overline{P_b^{1/\rho}}$; and hence for this code

$$P_b \leq (\overline{P_b^{1/\rho}})^\rho$$

$$\leq \left[\frac{(2^b - 1)}{(1 - 2^{-b[E_x(\rho, \mathbf{q})/(\rho R) - 1]})^2}\right]^\rho 2^{-KbE_x(\rho, \mathbf{q})/R} \tag{5.3.8}$$

We now choose ρ such that

$$(1 + \epsilon)\rho = \frac{E_x(\rho, \mathbf{q})}{R} \qquad \epsilon > 0 \tag{5.3.9}$$

Finally, maximizing over $\mathbf{q}$, we obtain

Theorem 5.3.1 (Viterbi and Odenwalder [1969]) For binary-input, output-symmetric channels, there exists a time-varying convolutional code of constraint length K and rate b/n bits per symbol for which the bit error probability with maximum likelihood decoding satisfies

$$P_b < \left[\frac{2^b - 1}{(1 - 2^{-b\epsilon})^2}\right]^{E_{\text{cex}}(R)/[R(1+\epsilon)]} 2^{-KbE_{\text{cex}}(R)/R} \tag{5.3.10}$$

where

$$E_{\text{cex}}(R) = \max_{\mathbf{q}} E_x(\rho, \mathbf{q}) \qquad 1 \leq \rho < \infty$$

$$R = \max_{\mathbf{q}} \frac{E_x(\rho, \mathbf{q})}{\rho(1 + \epsilon)} \qquad 0 < R \leq \frac{R_o}{1 + \epsilon} \tag{5.3.11}$$

$$\epsilon > 0$$

where we have used the fact that

$$\max_{\mathbf{q}} E_x(1, \mathbf{q}) = \max_{\mathbf{q}} E_o(1, \mathbf{q}) = R_o$$

Actually, we can obtain the exponent explicitly in terms of the rate, since, for binary-input, output-symmetric channels, we found in Sec. 3.3 that

$$\max_{\mathbf{q}} E_x(\rho, \mathbf{q}) = -\rho \ln \left(\frac{1 + Z^{1/\rho}}{2} \right) \tag{3.3.29}$$

where

$$Z = \sum_y \sqrt{p_0(y)p_1(y)}$$

Thus combining (5.3.11) and (3.3.29), we find

$$e^{-R(1+\epsilon)} = \frac{1 + Z^{1/\rho}}{2}$$

and, consequently, we have that

$$\rho = \frac{\ln Z}{\ln \left[2e^{-R(1+\epsilon)} - 1\right]} \tag{5.3.12}$$

Dividing the first equation of (5.3.11) by the second, and using (5.3.12), we obtain

Corollary 5.3.1 The exponent of (5.3.11) can alternatively be expressed as

$$\frac{E_{cex}(R)}{R} = \frac{(1 + \epsilon) \ln Z}{\ln \left[2e^{-R(1+\epsilon)} - 1\right]} \qquad 0 < R \le R_o/(1 + \epsilon) \tag{5.3.13}$$

Note, finally, from this that

$$\lim_{R \to 0} E_{cex}(R) = -\frac{1}{2} \ln Z \tag{5.3.14}$$

which is precisely the same as the zero-rate exponent (3.3.31) for block codes. The exponent (5.3.13) is plotted in Fig. 5.5 and compared with the corresponding exponent for block codes.

5.4 LOWER BOUND ON ERROR PROBABILITY

For a rate b/n trellis code, let $P_b(j)$ be the probability that any of the b information bits associated with node j are decoded incorrectly. Certainly the average bit error probability, P_b, is lower-bounded by the smallest such node bit error probability. Thus

$$P_b \ge \min_j P_b(j) \tag{5.4.1}$$

Assuming that path lengths are arbitrarily long ($L \to \infty$), we now proceed to lower-bound $P_b(j)$. First note that a decoding error at node j can be caused by many possible paths that diverge from the correct path at node j or earlier. Recall that $\Pi_k(j)$ is the probability that a path diverging from the correct path at node j and remerging at node $j + K + k$ causes an error event. Since this is only one of many possible events that can cause a decoding error at node j, we have

$$P_b(j) \geq \Pi_k(j)$$

for any k. Maximizing over k we get

$$P_b(j) \geq \max_k \Pi_k(j) \tag{5.4.2}$$

For arbitrary k, $\Pi_k(j)$ is the probability of a block decoding error with no more than 2^{bk} code vectors each of block length $(K + k)n$ channel symbols. Thus, this can be regarded as a highly constrained block code of length $N = (K + k)n$ and rate $\tilde{R}_k = (bk \ln 2)/[n(K + k)]$ nats per channel symbol.[8] Hence, using (3.6.45) and (3.6.46), we have

$$\begin{aligned} \Pi_k(j) &> e^{-N[E_{sp}(\tilde{R}_k) + o(N)]} \\ &= \exp\left\{-\frac{(K + k)b \ln 2}{R}[E_{sp}(R, \lambda) + o(K)]\right\} \qquad \lambda = k/K \end{aligned} \tag{5.4.3}$$

where
$$E_{sp}(R, \lambda) = E_o(\rho) - \rho E_o'(\rho) \tag{5.4.4a}$$

$$R = \frac{1 + \lambda}{\lambda}\tilde{R}_k = \frac{1 + \lambda}{\lambda}E_o'(\rho) \tag{5.4.4b}$$

with

$$E_o(\rho) = \max_{\mathbf{q}} E_o(\rho, \mathbf{q}) \tag{5.4.5}$$

Thus combining (5.4.1) through (5.4.5), we obtain

$$\begin{aligned} P_b(j) &\geq \max_{\lambda \geq 0} 2^{-Kb[(1+\lambda)E_{sp}(R, \lambda) + o(K)]/R} \\ &= 2^{-Kb \min_{\lambda \geq 0} [(1+\lambda)E_{sp}(R, \lambda) + o(K)]/R} \end{aligned} \tag{5.4.6}$$

where we assume K sufficiently large that λ can be any rational number; any inaccuracy resulting from this is compensated for by the $o(K)$ term. To minimize the exponent, we must take the lower envelope with respect to λ of $(1 + \lambda)E_{sp}(R, \lambda)$, which is defined parametrically by (5.4.4). We show now that this function is convex $\cup$, and thus we can obtain a minimum by setting the derivative equal to zero. For, from (5.4.4*a*), we have

$$\begin{aligned} \frac{d(1 + \lambda)E_{sp}(R, \lambda)}{d\lambda} &= E_o(\rho) - \rho E_o'(\rho) + (1 + \lambda)[-\rho E_o''(\rho)]\frac{d\rho}{d\lambda} \\ &= E_o(\rho) - \rho E_o'(\rho) - \frac{\rho R}{1 + \lambda} \end{aligned} \tag{5.4.7}$$

[8] Since the actual number of codewords is slightly less than 2^{bk}, the actual rate is slightly less than this. But for large K these differences are negligible and will be incorporated into $o(K)$ terms in our bound.

since from (5.4.4*b*) we have

$$E_o''(\rho)\frac{d\rho}{d\lambda} = \frac{R}{(1+\lambda)^2} \tag{5.4.8}$$

Differentiating (5.4.7) and using (5.4.8) and (3.2.5), we have

$$\frac{d^2[(1+\lambda)E_{sp}(R,\lambda)]}{d\lambda^2} = -\frac{R^2}{(1+\lambda)^3 E_o''(\rho)} \geq 0 \tag{5.4.9}$$

Thus we may set (5.4.7) equal to zero and obtain the absolute minimum as a function of λ. We obtain

$$\lambda = \frac{\rho R}{E_o(\rho) - \rho E_o'(\rho)} - 1 \tag{5.4.10}$$

and combining (5.4.10) with (5.4.4*b*) we have

$$R = \frac{E_o(\rho)}{\rho} \tag{5.4.11}$$

while (5.4.4*a*), (5.4.10), and (5.4.11) yield

$$\min_{\lambda \geq 0} (1+\lambda)E_{sp}(R,\lambda) = \rho R = E_o(\rho) \tag{5.4.12}$$

Finally, combining (5.4.6), (5.4.11), and (5.4.12), and recognizing that the arguments used assume no particular decoding algorithm, we have

Theorem 5.4.1: Convolutional coding lower bound (Viterbi [1967*a*]) The probability of bit error, for any convolutional code and any decoding algorithm, is lower-bounded by

$$P_b \geq 2^{-Kb[E_{csp}(R)+o(K)]/R} \tag{5.4.13}$$

where

$$\begin{aligned} E_{csp}(R) &= E_o(\rho) \qquad 0 < \rho < \infty \\ R &= \frac{E_o(\rho)}{\rho} \qquad 0 < R < C \end{aligned} \tag{5.4.14}$$

Thus the convolutional lower-bound exponent agrees with the upper-bound (5.1.34) for the range $R_o \leq R < C$ (ignoring the ϵ's), but diverges at lower rates. This parallels exactly the situation for block codes, except that the bounds for block codes diverge at the lower rate $E_o'(1) < E_o(1) = R_0$. We note also that at zero rate we have

$$E_{csp}(0) = \lim_{\rho\to\infty} E_o(\rho) = \lim_{\rho\to\infty} [E_o(\rho) - \rho E_o'(\rho)] = E_{sp}(0) \tag{5.4.15}$$

since either the monotonic increasing function $E_o(\rho)$ is bounded, in which case $\lim_{\rho \to \infty} \rho E_o'(\rho) = 0$, or it is unbounded, in which case both exponents are infinite at zero rate. Thus the convolutional and block code lower-bound exponents are equal at zero rate, and neither bound is tight.

To improve the convolutional lower-bound exponent at low rates, we utilize the zero-rate lower bound (3.7.19) instead of the sphere-packing bound. Then, in place of (5.4.3), we have

$$\begin{aligned} \Pi_k(j) &> e^{-N[E_{ex}(0) + o(N)]} \\ &= e^{-(K+k)n[E_{ex}(0) + o(K)]} \end{aligned} \tag{5.4.16}$$

Although we have used the zero-rate exponent, this result is valid for any rate, since the exponent must decrease monotonically with R and $\tilde{R}_k$. Hence (5.4.6) becomes

$$\begin{aligned} P_b(j) &\geq \max_k e^{-(K+k)n[E_{ex}(0) + o(K)]} \\ &= e^{-Kn[E_{ex}(0) + o(K)]} \\ &= 2^{-Kb[E_{ex}(0) + o(K)]/R} \end{aligned} \tag{5.4.17}$$

where $E_{ex}(0)$ is given by (3.3.27) (see also Sec. 5.3). We may state this result as

Corollary 5.4.1 : Low-rate lower bound For $0 \leq R < R_1 \leq R_0$, a tighter lower bound on bit error probability than that in Theorem 5.4.1 is

$$P_b > 2^{-Kb[E_{ex}(0) + o(K)]/R} \tag{5.4.18}$$

where R_1 is the rate at which $E_{csp}(R_1) = E_{ex}(0)$.

The exponent of this bound is sketched for a typical binary-input, output-symmetric channel in Fig. 5.5, where it is compared with the low-rate upper bound, the latter holding only for this class of channels. We note also that we could have used the low-rate lower bound of Sec. 3.8 (see Viterbi [1967]), but this would have yielded exactly the same results as (5.4.17).

We comment finally on the possibility of obtaining bounds which are asymptotically tight for all rates. The arguments of Sec. 3.9 for block codes apply equally for convolutional codes. If the Gilbert bound is tight [conjecture (3.9.4)], then the resulting lower bound (3.9.5) can be used in place of (5.4.4), yielding then a low-rate lower bound for binary-input, output-symmetric channels, which agrees everywhere with the upper bound of (5.3.13). Thus all aspects of block code exponents are paralleled in convolutional code exponents, which are, however, always significantly greater in the entire range $0 < R < C$.

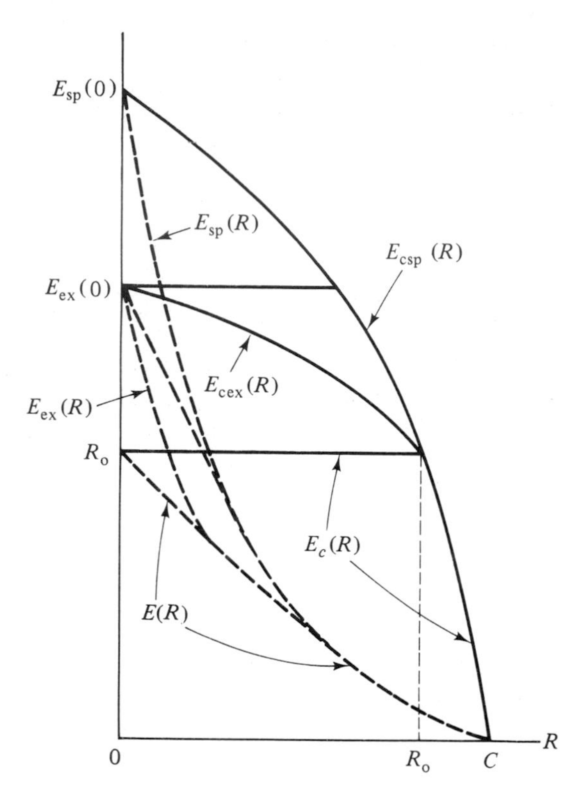

Figure 5.5 Expurgated ensemble and sphere-packing bounds for convolutional and block codes on binary-input, output-symmetric channel.

5.5 CRITICAL LENGTHS OF ERROR EVENTS*

The maximization carried out in connection with the lower bound of the preceding section [(5.4.2) and (5.4.6)] suggests that certain lengths of errors (unmerged paths) are more likely than others. Based on the lower bound, it appears that the most likely $\lambda \approx k/K$ is given by (5.4.10). Actually, to make this result precise, we must use a combination of upper and lower bounds. First of all, we found in Sec. 5.1 that the ensemble average probability of an error at node j caused by an unmerged path of length $K + k$ is bounded by (5.1.17) for rate $1/n$ codes, while for rate b/n this generalizes [see (5.1.27)] to

$$\overline{\Pi_k}(j) < (2^b - 1)(2^{bk})^{\rho} 2^{-(K+k)bE_o(\rho,\,\mathbf{q})/R} \qquad 0 \le \rho \le 1 \tag{5.5.1}$$

We shall call this an error event of length bk, since a run of errors will occur within k branches of b bits each, with no two errors separated by $K - 1$ or more

* May be omitted without loss of continuity.

branches,[9] each with b correct bits. Rewriting (5.5.1) in terms of

$$N = (K + k)n = (K + k)b\left(\frac{\ln 2}{R}\right)$$

and

$$\tilde{R}_k = \frac{Rk}{K + k} = R\frac{\lambda}{1 + \lambda}$$

we have

$$\overline{\Pi_k(j)} < (2^b - 1)\, e^{-N[E_o(\rho,\, \mathbf{q}) - \rho \tilde{R}_k]} \qquad 0 \le \rho \le 1 \tag{5.5.2}$$

Since the exponent is identical to that of the block coding bound (3.1.17), minimizing with respect to ρ and $\mathbf{q}$, we obtain the equivalent of (3.2.8), namely

$$\begin{aligned}\overline{\Pi_k(j)} &< (2^b - 1)\, e^{-NE(R,\, \lambda)} \\ &= (2^b - 1)2^{-Kb(1+\lambda)\, E(R,\, \lambda)/R}\end{aligned} \tag{5.5.3}$$

where

$$\lambda = k/K$$

$$E(R, \lambda) = E_o(\rho) - \rho E_o'(\rho) \qquad 0 \le \rho \le 1 \tag{5.5.4a}$$

$$\frac{\lambda R}{1 + \lambda} = \tilde{R}_k = E_o'(\rho) \qquad E_o'(1) \le \tilde{R}_k < C \tag{5.5.4b}$$

and

$$E_o(\rho) = \max_{\mathbf{q}} E_o(\rho, \mathbf{q})$$

Even though this is only a bound, we may expect to obtain an indication of the most likely run length of errors by maximizing (5.5.3) with respect to k (or, equivalently, λ). Since, other than for asymptotically unimportant terms, (5.5.3) is the same as the right side of (5.4.6), clearly the maximization (or minimization of the negative exponent) proceeds identically, and we obtain again (5.4.7) through (5.4.11). Let us call the length $k = \lambda K$ which maximizes (5.5.3) the *critical length*, k_{crit}. Thus from (5.4.10) and (5.4.11), we have

$$\lambda_{\text{crit}} \equiv \frac{k_{\text{crit}}}{K} = \frac{E_o(\rho)}{E_o(\rho) - \rho E_o'(\rho)} - 1 = \frac{\rho E_o'(\rho)}{E_o(\rho) - \rho E_o'(\rho)} \qquad 0 \le \rho \le 1 \tag{5.5.5}$$

[9] Note that this does not quite mean that $b(K - 1)$ correct bits cannot occur between two incorrect bits. For example, if $b = 2$ and the second bit of the first unmerged branch and the first bit of the $(K - 1)$st unmerged branch are correct (with the other bit on both these branches being incorrect), the number of correct bits between successive incorrect bits may be as large as $2(K - 2) + 2 = b(K - 1)$ in this case.

We will next show that, for large K, the run length of errors tends to concentrate around k_{crit}. More precisely, we prove

Theorem 5.5.1: Error run lengths (Forney [1972*b*], [1974]) Over the ensemble of time-varying convolutional codes, for any $\epsilon > 0$, the average fraction of error events of run length k outside the interval $k_{\text{crit}} - \epsilon K \le k \le k_{\text{crit}} + \epsilon K$ approaches 0 as $K \to \infty$, where

$$\frac{k_{\text{crit}}}{K} = \begin{cases} \dfrac{\rho E_o'(\rho)}{E_o(\rho) - \rho E_o'(\rho)} & 0 < \rho < 1,\ R_o < R < C \\ 0 & 0 \le R < R_o \end{cases} \tag{5.5.6}$$

Proof (5.4.13) is a lower bound on event error probability for the best code, but in the high-rate region, $R_o < R < C$, it agrees asymptotically with the ensemble average upper bound. Hence, in this region, this is an asymptotically exact expression for the ensemble average event error probability, $\overline{P}_e$. For lower rates, we have from (5.1.9) that

$$\overline{P}_e < 2^{-Kb[R_o + o(K)]/R} \qquad 0 < R < R_0 \tag{5.5.7}$$

But, over the same ensemble, this is also a lower bound to the average event error probability since P_e is lower-bounded by the average probability of pairwise errors for one incorrect path unmerged for the minimum length, which is just K branches. Averaged over the ensemble, this lower bound is the same as (5.1.5) except for a negligible $o(K)$ term, since that result is based on the Bhattacharyya bound (5.1.3), which can be shown to be asymptotically tight by the methods of Sec. 3.5. Hence

$$\overline{P}_e = \begin{cases} 2^{-Kb[R_o + o(K)]/R} & 0 < R < R_0 \\ 2^{-Kb[E_o(\rho^*) + o(K)]/R} & R_0 < R = E_o(\rho^*)/\rho^* < C \end{cases} \tag{5.5.8}$$

Combining (5.5.1) and (5.5.8), we obtain for the high-rate region

$$\begin{aligned} \frac{\Pr\{k \ge \lambda K\}}{\overline{P}_e} &\le \frac{\sum_{k=\lambda K}^{\infty} \overline{\Pi}_k(j)}{2^{-Kb[E_o(\rho^*) + o(K)]/R}} \\ &< \frac{(2^b - 1)2^{-KbE_o(\rho)/R} \sum_{k=\lambda K}^{\infty} (2^{-b[E_o(\rho)/R - \rho]})^k}{2^{-Kb[E_o(\rho^*) + o(K)]/R}} \\ &= \left(\frac{2^b - 1}{1 - 2^{-b[E_o(\rho)/R - \rho]}}\right) \\ &\quad \times 2^{-Kb\{[E_o(\rho) - E_o(\rho^*)]/R + \lambda[E_o(\rho)/R - \rho] + o(K)\}} \end{aligned} \tag{5.5.9}$$

where, from (5.5.8), we see that ρ^* satisfies

$$R = \frac{E_o(\rho^*)}{\rho^*} \tag{5.5.10}$$

and where ρ must satisfy the condition

$$\frac{E_o(\rho)}{R} - \rho > 0 \tag{5.5.11}$$

The exponent coefficient in (5.5.9) can be made positive for λ large enough. We next examine the critical value of λ where the exponent is zero in the limit as $\rho \to \rho^*$. The critical value of λ satisfies

$$\frac{E_o(\rho) - E_o(\rho^*)}{R} + \lambda\left[\frac{E_o(\rho)}{R} - \rho\right] = 0 \tag{5.5.12}$$

or

$$\lambda = \frac{E_o(\rho) - E_o(\rho^*)}{\rho R - E_o(\rho)} \tag{5.5.13}$$

Using (5.5.10), we have

$$\begin{aligned} \lambda &= \frac{\rho^*[E_o(\rho) - E_o(\rho^*)]}{\rho E_o(\rho^*) - \rho^* E_o(\rho)} \\ &= \frac{\rho^*[E_o(\rho) - E_o(\rho^*)]/(\rho - \rho^*)}{E_o(\rho) - \rho[E_o(\rho) - E_o(\rho^*)]/(\rho - \rho^*)} \end{aligned} \tag{5.5.14}$$

and

$$\begin{aligned} \lambda_{\text{crit}} &= \lim_{\rho \to \rho^*} \frac{\rho^*[E_o(\rho) - E_o(\rho^*)]/(\rho - \rho^*)}{E_o(\rho) - \rho[E_o(\rho) - E_o(\rho^*)]/(\rho - \rho^*)} \\ &= \frac{\rho^* E_o'(\rho^*)}{E_o(\rho^*) - \rho^* E_o'(\rho^*)} \end{aligned} \tag{5.5.15}$$

which is exactly (5.5.5). Hence by choosing $\lambda = \lambda_{\text{crit}} + \epsilon$, we have

$$\lim_{K \to \infty} \frac{\overline{\Pr\{k \geq k_{\text{crit}} + \epsilon K\}}}{\overline{P}_e} = 0 \tag{5.5.16}$$

Noting that k_{crit} maximizes the bound on $\overline{\Pi_k(j)}$, we can similarly show that

$$\lim_{K \to \infty} \frac{\overline{\Pr\{k \leq k_{\text{crit}} - \epsilon K\}}}{\overline{P}_e} = 0 \tag{5.5.17}$$

which completes the proof in the high-rate region.

In the low-rate region, we have from (5.5.1) with $\rho = 1$ and from (5.5.8)

$$\frac{\overline{\Pr\{k \geq \epsilon K\}}}{\overline{P_e}} \leq \frac{(2^b - 1)2^{-KbR_o/R} \sum_{k=\epsilon K}^{\infty} (2^{-b[R_o/R - 1]})^k}{2^{-Kb[R_o + o(K)]/R}}$$

$$= \left(\frac{2^b - 1}{1 - 2^{-b(R_o/R - 1)}}\right) 2^{-Kb[\epsilon(R_o/R - 1) + o(K)]} \tag{5.5.18}$$

Hence also

$$\lim_{K \to \infty} \frac{\overline{\Pr\{k \geq \epsilon K\}}}{\overline{P_e}} = 0 \qquad 0 < R < R_0 \tag{5.5.19}$$

and we have shown that the fraction of error events with lengths which deviate from k_{crit} of (5.5.6) by ϵK approaches zero as $K \to \infty$ for any $\epsilon > 0$. This proves the theorem.

Figure 5.6 shows the ratio $\lambda_{\text{crit}} = k_{\text{crit}}/K$ as a function of R for a typical memoryless channel. For the class of very noisy channels (see Sec. 5.2), we can, in fact, obtain an exact expression, since in this case $E_o(\rho) = \rho C/(1 + \rho)$ and $\rho = (C/R) - 1$ for $C/2 < R < C$, so that

$$\frac{k_{\text{crit}}}{K} \approx \begin{cases} 0 & 0 \leq R < C/2 \\ \dfrac{1}{(C/R) - 1} & C/2 < R < C \end{cases} \tag{5.5.20}$$

Thus, for asymptotically large constraint lengths, the "most likely" error length is very small for $R < R_0$, increases stepwise at R_0, and grows without bound as $R \to C$. For very noisy channels, the step increase at $R_0 = C/2$ is equal to one constraint length.

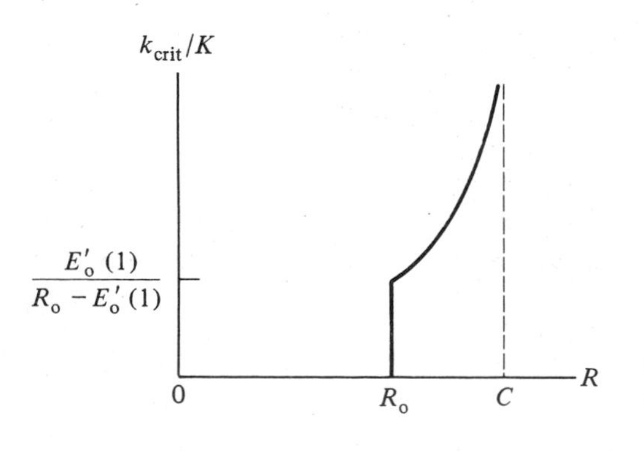

Figure 5.6 Normalized critical length of error runs.

5.6 PATH MEMORY TRUNCATION AND INITIAL SYNCHRONIZATION ERRORS

In Sec. 4.7, we indicated that practical storage constraints require limiting the path memory for each state to a finite length, usually a few constraint lengths. One way to truncate memory at t branches is to make a maximum likelihood decision among all paths which are not merged t branches back. It easily follows that a *truncation* error can occur only if an incorrect path which diverges from the correct path at the jth node, and remains *unmerged* from it for t branches, has higher metric than the correct path after t branches. For, if the paths merged before $t + 1$ branches, the path with higher likelihood would survive, whether or not truncation were employed. Thus, consider the set $\mathscr{X}(j; t)$ of paths which diverge from the correct path at node j and remain unmerged for exactly t branches. Now there are no more than 2^{bt} such paths. Thus, by exactly the same argument used in Sec. 5.1, analogous[10] to (5.1.17) but for $b \geq 1$, we find that the ensemble average probability that an incorrect path has higher metric than the correct path after t unmerged branches is bounded by

$$\overline{P_t(j)} < 2^{bt\rho} e^{-tnE_o(\rho, \mathbf{q})} = 2^{-bt[E_o(\rho, \mathbf{q}) - \rho R]/R} \qquad 0 < \rho \leq 1 \tag{5.6.1}$$

Thus, maximizing with respect to ρ and $\mathbf{q}$, we obtain the usual ensemble error upper bound for block codes of block length $b(\ln 2)t/R$.

$$\overline{P}_t < 2^{-bt\,E(R)/R} \tag{5.6.2}$$

where

$$E(R) = R_0 - R \qquad 0 \leq R < E'_o(1) \tag{5.6.3}$$

and for the high-rate region

$$\begin{aligned} E(R) &= E_o(\rho) - \rho E'_o(\rho) \qquad && 0 < \rho \leq 1 \\ R &= E'_o(\rho) && E'_o(1) \leq R < C \end{aligned} \tag{5.6.4}$$

Comparing (5.6.2) with (5.1.32) we may conclude that *truncation errors will not significantly (exponentially) affect the overall error probability* if the truncation length t is such that

$$tE(R) \geq KE_c(R) \tag{5.6.5}$$

where $E(R)$ of (5.6.3) and (5.6.4) is the block coding exponent, and $E_c(R)$ is the convolutional coding exponent of (5.1.33) and (5.1.34).

[10] This is just the block coding error bound for a code of nt symbols and 2^{bt} codewords.

For very noisy channels, condition (5.6.5) reduces to

$$t/K \geq \begin{cases} \dfrac{1}{1-2R/C} & 0 \leq R < C/4 \\ \dfrac{1}{2(1-\sqrt{R/C})^2} & C/4 \leq R \leq C/2 \\ \dfrac{1+\sqrt{R/C}}{1-\sqrt{R/C}} & C/2 < R < C \end{cases} \tag{5.6.6}$$

Note that, at $R = C/2 = R_0$, this indicates that the truncation length for very noisy channels should be $t \geq K/(\sqrt{2}-1)^2 \approx 5.8K$. In practice, truncation lengths of 4 to 5 constraint lengths have been found sufficient to ensure minor to negligible degradation.

Another problem arising in a practical decoder is that of *initial synchronization* at any node other than the initial node. As we indicated in Sec. 4.7, synchronization eventually occurs automatically once the initial symbol of each branch has been determined (which we assume here has already occurred). However, during the early stages of synchronization, many errors may occur. The situation in starting in midstream is that no initial state metrics are known. Thus we may take them all to be zero. In decoding in the usual way, we may regard as an *initial synchronization error*, any error which is caused by a path which is initially unmerged with the correct path, for an error caused by any path initially merged would have occurred anyway. Now s branches after decoding begins (in midstream with all metrics set to zero at the outset), there is a set of at most 2^{bs} initially unmerged paths, which are merging for the first time with the correct path. Clearly, this set is the dual (and the mirror image) of the set $\mathscr{X}(j;\, t)$ considered above in connection with truncation errors. Thus the probability of initial synchronization error decreases exponentially with s, the number of branches after initiation of decoding. In fact, the ensemble average upper bound on initial synchronization error is the same as (5.6.2) with t replaced by s. Thus after s branches, where

$$sE(R) \geq KE_c(R) \tag{5.6.7}$$

the effects of initial synchronization on error probability become insignificant. In practice, the first s branches ($s \approx 5K$) are usually discarded as unreliable, when the decoder is started in midstream.

5.7 ERROR BOUNDS FOR SYSTEMATIC CONVOLUTIONAL CODES

In Sec. 2.10, we showed that every linear block code is equivalent in performance to a systematic linear block code, and in Sec. 3.10 we showed that the best linear code, and hence the best systematic linear block code, performs as well asymptotically as the best block code with the same parameters. That this is not the case for systematic convolutional codes was intimated in Sec. 4.5 where we found that, in general, the best systematic codes have smaller free distance than the best nonsystematic codes.

We now proceed to obtain a more precise measure of the performance loss of systematic convolutional codes by deriving upper and lower bounds. We recall from Sec. 4.5 that a systematic rate b/n convolutional code is one in which, for each branch, the b data symbols[11] are transmitted uncoded, followed by $n - b$ parity symbols, which are generated just as for nonsystematic codes and consequently depend on the last Kb data symbols. The systematic constraint affects primarily the form of the code paths during remerging, for any incorrect path remerges with the correct path only when $(K - 1)b$ consecutive data symbols are identical to those of the correct path. But when this occurs, exactly this many of its code symbols are identical to the code symbols of the correct path (the first b symbols of each of the $K - 1$ branches just before remerging). Hence, the *effective length* of the unmerged code paths is reduced by $(K - 1)b$ code symbols, since identical code symbols are useless in discriminating between code paths.

We first determine the effect of this property on the upper bound of Sec. 5.1. The bound (5.1.27) applies in the same way, but now the effective length of incorrect code paths unmerged for $(K + k)$ branches is only

$$N' = (K + k)n - b(K - 1) = K(n - b) + kn + b \qquad (5.7.1)$$

rather than $(K + k)n$, for the kth term of the summation. Note, however, that over the first $(k + 1)$ branches all possible data symbols are used; hence the ensemble is not curtailed. Another viewpoint is that the kth term of (5.1.27) is an ensemble average upper bound for a block code of $2^{b(k+1)}$ code vectors of length $n(K + k)$; we showed in Sec. 3.10, based on Sec. 2.10, that the ensemble average upper bound for systematic block codes is the same as for nonsystematic block codes. Hence we may employ this result, but the "block code" resulting from considering $(2^b - 1)2^{bk}$ incorrect paths unmerged for $K + k$ branches has only N' rather than $(K + k)n$ effective code symbols. Thus substituting N' of (5.7.1) in place of $(K + k)n$ in the kth term of (5.1.27), we obtain

$$\begin{aligned}\overline{\Pi_k(j)} &< [(2^b - 1)2^{bk}]^{\rho}\, e^{-[K(n-b)+kn+b]E_o(\rho,\,\mathbf{q})} \\ &< (2^b - 1)2^{-Kb(1-r)E_o(\rho,\,\mathbf{q})/R}2^{-kb[E_o(\rho,\,\mathbf{q})/R-\rho]} \qquad 0 \le \rho \le 1 \qquad (5.7.2)\end{aligned}$$

where we have again used $R = b \ln 2/n$ and $r = b/n = R/\ln 2$. Thus inserting (5.7.2) for $\overline{\Pi_k(j)}$ in (5.1.29), we obtain, in place of (5.1.29)

$$\overline{E[n_b(j)]} < \frac{b(2^b - 1)2^{-KbE_o(\rho,\,\mathbf{q})(1-r)/R}}{[1 - 2^{-b\{[E_o(\rho,\,\mathbf{q})/R]-\rho\}}]^2} \qquad 0 \le \rho \le 1$$

[11] If the channel input is not binary but Q-ary, then $l = \nu n$ (where $\nu = \lceil \log Q \rceil$ is the least integer not less than $\log Q$). Each sequence of νb input bits is transmitted, after mapping, as b Q-ary symbols followed by $l - \nu b$ coded bits mapped into $(n - b)$ Q-ary symbols (see Fig. 5.1).

Proceeding with the remainder of the steps in Sec. 5.1, we find that there exists a systematic convolutional code whose bit error probability is bounded by

$$P_b < (2^b - 1)\frac{2^{-KbE_c(R)(1-r)/R}}{[1 - 2^{-b\epsilon E_c(R)/R}]^2} \tag{5.7.3}$$

where $E_c(R)$ is given by (5.1.33) and (5.1.34).

We now turn to the lower bound, modifying the derivation in Sec. 5.4 in the same way. Here again $b(K - 1)$ code symbols of remerging incorrect paths are constrained to be the same as those of the correct path. Hence, in (5.4.3), $N = (K + k)n$ must be replaced by N' of (5.7.1). This yields, in place of (5.4.3) through (5.4.5)

$$\begin{aligned}\Pi_k(j) &\geq e^{-N'[E_{sp}(\tilde{R}_k) + o(N)]} \\ &= e^{-N'[E_{sp}(\tilde{R}_k) + o(K)]} \\ &= e^{-[K(n-b) + kn + b][E_{sp}(\tilde{R}_k) + o(K)]} \\ &> 2^{-Kb[(1-r+\lambda)/R][E_{sp}(R,\,\lambda) + o(K)]}\end{aligned} \tag{5.7.4}$$

where

$$\lambda = \frac{k}{K}$$

$$r = \frac{b}{n}$$

$$E_{sp}(R, \lambda) = E_o(\rho) - \rho E_o'(\rho) \tag{5.7.5a}$$

$$\begin{aligned}R &= \frac{1 + \lambda - r}{\lambda}\tilde{R}_k \\ &= \frac{1 + \lambda - r}{\lambda}E_o'(\rho)\end{aligned} \tag{5.7.5b}$$

Then proceeding as in the remainder of Sec. 5.4, we have

$$\begin{aligned}P_b(j) &\geq 2^{-Kb\left[\min_{\lambda \geq 0} (1 + \lambda - r)E_{sp}(R,\,\lambda) + o(K)\right]/R} \\ &= 2^{-Kb[E_{csp}(R)(1-r) + o(K)]/R}\end{aligned} \tag{5.7.6}$$

where

$$\begin{aligned}E_{csp}(R) &= E_o(\rho) \qquad 0 < \rho < \infty \\ R &= \frac{E_o(\rho)}{\rho} \qquad 0 < R < C\end{aligned} \tag{5.7.7}$$

Thus the upper-bound and lower-bound exponents agree for $R_0 < R < C$. While we cannot, in general, obtain tight bounds for lower rates, we can improve the lower bound by using the zero-rate lower bound (3.7.19) in place of (5.7.5) with the result

$$P_b(j) > 2^{-Kb[E_{ex}(0)(1-r)+o(K)]/R} \qquad 0 < R < R_1 \leq R_0 \tag{5.7.8}$$

We summarize all these results as

Theorem 5.7.1: Systematic convolutional code bounds (Bucher and Heller [1970]) For systematic convolutional codes, all the upper and lower error bounds of nonsystematic codes hold with all numerator exponents multiplied by

$$1 - r = 1 - \frac{b}{n} = 1 - \frac{R}{\ln 2} \tag{5.7.9}$$

Note that there is a severe loss when b/n is close to unity. Even for $b/n = \frac{1}{2}$, the reduction in exponent requires doubling the constraint length to obtain with systematic codes the same asymptotic results as for nonsystematic codes.

5.8 TIME-VARYING CONVOLUTIONAL CODES ON INTERSYMBOL INTERFERENCE CHANNELS*

We conclude this chapter with an application of the ensemble average error probability analysis to the class of time-varying convolutional codes with the intersymbol interference (ISI) channel, first defined and analyzed in Secs. 4.9 and 4.10. Figure 5.7*a* and 5.7*b* illustrates the analog model and digital equivalent of the intersymbol interference channel, which are the same as in Figs. 4.20 and 4.21 but with a rate b/n convolutional encoder preceding the channel. In Sec. 4.10, we have shown that the maximum likelihood combined demodulator–decoder can be realized with a Viterbi algorithm of dimensionality $\lceil(\mathscr{L} - 1)/n\rceil + (K - 1)$ where the trellis diagram comes from combining the convolutional encoder and ISI linear filter into a single device. Here we shall assume such a maximum likelihood demodulator–decoder.

In the trellis diagram for the combined demodulator–decoder, a path that diverges from the correct path and later remerges for the first time can cause an error event only if it accumulates a higher metric than the correct path while unmerged. Such a path can correspond to a data sequence with a path in the convolutional code trellis diagram which diverges and remerges with the correct path more than once during the same span of branches over which it is totally unmerged in the coded ISI trellis. We shall first consider only those paths for which there is only one unmerged span in the code trellis corresponding to the

* May be omitted without loss of continuity.

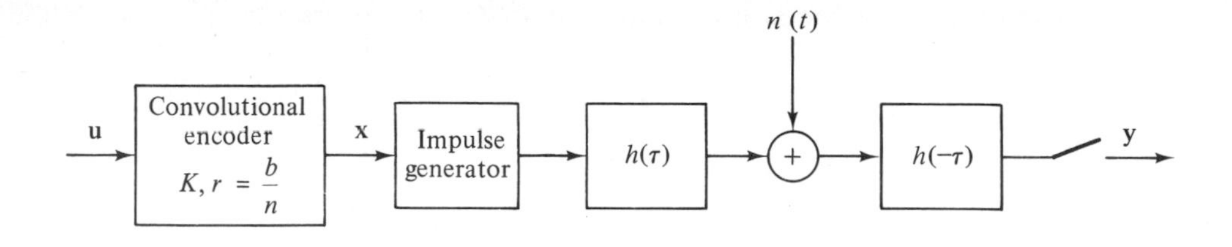

(a) Analog model

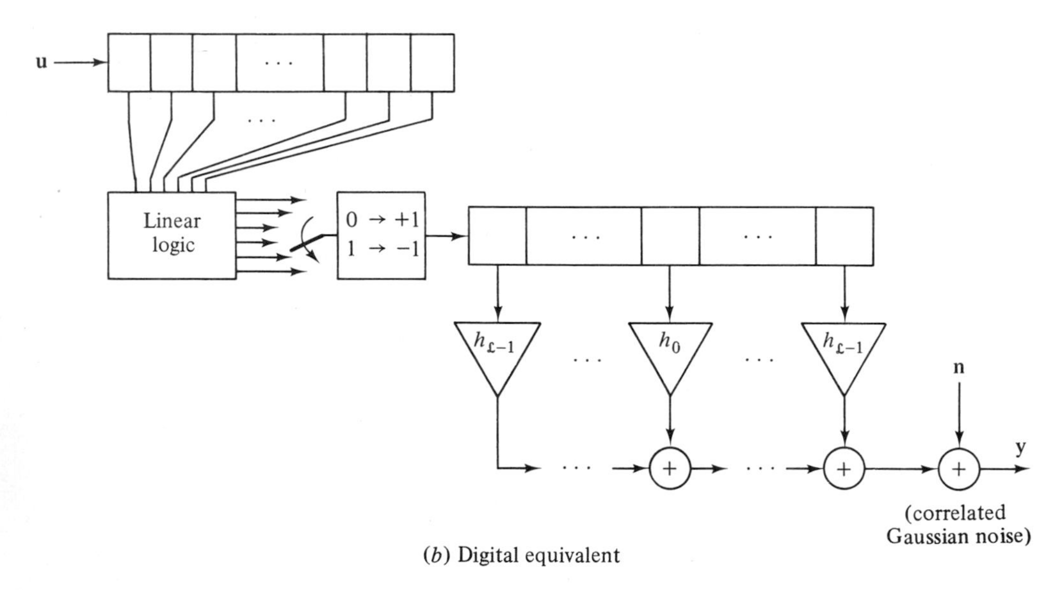

(b) Digital equivalent

Figure 5.7 Coded ISI channel model.

unmerged span of the coded ISI trellis. That is, we first limit our discussion to error events for which the unmerged span in the coded ISI trellis corresponds to paths in the convolutional code trellis which diverge and remerge only once.

Let $\{x_n\}$ be the channel symbols ($+1$ or -1) of the correct path and let $\{x'_n\}$ be the channel symbols corresponding to a path that diverges from the correct path and remerges for the first time after a span of N channel symbols. Here

$$x_n = x'_n \qquad n \leq 0,\ n \geq N+1 \tag{5.8.1}$$

Defining $\epsilon_n = \frac{1}{2}(x_n - x'_n)$, $n = 1, 2, \ldots, N$ we have from (4.9.18)

$$P_{E_1}(\epsilon) < \prod_{n=1}^{N} \exp\left\{-\frac{1}{N_o}\left(h_0 \epsilon_n^2 + 2\sum_{i=1}^{\mathscr{L}-1} h_i \epsilon_n \epsilon_{n-i}\right)\right\} \tag{5.8.2}$$

where the subscript E_1 indicates the restriction to an error event with paths that diverge and remerge only *once* in the convolutional code trellis during the span of N channel symbols. Suppose we could average $P_{E_1}(\boldsymbol{\epsilon})$ over all sequences $\boldsymbol{\epsilon} = (\epsilon_1, \epsilon_2, \ldots, \epsilon_N)$ using the product measure

$$\tilde{q}_N(\boldsymbol{\epsilon}) = \prod_{n=1}^{N} \tilde{q}(\epsilon_n) \tag{5.8.3}$$

where

$$\tilde{q}(\epsilon) = \begin{cases} \frac{1}{4} & \epsilon = 1, \ -1 \\ \frac{1}{2} & \epsilon = 0 \end{cases} \tag{5.8.4}$$

or, equivalently

$$\tilde{q}(\epsilon) = 2^{-(|\epsilon|+1)} \tag{5.8.5}$$

Averaging $P_{E_1}(\boldsymbol{\epsilon})$ over this ensemble yields

$$\overline{P_{E_1}(N)} \leq \sum_{\epsilon_1} \sum_{\epsilon_2} \cdots \sum_{\epsilon_N} \prod_{n=1}^{N} \tilde{q}(\epsilon_n) \exp\left\{ -\frac{1}{N_o} \left(h_0 \epsilon_n^2 + 2 \sum_{i=1}^{\mathscr{L}-1} h_i \epsilon_n \epsilon_{n-i} \right) \right\} \tag{5.8.6}$$

Note that this expression differs from (4.9.22) in that here the summation is over all sequences and there is an additional weighting of $1/2^N$. It remains, of course, to justify the validity of this weighting, as we now do by the following argument.

Figure 5.8 illustrates the generation of the terms inside the product in (5.8.6) for the two paths of N channel symbols which correspond to an incorrect path that diverges and remerges with the correct path in the code trellis diagram. Its right half resembles Figs. 4.22*c* and 4.23*c* (the uncoded cases), but the error sequence now depends on the code. The error sequence for a particular pair of (correct and incorrect) information sequences $\mathbf{u}$ and $\mathbf{u}'$ are generated as shown in the left half of Fig. 5.8. The information sequence $\mathbf{u}$ is encoded by the convolutional coder into the channel sequence $\mathbf{x}$. The binary sequence is mapped into the real channel inputs according to the convention "0" → +1 and "1" → −1. Since $x_k = \pm 1$, the error sequence term is given by

$$\epsilon_k \equiv \tfrac{1}{2}(x_k - x_k') = \frac{|x_k - x_k'|}{2} x_k \tag{5.8.7}$$

Because of the linearity of the convolutional code, we may form the vector

$$\mathbf{d} \equiv \tfrac{1}{2}|\mathbf{x} - \mathbf{x}'| \equiv (\tfrac{1}{2}|x_1 - x_1'|, \tfrac{1}{2}|x_2 - x_2'|, \ldots \tfrac{1}{2}|x_N - x_N'|)$$

by first forming the modulo-2 sum of the binary information sequences $\mathbf{v} = \mathbf{u} \oplus \mathbf{u}'$, encoding this sum using a convolutional encoder identical to that which encodes $\mathbf{u}$, and mapping the resulting binary sequence according to the convention "0" → 0 and "1" → +1. The error sequence is then obtained, as determined by (5.8.7), by multiplying this sequence by the coded information sequence. This explains the form of the error sequence generator shown in the left half of Fig. 5.8.

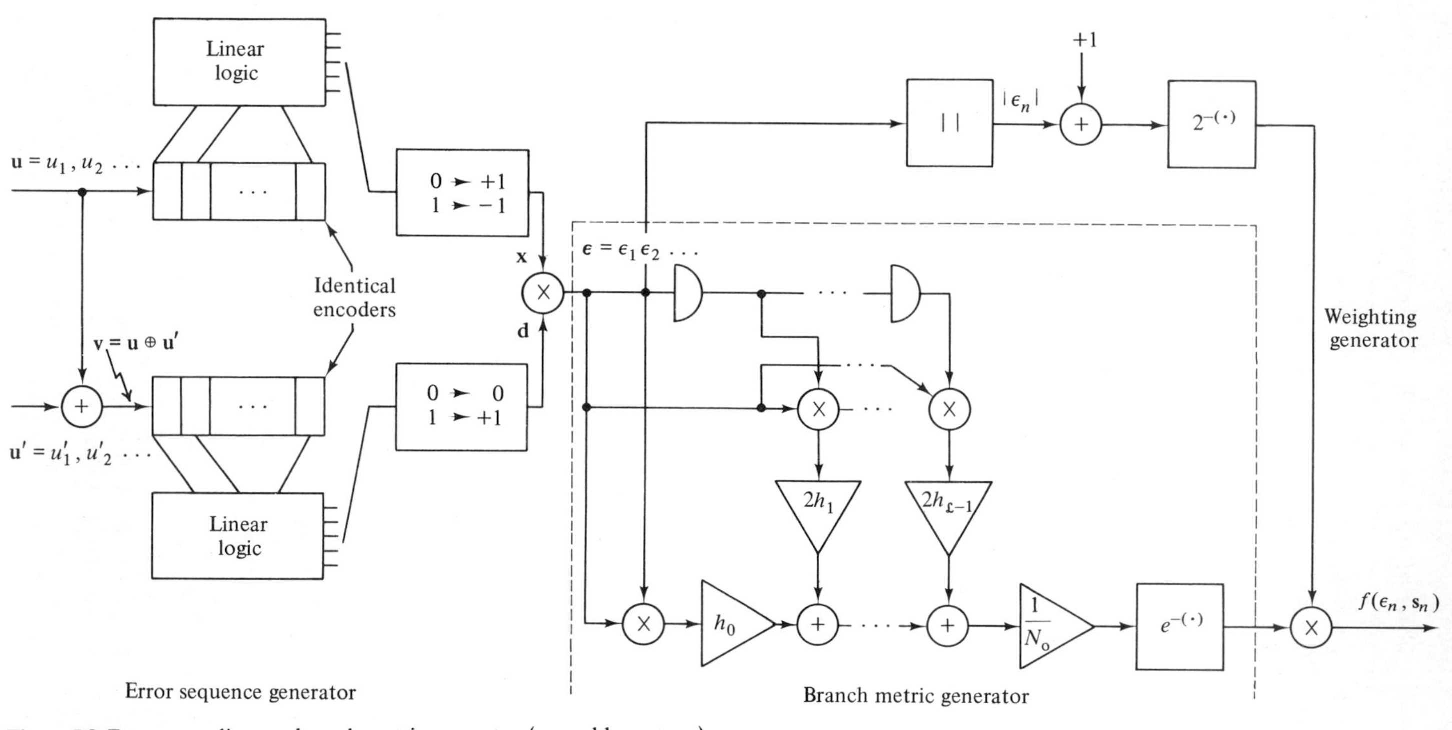

Figure 5.8 Error-state diagram branch metric generator (ensemble average).

Over the ensemble of time-varying convolutional codes, each component of the vector **d** is equally likely to be 0 or 1 provided **u** and **u**′ are on unmerged paths (or, equivalently, **v** has diverged from the all-zeros path). The bit error probability is averaged not only over the code ensemble but over the data sequence **u** as well. Since **v** varies over all binary sequences independent of **u**, the sequence **x** is independent of the sequence **d** even though the two generators shown are identical. Each component of **x** is equally likely to be a $+1$ or -1. Hence each component of the error sequence $\boldsymbol{\epsilon}$ is 0 with probability 1/2 and $+1$ or -1 each with probability 1/4, which verifies the weighting of (5.8.4).

The branch metric generator half of Fig. 5.8 is similar to that of Figs. 4.22*c* and 4.23*c* except that here the weighting has an additional $\frac{1}{2}$ factor to account for the code ensemble averaging. We now present a straightforward matrix version of the convolutional coded bit error bound discussed in Sec. 5.1 as modified for the ISI channel.

Define the state sequence, which corresponds to the contents of the last $\mathscr{L}-1$ stages of the branch metric generator

$$\mathbf{s}_n = (\epsilon_{n-(\mathscr{L}-1)}, \ldots, \epsilon_{n-2}, \epsilon_{n-1}) \qquad n = 1, 2, \ldots, N+1 \tag{5.8.8}$$

and the shift relationship

$$\mathbf{s}_{n+1} = \mathbf{g}(\epsilon_n, \mathbf{s}_n) = (\epsilon_{n+1-(\mathscr{L}-1)}, \ldots, \epsilon_{n-1}, \epsilon_n) \tag{5.8.9}$$

Let

$$\Delta_0 = \mathbf{0}, \Delta_1, \Delta_2, \ldots, \Delta_{3^{\mathscr{L}-1}-1}$$

be the $3^{\mathscr{L}-1}$ possible distinct states. Initially we must have $\mathbf{s}_1 = \Delta_0 = \mathbf{0}$ since, before unmerging, the error sequence is $\mathbf{0}$. Also define

$$f(\epsilon_n, \mathbf{s}_n) = \tilde{q}(\epsilon_n) \exp\left\{-\frac{1}{N_o}\left(h_0 \epsilon_n^2 + 2\sum_{i=1}^{\mathscr{L}-1} h_i \epsilon_n \epsilon_{n-i}\right)\right\} \tag{5.8.10}$$

and define the $3^{\mathscr{L}-1} \times 3^{\mathscr{L}-1}$ matrix

$$A = \{a_{ij}\} \tag{5.8.11}$$

where

$$a_{ij} = \begin{cases} f(\epsilon, \Delta_j) & \text{if } \Delta_i = \mathbf{g}(\epsilon, \Delta_j) \text{ for some } \epsilon \in \{-1, 0, 1\} \\ 0 & \text{otherwise} \end{cases} \tag{5.8.12}$$

Then (5.8.6) becomes

$$\overline{P_{E_1}(N)} \le \sum_{\epsilon_1}\sum_{\epsilon_2}\cdots\sum_{\epsilon_N}\prod_{n=1}^{N} f(\epsilon_n, \mathbf{s}_n)$$

$$= [1\ 1\ \cdots\ 1]A^N \begin{bmatrix} 1 \\ 0 \\ \vdots \\ 0 \end{bmatrix} \tag{5.8.13}$$

The matrix A is the state transition matrix of the intersymbol interference. It has only three nonzero components in each row and each column, where the nonzero components are branch values of a state diagram whose generation is shown in Fig. 5.8. For $\mathscr{L} = 2$, for example, it is the state transition matrix for Fig. 4.22d but with the "0" state included with a self-loop and all branches also weighted by the probability $\tilde{q}(\epsilon)$. Hence

$$A = \begin{bmatrix} f(0, 0) & f(0, -1) & f(0, 1) \\ f(-1, 0) & f(-1, -1) & f(-1, 1) \\ f(1, 0) & f(1, -1) & f(1, 1) \end{bmatrix} \qquad \begin{aligned} \Delta_0 &= 0 \\ \Delta_1 &= -1 \\ \Delta_2 &= 1 \end{aligned}$$

where

$$\begin{aligned} f(0, 0) = f(0, -1) = f(0, 1) &= \tfrac{1}{2} \\ f(-1, 0) = f(1, 0) \quad &= \tfrac{1}{4}a_0 \\ f(-1, -1) = f(1, 1) \quad &= \tfrac{1}{4}a_1 \\ f(-1, 1) = f(1, -1) &= \tfrac{1}{4}a_2 \end{aligned}$$

and a_0, a_1, a_2 are given in Fig. 5.9(a) which presents the state diagram for this case. Note that the bound in (5.8.13) represents the set of all paths of length N starting from the initial state $\mathbf{s}_1 = \mathbf{0}$. It can terminate in any state, however, since merger of the code path guarantees only that $\epsilon_n = 0$, but the state-vector $\mathbf{s}_n = (\epsilon_{n-(\mathscr{L}-1)}, \ldots, \epsilon_{n-2}, \epsilon_{n-1})$, the contents of the register of Fig. 5.8, is arbitrary. This also explains the fact that the premultiplying vector in (5.8.13) is $(1\ 1\ 1 \cdots 1)$.

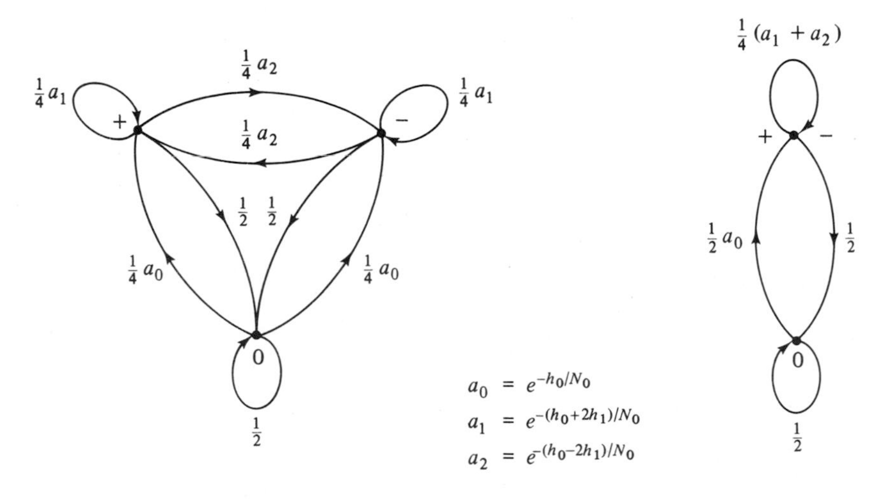

Figure 5.9 Coded ISI channel error state diagram (ensemble average) for $\mathscr{L} = 2$.

By symmetry, the set of all paths ending at state " -1 " is the same as the set of all paths ending at state "1." Hence, we have for $\mathscr{L} = 2$ (for $\mathscr{L} = 3$ see Prob. 5.11)

$$\overline{P_{E_1}(N)} \leq [1\ 1]\tilde{A}^N \begin{bmatrix} 1 \\ 0 \end{bmatrix}$$

where

$$\tilde{A} = \begin{bmatrix} f(0, 0) & f(0, \pm 1) \\ f(\pm 1, 0) & f(\pm 1, \pm 1) \end{bmatrix} \qquad \begin{matrix} \Delta_0 = 0 \\ \Delta_1 = \pm 1 \end{matrix}$$

where

$$f(0, 0) = f(0, \pm 1) = \tfrac{1}{2}$$
$$f(\pm 1, 0) = \tfrac{1}{2}a_0$$
$$f(\pm 1, \pm 1) = \tfrac{1}{4}(a_1 + a_2)$$

The corresponding reduced state diagram is shown in Fig. 5.9*b*.

In general for memory $\mathscr{L}$, the $3^{\mathscr{L}-1} \times 3^{\mathscr{L}-1}$ matrix A corresponds to a state diagram where the $3^{\mathscr{L}-1} - 1$ nonzero states come in equivalent pairs, for which the set of N-step transitions to these states starting at the zero state are the same. Hence we can always find a reduced state diagram and the corresponding square matrix $\tilde{A}$ of size $(3^{\mathscr{L}-1} - 1)/2 + 1$ such that (5.8.13) is expressed as

$$\overline{P_{E_1}(N)} \leq [1\ 1 \cdots 1]\tilde{A}^N \begin{bmatrix} 1 \\ 0 \\ \vdots \\ 0 \end{bmatrix} \tag{5.8.14}$$

Thus, in the following, the matrix $\tilde{A}$ can be used interchangeably with A, with concurrent reduction of the dimensionality of the vectors. Initially, however, for clarity of exposition we shall consider the unreduced diagram; the reduction will then follow immediately.

Recall that (5.8.13) is the convolutional code ensemble bound on the probability that a path diverging from the correct path and remerging N channel symbols later (in the convolutional code trellis) causes an error event. If the span over which the two paths are apart is $K + k$ branches, then $N = n(K + k)$. The code-ensemble average bit error bound due to these single code-merger error events is then (see Sec. 5.1)

$$\overline{P_{b_1}} \leq \frac{2^b - 1}{b} \sum_{k=0}^{\infty} b(k + 1)2^{bk}\overline{P_k} \tag{5.8.15}$$

where $\overline{P_k} = \overline{P_{E_1}(N)}$ with $N = n(K + k)$. Substituting (5.8.13) into (5.8.15), we see that $\overline{P_{b_1}}$ is bounded by

$$\overline{P_{b_1}} \leq \frac{2^b - 1}{b} \sum_{k=0}^{\infty} b(k + 1)2^{bk}[1\ 1 \cdots 1]A^{n(K+k)} \begin{bmatrix} 1 \\ 0 \\ \vdots \\ 0 \end{bmatrix} \tag{5.8.16}$$

The matrix A is nonnegative and irreducible. The Perron-Frobenius theorem (see, e.g., Gantmacher [1959]) states that such a matrix has a real maximum eigenvalue λ and an associated positive left eigenvector. Defining $\alpha > 0$ to be the largest component of the left eigenvector divided by its smallest component we have (Prob. 5.12) the inequalities

$$\frac{1}{\alpha}\lambda^N \leq [1\ 1 \cdots 1]A^N \begin{bmatrix} 1 \\ 0 \\ \vdots \\ 0 \end{bmatrix} \leq \alpha\lambda^N \tag{5.8.17}$$

Thus (5.8.16) can be expressed as

$$\overline{P_{b_1}} \leq \frac{\alpha(2^b - 1)}{(1 - 2^b\lambda^n)^2}\lambda^{nK} \qquad 2^b\lambda^n < 1 \tag{5.8.18}$$

Up to this point, we have restricted the error events to those paths that diverge and remerge only once in the convolutional code trellis during the unmerged span in the coded ISI trellis. Now consider again the transmitted convolutional coded sequence $\{x_n\}$ and another coded sequence $\{x'_n\}$ corresponding to an error event satisfying (5.8.1), but suppose that the paths merge twice in the convolutional code trellis, merging at N_1 but diverging again at N_2 where

$$nK \leq N_1 < N_2 < N_1 + (\mathscr{L} - 1) \tag{5.8.19}$$

This means that the code paths diverge again before the $\boldsymbol{\epsilon}$ register of Fig. 5.8 is allowed to clear, for that would require $N_2 \geq N_1 + (\mathscr{L} - 1)$. We thus have, in addition to (5.8.1)

$$x'_n = x_n \qquad n = N_1 + 1, N_1 + 2, \ldots, N_2 \tag{5.8.20}$$

This situation is sketched in Fig. 5.10 where the paths in the convolutional code trellis merge at N_1 and N. The error sequence for the N coded symbols is thus

$$\boldsymbol{\epsilon} = (\epsilon_1, \ldots, \epsilon_{N_1}, 0, \ldots, 0, \epsilon_{N_2+1}, \ldots, \epsilon_N) \tag{5.8.21}$$

Over the ensemble of time-varying convolutional codes with product measure given by (5.8.3), $\boldsymbol{\epsilon}$ has measure

$$\tilde{q}(\boldsymbol{\epsilon}) = \prod_{n=1}^{N_1} \tilde{q}(\epsilon_n) \prod_{k=N_2+1}^{N} \tilde{q}(\epsilon_k) \tag{5.8.22}$$

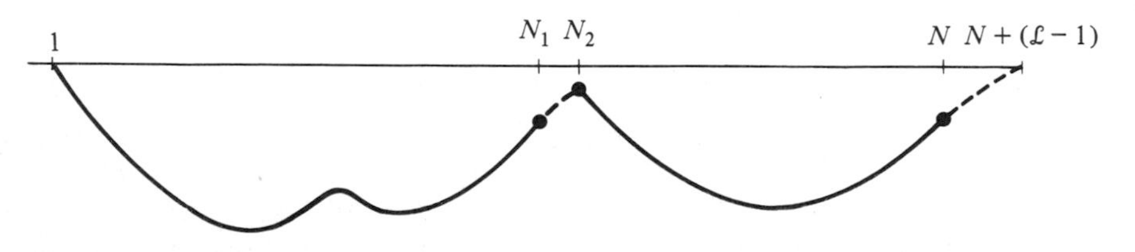

Figure 5.10 Typical two code-merger path in the coded ISI trellis.

For this error sequence, (5.8.2) becomes

$$P_{E_2}(\boldsymbol{\epsilon}) < \prod_{n=1}^{N_1} \exp\left\{-\frac{1}{N_o}\left(h_0 \epsilon_n^2 + 2\sum_{i=1}^{\mathscr{L}-1} h_i \epsilon_n \epsilon_{n-i}\right)\right\}$$
$$\times \prod_{k=N_2+1}^{N} \exp\left\{-\frac{1}{N_o}\left(h_0 \epsilon_k^2 + 2\sum_{i=1}^{\mathscr{L}-1} h_i \epsilon_k \epsilon_{k-i}\right)\right\} \tag{5.8.23}$$

and its average over the ensemble is

$$\overline{P_{E_2}(N_1, N - N_2)} \leq \sum_{\epsilon_1} \cdots \sum_{\epsilon_{N_1}} \prod_{n=1}^{N_1} f(\epsilon_n, \mathbf{s}_n)\left(\sum_{\epsilon_{N_2+1}} \cdots \sum_{\epsilon_N} \prod_{k=N_2+1}^{N} f(\epsilon_k, \mathbf{s}_k)\right)$$
$$= \sum_{\epsilon_1} \cdots \sum_{\epsilon_{N_1}} \prod_{n=1}^{N_1} f(\epsilon_n, \mathbf{s}_n)([1\ 1 \cdots 1]A^{N-N_2}\mathbf{i}(\mathbf{s}_{N_2+1})) \tag{5.8.24}$$

where $\mathbf{i}(\mathbf{s}_{N_2+1})$ is the $(3^{\mathscr{L}-1})$-dimensional column vector with "1" in the position corresponding to state $\mathbf{s}_{N_2+1}$ and "0" elsewhere.[12] An inequality similar to (5.8.17) also applies here (Prob. 5.12) to give

$$[1\ 1 \cdots 1]A^{N-N_2}\mathbf{i}(\mathbf{s})_{N_2+1}) \leq \alpha\lambda^{N-N_2} \tag{5.8.25}$$

This bound eliminates the dependence on state $\mathbf{s}_{N_2+1}$ and allows separation of the two code-trellis spans that make up the single-error event in the coded ISI trellis. Thus (5.8.13), (5.8.17), and (5.8.25) yield the further bound on (5.8.24)

$$\overline{P_{E_2}(N_1, N - N_2)} \leq (\alpha\lambda^{N_1})(\alpha\lambda^{N-N_2}) \tag{5.8.26}$$

For fixed N_1, N_2, and N given above, the number of paths that merge twice in the convolutional code trellis is bounded by $(2^b - 1)2^{bk_1}(2^b - 1)2^{bk_2}$, where $n(K + k_1) = N_1$ and $n(K + k_2) = N - N_2$. For such error events, there can be at most $b[(k_1 + 1) + (k_2 + 1)]$ coded binary symbol errors. Since

$$(k_1 + 1) + (k_2 + 1) \leq 2(k_1 + 1)(k_2 + 1) \tag{5.8.27}$$

(see Prob. 5.13 for generalizations to l code mergers), the code ensemble average bit error probability due to these two code-merger error events is bounded by

$$\overline{P_{b_2}} \leq \frac{1}{b} \sum_{k_1=0}^{\infty} \sum_{k_2=0}^{\infty} 2b(k_1 + 1)(k_2 + 1)(2^b - 1)2^{bk_1}(2^b - 1)2^{bk_2}$$
$$\times (\alpha\lambda^{n(K+k_1)})(\alpha\lambda^{n(K+k_2)})$$
$$= 2\left[\alpha(2^b - 1)\lambda^{nK} \sum_{k=0}^{\infty} (k + 1)(2^b\lambda^n)^k\right]^2$$
$$= 2\left[\frac{\alpha(2^b - 1)}{(1 - 2^b\lambda^n)^2}\lambda^{nK}\right]^2 \tag{5.8.28}$$

[12] This follows since here the initial state is not $\boldsymbol{\epsilon} = \mathbf{0}$ but rather the $\boldsymbol{\epsilon}$ corresponding to the contents of the register when the code paths diverge for the second time.

The bounds for two code-merger error events easily generalize to error events where there are l path mergers in the convolutional code trellis during the single unmerged span in the coded ISI trellis. For any integer l, the corresponding code-ensemble average bit error bound due to these events is

$$\overline{P_{b_l}} \le l \left[\frac{\alpha(2^b - 1)}{(1 - 2^b \lambda^n)^2} \lambda^{nK} \right]^l \qquad l = 1, 2, \ldots \tag{5.8.29}$$

Taking the union of events bound over all error events, we find that the code-ensemble average bit error is bounded by

$$\begin{aligned} \overline{P_b} &\le \sum_{l=1}^{\infty} \overline{P_{b_l}} \\ &\le \sum_{l=1}^{\infty} l \left[\frac{\alpha(2^b - 1)}{(1 - 2^b \lambda^n)^2} \lambda^{nK} \right]^l \\ &= \frac{\alpha(2^b - 1)/(1 - 2^b \lambda^n)^2}{\{1 - [\alpha(2^b - 1)/(1 - 2^b \lambda^n)^2] \lambda^{nK}\}^2} \lambda^{nK} \end{aligned} \tag{5.8.30}$$

From this we obtain

Theorem 5.8.1 For an additive Gaussian ISI channel with $\mathscr{L}$ nonzero coefficients $h_0, h_1, \ldots, h_{\mathscr{L}-1}$, there exists a time-varying convolutional code of constraint length K and rate b/n for which the bit error probability with maximum likelihood demodulation–decoding is bounded by

$$P_b \le \frac{\gamma(R) 2^{-KbR_0/R}}{[1 - \gamma(R) 2^{-KbR_0/R}]^2} \tag{5.8.31}$$

where

$$\gamma(R) = \frac{\alpha(2^b - 1)}{(1 - 2^{-b(R_0/R - 1)})^2}$$

$$R = \frac{b}{n} \ln 2 < R_0$$

$$R_0 = -\ln \lambda \qquad \text{nats/channel symbol} \tag{5.8.32}$$

and where λ is the maximum eigenvalue of the ISI channel transition matrix A, and α is the ratio of the maximum component over the minimum component of the positive left eigenvector associated with λ.

The maximum eigenvalue λ and the ratio of eigenvector components α are the same for both the state transition matrix A and the corresponding reduced-state transition matrix $\tilde{A}$ (Prob. 5.12). In the case of duobinary ISI where $h_0 = \mathscr{E}_s$ and $h_1 = \mathscr{E}_s/2$, we have the maximum eigenvalue

$$\lambda = \frac{a_0^2 + 3}{8} \left[1 + \sqrt{1 - 8 \left(\frac{a_0 - 1}{a_0^2 + 3} \right)^2} \right]$$

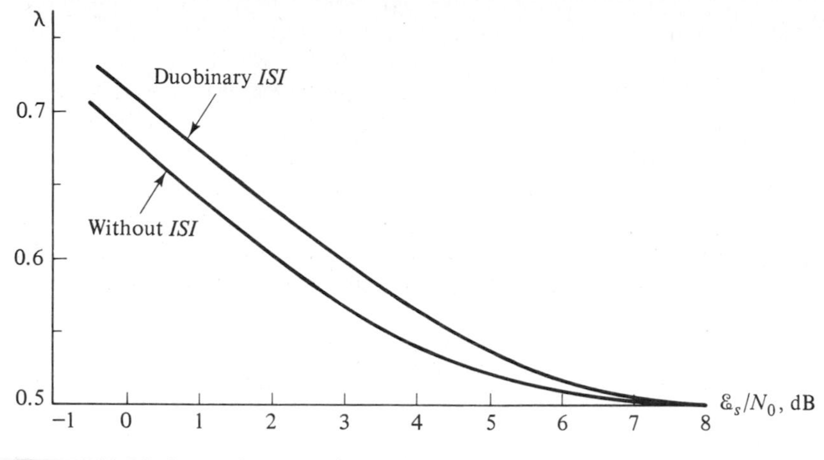

Figure 5.11 Maximum eigenvalue for duobinary ISI.

and ratio

$$\alpha = (2\lambda - 1)/a_0$$

where

$$a_0 = e^{-\mathscr{E}_s/N_o}$$

Figure 5.11 shows λ as a function of $\mathscr{E}_s/N_o$ for this special case, as well as for the non-ISI AWGN channel (where $h_0 = \mathscr{E}_s$ and $h_1 = 0$) for which the only nonzero eigenvalue is $(1 + a_o)/2$. It is interesting to note that rate $= \frac{1}{2}$ encoding together with duobinary digital linear filtering results in no net change in the signal spectrum; yet the performance loss relative to rate $= \frac{1}{2}$ coding only, as shown by Fig. 5.11 and (5.8.32), is less than 1 dB. Of course, there are now three signal levels rather than two.

5.9 BIBLIOGRAPHICAL NOTES AND REFERENCES

The basic upper and lower bounds on convolutional codes in Secs. 5.1, 5.2, and 5.4 first appeared in Viterbi [1967*a*]. The expurgated bound for binary-input, output-symmetric channels in Sec. 5.3 appeared in slightly weaker form in Viterbi and Odenwalder [1969]. The results on critical lengths of error events and memory truncation and initial synchronization errors in Secs. 5.5 and 5.6 are due to Forney [1974]. The modification of the results of the first four sections for systematic convolutional codes, treated in Sec. 5.7, is due to Bucher and Heller [1970]. Application of the ensemble average error probability techniques to the intersymbol interference channel with coding has not been published previously.

PROBLEMS

5.1 Find $E_c(R)$ and $E_{csp}(R)$ for the following channels and compare with the corresponding block exponents

(*a*) All channels of Prob. 3.2.
(*b*) All channels of Prob. 3.3.
(*c*) Channel of Prob. 3.5.
(*d*) Channel of Prob. 3.6.

5.2 Verify (5.6.6) and plot k_{crit}/K versus R for $0 \leq R < C$.

5.3 (Construction of a Block Code from a Convolutional Code by Termination with a Zero Tail, Forney [1974]) Suppose we construct a block code of length $(L + K - 1)n = N_b$ symbols by taking L branches of a rate b/n convolutional code and terminating it with a $(K - 1)$ branch tail of all-zero data.

(*a*) Show that the rate of this block code is given by $R_b = [L/(L + K - 1)]R$ where $R = (b/n) \ln 2$ is the convolutional code rate in nats per symbol.

(*b*) Show that the block error probability of this block code is upper-bounded by

$$P_E < \frac{L(2^b - 1)}{1 - 2^{-b[E_o(\rho)/R - \rho]}} e^{-N_b E_o(\rho)K/(L+K-1)} \qquad 0 < \rho < 1$$

(*c*) Letting

$$\theta \equiv \frac{L}{L + K - 1} \qquad 0 < \theta < 1$$

show that

$$P_E < \mathscr{K} e^{-N_b(1-\theta)E_c(R)}$$

where

$$E_c(R) = E_o(\rho) \qquad \frac{R_b}{\theta} = R = \frac{E_o(\rho)(1 - \epsilon)}{\rho}$$

and where $\mathscr{K}$ is a constant independent of K, for $\epsilon > 0$.

(*d*) Now, since L and K are arbitrary, choose θ so as to minimize the bound on P_E. Show then that

$$P_E < \mathscr{K} e^{-N_b E_b(R_b)}$$

where

$$E_b(R_b) = \max_{\theta,\, R:\, R_b = R\theta} \{(1 - \theta)E_c(R)\}$$

(*e*) Substituting the result of (*c*) into that of (*d*) show

$$E_b(R_b) = \max_{0 \leq \rho \leq 1} \left[E_o(\rho) - \frac{R_b}{1 - \epsilon} \rho \right]$$

Thus, aside from $\epsilon \ll 1$ and the constant $\mathscr{K}$, we have constructed a block code which is as good as the ensemble average upper bound on block codes (Chap. 3).

5.4 In Prob. 5.3, suppose that after step (*b*), we arbitrarily choose $L = k_{crit}$ of (5.5.8)—the critical run length of errors. Then show

$$R_b \approx \frac{k_{crit}}{k_{crit} + K} R = E_o'(\rho) \qquad 0 \leq \rho \leq 1$$

$$E_b(R_b) \approx \frac{K}{k_{crit} + K} E_o(\rho) = E_o(\rho) - \rho E_o'(\rho)$$

and thus obtain the same result as in 5.3(*e*).

5.5 (Lower Bound by a Termination with a Zero Tail Argument: Alternative Proof to Theorem 5.4.1, Forney [1974])

(*a*) Consider a terminated convolutional code as in Prob. 5.3. Show that this block code must have block error probability

$$P_E > 2^{-bK[E_{sp}(R_b)+o(K)]/[R(1-\theta)]}$$

where

$$N_b = (L + K - 1)n$$

$$R_b = \frac{L}{L+k-1} R$$

(*b*) Applying the definitions of Prob. 5.3(*c*) show that

$$P_E > 2^{-bK[E_{sp}(R_b)+o(K)]/[R(1-\theta)]}$$

where

$$E_{sp}(R_b) = E_o(\rho) - \rho E_o'(\rho) \qquad 0 \le \rho < \infty$$

$$R_b = E_o'(\rho) = R\theta \qquad 0 \le \theta \le 1$$

(*c*) Now show that the probability of *at least one error* in L branches of any convolutional code is lower-bounded by

$$P_e > 2^{-bK[E_{csp}(R)+o(K)]/R}$$

where

$$E_{csp}(R) \equiv \min_{\theta,\, R:\, R_b = R\theta} \left[\frac{E_{sp}(R_b)}{1-\theta}\right]$$

$$= \min_{0<\rho<\infty} \frac{E_o(\rho) - \rho E_o'(\rho)}{1 - E_o'(\rho)/R}$$

and this minimization yields

$$E_{csp}(R) = E_o(\rho) \qquad \text{where} \qquad R = \frac{E_o(\rho)}{\rho} \qquad 0 < \rho < \infty$$

5.6 (Upper Bound on Free Distance by a Termination with a Zero Tail Argument, Forney [1974])

(*a*) Show that, for a terminated convolutional code with parameter as in Prob. 5.3

$$d_{\min}(\text{block}) \ge d_{\text{free}}(\text{convolutional})$$

(*b*) Thus, given any upper bound for the block code

$$d_{\min}(\text{block}) \le D(R_b)$$

show that [using the definition of 5.3(*c*)]

$$\frac{d_{\text{free}}}{(K-1)n} \le \frac{d_{\min}}{N_b(1-\theta)} \le \frac{D(R_b)}{N_b(1-\theta)} \qquad \text{where} \qquad R_b = R\theta$$

and hence

$$\frac{d_{\text{free}}}{(K-1)n} \le \min_{0<\theta<1} \frac{D(R\theta)}{N_b(1-\theta)}$$

(*c*) Using the Plotkin bound $D/N_b \approx \frac{1}{2}(1 - R_b/\ln 2)$, show that (*b*) merely results in

$$\frac{d_{\text{free}}}{(K-1)n} \leq \frac{1}{2}$$

(Note that this agrees asymptotically with the result of Prob. 4.9. A tighter, more useful bound can be obtained from the Elias upper bound with considerably more manipulation.)

5.7 (Gilbert-Type Lower Bound on Free Distance)

(*a*) Suppose $d_{\text{free}} \leq \delta(R)$ for every binary convolutional code. Show that, on a binary-input output-symmetric channel, any such code yields

$$P_b \geq \left[\sum_y \sqrt{p_0(y)p_1(y)}\right]^{[\delta(R)-o(K)]} \approx Z^{\delta(R)}$$

(*b*) Suppose that

$$\frac{\delta(R)}{Kn} \leq \frac{-R}{\ln(2e^{-R}-1)}$$

Show that this would imply that, for every binary convolutional code used on a binary-input, output-symmetric channel

$$P_b \gtrsim 2^{-KbE_{\text{cex}}(R)/R}$$

where

$$\frac{E_{\text{cex}}(R)}{R} = \frac{\ln Z}{\ln(2e^{-R}-1)}$$

(*c*) Show that this is in direct contradiction to the upper bound of Theorem 5.3.1 and Corollary 5.3.1, and that hence there exists a convolutional code for which

$$\frac{\delta(R)}{Kn} \geq \frac{-R}{\ln(2e^{-R}-1)}$$

(*d*) Suppose we terminate this code in exactly the same manner as Probs. 5.3, 5.5 and 5.6. Show that there exists a resulting block code with

$$d_{\min} \geq \delta_b(R)$$

where δ_b satisfies

$$R = \ln 2 - \mathscr{H}(\delta_b) \qquad \text{(Gilbert bound)}$$

5.8 Consider an L-branch convolutional code of rate b/n. Show that, over some ensemble of convolutional codes, the average node error probability for any node j is bounded by

$$\overline{P_e(j)} \leq L\, 2^{-Kb[E_o(\rho)+o(K)]/R}$$

where ρ satisfies

$$R = \frac{E_o(\rho)}{\rho}$$

when $E_o(1) < R < C$, and $\rho = 1$ for $R \leq E_o(1)$.

5.9 Prove (5.5.17) of Theorem 5.5.1.

5.10 Consider a $K = 3$, $r = \frac{1}{2}$ time-varying convolutional encoder where at time i when the binary data symbol u_i enters the encoder the output binary symbols are $\mathbf{v}_i = (v_{i1}, v_{i2})$ as shown below, and $\mathbf{g}_0^{(i)}$, $\mathbf{g}_1^{(i)}$,

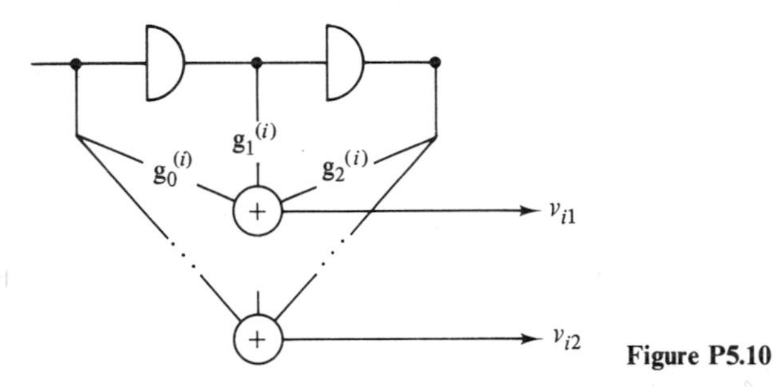

Figure P5.10

and $\mathbf{g}_2^{(i)}$ are the time-varying connection vectors of dimension 2. Assuming the all-zero data sequence is transmitted, we can consider the modified state diagram showing distances of all branches from the all-zero path branch at time i as

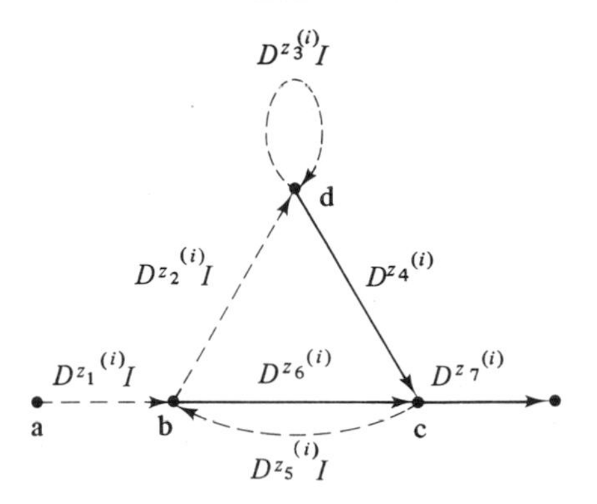

where, for $k = 1, 2, 3, \ldots, 7$,

$$z_k^{(i)} = v_{i1} + v_{i2}$$

is the sum of the encoder output binary symbols for the kth branch of the state diagram at time i.

(*a*) Define, for the above state diagram, $\xi_x(D, I; j, i)$ = transition function for all paths going from state **a** to state **b** at time j and going to state **x** at exactly time i, where **x** = **b**, **c**, **d**.

Let

$$\boldsymbol{\xi}(D, I; j, i) = \begin{bmatrix} \xi_b(D, I; j, i) \\ \xi_c(D, I; j, i) \\ \xi_d(D, I; j, i) \end{bmatrix}$$

and find $\mathbf{A}(i + 1)$ such that

$$\boldsymbol{\xi}(D, I; j, i + 1) = \mathbf{A}(i + 1)\boldsymbol{\xi}(D, I; j, i)$$

Initially we have

$$\boldsymbol{\xi}(D, I; j, j) = \begin{bmatrix} D^{z_1^{(j)}}I \\ 0 \\ 0 \end{bmatrix}$$

(*b*) For a binary-input, output-symmetric channel, show that the node error probability at node j is bounded by

$$P_e(j) \le \sum_{i=j}^{\infty} D^{z_7(i+1)} \xi_c(D, I; j, i) \Big|_{I=1,\, D=Z}$$

(*c*) Suppose at each time i the time-varying connection vectors are independently selected at random according to

$$P(\mathbf{g}_0^{(i)}, \mathbf{g}_1^{(i)}, \mathbf{g}_2^{(i)}) = (\tfrac{1}{2})^6$$

for all connections $\mathbf{g}_0^{(i)}$, $\mathbf{g}_1^{(i)}$, and $\mathbf{g}_2^{(i)}$. Over this ensemble of time-varying codes, show that

$$P_e(j) \le T(D, I)\big|_{I=1,\, D=[(1+Z)/2]^2}$$

and the averaged bit error probability is bounded by

$$\overline{P_b} \le \frac{\partial T(D, I)}{\partial I}\Big|_{I=1,\, D=[(1+Z)/2]^2}$$

where

$$T(D, I) = \frac{D^3 I}{1 - D(1 + D)I}$$

(*d*) Generalize (*c*) to arbitrary K and rate $r = 1/n$ where

$$T(D, I) = \frac{D^K(1 - D)I}{1 - D[1 + I(1 - D^{K-1})]}$$

and

$$D = \left(\frac{1 + Z}{2}\right)^n = 2^{-(R_0/R)}$$

This gives a bound which is exponentially the same as those of (5.1.23) for rates $R < R_0 = -\ln[(1 + Z)/2]$.

Hint: See $T(L, I)$ given by (4.6.5).

5.11 Show that, for $\mathscr{L} = 3$, the 9×9 matrix A defined in (5.8.11) reduces to the 5×5 matrix

$$\tilde{A} = \begin{bmatrix} \frac{1}{2} & 0 & 0 & 0 & \frac{1}{2} \\ a_0 & 0 & 0 & 0 & \frac{1}{2}(a_7 + a_8) \\ 0 & \frac{1}{2}a_1 & \frac{1}{2}a_3 & \frac{1}{2}a_6 & 0 \\ 0 & \frac{1}{2}a_2 & \frac{1}{2}a_4 & \frac{1}{2}a_5 & 0 \\ 0 & \frac{1}{2} & \frac{1}{2} & \frac{1}{2} & 0 \end{bmatrix} \qquad \begin{aligned} \Delta_0 &= (0, 0) \\ \Delta_1 &= (0, \pm 1) \\ \Delta_2 &= (\pm 1, \pm 1) \\ \Delta_3 &= (\pm 1, \mp 1) \\ \Delta_4 &= (\pm 1, 0) \end{aligned}$$

where $a_0, a_1, a_2, a_3, a_4, a_5, a_6, a_7$, and a_8 are defined by Fig. 4.23. Here the state at time n is $\mathbf{s}_n = (\epsilon_{n-2}, \epsilon_{n-1})$. Also sketch the reduced state diagram for this case and show that (5.8.13) becomes

$$\overline{P_E(N)} \le [1\ 1\ 1\ 1\ 1]\tilde{A}^N \begin{bmatrix} 1 \\ 0 \\ 0 \\ 0 \\ 0 \end{bmatrix}$$

5.12 Prove the inequalities (5.8.17) and (5.8.25) and show that λ and α are the same for the state transition matrix A and the reduced state transition matrix $\tilde{A}$. Note that α is the ratio of the largest component to the smallest component of the positive left eigenvector of A associated with the maximum eigenvalue λ.

5.13 For nonnegative integers $k_1, k_2, \ldots, k_l$, prove the inequality

$$\sum_{i=1}^{l} (k_i + 1) \le l \prod_{i=1}^{l} (k_i + 1)$$

This general form of (5.8.27) is required to prove the code-ensemble average bit error bound for l code-merger events given in (5.8.29).

5.14 Generalize the results of Sec. 5.8 to channels with an arbitrary but known finite memory part followed by a noisy memoryless part where, for channel input sequence $\mathbf{x} = (x_1, x_2, \ldots, x_N)$, the channel output sequence $\mathbf{y} = (y_1, y_2, \ldots, y_N)$ has conditional probability

$$p_N(\mathbf{y} \mid \mathbf{x}, \mathbf{s}_1) = \sum_{n=1}^{N} p(y_n \mid x_n, x_{n-1}, \ldots, x_{n-(\mathscr{L}-1)})$$

where $\mathbf{s}_1 = (x_{2-\mathscr{L}}, \ldots, x_{-1}, x_0)$. This is a channel with memory $\mathscr{L}$. Defining the state sequence

$$\mathbf{s}_n = (x_{n-(\mathscr{L}-1)}, \ldots, x_{n-2}, x_{n-1})$$

the channel conditional probability becomes

$$p_N(y \mid x, \mathbf{s}_1) = \sum_{n=1}^{N} p(y_n \mid x_n, \mathbf{s}_n)$$

where there is a state transition equation

$$\mathbf{s}_{n+1} = \mathbf{g}(x_n, \mathbf{s}_n)$$

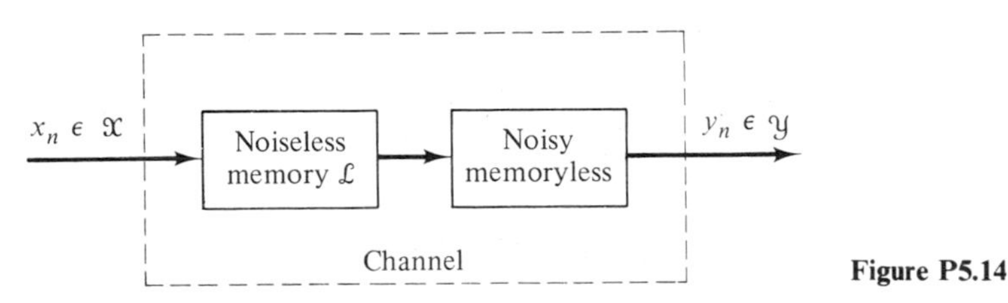

Figure P5.14

(*a*) Assume two input sequences

$$\mathbf{x} = (x_1, x_2, \ldots, x_N)$$

$$\mathbf{x}' = (x_1', x_2', \ldots, x_N')$$

and initial states $\mathbf{s}_1$ and $\mathbf{s}_1'$. Show that, for the maximum likelihood decision rule, the two-signal error probability is bounded as

$$P_E(\mathbf{x}, \mathbf{x}' \mid \mathbf{s}_1, \mathbf{s}_1') \le \sum_{\mathbf{y}} \sum_{n=1}^{N} \sqrt{p(y_n \mid x_n, \mathbf{s}_n) p(y_n \mid x_n', \mathbf{s}_n')}$$

$$= \sum_{n=1}^{N} \sum_{y} \sqrt{p(y_n \mid x_n, \mathbf{s}_n) p(y_n \mid x_n', \mathbf{s}_n')}$$

(*b*) Select the components of $\mathbf{x}$ and $\mathbf{x}'$ independently according to the probability distribution $q(x)$, $x \in \mathscr{X}$. Then show that

$$\overline{P_{E_1}(\mathbf{x}, \mathbf{x}' \mid \mathbf{s}_1, \mathbf{s}_1')} \le \sum_{x_1} \sum_{x_1'} \sum_{x_2} \sum_{x_2'} \cdots \sum_{x_N} \sum_{x_N'} \prod_{n=1}^{N} q(x_n) q(x_n') \left(\sum_{y} \sqrt{p(y \mid x_n, \mathbf{s}_n) p(y \mid x_n', \mathbf{s}_n')} \right)$$

(*c*) Define the "super state"

$$\hat{\mathbf{s}}_n = (\mathbf{s}_n, \mathbf{s}_n') \in \{\Delta_1, \Delta_2, \ldots, \Delta_{K^{2(\mathscr{L}-1)}}\} = \Lambda$$

where $K = |\mathscr{X}|$ is the number of channel input letters and Λ are the $K^{2(\mathscr{L}-1)}$ distinct "super states." Defining $\hat{\mathbf{x}} = (x, x')$, $q(\hat{\mathbf{x}}) = q(x)q(x')$, and super-state transition expression $\hat{\mathbf{s}}_{k+1} = \mathbf{g}(\hat{\mathbf{x}}_k, \hat{\mathbf{s}}_k)$, show that

$$P_{E_1}(\mathbf{x}, \mathbf{x}'|\hat{\mathbf{s}}_1) \le \sum_{\hat{\mathbf{x}}_1}\sum_{\hat{\mathbf{x}}_2}\cdots\sum_{\hat{\mathbf{x}}_N}\prod_{n=1}^{N} q(\hat{\mathbf{x}}_n)\left(\sum_y \sqrt{p(y|x_n, \mathbf{s}_n)p(y|x_n', \mathbf{s}_n)}\right)$$

$$= [1\ 1 \cdots 1]\ A^N \mathbf{i}(\hat{\mathbf{s}})$$

where $\mathbf{i}(\mathbf{s}_1)$ is the $(K^{2(\mathscr{L}-1)})$-dimensional column vector with "1" in the position corresponding to state $\mathbf{s}_1$ and "0" elsewhere, and where

$$A = \{a_{ij}\}$$

is the $K^{2(\mathscr{L}-1)} \times K^{2(\mathscr{L}-1)}$ matrix with

$$a_{ij} = \begin{cases} f(\mathbf{x}, \Delta_j) & \text{if } \Delta_i = \mathbf{g}(\hat{\mathbf{x}}, \Delta_j) \text{ for some } \hat{\mathbf{x}} = (x, x') \\ 0 & \text{otherwise} \end{cases}$$

and

$$f(\hat{\mathbf{x}}, \hat{\mathbf{s}}) = q(\mathbf{x})\left(\sum_y \sqrt{p(y|x, \mathbf{s})p(y|x', \mathbf{s}')}\right)$$

(*d*) Verify that Theorem 5.8.1 generalizes to this general finite memory channel.

CHAPTER

SIX

SEQUENTIAL DECODING OF CONVOLUTIONAL CODES

6.1 FUNDAMENTALS AND A BASIC STACK ALGORITHM

In the last two chapters, we described and analyzed maximum likelihood decoders for convolutional codes. While their performance is significantly superior to that of maximum likelihood decoders for block codes, they suffer from the same disadvantage that computational complexity grows exponentially with constraint length. Thus, even though error probability decreases exponentially with the same parameter, the net effect is that error probability decreases only algebraically with computational complexity. The same is true for block coding, but of course the rate of decrease is much greater with convolutional codes.

This situation could be improved if there were a way to avoid computing the likelihood, or metric, of every path in the trellis and concentrate only on those with higher metrics which presumably should include the correct path.[1] It is practically intuitive, based on our previous analyses, that while an incorrect path is unmerged from the correct path, its metric increments are much lower than those of the correct path over this segment. We can support this observation quantitatively by again considering the ensemble of all possible convolutional codes of a given constraint length for a given channel. Let $\mathbf{x}$ and $\mathbf{x}'$ be the code-vectors for the correct and an incorrect path over a segment where the two are unmerged, and let $\mathbf{y}$ be the received output vector from the memoryless channel

[1] An extension of a given path is regarded as another path.

over this segment. We now indicate the nth symbol of each vector by the subscript n. Suppose we arbitrarily choose for our metric

$$M(\mathbf{x}) = \sum_n m(x_n) \tag{6.1.1}$$

where

$$m(x_n) = \ln \left[\frac{p(y_n \mid x_n)}{p(y_n)}\right] - R \tag{6.1.2}$$

and where we define

$$p(y_n) = \sum_{x_n} q(x_n) p(y_n \mid x_n) \tag{6.1.3}$$

and $q(x)$ is the arbitrary weighting distribution imposed on the code ensemble (see Sec. 5.1).

We note, first of all, that this choice of metric is consistent with the maximum likelihood metric used previously. For, in maximum likelihood decoding, only the difference between the metrics of the paths being compared is utilized. Thus, as we previously defined in (4.4.1) and (5.1.1), the metric difference is

$$\Delta M(\mathbf{x}, \mathbf{x}') = M(\mathbf{x}) - M(\mathbf{x}') = \sum_n \ln \left[\frac{p(y_n \mid x_n)}{p(y_n \mid x_n')}\right] \tag{6.1.4}$$

where the sum is over the symbols in the unmerged span. Consequently, the terms $p(y_n)$ and R do not appear in the metric difference, and hence are immaterial in maximum likelihood decoding. On the other hand, in any algorithm which does not inspect every possible path in making a decision but must choose among paths of *different lengths*, these terms introduce a *bias* which is critical in optimizing the performance of the algorithm.[2] To illustrate the effect of these terms, consider the average metric increase for any symbol of the correct path. As usual, we take both the expectation with respect to the channel output conditional distribution $p(y_n \mid x_n)$ and the ensemble average with respect to the input weighting distribution $q(x_n)$. Thus we have

$$\begin{aligned} E_{x_n, y_n}[m(x_n)] &= \sum_{x_n} q(x_n) \sum_{y_n} p(y_n \mid x_n) m(x_n) \\ &= \sum_{x_n} \sum_{y_n} q(x_n) p(y_n \mid x_n) \left\{ \ln \left[\frac{p(y_n \mid x_n)}{p(y_n)}\right] - R \right\} \\ &= I(\mathbf{q}) - R \end{aligned} \tag{6.1.5}$$

and, if we choose the weighting vector $\mathbf{q}$ to maximize $I(\mathbf{q})$ and thus make it equal to channel capacity

$$E_{x_n, y_n}[m(x_n)] = C - R > 0 \qquad \text{for all } R < C \tag{6.1.6}$$

[2] Massey [1972] has given analytical justification that the metric (6.1.2) is the optimum decoding metric. This metric was first introduced by Fano [1963] and is referred to as the Fano metric (see Prob. 6.7).

On the other hand, for any symbol on an unmerged incorrect path

$$E_{x_n, x_n', y_n}[m(x_n')] = \sum_{x_n'} q(x_n') \sum_{y_n} \sum_{x_n} p(y_n | x_n) q(x_n) m(x_n')$$

$$= \sum_{x_n'} \sum_{y_n} q(x_n') p(y_n) \left\{ \ln \left[\frac{p(y_n | x_n')}{p(y_n)} \right] - R \right\}$$

$$\leq \sum_{x_n'} \sum_{y_n} q(x_n') p(y_n) \left[\frac{p(y_n | x_n')}{p(y_n)} - 1 \right] - R$$

where we have used (6.1.3) and the inequality $\ln x \leq x - 1$. Then since the summation in the last inequality is identically zero we have

$$E_{x_n, x_n', y_n}[m(x_n')] \leq -R \tag{6.1.7}$$

The reason that we had to average over the weighting of x_n, the corresponding symbol of the correct path, is that the distribution of the channel output y_n is conditioned on it.

Thus, we have the heuristic result that the "average" metric[3] increment per symbol of the correct path is always positive for $R < C$, while on an unmerged incorrect path it is always negative. Obviously, any bias term less than C could be used in place of R, but this choice minimizes the computational complexity. The main conclusion to be drawn from this is that, on a long constraint length convolutional code, it should be possible to search out the correct path, since only its metric will rise on the average, while that of any unmerged incorrect path will fall on the average. By making the constraint length K sufficiently long, the fall in any unmerged span can be detected and the path discarded, usually soon after diverging.

Before we can substantiate these heuristic generalities, we must describe an algorithm which somehow recognizes and utilizes these properties. We begin by *defining* a *sequential decoding algorithm* as an algorithm which computes the metric of paths by extending, by one branch only, a path which has already been examined, *and* which bases the decision on which path to extend *only* on the metrics of already examined paths.

Probably the most basic algorithm in this class, and certainly the simplest to describe, is the *stack sequential decoding algorithm* whose flowchart is shown in Table 6.1 for a rate b/n convolutional code. We adopt the notation $\mu(\mathbf{u}, \mathbf{w})$ for the branch metrics, which consist of the sum of n symbol metrics and depend on the b data symbols $\mathbf{w}$ of the given branch as well as on the $(K-1)b$ preceding data symbols $\mathbf{u}$ of the path which determine the state of the node. Thus the algorithm creates a stack of already searched paths of varying lengths, ordered according to their metric values. At each step, the path at the top of the stack is replaced by its

[3] This average, of course, is over the ensemble of codes defined by the arbitrary weighting distribution $q(x)$. From this we can not necessarily conclude at this point that the same will be true for a particular code. To deduce this from the ensemble average can only be considered a heuristic argument.

Table 6.1 Stack algorithm flow chart

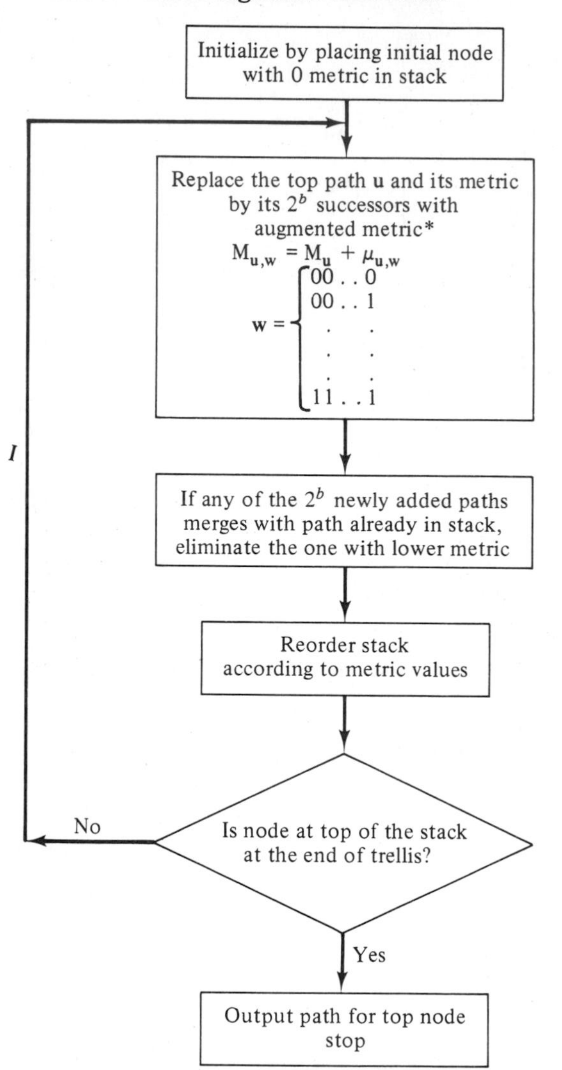

* The metric subscripts **u** and **w** indicate data vectors; in the next section we shall identify metrics by their code vectors **x** used as arguments of $M(\cdot)$.

2^b successors extended by one branch, with correspondingly augmented metrics. If any one of the newly added paths merge with any other trellis path already in the stack, the one with lower metric is eliminated. The algorithm continues in this way until the end of the trellis is reached.

An example of the basic stack algorithm search is illustrated in Fig. 6.1 which shows the tree and path metrics for the $K = 3$, $r = \frac{1}{2}$, convolutional code, first studied in Chap. 4 (Fig. 4.2), transmitted over a BSC with $p = 0.03$. To determine

Information	1	0	1	0	0
Transmitted sequence	11	10	00	10	11
Received sequence	01	10	01	10	11

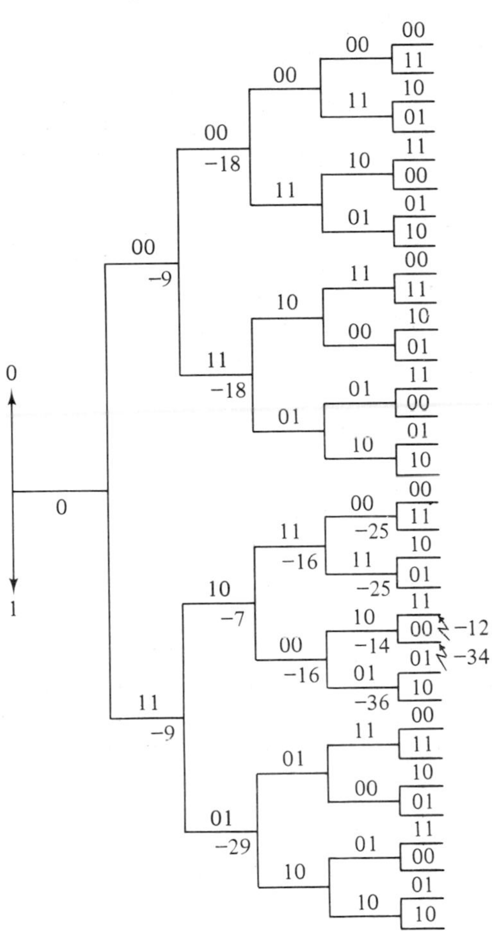

Stack contents after reordering
(path followed by metric)

Time
1 0, −9; 1, −9
2 1, −9; 00, −18; 01, −18
3 10, −7; 00, −18; 01, −18; 11, −29
4 100, −16; 101, −16; 00, −18; 01, −18; 11, −29
5 101, −16; 00, −18; 01, −18; 1000, −25; 1001, −25; 11, −29
6 1010, −14; 00, −18; 01, −18; 1000, −25; 1001, −25; 11, −29; 1011, −36
7 10100, −12; 00, −18; 01, −18; 1000, −25; 1001, −25; 11, −29; 10101, −34; 1011, −36

Figure 6.1 Stack algorithm decoding example.

the symbol metrics, we note first that $R = r \ln 2 = 0.347$ and $p(y_n) = \frac{1}{2}$ for $y_n = 0$ and 1. Thus from (6.1.2) we have

$$m(x_n) = \begin{cases} \ln[2(1-p)] - R = 0.316 & \text{for } x_n = y_n \\ \ln(2p) - R = -3.160 & \text{for } x_n \neq y_n \end{cases}$$

Since the order of the search is unaffected if the symbol metrics are all multiplied by the same positive constant, we may equally use

$$m(x_n) = \begin{cases} +1 & \text{for } x_n = y_n \\ -10 & \text{for } x_n \neq y_n \end{cases}$$

and thus simplify the bookkeeping and the diagram. Figure 6.1 shows the first seven steps of the search, indicating the path and metric values after each new pair of branches have been searched and the stack reordered. Since no two equal length paths with the same terminal state appear in the stack shown through the seventh step, no eliminations occur due to merging up to this point. If, for example, the correct data sequence had been 1 0 1 0 0 so that the received code sequence contains two errors, in the first and third branches (underlined), then it appears that by the fifth step the correct path has reached the top of the stack and remains there at least through the seventh step. Assuming that, of the paths shown in Fig. 6.1, no path other than the top path is further extended (which would certainly be the case if no further errors occurred), we see that, from the third node (where the trellis reaches its full size) through the sixth node, only eight branch metric computations were required by this sequential stack algorithm as compared to the 24 computations required in maximum likelihood decoding. Obviously this comparison becomes ever more impressive as the code constraint length grows.

Nevertheless, each step of the sequential stack algorithm does not necessarily advance the search by one branch. It is clear from the example that the number of incorrect paths searched varies from node to node. At each node of the correct path, we define the *incorrect subset* to be the set of all paths which diverge from the correct path at this node. For a rate $1/n$ code, exactly half the paths emanating from a given node are in its incorrect subset. In the example, assuming again that no further search occurs within the first six branching levels, we see that three paths were searched in the incorrect subset of the first node, one path in that of the second node, and three in that of the third node. Let us define a branch computation as the calculation of the metric of a single path by extension of one branch of a previously examined path. Thus the number of branch computations per node level is just one more than the number of branch computations in the incorrect subset of that node. As shown more generally in Fig. 6.2, there are $\tilde{C}_j$ paths (branch computations) in the incorrect subset of node j, and hence $\tilde{C}_j + 1$ computations required ultimately to reach node level $j + 1$ from node j without ever again retreating.[4] Clearly $\tilde{C}_j$ is a random variable, but, as we shall see in the next

[4] Note that the jth incorrect subset may be revisited at any later time, but we take $\tilde{C}_j$ as the total number of branch metrics computed in this subset over all visits.

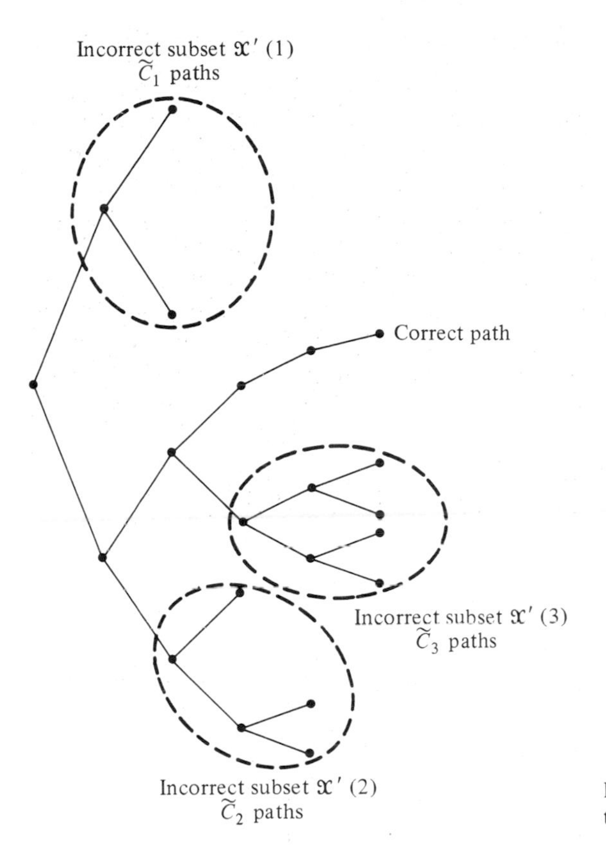

Figure 6.2 Incorrect subsets for first three nodes.

section, its distribution is independent of the constraint length of the code, although it does depend on the rate R. Equally important is the fact that, even though this algorithm is suboptimal, asymptotically for large constraint length it performs essentially as well as maximum likelihood decoding.

We examine the distribution of the number of computations in Sec. 6.2 and the error probability in Sec. 6.3.

6.2 DISTRIBUTION OF COMPUTATIONS: UPPER BOUND

Let $\mathbf{x}$ be the correct path through the trellis and let $\mathbf{x}'_j$ be any incorrect path which diverges from $\mathbf{x}$ at node j; that is, $\mathbf{x}'_j$ is a path in the incorrect subset of node j. Further, let $M[\mathbf{x}(i)]$ be the metric up to node i of the correct path, and let $M[\mathbf{x}'_j(k)]$ be the metric at node k of $\mathbf{x}'_j$ where $k > j$. The number of computations in the jth incorrect subset will depend on the relative values of the metrics $M[\mathbf{x}'_j(k)]$ for all incorrect paths in the subset and on $M[\mathbf{x}(i)]$ where both $k > j$ and $i \geq j$. Precisely, we have the following condition:

Lemma 6.2.1 The incorrect path $\mathbf{x}'_j$ in the jth incorrect subset may have to be searched beyond node $k > j$ only if

$$M[\mathbf{x}'_j(k)] \geq \min_{i \geq j} M[\mathbf{x}(i)] \equiv \gamma_j \tag{6.2.1}$$

Proof A path is searched further if and only if it reaches the top of the stack. We may assume node j on the correct path has been reached; otherwise the incorrect subset for node j will be empty. The algorithm guarantees that, if $M[\mathbf{x}'_j(k)] < M[\mathbf{x}(j)]$, then this incorrect path $\mathbf{x}'_j$ cannot be searched further until after $\mathbf{x}$ has been searched to a point at which its metric falls below $M[\mathbf{x}'_j(k)]$, and hence its position in the stack falls below that of $\mathbf{x}'_j$. But if

$$\min_{i \geq j} M[\mathbf{x}(i)] > M[\mathbf{x}'_j(k)]$$

then this never happens and consequently the incorrect path in question is never searched again, which proves the lemma. Note that we have ignored mergers, but since Lemma 6.2.1 is only a necessary, and not a sufficient, condition for further search, the side condition which causes the pruning of merging paths can be ignored.

This lemma is all that we need to determine the upper bound on the distribution of computation in the jth incorrect subset, which we henceforth denote $\mathscr{X}'(j)$. We note first that the number of computations $\tilde{C}_j$ in this subset will exceed L only if L paths in $\mathscr{X}'(j)$ satisfy condition (6.2.1). Hence

$$\Pr\{\tilde{C}_j \geq L\} \leq \sum_{\mathbf{y}} p(\mathbf{y} \mid \mathbf{x}) \phi_{\mathbf{y}}(L) \tag{6.2.2}$$

where the received code vector[5] runs over all symbols beyond node j, and

$$\phi_{\mathbf{y}}(L) = \begin{cases} 1 & \text{if } M[\mathbf{x}'_j(k)] \geq \gamma_j \text{ for at least } L \text{ paths } \mathbf{x}'_j(k) \in \mathscr{X}'(j) \\ 0 & \text{otherwise} \end{cases} \tag{6.2.3}$$

We proceed to upper-bound (6.2.3) by noting that if, for a given $\mathbf{y}$, $\phi_{\mathbf{y}}(L) = 1$, then by definition

$$M[\mathbf{x}'_j(k)] - \gamma_j \geq 0 \qquad \text{for at least } L \text{ paths } \mathbf{x}'_j(k) \in \mathscr{X}'(j)$$

and consequently

$$e^{\alpha\{M[\mathbf{x}'_j(k)] - \gamma_j\}} \geq 1 \qquad \text{for at least } L \text{ paths } \mathbf{x}'_j(k) \in \mathscr{X}'(j),\ \alpha \geq 0$$

and is nonnegative for all other paths. Thus, summing over all paths in the incorrect subset, we obtain that for any $\mathbf{y}$ for which $\phi_{\mathbf{y}}(L) = 1$

$$\sum_{\mathbf{x}'_j(k) \in \mathscr{X}'(j)} e^{\alpha\{M[\mathbf{x}'_j(k)] - \gamma_j\}} \geq L \qquad \text{for any } \alpha > 0$$

[5] Notation and discussion is simplified if we do not specify the dimensions of vectors; these are either implicit or specifically designated after each equation.

Equivalently,

$$\left[\frac{1}{L} \sum_{\mathbf{x}'_j(k) \in \mathscr{X}'(j)} e^{\alpha\{M[\mathbf{x}'_j(k)] - \gamma_j\}}\right]^\rho \geq 1 = \phi_\mathbf{y}(L) \qquad \text{for any } \alpha > 0 \text{ and } \rho > 0 \quad (6.2.4)$$

The inequality (6.2.4) also holds trivially (as a direct inequality without the intermediate unity term) for $\mathbf{y}$ such that $\phi_\mathbf{y}(L) = 0$. Also, from the definition (6.2.1) of γ_j, it follows that

$$e^{-\alpha\rho\gamma_j} = \exp\left\{-\alpha\rho \min_{i \geq j} M[\mathbf{x}(i)]\right\}$$

and hence

$$e^{-\alpha\rho\gamma_j} \leq \sum_{i=j}^{\infty} e^{-\alpha\rho M[\mathbf{x}(i)]} \qquad (6.2.5)$$

Thus combining (6.2.4) and (6.2.5), we have

$$L^{-\rho}\left\{\sum_{\mathbf{x}'_j(k) \in \mathscr{X}'(j)} e^{\alpha M[\mathbf{x}'_j(k)]}\right\}^\rho \sum_{i=j}^{\infty} e^{-\alpha\rho M[\mathbf{x}(i)]} \geq \phi_\mathbf{y}(L) \qquad (6.2.6)$$

for all $\mathbf{y}$ and any $\alpha > 0$, $\rho > 0$. Substituting into (6.2.2) we obtain

Lemma 6.2.2 The distribution of computation in the jth incorrect subset is upper-bounded by

$$\Pr\{\tilde{C}_j \geq L\} \leq L^{-\rho} \sum_\mathbf{y} p(\mathbf{y} \mid \mathbf{x}) \sum_{i=j}^{\infty} e^{-\alpha\rho M[\mathbf{x}(i)]} \left\{\sum_{\mathbf{x}'_j(k) \in \mathscr{X}'(j)} e^{\alpha M[\mathbf{x}'_j(k)]}\right\}^\rho \qquad \begin{array}{l} \alpha > 0 \\ 0 < \rho \leq 1 \end{array} \quad (6.2.7)$$

Note, of course, that the metrics $M[\,\cdot\,]$, as defined by (6.1.1) and (6.1.2), are functions of $\mathbf{y}$ as well as of $\mathbf{x}$ or $\mathbf{x}'$.

To proceed, we again consider the ensemble of time-varying convolutional codes, first described and used in Sec. 5.1. Averaging over this ensemble, and arguing just as in (5.1.14) and (5.1.15) by restricting ρ to the unit interval and using the Jensen inequality, we obtain[6]

$$\overline{\Pr\{\tilde{C}_j \geq L\}} \leq L^{-\rho} \sum_\mathbf{y} p(\mathbf{y} \mid \mathbf{x}) \overline{\sum_{i=j}^{\infty} e^{-\alpha\rho M[\mathbf{x}(i)]}} \left\{\sum_{\mathbf{x}'_j(k) \in \mathscr{X}'(j)} \overline{e^{\alpha M[\mathbf{x}'_j(k)]}}\right\}^\rho \qquad \begin{array}{l} \alpha > 0 \\ 0 < \rho \leq 1 \end{array}$$

and where the first and second overbars on the right side indicate averages with respect to the weighting distributions $q[\mathbf{x}(i)]$ and $q[\mathbf{x}'_j(k)]$, respectively. Finally,

[6] Note that in taking this ensemble average, we are again ignoring possible merging of the correct and incorrect paths. But, if merging occurs, we would not need to make any further computations on the incorrect path in question; thus ignoring merging merely adds additional terms to the upper bound, which is therefore still valid.

recognizing that in a rate b/n code, ignoring mergers, there are less than $2^{b(k-j)}$ paths $\mathbf{x}'_j(k)$ for $k \geq j$ and that all averages are the same, we obtain, with the aid of inequality (g) of App. 3A

$$\overline{\Pr\{\tilde{C}_j \geq L\}} \leq L^{-\rho} \sum_{\mathbf{y}} \overline{p(\mathbf{y}|\mathbf{x}) \sum_{i=j}^{\infty} e^{-\alpha\rho M[\mathbf{x}(i)]}} \sum_{k=j}^{\infty} 2^{b(k-j)\rho} \{\overline{e^{\alpha M[\mathbf{x}'_j(k)]}}\}^{\rho}$$

To simplify the notation, we let $t = i - j$ and $\tau = k - j$ and summarize the above results as

Lemma 6.2.3 The ensemble average computational distribution in the jth incorrect subset is upper-bounded by

$$\overline{\Pr\{\tilde{C}_j \geq L\}} \leq L^{-\rho} \sum_{t=0}^{\infty} \sum_{\tau=0}^{\infty} T(t, \tau) \tag{6.2.8}$$

where

$$T(t, \tau) \equiv 2^{b\tau\rho} \sum_{\mathbf{y}} \sum_{\mathbf{x}(t)} p[\mathbf{y}|\mathbf{x}(t)]q[\mathbf{x}(t)]e^{-\alpha\rho M[\mathbf{x}(t)]} \left\{ \sum_{\mathbf{x}'(\tau)} q[\mathbf{x}'(\tau)]e^{\alpha M[\mathbf{x}'(\tau)]} \right\}^{\rho} \qquad \begin{matrix} \alpha > 0 \\ 0 < \rho \leq 1 \end{matrix} \tag{6.2.9}$$

and where $\mathbf{x}(t)$ and $\mathbf{x}'(\tau)$ are codeword segments of t and τ branches, respectively.

This bound is clearly independent of j. To evaluate (6.2.9), it is necessary to distinguish the cases $\tau < t$ and $\tau > t$. As shown in Fig. 6.3, the former case corresponds to the case where the correct path segment under consideration is longer than the incorrect, and vice versa for the latter. Then, since the channel is memoryless, it follows from the definitions (6.1.1) through (6.1.3) that, for $\tau < t$

$$T(t, \tau) = 2^{b\tau\rho} e^{-(t-\tau)nE_C(\alpha, \rho)} e^{-\tau nE_{CI}(\alpha, \rho)} \tag{6.2.10a}$$

where

$$e^{-E_C(\alpha, \rho)} = \sum_y \sum_x q(x)p(y|x) \left[\frac{p(y|x)}{p(y)} e^{-R} \right]^{-\alpha\rho} \tag{6.2.11}$$

$$e^{-E_{CI}(\alpha, \rho)} = \sum_y \sum_x q(x)p(y|x) \left[\sum_{x'} q(x') \left(\frac{p(y|x')}{p(y|x)} \right)^{\alpha} \right]^{\rho} \tag{6.2.12}$$

while for $\tau > t$

$$T(t, \tau) = 2^{b\tau\rho} e^{-E_I(\alpha, \rho)(\tau - t)n} e^{-tnE_{CI}(\alpha, \rho)} \tag{6.2.10b}$$

where

$$e^{-E_I(\alpha, \rho)} = \sum_y p(y) \left\{ \sum_{x'} q(x') \left[\frac{p(y|x')}{p(y)} e^{-R} \right]^{\alpha} \right\}^{\rho} \tag{6.2.13}$$

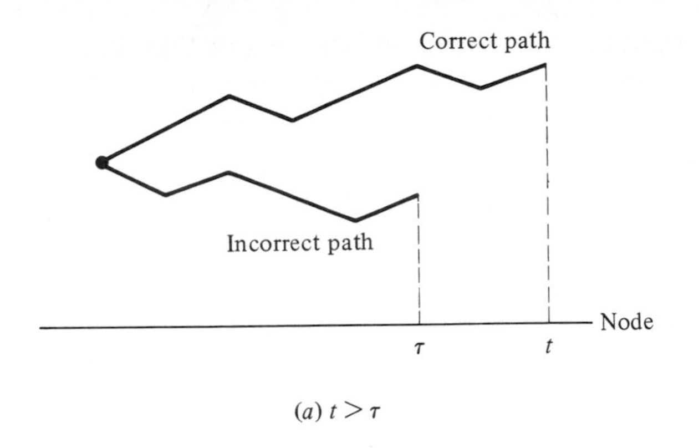

(a) $t > \tau$

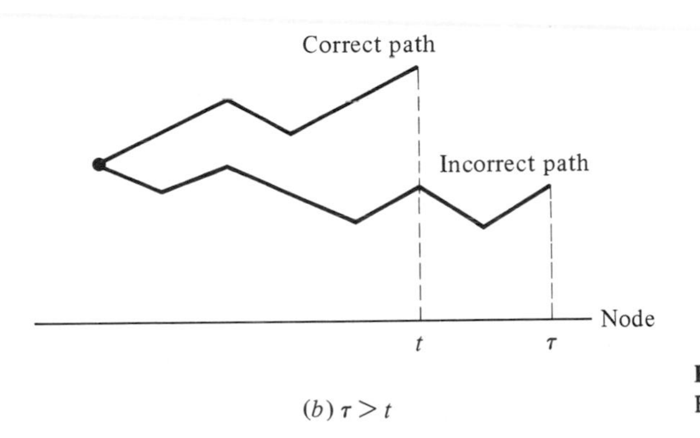

(b) $\tau > t$

Figure 6.3 Relative node depths for Eq. (6.2.9).

It should be clear that the single subscripts C and I correspond to segments which contain only the correct or incorrect path branches, respectively, while the double subscript CI corresponds to segments which contain branches of both the correct and incorrect paths (see Fig. 6.3).

Thus, since $R = (b/n) \ln 2$, we may rewrite $T(t, \tau)$ as

$$T(t, \tau) = \begin{cases} \exp\left[-n\{(t-\tau)E_C(\alpha, \rho) + \tau[E_{CI}(\alpha, \rho) - \rho R]\}\right] & \tau \le t \\ \exp\left[-n\{(\tau - t)[E_I(\alpha, \rho) - \rho R] + t[E_{CI}(\alpha, \rho) - \rho R]\}\right] & \tau \ge t \end{cases} \tag{6.2.14}$$

Finally, applying the Hölder inequality (App. 3A) to each component of the exponents, using the definitions (6.2.11) through (6.2.13), we find

$$e^{-E_C(\alpha, \rho)} \le e^{\alpha\rho R - (1-\alpha\rho)E_o[\alpha\rho/(1-\alpha\rho)]} \equiv \delta_C \tag{6.2.15}$$

$$e^{-[E_I(\alpha, \rho) - \rho R]} \le e^{\rho(1-\alpha)R - \alpha\rho E_o[(1-\alpha)/\alpha]} \equiv \delta_I \tag{6.2.16}$$

$$e^{-[E_{CI}(\alpha, \rho) - \rho R]} \le e^{\rho R - (1-\alpha\rho)E_o[\alpha\rho/(1-\alpha\rho)] - \alpha\rho E_o[(1-\alpha)/\alpha]} = \delta_C \delta_I \tag{6.2.17}$$

where $0 < \alpha\rho < 1$ and where $E_o(\rho)$ is the Gallager function[7] of (3.1.18). Thus

$$T(t, \tau) \leq \delta_C^{nt}\, \delta_I^{n\tau} \qquad \text{for all } t \geq 0,\ \tau \geq 0 \tag{6.2.18}$$

Now in order for the double summation (6.2.8) to be bounded, we must have $\delta_C < 1$ and $\delta_I < 1$; but according to (6.2.15) and (6.2.16)

$$\delta_C < 1$$

$$\text{if} \quad R < \frac{1-\alpha\rho}{\alpha\rho} E_o\left(\frac{\alpha\rho}{1-\alpha\rho}\right) \quad \text{or} \quad R < \frac{E_o(\gamma)}{\gamma} \quad \text{where } \gamma = \frac{\alpha\rho}{1-\alpha\rho} > 0$$

$$\delta_I < 1$$

$$\text{if} \quad R < \frac{\alpha}{1-\alpha} E_o\left(\frac{1-\alpha}{\alpha}\right) \quad \text{or} \quad R < \frac{E_o(\delta)}{\delta} \quad \text{where } \delta = \frac{1-\alpha}{\alpha} > 0$$

Thus for $\alpha = 1/(1 + \rho)$, both conditions reduce to

$$\delta_C < 1,\ \delta_I < 1 \quad \text{if} \quad R < \frac{E_o(\rho)}{\rho} \qquad 0 < \rho \leq 1 \tag{6.2.19}$$

Finally, choosing ρ such that

$$R = (1 - \epsilon)\frac{E_o(\rho)}{\rho} \qquad \epsilon > 0$$

we have from (6.2.8), (6.2.18), and (6.2.19)

$$\overline{\Pr\{\tilde{C}_j \geq L\}} \leq AL^{-\rho}$$

where

$$A = \frac{1}{(1 - \delta_C^n)(1 - \delta_I^n)} \qquad 0 < \rho \leq 1$$

Thus, we may conclude with

Theorem 6.2.1 There exists a time-varying, rate b/n, convolutional code whose distribution of computation in any incorrect subset (and hence of computation required to advance one branch) is bounded by

$$\Pr\{\tilde{C} \geq L\} < AL^{-\rho} \qquad 0 < \rho \leq 1 \tag{6.2.20}$$

where A is a constant and ρ is related to the rate $R = (b/n) \ln 2$ by the parametric equation

$$R = (1 - \epsilon)\frac{E_o(\rho)}{\rho} \qquad R_0 < \frac{R}{1-\epsilon} < C \tag{6.2.21}$$

[7] Maximization of the exponent with respect to $q(x)$ is implied here.

and ϵ is any positive constant. The distribution described in (6.2.20) is called a *Pareto distribution.* Note that the power ρ goes to unity as $R \to R_0$ and to zero as $R \to C$ when we let $\epsilon \to 0$.

Obviously, the condition (6.2.19) also yields an upper bound for lower rates ($R < R_0$). We may take $\rho = 1$ so that

$$\Pr\{\tilde{C} \geq L\} < \frac{A}{L} \qquad R < R_0 \tag{6.2.22}$$

However, one would expect a more rapid decrease with L for low rates, and in fact, if we remove the linearity condition on our code, a tighter result can be proved. Precisely, for a time-varying trellis code,[8] it can be shown (Savage [1966]) that

$$\Pr\{\tilde{C} \geq L\} < AL^{-\rho} \qquad 0 < \rho < \infty \tag{6.2.23}$$

where

$$R = (1-\epsilon)\frac{E_o(\rho)}{\rho} \qquad 0 < R < C(1-\epsilon)$$

We shall show in Sec. 6.4 that this is the best possible computational distribution by deriving a lower bound for any sequential decoding algorithm. But before we do this, in Sec. 6.3 we upper-bound the error probability for this algorithm, to show that it is asymptotically optimum for large K.

6.3 ERROR PROBABILITY UPPER BOUND

The calculation of an upper bound on node or bit error probability for sequential decoding is almost the same as that for the distribution of computations. We now concentrate on the merging of paths, but rather than consider the probability that an incorrect path metric exceeds the correct path metric upon merging, we recognize that an incorrect path in the jth incorrect subset does not even get a chance to reach the merging point if its metric at the merging point is below the minimum metric of the correct path after node j. That is, consider the incorrect path $\mathbf{x}'_j(k)$ which diverges from the correct path at node j and remerges at node k. If

$$M[\mathbf{x}'_j(k)] < \min_{i \geq j} M[\mathbf{x}(i)]$$

then the incorrect path does not even get a chance to be compared with the correct path at this point.[9] Alternatively, we can state this in the same form as Lemma 6.2.1.

[8] A general time-varying trellis code of constraint length K can be generated by the same K-stage shift register(s) as a convolutional code, but with time-varying arbitrary logic ("and" and "or" gates) in place of linear logic (modulo-2 addition).

[9] This implies also that the step in the Stack algorithm (Table 6.1) which eliminates merging paths may be omitted. (See Sec. 6.5.)

Lemma 6.3.1 An error may be caused by selecting an incorrect path $\mathbf{x}_j'(k)$ which diverged from the correct path at node j and remerged with it at node k *only if*

$$M[\mathbf{x}_j'(k)] \geq \min_{i \geq j} M[\mathbf{x}(i)] \equiv \gamma_j \tag{6.3.1}$$

Again this condition is necessary, but clearly not sufficient for an error to occur.

From this point, much of the derivation closely follows that of the previous section. There is, however, one important difference. While $\mathbf{x}_j'(k)$ in Sec. 6.2 represented any path in the jth incorrect subset, it now represents only such a path which merges at node k. Thus the steps leading to Lemma 6.2.2 are essentially the same, as is the lemma itself, but now the set $\mathscr{X}'(j)$ must be replaced by the union of subsets $\bigcup_{k=j+K}^{\infty} \mathscr{X}'(j; k) \subset \mathscr{X}'(j)$ where $\mathscr{X}'(j; k)$ contains all paths in $\mathscr{X}'(j)$ which remerge with the correct path at node k. We can thus prove

Lemma 6.3.2 The node error probability at node j is upper-bounded by

$$P_e(j) \leq \sum_{\mathbf{y}} p(\mathbf{y} \mid \mathbf{x}) \sum_{i=j}^{\infty} e^{-\alpha\rho M[\mathbf{x}(i)]} \sum_{k=j+K}^{\infty} \left\{ \sum_{\mathbf{x}_j'(k) \in \mathscr{X}'(j;\, k)} e^{\alpha M[\mathbf{x}_j'(k)]} \right\}^{\rho} \qquad \begin{array}{c} \alpha > 0 \\ 0 < \rho \leq 1 \end{array} \tag{6.3.2}$$

and the expected number of bit errors caused by a path which diverged at node j is upper-bounded by

$$E[n_b(j)] \leq \sum_{\mathbf{y}} p(\mathbf{y} \mid \mathbf{x}) \sum_{i=j}^{\infty} e^{-\alpha\rho M[\mathbf{x}(i)]} \sum_{k=j+K}^{\infty} b[k - j - (K-1)]$$
$$\times \left\{ \sum_{\mathbf{x}_j'(k) \in \mathscr{X}'(j;\, k)} e^{\alpha M[\mathbf{x}_j'(k)]} \right\}^{\rho} \qquad \begin{array}{c} \alpha > 0 \\ 0 < \rho \leq 1 \end{array} \tag{6.3.3}$$

Proof Let $P_e(j; k)$ be the probability of an error at node j caused by a path which remerges at node k. Analogously to (6.2.2), we have, using Lemma 6.3.1

$$P_e(j; k) \leq \sum_{\mathbf{y}} p(\mathbf{y} \mid \mathbf{x}) \phi_{\mathbf{y}}(1) \tag{6.3.4}$$

where recall from (6.2.3) that

$$\phi_{\mathbf{y}}(1) = \begin{cases} 1 & \text{if } M[\mathbf{x}_j'(k)] \geq \gamma_j \text{ for some } \mathbf{x}_j'(k) \in \mathscr{X}'(j;\, k) \\ 0 & \text{otherwise} \end{cases}$$

Thus if for a given $\mathbf{y}$, $\phi_{\mathbf{y}}(1) = 1$, then

$$e^{\alpha\{M[\mathbf{x}_j'(k)] - \gamma_j\}} \geq 1$$

for some $\mathbf{x}'_j(k) \in \mathscr{X}'(j; k)$. Hence for this $\mathbf{y}$

$$\left[\sum_{\mathbf{x}'_j(k) \in \mathscr{X}'(j;k)} e^{\alpha\{M[\mathbf{x}'_j(k)] - \gamma_j\}} \right]^\rho \geq 1 = \phi_\mathbf{y}(1) \qquad \begin{array}{l} \alpha > 0 \\ \rho \geq 0 \end{array} \tag{6.3.5}$$

while if $\phi_\mathbf{y}(1) = 0$, (6.3.5) holds trivially without the intermediate unity term. At the same time, $e^{-\alpha\rho\gamma_j}$ may be bounded just as in (6.2.5). Thus substituting (6.3.5) for $\phi_\mathbf{y}(1)$ and (6.2.5) for $e^{-\alpha\rho\gamma_j}$ yields

$$P_e(j; k) \leq \sum_\mathbf{y} p(\mathbf{y} \mid \mathbf{x}) \sum_{i=j}^{\infty} e^{-\alpha\rho M[\mathbf{x}(i)]} \left\{ \sum_{\mathbf{x}'_j(k) \in \mathscr{X}'(j;k)} e^{\alpha M[\mathbf{x}'_j(k)]} \right\}^\rho \tag{6.3.6}$$

It takes at least K branches for a path to remerge; thus

$$P_e(j) \leq \sum_{k=j+K}^{\infty} P_e(j; k) \tag{6.3.7}$$

Combining (6.3.6) and (6.3.7) yields (6.3.2). To find the expected number of bit errors caused by such a node error, we observe, as in Sec. 5.1, that the number of bit errors caused by an incorrect path unmerged for $k - j$ branches cannot be greater than $b[k - j - (K - 1)]$ [since the last $K - 1$ branches, or $b(K - 1)$ symbols, must be the same as for the correct path]. Thus

$$E[n_b(j)] \leq \sum_{k=j+K}^{\infty} b[k - j - (K - 1)]P_e(j; k) \tag{6.3.8}$$

Combining (6.3.6) and (6.3.8) yields (6.3.3), and thus proves the lemma.

If we now proceed as in Sec. 6.2, by averaging (6.3.3) over the same code ensemble, restricting ρ to the unit interval and applying the Jensen inequality, we obtain

$$\overline{E[n_b(j)]} \leq \overline{\sum_\mathbf{y} p(\mathbf{y} \mid \mathbf{x}) \sum_{i=j}^{\infty} e^{-\alpha\rho M[\mathbf{x}(i)]}} \sum_{k=j+K}^{\infty} b(k - j - K + 1) \times \left\{ \sum_{\mathbf{x}'_j(k) \in \mathscr{X}'(j;k)} \overline{e^{\alpha M[\mathbf{x}'_j(k)]}} \right\}^\rho \qquad \begin{array}{l} \alpha > 0 \\ 0 < \rho \leq 1 \end{array} \tag{6.3.9}$$

But the set $\mathscr{X}'(j; k)$ of incorrect paths diverging at node j and remerging at node k contains no more than $(2^b - 1)2^{b[(k-j)-K]}$ paths, since the first branch must differ from the correct path while, of the remaining $(k - j - 1)$ branches, the last $(K - 1)$ branches must be identical to it. Thus, since the same weighting distribution is used for all path branches

$$\overline{E[n_b(j)]} \leq \overline{\sum_\mathbf{y} p(\mathbf{y} \mid \mathbf{x}) \sum_{i=j}^{\infty} e^{-\alpha\rho M[\mathbf{x}(i)]}} \times \sum_{k=j+K}^{\infty} b(k - j - K + 1)(2^b - 1)^\rho 2^{b[(k-j)-K]\rho} \{\overline{e^{\alpha M[\mathbf{x}_j'(k)]}}\}^\rho$$

Finally, since by (5.1.32)

$$\overline{P_b} \le \frac{\overline{E[n_b(j)]}}{b}$$

letting $t = i - j$ and $\tau = k - j$, we have

Lemma 6.3.3 The ensemble average bit error probability is upper-bounded by

$$\overline{P_b} \le (2^b - 1)^\rho 2^{-bK\rho} \sum_{t=0}^{\infty} \sum_{\tau=K}^{\infty} [\tau - (K-1)] T(t, \tau) \tag{6.3.10}$$

where

$$T(t, \tau) = 2^{b\tau\rho} \sum_{\mathbf{y}} \sum_{\mathbf{x}} p(\mathbf{y} \mid \mathbf{x}) q(\mathbf{x}) e^{-\alpha\rho M[\mathbf{x}(t)]} \left\{ \sum_{\mathbf{x}'(\tau)} q[\mathbf{x}'(\tau)] e^{\alpha M[\mathbf{x}'(\tau)]} \right\}^\rho \qquad \begin{matrix} \alpha > 0 \\ 0 < \rho \le 1 \end{matrix} \tag{6.2.9}$$

But $T(t, \tau)$ is identical to the function defined in Sec. 6.2, and we have shown there that

$$T(t, \tau) \le \delta_C^{nt} \delta_I^{n\tau} \qquad \text{for all } t \ge 0, \tau \ge 0 \tag{6.2.18}$$

with

$$\delta_C < 1, \delta_I < 1 \qquad \text{if } \alpha = \frac{1}{1+\rho} \text{ and } R < \frac{E_o(\rho)}{\rho} \tag{6.2.19}$$

Thus letting $R = (1 - \epsilon)E_o(\rho)/\rho$, we have that the sum of (6.3.10) is bounded by

$$\overline{P_b} \le \frac{(2^b - 1)\delta_I^{Kn}}{(1 - \delta_C^n)(1 - \delta_I^n)^2} 2^{-bK\rho} \qquad \begin{matrix} 0 < \rho \le 1 \\ R_0(1-\epsilon) \le R \le C(1-\epsilon) \end{matrix} \tag{6.3.11}$$

For $R < R_0$, as usual we choose $\rho = 1$. Thus, using the terminology of Sec. 5.1 (5.1.34)

$$E_c(R) = E_o(\rho)$$

$$R = \frac{(1-\epsilon)E_o(\rho)}{\rho}$$

and taking $\epsilon = |\ln \delta_I|/E_c(R)$, we have the following theorem.

Theorem 6.3.1: Error probability with sequential decoding (Yudkin [1964]) The ensemble average bit error probability of a sequentially decoded time-varying convolutional code of rate b/n is upper-bounded by

$$\overline{P_b} \le \begin{cases} D2^{-Kb} & 0 \le R \le R_0(1-\epsilon) \\ D2^{-KbE_c(R)/R} & R_0(1-\epsilon) \le R \le C(1-\epsilon) \end{cases} \tag{6.3.12}$$

where $E_c(R)$ is given by (5.1.34) and[10]

$$D \leq \frac{2^b - 1}{(1 - \delta_C^{b \ln 2/R})[1 - 2^{-\epsilon b E_c(R)/R}]^2} < \frac{2^b - 1}{[1 - 2^{-\epsilon b E_c(R)/R}]^3} \tag{6.3.13}$$

The exponent of (6.3.12) has the same form as that of (5.1.32), the upper bound for Viterbi decoding at high rates[11] [except that ϵ here is related to δ_I whereas in (5.1.32) it is an arbitrary positive number]. On the other hand, for lower rates $R < R_0$, the exponent is reduced from $R_0/R > 1$ to unity. It would be possible to increase this exponent, as well as that of (6.2.22), by a different choice of bias term [R replaced by $R_0(1 - \epsilon)$] in the metric (6.1.2), but only at the cost of a worse distribution of computation at higher rates (see Prob. 6.2).

There remains one issue to resolve. Although we proved in Sec. 6.2 that there exists a code for which $\Pr(\tilde{C} \geq L) < AL^{-\rho}$, and although it follows from Theorem 6.3.1 that there exists a code for which $P_b \leq \overline{P_b}$ is bounded by (6.3.12), these bounds may not both hold simultaneously for the same code. The resolution of this dilemma is arrived at by an argument similar to that used in Sec. 3.2. Assuming, for the moment, a uniform weighting of the ensemble, there exist α and β on the unit interval such that all but a fraction α of the codes satisfy

$$\Pr\{\tilde{C} \geq L\} < \frac{A}{\alpha} L^{-\rho} \tag{6.3.14}$$

while all but a fraction β of the codes satisfy

$$P_b < \overline{P_b}/\beta \tag{6.3.15}$$

Thus, at most a fraction $\alpha + \beta$ fail to satisfy at least one of these bounds, and consequently a fraction $(1 - \alpha - \beta)$ must satisfy both. With nonuniform ensemble weighting, an essentially probabilistic statement must replace this simple argument. In any case, there exists at least one code which, within unimportant multiplicative constants, simultaneously satisfies the upper bounds of both Theorems 6.2.1 and 6.3.1.

6.4 DISTRIBUTION OF COMPUTATION: LOWER BOUND

We now proceed to show that the upper bound of Theorem 6.2.1 for convolutional codes is asymptotically tight at least for $R \geq R_0$, and that the result (6.2.23) for trellis codes is asymptotically tight for $R < R_0$ as well. The proof is based on comparing the list of paths searched by a sequential decoder with the list of the L paths of highest metric for a fixed block decoder, and employing the lower bound of Lemma 3.8.1 on list-of-L block decoding.

[10] The last inequality in (6.3.13) follows from the choice of ϵ and substitution of (6.2.19) in (6.2.15) and (6.2.16).

[11] For systematic codes, the exponent is reduced by the factor of $1 - r = 1 - R/\ln 2$. This is shown by applying the same arguments as used in Sec. 5.7.

We begin by considering a sequential decoder aided by a benevolent genie who oversees the decoder action on each incorrect subset. If any incorrect path of the jth incorrect subset is searched to length l branches ($N = ln$ symbols) beyond node j, the genie stops the decoder and informs it to stop searching this path. Provided no decoding error is made at the jth node, the distribution of computation on the jth incorrect subset $\Pr\{\tilde{C}_j \geq L\}$ is lower-bounded by the probability that the genie stops the decoder L times. For first of all, a computation has been defined as a branch computation, and L is just the number of computations on the last branch of all the incorrect paths stopped by the genie. Hence we are ignoring all but the last branch of each path in computing the lower bound. Furthermore, many other paths may have been searched, but not to depth l branches. Finally, if the genie were not present, the incorrect paths might be allowed to continue for even more operations; but if no errors are made in the jth subset, we will ultimately return, just as if the genie were present. Thus in the absence of errors

$$\Pr\{\tilde{C}_j \geq L\} > P_g(L) \tag{6.4.1}$$

where

$$P_g(L) \equiv \Pr\begin{Bmatrix}\text{genie stops decoder at depth } l \text{ of } j\text{th incorrect} \\ \text{subset more than } L \text{ times}\end{Bmatrix} \tag{6.4.2}$$

Naturally, when the correct path arrives at depth l beyond node j, it is allowed through. Thus suppose we construct a list $\mathscr{X}_L(j)$ of the first L paths (incorrect or correct) emanating from node j of the correct path and examined by the genie at node $j + l$. Then letting $\overline{\mathscr{X}_L}(j)$ be the complementary set of $2^{bl} - L$ paths *not* on this list, the probability that the genie stops the decoder more than L times for a given received vector $\mathbf{y}$ is

$$P_g(L \mid \mathbf{y}) = \Pr\{\mathbf{x} \in \overline{\mathscr{X}_L}(j) \mid \mathbf{y}\} \tag{6.4.3}$$

where $\mathbf{x}$ is the correct path over the given ln-symbol segment. Then, since all 2^{bl} paths of this length emanating from a common node j are a priori equiprobable, it follows that

$$P_g(L) = \sum_{\mathbf{y}} \sum_{\mathbf{x} \in \overline{\mathscr{X}_L}(j)} \frac{1}{2^{bl}} p_N(\mathbf{y} \mid \mathbf{x}) \tag{6.4.4}$$

This procedure should remind us of the list-of-L decoder described in Sec. 3.8 and Prob. 3.16. A maximum likelihood list-of-L decoder for a code of M code-vectors produces a list consisting of the L code-vectors with highest likelihood functions (metrics). Suppose the number of code vectors is $M = 2^{bl}$. Let the list of the L most likely code-vectors be denoted $\mathscr{U}(L)$ and the complementary set, consisting of the $2^{bl} - L$ code-vectors not on the list, be denoted $\overline{\mathscr{U}}(L)$. Then for any block code of 2^{bl} a priori equiprobable code vectors of length N, the block error probability of such a decoder is

$$P_E(L) = \sum_{\mathbf{y}} \sum_{\mathbf{x} \in \overline{\mathscr{U}}(L)} \frac{1}{2^{bl}} p_N(\mathbf{y} \mid \mathbf{x}) \tag{6.4.5}$$

Now the genie-aided sequential decoding of all paths of length N symbols emanating from the jth node can also be regarded as a decoding operation on a somewhat constrained (truncated convolutional) block code of 2^{bl} vectors. However, while it does produce a list-of-L output, this list does not correspond to maximum likelihood decoding. Thus it follows that for every $\mathbf{x}_a \in \mathscr{X}_L(j)$, there is some $\mathbf{x}_b \in \mathscr{U}(L)$ such that

$$p_N(\mathbf{y} \mid \mathbf{x}_a) \le p_N(\mathbf{y} \mid \mathbf{x}_b) \qquad \begin{array}{l} \mathbf{x}_a \in \mathscr{X}_L(j) \\ \mathbf{x}_b \in \mathscr{U}(L) \end{array}$$

Since $\mathscr{U}(L) + \overline{\mathscr{U}(L)} = \mathscr{X}_L(j) + \overline{\mathscr{X}_L}(j)$ it follows that if, for a given $\mathbf{y}$, we sum the $2^{bl} - L$ elements of the complementary sets, then

$$\sum_{\mathbf{x} \in \overline{\mathscr{X}}_L(j)} p_N(\mathbf{y} \mid \mathbf{x}) \ge \sum_{\mathbf{x} \in \overline{\mathscr{U}}(L)} p_N(\mathbf{y} \mid \mathbf{x}) \tag{6.4.6}$$

since $\overline{\mathscr{U}(L)}$ consists of the $(2^{bl} - L)$ vectors with lowest likelihood, while $\overline{\mathscr{X}_L}(j)$ may have some elements which are contained in $\mathscr{U}(L)$.

Finally combining (6.4.1) and (6.4.4) and employing (6.4.6) to compare this with (6.4.5), we have

$$\begin{aligned} \Pr\{\tilde{C}_j \ge L\} > P_g(L) &= \sum_{\mathbf{y}} \sum_{\mathbf{x} \in \overline{\mathscr{X}}_L(j)} 2^{-bl} p_N(\mathbf{y} \mid \mathbf{x}) \\ &\ge \sum_{\mathbf{y}} \sum_{\mathbf{x} \in \overline{\mathscr{U}}(L)} 2^{-bl} p_N(\mathbf{y} \mid \mathbf{x}) \\ &= P_E(L) \end{aligned} \tag{6.4.7}$$

At this point we may use Lemma 3.8.1 which lower-bounds the list decoding error probability $P_E(L) = P_E(N, 2^{bl}, L)$ to obtain

$$\Pr\{\tilde{C}_j \ge L\} > e^{-N[E_{sp}(\tilde{R}) + o(L)]} \tag{3.8.2}$$

where

$$\tilde{R} = \frac{\ln(2^{bl}/L)}{N} \qquad N = nl \tag{3.8.3}$$

and

$$\begin{aligned} E_{sp}(\tilde{R}) &= E_o(\rho) - \rho E_o'(\rho) \qquad & 0 \le \rho < \infty \\ \tilde{R} &= E_o'(\rho) & 0 \le R < C \end{aligned} \tag{3.6.46}$$

To utilize this result, we must choose l or $N = nl$, the genie's vantage point. Suppose we arbitrarily pick[12]

$$nl = nl_{\text{crit}} = \frac{\rho \ln L}{E_o(\rho) - \rho E_o'(\rho)} \tag{6.4.8}$$

[12] The connection between l_{crit} and k_{crit} of (5.5.5) is noteworthy (see Prob. 6.5).

Combining (3.8.2), (3.8.3), (3.6.46), and (6.4.8), we obtain[13]

$$\begin{aligned}\Pr\{\tilde{C}_j \geq L\} &> e^{-nl_{\text{crit}}[E_o(\rho) - \rho E_o'(\rho) + o(l_{\text{crit}})]} \\ &= e^{-\rho \ln L[1+o(L)]} \\ &= L^{-\rho}[1 - o(L)] \qquad 0 \leq \rho < \infty \end{aligned} \tag{6.4.9}$$

To determine the relationships between rate and ρ, we have from (3.6.46), (3.8.3), and (6.4.8)

$$\begin{aligned} E_o'(\rho) = \tilde{R} &= \frac{\ln (2^{bl_{\text{crit}}})}{nl_{\text{crit}}} - \frac{\ln L}{nl_{\text{crit}}} \\ &= R - \left[\frac{E_o(\rho)}{\rho} - E_o'(\rho)\right] \end{aligned}$$

Thus

$$R = \frac{E_o(\rho)}{\rho} \qquad 0 \leq \rho < \infty \tag{6.4.10}$$

Hence we obtain the following theorem.

Theorem 6.4.1: Computational distribution lower bound (Jacobs and Berlekamp [1967]) The computational distribution of any convolutional (or trellis) code, on any incorrect subset where no decoding error occurs, is lower-bounded by

$$\Pr\{\tilde{C} \geq L\} > L^{-\rho}[1 - o(L)] \tag{6.4.11}$$

where

$$R = \frac{E_o(\rho)}{\rho} \qquad \begin{matrix} 0 < \rho < \infty \\ 0 < R < C \end{matrix} \tag{6.4.12}$$

Thus, by comparing Theorems 6.2.1 and 6.4.1, we see that the bounds in both theorems are asymptotically tight for $R_0 \leq R < C$. For lower rates $0 < R < R_0$, the lower bound (6.4.11) has been shown to be asymptotically tight only for time-varying trellis (nonlinear convolutional) codes. For linear convolutional codes, the lower-bound exponent of (6.4.11) does not agree for the lower rates with the upper-bound exponent of (6.2.22). It is not known whether either bound is tight.

Given the significance of this Pareto distribution for the operation of a sequential decoder, it is worthwhile to examine how the key parameter ρ, known as the *Pareto exponent*, varies with the channel probability distribution for specific commonly used channels. For the BSC derived from the binary-input AWGN

[13] Here $o(L) \sim 1/\sqrt{\ln L}$.

channel by hard quantization of the channel output ($J = 2$), the function $E_o(\rho)$, first derived in Sec. 3.4, depends only on the symbol energy-to-noise density $\mathscr{E}_s/N_o$ [see (3.4.1) with p given by (3.4.18)]. Then solving the parametric equation (6.4.12) for ρ, with various values of code rate $r = R/\ln 2$, results in the curves shown in Fig. 6.4, where ρ is plotted as a function of $\mathscr{E}_b/N_o = (\mathscr{E}_s/N_o)/r$ in dB.

Of considerable interest is the behavior of the decoder when soft (multilevel) quantization is used on the AWGN channel output. Figure 6.5 shows the corresponding results for the octal (3-bit) quantizer of Fig. 2.13 and the corresponding channel of Fig. 2.14, with the quantization step $a = 0.58\sqrt{N_o/2}$. For this case, $E_o(\rho)$ is obtained from the general expression (3.1.18) with the transition probabilities given by (2.8.1). We note that the improvement over the hard-quantized case is very nearly $\pi/2$ (2 dB), the same improvement factor found for small $\mathscr{E}_s/N_o$ in Sec. 3.4 (Fig. 3.8).

Note also that $\rho = 1$ corresponds to $R = R_0 = E_o(1) = E(0)$, and thus the intercepts of the line $\rho = 1$ for each curve in Figs. 6.4 and 6.5 can be derived from the $J = 2$ and $J = 8$ curves of Fig. 3.8(b) by finding the point at which $E(0) = R = r \ln 2$.

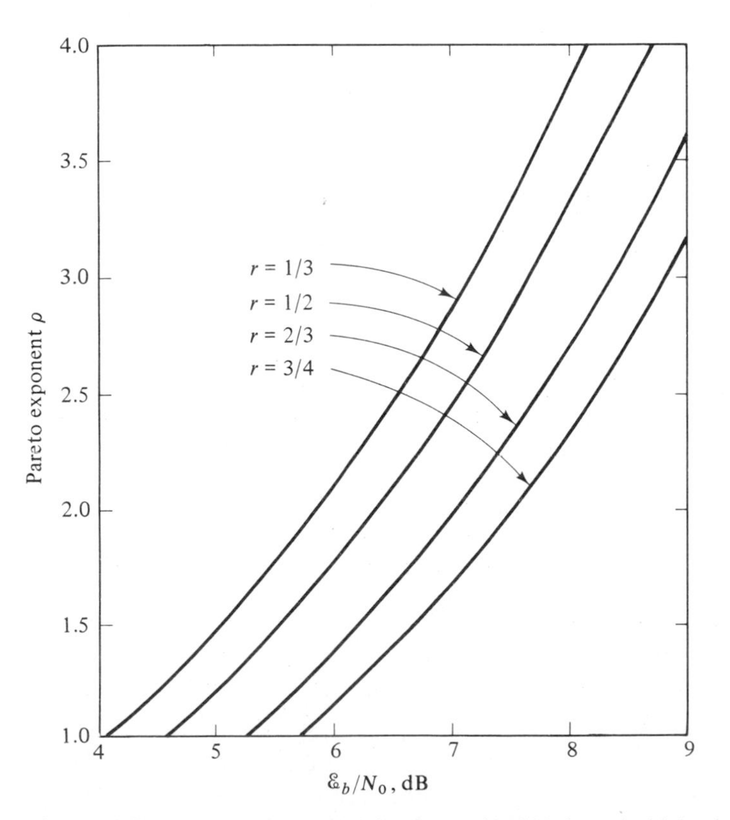

Figure 6.4 Pareto exponent versus $\mathscr{E}_b/N_o$ for an AWGN channel with hard quantization.

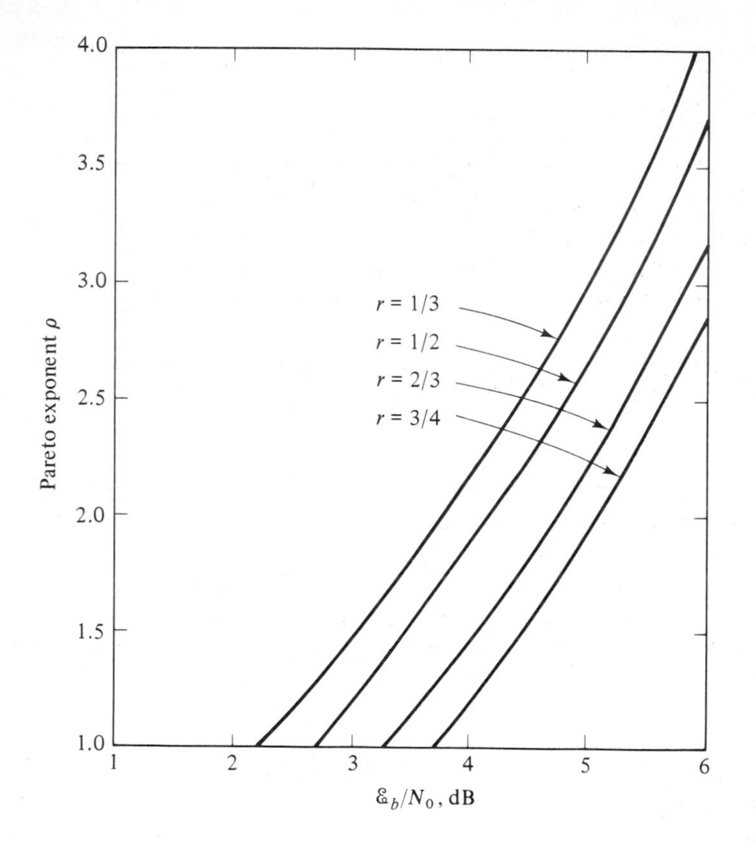

Figure 6.5 Pareto exponent versus $\mathcal{E}_b/N_o$ for an AWGN channel with octal quantization ($a = 0.58\sqrt{N_o/2}$).

6.5 THE FANO ALGORITHM AND OTHER SEQUENTIAL DECODING ALGORITHMS

The basic stack sequential decoding algorithm is a distillation and ultimate simplification of a number of successively discovered algorithms, each of which was progressively simpler to describe and analyze. The original sequential decoding algorithm, proposed and analyzed by Wozencraft [1957], utilized a sequence of progressively looser thresholds to eliminate all paths in the incorrect subset of node j before proceeding to search the paths emanating from node $j + 1$. This technique is mainly of historical importance. The next important step was the algorithm described by Fano [1963], whose complete analysis appears in the work of Yudkin [1964], Wozencraft and Jacobs [1965], and Gallager [1968]. From a practical viewpoint, the Fano algorithm is still probably the most important and will be discussed further below. Stack algorithms, which form the basis of the algorithm treated in Secs. 6.1 to 6.4 were proposed and analyzed independently by Zigangirov [1966] and Jelinek [1969*a*]. Also of some tutorial value is the semi-sequential algorithm proposed by Viterbi [1967*a*] (Prob. 6.4) and extended by Forney [1974].

The Zigangirov and Jelinek algorithms are most similar to the one considered here. They differ, however, in certain features designed to render them more practical for implementation. First, *both ignore merging* and thus make no provisions for comparing the metric of a path newly added to the stack with that of a previously inserted path of the same length terminating in the same state. But this does not significantly increase the probability of error, for in Sec. 6.3, we upper-bounded P_e by determining the probability that an incorrect path was searched up to the point of merging. This is tantamount to assuming that errors always occur if an incorrect path is allowed to merge, and so the already calculated error bound is valid even if comparisons of merging paths are not performed. As for the computational distribution, it is possible that, by not eliminating merging paths, more computations are required, since excess (duplicate) paths are carried along in the stack. But as we have just noted, the probability of this event is on the order of the error probability, which decreases exponentially with constraint length, K. Moreover, the computational distribution upper bound is independent of K, which suggests that K can be made very large—much larger than for maximum likelihood decoding, as we shall discuss further in the next section; in that case, both error probability and the additional computation due to ignoring mergers will be negligible. From a practical viewpoint, ignoring mergers is very useful, for carrying out the merge-elimination step in the flowchart of Table 6.1 would contribute heavily to the computation time for each branch.

A much more serious weakness of the basic stack algorithm is that the stack size, and hence required memory, increment for node j is proportional to $\tilde{C}_j$, the number of computations in the incorrect subset, and hence it too is a Pareto distributed random variable. In the Zigangirov algorithm, this drawback is partially remedied by discarding a path from the stack whenever its metric falls more than a fixed amount β below the metric of the top path. The probability of eliminating the correct path in this way decreases exponentially with β, so that the effect on performance can be made negligible.

A third, and possibly most undesirable, drawback of the basic stack algorithm is that the stack must be reordered for each new entry, requiring potentially a very large number of comparisons each time. The Jelinek algorithm partially avoids this by ordering paths only grossly; that is, all paths with metrics in the range $M_m \le M < M_m + \Delta$ are placed in the mth "bin" and paths in the top bin are further searched in inverse order of their arrival in the bin (last-in first-out or "push down" stack). This requires then that any path not in the bin has its metric compared only with one metric for all the paths in the bin. The effect of this gross ordering is easily determined. The basic condition for further search of an incorrect path (6.2.1) is modified to become

$$M[\mathbf{x}'_j(k)] \ge \gamma_j - \Delta \qquad k > j \tag{6.5.1}$$

The remainder of the derivation of the computational distribution of Sec. 6.2 follows in exactly the same way, with the result that the additional factor $e^{\alpha\rho\Delta}$ is carried throughout. Since in the final steps we choose $\alpha = 1/(1+\rho)$, the final effect is to multiply the factor A of (6.2.20) by $e^{\Delta\rho/(1+\rho)}$, which obviously is asymptotically insignificant. For the same reasons, the same factor also multiplies $\bar{P}_b$ of (6.3.12).

This brings us finally to the *Fano algorithm*, which is generally considered to be the most practical to implement. It too utilizes a sequence of metric thresholds spaced at intervals of Δ. Its most desirable feature is that it examines only one path at a time, thus eliminating the storage of all but one path and its metric. Basically, it continues to search further along a given path as long as its metric is growing. Whenever the metric begins to decrease significantly, it backs up and searches other paths stemming from previous nodes on the already travelled path. It accomplishes this by varying a comparison threshold in steps of magnitude Δ. The threshold is tightened (raised by Δ) whenever the metric is growing sufficiently on a forward search and relaxed (lowered by Δ) during backward searches. This is done in such a way that no node is ever searched forward twice with the same threshold setting—on each successive forward search, the threshold must be lower than when it was previously searched.

The details of the Fano algorithm can be explained by examining the flowchart of Fig. 6.6. In the first block, looking forward on the better node of a binary tree refers to computing both branch metrics and tentatively augmenting the current node metric by the greater of the two branch metrics. If the better node has just been searched and the running threshold, T, violated, the forward look must be to the worse node. This will occur if the first block is entered from point (A), which corresponds to a single pass through the backward search. In either case, the metric of the node arrived at is compared with T, and if it is satisfied ($M \geq T$), the search pointer is moved forward to that node. The next test is to determine whether this is the first time this node has been visited in the sequential decoding search.[14] It can be shown (Gallager [1968]) that if this is the case, the metric of the preceding node will violate $T + \Delta$. If so, we may attempt to tighten the threshold by increasing T by integer multiples of Δ until $M < T + \Delta$, and continue to look forward. If the node has been searched before, it is essential that we not tighten the threshold prior to searching further, for otherwise we may enter a closed loop and repeat the same moves endlessly.

If, in the first block, upon forward search the new node has metric $M < T$, we must enter the backward search mode. This involves subtracting the previous branch metric from the current node metric. If this satisfies T, then the pointer is moved back; if the branch upon which the backward move was made was the better of the two emanating from the node just reached, the worse has yet to be searched. Thus we return to the forward search via (A). If it was a worse branch, there are no more branches to search forward from this node; hence we must continue the backward search. If upon a backward look the current threshold T is

[14] If the code tree is of finite length, this is also the point at which we should test for the end of the tree tail and terminate when this is reached.

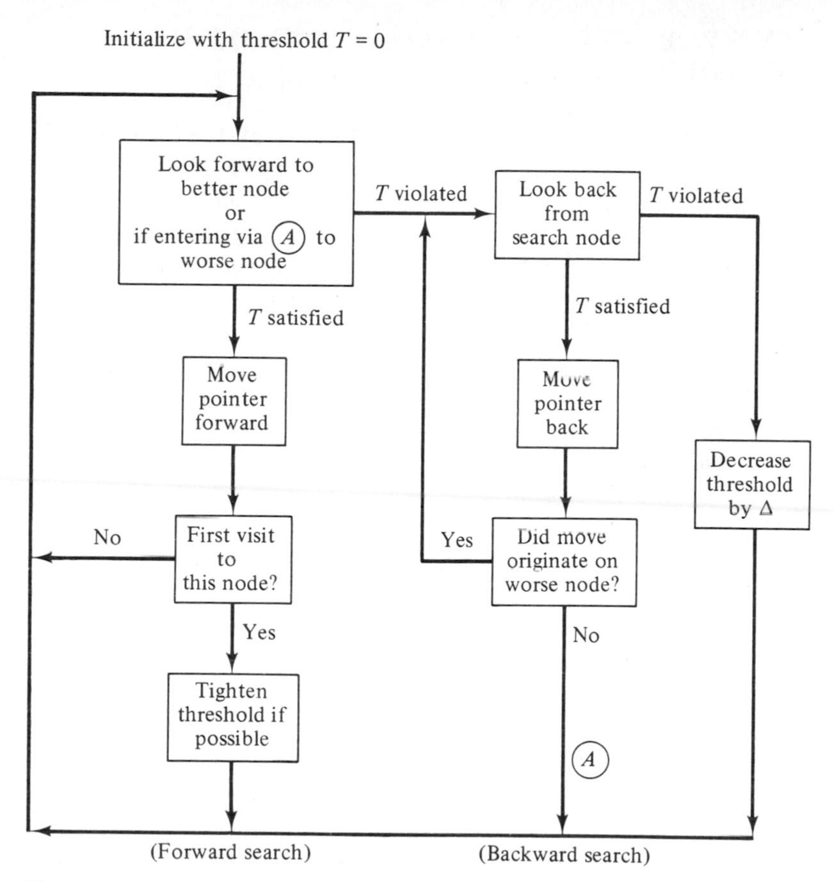

Figure 6.6 Fano sequential decoding algorithm for binary tree.

violated, we cannot move back. When this occurs, all paths accessible from here with the current T in effect have been searched and found to eventually violate T. The threshold is now decreased by Δ and forward search is again attempted. Note that, when a node is searched two or more times, each successive time it will be searched with a lower current threshold; hence endless loops are avoided.

Extensive treatments of the Fano algorithm are contained in Wozencraft and Jacobs [1965] and Gallager [1968]. Its performance, as well as its analysis, is essentially the same as that of the stack algorithm. In fact, the threshold increment Δ of the Fano algorithm has exactly the same effect as the bin size Δ of the Jelinek algorithm. Geist [1973] has shown that, under some weak conditions, the Fano algorithm always finds the same path through the tree as the stack algorithm. The only difference is that in the Fano algorithm a path node may be searched several times, while in the stack it needs to be searched only once. The effect is a modest increase in number of branch computations, which can be accounted for by an additional multiplicative factor in Theorem 6.2.1. This disadvantage is usually more than offset by the advantage of a considerable reduction in storage requirements.

6.6 COMPLEXITY, BUFFER OVERFLOW, AND OTHER SYSTEM CONSIDERATIONS

For maximum likelihood decoding of convolutional codes by the Viterbi algorithm, complexity is easily defined, for if the constraint length is K and the code rate is b/n, the number of branch metric computations per branch (b bits) is 2^{Kb}, while the number of comparisons, and the number of storage registers required for path memories and metrics, is $2^{(K-1)b}$. Thus, if we define *complexity for Viterbi decoding* as the number of branch metric computations per bit, that is

$$\chi \equiv \frac{2^{Kb}}{b} \tag{6.6.1}$$

then it follows from (5.1.32) and (5.4.13) that the bit error probability is, asymptotically[15] for large χ, and for $R_0 < R < C$

$$P_b \sim 2^{-KbE_c(R)/R} \sim \chi^{-E_c(R)/R} = \chi^{-\rho} \tag{6.6.2}$$

where

$$\frac{E_c(R)}{R} = \frac{E_o(\rho)}{E_o(\rho)/\rho} = \rho \qquad \begin{matrix} 0 < \rho \le 1 \\ R_0 \le R < C \end{matrix}$$

We have already seen in Sec. 5.2 that convolutional code behavior as a function of complexity is much more favorable than that of block codes. In the present context, for a K-bit block code, we should define $\chi = 2^K/K$, the number of code-vector metric computations per bit. Then from (3.2.14) and (3.6.45), it follows that the block error probability for $E_o'(1) < R < C$ is asymptotically

$$P_E \sim e^{-NE(R)} = 2^{-KE(R)/R} \sim \chi^{-E(R)/R} \qquad E_o'(1) \le R < C \tag{6.6.3}$$

But since $E(R)$ is significantly smaller than $E_c(R)$ for $R_0 \le R < C$, the magnitude of the negative exponent of (6.6.2) is significantly greater than that of (6.6.3); hence the superiority of convolutional codes with Viterbi decoding.

The definition of complexity for sequential decoding is somewhat less obvious. One possible definition would be the *maximum* number of branch metric computations per bit; that is, the maximum number of computations in the incorrect subset of each node, normalized by b, the number of bits decoded for each node advanced. The problem is that this is a random variable, $\tilde{C}/b$, and for an infinite length tree $\tilde{C}$ has a Pareto distribution with no maximum. On the other hand, for practical reasons discussed further below, we must limit the number of

[15] In this asymptotic expression, we ignore all terms which do not depend on K; hence both the multiplicative constant and ϵ are omitted.

computations in any given incorrect subset or we might never complete decoding.[16] Thus if we require $\tilde{C} < L_{\max}$ for each incorrect subset, we may define the complexity for sequential decoding as

$$\chi = \frac{L_{\max}}{b} \tag{6.6.4}$$

Then we have from (6.2.20) and (6.4.9) that the decoder will fail to decode a given node, by virtue of requiring more computations for that node than are available, with probability

$$P_{\text{failure}} \sim L_{\max}^{-\rho} \sim \chi^{-\rho} \tag{6.6.5}$$

where

$$\rho = \frac{E_c(R)}{R} \qquad \begin{matrix} 0 < \rho \le 1 \\ R_0 \le R < C \end{matrix}$$

Thus, interestingly enough, we note by comparing (6.6.5) with (6.6.2) that the probability of sequential decoding failure, when the number of computations per branch is limited, asymptotically bears the same relation to complexity as does the bit error probability for Viterbi (maximum likelihood) decoding. Note, however, that in sequential decoding, the constraint length K does not appear and it would almost seem that, since complexity is independent of K, we should make this arbitrarily large,[17] thus eliminating the possibility of ordinary error and replacing it by the kind of decoding failure just described.

Comparison of (6.6.2) and (6.6.5), or of (6.6.1) and (6.6.4), suggests choosing $L_{\max}$ for sequential decoding such that

$$L_{\max} = 2^{Kb}$$

where K pertains to Viterbi decoding. Thus, the effective constraint length for sequential decoding is

$$K_{\text{eff}} = \frac{\log L_{\max}}{b}$$

which measures the effective complexity of the algorithm in the same way as does the ordinary constraint length in Viterbi decoding.

However, our definition of complexity for sequential decoding is somewhat misleading, for it is based on the maximum number of computations per bit, whereas normally, for most nodes, $\tilde{C}_j$ will be much less than $L_{\max}$. This scheme of limiting $\tilde{C}_j$ is also impractical by itself since a decoding failure may well be

[16] There is also the issue of the size of the stack, which grows with $\tilde{C}$ for each node; however, by using the Fano algorithm, all this storage is avoided at the cost of increased computation.

[17] For other practical system considerations, discussed below, this is really neither feasible nor desirable, but we might make K sufficiently large that P_b is negligible compared to the probability of failure as given by (6.6.5).

"catastrophic" in the sense[18] that the decoder may possibly never recover from it to return to correct decoding. These issues suggest that, for any real sequential decoder, we need to provide some additional features and basic operational techniques, before we can realistically consider its performance and complexity.

The best place to begin is to establish the size of the memory or buffer which contains the symbols of the received code-vector $\mathbf{y}$ as they await their turn to be searched by the decoder. Let this be fixed at B branches, or Bn channel symbols. Assuming a J-ary output channel, or equivalently a J-level quantized continuous channel, this will require at most $Bn\lceil \log_2 J \rceil$ bits of storage. (This does not include any of the memory required by the stack but, as already noted, we can avoid this altogether by using the Fano algorithm.)[19] Next, suppose the decoder can perform μ branch computations during the interarrival time between two successive received branches—thus μ is the number of computations for every b bit times and is generally called the *decoder speed factor*. Then, if the number of computations required in the jth incorrect subset is

$$\tilde{C}_j > \mu B \tag{6.6.6}$$

it is clear that a failure will occur. For, even if the buffer is empty when the channel symbols of the jth branch are received, if $\tilde{C}_j > \mu B$ computations are required in the jth subset, then clearly the received symbols for the jth branch cannot be discarded for at least $\tilde{C}_j/\mu > B$ branch times, since we may need to use these to compute a metric at any time until the jth branch decision is finally concluded. But in this time B more branches will have arrived and require storage, which is impossible unless the jth branch is discarded. This type of failure is called a buffer overflow for obvious reasons, and it follows from (6.6.6) and the lower bound of Theorem 6.4.1 that at the jth node

$$P_{\text{overflow}} > (\mu B)^{-\rho}[1 - o(\mu B)] \tag{6.6.7}$$

where

$$R = \frac{E_o(\rho)}{\rho} \qquad \begin{matrix} 0 < \rho < \infty \\ 0 < R < C \end{matrix} \tag{6.6.8}$$

We also know from Theorem 6.2.1 that this result is asymptotically tight for $R_0 \le R < C$, provided the buffer is assumed initially empty. Moreover, if we widen our horizon to include arbitrary time-varying trellis (nonlinear convolutional) codes, the result is asymptotically tight for all rates, according to (6.2.23), as shown by Savage [1966]. Assuming this wider class of codes[20] in the

[18] This is to be distinguished from the definition of *catastrophic codes* given in Chap. 4.

[19] Arguments in favor of the stack algorithm point out that, if enough storage is available, the stack algorithm is preferable because of the reduced computational distribution (by a moderate factor, independent of L). But the counterargument can be made that, if properly organized, this additional stack memory can be devoted to the input data buffer in the Fano algorithm, which does not require the stack, and that this advantage will more than overcome the required increase in computation by significantly increasing B while only moderately increasing $\mathcal{K}$ [see (6.6.9)].

following, we thus conclude that at the jth node with an initially empty buffer

$$P_{\text{overflow}} \sim \mathscr{K}(\mu B)^{-\rho} \tag{6.6.9}$$

where $\mathscr{K}$ is a constant. Experimental evidence (Forney and Bower [1971] Gilhousen et al. [1971]) indicates that $\mathscr{K}$ is on the order of 1 to 10, and that long searches are sufficiently rare that the assumption of a nearly empty buffer at the beginning of each search is reasonably accurate. Then, for a sufficiently low overflow probability per node, which must be the case for efficient operation, we would have

$$\Pr\{\text{overflow in an } \mathscr{L}\text{-branch trellis}\} \sim \mathscr{L}\mathscr{K}(\mu B)^{-\rho} \tag{6.6.10}$$

where ρ is related parametrically to R by (6.6.8).

Since overflow is almost certainly "catastrophic," it appears[21] that one way to operate a sequential decoder, with finite buffer size and speed factor, is to block off the data in $\mathscr{L}$-branch ($\mathscr{L}b$ bit) blocks and to insert, between successive blocks, tails consisting of $(K - 1)$ branches each containing b zeros. In this way, even if catastrophic overflow occurs in one $\mathscr{L}$-branch block, the tail allows us to reset the decoder to the correct state and recommence decoding with a loss of at most $\mathscr{L}b$ bits. Of course, the insertion of tails introduces a reduction of rate by $(K - 1)/\mathscr{L}$, and complicates the timing of the decoder. Thus, to keep the degradation small, $K/\mathscr{L}$ should be kept small. At the same time, $\mathscr{L}$ cannot be made excessively large because it appears as a multiplicative factor in block overflow probability (6.6.10). Typical values used in sequential decoders are $\mathscr{L} \approx 500$ to 2000, $K \approx 20$ to 40, and buffer size in branches[22] $B \approx 10^4$ to 10^5. The speed factor μ depends, of course, on the data rate in bits per second, and on the speed and complexity of the digital logic required for the computations. For example, if we are limited, by a maximum logic speed, to 10^7 branch computations/s, and have a data rate of 10^6 bits/s, then $\mu = 10$. Clearly, we must have $\mu > 1$ just to keep up with the arriving data. Thus, for low enough data rates (less than 100 K bits/s), μB products in excess of 10^7 are possible. Of course, μ also depends on the complexity of the metric calculation. Obviously, computation of the Hamming distance metric for the BSC is far simpler than metric computation for an octal output channel; thus, μ will be several times greater for the BSC.

[20] Experimental evidence, (Forney and Bower [1971], Gilhousen et al. [1971]) indicates that this behavior is accurate even for time-invariant linear convolutional codes.

[21] There is, however, another strategy which has been implemented effectively with systematic codes and even some nonsystematic codes. As soon as an overflow occurs, the strategy is to guess the correct state of the code at this time and start to decode at this point. The most likely state corresponds to the last $(K - 1)b$ bits (which are transmitted uncoded in a systematic code). If the guess is wrong, the decoder will again overflow and then the state is again guessed at that time. After several false starts, the decoder ultimately "synchronizes."

[22] As noted above, this translates into a memory size of $Bn\lceil \log_2 J \rceil$ bits. Thus if we have 2×10^5 bits available, for a BSC with $r = \frac{1}{2}(n = 2)$, this translates to $B = 10^5$ branches of buffer storage, while for an octal output channel with $r = \frac{1}{3}$ this translates to $B = 2.2 \times 10^4$ branches.

We see by comparing (6.6.9) with (6.6.2) that, in sequential decoding, μB plays a role similar to 2^{Kb} in Viterbi decoding. Of course, as we noted, μB may be of the order of 10^7 at low data rates, while, since $2^{(K-1)b}$ is the number of path memory-and-metric storage registers in maximum likelihood decoding, it is not feasible to make this much greater than 10^3. On the other hand, at high data rates (10^7 bit/s or above), it is not practical to make μ sufficiently greater than unity, as required for effective sequential decoding, except for a binary-output channel, and even then this requires very fast digital logic. With Viterbi decoding, however, by providing a separate metric calculator for each state, we require only that $\mu = 1$. Also, the highly repetitive "pipeline" nature of a Viterbi decoder, as described in Chap. 4, serves to reduce its hardware complexity.

Another aspect to be considered is the decoding delay. With sequential decoding, this must be Bb bits; for, in order for the data to be output in the same order that it was encoded, the same (maximum) delay must be provided for all bits. For Viterbi decoding, we found in Sec. 5.6 that the maximum delay need only be on the order of a small multiple of Kb; on the other hand, B is typically two orders of magnitude greater than K.

The final major consideration which must be included in any choice between Viterbi decoding and sequential decoding concerns their relative sensitivity to channel parameter variations, i.e., their robustness. In this category, the sequential decoder is inferior, for its performance is strongly influenced by the choice of metric, which depends on the channel parameters (e.g., on the channel error probability for a BSC, and on the energy-to-noise ratio for an AWGN channel). Another source of channel variation is the phase tracking inaccuracy (see Sec. 2.5). In fact, it has been demonstrated that both phase and gain (amplitude) variations affect sequential decoders more detrimentally than they do Viterbi decoders (Heller and Jacobs [1971], Gilhousen et al. [1971]). A revealing indication of the robustness of Viterbi decoders is that, in some cases, the decoder partially offsets imperfections of the demodulator which precedes it (Jacobs [1974]).

6.7 BIBLIOGRAPHICAL NOTES AND REFERENCES

As was noted previously, the original sequential decoding algorithm was proposed and analyzed by Wozencraft [1957]. The Fano algorithm [1963], with various minor modifications, has been analyzed by Yudkin [1964], Wozencraft and Jacobs [1965], Gallager [1968], and Jelinek [1968a]. Two versions of stack algorithms and their performance analyses are due to Zigangirov [1966] and Jelinek [1969a]. The precise form of the Pareto distribution on computation emerged from the works of Savage [1966] for the upper bound, and of Jacobs and Berlekamp [1967] for the lower bound.

The development of Secs. 6.2 through 6.4 follows closely the tutorial presentation of Forney [1974].

PROBLEMS

6.1 Apply the Hölder inequality

$$\sum_y a(y)b(y) \le \left[\sum_y a(y)^{1/\theta}\right]^{\theta} \left[\sum_y b(y)^{1/(1-\theta)}\right]^{1-\theta}$$

to (6.2.11) through (6.2.13) to verify inequalities (6.2.15) through (6.2.17).

6.2 Suppose the metric defined in (6.1.2) is modified to utilize an arbitrary bias β. That is,

$$m(x_n) = \ln\left[\frac{p(y_n|x_n)}{p(y_n)}\right] - \beta$$

(*a*) Show that the correct path mean is positive and the incorrect mean negative, provided $\beta < C$.

(*b*) Show that this modifies (6.2.11) through (6.2.13) by replacing R by β, and similarly for (6.2.15), but (6.2.16) now involves both R and β, while (6.2.17) only involves R.

(*c*) Find the effect on (6.2.19) and Theorem 6.2.1 of using $\beta = R_0(1-\epsilon)$ (choose $\alpha\rho = \frac{1}{2}$) and thus show that (6.2.22) is replaced by

$$\Pr\{C > L\} < AL^{-(R_0/R)(1-\epsilon)} \qquad 0 \le R \le R_0(1-\epsilon)$$

Find the effect on error probability (6.3.12) and (6.3.13) and thus show that, for low rates, (6.3.12) is replaced by

$$\overline{P_b} \le D2^{-KbR_0(1-\epsilon)/R} \qquad 0 \le R \le R_0(1-\epsilon)$$

6.3 If $\Pr\{\tilde{C} \ge L\} = \mathscr{K} L^{-\rho}$ where $R = E_o(\rho)/\rho$, $0 < \rho < \infty$

(*a*) Find the rate $R^{(1)}$ below which the mean $E(\tilde{C})$ is finite.

(*b*) Find the rate $R^{(2)}$ below which the second moment $E(\tilde{C}^2)$ is finite.

(*c*) Find the rate $R^{(k)}$ below which the kth moment $E(\tilde{C}^k)$ is finite.

6.4 (Semisequential Decoding) Consider a constraint length K, rate b/n, convolutional code of B branches terminated by $K-1$ zeros. Suppose we station a genie at the end of the terminated code, and that we utilize a maximum likelihood decoder of a code of shorter constraint length $k \le K$. Precisely, let the decoder and genie operate as follows:

1. Suppose $k = 1$ and decode on this basis the entire B-branch code. If all the right decisions are made, the genie accepts the result; otherwise, he sends us back to the beginning and step 2.
2. Suppose $k = 2$ and repeat. Again the genie either accepts the result or sends us back to step 3.
3. Repeat for $k = 3$ and continue until either the genie accepts or $k = K$.

Using the results of Chap. 5, show that the probability that the number of computations per branch exceeds 2^k is upper-bounded by

$$\Pr\{\tilde{C} \ge 2^{bk}\} < D\frac{(2^b - 1)2^{-bkE_c(R)/R}}{1 - 2^{-b\epsilon E_c(R)/R}} \qquad 0 < \rho < 1$$

and hence, letting $L = 2^{bk}$

$$\Pr\{\tilde{C} > L\} < D'L^{-\rho} \qquad 0 < \rho < 1$$

where $R = E_o(\rho)/\rho$ and D' is a constant independent of L.

6.5 (*a*) Show the relationship between

$$\frac{l_{\text{crit}}}{K} \quad \text{and} \quad \frac{k_{\text{crit}} + K}{K} = \frac{k_{\text{crit}}}{K} + 1$$

where l_{crit} is given by (6.4.8) and k_{crit} is given by (5.5.5).

(*b*) Justify this result intuitively.

6.6 Consider a binary tree of depth $L + T$ where two branches diverge from each node at depth less than L and only one branch emanates from each node from depth L to the final terminal node at depth $L + T$. Assume each branch of the tree has n channel symbols independently selected according to distribution $q(x)$, $x \in \mathscr{X}$. Suppose one path in the tree is the actual transmitted sequence and let E_i, $1 \le i \le L$, be the event that some path to the terminal node diverging from the correct path at node depth $(L - i)$ is incorrectly decoded. The probability that an incorrect path is decoded when using maximum likelihood decoding is therefore bounded by

$$P_E \le \sum_{i=1}^{L} P(E_i)$$

For any DMC with input alphabet $\mathscr{X}$ show that for P_E averaged over an ensemble of such tree codes defined by $q(x)$, $x \in \mathscr{X}$, we have

$$\overline{P_E} \le \frac{e^{-(T+1)nE_o(\rho, \mathbf{q})}}{1 - 2^{\rho} e^{-nE_o(\rho, \mathbf{q})}}$$

where

$$E_o(\rho, \mathbf{q}) = -\ln \sum_y \left(\sum_x q(x) p(y|x)^{1/(1+\rho)} \right)^{1+\rho} \qquad \text{and} \qquad 0 < \rho \le 1$$

Note that this bound is independent of L. Show that, for any rate $r = 1/n$ bits per channel symbol, less than capacity, the bound can be made to decrease exponentially with T. Generalize this result to rate $r = b/n$ bits per channel symbol using a 2^b-ary tree of depth $L + T$ (Massey [1974]).

6.7 (The Fano Metric, Massey [1974]) Assume a variable length code $\{\mathbf{x}_1, \mathbf{x}_2, \ldots, \mathbf{x}_m\}$ where codeword $\mathbf{x}_m$ has a priori probability π_m and length N_m. To each codeword, add a random tail sequence to extend the codewords to length $N = \max_m N_m$. That is, for codeword $\mathbf{x}_m$, add the tail $\mathbf{t}_m = (t_1, t_2, \ldots, t_{N-N_m})$ where $\mathbf{t}_m$ is randomly chosen according to probability distribution

$$q_{N-N_m}(\mathbf{t}_m) = \prod_{k=1}^{N-N_m} q(t_k)$$

By adding independent random tails to each codeword, a code $\{\mathbf{z}_1, \mathbf{z}_2, \ldots, \mathbf{z}_m\}$ of fixed block length N, where $\mathbf{z} = (\mathbf{x}_m, \mathbf{t}_m)$ for each m, is obtained.

(*a*) Suppose that code $\{\mathbf{z}_1, \mathbf{z}_2, \ldots, \mathbf{z}_m\}$ is used over a DMC where the decoder does not know which random tails are used (only their probability distribution). Show that the minimum-probability-of-error decision rule is to choose m that maximizes $L(m, \mathbf{y})$ for channel output sequence $\mathbf{y} = (y_1, y_2, \ldots, y_N)$ where

$$L(m, \mathbf{y}) = \sum_{n=1}^{N_m} \left[\ln \frac{p(y_n | x_{mn})}{p(y_n)} + \frac{1}{N_m} \ln \pi_m \right]$$

and

$$p(y_n) = \sum_x p(y_n | x) q(x)$$

where $p(y|x)$ is the transition probability of the DMC.

(*b*) In a sequential decoder, suppose $\{\mathbf{x}_1, \mathbf{x}_2, \ldots, \mathbf{x}_m\}$ above represents all the paths in the encoding tree that have been explored up to the present time. The decoder is assumed to know nothing about the symbols in the unexplored part of the encoded tree except that they are selected independently according to $q(\cdot)$. In order for the decoder to learn the branch symbols that extend any already explored path, it must pay the price of one computation. (Any sequential decoding algorithm can be thought of as a rule for deciding which already-explored path to extend.) Show that, when the information bits are independent and equally likely, then $L(m, \mathbf{y})$ is the Fano metric given by (6.1.1) and (6.1.2). Hence the basic stack algorithm always extends the path which is chosen according to the minimum probability of error criterion.

6.8 (Massey [1973]) Suppose we have an $r = \frac{1}{2}$ binary tree code used over the BEC with erasure probability p. Using the stack decoding algorithm, we note that any path that disagrees with the received sequence in any unerased position has metric $-\infty$ and can never reach the top of the stack. Over the ensemble of tree codes and received sequences, we now find bounds on the average computation per node, $\overline{\tilde{C}}_j$.

Following the notation of Sec. 6.2, define the random variable

$$e(\mathbf{x}, \mathbf{x}'_j(k), \mathbf{y}) = \begin{cases} 1 & \text{path } \mathbf{x}'_j(k) \in \mathscr{X}'(j) \text{ is extended by the algorithm} \\ 0 & \text{otherwise} \end{cases}$$

and thus

$$\tilde{C}_j = \sum_{k=j+1}^{\infty} \sum_{i=1}^{2^{k-j-1}} e(\mathbf{x}, \mathbf{x}'_{ji}(k), \mathbf{y})$$

where $\mathbf{x}'_{ji}(k)$ is the ith path in $\mathscr{X}'(j)$ at node depth k. (There are 2^{k-j-1} such paths.)

(*a*) Show that, over the ensemble of tree codes and received sequences,

$$\begin{aligned} \Pr\{e(\mathbf{x}, \mathbf{x}'_{ji}(k), \mathbf{y}) = 1\} &\le \Pr\{\text{path } \mathbf{x}'_{ji}(k) \text{ agrees with } \mathbf{y} \text{ in all unerased positions}\} \\ &= (1 - \tfrac{1}{2}q)^{2(k-j)} \qquad q = 1 - p \\ &= 2^{-2(k-j)r_0} \qquad r_0 = -\log(1 - \tfrac{1}{2}q) \end{aligned}$$

Then show that

$$\overline{\tilde{C}}_j \le \frac{2^{-2r_0}}{1 - 2^{[1-2r_0]}} \qquad \text{provided } r = \tfrac{1}{2} < r_0$$

(*b*) Next observe that, whenever path $\mathbf{x}'_{ji}(k)$ reaches the top of the stack before $\mathbf{x}(k)$, then $e(\mathbf{x}, \mathbf{x}'_{ji}(k), \mathbf{y}) = 1$. Show that

$$\Pr\{e(\mathbf{x}, \mathbf{x}'_{ji}(k), \mathbf{y}) = 1\} \ge \tfrac{1}{2}(2^{-2(k-j)r_0})$$

and thus

$$\overline{\tilde{C}}_j \ge \frac{1}{2} \frac{2^{-2r_0}}{1 - 2^{[1-2r_0]}} \qquad \text{provided } r = \tfrac{1}{2} < r_0$$

PART THREE

SOURCE CODING FOR DIGITAL COMMUNICATION

CHAPTER

SEVEN

RATE DISTORTION THEORY: FUNDAMENTAL CONCEPTS FOR MEMORYLESS SOURCES

7.1 THE SOURCE CODING PROBLEM

Rate distortion theory is the fundamental theory of data compression. It establishes the theoretical minimum average number of binary digits per source symbol (or per unit time), i.e., the *rate*, required to represent a source so that it can be reconstructed to satisfy a given fidelity criterion, one within the allowed *distortion*. Although the foundations were laid by Shannon in 1948, it was not until 1959 that Shannon fully developed this theory when he established the fundamental theorems for the rate distortion function of a source with respect to a fidelity criterion which endow this function with its operational significance. Initially, rate distortion theory did not receive as much attention as the better known channel coding theory treated in Chaps. 2 through 6. Ultimately, however, interest grew in expanding this theory and in the insights it affords into data compression practice.

Let us now re-examine the general basic block diagram of a communication system depicted in Fig. 7.1. As always we assume that we have no control over the source, channel, and user.[1] We are free to construct only the encoders and decoders. In Chap. 1 we determined the minimum number of binary symbols per source symbol such that the original source sequence can be perfectly reconstructed by observing the binary sequence. There we found that Shannon's noiseless coding

[1] In earlier chapters we referred to the user as the destination. To emphasize the active role of the user of information in determining the fidelity measure, we now call the final destination point the user.

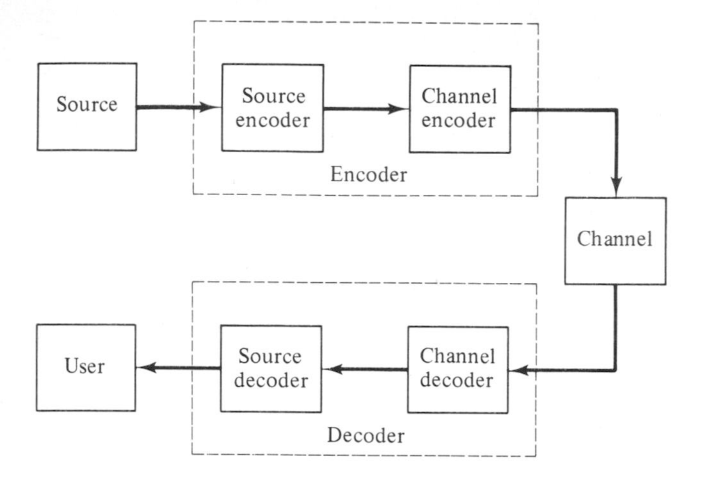

Figure 7.1 Communication system model.

theorem gave operational significance to the entropy function of a source. In this chapter we generalize the theory of noiseless source coding in Chap. 1 by defining a distortion measure and examining the problem of representing source symbols within a given fidelity criterion. We shall examine the tradeoff between the rate of information needed to represent the source symbols and the fidelity with which source symbols can be reconstructed from this information.

Chapters 2 through 6 were devoted to the channel coding problem where we restricted our attention to only the part of the block diagram of Fig. 7.1 consisting of the channel encoder, channel, and channel decoder. In these chapters, we showed that channel encoders and decoders can be found which ensure an arbitrarily small error probability for messages transmitted through the channel encoder, channel, and channel decoder as long as the message rate is less than the channel capacity. For the development of rate distortion theory, we assume that ideal channel encoders and decoders are employed so that the link between the source encoder and source decoder is noiseless as shown in Fig. 7.2.[2] This requires the assumption that the rate on this link is less than the channel capacity.

The assumption that source and channel encoders can be considered separately will be justified on the basis that, in the limit of arbitrarily complex overall encoders and decoders, no loss in performance results from separating source and channel coding in this way. Representing the source output by a sequence of binary digits also isolates the problem of source representation from that of information transmission. From a practical viewpoint, this separation is desirable since it allows channel encoders and decoders to be designed independently of the actual source and user. The source encoder and source decoder in effect adapt the source and user to the channel coding system.

[2] This is also a natural model for storage of data in a computer. In this case the capacity of the noiseless channel represents the limited amount of memory allowed per source symbol.

Figure 7.2 Source coding model.

We begin by defining a source alphabet $\mathscr{U}$, a user alphabet $\mathscr{V}$ (sometimes called the representation alphabet), a distortion measure $d(u, v)$ for each pair of symbols in $\mathscr{U}$ and $\mathscr{V}$, and a statistical characterization of the source. With these definitions and assumptions, we can begin our discussion of rate distortion theory. For this chapter we will consider discrete-time memoryless sources that emit a symbol u belonging to alphabet $\mathscr{U}$ each unit of time, say every T_s seconds. Here the user alphabet $\mathscr{V}$ depends on the user, although in many cases it is the same as the source alphabet. Throughout this chapter we will also assume a single-letter distortion measure between any source symbol u and any user symbol v represented by $d(u, v)$ and satisfying

$$d(u, v) \geq 0 \tag{7.1.1}$$

This is sometimes referred to as a *context-free distortion measure* since it does not depend on the other terms in the sequence of source and user symbols.

Referring to Fig. 7.2 we now consider the problem of source encoding and decoding so as to achieve an average distortion no greater than D. Suppose we consider all possible encoder–decoder pairs that achieve average distortion D or less and denote by $\mathscr{R}_D$ the set of rates required by these encoder–decoder pairs. By rate R, we mean the average number of nats per source symbol[3] transmitted over the link between source encoder and source decoder in Fig. 7.2. We now define the rate distortion function for a given D as the minimum possible rate R necessary to achieve average distortion D or less. Formally, we define[4]

$$R^*(D) \equiv \min_{R \in \mathscr{R}_D} R \qquad \text{nats/source symbol} \tag{7.1.2}$$

Naturally this function depends on the particular source statistics and the distortion measure. This direct definition of the rate distortion function does not allow us actually to evaluate $R^*(D)$ for various values of D. However, we shall see that this definition is meaningful for all stationary ergodic discrete-time sources with a single-letter distortion measure, and for these cases we will show that $R^*(D)$ can be expressed in terms of an average mutual information function, $R(D)$, which will be derived in Sec. 7.2.

There is another way of looking at this same problem, namely the distortion rate viewpoint. Suppose we consider all source encoder–decoder pairs that require fixed rate R and let $\mathscr{D}_R$ be the set of all the average distortions of these encoder–

[3] Recall that $R = r \ln 2$ nats per symbol where r is the rate measured in bits per symbol.

[4] Strictly speaking, the "minimum" here should be "infimum."

decoder pairs. Then, analogously to the previous definition, we define the distortion rate function as

$$D^*(R) \equiv \min_{D \in \mathscr{D}_R} D \tag{7.1.3}$$

For stationary ergodic sources with single-letter distortion measures, the definitions of $R^*(D)$ and $D^*(R)$ yield equivalent results, the only difference being the choice of dependent and independent variables.

The study of rate distortion theory can be divided roughly into three areas. First, for each kind of source and distortion measure, one must find an explicit function $R(D)$ and prove coding theorems which show that it is possible to achieve an average distortion of D or less with an encoding and decoding scheme of rate R for any rate $R > R(D)$. A converse must also be derived which shows that if an encoder–decoder pair has rate $R < R(D)$, then it is impossible to achieve average distortion of D or less with this pair. These two theorems (direct and converse) establish that $R^*(D) = R(D)$ and give operational significance to the function $R(D)$. The second area concerns the actual determination of the optimal attainable performance, and this requires finding the form of the rate distortion function, $R^*(D)$, for various sources and distortion measures. Often when this is difficult, tight bounds on $R^*(D)$ can be obtained. The final category of study deals with the application of rate distortion theory to data compression practice. Developing effective sets of implementation techniques for source encoding which produces rates approaching $R^*(D)$, finding meaningful measures of distortion that agree well with users' needs, and finding reasonable statistical models for important sources are the three main problems associated with application of this theory to practice.

In this chapter, we develop the basic theory for memoryless sources, beginning with block codes for discrete memoryless sources in the next section, and its relationship to channel coding theory in Sec. 7.3. Results on tree codes and trellis codes are presented in Sec. 7.4. All these results are extended to continuous-amplitude (discrete-time) memoryless sources in Sec. 7.5. Sections 7.6 and 7.7 treat the evaluation of the rate distortion function for discrete memoryless sources and continuous-amplitude memoryless sources, respectively. Various generalizations of the theory are presented in Chap. 8, including sources with memory and universal coding concepts.

7.2 DISCRETE MEMORYLESS SOURCES—BLOCK CODES

In this section and the following two sections we shall restrict our study of source coding with a fidelity criterion to the case of a discrete memoryless source with alphabet $\mathscr{U} = \{a_1, a_2, \ldots, a_A\}$ and letter probabilities $Q(a_1), Q(a_2), \ldots, Q(a_A)$. Then in each unit of time, say T_s seconds, the source emits a symbol $u \in \mathscr{U}$ according to these probabilities and independent of past or future outputs. The user alphabet is denoted $\mathscr{V} = \{b_1, b_2, \ldots, b_B\}$ and there is a nonnegative distortion measure $d(u, v)$ defined for each pair (u, v) in $\mathscr{U} \times \mathscr{V}$. Since the alphabet is finite, we may assume that there exists a finite number d_0 such that for all $u \in \mathscr{U}$ and $v \in \mathscr{V}$

$$0 \leq d(u, v) \leq d_0 < \infty \tag{7.2.1}$$

In this section, we consider block source coding where sequences of N source symbols will be represented by sequences of N user symbols. The *average* amount of *distortion* between N source output symbols $\mathbf{u} = (u_1, u_2, \ldots, u_N)$ and N representation symbols $\mathbf{v} = (v_1, v_2, \ldots, v_N)$ is given by

$$d_N(\mathbf{u}, \mathbf{v}) \equiv \frac{1}{N} \sum_{n=1}^{N} d(u_n, v_n) \tag{7.2.2}$$

Let $\mathscr{B} = \{\mathbf{v}_1, \mathbf{v}_2, \ldots, \mathbf{v}_M\}$ be a set of M representation sequences of N user symbols each. This is called a block source code of size M and block length N, and each sequence in $\mathscr{B}$ is called a codeword. Code $\mathscr{B}$ will be used to encode a source sequence $\mathbf{u} \in \mathscr{U}_N$ by choosing the codeword $\mathbf{v} \in \mathscr{B}$ which minimizes $d_N(\mathbf{u}, \mathbf{v})$. We denote this minimum by

$$d(\mathbf{u} \mid \mathscr{B}) \equiv \min_{\mathbf{v} \in \mathscr{B}} d_N(\mathbf{u}, \mathbf{v}) \tag{7.2.3}$$

and we define in a natural way the average distortion achieved with code $\mathscr{B}$ as

$$d(\mathscr{B}) \equiv \sum_{\mathbf{u}} Q_N(\mathbf{u}) d(\mathbf{u} \mid \mathscr{B}) \tag{7.2.4}$$

where

$$Q_N(\mathbf{u}) \equiv \prod_{n=1}^{N} Q(u_n) \tag{7.2.5}$$

as follows from the assumption that the source is memoryless.

Each N units of time when N source symbols are collected by the source encoder, the encoder selects a codeword according to the minimum distortion rule (7.2.3). The *index* of the selected codeword is then transmitted over the link between source encoder and source decoder. The source decoder then selects the codeword with this transmitted index and presents it to the user. This block source coding system is shown in Fig. 7.3. Since, for each sequence of N source symbols, one of M indices is transmitted over the noiseless channel between the encoder and decoder (which can be represented by a distinct binary sequence whose length is the smallest integer greater than or equal to $\log M$) the required

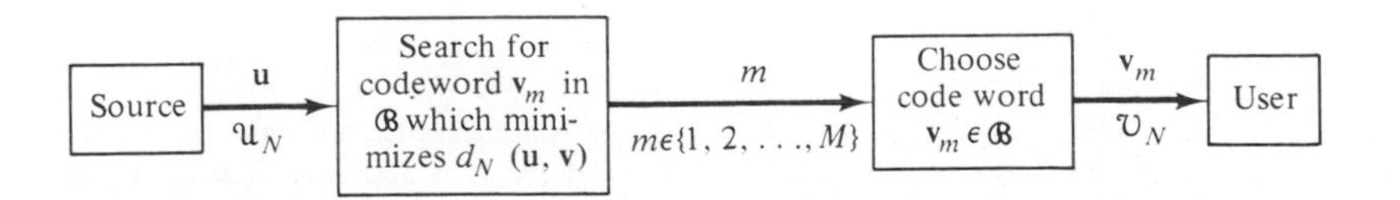

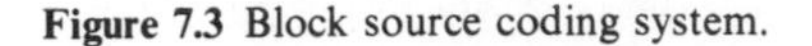
Figure 7.3 Block source coding system.

rate[5] is $R = (\ln M)/N$ nats per source symbol. In the following we will refer to code $\mathscr{B}$ as a block code of block length N and rate R.

For a given fidelity criterion D, we are interested in determining how small a rate R can be achieved when $d(\mathscr{B}) \leq D$. Unfortunately, for any given code $\mathscr{B}$, the average distortion $d(\mathscr{B})$ is generally difficult to evaluate. Indeed, the evaluation of $d(\mathscr{B})$ is analogous to the evaluation of error probabilities for specific codes in channel coding. Just as we did in channel coding, we now use ensemble average coding arguments to get around this difficulty and show how well the above block source coding system can perform. Thus we proceed to prove coding theorems that establish the theoretically minimum possible rate R for a given distortion D.

Let us first introduce an arbitrary conditional probability distribution $\{P(v \mid u) : v \in \mathscr{V},\ u \in \mathscr{U}\}$.[6] For sequences $\mathbf{u} \in \mathscr{U}_N$ and $\mathbf{v} \in \mathscr{V}_N$, we assume conditional independence in this distribution so that

$$P_N(\mathbf{v} \mid \mathbf{u}) = \prod_{n=1}^{N} P(v_n \mid u_n) \tag{7.2.6}$$

Corresponding marginal probabilities are thus given by

$$\begin{aligned} P_N(\mathbf{v}) &= \sum_{\mathbf{u}} P_N(\mathbf{v} \mid \mathbf{u}) Q_N(\mathbf{u}) \\ &= \prod_{n=1}^{N} P(v_n) \end{aligned} \tag{7.2.7}$$

where

$$P(v) = \sum_{u} P(v \mid u) Q(u)$$

Similarly, applying Bayes' rule, we have the backward conditional probabilities

$$\begin{aligned} Q_N(\mathbf{u} \mid \mathbf{v}) &= \frac{P_N(\mathbf{v} \mid \mathbf{u}) Q_N(\mathbf{u})}{P_N(\mathbf{v})} \\ &= \prod_{n=1}^{N} Q(u_n \mid v_n) \end{aligned} \tag{7.2.8}$$

where

$$Q(u \mid v) = \frac{P(v \mid u) Q(u)}{P(v)}$$

We attach no physical significance to the conditional probabilities $\{P(v \mid u) : v \in \mathscr{V},\ u \in \mathscr{U}\}$, but merely use them as a convenient tool for deriving bounds on the average distortion when using a code $\mathscr{B}$ of size M and block length N.

[5] M is usually taken to be a power of 2; however, even if this is not the case, we may combine the transmission of several indices into one larger channel codeword and thus approach R as closely as desired.

[6] We shall denote all probability distribution and density functions associated with source coding by capital letters.

Recall from (7.2.4) that the average distortion achieved using code $\mathscr{B}$ is

$$d(\mathscr{B}) = \sum_{\mathbf{u}} Q_N(\mathbf{u}) d(\mathbf{u} | \mathscr{B}) \tag{7.2.4}$$

Since

$$\sum_{\mathbf{v}} P_N(\mathbf{v} | \mathbf{u}) = 1$$

we can also write this as

$$d(\mathscr{B}) = \sum_{\mathbf{u}} \sum_{\mathbf{v}} Q_N(\mathbf{u}) P_N(\mathbf{v} | \mathbf{u}) d(\mathbf{u} | \mathscr{B}) \tag{7.2.9}$$

Here $\mathbf{v} \in \mathscr{V}_N$ is not a codeword but only a dummy variable of summation. We now split the summation over $\mathbf{u}$ and $\mathbf{v}$ into two disjoint regions by defining the indicator function

$$\Phi(\mathbf{u}, \mathbf{v}; \mathscr{B}) = \begin{cases} 1 & d_N(\mathbf{u}, \mathbf{v}) < d(\mathbf{u} | \mathscr{B}) \\ 0 & d_N(\mathbf{u}, \mathbf{v}) \geq d(\mathbf{u} | \mathscr{B}) \end{cases} \tag{7.2.10}$$

Since $(1 - \Phi) + \Phi = 1$, we have

$$\begin{aligned} d(\mathscr{B}) &= \sum_{\mathbf{u}} \sum_{\mathbf{v}} Q_N(\mathbf{u}) P_N(\mathbf{v} | \mathbf{u}) d(\mathbf{u} | \mathscr{B})[1 - \Phi(\mathbf{u}, \mathbf{v}; \mathscr{B})] \\ &\quad + \sum_{\mathbf{u}} \sum_{\mathbf{v}} Q_N(\mathbf{u}) P_N(\mathbf{v} | \mathbf{u}) d(\mathbf{u} | \mathscr{B}) \Phi(\mathbf{u}, \mathbf{v}; \mathscr{B}) \end{aligned} \tag{7.2.11}$$

Using the inequality, which results from definition (7.2.10)

$$d(\mathbf{u} | \mathscr{B})[1 - \Phi(\mathbf{u}, \mathbf{v}; \mathscr{B})] \leq d_N(\mathbf{u}, \mathbf{v}) \tag{7.2.12}$$

in the first summation and using the inequality, which follows from (7.2.1)

$$d(\mathbf{u} | \mathscr{B}) = \min_{\mathbf{v} \in \mathscr{B}} d_N(\mathbf{u}, \mathbf{v}) \leq d_0 \tag{7.2.13}$$

in the second summation in (7.2.11), we obtain the bound

$$d(\mathscr{B}) \leq \sum_{\mathbf{u}} \sum_{\mathbf{v}} Q_N(\mathbf{u}) P_N(\mathbf{v} | \mathbf{u}) d_N(\mathbf{u}, \mathbf{v}) + d_0 \sum_{\mathbf{u}} \sum_{\mathbf{v}} Q_N(\mathbf{u}) P_N(\mathbf{v} | \mathbf{u}) \Phi(\mathbf{u}, \mathbf{v}; \mathscr{B}) \tag{7.2.14}$$

The first term in this bound simplifies to

$$\begin{aligned} \sum_{\mathbf{u}} \sum_{\mathbf{v}} Q_N(\mathbf{u}) P_N(\mathbf{v} | \mathbf{u})\, d_N(\mathbf{u}, \mathbf{v}) &= \sum_{\mathbf{u}} \sum_{\mathbf{v}} Q_N(\mathbf{u}) P_N(\mathbf{v} | \mathbf{u}) \frac{1}{N} \sum_{n=1}^{N} d(u_n, v_n) \\ &= \frac{1}{N} \sum_{n=1}^{N} \sum_{u_n} \sum_{v_n} Q(u_n) P(v_n | u_n)\, d(u_n, v_n) \\ &= \sum_{u} \sum_{v} Q(u) P(v | u) d(u, v) \\ &\equiv D(\mathbf{P}) \end{aligned} \tag{7.2.15}$$

To bound the second term, we need to apply an ensemble average argument. In particular, we consider an ensemble of block codes of size M and block length

N where $\mathscr{B} = \{\mathbf{v}_1, \mathbf{v}_2, \ldots, \mathbf{v}_M\}$ is assigned the product measure

$$P(\mathscr{B}) = \prod_{m=1}^{M} P_N(\mathbf{v}_m) \tag{7.2.16}$$

where $P_N(\mathbf{v})$ is defined by (7.2.7) and is the marginal distribution corresponding to the given conditional probability distribution $\{P(v\,|\,u): v \in \mathscr{V}, u \in \mathscr{U}\}$. Averages over this code ensemble will be denoted by an upper bar $\overline{(\cdot)}$. The desired bound for the ensemble average of the second term in (7.2.14) is given by the following lemma.

Lemma 7.2.1

$$\overline{\sum_{\mathbf{u}} \sum_{\mathbf{v}} Q_N(\mathbf{u}) P_N(\mathbf{v}\,|\,\mathbf{u}) \Phi(\mathbf{u}, \mathbf{v}; \mathscr{B})} \le e^{-NE(R;\,\rho,\,\mathbf{P})} \tag{7.2.17}$$

where

$$E(R;\, \rho, \mathbf{P}) = -\rho R + E_o(\rho, \mathbf{P}) \tag{7.2.18}$$

$$E_o(\rho, \mathbf{P}) = -\ln \sum_{u} \left[\sum_{v} P(v) Q(u\,|\,v)^{1/(1+\rho)}\right]^{1+\rho} \qquad -1 \le \rho \le 0$$

$$R = \frac{\ln M}{N}$$

PROOF Using the Hölder inequality (see App. 3A), we have, for any $-1 \le \rho \le 0$,

$$\begin{aligned}
&\sum_{\mathbf{u}} \sum_{\mathbf{v}} Q_N(\mathbf{u}) P_N(\mathbf{v}\,|\,\mathbf{u}) \Phi(\mathbf{u}, \mathbf{v}; \mathscr{B}) \\
&\quad = \sum_{\mathbf{u}} \sum_{\mathbf{v}} P_N(\mathbf{v}) Q_N(\mathbf{u}\,|\,\mathbf{v}) \Phi(\mathbf{u}, \mathbf{v}; \mathscr{B}) \\
&\quad \le \sum_{\mathbf{u}} \left[\sum_{\mathbf{v}} P_N(\mathbf{v}) Q_N(\mathbf{u}\,|\,\mathbf{v})^{1/(1+\rho)}\right]^{1+\rho} \left[\sum_{\mathbf{v}} P_N(\mathbf{v}) \Phi(\mathbf{u}, \mathbf{v}; \mathscr{B})\right]^{-\rho}
\end{aligned} \tag{7.2.19}$$

since it follows from definition (7.2.10) that $\Phi^{-1/\rho} = \Phi$. Averaging this over the code ensemble and applying the Jensen inequality over the same range of ρ yields

$$\begin{aligned}
&\overline{\sum_{\mathbf{u}} \sum_{\mathbf{v}} Q_N(\mathbf{u}) P_N(\mathbf{v}\,|\,\mathbf{u}) \Phi(\mathbf{u}, \mathbf{v}; \mathscr{B})} \\
&\quad \le \sum_{\mathbf{u}} \left[\sum_{\mathbf{v}} P_N(\mathbf{v}) Q_N(\mathbf{u}\,|\,\mathbf{v})^{1/(1+\rho)}\right]^{1+\rho} \overline{\left[\sum_{\mathbf{v}} P_N(\mathbf{v}) \Phi(\mathbf{u}, \mathbf{v}; \mathscr{B})\right]^{-\rho}} \\
&\quad \le \sum_{\mathbf{u}} \left[\sum_{\mathbf{v}} P_N(\mathbf{v}) Q_N(\mathbf{u}\,|\,\mathbf{v})^{1/(1+\rho)}\right]^{1+\rho} \left[\overline{\sum_{\mathbf{v}} P_N(\mathbf{v}) \Phi(\mathbf{u}, \mathbf{v}; \mathscr{B})}\right]^{-\rho}
\end{aligned} \tag{7.2.20}$$

The second bracketed term above is simply

$$\begin{aligned}\overline{\sum_{\mathbf{v}} P_N(\mathbf{v})\Phi(\mathbf{u}, \mathbf{v}; \mathscr{B})} &= \sum_{\mathbf{v}} \sum_{\mathbf{v}_1} \cdots \sum_{\mathbf{v}_M} P_N(\mathbf{v})P_N(\mathbf{v}_1) \cdots P_N(\mathbf{v}_M)\Phi(\mathbf{u}, \mathbf{v}; \mathscr{B}) \\ &= \Pr\{d_N(\mathbf{u}, \mathbf{v}) < \min(d_N(\mathbf{u}, \mathbf{v}_1), d_N(\mathbf{u}, \mathbf{v}_2), \ldots, d_N(\mathbf{u}, \mathbf{v}_M))\} \\ &\le \frac{1}{M+1} \\ &< \frac{1}{M} \end{aligned} \tag{7.2.21}$$

since the code $\mathscr{B}$ has the product measure given in (7.2.16) and thus, for a fixed $\mathbf{u}$, each of the random variables $d_N(\mathbf{u}, \mathbf{v})$, $d_N(\mathbf{u}, \mathbf{v}_1)$, $\ldots$, $d_N(\mathbf{u}, \mathbf{v}_M)$, which are independent and identically distributed, has the same probability of being the minimum. Using (7.2.21) in (7.2.20), we have

$$\begin{aligned}\overline{\sum_{\mathbf{u}} \sum_{\mathbf{v}} Q_N(\mathbf{u})P_N(\mathbf{v} \mid \mathbf{u})\Phi(\mathbf{u}, \mathbf{v}; \mathscr{B})} &\le M^\rho \sum_{\mathbf{u}} \left[\sum_{\mathbf{v}} P_N(\mathbf{v})Q_N(\mathbf{u} \mid \mathbf{v})^{1/(1+\rho)}\right]^{1+\rho} \\ &= e^{N\rho R} \sum_{\mathbf{u}} \left[\sum_{\mathbf{v}} \prod_{n=1}^{N} P(v_n)Q(u_n \mid v_n)^{1/(1+\rho)}\right]^{1+\rho} \\ &= e^{N\rho R} \sum_{\mathbf{u}} \left[\prod_{n=1}^{N} \sum_{v} P(v)Q(u_n \mid v)^{1/(1+\rho)}\right]^{1+\rho} \\ &= e^{N\rho R} \sum_{\mathbf{u}} \prod_{n=1}^{N} \left[\sum_{v} P(v)Q(u_n \mid v)^{1/(1+\rho)}\right]^{1+\rho} \\ &= e^{N\rho R} \prod_{n=1}^{N} \sum_{u} \left[\sum_{v} P(v)Q(u \mid v)^{1/(1+\rho)}\right]^{1+\rho} \\ &= e^{N\rho R} \left\{\sum_{u} \left[\sum_{v} P(v)Q(u \mid v)^{1/(1+\rho)}\right]^{1+\rho}\right\}^N \\ &= e^{-NE(R;\, \rho, \mathbf{P})} \end{aligned} \tag{7.2.22}$$

Let us briefly examine the behavior of this bound for various parameter values. As stated in the above lemma, the bound given in (7.2.17) applies for all ρ in the range $-1 \le \rho \le 0$ and for any choice of the conditional probability $\{P(v \mid u) : v \in \mathscr{V},\ u \in \mathscr{U}\}$. The expression $E(R; \rho, \mathbf{P})$ is identical to the random coding exponent in channel coding theory introduced in Sec. 3.1. The only difference is that here the parameter ρ ranges between -1 and 0 while for channel coding this parameter ranges from 0 to 1. Also, here we can pick an arbitrary conditional probability $\{P(v \mid u)\}$ which influences both $P(v)$ and $Q(u \mid v)$, while in the channel random coding exponent the channel conditional probability is fixed and only the distribution of the code ensemble is allowed to change. In the following lemmas, we draw upon our earlier examination of the random coding bound for channel coding. Here $E_o(\rho, \mathbf{P})$ is a form of the Gallager function first defined in (3.1.18).

Lemma 7.2.2

$$E_o(\rho, \mathbf{P}) = -\ln \sum_u \left[\sum_v P(v)Q(u \mid v)^{1/(1+\rho)} \right]^{1+\rho} \tag{7.2.23}$$

has the following properties for $-1 \le \rho \le 0$:

$$\begin{aligned} &E_o(\rho, \mathbf{P}) \le 0 \\ &\frac{\partial E_o(\rho, \mathbf{P})}{\partial \rho} \ge I(\mathbf{P}) \ge 0 \\ &\frac{\partial^2 E_o(\rho, \mathbf{P})}{\partial \rho^2} \le 0 \\ &E_o(0, \mathbf{P}) = 0 \\ &E_o'(0, \mathbf{P}) = \left. \frac{\partial E_o(\rho, \mathbf{P})}{\partial \rho} \right|_{\rho=0} = I(\mathbf{P}) \end{aligned} \tag{7.2.24}$$

where[7]

$$I(\mathbf{P}) = \sum_u \sum_v Q(u)P(v \mid u) \ln \frac{P(v \mid u)}{P(v)} \tag{7.2.25}$$

is the usual average mutual information function.

PROOF This lemma is the same as Lemma 3.2.1. Its proof is given in App. 3A.

Since we are free to choose any ρ in the interval $-1 \le \rho \le 0$, the bound in Lemma 7.2.1 can be minimized with respect to ρ or, equivalently, the negative exponent can be maximized. We first establish that the minimum always corresponds to a negative exponent, and then show how to determine its value.

Lemma 7.2.3

$$\max_{-1 \le \rho \le 0} E(R; \rho, \mathbf{P}) > 0 \qquad \text{for} \qquad R > I(\mathbf{P}) \tag{7.2.26}$$

PROOF It follows from the properties given in Lemma 7.2.2 and the mean value theorem that, for any $\delta > 0$, there exists a ρ_o in the interval $-1 < \rho_o < 0$ such that[8]

$$E_o'(0, \mathbf{P}) < \frac{E_o(0, \mathbf{P}) - E_o(\rho_o, \mathbf{P})}{0 - \rho_o} \le E_o'(0, \mathbf{P}) + \delta$$

[7] $I(\mathbf{P}) = I(\mathscr{U}; \mathscr{V})$ was first defined in Sec. 1.2. Henceforth, the conditional probability distribution is used as the argument because this is the variable over which we optimize.

[8] We assume $E_o(\rho, \mathbf{P})$ is strictly convex $\cap$ in ρ. Otherwise this proof is trivial.

which, since $E_o(0, \mathbf{P}) = 0$ and $E_o'(0, \mathbf{P}) = I(\mathbf{P})$, implies

$$E_o(\rho_o, \mathbf{P}) \geq \rho_o[I(\mathbf{P}) + \delta] \tag{7.2.27}$$

Hence

$$\begin{aligned}\max_{-1 \leq \rho \leq 0} E(R; \rho, \mathbf{P}) &= \max_{-1 \leq \rho \leq 0} [-\rho R + E_o(\rho, \mathbf{P})] \\ &\geq -\rho_o R + E_o(\rho_o, \mathbf{P}) \\ &\geq -\rho_o R + \rho_o[I(\mathbf{P}) + \delta] \\ &= -\rho_o[R - I(\mathbf{P}) - \delta]\end{aligned}$$

We can choose $\delta = [R - I(\mathbf{P})]/2 > 0$ so that

$$\max_{-1 \leq \rho \leq 0} E(R; \rho, \mathbf{P}) \geq -\rho_o\left(\frac{R - I(\mathbf{P})}{2}\right) > 0 \tag{7.2.28}$$

Analogously to the channel coding bound for fixed conditional probability distribution $\{P(v \mid u): v \in \mathscr{V}, u \in \mathscr{U}\}$, the value of the exponent

$$\max_{-1 \leq \rho \leq 0} E(R; \rho, \mathbf{P})$$

is determined by the parametric equation

$$\max_{-1 \leq \rho \leq 0} E(R; \rho, \mathbf{P}) = -\rho^* R + E_o(\rho^*, \mathbf{P})$$

$$R = \left.\frac{\partial E_o(\rho, \mathbf{P})}{\partial \rho}\right|_{\rho = \rho^*} \tag{7.2.29}$$

for

$$I(\mathbf{P}) < R < \left.\frac{\partial E_o(\rho, \mathbf{P})}{\partial \rho}\right|_{\rho = -1}$$

and $-1 < \rho^* < 0$. In Fig. 7.4 we sketch these relationships.

Now let us combine these results into a bound on the average distortion using codes of block length N and rate R. We take the code ensemble average of $d(\mathscr{B})$ given by (7.2.14) and bound this by the sum of (7.2.15) and the bound in Lemma 7.2.1. This results in the bound on $\overline{d(\mathscr{B})}$ given by

$$\overline{d(\mathscr{B})} \leq D(\mathbf{P}) + d_0\, e^{-NE(R; \rho, \mathbf{P})} \tag{7.2.30}$$

for any $-1 \leq \rho \leq 0$. Minimizing the bound with respect to ρ yields

$$\overline{d(\mathscr{B})} \leq D(\mathbf{P}) + d_0 \exp\left\{-N\left[\max_{-1 \leq \rho \leq 0} E(R; \rho, \mathbf{P})\right]\right\} \tag{7.2.31}$$

where

$$\max_{-1 \leq \rho \leq 0} E(R; \rho, \mathbf{P}) > 0 \qquad \text{for } R > I(\mathbf{P})$$

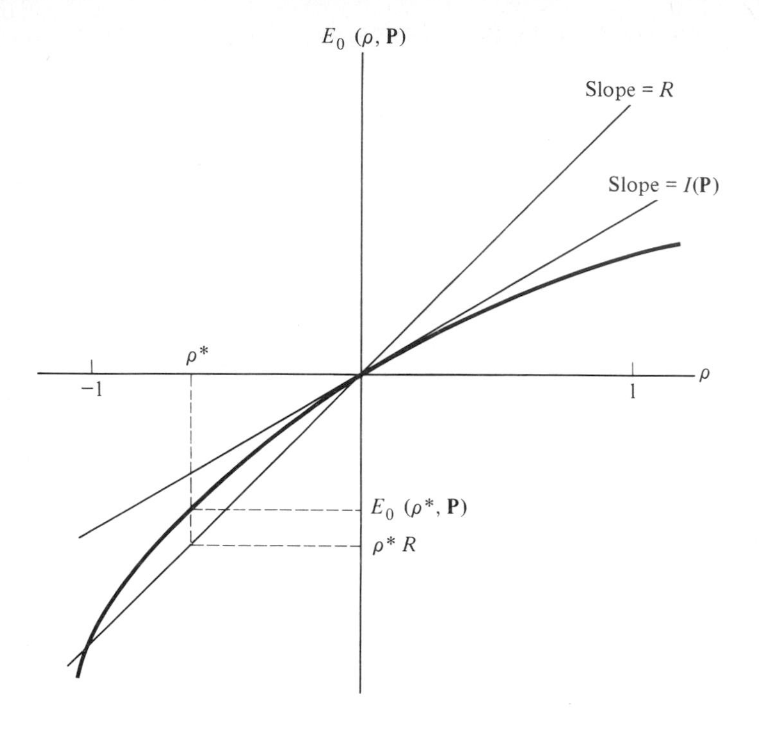

Figure 7.4 $E_0(\rho, P)$ curve.

and

$$D(\mathbf{P}) = \sum_u \sum_v Q(u)P(v \mid u)d(u, v)$$

At this point we are free to choose the conditional probability $\{P(v \mid u)\}$ to minimize the bound on $\overline{d(\mathscr{B})}$ further. Suppose we are given a fidelity criterion D which we wish to satisfy with the block source encoder and decoder system of Fig. 7.3. Let us next define the set of conditional probabilities that satisfy the condition $D(\mathbf{P}) \leq D$

$$\mathscr{P}_D = \{P(v \mid u) \colon D(\mathbf{P}) \leq D\} \tag{7.2.32}$$

It follows that $\mathscr{P}_D$ is a nonempty, closed, convex set for all

$$D \geq \sum_u Q(u) \min_{v \in \mathscr{V}} d(u, v) \equiv D_{\min} \tag{7.2.33}$$

since in defining $v(u)$ by the relation $d(u, v(u)) = \min_v d(u, v)$ we may construct the conditional distribution

$$P_{\min}(v \mid u) = \begin{cases} 1 & v = v(u) \\ 0 & v \neq v(u) \end{cases} \tag{7.2.34}$$

which belongs to $\mathscr{P}_D$ and achieves the lower bound. Now we define the source reliability function

$$E(R, D) \equiv \max_{\mathbf{P} \in \mathscr{P}_D} \max_{-1 \leq \rho \leq 0} E(R; \rho, \mathbf{P}) \tag{7.2.35}$$

and the function

$$R(D) \equiv \min_{\mathbf{P} \in \mathscr{P}_D} I(\mathbf{P}) \tag{7.2.36}$$

We will soon show that in fact $R(D)$ *is the rate distortion function* as defined in (7.1.2), but for the moment we shall treat it only as a candidate for the rate distortion function. With these definitions we have the source coding theorem.

Theorem 7.2.1: Source coding theorem For any block length N and rate R, there exists a block code $\mathscr{B}$ with average distortion $d(\mathscr{B})$ satisfying

$$d(\mathscr{B}) \leq D + d_0 e^{-NE(R, D)} \tag{7.2.37}$$

where

$$E(R, D) > 0 \qquad \text{for } R > R(D)$$

PROOF Suppose $\mathbf{P}^* \in \mathscr{P}_D$ achieves the maximization (7.2.35) in the source reliability function. Then from (7.2.31) we have

$$\overline{d(\mathscr{B})} \leq D(\mathbf{P}^*) + d_0 e^{-NE(R, D)} \tag{7.2.38}$$

where

$$E(R, D) > 0 \qquad \text{for } R > I(\mathbf{P}^*)$$

But by definition (7.2.32) of $\mathscr{P}_D$, we have $D(\mathbf{P}^*) \leq D$. Also since

$$E(R, D) \geq \max_{-1 \leq \rho \leq 0} E(R; \rho, \mathbf{P}) > 0 \qquad \text{for } R > I(\mathbf{P})$$

where $\mathbf{P}$ can be any $\mathbf{P} \in \mathscr{P}_D$, we have

$$E(R, D) > 0 \qquad \text{for } R > \min_{\mathbf{P} \in \mathscr{P}_D} I(\mathbf{P}) = R(D)$$

Hence

$$\overline{d(\mathscr{B})} \leq D + d_0 e^{-NE(R, D)} \tag{7.2.39}$$

where $E(R, D) > 0$ for $R > R(D)$. Since this bound holds for the ensemble average over all codes of block length N and rate R, we know that there exists at least one code whose distortion is less than or equal to $\overline{d(\mathscr{B})}$, thus completing the proof.

Example (Binary symmetric source, error distortion) Let $\mathscr{U} = \mathscr{V} = \{0, 1\}$ and $d(u, v) = 1 - \delta_{uv}$. Also suppose $Q(0) = Q(1) = \frac{1}{2}$. By symmetry, the distribution $\mathbf{P} \in \mathscr{P}_D$ that achieves both $E(R, D)$ and $R(D)$ is given by

$$P(v \mid u) = \begin{cases} D & v \neq u \\ 1 - D & v = u \end{cases} \qquad \text{where} \qquad 0 \leq D \leq \tfrac{1}{2} \tag{7.2.40}$$

Then the parametric equations (7.2.29) become (see also Sec. 3.4)

$$E(R, D) = E(R; \rho^*, \mathbf{P}) = -\delta_D \ln D - (1 - \delta_D) \ln (1 - D) - \mathscr{H}(\delta_D) \tag{7.2.41}$$

and

$$R = \ln 2 - \mathscr{H}(\delta_D) \tag{7.2.42}$$

where

$$\delta_D = \frac{D^{1/(1+\rho)}}{D^{1/(1+\rho)} + (1 - D)^{1/(1+\rho)}} \qquad -1 < \rho < 0 \tag{7.2.43}$$

$E(R, D)$ is sketched in Fig. 7.5 for $0 \le D \le \frac{1}{2}$ and $R(D) \le R \le \ln 2$ where $R(D) = \ln 2 - \mathscr{H}(D)$.

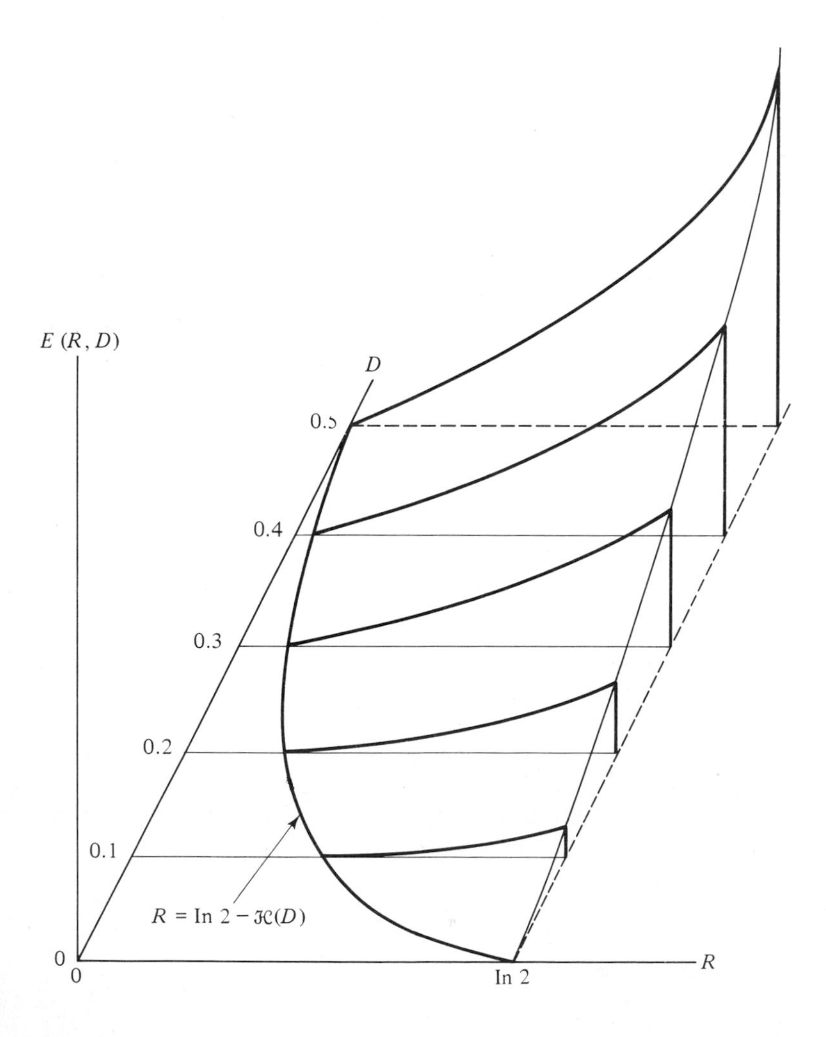

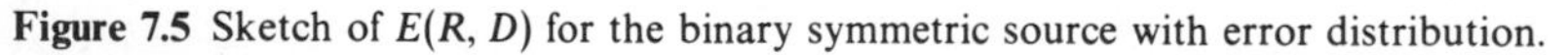

Figure 7.5 Sketch of $E(R, D)$ for the binary symmetric source with error distribution.

Theorem 7.2.1 shows that, as block length increases, we can find a code of any rate $R > R(D)$ whose average distortion is arbitrarily close to D. A weaker but more common form of this theorem is given next.

Corollary 7.2.2 Given any $\epsilon > 0$, there exists a block code $\mathscr{B}$ of rate $R \le R(D) + \epsilon$ with average distortion $d(\mathscr{B}) \le D + \epsilon$.

PROOF Let R satisfy

$$R(D) < R \le R(D) + \epsilon$$

and choose N large enough so that

$$d_0 e^{-NE(R, D)} \le \epsilon$$

In order to show that $R(D)$ is indeed the rate distortion function, we must show that it is impossible to achieve an average distortion of D or less with any source encoder–decoder pair that has rate $R < R(D)$. To show this we first need two properties of $I(\mathbf{P})$. First let $\{P_N(\mathbf{v} \mid \mathbf{u}) \colon \mathbf{v} \in \mathscr{V}_N, \mathbf{u} \in \mathscr{U}_N\}$ be any arbitrary conditional distribution on sequences of length N. Also let $P^{(n)}(v_n \mid u_n)$ be the marginal conditional distribution for the nth pair (v_n, u_n) derived from this distribution. Defining

$$I(\mathbf{P}_N) = \sum_{\mathbf{u}} \sum_{\mathbf{v}} Q_N(\mathbf{u}) P_N(\mathbf{v} \mid \mathbf{u}) \ln \frac{P_N(\mathbf{v} \mid \mathbf{u})}{P_N(\mathbf{v})} \tag{7.2.44}$$

and

$$I(\mathbf{P}^{(n)}) = \sum_{u} \sum_{v} Q(u) P^{(n)}(v \mid u) \ln \frac{P^{(n)}(v \mid u)}{P^{(n)}(v)} \tag{7.2.45}$$

where

$$Q_N(\mathbf{u}) = \prod_{n=1}^{N} Q(u_n)$$

and

$$P^{(n)}(v) = \sum_{u} Q(u) P^{(n)}(v \mid u)$$

we have the following inequalities

$$I\left(\frac{1}{N} \sum_{n=1}^{N} \mathbf{P}^{(n)}\right) \le \frac{1}{N} \sum_{n=1}^{N} I(\mathbf{P}^{(n)}) \tag{7.2.46}$$

and

$$\frac{1}{N} \sum_{n=1}^{N} I(\mathbf{P}^{(n)}) \le \frac{1}{N} I(\mathbf{P}_N) \tag{7.2.47}$$

Inequality (7.2.46) is the statement that $I(\mathbf{P})$ is a convex $\cup$ function of $\mathbf{P}$. This statement is given in Lemma 1A.2 in App. 1A. Inequality (7.2.47) can be shown using an argument analogous to the proof of Lemma 1.2.2 for $I(\mathscr{X}_N; \mathscr{Y}_N)$ given in Chap. 1 (see Prob. 7.1).

Theorem 7.2.3: Converse source coding theorem For any source encoder–decoder pair it is impossible to achieve average distortion less than or equal to D whenever the rate R satisfies $R < R(D)$.

PROOF Any encoder–decoder pair defines a mapping from source sequences to user sequences. For any length N, consider the mapping from $\mathscr{U}_N$ to $\mathscr{V}_N$ where we let M be the number of distinct sequences in $\mathscr{V}_N$ into which the sequences of $\mathscr{U}_N$ are mapped. Define the conditional distribution

$$P_N(\mathbf{v} \mid \mathbf{u}) \equiv \begin{cases} 1 & \text{if } \mathbf{u} \text{ is mapped into } \mathbf{v} \\ 0 & \text{otherwise} \end{cases} \tag{7.2.48}$$

and let $P^{(n)}(v \mid u)$ be the resulting marginal conditional distribution on the nth terms in the sequences. Also, define the conditional distribution

$$\hat{P}(v \mid u) \equiv \frac{1}{N} \sum_{n=1}^{N} P^{(n)}(v \mid u) \tag{7.2.49}$$

Now let us assume that the mapping results in an average distortion of D or less. Then

$$\begin{aligned} D(\mathbf{P}_N) &= \sum_{\mathbf{u}} \sum_{\mathbf{v}} Q_N(\mathbf{u}) P_N(\mathbf{v} \mid \mathbf{u}) d_N(\mathbf{u} \mid \mathbf{v}) \\ &= \sum_{\mathbf{u}} Q_N(\mathbf{u}) d_N(\mathbf{u}, \mathbf{v}(\mathbf{u})) \\ &\leq D \end{aligned} \tag{7.2.50}$$

where $\mathbf{u}$ is mapped into $\mathbf{v}(\mathbf{u})$. But by definition (7.2.2)

$$\begin{aligned} D(\mathbf{P}_N) &= \sum_{\mathbf{u}} \sum_{\mathbf{v}} Q_N(\mathbf{u}) P_N(\mathbf{v} \mid \mathbf{u}) \frac{1}{N} \sum_{n=1}^{N} d(u_n, v_n) \\ &= \frac{1}{N} \sum_{n=1}^{N} \sum_{\mathbf{u}} \sum_{\mathbf{v}} Q_N(\mathbf{u}) P_N(\mathbf{v} \mid \mathbf{u}) d(u_n, v_n) \\ &= \frac{1}{N} \sum_{n=1}^{N} \sum_{u} \sum_{v} Q(u) P^{(n)}(v \mid u) d(u, v) \\ &= \sum_{u} \sum_{v} Q(u) \left[\frac{1}{N} \sum_{n=1}^{N} P^{(n)}(v \mid u) \right] d(u, v) \\ &\leq D \end{aligned} \tag{7.2.51}$$

where the inequality follows from (7.2.50). Hence $\hat{P}(v \mid u)$ given by (7.2.49) belongs to $\mathscr{P}_D$ and so

$$\begin{aligned} R(D) &\le I(\hat{\mathbf{P}}) \\ &= I\left(\frac{1}{N}\sum_{n=1}^{N} \mathbf{P}^{(n)}\right) \\ &\le \frac{1}{N}\sum_{n=1}^{N} I(\mathbf{P}^{(n)}) \\ &\le \frac{1}{N} I(\mathbf{P}_N) \\ &\le \frac{1}{N} \ln M \\ &= R \end{aligned} \tag{7.2.52}$$

We used here inequalities (7.2.46), (7.2.47), and $I(\mathbf{P}_N) \le \ln M$ (see Prob. 1.7).[9] Hence, $D(\mathbf{P}_N) \le D$ implies that $R(D) \le R$, which proves the theorem.

Note that this converse source coding theorem applies to all source encoder–decoder pairs and is not limited to block coding. For any encoder–decoder pair and any sequence of length N, there is some mapping defined from $\mathscr{U}_N$ to $\mathscr{V}_N$ and that is all that is required in the proof. Later in Sec. 7.3 when we consider non-block codes called trellis codes, this theorem will still be applicable.

The source coding theorem (Theorem 7.2.1) and the converse source coding theorem (Theorem 7.2.3) together show that $R(D)$ is the rate distortion function. Hence for discrete memoryless sources we have $R^*(D) = R(D)$ where

$$\begin{aligned} R(D) &= \min_{\mathbf{P} \in \mathscr{P}_D} I(\mathbf{P}) \qquad \text{nats/source symbol} \\ I(\mathbf{P}) &= \sum_u \sum_v Q(u)P(v \mid u) \ln \frac{P(v \mid u)}{P(v)} \\ \mathscr{P}_D &= \left\{ P(v \mid u): \sum_u \sum_v Q(u)P(v \mid u)d(u, v) \le D \right\} \end{aligned} \tag{7.2.53}$$

Thus for this case we have an explicit form of the rate distortion function in terms of a minimization of average mutual information.

The preceding source coding theorem and its converse establish that the rate distortion function $R(D)$ given by (7.2.53) specifies the minimum rate at which the source decoder must receive information about the source outputs in order to be able to represent it to the user with an average distortion that does not exceed D.

[9] With entropy source coding discussed in Chap. 1 it may be possible to reduce the rate below $(\ln M)/N$, but never below $I(\mathbf{P}_N)/N$.

Theorem 7.2.1 also shows that block codes can achieve distortion D with rate $R(D)$ in the limit as the block length N goes to infinity. For a block code $\mathscr{B}$ of finite block length N and rate R, it is natural to ask how close to the rate distortion limit $(D, R(D))$ we can have $(d(\mathscr{B}), R)$. The following theorem provides a bound on the rate of convergence to the limit $(D, R(D))$.

Theorem 7.2.4 There exists a code $\mathscr{B}$ of block length N and rate R such that

$$0 \leq d(\mathscr{B}) - D \leq d_0 e^{-N\delta^2(N)/2C_o} \tag{7.2.54}$$

when

$$0 < \delta(N) = R - R(D) \leq \tfrac{1}{2}C_o$$

where $C_o = 2 + 16[\ln A]^2$ is a constant such that for all $\mathbf{P}$

$$\frac{\partial^2 E_o(\rho, \mathbf{P})}{\partial \rho^2} \geq -C_o \qquad -\tfrac{1}{2} \leq \rho \leq 0$$

PROOF From (7.2.30) we know that, for each ρ in the interval $-1 \leq \rho \leq 0$ and for the conditional probability $\{P(v \mid u)\colon v \in \mathscr{V}, u \in \mathscr{U}\}$, there exists a code $\mathscr{B}$ of block length N and rate R such that

$$d(\mathscr{B}) \leq D(\mathbf{P}) + d_0 e^{-NE(R;\,\rho,\,\mathbf{P})} \tag{7.2.55}$$

Recall from (7.2.18) that

$$\begin{aligned} E(R;\, \rho, \mathbf{P}) &= -\rho R + E_o(\rho, \mathbf{P}) \\ E_o(\rho, \mathbf{P}) &= -\ln \sum_u \left[\sum_v P(v)Q(u \mid v)^{1/(1+\rho)}\right]^{1+\rho} \end{aligned} \tag{7.2.56}$$

For fixed $\mathbf{P}$, twice integrating $E_o''(\rho, \mathbf{P}) = \partial^2 E_o(\rho, \mathbf{P})/\partial\rho^2$ yields

$$\int_0^\rho \int_0^\beta E_o''(\alpha, \mathbf{P})\, d\alpha\, d\beta = -\rho E_o'(0, \mathbf{P}) + E_o(\rho, \mathbf{P}) - E_o(0, \mathbf{P}) \tag{7.2.57}$$

Since $E_o(0, \mathbf{P}) = 0$ and $E_o'(0, \mathbf{P}) = I(\mathbf{P})$, we have

$$E_o(\rho, \mathbf{P}) = \rho I(\mathbf{P}) + \int_0^\rho \int_0^\beta E_o''(\alpha, \mathbf{P})\, d\alpha\, d\beta \tag{7.2.58}$$

Let C_o be any constant upper bound to $-E_o''(\rho, \mathbf{P})$. (See Prob. 7.3, where we show that $C_o = 2 + 16[\ln A]^2$ is such a bound for $-\frac{1}{2} \leq \rho \leq 0$.) Then

$$\begin{aligned} E_o(\rho, \mathbf{P}) &\geq \rho I(\mathbf{P}) - \int_0^\rho \int_0^\beta C_o\, d\alpha\, d\beta \\ &= \rho I(\mathbf{P}) - \frac{\rho^2}{2} C_o \qquad -\tfrac{1}{2} \leq \rho \leq 0 \end{aligned} \tag{7.2.59}$$

Hence

$$E(R; \rho, \mathbf{P}) \geq -\rho R + \rho I(\mathbf{P}) - \frac{\rho^2}{2} C_o \tag{7.2.60}$$

Now choose $\mathbf{P}^* \in \mathscr{P}_D$ such that $I(\mathbf{P}^*) = R(D)$. Then

$$E(R; \rho, \mathbf{P}^*) \geq -\rho[R - R(D)] - \frac{\rho^2}{2} C_o \tag{7.2.61}$$

Defining $\delta(N) = R - R(D)$, we choose

$$\rho^* = -\frac{\delta(N)}{C_o} \tag{7.2.62}$$

where $\delta(N)$ is assumed small enough to guarantee $-\frac{1}{2} \leq \rho^* \leq 0$. Then

$$E(R; \rho^*, \mathbf{P}^*) \geq \frac{\delta^2(N)}{2C_o} \tag{7.2.63}$$

and putting this into (7.2.55) gives

$$\begin{aligned} d(\mathscr{B}) &\leq D(\mathbf{P}^*) + d_0 e^{-NE(R;\, \rho^*,\, \mathbf{P}^*)} \\ &\leq D + d_0 e^{-N\delta^2(N)/2C_o} \end{aligned} \tag{7.2.64}$$

There are many ways in which the bound on $(d(\mathscr{B}), R)$ can be made to converge to $(D, R(D))$. For example, for some constant $\alpha > 0$

$$\delta(N) = R - R(D) = \alpha N^{-3/8} \tag{7.2.65}$$

yields

$$0 \leq d(\mathscr{B}) - D \leq d_0 \exp\left\{-\frac{\alpha^2 N^{1/4}}{2C_o}\right\} \tag{7.2.66}$$

A different choice of

$$\delta(N) = R - R(D) = \alpha\sqrt{\frac{\ln N}{N}} \tag{7.2.67}$$

yields

$$0 \leq d(\mathscr{B}) - D \leq \frac{d_0}{N^{(\alpha^2/2C_o)}} \tag{7.2.68}$$

which shows that, if $R \to R(D)$ as $\sqrt{(\ln N)/N}$, we can have $d(\mathscr{B}) \to D$ as $N^{-\gamma}$ for any fixed $\gamma > 0$.

Although Theorem 7.2.4 does not yield the tightest known bounds on the convergence of $(d(\mathscr{B}), R)$ to $(D, R(D))$ (cf. Berger [1971], Gallager [1968], Pilc [1968]), the bounds are easy to evaluate. It turns out that some sources called symmetric sources have block source coding schemes that can be shown to converge much faster with block length (see Chap. 8, Sec. 8.5).

7.3 RELATIONSHIPS WITH CHANNEL CODING

There are several relationships between the channel coding theory of Chaps. 2 through 6 and rate distortion theory. Some of these appear simply because the same mathematical tools are applied in both theories, while others are of a more fundamental nature.

Suppose we no longer assume a noiseless channel and consider both source and channel block coding as shown in Fig. 7.6. Assume the discrete memoryless source emits a symbol once every T_s seconds and that we have a source encoder and decoder for a source block code, $\mathscr{B}$, of block length N and rate R nats per symbol of duration T_s seconds. For each NT_s seconds, a minimum distortion codeword in $\mathscr{B} = \{\mathbf{v}_1, \mathbf{v}_2, \ldots, \mathbf{v}_M\}$ is chosen to represent the source sequence $\mathbf{u} \in \mathscr{U}_N$ and the codeword index m is sent over the channel. Hence, once every NT_s seconds, one of $M = e^{NR}$ messages is sent over the channel. We assume that the memoryless channel is used once every T_c seconds and has a channel capacity of $\tilde{C}$ nats per channel use of duration T_c seconds. The channel encoder and decoder use a channel block code, $\mathscr{C}$, of block length $\tilde{N}$ and rate $\tilde{R}$ nats per channel use where[10]

$$\begin{aligned} T_c \tilde{N} &= T_s N \\ T_c \tilde{R} &= T_s R \end{aligned} \tag{7.3.1}$$

[10] It is not strictly necessary for the channel block length to satisfy (7.3.1) since the channel encoder can regard sequences of source encoder outputs as channel input symbols; that is, $\tilde{N}$ could be any multiple of its value as given by (7.3.1).

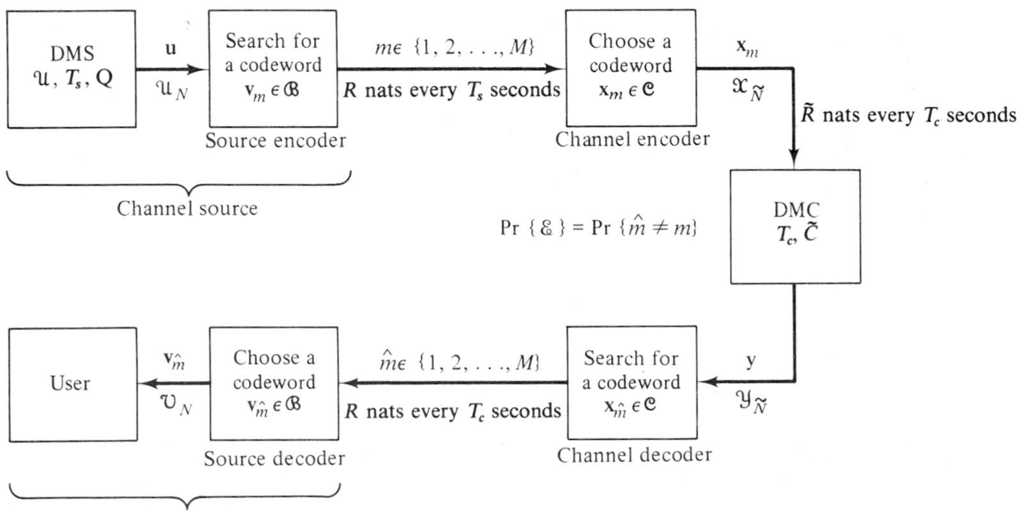

Figure 7.6 Combined source and channel coding.

Here let $\mathscr{E} = \{\hat{m} \neq m\}$ be the event that a channel message error occurs and let $\bar{\mathscr{E}} = \{\hat{m} = m\}$ denote its complement. The average distortion attained when using source code $\mathscr{B}$ and channel code $\mathscr{C}$ is

$$\begin{aligned} d(\mathscr{B}, \mathscr{C}) &= E\{d_N(\mathbf{u}, \mathbf{v}_{\hat{m}}) \mid \mathscr{B}, \mathscr{C}\} \\ &= E\{d_N(\mathbf{u}, \mathbf{v}_{\hat{m}}) \mid \mathscr{B}, \mathscr{C}, \bar{\mathscr{E}}\} \Pr\{\bar{\mathscr{E}}\} + E\{d_N(\mathbf{u}, \mathbf{v}_{\hat{m}}) \mid \mathscr{B}, \mathscr{C}, \mathscr{E}\} \Pr\{\mathscr{E}\} \end{aligned} \tag{7.3.2}$$

where the expectation $E\{\cdot\}$ is over both source output random variables and noisy channel outputs. When no channel errors occur, we have

$$d_N(\mathbf{u}, \mathbf{v}_{\hat{m}}) = d_N(\mathbf{u}, \mathbf{v}_m) = d(\mathbf{u} \mid \mathscr{B}) = \min_{\mathbf{v} \in \mathscr{B}} d_N(\mathbf{u}, \mathbf{v})$$

From (7.2.1), we have

$$E\{d_N(\mathbf{u}, \mathbf{v}_{\hat{m}}) \mid \mathscr{B}, \mathscr{C}, \mathscr{E}\} \le d_0 \tag{7.3.3}$$

Substituting this bound and

$$\Pr\{\bar{\mathscr{E}}\} \le 1 \tag{7.3.4}$$

in (7.3.2), we have

$$d(\mathscr{B}, \mathscr{C}) \le \sum_{\mathbf{u}} Q_N(\mathbf{u}) d(\mathbf{u} \mid \mathscr{B}) + d_0 \Pr\{\mathscr{E}\} \tag{7.3.5}$$

From channel coding theory (Theorem 3.2.1), we know that there exists a channel code $\mathscr{C}$ such that the probability of a channel message error $\Pr\{\mathscr{E}\}$ is bounded by

$$\begin{aligned} \Pr\{\mathscr{E}\} &\le e^{-\tilde{N}E(\tilde{R})} \\ &= e^{-(T_s/T_c)NE(T_sR/T_c)} \end{aligned} \tag{7.3.6}$$

where

$$E\left(\frac{T_s R}{T_c}\right) > 0 \qquad \text{when } \tilde{R} = \frac{T_s R}{T_c} < \tilde{C}$$

Similarly from Theorem 7.2.1, we know that there exists a source code $\mathscr{B}$ such that

$$\sum_{\mathbf{u}} Q_N(\mathbf{u}) d(\mathbf{u} \mid \mathscr{B}) \le D + d_0 e^{-NE(R, D)} \tag{7.3.7}$$

where $E(R, D) > 0$ for $R > R(D)$. Applying these codes to the combined source and channel coding scheme of Fig. 7.6, substituting (7.3.6) and (7.3.7) in (7.3.5), yields the average distortion given by the following theorem.

Theorem 7.3.1 For the combined source and channel coding scheme of Fig. 7.6 discussed above, there exists a source code $\mathscr{B}$ of rate R and block length N and a channel code $\mathscr{C}$ of rate $\tilde{R}$ and block length $\tilde{N}$ satisfying (7.3.1) such that the average distortion is bounded by

$$d(\mathscr{B}, \mathscr{C}) \le D + d_0 e^{-NE(R, D)} + d_0 e^{-(T_s/T_c)NE(T_sR/T_c)} \tag{7.3.8}$$

where

$$E(R, D) > 0 \qquad \text{and} \qquad E\left(\frac{T_s R}{T_c}\right) > 0$$

for R satisfying

$$R(D) < R < C \tag{7.3.9}$$

where

$$C = \frac{T_c}{T_s} \tilde{C} \tag{7.3.10}$$

is the channel capacity in nats per T_s seconds.

As long as the rate distortion function is less than the channel capacity, $R(D) < C$, we can achieve average distortion arbitrarily close to D. When $R(D) > C$, this is impossible, as established by the following.

Theorem 7.3.2 It is impossible to reproduce the source in Theorem 7.3.1 with fidelity D at the receiving end of any discrete memoryless channel of capacity $C < R(D)$ nats per source letter.

PROOF The proof of this converse follows directly from the data-processing theorem (Theorem 1.2.1) and the converse source coding theorem (Theorem 7.2.3) (see Prob. 7.5).

The above converse theorem is true regardless of what type of encoders and decoders are used. In fact, they need not be separated as shown in Fig. 7.6, nor do they need to be block coding schemes for Theorem 7.3.2 to be true. Since Theorem 7.3.1 is true for the block source and channel coding scheme of Fig. 7.6, we see that in the limit of large block lengths there is no loss of generality in assuming a complete separation of source coding and channel coding. From a practical viewpoint, this separation is desirable since it allows channel encoders and decoders to be designed independently of the actual source and user. The source encoder and decoder in effect adapts the source and user to any channel coding system which has sufficient capacity. As block length increases, the source encoder outputs become equally likely (asymptotic equipartition property) so that, in the limit of large block lengths, all source encoder outputs depend only on the rate of the encoder and not on the detailed nature of the source.

From Fig. 7.6, we see a natural duality between source and channel block coding. The source encoder performs an operation similar to the channel decoder, while the channel encoder is similar to the source decoder. Generally, in channel coding, the channel decoder is the more complex device, while in source coding the source encoder is the more complex device. We shall see in Sec. 7.4 that this duality also holds for trellis coding systems. Finally, we note that, although the source encoder removes redundancy from source sequences and channel encoding adds redundancy, these operations are done for quite different reasons. The source encoder takes advantage of the statistical regularity of long sequences of the source output in order to represent the source outputs with a limited rate $R(D)$. The channel encoder adds redundancy so as to achieve immunity to channel errors.

We next show an interesting channel coding interpretation for the source coding theorems of Sec. 7.2. For the general discrete memoryless *source*, representation alphabet, and distortion measure defined earlier, consider $\mathscr{P}_D = \{P(v \mid u): D(\mathbf{P}) \le D\}$ for some fidelity D. For any $\mathbf{P} \in \mathscr{P}_D$, define the channel transition probability for a discrete memoryless *channel* with input alphabet $\mathscr{V}$ and output alphabet $\mathscr{U}$ as

$$Q(u \mid v) = \frac{P(v \mid u)Q(u)}{\sum_{u'} P(v \mid u')Q(u')} \qquad \text{for all } u \in \mathscr{U},\ v \in \mathscr{V} \tag{7.3.11}$$

This is sometimes referred to as the "backward test channel." Now consider any source code $\mathscr{B} = \{\mathbf{v}_1, \mathbf{v}_2, \ldots, \mathbf{v}_M\}$ of rate R and block length N. We can regard $\{\mathbf{v}_0, \mathbf{v}_1, \ldots, \mathbf{v}_M\}$ as a channel code[11] for the above backward test channel as shown in Fig. 7.7. Assume that the codewords are equally likely so that the maximum probability of correct detection, denoted $P_c(\mathbf{v}_0, \mathbf{v}_1, \ldots, \mathbf{v}_M)$, would be achieved by the usual maximum likelihood decoder. But suppose we use a suboptimum channel decoder which uses the decision rule, for given channel output $\mathbf{u} \in \mathscr{U}_N$

$$\text{choose} \qquad \mathbf{v} \in \{\mathbf{v}_0, \mathbf{v}_1, \ldots, \mathbf{v}_M\} \qquad \text{which minimizes} \qquad d_N(\mathbf{u}, \mathbf{v}) \tag{7.3.12}$$

Then for this suboptimum decoder, the probability of a correct decision, denoted $\hat{P}_c(\mathbf{v}_0, \mathbf{v}_1, \ldots, \mathbf{v}_M)$, is upper-bounded by

$$\begin{aligned}\hat{P}_c(\mathbf{v}_0, \mathbf{v}_1, \ldots, \mathbf{v}_M) &= \frac{1}{M+1} \sum_{m=0}^{M} \Pr\left\{ d_N(\mathbf{u}, \mathbf{v}_m) < \min_{m' \neq m} d_N(\mathbf{u}, \mathbf{v}_{m'}) \,\middle|\, \mathbf{v}_m \text{ is sent} \right\} \\ &\le P_c(\mathbf{v}_0, \mathbf{v}_1, \ldots, \mathbf{v}_M) \\ &\le e^{-N[E_o(\rho, \mathbf{P}) - \rho R]} \qquad -1 < \rho < 0 \end{aligned} \tag{7.3.13}$$

where the last inequality follows from the strong converse to the coding theorem (Theorem 3.9.1). We now use (7.3.13) to show why in the source coding theorem

[11] The vector $\mathbf{v}_0$ plays the same role as the dummy vector $\mathbf{v}$ in the proof of Lemma 7.2.1.

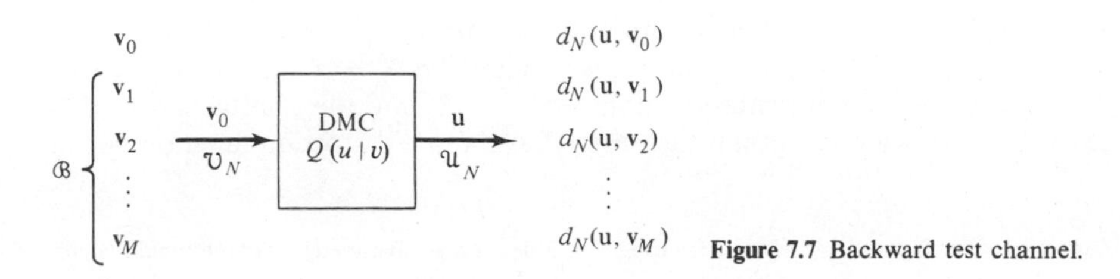

Figure 7.7 Backward test channel.

(Theorem 7.2.1, also see Lemma 7.2.1) the source coding exponent, $E(R, D)$, is essentially the exponent in the strong converse to the coding theorem.

We are primarily interested in the term $\Pr\{d_N(\mathbf{u}, \mathbf{v}_0) < \min_{m \neq 0} d_N(\mathbf{u}, \mathbf{v}_m) \mid \mathbf{v}_0 \text{ is sent}\}$ which may or may not be larger than $\hat{P}_c(\mathbf{v}_0, \mathbf{v}_1, \ldots, \mathbf{v}_M)$. However, if we average (7.3.13) over the ensemble of codewords $\{\mathbf{v}_0, \mathbf{v}_1, \ldots, \mathbf{v}_M\}$ where all components are chosen independently according to $\{P(v): v \in \mathscr{V}\}$, we have[12]

$$\begin{aligned}
\overline{\Pr\left\{d_N(\mathbf{u}, \mathbf{v}_0) < \min_{m \neq 0} d_N(\mathbf{u}, \mathbf{v}_m) \,\middle|\, \mathbf{v}_0 \text{ is sent}\right\}}
&= \overline{\hat{P}_c(\mathbf{v}_0, \mathbf{v}_1, \ldots, \mathbf{v}_M)} \\
&\leq \overline{P_c(\mathbf{v}_0, \mathbf{v}_1, \ldots, \mathbf{v}_M)} \\
&\leq e^{-N[E_o(\rho, \mathbf{P}) - \rho R]} \qquad -1 \leq \rho \leq 0 \qquad (7.3.14)
\end{aligned}$$

which is exactly Lemma 7.2.1. Then, as in Sec. 7.2, for $\mathbf{P} \in \mathscr{P}_D$ we have average distortion

$$\begin{aligned}
\overline{d(\mathscr{B})} &\leq D + d_0 \overline{\Pr\left\{d_N(\mathbf{u}, \mathbf{v}_0) < \min_{m \neq 0} d_N(\mathbf{u}, \mathbf{v}_m) \,\middle|\, \mathbf{v}_0 \text{ is sent}\right\}} \\
&\leq D + d_0 e^{-N[E_o(\rho, \mathbf{P}) - \rho R]} \qquad (7.3.15)
\end{aligned}$$

where

$$\max_{-1 \leq \rho \leq 0} [E_o(\rho, \mathbf{P}) - \rho R] > 0 \qquad \text{for } R > I(\mathbf{P})$$

Here we see that the source coding theorem can be derived directly from the strong converse to the coding theorem due to Arimoto [1973] by applying it to the backward test channel corresponding to any $\mathbf{P} \in \mathscr{P}_D$ as shown in Fig. 7.7. Since the strong converse to the coding theorem results in an exponent that is dual to the ensemble average error exponent, the source coding exponent is dual to the ensemble average error exponent.

Perhaps the least direct relationship between channel and source coding theories is the relationship between the low-rate expurgated error bounds of channel coding theory and the natural rate distortion function associated with the Bhattacharyya distance measure of the channel. In particular, suppose we have a DMC with input alphabet $\mathscr{X}$, output alphabet $\mathscr{Y}$, and transition conditional probabilities $\{p(y \mid x): y \in \mathscr{Y}, x \in \mathscr{X}\}$. For any two channel input letters $x, x' \in \mathscr{X}$, we have the Bhattacharyya distance defined [see (2.3.15)] as

$$d(x, x') \equiv -\ln \sum_y \sqrt{p(y \mid x) p(y \mid x')} \qquad (7.3.16)$$

and we suppose that the channel input letters have a probability distribution $\{q(x): x \in \mathscr{X}\}$. Alternatively, for a source with alphabet $\mathscr{U} = \mathscr{X}$, probability distribution $\{q(x): x \in \mathscr{X}\}$, representation alphabet $\mathscr{V} = \mathscr{X}$, and the Bhattacharyya distance in (7.3.16) as a distortion measure, we have a rate distortion function which

[12] We again use the overbar to denote the code ensemble average. Symmetry gives the equality here.

we denote as $R(D; \mathbf{q})$. This leads us to define the *natural rate distortion function* for the Bhattacharyya distance (7.3.16) as

$$R(D) = \max_{\mathbf{q}} R(D; \mathbf{q}) \tag{7.3.17}$$

To show the relationship between $R(D)$ and the expurgated exponent for the DMC, let us consider the BSC with crossover probability p. Here $\mathscr{U} = \mathscr{V} = \{0, 1\}$ and the distortion measure is

$$d(x, x') = \begin{cases} 0 & x = x' \\ -\ln \sqrt{4p(1-p)} & x \neq x' \end{cases} \tag{7.3.18}$$

Thus letting $\alpha = -\ln \sqrt{4p(1-p)}$, we see that the Bhattacharyya distance is proportional to the Hamming distance. It is easy to show (Sec. 7.6) that

$$\begin{aligned} R(D) &= \max_{\mathbf{q}} \left\{ \mathscr{H}(q) - \mathscr{H}\left(\frac{D}{\alpha}\right) \right\} \\ &= \ln 2 - \mathscr{H}\left(\frac{D}{\alpha}\right) \end{aligned} \tag{7.3.19}$$

and the corresponding source is the Binary Symmetric Source (BSS).

Recall from Sec. 3.4 [see (3.4.8)] that, by the expurgated bound for the BSC, there exists a block code $\mathscr{C}$ of block length N and rate R such that

$$P_E \leq e^{-NE_{\text{ex}}(R)} \tag{7.3.20}$$

where $D = E_{\text{ex}}(R)$ satisfies $R = R(D)$, and $R(D)$ is given by (7.3.19). Hence, we see that the natural rate distortion function for the BSC yields the expurgated exponent as the distortion level.

We can also prove the Gilbert bound discussed in Sec. 3.9 by using the above relationship with rate distortion theory. Let

$$d(N, R) = \max_{\mathscr{C}} d_{\min}(\mathscr{C}) \tag{7.3.21}$$

where

$$d_{\min}(\mathscr{C}) = \min_{\substack{\mathbf{x}, \mathbf{x}' \in \mathscr{C} \\ \mathbf{x} \neq \mathbf{x}'}} d_N(\mathbf{x}, \mathbf{x}') \tag{7.3.22}$$

and where the maximization is over all codes of block length N and rate R. Next let $\mathscr{C}^*$ be a code of block length N and rate R that achieves the maximum minimum distance with the fewest codeword pairs that have the minimum distance $d(N, R)$. Hence

$$\begin{aligned} d(N, R) &= d_{\min}(\mathscr{C}^*) \\ &\geq d(\mathbf{x} \mid \mathscr{C}^*) \qquad \text{for all } \mathbf{x} \in \mathscr{X}_N \end{aligned} \tag{7.3.23}$$

where

$$d(\mathbf{x} \mid \mathscr{C}^*) = \min_{\mathbf{x}' \in \mathscr{C}^*} d_N(\mathbf{x}, \mathbf{x}')$$

This inequality follows from the fact that if there exists an $\mathbf{x}^* \in \mathscr{X}_N$ such that $d(\mathbf{x}^* | \mathscr{C}^*) > d_{\min}(\mathscr{C}^*)$, then by interchanging $\mathbf{x}^*$ with a codeword in $\mathscr{C}^*$ that achieves the minimum distance when paired with another codeword, there would result a new code with fewer pairs of codewords that achieve the minimum distance. This contradicts the definition of $\mathscr{C}^*$. With (7.3.23), we can now prove the Gilbert bound.

Theorem 7.3.3: Gilbert bound

$$d(N, R) \geq D$$

where

$$R = R(D) = \ln 2 - \mathscr{H}\left(\frac{D}{\alpha}\right) \tag{7.3.24}$$

and $D_H = D/\alpha$ is the Hamming distance.

Proof $\mathscr{C}^*$ defined above is a code of rate R which has average distortion $d(\mathscr{C}^*)$ satisfying

$$\begin{aligned} d(\mathscr{C}^*) &\equiv \sum_{\mathbf{x}} q_N(\mathbf{x}) d(\mathbf{x} | \mathscr{C}^*) \\ &\leq d_{\min}(\mathscr{C}^*) \\ &= d(N, R) \end{aligned} \tag{7.3.25}$$

where (7.3.23) is used in this inequality. Here we consider $\mathscr{C}^*$ as a source block code. The converse source coding theorem (Theorem 7.2.3) states that any source code $\mathscr{C}^*$ with distortion $d(\mathscr{C}^*)$ must have

$$R \geq R(d(\mathscr{C}^*)) \tag{7.3.26}$$

Since D is given by (7.3.24), we must have $R(D) = R \geq R(d(\mathscr{C}^*))$. Then since $R(D)$ is a strictly decreasing function of D on $0 < D < \alpha/2$, we have

$$\begin{aligned} d(N, R) &\geq d(\mathscr{C}^*) \\ &\geq D \end{aligned}$$

The results for the BSC generalize to all DMCs, when we use the Bhattacharyya distance, if for the parameter s such that $D = D_s$, the matrix $[e^{sd(x, x')}]$ is positive definite (see Jelinek [1968*b*] and Lesh [1976]). This positive definite condition holds for all $s \leq 0$ in most channels of interest. This shows that, for an arbitrary DMC, the Bhattacharyya distance is the natural generalization to the Hamming distance for binary codes used over the BSC, and a generalized Gilbert bound analogous to Theorem 7.3.3 can be found (see Probs. 7.8 and 7.9).

7.4 DISCRETE MEMORYLESS SOURCES—TRELLIS CODES

For block codes we have demonstrated a duality between source and channel coding where the source encoder performs in a manner similar to the channel decoder and the source decoder performs like a channel encoder (see Fig. 7.6). This duality holds also for trellis codes. We now proceed to show that trellis codes can be used for source coding where the source encoder performs the operations that are essentially the operations of the maximum likelihood trellis decoding algorithm of channel coding, while the trellis source decoder is essentially a trellis channel encoder. In particular, we show that it is possible to use trellis codes, which are general forms of convolutional codes, to achieve the rate distortion limit $(D, R(D))$ of a discrete memoryless source.

Furthermore, the same algorithm which attains the channel coding bound with convolutional channel codes (Viterbi [1967*a*]) also attains the source coding bound with trellis (generalized convolutional) source codes. In this context, however, the term "maximum likelihood" does not apply.

We again consider a discrete memoryless source with alphabet $\mathscr{U} = \{a_1, a_2, \ldots, a_A\}$ and nonzero letter probabilities $Q(a_1), Q(a_2), \ldots, Q(a_A)$. The user alphabet is denoted by $\mathscr{V} = \{b_1, b_2, \ldots, b_B\}$, and there is a nonnegative bounded distortion measure $d(u, v)$ which satisfies

$$0 \le d(u, v) \le d_0 \tag{7.4.1}$$

for all $u \in \mathscr{U}$, $v \in \mathscr{V}$ and some $d_0 < \infty$.

Trellis codes are generalized convolutional codes generated by the same shift register encoder as convolutional codes, but with arbitrary delayless nonlinear operations replacing the linear combinatorial logic of the latter. Whether fixed or time-varying, they can most conveniently be described and analyzed by means of the familiar trellis diagram of Chap. 4. Figure 7.8 shows a trellis source decoder and Fig. 7.9 shows the corresponding trellis diagram for the binary-trellis code with $K - 1$ delay elements and a delayless transformation. Following the same convention as for channel convolutional codes, we will refer to K as the constraint length of the trellis code. We assume for the present a binary-trellis code with n destination symbols per branch, resulting in a code rate $r = 1/n$ bits per source

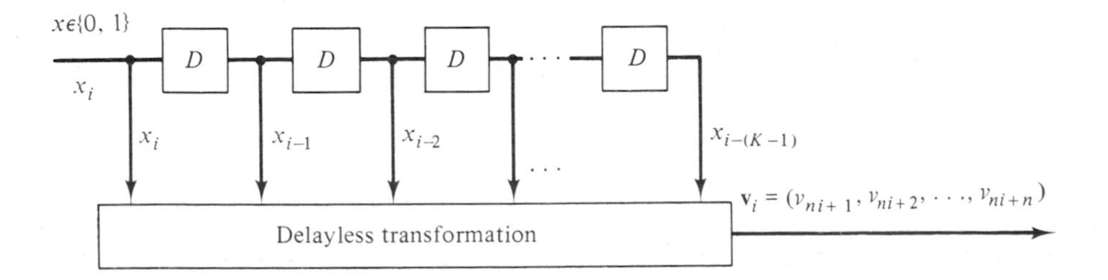

Figure 7.8 Trellis source decoder.

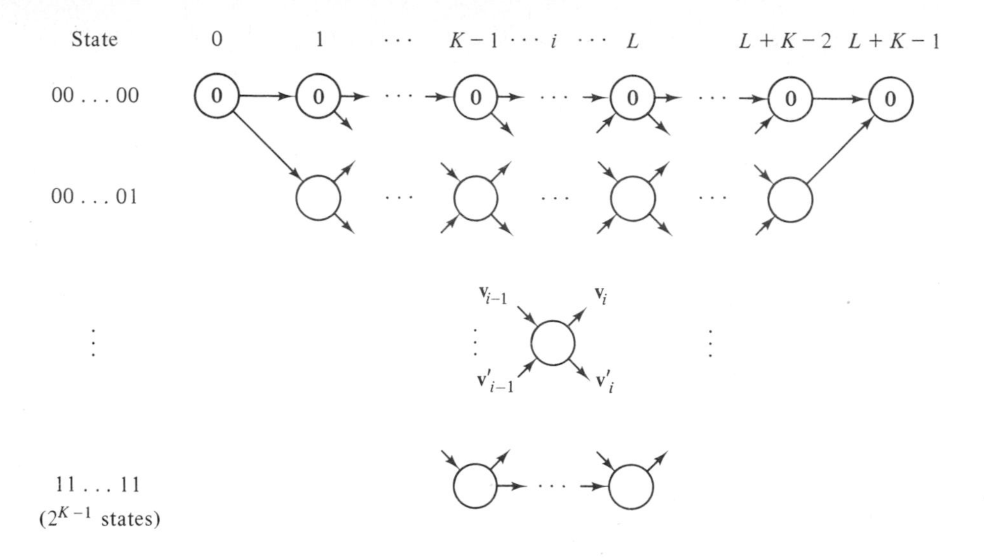

Figure 7.9 Trellis diagram.

symbol. This means that, for each binary input, the trellis source decoder emits n symbols from $\mathscr{V}$, and a sequence of binary input symbols defines a path in the trellis diagram. We can easily generalize to nonbinary trellis source decoders later. Here, each branch of the diagram is labelled with the corresponding n-dimensional destination vector in $\mathscr{V}_n$, and the states (contents of the source decoder's first $K - 1$ delay registers) are denoted by the vertical position in the diagram, also shown at the left of the trellis diagram. The trellis is assumed to be initiated and terminated in the $\mathbf{0}$ state, and no encoding or decoding is performed during the final merging in what we will call the "tail" of the trellis. There are 2^{K-1} states, and we assume that the trellis source coding operates continuously for many source symbols so that the effects of the tail can be ignored. We let the total code length be L branches, while the tail requires $K - 1$ further branches.

The source encoder searches for that path in the trellis whose destination (user) sequence $\mathbf{v}$ most closely resembles (in the sense of minimum distortion) the source sequence $\mathbf{u}$. Once the source encoder picks a path, then it sends binary symbols $\mathbf{x}$ through the channel (again taken to be noiseless) which drives the trellis source decoder through the desired sequence of states yielding the desired path $\mathbf{v}$ as the trellis source decoder output. Figure 7.10 shows the block diagram for the trellis source coding system.

We assume that the trellis source coding system operates continuously for a long time between initial fan-out and final merging. This means we assume that $L \gg K$ and that the effects of the tail can be ignored. In particular, we will ignore the last $K - 1$ branches where all paths merge to the zero state. Hence, the total code length is taken to be L branches and we have a total source sequence length of $N_L = nL$. There are many possible paths or trellis codewords of length N_L, one of which must be chosen to represent the source sequence. For a given source sequence **u** and any trellis codeword **v**, we have the distortion measure

$$d_{N_L}(\mathbf{u}, \mathbf{v}) = \frac{1}{N_L} \sum_{t=1}^{N_L} d(u_t, v_t) \tag{7.4.2}$$

The source encoder chooses the path corresponding to the trellis source decoder output **v** that minimizes $d_{N_L}(\mathbf{u}, \mathbf{v})$. Defining, for each index $i \in \{0, 1, 2, \ldots, L-1\}$, the subsequences of length n

$$\begin{aligned} \mathbf{u}_i &= (u_{ni+1}, u_{ni+2}, \ldots, u_{ni+n}) \\ \mathbf{v}_i &= (v_{ni+1}, v_{ni+2}, \ldots, v_{ni+n}) \end{aligned} \tag{7.4.3}$$

and branch distortion measures

$$d_n(\mathbf{u}_i, \mathbf{v}_i) = \frac{1}{n} \sum_{t=1}^{n} d(u_{ni+t}, v_{ni+t}), \tag{7.4.4}$$

we can rewrite $d_{N_L}(\mathbf{u}, \mathbf{v})$ as

$$d_{N_L}(\mathbf{u}, \mathbf{v}) = \frac{1}{L} \sum_{i=0}^{L-1} d_n(\mathbf{u}_i, \mathbf{v}_i) \tag{7.4.5}$$

In this form it is clear that the source encoder selects a path in the trellis which consists of a sequence of L connected branches, where each branch adds an amount of distortion that is independent of the distortion values of other branches in the path. For a given source sequence **u**, the source encoder's search for the path

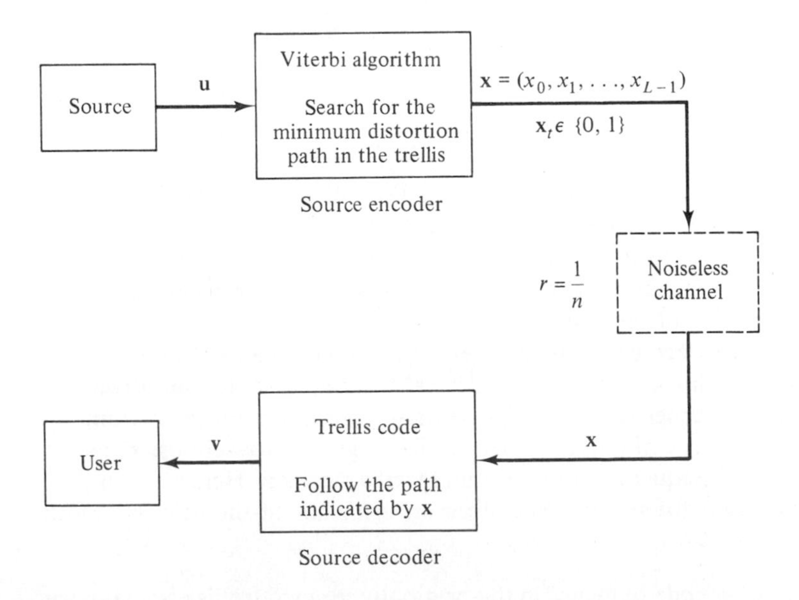

Figure 7.10 Trellis source coding system.

in the trellis that minimizes $d_{N_L}(\mathbf{u}, \mathbf{v})$ is equivalent to the channel decoding search problem where the Viterbi algorithm was used to find the path, or convolutional codeword, that minimizes the negative of the log-likelihood function. Hence the source encoder for trellis codes can be realized with the Viterbi algorithm.

For the given source and distortion measure, we have shown in Sec. 7.2 that the rate distortion function $R(D)$ is given by (7.2.53). Regardless of what type of source coding system we consider, the converse source coding theorem (Theorem 7.2.3) has shown that it is impossible to achieve average distortion of D or less with a system using rate less than $R(D)$. This converse theorem applies to trellis source coding as well as to block source coding (Sec. 7.2). We have also shown that, in the limit of large block lengths, block source coding systems can achieve average distortion D with rate $R(D)$ nats per source symbol, thus justifying $R(D)$ as the rate distortion function. In this section, we will show that, in the limit of large constraint length K, trellis codes can also achieve the rate distortion limit.

We again appeal to an ensemble coding argument where we consider an ensemble of binary trellis source codes of constraint length K and bit rate $r = 1/n$. The ensemble and the corresponding distribution are so chosen that each branch of the trellis diagram has associated with it a user or representation sequence consisting of symbols with common probability distribution $\{P(v): v \in \mathscr{V}\}$ with independence among all symbols. Now for any given source sequence $\mathbf{u}$ and any given trellis code, we denote the minimum distortion path sequence as $\mathbf{v}(\mathbf{u})$. Thus by definition, we have the bound $d_{N_L}(\mathbf{u}, \mathbf{v}(\mathbf{u})) \le d_{N_L}(\mathbf{u}, \mathbf{v})$ for any other path sequence $\mathbf{v}$ belonging to the trellis code. We now choose $\mathbf{v} = \mathbf{v}^*$ as follows:

1. For a given trellis code and the given source sequence $\mathbf{u}$, replace the representation sequence of the all-zeros state path by the sequence $\mathbf{v}_0$ randomly selected according to the conditional probability

$$P(\mathbf{v}_0 \mid \mathbf{u}) = \prod_{t=1}^{N_L} P(v_{0t} \mid u_t) \tag{7.4.6}$$

   This results in a new trellis code which differs from the original trellis code only in the branch values of the all-zeros state path. We call this modified trellis code a *forbidden code*, since in general we are not allowed to select parts of a trellis code after observing the source output sequence $\mathbf{u}$. Note that the original code and the corresponding forbidden code differ only in the *forbidden code path* corresponding to the all-zeros state path.
2. Given a source sequence $\mathbf{u}$, for the above forbidden code, let $\mathbf{v}^{**}$ be the minimum distortion path sequence. That is, let $\mathbf{v}^{**}$ correspond to the forbidden trellis code output sequence which represents $\mathbf{u}$ with minimum distortion.
3. $\mathbf{v}^{**}$ defines a path through the forbidden trellis diagram. Now choose $\mathbf{v}^*$ as the corresponding path sequence in the original trellis diagram. Hence $\mathbf{v}^{**}$ and $\mathbf{v}^*$ are the same except for the subsequences on branches of the all-zeros state path.

Note that $\mathbf{v}^*$ is a trellis code sequence in the originally selected trellis code, and we introduced the forbidden trellis code only as a means of selecting this trellis code sequence. We never use the forbidden trellis code in the actual encoding of source sequences and require it only to derive the following bounds. Since $\mathbf{v}^*$ is a path sequence in the trellis code, we have from the definition of $\mathbf{v}(\mathbf{u})$

$$d_{N_L}(\mathbf{u}, \mathbf{v}(\mathbf{u})) \le d_{N_L}(\mathbf{u}, \mathbf{v}^*) \tag{7.4.7}$$

We now derive a bound on $\overline{d_{N_L}(\mathbf{u}, \mathbf{v}(\mathbf{u}))}$, where $\overline{(\cdot)}$ denotes an average over all source sequences and trellis codes in the ensemble. We do this by bounding $\overline{d_{N_L}(\mathbf{u}, \mathbf{v}^*)}$.

Lemma 7.4.1

$$\overline{d_{N_L}(\mathbf{u}, \mathbf{v}(\mathbf{u}))} \le D(\mathbf{P}) + \frac{d_0}{L} \sum_{j=0}^{L-1} \sum_{k=1}^{L-j-1} k P_{jk} \tag{7.4.8}$$

where

$$P_{jk} \equiv \Pr \left\{ \begin{array}{l} \mathbf{v}^* \text{ merges with the all-zeros state} \\ \text{path at node } j \text{ and remains merged} \\ \text{for exactly } k \text{ branches} \end{array} \right\} \tag{7.4.9}$$

and

$$D(\mathbf{P}) = \sum_u \sum_v Q(u)P(v \mid u)d(u, v) \tag{7.4.10}$$

PROOF For a given source sequence $\mathbf{u}$ and for $\mathbf{v}^*$ as selected above, let $\mathscr{Z} = \{i: \mathbf{v}_i^* \text{ is a branch output vector of the all-zeros state path}\}$. Then

$$\begin{aligned} L d_{N_L}(\mathbf{u}, \mathbf{v}^*) &= \sum_{i=0}^{L-1} d_n(\mathbf{u}_i, \mathbf{v}_i^*) \\ &= \sum_{i \notin \mathscr{Z}} d_n(\mathbf{u}_i, \mathbf{v}_i^*) + \sum_{i \in \mathscr{Z}} d_n(\mathbf{u}_i, \mathbf{v}_i^*) \end{aligned} \tag{7.4.11}$$

For $i \in \mathscr{Z}$ we use the bound $d_n(\mathbf{u}_i, \mathbf{v}_i^*) \le d_0$, while for $i \notin \mathscr{Z}$ we have $d_n(\mathbf{u}_i, \mathbf{v}_i^*) = d_n(\mathbf{u}, \mathbf{v}_i^{**})$.

Hence

$$\begin{aligned} L d_{N_L}(\mathbf{u}, \mathbf{v}^*) &\le \sum_{i \notin \mathscr{Z}} d_n(\mathbf{u}_i, \mathbf{v}_i^{**}) + \sum_{i \in \mathscr{Z}} d_0 \\ &\le \sum_{i=0}^{L-1} d_n(\mathbf{u}_i, \mathbf{v}_i^{**}) + \sum_{i \in \mathscr{Z}} d_0 \\ &\le \sum_{i=0}^{L-1} d_n(\mathbf{u}_i, \mathbf{v}_{0i}) + \sum_{i \in \mathscr{Z}} d_0 \end{aligned} \tag{7.4.12}$$

where $\mathbf{v}_{0i}$ is the ith branch output vector of the all-zeros path of the forbidden code. This last inequality follows from the fact that, by the definition of $\mathbf{v}^{**}$, we have

$$d_{N_L}(\mathbf{u}, \mathbf{v}^{**}) \le d_{N_L}(\mathbf{u}, \mathbf{v}_0) \tag{7.4.13}$$

in the forbidden trellis code where $\mathbf{v}_0$ is the all-zeros state output sequence. From (7.4.7) and (7.4.12), we obtain the inequality

$$d_{N_L}(\mathbf{u}, \mathbf{v}(\mathbf{u})) \le d_{N_L}(\mathbf{u}, \mathbf{v}_0) + \sum_{i \in \mathscr{X}} \frac{d_0}{L} \tag{7.4.14}$$

When we average (7.4.14) over all source sequences and over the trellis code ensemble, the first term becomes $D(\mathbf{P})$. Using the definition of P_{jk} given in (7.4.9), we employ the union-of-events bound on the second term to get the desired result.

There remains only the evaluation of a tight bound for P_{jk}. This is computed over the ensemble of forbidden trellis codes which consist of the normal codes with the branch vectors of the all-zeros state path $\mathbf{v}_o$ selected according to (7.4.6) for each source sequence $\mathbf{u}$. Note that when $\mathbf{v}^*$ merges with the all-zeros state path at node j and remains merged for exactly k branches, in the corresponding forbidden code $\mathbf{v}^{**}$ also is merged with the all-zeros state for the same span. Hence P_{jk} is also the probability that, in the forbidden trellis codes, $\mathbf{v}^{**}$ (the minimum distortion path) merges with the all-zeros state path at node j and remains merged for exactly k branches.

Let $\mathbf{x}^{**}$ be the binary input sequence to the forbidden trellis decoder that yields the minimum distortion codeword $\mathbf{v}^{**}$. If $\mathbf{v}^{**}$ merges with the all-zeros state for exactly k branches starting with the jth node, the binary sequence $\mathbf{x}^{**}$ has the form

$$\begin{array}{cccc} \cdots a_1\, a_2 \cdots a_{K-1}\; 1\; 0\; 0 & \cdots 0\; 0\; 0 \cdots 0 & 1\; b_1\; b_2 \cdots & b_{K-1} \cdots \\ \uparrow & \uparrow \qquad \uparrow & & \uparrow \\ \text{node } j-K & \text{node } j \quad \text{node } j+k & & \text{node } j+k+K \end{array} \tag{7.4.15}$$

At node $j - K$, we take the forbidden trellis decoder to be in state $\mathbf{a} = (a_1, a_2, \ldots, a_{K-1})$, and at node $j + k + K$ to be in state $\mathbf{b} = (b_1, b_2, \ldots, b_{K-1})$. The "1" immediately following node $j - K$ is required, for otherwise merging could not start exactly at node j. Similarly a "1" must follow node $j + k$, for otherwise the merged span would be longer than exactly k as assumed. The merged span is shown in Fig. 7.11. Note that states $\mathbf{a}$ and $\mathbf{b}$ are unrestricted, and either or both may possibly be the all-zeros state.

Now for the moment let us assume that states $\mathbf{a}$ and $\mathbf{b}$ are fixed. That is, the trellis path corresponding to the minimum-distortion forbidden trellis decoder output, $\mathbf{v}^{**}$, is assumed to have passed into state $\mathbf{a}$ at node $j - K$ and state $\mathbf{b}$ at node $j + k + K$. Then we seek the probability that the subpath with decoder input sequence

$$\mathbf{a}\; 1\; 0\; 0 \cdots 0\; 0\; 1\; \mathbf{b} \tag{7.4.16}$$

is the minimum distortion path (subsequence of $\mathbf{x}^{**}$) from state $\mathbf{a}$ to state $\mathbf{b}$ in the forbidden trellis code. Any other path from $\mathbf{a}$ to $\mathbf{b}$ has an input of the general form

$$\mathbf{a}\; x_{j-K}\; \mathbf{x}\; x_{j+k}\; \mathbf{b} \tag{7.4.17}$$

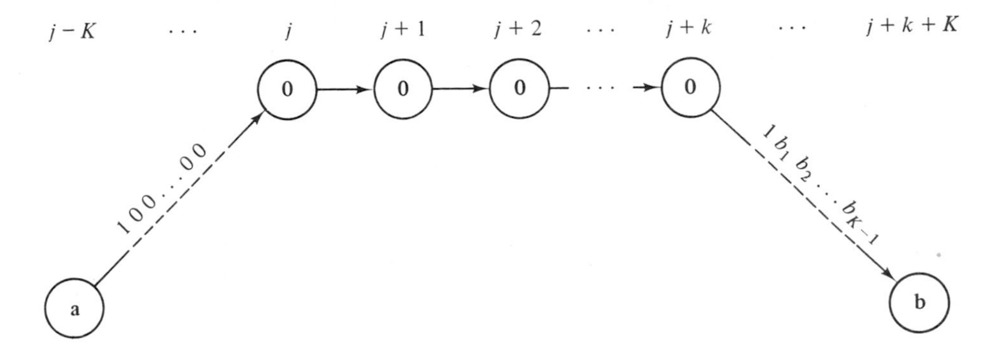

Figure 7.11 Merger with the all-zeros state path.

where $\mathbf{x} = (x_{j-K+1}, \ldots, x_{j+k-1})$. Since the probability that path **a** 1 **0** 1 **b** is the minimum distortion path among all paths of the general form **a** x_{j-K} **x** x_{j+k} **b** is upper-bounded by the probability that path **a** 1 **0** 1 **b** is the minimum distortion path among all paths of the restricted form **a** 1 **x** 1 **b**, we now consider only paths of this restricted form. Let $\mathbf{v}(\mathbf{x})$ be the forbidden trellis decoder output for the $(k + 2K)$ branches going from state **a** to state **b** corresponding to the input **a** 1 **x** 1 **b**. Then for random source subsequences of length $n(k + 2K)$, denoted **u**, and for the ensemble of forbidden trellis codes, we seek to bound P_{jk} by first bounding the probability[13]

$$P_{jk}(\mathbf{a}, \mathbf{b}) = \Pr\left\{d(\mathbf{u}, \mathbf{v}(\mathbf{0})) < \min_{\mathbf{x} \neq \mathbf{0}} d(\mathbf{u}, \mathbf{v}(\mathbf{x})) \,\middle|\, \mathbf{a}, \mathbf{b}\right\}$$

By restricting our attention to subpaths from state **a** to state **b** of a forbidden code, we have formulated the problem as a block source coding problem. Our bound on P_{jk} will be developed in a way analogous to the block coding bound of Sec. 7.2.

Lemma 7.4.2 Over the trellis code ensemble just defined,

$$P_{jk} \leq 2^{(K-1)\rho} 2^{-k(E_o(\rho, \mathbf{P})/R - \rho)} \tag{7.4.18}$$

where

$$E_o(\rho, \mathbf{P}) = -\ln \sum_u \left(\sum_v P(v) Q(u \mid v)^{1/(1+\rho)}\right)^{1+\rho} \qquad -1 < \rho < 0 \tag{7.4.19}$$

and

$$R = r \ln 2 = (\ln 2)/n$$

[13] To simplify the notation, in the following, when the subscript on the distortion $d(\cdot\,,\cdot)$ is missing, we assume that, as always, it is defined by the dimensions of the vectors involved.

PROOF We now require some notation to separate branch vectors of the all-zeros path from other branch vectors of the forbidden trellis. As was discussed above, we are concerned only with branch vectors associated with paths in the trellis of the form **a** 1 **x** 1 **b**. Hence our notation refers only to quantities associated with these paths.

$\mathbf{u}^c$ denotes the source subsequence over the central k branches

$\mathbf{u}_{jk}$ denotes the source subsequence over the first K and final K branches of the subtrellis under consideration

$\mathbf{v}^c(\mathbf{0})$ denotes the branch vectors of the all-zeros state path over the central k branches

$\mathscr{V}_{jk}$ denotes the collection of all branch vectors over the central k branches not belonging to the all-zeros state path

If **u** is the subsequence of the source in going from state **a** to state **b**, then we have $Q(\mathbf{u}) = Q(\mathbf{u}_{jk})Q(\mathbf{u}^c)$, since all components of **u** are independent and identically distributed. The term $\mathbf{v}^c(\mathbf{0})$ also represents the only part of the all-zeros path of the forbidden trellis that is relevant; it is a random sequence selected according to $P(\mathbf{v}^c(\mathbf{0})\,|\,\mathbf{u}^c)$ and is independent of $\mathscr{V}_{jk}$ · Vectors $\mathbf{v}^c(\mathbf{0})$ and $\mathscr{V}_{jk}$ comprise all the branch vectors corresponding to paths in the forbidden trellis code with binary subsequences of the form **a** 1 **x** 1 **b**. Hence all the quantities of interest have the joint probability distribution[14]

$$P(\mathscr{V}_{jk}, \mathbf{v}^c(\mathbf{0}), \mathbf{u}_{jk}, \mathbf{u}^c) = P(\mathscr{V}_{jk})Q(\mathbf{u}_{jk})Q(\mathbf{u}^c)P(\mathbf{v}^c(\mathbf{0})\,|\,\mathbf{u}^c)$$

Now we define the indicator function

$$\Phi(\mathbf{u}, \mathbf{v}^c(\mathbf{0}); \mathscr{V}_{jk}) = \begin{cases} 1 & d(\mathbf{u}, \mathbf{v}(\mathbf{0})) < \min\limits_{\mathbf{x} \neq \mathbf{0}} d(\mathbf{u}, \mathbf{v}(\mathbf{x})) \\ 0 & \text{otherwise} \end{cases} \tag{7.4.20}$$

Then

$$\begin{aligned} P_{jk}(\mathbf{a}, \mathbf{b}) &= \Pr\left\{ d(\mathbf{u}, \mathbf{v}(\mathbf{0})) < \min_{\mathbf{x} \neq \mathbf{0}} d(\mathbf{u}, \mathbf{v}(\mathbf{x})) \,\middle|\, \mathbf{a}, \mathbf{b} \right\} \\ &= \sum_{\mathscr{V}_{jk}} \sum_{\mathbf{u}_{jk}} \sum_{\mathbf{u}^c} \sum_{\mathbf{v}^c(\mathbf{0})} P(\mathscr{V}_{jk})Q(\mathbf{u}_{jk})Q(\mathbf{u}^c)P(\mathbf{v}^c(\mathbf{0})\,|\,\mathbf{u}^c)\Phi(\mathbf{u}, \mathbf{v}^c(\mathbf{0}); \mathscr{V}_{jk}) \\ &= \sum_{\mathscr{V}_{jk}} \sum_{\mathbf{u}_{jk}} \sum_{\mathbf{u}^c} \sum_{\mathbf{v}^c(\mathbf{0})} P(\mathscr{V}_{jk})Q(\mathbf{u}_{jk})P(\mathbf{v}^c(\mathbf{0}))Q(\mathbf{u}^c\,|\,\mathbf{v}^c(\mathbf{0}))\Phi(\mathbf{u}, \mathbf{v}^c(\mathbf{0}); \mathscr{V}_{jk}) \\ &\leq \sum_{\mathscr{V}_{jk}} \sum_{\mathbf{u}_{jk}} \sum_{\mathbf{u}^c} P(\mathscr{V}_{jk})Q(\mathbf{u}_{jk}) \left[\sum_{\mathbf{v}^c(\mathbf{0})} P(\mathbf{v}^c(\mathbf{0}))Q(\mathbf{u}^c\,|\,\mathbf{v}^c(\mathbf{0}))^{1/(1+\rho)} \right]^{1+\rho} \\ &\quad \times \left[\sum_{\mathbf{v}^c(\mathbf{0})} P(\mathbf{v}^c(\mathbf{0}))\Phi(\mathbf{u}, \mathbf{v}^c(\mathbf{0}); \mathscr{V}_{jk}) \right]^{-\rho} \end{aligned} \tag{7.4.21}$$

[14] Note that $\mathbf{u}_{jk}$ and $\mathscr{V}_{jk}$ are independent since they refer to disjoint segments.

where the Hölder inequality is used with $-1 < \rho < 0$. Next the Jensen inequality yields the further bound

$$P_{jk}(\mathbf{a}, \mathbf{b}) \le \sum_{\mathbf{u}_{jk}} Q(\mathbf{u}_{jk}) \sum_{\mathbf{u}^c} \left[\sum_{\mathbf{v}^c(\mathbf{0})} P(\mathbf{v}^c(\mathbf{0}))Q(\mathbf{u}^c \mid \mathbf{v}^c(\mathbf{0}))^{1/(1+\rho)} \right]^{1+\rho}$$

$$\times \left[\sum_{\mathscr{V}_{jk}} \sum_{\mathbf{v}^c(\mathbf{0})} P(\mathscr{V}_{jk})P(\mathbf{v}^c(\mathbf{0}))\Phi(\mathbf{u}, \mathbf{v}^c(\mathbf{0}); \mathscr{V}_{jk}) \right]^{-\rho} \tag{7.4.22}$$

In the last bracketed term, we note that there is now complete symmetry for all paths involved since the section of the all-zeros state path $\mathbf{v}^c(\mathbf{0})$ has the probability $P(\mathbf{v}^c(\mathbf{0}))$ induced by definition (7.4.6), which is the same for all branch vectors in $\mathscr{V}_{jk}$ and thus, since all of the 2^{k+K-1} paths[15] of the form $\mathbf{a}\ 1\ \mathbf{x}\ 1\ \mathbf{b}$ have the same statistical properties, we have

$$\sum_{\mathscr{V}_{jk}} \sum_{\mathbf{v}^c(\mathbf{0})} P(\mathscr{V}_{jk})P(\mathbf{v}^c(\mathbf{0}))\Phi(\mathbf{u}, \mathbf{v}^c(\mathbf{0}); \mathscr{V}_{jk}) = \frac{1}{2^{k+K-1}} \tag{7.4.23}$$

independent of $\mathbf{u}$. Hence

$$\begin{aligned} P_{jk}(\mathbf{a}, \mathbf{b}) &\le \sum_{\mathbf{u}^c} \left[\sum_{\mathbf{v}^c(\mathbf{0})} P(\mathbf{v}^c(\mathbf{0}))Q(\mathbf{u}^c \mid \mathbf{v}^c(\mathbf{0}))^{1/(1+\rho)} \right]^{1+\rho} 2^{(k+K-1)\rho} \\ &= 2^{(k+K-1)\rho} \left[\sum_{u} \left(\sum_{v} P(v)Q(u \mid v)^{1/(1+\rho)} \right)^{1+\rho} \right]^{kn} \\ &= 2^{(K-1)\rho} 2^{-k[E_o(\rho, \mathbf{P})/R - \rho]} \end{aligned} \tag{7.4.24}$$

Here we use the fact that all components of all vectors are statistically independent of each other. Since the bound on $P_{jk}(\mathbf{a}, \mathbf{b})$ is independent of states $\mathbf{a}$ and $\mathbf{b}$, we obtain the desired result.

Using this bound on P_{jk}, we now obtain from (7.4.8)

$$\begin{aligned} \overline{d_{N_L}(\mathbf{u}, \mathbf{v} \mid \mathbf{u})} &\le D(\mathbf{P}) + \frac{d_0}{L} \sum_{j=0}^{L-1} \sum_{k=1}^{L-j-1} k 2^{(K-1)\rho} 2^{-k[E_o(\rho, \mathbf{P})/R - \rho]} \\ &\le D(\mathbf{P}) + d_0 \sum_{k=0}^{\infty} k 2^{(K-1)\rho} 2^{-k[E_o(\rho, \mathbf{P})/R - \rho]} \\ &= D(\mathbf{P}) + d_0 2^{(K-1)\rho} \sum_{k=0}^{\infty} k 2^{-k[E_o(\rho, \mathbf{P})/R - \rho]} \\ &= D(\mathbf{P}) + \frac{d_0 2^{(K-1)\rho}}{[1 - 2^{-[E_o(\rho, \mathbf{P})/R - \rho]}]^2} \end{aligned} \tag{7.4.25}$$

provided $E_o(\rho, \mathbf{P})/R - \rho > 0$. Recall that $E_o(\rho, \mathbf{P})$ is the Gallager function whose properties are given in Lemma 7.2.2. From (7.2.58), we have

$$E_o(\rho, \mathbf{P}) = \rho I(\mathbf{P}) + \int_0^{\rho} \int_0^{\beta} E_o''(\alpha, \mathbf{P})\, d\alpha\, d\beta$$

[15] This corresponds to all paths over the k central branches of the subtrellis starting in any one of the 2^{K-1} possible states.

where

$$I(\mathbf{P}) = \sum_u \sum_v Q(u)P(v \mid u) \ln \frac{P(v \mid u)}{P(v)}$$

For $-\frac{1}{2} \leq \rho \leq 0$, we have the bound (see Prob. 7.3)[16]

$$E_o''(\alpha, \mathbf{P}) \geq -C_o = -2 - 16[\ln A]^2 \tag{7.4.26}$$

which yields

$$E_o(\rho, \mathbf{P}) \geq \rho I(\mathbf{P}) - C_o \frac{\rho^2}{2} \tag{7.4.27}$$

This inequality is then used to bound

$$\begin{aligned} \frac{E_o(\rho, \mathbf{P})}{R} - \rho &\geq \rho \frac{I(\mathbf{P})}{R} - \rho - \frac{C_o}{R}\left(\frac{\rho^2}{2}\right) \\ &= \rho \frac{I(\mathbf{P}) - R}{R} - \frac{C_o}{R}\left(\frac{\rho^2}{2}\right) \end{aligned} \tag{7.4.28}$$

Next we choose

$$\rho = \frac{I(\mathbf{P}) - R}{C_o} < 0 \tag{7.4.29}$$

so that the lower bound in (7.4.28) becomes

$$\rho\left[\frac{I(\mathbf{P}) - R}{R}\right] - \frac{C_o}{R}\left(\frac{\rho^2}{2}\right) = \frac{(I(\mathbf{P}) - R)^2}{2RC_o} \tag{7.4.30}$$

Defining

$$E(R; \mathbf{P}) \equiv -\rho = \frac{R - I(\mathbf{P})}{C_o}$$

we have

$$\overline{d_{N_L}(\mathbf{u}, \mathbf{v}(\mathbf{u}))} \leq D(\mathbf{P}) + \frac{d_0 2^{-(K-1)E(R;\mathbf{P})}}{[1 - 2^{-(C_o/2R)E^2(R;\mathbf{P})}]^2} \tag{7.4.31}$$

where $E(R; \mathbf{P}) > 0$ for $R > I(\mathbf{P})$.

Recall from (7.2.53) that the rate distortion function is

$$R(D) = \min_{\mathbf{P} \in \mathscr{P}_D} I(\mathbf{P})$$

[16] Actually any bounded number larger than $2 + 16[\ln A]^2$ will suffice. By choosing C_o large enough we can always choose ρ in (7.4.29) such that $\rho \geq -\frac{1}{2}$.

where

$$\mathscr{P}_D = \left\{P(v \mid u): \sum_u \sum_v Q(u)P(v \mid u)d(u, v) \le D\right\}$$

For $\mathbf{P}^* \in \mathscr{P}_D$ that achieves $R(D) = I(\mathbf{P}^*)$, we define

$$E_c(R, D) \equiv E(R; \mathbf{P}^*) = \frac{R - R(D)}{C_o}$$

and we have the source coding theorem.

Theorem 7.4.1: Trellis source coding theorem Given distortion D, for any constraint length K and rate $R = (\ln 2)/n > R(D)$ for any integer n, there exists a binary trellis code T_K with average distortion $d(T_K)$ satisfying

$$d(T_K) \le D + \frac{d_0 2^{-(K-1)E_c(R, D)}}{[1 - 2^{-(C_o/2R)E_c^2(R, D)}]^2} \tag{7.4.32}$$

where

$$E_c(R, D) = \frac{R - R(D)}{C_o} > 0 \tag{7.4.33}$$

PROOF The only additional observation we make from (7.4.31) is that at least one code has average distortion less than or equal to the ensemble average distortion.

This theorem shows that in the limit of large constraint length K we can achieve the rate distortion limit $(D, R(D))$ with the trellis source coding system shown in Fig. 7.10. Furthermore, it gives a bound on the distortion achievable with finite constraint length.

Up to this point we have considered trellis decoders with only binary inputs, which corresponds to a trellis diagram where only two branches leave each node. We can easily generalize to the case where the decoder has one of q inputs so that the corresponding trellis diagram has q branches leaving each node. Over the noiseless channel, the encoder sends q-ary symbols for each n source symbols so that, for these codes, the rate is

$$r = \frac{\log q}{n} \quad \text{bits/source symbol}$$

or

$$R = \frac{\ln q}{n} \quad \text{nats/source symbol} \tag{7.4.34}$$

There are still n representation symbols for each branch. The proof is essentially the same as for the binary case where $q = 2$, but it requires conditioning on states

a, **b** and on the two nonzero symbols that follow **a** and precede **b**. For arbitrary integer q, (7.4.8), (7.4.9), and (7.4.10) are the same, but now P_{jk} is bounded by

$$P_{jk} \leq q^{(K-1)\rho} q^{-k[E_o(\rho, \mathbf{P})/R - \rho]} \tag{7.4.35}$$

Hence, for this more general case, we have the same source coding theorem with (7.4.32) replaced by

$$d(T_K) \leq D + \frac{d_0 q^{-(K-1)E_c(R, D)}}{[1 - q^{-(C_o/2R)E_c^2(R, D)}]^2} \tag{7.4.36}$$

where

$$E_c(R, D) = \frac{R - R(D)}{C_o}$$

To examine the rate of convergence to the rate distortion limit $(D, R(D))$ as constraint length K increases, we merely substitute $E_c(R, D)$ into the bound (7.4.36) and rewrite this as

$$\begin{aligned} d(T_K) &\leq D + \frac{d_0 q^{-(K-1)(R-R(D))/C_o}}{[1 - q^{-(R-R(D))^2/2RC_o}]^2} \\ &= D + \frac{d_0 q^{(R-R(D))/C_o}}{[1 - q^{-(R-R(D))^2/2RC_o}]^2} e^{-N_t R(R-R(D))/C_o} \end{aligned} \tag{7.4.37}$$

where $N_t = nK = (K/R) \ln q$ is the equivalent block length. Comparing this with the convergence of block source coding given by Theorem 7.2.4, we see that this bound on distortion has an exponent proportional to $R[R - R(D)]$, whereas with block codes the exponent is proportional to $[R - R(D)]^2/2$. We observed similar superiority for convolutional codes over block codes in channel coding.

In this section we described and analyzed trellis source decoders and the optimum trellis source encoder implemented by the Viterbi algorithm. As with channel coding, the computational complexity of the optimum source encoder grows exponentially with constraint length. It is natural to consider suboptimum path search algorithms such as the sequential decoding algorithms for channel convolutional codes. These algorithms can reduce the computation required per source symbol.

For the most part, sequential algorithms for source encoding are best analyzed in terms of tree codes which are trellis codes with infinite constraint length, $K = \infty$. This results in a trellis diagram that never has merging nodes but continues to branch out forever with independent random representation vectors on all branches. For a tree source decoder, the optimum source encoder finds the path in the tree that can represent a source sequence with minimum distortion. Jelinek [1969], by using branching theory arguments (see Probs. 7.10 and 7.11), was the first to show that tree codes can achieve the rate distortion limit $(D, R(D))$. We obtain the same result by letting $K = \infty$ in (7.4.37).

Note finally that the source trellis or tree encoder need not necessarily find the unique path that represents the given source sequence with minimum distortion. There may, in fact, be many paths that can represent a source sequence within a desired fidelity criterion D and so it is natural to consider various sequential search algorithms which choose the first subpath that meets a fidelity criterion. Anderson and Jelinek [1973] and Gallager [1974] have proposed and analyzed such algorithms and have shown convergence to the rate distortion limit for various sources. Sequential algorithms of this type, although suboptimum, yield less complex trellis or tree source encoders and still achieve the rate distortion limit.

7.5 CONTINUOUS AMPLITUDE MEMORYLESS SOURCES

Many sources, such as sampled speech, can be modeled as discrete-time sources with source outputs which are real numbers; that is, a source with alphabet $\mathscr{R} = (-\infty, \infty)$. We now consider such discrete-time continuous-amplitude memoryless sources where the source and representation alphabets are the real numbers, the source output at time n is a random variable u_n with probability density function $\{Q(u): -\infty < u < \infty\}$,[17] and we have a possibly unbounded nonnegative distortion measure $d(u, v)$ for each $u, v \in \mathscr{R}$. All outputs of the source are independent and identically distributed. The distortion between sequences $\mathbf{u}$ and $\mathbf{v}$ of length N is again defined as $d_N(\mathbf{u}, \mathbf{v}) = (1/N) \sum_{n=1}^{N} d(u_n, v_n)$. Besides the fact that the source outputs are now continuous real random variables, the main difference from the previous sections is the fact that the single-letter distortion measure can be unbounded. This is to allow many common distortions such as the magnitude error, $d(u, v) = |u - v|$, and the squared error, $d(u, v) = (u - v)^2$, distortion measures. To overcome the fact that we no longer have a bounded distortion measure, we require instead the condition

$$\int_{-\infty}^{\infty} Q(u) d^2(u, 0)\, du \leq d_0^2 \tag{7.5.1}$$

for some finite number d_0. This is the condition that the random variable $d(u, 0)$ has bounded mean[18] and bounded variance which is satisfied in most cases of interest. Throughout the following we will assume this condition for continuous amplitude sources and distortion measures.

[17] We shall denote all probability density functions associated with source coding with capital letters.

[18] Hölder's inequality (App. 3A) applied to (7.5.1), the bounded variance condition, implies a bounded mean, that is

$$\int_{-\infty}^{\infty} Q(u) d(u, 0)\, du \leq d_0$$

7.5.1 Block Coding Theorems for Continuous-Amplitude Sources

Again referring to Fig. 7.3 for the basic block source coding system, let $\mathscr{B} = \{\mathbf{v}_1, \mathbf{v}_2, \ldots, \mathbf{v}_M\}$ be a set of M representation sequences of N user symbols each, which we call a block code of length N and rate $R = (\ln M)/N$ nats per source symbol. For this code the average distortion is now

$$d(\mathscr{B}) = \int_{-\infty}^{\infty} \cdots \int_{-\infty}^{\infty} Q_N(\mathbf{u}) d(\mathbf{u} \mid \mathscr{B})\, d\mathbf{u} \tag{7.5.2}$$

where

$$d(\mathbf{u} \mid \mathscr{B}) = \min_{\mathbf{v} \in \mathscr{B}} d_N(\mathbf{u}, \mathbf{v})$$

$$Q_N(\mathbf{u}) = \prod_{n=1}^{N} Q(u_n)$$

In proving coding theorems for block codes we essentially follow our earlier proofs for the discrete memoryless source presented in Sec. 7.2, the main difference being that integrals of probability density functions replace summations of probabilities. As before, we use an ensemble average coding argument by first introducing the conditional probability density function

$$P_N(\mathbf{v} \mid \mathbf{u}) = \prod_{n=1}^{N} P(v_n \mid u_n) \tag{7.5.3}$$

and the corresponding marginal probability density on $\mathscr{R}_N$

$$\begin{aligned} P_N(\mathbf{v}) &= \int_{-\infty}^{\infty} \cdots \int_{-\infty}^{\infty} Q_N(\mathbf{u}) P_N(\mathbf{v} \mid \mathbf{u})\, d\mathbf{u} \\ &= \prod_{n=1}^{N} P(v_n) \end{aligned} \tag{7.5.4}$$

where

$$P(v) = \int_{-\infty}^{\infty} Q(u) P(v \mid u)\, du \tag{7.5.5}$$

Proceeding exactly as in Sec. 7.2 [Eqs. (7.2.8) through (7.2.11)], but with summations replaced by integrals, we obtain

$$\begin{aligned} d(\mathscr{B}) = &\int_{-\infty}^{\infty} \cdots \int_{-\infty}^{\infty} Q_N(\mathbf{u}) P_N(\mathbf{v} \mid \mathbf{u}) d(\mathbf{u} \mid \mathscr{B})[1 - \Phi(\mathbf{u}, \mathbf{v}; \mathscr{B})]\, d\mathbf{u}\, d\mathbf{v} \\ &+ \int_{-\infty}^{\infty} \cdots \int_{-\infty}^{\infty} Q_N(\mathbf{u}) P_N(\mathbf{v} \mid \mathbf{u}) d(\mathbf{u} \mid \mathscr{B}) \Phi(\mathbf{u}, \mathbf{v}; \mathscr{B})\, d\mathbf{u}\, d\mathbf{v} \end{aligned} \tag{7.5.6}$$

where

$$\Phi(\mathbf{u}, \mathbf{v}; \mathscr{B}) = \begin{cases} 1 & d_N(\mathbf{u}, \mathbf{v}) < d(\mathbf{u} \mid \mathscr{B}) \\ 0 & d_N(\mathbf{u}, \mathbf{v}) \ge d(\mathbf{u} \mid \mathscr{B}) \end{cases} \tag{7.2.10}$$

Now, defining (as in 7.2.15)

$$D(\mathbf{P}) = \int_{-\infty}^{\infty} \int_{-\infty}^{\infty} Q(u)P(v \mid u)d(u, v)\, du\, dv \tag{7.5.7}$$

we see that since $1 - \Phi \leq 1$, the first integral is easily bounded to yield

$$d(\mathscr{B}) \leq D(\mathbf{P}) + \int_{-\infty}^{\infty} \cdots \int_{-\infty}^{\infty} Q_N(\mathbf{u})P_N(\mathbf{v} \mid \mathbf{u})d(\mathbf{u} \mid \mathscr{B})\Phi(\mathbf{u}, \mathbf{v}; \mathscr{B})\, d\mathbf{u}\, d\mathbf{v} \tag{7.5.8}$$

To bound the second term we can no longer appeal to the argument that $d(\mathbf{u} \mid \mathscr{B})$ is bounded by d_0. Instead we use a simple form of the Hölder inequality (App. 3A)

$$\begin{aligned}\int_{-\infty}^{\infty} \cdots \int_{-\infty}^{\infty} & Q_N(\mathbf{u})P_N(\mathbf{v} \mid \mathbf{u})d(\mathbf{u} \mid \mathscr{B})\Phi(\mathbf{u}, \mathbf{v}; \mathscr{B})\, d\mathbf{u}\, d\mathbf{v} \\ &\leq \left[\int_{-\infty}^{\infty} \cdots \int_{-\infty}^{\infty} Q_N(\mathbf{u})P_N(\mathbf{v} \mid \mathbf{u})(d(\mathbf{u} \mid \mathscr{B}))^2\, d\mathbf{u}\, d\mathbf{v}\right]^{1/2} \\ &\quad \times \left[\int_{-\infty}^{\infty} \cdots \int_{-\infty}^{\infty} Q_N(\mathbf{u})P_N(\mathbf{v} \mid \mathbf{u})\Phi(\mathbf{u}, \mathbf{v}; \mathscr{B})\, d\mathbf{u}\, d\mathbf{v}\right]^{1/2}\end{aligned} \tag{7.5.9}$$

where we noted that $\Phi^2 = \Phi$. Next we assume that $\mathbf{v}_1 \in \mathscr{B} = \{\mathbf{v}_1, \mathbf{v}_2, \ldots, \mathbf{v}_M\}$ is the all-zeros vector; that is, $\mathbf{v}_1 = \mathbf{0}$. Then $d(\mathbf{u} \mid \mathscr{B}) \leq d_N(\mathbf{u}, \mathbf{v}_1) = d_N(\mathbf{u}, \mathbf{0})$ and

$$\begin{aligned}\int_{-\infty}^{\infty} \cdots \int_{-\infty}^{\infty} Q_N(\mathbf{u})P_N(\mathbf{v} \mid \mathbf{u})(d(\mathbf{u} \mid \mathscr{B}))^2\, d\mathbf{u}\, d\mathbf{v} &= \int_{-\infty}^{\infty} \cdots \int_{-\infty}^{\infty} Q_N(\mathbf{u})(d(\mathbf{u} \mid \mathscr{B}))^2\, d\mathbf{u} \\ &\leq \int_{-\infty}^{\infty} \cdots \int_{-\infty}^{\infty} Q_N(\mathbf{u})(d_N(\mathbf{u}, \mathbf{0}))^2\, d\mathbf{u} \\ &= \int_{-\infty}^{\infty} \cdots \int_{-\infty}^{\infty} Q_N(\mathbf{u})\left[\frac{1}{N} \sum_{n=1}^{N} d(u_n, 0)\right]^2 d\mathbf{u} \\ &\leq \int_{-\infty}^{\infty} \cdots \int_{-\infty}^{\infty} Q_N(\mathbf{u})\left[\frac{1}{N} \sum_{n=1}^{N} d^2(u_n, 0)\right] d\mathbf{u} \\ &\leq d_0^2\end{aligned} \tag{7.5.10}$$

where the last inequality follows from (7.5.1). Hence when $\mathbf{v}_1 = \mathbf{0} \in \mathscr{B}$, we have

$$d(\mathscr{B}) \leq D(\mathbf{P}) + d_0\left[\int_{-\infty}^{\infty} \cdots \int_{-\infty}^{\infty} Q_N(\mathbf{u})P_N(\mathbf{v} \mid \mathbf{u})\Phi(\mathbf{u}, \mathbf{v}; \mathscr{B})\, d\mathbf{u}\, d\mathbf{v}\right]^{1/2} \tag{7.5.11}$$

We now proceed to bound the ensemble average of $d(\mathscr{B})$. We consider an ensemble of codes in which $\mathbf{v}_1 = \mathbf{0}$ is fixed and the ensemble weighting for the remaining $M - 1$ codewords is according to a product measure corresponding to independent identically distributed components having common probability density $\{P(v)\colon -\infty < v < \infty\}$. Now for any code $\mathscr{B} = \{\mathbf{v}_1, \mathbf{v}_2, \ldots, \mathbf{v}_M\}$, define $\tilde{\mathscr{B}} = \{\mathbf{v}_2, \mathbf{v}_3, \ldots, \mathbf{v}_M\}$ which is the code without codeword $\mathbf{v}_1 = \mathbf{0}$. Then clearly

$$d(\mathbf{u} \mid \mathscr{B}) \le d(\mathbf{u} \mid \tilde{\mathscr{B}}) \tag{7.5.12}$$

and

$$\Phi(\mathbf{u}, \mathbf{v}; \mathscr{B}) \le \Phi(\mathbf{u}, \mathbf{v}; \tilde{\mathscr{B}}) \tag{7.5.13}$$

Hence for any code $\mathscr{B}$, we have from (7.5.11) and (7.5.13)

$$d(\mathscr{B}) \le D(\mathbf{P}) + d_0 \left[\int_{-\infty}^{\infty} \cdots \int_{-\infty}^{\infty} Q_N(\mathbf{u}) P_N(\mathbf{v} \mid \mathbf{u}) \Phi(\mathbf{u}, \mathbf{v}; \tilde{\mathscr{B}})\, d\mathbf{u}\, d\mathbf{v} \right]^{1/2} \tag{7.5.14}$$

Now averaging this over the code ensemble and using the Jensen inequality yields

$$\begin{aligned} \overline{d(\mathscr{B})} &\le D(\mathbf{P}) + d_0 \overline{\left[\int_{-\infty}^{\infty} \cdots \int_{-\infty}^{\infty} Q_N(\mathbf{u}) P_N(\mathbf{v} \mid \mathbf{u}) \Phi(\mathbf{u}, \mathbf{v}; \tilde{\mathscr{B}})\, d\mathbf{u}\, d\mathbf{v} \right]^{1/2}} \\ &\le D(\mathbf{P}) + d_0 \left[\int_{-\infty}^{\infty} \cdots \int_{-\infty}^{\infty} \overline{Q_N(\mathbf{u}) P_N(\mathbf{v} \mid \mathbf{u}) \Phi(\mathbf{u}, \mathbf{v}; \tilde{\mathscr{B}})}\, d\mathbf{u}\, d\mathbf{v} \right]^{1/2} \end{aligned} \tag{7.5.15}$$

The term inside the bracket can now be bounded by following the proof of Lemma 7.2.1 [(7.2.20) through (7.2.22)], replacing summations of probabilities with integrals of probability densities. This yields the bound

$$\int_{-\infty}^{\infty} \cdots \int_{-\infty}^{\infty} \overline{Q_N(\mathbf{u}) P_N(\mathbf{v} \mid \mathbf{u}) \Phi(\mathbf{u}, \mathbf{v}; \tilde{\mathscr{B}})}\, d\mathbf{u}\, d\mathbf{v} \le e^{-NE(R;\, \rho,\, \mathbf{P})} \tag{7.5.16}$$

where

$$E(R; \rho, \mathbf{P}) = -\rho R + E_o(\rho, \mathbf{P})$$

$$-1 < \rho < 0$$

$$E_o(\rho, \mathbf{P}) = -\ln \int_{-\infty}^{\infty} \left[\int_{-\infty}^{\infty} P(v) Q(u \mid v)^{1/(1+\rho)}\, dv \right]^{1+\rho} du \tag{7.5.17}$$

The properties of $E_o(\rho, \mathbf{P})$ are the same as those given in Lemma 7.2.2 where now $I(\mathbf{P})$ is

$$I(\mathbf{P}) = \int_{-\infty}^{\infty} \int_{-\infty}^{\infty} Q(u) P(v \mid u) \ln \frac{P(v \mid u)}{P(v)}\, du\, dv \tag{7.5.18}$$

the average mutual information. Then it follows from Lemma 7.2.3 that

$$\max_{-1 \le \rho \le 0} E(R; \rho, \mathbf{P}) > 0 \qquad \text{for } R > I(\mathbf{P}) \tag{7.5.19}$$

Combining these extensions of earlier results into (7.5.15) yields

$$\overline{d(\mathscr{B})} \le D(\mathbf{P}) + d_0 e^{-(1/2)NE(R;\, \rho,\, \mathbf{P})} \tag{7.5.20}$$

where

$$\max_{-1 \le \rho \le 0} E(R; \rho, \mathbf{P}) > 0 \qquad \text{for } R > I(\mathbf{P})$$

At this point we are still free to choose the conditional probability density $\{P(v \mid u)\colon u, v \in \mathscr{R}\}$ to minimize the bound on $\overline{d(\mathscr{B})}$. Suppose the fidelity criterion to be satisfied by the block source coding system is specified as $D(\mathbf{P}) \le D$. Then let

$$\mathscr{P}_D = \{P(v \mid u)\colon D(\mathbf{P}) \le D\} \tag{7.5.21}$$

and define

$$E(R, D) \equiv \sup_{\mathbf{P} \in \mathscr{P}_D} \max_{-1 \le \rho \le 0} E(R; \rho, \mathbf{P}) \tag{7.5.22}$$

and the rate distortion function

$$R(D) \equiv \inf_{\mathbf{P} \in \mathscr{P}_D} I(\mathbf{P}) \tag{7.5.23}$$

Applying these to (7.5.20) yields the coding theorem for continuous-amplitude memoryless sources.

Theorem 7.5.1: Source coding theorem For any block length N and rate R there exists a block code with average distortion $d(\mathscr{B})$ satisfying

$$d(\mathscr{B}) \le D + d_0 e^{-(1/2)NE(R, D)} \tag{7.5.24}$$

where

$$E(R, D) > 0 \qquad \text{for } R > R(D)$$

PROOF See the proof of Theorem 7.2.1.

We defined $R(D)$ in (7.5.23) as the rate distortion function for a continuous-amplitude memoryless source, where the unbounded single-letter distortion measure satisfies a bounded variance condition. To justify this definition we need to prove a converse theorem. This is easily done using the same basic proof given earlier for the discrete memoryless sources (see Theorem 7.2.3).

Theorem 7.5.2: Converse source coding theorem For any source encoder–decoder pair, it is impossible to achieve average distortion less than or equal to D whenever the rate R satisfies $R < R(D)$.

The proof of the direct coding theorem given in this section certainly applies as well for discrete memoryless sources with *unbounded* distortion measure as long as the bounded variance condition is satisfied. Similarly for discrete sources with a countably infinite alphabet we can establish coding theorems similar to Theorem 7.5.1. An example of such a source is one which emits a Poisson random variable and which has a magnitude distortion measure (see Probs. 7.25, 7.26, and 7.27).

Here we have shown that coding theorems can be obtained for continuous amplitude sources using proofs that are essentially the same as those for discrete memoryless sources with bounded single-letter distortion measures. All of the earlier discussion concerning the relationship between channel and source coding also applies. In fact, the trellis coding theorem can also be extended in this way, as will be shown next.

7.5.2 Trellis Coding Theorems for Continuous-Amplitude Sources

We extend the results of Sec. 7.4 to the case of continuous-amplitude memoryless sources with unbounded distortion measures that satisfy the bounded variance condition of (7.5.1). The basic trellis source coding system is again presented in Fig. 7.10 with the only difference here being that the source and representation alphabet is the real line, $\mathscr{R} = (-\infty, \infty)$, and the distortion measure is possibly unbounded.

Following the same discussion which led to (7.4.7), we have

$$d_{N_L}(\mathbf{u}, \mathbf{v}(\mathbf{u})) \le d_{N_L}(\mathbf{u}, \mathbf{v}^*) \tag{7.5.25}$$

where $\mathbf{v}^*$ is a trellis decoder output sequence that is selected by finding $\mathbf{v}^{**}$, the minimum-distortion path sequence of the corresponding forbidden trellis code. Then defining $\mathscr{Z} = \{i: \mathbf{v}_i^* \text{ is a branch output vector of the all-zeros state path}\}$ we have again (7.4.11)

$$\begin{aligned} L d_{N_L}(\mathbf{u}, \mathbf{v}^*) &= \sum_{i=0}^{L-1} d_n(\mathbf{u}_i, \mathbf{v}_i^*) \\ &= \sum_{i \notin \mathscr{Z}} d_n(\mathbf{u}_i, \mathbf{v}_i^*) + \sum_{i \in \mathscr{Z}} d_n(\mathbf{u}_i, \mathbf{v}_i^*) \end{aligned} \tag{7.5.26}$$

For $i \notin \mathscr{Z}$, recall that $d_n(\mathbf{u}, \mathbf{v}_i^*) = d_n(\mathbf{u}, \mathbf{v}_i^{**})$ and so

$$\begin{aligned} L d_{N_L}(\mathbf{u}, \mathbf{v}^*) &= \sum_{i \notin \mathscr{Z}} d_n(\mathbf{u}_i, \mathbf{v}_i^{**}) + \sum_{i \in \mathscr{Z}} d_n(\mathbf{u}_i, \mathbf{v}_i^*) \\ &\le \sum_{i=0}^{L-1} d_n(\mathbf{u}_i, \mathbf{v}_i^{**}) + \sum_{i \in \mathscr{Z}} d_n(\mathbf{u}_i, \mathbf{v}_i^*) \\ &\le \sum_{i=0}^{L-1} d_n(\mathbf{u}_i, \mathbf{v}_{0i}) + \sum_{i \in \mathscr{Z}} d_n(\mathbf{u}_i, \mathbf{v}_i^*) \end{aligned}$$

or

$$d_{N_L}(\mathbf{u}, \mathbf{v}^*) \le d_{N_L}(\mathbf{u}, \mathbf{v}_0) + \frac{1}{L} \sum_{i \in \mathscr{Z}} d_n(\mathbf{u}_i, \mathbf{v}_i^*) \tag{7.5.27}$$

since for the forbidden trellis code $d_{N_L}(\mathbf{u}, \mathbf{v}^{**}) \le d_{N_L}(\mathbf{u}, \mathbf{v}_0)$, where $\mathbf{v}_0$ is the all-zeros state output sequence of the forbidden trellis code.

Thus, for any trellis code, output sequence $\mathbf{u}$, and the corresponding forbidden trellis code, we have from (7.5.25) and (7.5.27) the bound

$$d_{N_L}(\mathbf{u}, \mathbf{v}(\mathbf{u})) \le d_{N_L}(\mathbf{u}, \mathbf{v}_0) + \frac{1}{L} \sum_{i \in \mathscr{Z}} d_n(\mathbf{u}_i, \mathbf{v}_i^*) \tag{7.5.28}$$

The only difference between this construction and that used in Sec. 7.4 is that we now consider only trellis codes where all branch outputs of the zero state are zero. This does not change $\mathbf{v}_0$ of the forbidden trellis code but does imply that $d_n(\mathbf{u}_i, \mathbf{v}_i^*) = d(\mathbf{u}_i, \mathbf{0})$ for all $i \in \mathscr{L}$. Hence

$$d_{N_L}(\mathbf{u}, \mathbf{v}(\mathbf{u})) \le d_{N_L}(\mathbf{u}, \mathbf{v}_0) + \frac{1}{L} \sum_{i \in \mathscr{L}} d_n(\mathbf{u}_i, \mathbf{0}) \tag{7.5.29}$$

Let us define the indicator function

$$\Phi_i(\mathscr{L}) = \begin{cases} 1 & i \in \mathscr{L} \\ 0 & i \notin \mathscr{L} \end{cases} \tag{7.5.30}$$

Then

$$d_{N_L}(\mathbf{u}, \mathbf{v}(\mathbf{u})) \le d_{N_L}(\mathbf{u}, \mathbf{v}_0) + \frac{1}{L} \sum_{i=0}^{L-1} d_n(\mathbf{u}_i, \mathbf{0}) \Phi_i(\mathscr{L}) \tag{7.5.31}$$

Now averaging over all source sequences $\mathbf{u}$ and $\mathbf{v}_0$ of the forbidden code we have for the given trellis code

$$\overline{d_{N_L}(\mathbf{u}, \mathbf{v}(\mathbf{u}))} \le D(\mathbf{P}) + \frac{1}{L} \sum_{i=0}^{L-1} \int_{-\infty}^{\infty} \cdots \int_{-\infty}^{\infty} Q_{N_L}(\mathbf{u}) P_{N_L}(\mathbf{v}_0 \mid \mathbf{u}) d_n(\mathbf{u}_i, \mathbf{0}) \Phi_i(\mathscr{L}) \, d\mathbf{u} \, d\mathbf{v}_0 \tag{7.5.32}$$

where

$$D(\mathbf{P}) = \int_{-\infty}^{\infty} \int_{-\infty}^{\infty} Q(u) P(v \mid u) d(u, v) \, dv \, du$$

The second term can be further bounded using the Hölder inequality and the bounded variance condition of (7.5.1).

$$\begin{aligned}
&\int_{-\infty}^{\infty} \cdots \int_{-\infty}^{\infty} Q_{N_L}(\mathbf{u}) P_{N_L}(\mathbf{v}_0 \mid \mathbf{u}) d_n(\mathbf{u}_i, \mathbf{0}) \Phi_i(\mathscr{L}) \, d\mathbf{u} \, d\mathbf{v}_0 \\
&\quad \le \left[\int_{-\infty}^{\infty} \cdots \int_{-\infty}^{\infty} Q_{N_L}(\mathbf{u}) P_{N_L}(\mathbf{v}_0 \mid \mathbf{u}) [d_n(\mathbf{u}_i, \mathbf{0})]^2 \, d\mathbf{u} \, d\mathbf{v}_0 \right]^{1/2} \\
&\qquad \times \left[\int_{-\infty}^{\infty} \cdots \int_{-\infty}^{\infty} Q_{N_L}(\mathbf{u}) P_{N_L}(\mathbf{v}_0 \mid \mathbf{u}) \Phi_i(\mathscr{L}) \, d\mathbf{u} \, d\mathbf{v}_0 \right]^{1/2} \\
&\quad = \left[\int_{-\infty}^{\infty} \cdots \int_{-\infty}^{\infty} Q_{N_L}(\mathbf{u}) (d_n(\mathbf{u}, \mathbf{0}))^2 \, d\mathbf{u} \right]^{1/2} \\
&\qquad \times \left[\int_{-\infty}^{\infty} \cdots \int_{-\infty}^{\infty} Q_{N_L}(\mathbf{u}) P_{N_L}(\mathbf{v}_0 \mid \mathbf{u}) \Phi_i(\mathscr{L}) \, d\mathbf{u} \, d\mathbf{v}_0 \right]^{1/2} \\
&\quad \le d_0 \left[\int_{-\infty}^{\infty} \cdots \int_{-\infty}^{\infty} Q_{N_L}(\mathbf{u}) P_{N_L}(\mathbf{v}_0 \mid \mathbf{u}) \Phi_i(\mathscr{L}) \, d\mathbf{u} \, d\mathbf{v}_0 \right]^{1/2}
\end{aligned} \tag{7.5.33}$$

Thus combining (7.5.32) and (7.5.33) we have the bound

$$\overline{d_{N_L}(\mathbf{u}, \mathbf{v}(\mathbf{u}))} \le D(\mathbf{P}) + \frac{d_0}{L} \sum_{i=0}^{L-1} \left[\int_{-\infty}^{\infty} \cdots \int_{-\infty}^{\infty} Q_{N_L}(\mathbf{u}) P_{N_L}(\mathbf{v}_0 \,|\, \mathbf{u}) \Phi_i(\mathscr{L})\, d\mathbf{u}\, d\mathbf{v}_0 \right]^{1/2}$$

$$\le D(\mathbf{P}) + d_0 \left[\frac{1}{L} \sum_{i=0}^{L-1} \int_{-\infty}^{\infty} \cdots \int_{-\infty}^{\infty} Q_{N_L}(\mathbf{u}) P_{N_L}(\mathbf{v}_0 \,|\, \mathbf{u}) \Phi_i(\mathscr{L})\, d\mathbf{u}\, d\mathbf{v}_0 \right]^{1/2} \tag{7.5.34}$$

We now consider an ensemble of trellis codes that have zero branch vectors on the all-zeros state path, and on all nonzero state branch vectors have independent identically distributed random variables with common probability density $\{P(v), -\infty < v < \infty\}$. Proceeding as in the proof of Lemmas 7.4.1 and 7.4.2, we obtain

$$\overline{d_{N_L}(\mathbf{u}, \mathbf{v}(\mathbf{u}))} \le D(\mathbf{P}) + d_0 \left[\sum_{j=0}^{L-1} \sum_{k=1}^{L-j-1} \frac{k}{L} P_{jk} \right]^{1/2} \tag{7.5.35}$$

where P_{jk} is defined in (7.4.9) and bounded by

$$P_{jk} \le 2^{(K-1)\rho} 2^{-k[E_o(\rho, \mathbf{P})/R - \rho]} \tag{7.5.36}$$

where in this case

$$E_o(\rho, \mathbf{P}) = -\ln \int_{-\infty}^{\infty} \left[\int_{-\infty}^{\infty} P(v) Q(u \,|\, v)^{1/(1+\rho)}\, dv \right]^{1+\rho} du \qquad -1 < \rho < 0$$

Since P_{jk} depends on the forbidden trellis code which is the same as in Sec. 7.4, the bound (7.5.36) follows from the proof of Lemma 7.4.2 when sums of probabilities are replaced by integrals of probability densities. Thus we have finally, as in (7.4.25),

$$\overline{d_{N_L}(\mathbf{u}, \mathbf{v}(\mathbf{u}))} \le D(\mathbf{P}) + \frac{d_0 2^{(1/2)(K-1)\rho}}{[1 - 2^{-[E_o(\rho, \mathbf{P})/R - \rho]}]^2} \tag{7.5.37}$$

and have established the trellis source coding theorem for continuous-amplitude memoryless sources.

Theorem 7.5.3: Trellis source coding theorem Given any fidelity D, constraint length K and rate $R = (\ln q)/n > R(D)$ for some q and n, there exists a trellis code T_K with average distortion $d(T_K)$ satisfying

$$d(T_K) \le D + \frac{d_0 q^{-(K-1)[R - R(D)]/2C_o}}{[1 - q^{-[R - R(D)]^2/2RC_o}]^2} \tag{7.5.38}$$

PROOF Having established the bound (7.5.37), the proof follows the proof of Theorem 7.4.1.

7.6 EVALUATION OF $R(D)$—DISCRETE MEMORYLESS SOURCES*

For discrete memoryless sources the rate distortion function $R(D)$ is given in (7.2.53). This definition is analogous to that of channel capacity in channel coding theory where the channel capacity is the maximum rate below which the random coding error exponent $E(R)$ is positive. In the source coding theorem, $R(D)$ is the minimum rate above which the exponent $E(R, D)$ is positive. Analogous converse theorems also exist. Thus both channel capacity and rate distortion functions are defined in terms of extreme values of average mutual information over some constrained space of probability distributions; hence, it is not surprising to find that techniques for evaluating rate distortion functions are similar to those for finding channel capacity. In fact, it is not surprising as a result that, while channel capacity was shown to be the maximum average mutual information, $R(D)$ appears as a minimum of average mutual information subject to the distortion measure constraint. In App. 3C, we presented a simple computational algorithm for channel capacity. A similar algorithm can be used to find $R(D)$ and this is given in App. 7A.

We now examine ways of finding the rate distortion function for various sources and distortion measures. First we examine some properties of $R(D)$. Note that in general (see Prob. 1.7)

$$\begin{aligned} I(\mathbf{P}) &= \sum_u \sum_v Q(u)P(v \mid u) \ln \frac{P(v \mid u)}{P(v)} \\ &\le \sum_u Q(u) \ln \frac{1}{Q(u)} \\ &= H(\mathscr{U}) \\ &\le \ln A \end{aligned} \tag{7.6.1}$$

where A is the alphabet size of the discrete memoryless source and

$$I(\mathbf{P}) \ge 0$$

Hence we have the bound

$$0 \le R(D) \le H(\mathscr{U}) \le \ln A \tag{7.6.2}$$

Let us next examine the range of values of D for which $R(D)$ exists. Recall from Sec. 7.2 that

$$\mathscr{P}_D = \left\{ P(v \mid u) \colon D(\mathbf{P}) = \sum_u \sum_v Q(u)P(v \mid u)d(u, v) \le D \right\}$$

is a nonempty closed convex set for $D \ge D_{\min}$ where

$$D_{\min} \equiv \sum_u Q(u) \min_{v \in \mathscr{V}} d(u, v) \tag{7.6.3}$$

* May be omitted without loss of continuity.

is the minimum possible average distortion. For $D < D_{min}$, $R(D)$ is not defined. Since $I(\mathbf{P})$ is a continuous, real-valued function of $\mathbf{P}$, it must assume a minimum value in a nonempty, closed set and therefore, $R(D)$ exists for all $D \geq D_{min}$.

Let D_{max} be the least value of D for which $R(D) = 0$. This is equivalent to finding the conditional probability $\{P(v \mid u)\}$ satisfying

$$D(\mathbf{P}) = \sum_u \sum_v Q(u)P(v \mid u)d(u, v) \leq D_{max} \tag{7.6.4}$$

and for which $I(\mathbf{P}) = 0$. But $I(\mathbf{P}) = 0$ if and only if $\mathscr{U}$ and $\mathscr{V}$ are independent (see Lemma 1.2.1 given in Chap. 1); that is

$$P(v \mid u) = P(v) \qquad \text{for all } u \in \mathscr{U},\ v \in \mathscr{V} \tag{7.6.5}$$

Hence

$$D(\mathbf{P}) = \sum_v P(v) \sum_u Q(u)d(u, v) \tag{7.6.6}$$

which we can minimize over $\{P(v)\}$ to obtain

$$D_{max} = \min_{v \in \mathscr{V}} \sum_u Q(u)d(u, v) \tag{7.6.7}$$

where the minimizing $\{P(v)\}$ is zero everywhere but at the value of v which minimizes $d(u, v)$ [see (7.6.10)]. From this we see that $R(D)$ is positive for $D_{min} < D < D_{max}$. $R(D)$ is clearly a nonincreasing function of D since $D_1 \leq D_2$ implies $\mathscr{P}_{D_1} \subset \mathscr{P}_{D_2}$ which in turn implies $R(D_1) \geq R(D_2)$. Otherwise, the most important property of $R(D)$ is its convexity, which we state in the following lemma.

Lemma 7.6.1 For $D_{min} \leq D_1 \leq D_{max}$, $D_{min} \leq D_2 \leq D_{max}$, and any $0 < \theta < 1$

$$R(\theta D_1 + (1 - \theta)D_2) \leq \theta R(D_1) + (1 - \theta)R(D_2) \tag{7.6.8}$$

PROOF Let $\mathbf{P}_1 \in \mathscr{P}_{D_1}$ and $\mathbf{P}_2 \in \mathscr{P}_{D_2}$ be such that $R(D_1) = I(\mathbf{P}_1)$ and $R(D_2) = I(\mathbf{P}_2)$. Then since $\theta \mathbf{P}_1 + (1 - \theta)\mathbf{P}_2 \in \mathscr{P}_{\theta D_1 + (1-\theta)D_2}$ using the convexity of $I(\cdot)$, we have

$$\begin{aligned} R(\theta D_1 + (1 - \theta)D_2) &= \min_{\mathbf{P} \in \mathscr{P}_{\theta D_1 + (1-\theta)D_2}} I(\mathbf{P}) \\ &\leq I(\theta \mathbf{P}_1 + (1 - \theta)\mathbf{P}_2) \\ &\leq \theta I(\mathbf{P}_1) + (1 - \theta)I(\mathbf{P}_2) \\ &= \theta R(D_1) + (1 - \theta)R(D_2) \end{aligned}$$

Thus $R(D)$ is a convex $\cup$, continuous, strictly decreasing function of D, for $D_{min} < D < D_{max}$. The strictly decreasing property of $R(D)$ further implies that if $\mathbf{P} \in \mathscr{P}_D$ yields $R(D) = I(\mathbf{P})$ then $D(\mathbf{P}) = D$; that is, the minimizing conditional probability that yields $R(D)$ satisfies the constraint with equality and therefore lies on the boundary of $\mathscr{P}_D$. Figure 7.12 shows a typical rate distortion function.

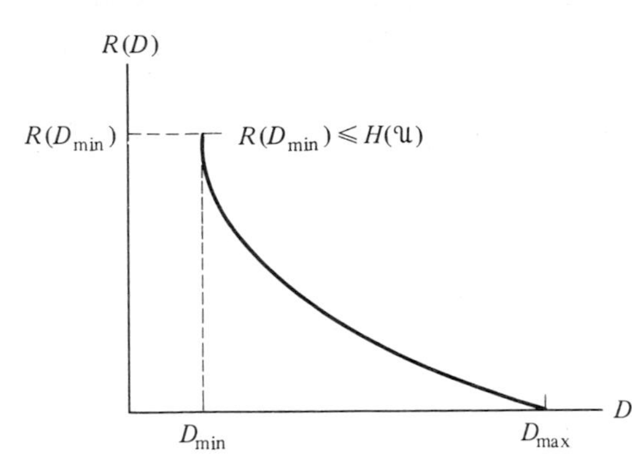

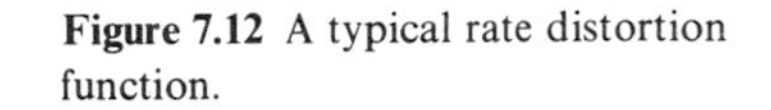
Figure 7.12 A typical rate distortion function.

Next we have from (7.6.2)

$$R(D_{\min}) \leq H(\mathscr{U}) = -\sum_{u} Q(u) \ln Q(u) \tag{7.6.9}$$

The only conditional probabilities $\{P_{\min}(v \mid u)\}$ that yield $R(D_{\min}) = I(\mathbf{P}_{\min})$ are

$$P_{\min}(v \mid u) = \begin{cases} 1 & v = v(u) \\ 0 & v \neq v(u) \end{cases} \tag{7.6.10}$$

where $v(u)$ satisfies

$$d(u, v(u)) = \min_{v \in \mathscr{V}} d(u, v)$$

Here

$$\begin{aligned} R(D_{\min}) &= I(\mathbf{P}_{\min}) \\ &= -\sum_{u} Q(u) \ln P_{\min}(v(u)) \end{aligned} \tag{7.6.11}$$

where

$$P_{\min}(v) = \sum_{u} Q(u) P_{\min}(v \mid u)$$

From this it is clear that, for the condition $v(u) \neq v(u')$ for $u \neq u'$, we have $P_{\min}(v(u)) = Q(u)$ and $R(D_{\min}) = H(\mathscr{U})$. This condition is typical for most cases of interest when the number of letters in $\mathscr{V}$, B, is greater than or equal to the number of letters in $\mathscr{U}$, A.

We now find necessary and sufficient conditions for the conditional probability distribution $\mathbf{P} \in \mathscr{P}_D$ that achieves $R(D) = I(\mathbf{P})$. We seek to minimize

$$I(\mathbf{P}) = \sum_{u} \sum_{v} Q(u) P(v \mid u) \ln \frac{P(v \mid u)}{\sum_{u'} P(v \mid u') Q(u')} \tag{7.6.12}$$

with respect to the AB variables $\{P(v \mid u) : v \in \mathscr{V}, u \in \mathscr{U}\}$ subject to the constraints

$$P(v \mid u) \geq 0 \qquad \text{for all } u \in \mathscr{U}, v \in \mathscr{V} \tag{7.6.13}$$

$$\sum_v P(v \mid u) = 1 \qquad \text{for all } u \in \mathscr{U} \tag{7.6.14}$$

$$\sum_u \sum_v Q(u)P(v \mid u)d(u, v) = D \tag{7.6.15}$$

Without the inequality constraints (7.6.13) this would be a straightforward Lagrange multiplier minimization problem. We proceed initially as if this were the case and let $\{\alpha(u) : u \in \mathscr{U}\}$ and s be Lagrange multipliers for the equality constraints (7.6.14) and (7.6.15), respectively, and consider the minimization of

$$J(\mathbf{P}; \boldsymbol{\alpha}, s) = I(\mathbf{P}) - \sum_u \alpha(u) \sum_v P(v \mid u) - s \sum_u \sum_v Q(u)P(v \mid u)d(u, v) \tag{7.6.16}$$

but keeping in mind ultimately the requirement of the inequality constraints (7.6.13). We find it convenient to define

$$\lambda(u) = e^{\alpha(u)/Q(u)} \qquad \text{for all } u \in \mathscr{U} \tag{7.6.17}$$

so that (7.6.16) can be written as

$$J(\mathbf{P}; \boldsymbol{\lambda}, s) = \sum_u \sum_v Q(u)P(v \mid u) \ln \frac{P(v \mid u)}{\lambda(u)P(v)e^{sd(u, v)}} \tag{7.6.18}$$

We now assume that $\boldsymbol{\lambda}$ and s are fixed (later we choose them to satisfy the equality constraints) and we find conditions for the minimization of $J(\mathbf{P}; \boldsymbol{\lambda}, s)$ with respect to the AB variables $\{P(v \mid u)\}$ subject only to the inequality constraints (7.6.13).

Since $I(\mathbf{P})$ and thus $J(\mathbf{P}; \boldsymbol{\lambda}, s)$ are convex $\cup$ functions of $\{P(v \mid u)\}$, a local minimization of $J(\mathbf{P}; \boldsymbol{\lambda}, s)$ is an absolute minimization. We use this in proving the following theorem.

Theorem 7.6.1 A necessary and sufficient condition for the AB variables $\{P^*(v \mid u) : v \in \mathscr{V}, u \in \mathscr{U}\}$ to minimize $J(\mathbf{P}; \boldsymbol{\lambda}, s)$ of (7.6.18), subject only to the inequality constraint (7.6.13), is that they satisfy

$$P^*(v \mid u) = \lambda(u)P^*(v)e^{sd(u, v)} \qquad \text{if } P^*(v) > 0 \tag{7.6.19}$$

and

$$\sum_u \lambda(u)Q(u)e^{sd(u, v)} \leq 1 \qquad \text{if } P^*(v) = 0$$

where

$$P^*(v) = \sum_u P^*(v \mid u)Q(u) \qquad \text{for all } v \in \mathscr{V}$$

PROOF (Sufficiency) Let $\{P^*(v \mid u)\}$ satisfy conditions (7.6.19). For any $\epsilon > 0$, taking a variation $\epsilon\eta(v \mid u)$ about $P^*(v \mid u)$ such that

$$P^*(v \mid u) + \epsilon\eta(v \mid u) \geq 0 \qquad \text{for all } u \in \mathscr{U}, v \in \mathscr{V} \tag{7.6.20}$$

and defining

$$\eta(v) = \sum_u Q(u)\eta(v \mid u) \qquad \text{for all } u \in \mathscr{U}$$

we have

$$\begin{aligned}
\Delta J(\epsilon) &\equiv J(\mathbf{P}^* + \epsilon\boldsymbol{\eta}; \boldsymbol{\lambda}, s) - J(\mathbf{P}^*; \boldsymbol{\lambda}, s) \\
&= \sum_u \sum_v Q(u)P^*(v \mid u) \ln \left[\frac{(P^*(v \mid u) + \epsilon\eta(v \mid u))P^*(v)}{P^*(v \mid u)(P^*(v) + \epsilon\eta(v))}\right] \\
&\quad + \sum_u \sum_v Q(u)\epsilon\eta(v \mid u) \ln \left[\frac{P^*(v \mid u) + \epsilon\eta(v \mid u)}{\lambda(u)(P^*(v) + \epsilon\eta(v))e^{sd(u,v)}}\right]
\end{aligned} \tag{7.6.21}$$

The first term in (7.6.21) is[19]

$$\begin{aligned}
\sum_u \sum_v & Q(u)P^*(v \mid u) \ln \left[\frac{1 + \epsilon\eta(v \mid u)/P^*(v \mid u)}{1 + \epsilon\eta(v)/P^*(v)}\right] \\
&= \sum_u \sum_v Q(u)P^*(v \mid u)\left[\frac{\epsilon\eta(v \mid u)}{P^*(v \mid u)} - \frac{\epsilon\eta(v)}{P^*(v)} + O(\epsilon^2)\right] \\
&= O(\epsilon^2)
\end{aligned} \tag{7.6.22}$$

while the second term is

$$\begin{aligned}
\epsilon \sum_u \sum_v & Q(u)\eta(v \mid u) \ln \left[\frac{P^*(v \mid u) + \epsilon\eta(v \mid u)}{(P^*(v) + \epsilon\eta(v))\lambda(u)e^{sd(u,v)}}\right] \\
&= \epsilon \sum_u \sum_{v:\, P^*(v) > 0} Q(u)\eta(v \mid u) \ln \left[\frac{P^*(v \mid u)}{P^*(v)\lambda(u)e^{sd(u,v)}}\right] + O(\epsilon^2) \\
&\quad + \epsilon \sum_u \sum_{v:\, P^*(v) = 0} Q(u)\eta(v \mid u) \ln \left[\frac{\eta(v \mid u)}{\eta(v)\lambda(u)e^{sd(u,v)}}\right] \\
&= \epsilon \sum_u \sum_{v:\, P^*(v) = 0} Q(u)\eta(v \mid u) \ln \left[\frac{\eta(v \mid u)}{\eta(v)\lambda(u)e^{sd(u,v)}}\right] + O(\epsilon^2)
\end{aligned} \tag{7.6.23}$$

since for $P^*(v) > 0$ we have

$$\frac{P^*(v \mid u)}{P^*(v)\lambda(u)e^{sd(u,v)}} = 1$$

by (7.6.19), which is true by hypothesis. Hence

$$\Delta J(\epsilon) = \epsilon \sum_u \sum_{v:\, P^*(v) = 0} Q(u)\eta(v \mid u) \ln \left[\frac{\eta(v \mid u)}{\eta(v)\lambda(u)e^{sd(u,v)}}\right] + O(\epsilon^2) \tag{7.6.24}$$

[19] The term $O(x)$ is proportional to x.

Now using the inequality $\ln x \geq 1 - (1/x)$ [see (1.1.6)], we have

$$\begin{aligned}\Delta J(\epsilon) &\geq \epsilon \sum_u \sum_{v:\, P^*(v)=0} Q(u)\eta(v\,|\,u)\left[1 - \frac{\eta(v)\lambda(u)e^{sd(u,\,v)}}{\eta(v\,|\,u)}\right] + O(\epsilon^2) \\ &= \epsilon \sum_{v:\, P^*(v)=0} \eta(v)\left[1 - \sum_u Q(u)\lambda(u)e^{sd(u,\,v)}\right] + O(\epsilon^2) \\ &\geq O(\epsilon^2) \end{aligned} \tag{7.6.25}$$

since by hypothesis for $P^*(v) = 0$

$$\sum_u Q(u)\lambda(u)e^{sd(u,\,v)} \leq 1 \qquad \text{and} \qquad \eta(v) \geq 0$$

Hence

$$\begin{aligned}\lim_{\epsilon \downarrow 0} \frac{\Delta J(\epsilon)}{\epsilon} &= \lim_{\epsilon \downarrow 0} \frac{J(\mathbf{P}^* + \epsilon\boldsymbol{\eta};\, \boldsymbol{\lambda}, s) - J(\mathbf{P}^*;\, \boldsymbol{\lambda}, s)}{\epsilon} \\ &\geq 0 \end{aligned} \tag{7.6.26}$$

which assumes a local minimum at $\mathbf{P}^*$. By convexity of $J(\mathbf{P};\, \boldsymbol{\lambda}, s)$, this must be an absolute minimum.

(Necessity) Let $\mathbf{P}^*$ minimize $J(\mathbf{P};\, \boldsymbol{\lambda}, s)$ subject to the inequality constraint (7.6.13). From above we have for any $\epsilon > 0$ and numbers $\{P^*(v\,|\,u)\}$ such that $P^*(v\,|\,u) + \epsilon\eta(v\,|\,u) \geq 0$, for all $u \in \mathscr{U}$, $v \in \mathscr{V}$

$$\begin{aligned}\Delta J(\epsilon) &\equiv J(\mathbf{P}^* + \epsilon\boldsymbol{\eta};\, \boldsymbol{\lambda}, s) - J(\mathbf{P}^*;\, \boldsymbol{\lambda}, s) \\ &= \epsilon \sum_u \sum_{v:\, P^*(v)>0} Q(u)\eta(v\,|\,u) \ln\left[\frac{P^*(v\,|\,u)}{P^*(v)\lambda(u)e^{sd(u,\,v)}}\right] \\ &\quad + \epsilon \sum_u \sum_{v:\, P^*(v)=0} Q(u)\eta(v\,|\,u) \ln\left[\frac{\eta(v\,|\,u)}{\eta(v)\lambda(u)e^{sd(u,\,v)}}\right] + O(\epsilon^2) \end{aligned} \tag{7.6.27}$$

First let us choose $\eta(v\,|\,u) = 0$ for all v where $P^*(v) = 0$. Then

$$\Delta J(\epsilon) = \epsilon \sum_u \sum_{v:\, P^*(v)>0} Q(u)\eta(v\,|\,u) \ln\left[\frac{P^*(v\,|\,u)}{P^*(v)\lambda(u)e^{sd(u,\,v)}}\right] + O(\epsilon^2) \tag{7.6.28}$$

where $\eta(v|u)$ can be any set of positive or negative numbers as long as $P^*(v\,|\,u) + \epsilon\eta(v\,|\,u) \geq 0$. Hence, for $\Delta J(\epsilon) \geq 0$ for arbitrarily small $\epsilon \geq 0$, we require

$$P^*(v\,|\,u) = P^*(v)\lambda(u)e^{sd(u,\,v)} \qquad \text{if } P^*(v) > 0$$

Suppose next in (7.6.27) we choose

$$\eta(v\,|\,u) = \begin{cases} 0 & P^*(v) > 0 \\ \dfrac{\eta(v)\lambda(u)e^{sd(u,\,v)}}{\sum_{u'} Q(u')\lambda(u')e^{sd(u',\,v)}} & P^*(v) = 0 \end{cases} \tag{7.6.29}$$

Then

$$\Delta J(\epsilon) = \epsilon \sum_{u} \sum_{v:\, P^*(v)=0} Q(u)\eta(v \mid u) \ln \left[\frac{1}{\sum_{u'} Q(u')\lambda(u')e^{sd(u',\, v)}} \right] + O(\epsilon^2)$$

$$= -\epsilon \sum_{v:\, P^*(v)=0} \eta(v) \ln \left[\sum_{u'} Q(u')\lambda(u')e^{sd(u',\, v)} \right] + O(\epsilon^2) \qquad (7.6.30)$$

Since $\eta(v) \geq 0$ when $P^*(v) = 0$, in order for $\Delta J(\epsilon) \geq 0$ for all $\epsilon > 0$, we require

$$\sum_{u} Q(u)\lambda(u)e^{sd(u,\, v)} \leq 1 \qquad \text{if } P^*(v) = 0$$

To find necessary and sufficient conditions for $\mathbf{P}^* \in \mathscr{P}_D$ that yield $R(D)$, in addition to (7.6.19) we need only choose Lagrange multipliers $\boldsymbol{\lambda}$ and s to satisfy the equality constraints (7.6.14) and (7.6.15). Hence from (7.6.14) and (7.6.19) it follows that $\boldsymbol{\lambda}$ is given by

$$\lambda(u) = \left(\sum_{v} P(v)e^{sd(u,\, v)} \right)^{-1} \qquad \text{for all } u \in \mathscr{U} \qquad (7.6.31)$$

It is more convenient to keep s as a free parameter and express the distortion $D = D_s$ and rate distortion function $R(D) = R(D_s)$ in terms of s.

Theorem 7.6.2 Necessary and sufficient conditions for a conditional probability $\{P(v \mid u)\}$ to yield the rate distortion function $R(D)$ at distortion D are that the conditions of Theorem 7.6.1 be satisfied, where Lagrange multipliers $\boldsymbol{\lambda}$ satisfy (7.6.31) and s satisfies the parametric equations

$$D_s = \sum_{u} \sum_{v} \lambda(u)Q(u)P(v)e^{sd(u,\, v)}d(u, v) \qquad (7.6.32)$$

and

$$R(D_s) = sD_s + \sum_{u} Q(u) \ln \lambda(u) \qquad (7.6.33)$$

PROOF We need only to use $P(v \mid u) = \lambda(u)P(v)e^{sd(u,\, v)}$ in $D = D(\mathbf{P})$ and $R(D) = I(\mathbf{P})$ to obtain (7.6.32) and (7.6.33).

Although this theorem gives us necessary and sufficient conditions for the conditional probabilities that yield points on the $R(D)$ curve, actual evaluation of $R(D)$ is difficult in most cases. Usually we must guess at a conditional probability and check the above conditions. There are, however, a few relationships which are helpful in evaluating $R(D)$.

Lemma 7.6.2 The parameter s in (7.6.32) and (7.6.33) is the slope of the rate distortion function at the point $D = D_s$. That is,

$$R'(D_s) = \left. \frac{dR(D)}{dD} \right|_{D = D_s} = s \qquad (7.6.34)$$

PROOF The chain rule yields the relation

$$R'(D) = \frac{dR}{dD} = \frac{\partial R}{\partial D} + \frac{\partial R}{\partial s}\left(\frac{ds}{dD}\right) + \sum_u \frac{\partial R}{\partial \lambda(u)} \frac{d\lambda(u)}{dD} \tag{7.6.35}$$

Using (7.6.33) we have

$$\begin{aligned} R'(D) &= s + D\left(\frac{ds}{dD}\right) + \sum_u \frac{Q(u)}{\lambda(u)} \frac{d\lambda(u)}{dD} \\ &= s + \left[D + \sum_u \frac{Q(u)}{\lambda(u)} \frac{d\lambda(u)}{ds}\right]\frac{ds}{dD} \end{aligned} \tag{7.6.36}$$

Recall that for $P(v \mid u) > 0$ we have

$$P(v \mid u) = \lambda(u)P(v)e^{sd(u, v)}$$

Multiplying by $Q(u)$ and summing over $u \in \mathscr{U}$ gives the relation

$$\sum_u \lambda(u)Q(u)e^{sd(u, v)} = 1 \tag{7.6.37}$$

when $P(v) > 0$. Differentiating with respect to s yields

$$\sum_u \left(\lambda(u)d(u, v) + \frac{d\lambda(u)}{ds}\right)Q(u)e^{sd(u, v)} = 0 \tag{7.6.38}$$

Multiplying by $P(v)$ and summing over $v \in \mathscr{V}$ gives

$$\sum_u \sum_v \lambda(u)Q(u)P(v)e^{sd(u, v)} d(u, v) + \sum_u Q(u) \frac{d\lambda(u)}{ds} \sum_v P(v)e^{sd(u, v)} = 0 \tag{7.6.39}$$

The first term is $D_s = D$ and

$$\sum_v P(v)e^{sd(u, v)} = \frac{1}{\lambda(u)} \tag{7.6.40}$$

which yields the relationship

$$D + \sum_u \frac{Q(u)}{\lambda(u)} \frac{d\lambda(u)}{ds} = 0 \tag{7.6.41}$$

Hence from (7.6.36) it follows that $R'(D_s) = s$.

Since $R(D)$ is a decreasing function of D for $D_{\min} < D < D_{\max}$, this lemma implies that the parameter values of interest satisfy $s \leq 0$. We next show that the slope of $R(D)$ is also continuous in this range.

Lemma 7.6.3 The derivative $R'(D)$ is continuous for $D_{\min} < D < D_{\max}$.

PROOF Let $D_{\min} < D^* < D_{\max}$ and consider the parameters

$$s_- = \lim_{D \uparrow D^*} R'(D) \tag{7.6.42}$$

and

$$s_+ = \lim_{D \downarrow D^*} R'(D) \tag{7.6.43}$$

These are defined since $R(D)$ is a continuous, convex $\cup$ function of $D_{min} < D < D_{max}$. We let $\mathbf{P}_+$ and $\mathbf{P}_-$ be corresponding conditional probabilities. By continuity of $R(D)$ we have

$$R(D^*) = I(\mathbf{P}_+) = I(\mathbf{P}_-) \tag{7.6.44}$$

For any $0 < \theta < 1$ let $\mathbf{P}_\theta = \theta\mathbf{P}_+ + (1-\theta)\mathbf{P}_-$. Certainly $\mathbf{P}_\theta$ satisfies $D(\mathbf{P}_\theta) = D^*$ so that

$$\begin{aligned} R(D^*) &\le I(\mathbf{P}_\theta) \\ &\le \theta I(\mathbf{P}_+) + (1-\theta)I(\mathbf{P}_-) \end{aligned} \tag{7.6.45}$$

The second inequality follows from convexity as proved in Lemma 1A.2. Since $I(\mathbf{P}_+) = I(\mathbf{P}_-) = R(D^*)$, we have

$$R(D^*) \le I(\mathbf{P}_\theta) \le R(D^*) \tag{7.6.46}$$

Thus we must have equality in each of the above steps. On examining the proof of Lemma 1A.2 in App. 1A for $P_\theta(v) > 0$, we have

$$\begin{aligned} \frac{P_\theta(v \mid u)}{P_\theta(v)} &= \frac{P_+(v \mid u)}{P_+(v)} = \frac{P_-(v \mid u)}{P_-(v)} \\ &= \lambda_+(u)e^{s_+ d(u,\, v)} \\ &= \lambda_-(u)e^{s_- d(u,\, v)} \end{aligned}$$

or

$$\frac{\lambda_+(u)}{\lambda_-(u)} = e^{(s_+ - s_-)d(u,\, v)} \tag{7.6.47}$$

Here $\lambda_+(u)$ and $\lambda_-(u)$ are the $\lambda(u)$ corresponding to $P_+(v \mid u)$ and $P_-(v \mid u)$, respectively. Since v does not appear on the left side, either $s_+ = s_-$ or $d(u, v) = d(u)$, independent of v. If $d(u, v) = d(u)$, then

$$P_+(v \mid u) = \lambda_+(u)e^{s_+ d(u)}P_+(v) \tag{7.6.48}$$

or summing over all v where $P_\theta(v) > 0$

$$1 = \lambda_+(u)e^{s_+ d(u)} \tag{7.6.49}$$

Hence

$$P_+(v \mid u) = P_+(v) \tag{7.6.50}$$

and consequently $D^* \ge D_{max}$ since $R(D^*) = I(\mathbf{P}_+) = 0$. But since $D < D_{max}$ we conclude that $s_+ = s_-$.

It has been shown further (Gallager [1968], Berger [1971]) that $R'(D)$ goes to $-\infty$ as D approaches $D_{\min}$, and that the only place a discontinuity of $R'(D)$ can occur is at $D = D_{\max}$. We next derive another form of $R(D)$ which is useful in obtaining lower bounds to $R(D)$.

Theorem 7.6.3 The rate distortion function can also be expressed as

$$R(D) = \max_{s \leq 0,\ \boldsymbol{\lambda} \in \Lambda_s} \left[sD + \sum_u Q(u) \ln \lambda(u) \right] \tag{7.6.51}$$

where

$$\Lambda_s \equiv \left\{ \lambda(u) \colon \sum_u \lambda(u) Q(u) e^{sd(u,\, v)} \leq 1 \right\} \tag{7.6.52}$$

Necessary and sufficient conditions for s and $\boldsymbol{\lambda}$ to achieve the maximum are the same as those given in Theorem 7.6.2.

PROOF Let $s \leq 0$, $\boldsymbol{\lambda} \in \Lambda_s$, and $\mathbf{P} \in \mathscr{P}_D$. Then using $D(\mathbf{P}) \leq D$ we have

$$I(\mathbf{P}) - sD - \sum_u Q(u) \ln \lambda(u) \geq I(\mathbf{P}) - sD(\mathbf{P}) - \sum_u \sum_v Q(u) P(v \mid u) \ln \lambda(u)$$

$$= \sum_u \sum_v Q(u) P(v \mid u) \ln \frac{P(v \mid u)}{P(v) \lambda(u) e^{sd(u,\, v)}} \tag{7.6.53}$$

Again using the inequality $\ln x \geq 1 - (1/x)$, we have

$$\begin{aligned} I(\mathbf{P}) - sD - \sum_u Q(u) \ln \lambda(u) &\geq \sum_u \sum_v Q(u) P(v \mid u) \left[1 - \frac{P(v) \lambda(u) e^{sd(u,\, v)}}{P(v \mid u)} \right] \\ &= 1 - \sum_v P(v) \sum_u \lambda(u) Q(u) e^{sd(u,\, v)} \\ &\geq 1 - \sum_v P(v) \\ &= 0 \end{aligned}$$

Hence for each $\mathbf{P} \in \mathscr{P}_D$ we have

$$I(\mathbf{P}) \geq sD + \sum_u Q(u) \ln \lambda(u)$$

and clearly

$$I(\mathbf{P}) \geq \max_{s \leq 0,\ \boldsymbol{\lambda} \in \Lambda_s} \left[sD + \sum_u Q(u) \ln \lambda(u) \right] \tag{7.6.54}$$

But from Theorem 7.6.2 we know that there exists a $\mathbf{P}^* \in \mathscr{P}_D$, $s^* \leq 0$, and $\boldsymbol{\lambda}^* \in \Lambda_{s^*}$ such that

$$R(D) = I(\mathbf{P}^*) = s^* D + \sum_u Q(u) \ln \lambda^*(u) \tag{7.6.55}$$

Hence

$$R(D) = \max_{s \le 0,\ \lambda \in \Lambda_s} \left[sD + \sum_u Q(u) \ln \lambda(u) \right]$$

We now examine a few examples. It will be clear that even for simple cases, unless certain symmetries hold, it is difficult to evaluate the rate distortion function. Fortunately, there is a very useful computational algorithm available for computing rate distortion functions as well as channel capacities. In App. 7A we present this algorithm, which is due to Blahut [1972].

Example (Binary source, error distortion) Consider the simple binary source, error distortion case where $\mathscr{U} = \mathscr{V} = \{0, 1\}$, $Q(0) = q \le \frac{1}{2}$, $Q(1) = 1 - q$, and $d(u, v) = 1 - \delta_{uv}$. To find $R(D)$, first we observe that $D_{\min} = 0$ and

$$D_{\max} = \min_v \{qd(0, v) + (1 - q)d(1, v)\} = q$$

Also for this case we see that

$$R(0) = \mathscr{H}(q) = -q \ln q - (1 - q) \ln (1 - q) \tag{7.6.56}$$

We now find $R(D)$ for $0 \le D \le q$. Clearly, if for any $\mathbf{P} \in \mathscr{P}_D$ we have $P(0) = 0$, then $D(\mathbf{P}) = q$; and if $P(1) = 0$ it follows that $D(\mathbf{P}) = 1 - q > q$. Hence for $0 \le D < q$ we must have, for any $\mathbf{P} \in \mathscr{P}_D$, the condition $P(0) > 0$ and $P(1) > 0$. The conditional probabilities that achieve the rate distortion function must then satisfy

$$P(v \mid u) = \lambda(u) P(v) e^{sd(u, v)}$$

Multiplying by $Q(u)$ and summing over $u \in \mathscr{U} = \{0, 1\}$ yields equations

$$\lambda(0) q e^s + \lambda(1)(1 - q) = 1$$
$$\lambda(0) q + \lambda(1)(1 - q) e^s = 1$$

which have solutions

$$\lambda(0) = \frac{1}{q(1 + e^s)} \qquad \lambda(1) = \frac{1}{(1 - q)(1 + e^s)} \tag{7.6.57}$$

Now we attempt to find $P(0)$ and $P(1)$ of the optimum conditional probability in $\mathscr{P}_D$. From (7.6.31)

$$\lambda(0) = \frac{1}{P(0) + P(1)e^s} \qquad \lambda(1) = \frac{1}{P(0)e^s + P(1)} \tag{7.6.58}$$

which combined with (7.6.57) yield equations

$$q(1 + e^s) = P(0) + P(1)e^s$$
$$(1 - q)(1 + e^s) = P(0)e^s + P(1)$$

yielding solutions

$$P(0) = \frac{q - (1 - q)e^s}{1 - e^s}$$
$$P(1) = \frac{(1 - q) - qe^s}{1 - e^s} \tag{7.6.59}$$

This then gives the parametric equation for $D = D_s$

$$\begin{aligned} D_s &= \sum_u \sum_v \lambda(u)Q(u)P(v)e^{sd(u,\, v)}d(u, v) \\ &= \lambda(0)Q(0)P(1)e^s + \lambda(1)Q(1)P(0)e^s \\ &= \frac{e^s}{1 + e^s} \end{aligned} \tag{7.6.60}$$

Hence the Lagrange multiplier s must satisfy

$$s = \ln\left(\frac{D}{1 - D}\right) \tag{7.6.61}$$

Now we have for $R(D)$, using (7.6.33)

$$\begin{aligned} R(D) &= sD + \sum_u Q(u) \ln \lambda(u) \\ &= D \ln\left(\frac{D}{1 - D}\right) + q \ln\left(\frac{1 - D}{q}\right) + (1 - q) \ln\left(\frac{1 - D}{1 - q}\right) \\ &= \mathscr{H}(q) - \mathscr{H}(D) \qquad 0 \le D \le q \end{aligned} \tag{7.6.62}$$

Note that since $\mathscr{H}(q) \le \mathscr{H}(\frac{1}{2}) = 1$, the rate distortion function for a binary *symmetric* source requires the highest rate of any binary source to achieve a given average distortion D. This is expected since there is greatest uncertainty in the outputs of the binary symmetric source. The natural generalization of this example will be examined next. Except for a very special case of this next example, the rate distortion function seems too complex to merit detailed presentation here (see, however, Berger [1971]). Instead we use Theorem 7.6.3 to find a lower bound to $R(D)$.

Example (Error distortion) Consider the natural generalization of the previous example where we are given alphabets $\mathscr{U} = \mathscr{V} = \{1, 2, \ldots, A\}$; source probabilities $Q(1), Q(2), \ldots, Q(A)$; and distortion measure $d(u, v) = 1 - \delta_{uv}$. Rather than derive the exact expression for $R(D)$, we develop an important lower bound to it. Recall from Theorem 7.6.3 that

$$R(D) \ge sD + \sum_u Q(u) \ln \lambda(u)$$

for any $s \le 0$ and $\lambda(1), \lambda(2), \ldots, \lambda(A)$ that satisfy

$$\sum_{k=1}^{A} \lambda(k)Q(k)e^{sd(k,\, j)} \le 1$$

Suppose we choose $\lambda(k)Q(k)$ to be a constant for $k = 1, 2, \ldots, A$ and require

$$\sum_{k=1}^{A} \lambda(k)Q(k)e^{sd(k,\, j)} = 1$$

Then

$$\lambda(k)Q(k) = \frac{1}{(A-1)e^s + 1} \tag{7.6.63}$$

Now choose

$$s = \ln\left[\frac{D}{(A-1)(1-D)}\right] \tag{7.6.64}$$

and so

$$\lambda(k)Q(k) = 1 - D \qquad k = 1, 2, \ldots, A \tag{7.6.65}$$

For this choice of $s \leq 0$ and $\boldsymbol{\lambda} \in \Lambda_s$

$$\begin{aligned} R(D) &\geq D \ln\left[\frac{D}{(A-1)(1-D)}\right] + \sum_{k=1}^{A} Q(k) \ln\left[\frac{1-D}{Q(k)}\right] \\ &= H(\mathscr{U}) - \mathscr{H}(D) - D \ln(A-1) \end{aligned} \tag{7.6.66}$$

Note that for $A = 2$, our previous example, this lower bound gives the exact expression for $R(D)$. Also for the special case where $Q(1) = Q(2) = \cdots = Q(A) = 1/A$ we can easily check that $P(1) = P(2) = \cdots = P(A) = 1/A$, with s and $\boldsymbol{\lambda}$ chosen above, satisfy the necessary and sufficient conditions, and again this lower bound is the exact rate distortion function. It turns out, in fact, that for

$$0 \leq D \leq (A-1) \min_k Q(k)$$

this lower bound is the exact rate distortion function for the general case. For

$$(A-1) \min_k Q(k) \leq D \leq D_{\max}$$

where

$$D_{\max} = 1 - \max_k Q(k)$$

the exact form of $R(D)$ is more complex and the lower bound is no longer tight (see Jelinek [1967]).

In the above example, for equally likely source outputs we had a symmetric condition which rendered easy the determination of the exact rate distortion function. This case is a special example of a class of sources and distortion measures referred to as *symmetric sources with balanced distortion.*

Example (Symmetric source and balanced distortion) Given $\mathscr{U} = \mathscr{V} = \{1, 2, \ldots, A\}$ and equally likely source probabilities $Q(1) = Q(2) = \cdots = Q(A) = 1/A$, suppose the distortion matrix $\{d(k, j)\}$ has the same set of entries in every row and column. That is, there exist nonnegative numbers $d_1, d_2, \ldots, d_A$ such that

$$\{d(k, j); j = 1, 2, \ldots, A\} = \{d_1, d_2, \ldots, d_A\} \qquad \text{for } k = 1, 2, \ldots, A$$

and

$$\{d(k, j); k = 1, 2, \ldots, A\} = \{d_1, d_2, \ldots, d_A\} \qquad \text{for } j = 1, 2, \ldots, A$$

In this case $\{d(k, j)\}$ is called a balanced distortion matrix, and we now compute the exact rate distortion function. By symmetry, we guess that $P(1) = P(2) = \cdots = P(A) = 1/A$ and $\lambda(1) = \lambda(2) = \cdots = \lambda(A)$. We now check to see if the necessary and sufficient conditions of Theorem 7.6.2 are satisfied for this guess. The conditional probability must satisfy

$$P(j \mid k) = \frac{\lambda}{A} e^{sd(k, j)} \qquad \text{for all } j, k \tag{7.6.67}$$

and from (7.6.31)

$$\lambda = \frac{A}{\sum_{k=1}^{A} e^{sd_k}} \tag{7.6.68}$$

This conditional probability satisfies the conditions (7.6.19) with the required λ value. The rate distortion function is given in parametric form by (7.6.32) and (7.6.33) which reduces to

$$D = D_s = \frac{\sum_{k=1}^{A} d_k e^{sd_k}}{\sum_{k=1}^{A} e^{sd_k}} \tag{7.6.69}$$

and

$$R(D_s) = sD_s + \ln A - \ln \left(\sum_{k=1}^{A} e^{sd_k} \right) \tag{7.6.70}$$

The symmetric source with balanced distortion example suggests a general way of obtaining a lower bound to $R(D)$ for arbitrary discrete memoryless sources.

Lemma 7.6.4 A lower bound to the rate distortion function for a discrete memoryless source with entropy $H(\mathscr{U})$ is given by

$$R(D) \geq R_{LB}(D) = sD + H(\mathscr{U}) - \ln \left(\sum_{u} e^{sd(u, v^*)} \right) \tag{7.6.71}$$

where v^* satisfies

$$\sum_{u} e^{sd(u, v^*)} = \max_{v \in \mathscr{V}} \sum_{u} e^{sd(u, v)} \tag{7.6.72}$$

and s satisfies the constraint

$$D = \frac{\sum_{u} d(u, v^*) e^{sd(u, v^*)}}{\sum_{u} e^{sd(u, v^*)}} \tag{7.6.73}$$

PROOF Choose $\{\lambda(u) \colon u \in \mathscr{U}\}$ such that

$$Q(u)\lambda(u) = \frac{1}{\sum_{u} e^{sd(u, v^*)}} \tag{7.6.74}$$

Then

$$\sum_u \lambda(u)Q(u)e^{sd(u,\,v)} = \frac{\sum_u e^{sd(u,\,v)}}{\sum_u e^{sd(u,\,v*)}} \le 1 \tag{7.6.75}$$

and thus $\boldsymbol{\lambda} \in \Lambda_s$. From Theorem 7.6.3 we have, for this choice of $\boldsymbol{\lambda} \in \Lambda_s$

$$R(D) \ge sD + H(\mathscr{U}) - \ln\left(\sum_u e^{sd(u,\,v*)}\right)$$

for any $s \le 0$. We now choose s to maximize this lower bound. By direct differentiation of the lower bound with respect to s and setting the derivative to zero, we find that s must satisfy (7.6.73).

Evaluation of $R(D)$ requires finding $\mathbf{P} \in \mathscr{P}_D$ that satisfy the necessary and sufficient conditions given in Theorem 7.6.2. Except for examples with certain symmetry properties this is difficult. Using the lower bound, which is often tight for small values of D, is a convenient way to find an approximation to $R(D)$. Another approach to evaluating $R(D)$ for a specific example is to use the computational algorithms of App. 7A.

7.7 EVALUATION OF $R(D)$—CONTINUOUS-AMPLITUDE MEMORYLESS SOURCES*

The conditions for the evaluation of $R(D)$ for continuous-amplitude memoryless sources are similar to those for discrete memoryless sources. Recall that the rate distortion function is defined by (7.5.23), (7.5.18), and (7.5.21) as

$$R(D) = \inf_{\mathbf{P} \in \mathscr{P}_D} I(\mathbf{P}) \qquad \text{nats/source symbol}$$

where

$$I(\mathbf{P}) = \int_{-\infty}^{\infty}\int_{-\infty}^{\infty} Q(u)P(v\,|\,u) \ln \frac{P(v\,|\,u)}{P(v)}\, dv\, du$$

and

$$\mathscr{P}_D = \left\{P(v\,|\,u)\colon D(\mathbf{P}) = \int_{-\infty}^{\infty}\int_{-\infty}^{\infty} Q(u)P(v\,|\,u)d(u,v)\, dv\, du \le D\right\}$$

As with discrete sources, $R(D)$ is a continuous, strictly decreasing function of D for $D_{\min} < D < D_{\max}$, where here

$$D_{\min} = \int_{-\infty}^{\infty} Q(u) \inf_v d(u, v)\, du \tag{7.7.1}$$

* May be omitted without loss of continuity.

and

$$D_{\max} = \inf_{v} \int_{-\infty}^{\infty} Q(u)d(u, v)\, du \tag{7.7.2}$$

The strictly decreasing property of $R(D)$ further implies that if $\mathbf{P} \in \mathscr{P}_D$ yields $R(D) = I(\mathbf{P})$, then $D(\mathbf{P}) = D$.

To find $R(D)$, we want to minimize

$$I(\mathbf{P}) = \int_{-\infty}^{\infty} \int_{-\infty}^{\infty} Q(u)P(v \mid u) \ln \left[\frac{P(v \mid u)}{P(v)}\right] dv\, du \tag{7.7.3}$$

subject to the conditions on $P(v \mid u)$

$$P(v \mid u) \geq 0 \qquad \text{for all } u, v \in \mathscr{R} \tag{7.7.4}$$

$$\int_{-\infty}^{\infty} P(v \mid u)\, dv = 1 \qquad \text{for all } u \in \mathscr{R} \tag{7.7.5}$$

$$\int_{-\infty}^{\infty} \int_{-\infty}^{\infty} Q(u)P(v \mid u)d(u, v)\, du\, dv = D \tag{7.7.6}$$

Using Lagrange multipliers for the equality constraints, (7.7.5) and (7.7.6), and the calculus of variations, we can obtain the continuous-amplitude form of Theorem 7.6.1, given in the following theorem (see Berger [1971], chap. 4).

Theorem 7.7.1 Necessary and sufficient conditions for a conditional probability $\mathbf{P} \in \mathscr{P}_D$ to yield the rate distortion function $R(D)$ at distortion D are that it satisfy[20]

$$P(v \mid u) = \lambda(u)P(v)e^{sd(u, v)} \qquad \text{if } P(v) > 0 \tag{7.7.7}$$

$$\int_{-\infty}^{\infty} \lambda(u)Q(u)e^{sd(u, v)}\, du \leq 1 \qquad \text{if } P(v) = 0 \tag{7.7.8}$$

where

$$\lambda(u) = \left[\int_{-\infty}^{\infty} P(v)e^{sd(u, v)}\, dv\right]^{-1} \tag{7.7.9}$$

and where for $s \leq 0$, $R(D)$ and D satisfy the parametric equations

$$D = \int_{-\infty}^{\infty} \int_{-\infty}^{\infty} \lambda(u)Q(u)P(v)e^{sd(u, v)}d(u, v)\, du\, dv \tag{7.7.10}$$

$$R(D) = sD + \int_{-\infty}^{\infty} Q(u) \ln \lambda(u)\, du \tag{7.7.11}$$

Following the same arguments as for the discrete case we have the following lemmas.

[20] In a strict sense, these relations hold for almost all $v \in \mathscr{V}$.

Lemma 7.7.1 The parameter s is the slope of the rate distortion function at the point $D = D_s$. That is

$$R'(D_s) = \left.\frac{dR(D)}{dD}\right|_{D=D_s} = s \tag{7.7.12}$$

Lemma 7.7.2 The derivative $R'(D)$ is continuous for $D_{\min} < D < D_{\max}$.

Theorem 7.7.2 The rate distortion function can be expressed as

$$R(D) = \sup_{s \leq 0,\, \boldsymbol{\lambda} \in \Lambda_s} \left[sD + \int_{-\infty}^{\infty} Q(u) \ln \lambda(u)\, du \right] \tag{7.7.13}$$

where

$$\Lambda_s = \left\{ \lambda(u) \colon \int_{-\infty}^{\infty} \lambda(u) Q(u) e^{sd(u,\, v)} \leq 1,\ -\infty < v < \infty \right\} \tag{7.7.14}$$

Necessary and sufficient conditions for s and $\boldsymbol{\lambda}$ to realize the maximum are the same as those given in Theorem 7.7.1.

The main difference between the rate distortion functions for continuous and discrete sources is that $R(D) \to \infty$ as $D \to D_{\min}$, since the entropy of a continuous amplitude source is infinite. For continuous amplitude sources there are only a few examples of explicit analytical evaluation of the rate distortion function. We present first the well-known, most commonly used example of a memoryless Gaussian source with a squared-error distortion measure.

Example (Gaussian source, squared-error distortion) Consider a source that outputs an independent Gaussian random variable each symbol time with probability density

$$Q(u) = \frac{1}{\sqrt{2\pi\sigma^2}} e^{-u^2/2\sigma^2} \qquad -\infty < u < \infty \tag{7.7.15}$$

and assume a squared-error distortion measure $d(u, v) = (u - v)^2$. For this distortion and source we have $D_{\min} = 0$ and $D_{\max} = \sigma^2$. We next seek a conditional probability density $\mathbf{P} \in \mathscr{P}_D$ which satisfies the necessary and sufficient conditions of Theorem 7.7.1 for $0 < D < \sigma^2$. A natural choice is to choose, for some β^2

$$P(v) = \frac{1}{\sqrt{2\pi\beta^2}} e^{-v^2/2\beta^2} \qquad -\infty < v < \infty \tag{7.7.16}$$

This then yields the Lagrange multiplier, $\lambda(\,\cdot\,)$, which satisfies

$$\begin{aligned}
[\lambda(u)]^{-1} &= \int_{-\infty}^{\infty} P(v) e^{sd(u,\, v)}\, dv \\
&= \int_{-\infty}^{\infty} P(v) e^{-(u-v)^2/2\alpha^2}\, dv \\
&= \sqrt{2\pi\alpha^2} \frac{1}{\sqrt{2\pi(\alpha^2 + \beta^2)}} e^{-u^2/2(\alpha^2+\beta^2)}
\end{aligned} \tag{7.7.17}$$

where $\alpha^2 = -1/(2s)$. This choice of $P(v)$ then requires $P(v \mid u)$ of the form

$$\begin{aligned} P(v \mid u) &= \lambda(u)P(v)e^{sd(u,\,v)} \\ &= \lambda(u)P(v)e^{-(u-v)^2/2\alpha^2} \\ &= \frac{1}{\sqrt{2\pi[\alpha^2\beta^2/(\alpha^2+\beta^2)]}} \exp\left\{-\frac{\{v-[\beta^2/(\alpha^2+\beta^2)]u\}^2}{2\alpha^2\beta^2/(\alpha^2+\beta^2)}\right\} \end{aligned} \tag{7.7.18}$$

All that remains is to satisfy the parametric equations for D and $R(D)$. First,

$$\begin{aligned} D &= \int_{-\infty}^{\infty} Q(u)P(v \mid u)d(u, v)\, du\, dv \\ &= \frac{\alpha^2\beta^2}{\alpha^2+\beta^2} + \left(\frac{\alpha^2}{\alpha^2+\beta^2}\right)^2 \sigma^2 \end{aligned}$$

So far α^2 is directly related to the parameter s, whereas β^2 is unrestricted. We choose β^2 to satisfy $\alpha^2 + \beta^2 = \sigma^2$. This forces the relation on s given by

$$\begin{aligned} D &= \alpha^2 \\ &= -\frac{1}{2s} \end{aligned} \tag{7.7.19}$$

The expression for $R(D)$ then becomes

$$\begin{aligned} R(D) &= sD + \int_{-\infty}^{\infty} Q(u) \ln \lambda(u)\, du \\ &= -\frac{1}{2} - \int_{-\infty}^{\infty} Q(u)\left(\tfrac{1}{2} \ln \frac{D}{\sigma^2} - \frac{u^2}{2\sigma^2}\right) du \end{aligned}$$

or

$$R(D) = \tfrac{1}{2} \ln \frac{\sigma^2}{D} \qquad \text{nats/source symbol} \qquad 0 < D < \sigma^2 \tag{7.7.20}$$

The above is the simplest example. We next present without proof other known examples.

Example (Gaussian source, magnitude error distortion) Consider next the same Gaussian source with probability density given by (7.7.15) and assume now a distortion measure $d(u, v) = |u - v|$. Here $D_{min} = 0$ and $D_{max} = \sqrt{2\sigma^2/\pi}$. For $0 < D < D_{max}$, the rate distortion function (Tan and Yao [1975]) is given parametrically by

$$R(D) = -\left[\left(\frac{1}{2} + \frac{\theta^2}{2}\right)(1 - 2Q(\theta)) + \frac{\theta}{\sqrt{2\pi}} e^{-\theta^2/2}\right] - \ln\,(2Q(\theta)) \tag{7.7.21}$$

$$D_\theta = \sigma\left\{\frac{1}{\sqrt{2\pi}}(1 - 2Q(\theta))e^{\theta^2/2}Q(\theta) + \sqrt{2/\pi}\, e^{-\theta^2/2} - 2\theta Q(\theta)\right\} \tag{7.7.22}$$

where $0 \leq \theta < \infty$. Similar analytical evaluation of rate distortion functions for classes of sources of probability densities with constrained tail decays under magnitude error distortion are also given in Tan and Yao [1975]. [In this example only $Q(\cdot)$ is the Gaussian integral function defined by (2.3.11).]

Example (Exponential source, magnitude error distortion) Suppose the source probability density is

$$Q(u) = \frac{\alpha}{2} e^{-\alpha|u|} \qquad -\infty < u < \infty \tag{7.7.23}$$

with a distortion measure $d(u, v) = |u - v|$. Then $D_{min} = 0$ and $D_{max} = 1/\alpha$. For $0 < D < 1/\alpha$, the choice (Berger [1971])

$$P(v) = \alpha^2 D^2 \, \delta(v) + \frac{\alpha}{2}(1 - \alpha^2 D^2) e^{-\alpha|v|} \tag{7.7.24}$$

yields the rate distortion function

$$R(D) = -\ln(\alpha D) \qquad \text{nats/source symbol} \tag{7.7.25}$$

Example (Uniform source, magnitude error distortion) Consider a source with uniform probability density

$$Q(u) = \begin{cases} 1/(2A) & |u| \le A \\ 0 & |u| > A \end{cases} \tag{7.7.26}$$

and a distortion measure $d(u, v) = |u - v|$. Then $D_{min} = 0$ and $D_{max} = A/2$. For $0 < D < A/2$, we have (Tan and Yao [1975])

$$R(D) = -\ln[1 - (1 - 2D/A)^{1/2}] - (1 - 2D/A)^{1/2} \tag{7.7.27}$$

Finally we note that Rubin [1973] has evaluated the rate distortion function for the Poisson source under the magnitude error distortion criterion. Evaluations of rate distortion functions for most other cases are limited to a low range of distortion values, wherein often a simple lower bound to the rate distortion function coincides with the actual rate distortion function.

Since $R(D)$ is generally difficult to evaluate, it is natural to consider various bounds on the rate distortion function. Upper bounds follow easily from the definition, since

$$\begin{aligned} R(D) &= \inf_{\mathbf{P} \in \mathscr{P}_D} I(\mathbf{P}) \\ &\le I(\mathbf{P}) \end{aligned}$$

for any $\mathbf{P} \in \mathscr{P}_D$. The trick is to choose a convenient form for $\mathbf{P} \in \mathscr{P}_D$. Often, for a given distortion measure, there is a natural choice for the conditional probability density that yields a simple, convenient upper bound. For example, for the squared-error distortion $d(u, v) = (u - v)^2$, a natural choice was to let $\mathbf{P} \in \mathscr{P}_D$ be the Gaussian density.

Theorem 7.7.3 Let $Q(\cdot)$ be any source probability density with mean zero and variance σ^2. That is, suppose

$$\int_{-\infty}^{\infty} uQ(u)\, du = 0 \tag{7.7.28}$$

and
$$\int_{-\infty}^{\infty} u^2 Q(u)\, du = \sigma^2 \tag{7.7.29}$$

For this source probability density and the squared-error distortion measure, $d(u, v) = (u - v)^2$, the rate distortion function is bounded by

$$R(D) \le \tfrac{1}{2} \ln \frac{\sigma^2}{D} \qquad \text{nats/source symbol} \qquad 0 \le D \le \sigma^2 \tag{7.7.30}$$

where equality holds if and only if $Q(\cdot)$ is the Gaussian density.

PROOF For a given D in the interval $0 < D < \sigma^2$, let

$$P(v \mid u) = \frac{1}{\sqrt{2\pi D(1 - D/\sigma^2)}} e^{-[v-(1-D/\sigma^2)u]^2/2D(1-D/\sigma^2)} \tag{7.7.31}$$

Then

$$\int_{-\infty}^{\infty} d(u, v) P(v \mid u)\, dv = D\left(1 - \frac{D}{\sigma^2}\right) + \left(\frac{D}{\sigma^2}\right)^2 u^2$$

and

$$D(\mathbf{P}) = \int_{-\infty}^{\infty} \int_{-\infty}^{\infty} d(u, v) Q(u) P(v \mid u)\, dv\, du$$
$$= D \tag{7.7.32}$$

Hence $\mathbf{P} \in \mathscr{P}_D$ and we have $R(D) \le I(\mathbf{P})$. But

$$I(\mathbf{P}) = \int_{-\infty}^{\infty} \int_{-\infty}^{\infty} Q(u) P(v \mid u) \ln \frac{P(v \mid u)}{P(v)}\, dv\, du$$
$$= \int_{-\infty}^{\infty} P(v) \ln \frac{1}{P(v)}\, dv + \int_{-\infty}^{\infty} \int_{-\infty}^{\infty} Q(u) P(v \mid u) \ln P(v \mid u)\, dv\, du \tag{7.7.33}$$

Letting
$$h(\mathscr{V}) \equiv \int_{-\infty}^{\infty} P(v) \ln \frac{1}{P(v)}\, dv \tag{7.7.34}$$

be the differential entropy of $P(v)$, and noting that

$$\int_{-\infty}^{\infty} \int_{-\infty}^{\infty} Q(u) P(v \mid u) \ln P(v \mid u)\, dv\, du$$
$$= \int_{-\infty}^{\infty} \int_{-\infty}^{\infty} Q(u) P(v \mid u) \left\{ -\frac{[v - (1 - D/\sigma^2)u]^2}{2D(1 - D/\sigma^2)} - \frac{1}{2} \ln \left[2\pi D\left(1 - \frac{D}{\sigma^2}\right)\right]\right\} dv\, du$$
$$= -\tfrac{1}{2} - \tfrac{1}{2} \ln \left[2\pi D\left(1 - \frac{D}{\sigma^2}\right)\right]$$
$$= -\tfrac{1}{2} \ln \left[2\pi e D\left(1 - \frac{D}{\sigma^2}\right)\right] \tag{7.7.35}$$

it follows that

$$R(D) \le I(\mathbf{P})$$
$$= h(\mathscr{V}) - \tfrac{1}{2} \ln [2\pi e D(1 - D/\sigma^2)] \tag{7.7.36}$$

for the choice of $\mathbf{P}$ of (7.7.31). Note from (7.7.28), (7.7.29), and (7.7.31) that

$$\int_{-\infty}^{\infty} vP(v)\, dv = 0 \tag{7.7.37}$$

and
$$\int_{-\infty}^{\infty} v^2 P(v)\, dv = \int_{-\infty}^{\infty} Q(u) \left\{ \int_{-\infty}^{\infty} v^2 P(v \mid u)\, dv \right\} du$$
$$= \int_{-\infty}^{\infty} Q(u)\{D(1 - D/\sigma^2) + (1 - D/\sigma^2)^2 u^2\}\, du$$
$$= (1 - D/\sigma^2)\sigma^2$$
$$= \sigma^2 - D \tag{7.7.38}$$

It follows also, from Prob. 1.13, that the differential entropy for any probability density is upper-bounded by the differential entropy of the Gaussian density having the same mean and variance. Hence, using (7.7.37) and (7.7.38), we have

$$h(\mathscr{V}) \le \tfrac{1}{2} \ln [2\pi e(\sigma^2 - D)] \tag{7.7.39}$$

which in turn yields the desired bound.

Thus, for a given variance, the Gaussian source yields the maximum rate distortion function with respect to a squared-error criterion. It follows that, for any given source of variance σ^2 and squared-error fidelity criterion D, there exists a block code of fixed rate $R > \frac{1}{2} \ln (\sigma^2/D)$ nats per symbol that can achieve average distortion D. In fact, Sakrison [1975] has shown that for $R > \frac{1}{2} \ln (\sigma^2/D)$, codes that are designed to achieve average distortion D for the Gaussian source will be good (in the sense of also achieving distortion D) for any other source with the same variance. Similar results were obtained for sources with fixed moments other than the second.

Most of the efforts in evaluating rate distortion functions have concentrated on deriving lower bounds to $R(D)$. This is due in part to the fact that, for many sources and distortion measures, a convenient lower bound due to Shannon [1959] coincides with the actual rate distortion function for some lower range of values of the fidelity criterion D. To derive lower bounds to $R(D)$, we examine the form of the rate distortion function given in Theorem 7.7.2. Specifically

$$R(D) = \sup_{s \le 0,\, \lambda \in \Lambda_s} \left[sD + \int_{-\infty}^{\infty} Q(u) \ln \lambda(u)\, du \right]$$
$$\ge sD + \int_{-\infty}^{\infty} Q(u) \ln \lambda(u)\, du \tag{7.7.40}$$

for any $s \leq 0$ and any $\boldsymbol{\lambda} \in \Lambda_s$, where

$$\Lambda_s = \left\{ \lambda(u) : \int_{-\infty}^{\infty} \lambda(u) Q(u) e^{sd(u, v)} \, du \leq 1, \qquad -\infty < v < \infty \right\}$$

Again we seek a convenient choice of $\boldsymbol{\lambda} \in \Lambda_s$. For difference distortion measures $d(u, v) = d(u - v)$, which depends only on the difference $u - v$, we have the following lower bound, $R_{LB}(D)$.

Theorem 7.7.4: Shannon lower bound For a source with probability density function $Q(\cdot)$ and difference distortion measure $d(u, v) = d(u - v)$

$$R(D) \geq R_{LB}(D) = \sup_{s \leq 0} \left[h(\mathscr{U}) + sD - \ln \int_{-\infty}^{\infty} e^{sd(z)} \, dz \right] \tag{7.7.41}$$

where

$$h(\mathscr{U}) = -\int_{-\infty}^{\infty} Q(u) \ln Q(u) \, du \tag{7.7.42}$$

is the differential entropy of the source.

PROOF Let $\lambda(u)$ be chosen according to

$$[\lambda(u)]^{-1} = Q(u) \int_{-\infty}^{\infty} e^{sd(z)} \, dz \tag{7.7.43}$$

Then

$$\int_{-\infty}^{\infty} \lambda(u) Q(u) e^{sd(u-v)} \, du = \frac{\int_{-\infty}^{\infty} e^{sd(u-v)} \, du}{\int_{-\infty}^{\infty} e^{sd(z)} \, dz} = 1$$

which establishes $\boldsymbol{\lambda} \in \Lambda_s$. Substituting (7.7.43) in (7.7.40) yields the desired result.

Using direct differentiation with respect to s on the lower bound (7.7.41), we can easily obtain two special cases.

Corollary 7.7.5: Squared error For $d(u, v) = (u - v)^2$ in the above lemma we have

$$R(D) \geq R_{LB}(D) = h(\mathscr{U}) - \tfrac{1}{2} \ln (2\pi e D) \qquad \text{nats/source symbol} \tag{7.7.44}$$

Corollary 7.7.6: Magnitude error For $d(u, v) = |u - v|$ in the above lemma we have

$$R(D) \geq R_{LB}(D) = h(\mathscr{U}) - \ln (2eD) \qquad \text{nats/source symbol} \tag{7.7.45}$$

In many cases the Shannon lower bound is tight. This occurs when $\lambda(\cdot)$ given in (7.7.43) also meets the conditions of Theorem 7.7.1, which are satisfied if and only if a probability density $P_s(\cdot)$ can be found that satisfies (see Prob. 7.18)

$$Q(u) = \frac{\int_{-\infty}^{\infty} P_s(v) e^{sd(u-v)}\, dv}{\int_{-\infty}^{\infty} e^{sd(z)}\, dz} \tag{7.7.46}$$

for some $s \geq 0$. For these values of s, we have $R(D_s) = R_{LB}(D_s)$.

For the Gaussian source with squared-error distortion measure, the Shannon lower bound is tight everywhere; that is, $R(D) = R_{LB}(D)$ for all $0 < D < \sigma^2$. This is also true of the source with the two-sided exponential density (7.7.23) with a magnitude error criterion whose $R(D)$ is given by (7.7.25). For a case in which the lower bound is nowhere tight consider the following.

Example (Gaussian source, magnitude distortion) For the Gaussian source with probability density

$$Q(u) = \frac{1}{\sqrt{2\pi\sigma^2}} e^{-u^2/2\sigma^2} \qquad -\infty < u < \infty \tag{7.7.47}$$

and the distortion measure $d(u, v) = |u - v|$, we have

$$h(\mathscr{U}) = \tfrac{1}{2} \ln (2\pi e \sigma^2) \tag{7.7.48}$$

and

$$R_{LB}(D) = \tfrac{1}{2} \ln (\pi\sigma^2/2eD^2) \tag{7.7.49}$$

for

$$0 < D < \sqrt{\frac{\pi\sigma^2}{2e}}$$

Here in general the true rate distortion function [see the example resulting in (7.7.21) and (7.7.22)] is strictly greater than the Shannon lower bound. However, by numerical calculations, Tan and Yao [1975] have shown that the maximum of $R(D) - R_{LB}(D)$ is roughly 0.036 nat per source symbol, and that at rates above one nat per source symbol the difference is less than one part in a million. Thus one can conclude that $R_{LB}(D)$ is a very good approximation of $R(D)$ for this source (see Prob. 7.21).

7.8 BIBLIOGRAPHICAL NOTES AND REFERENCES

The seeds of rate distortion theory can be found in Shannon's original 1948 paper. It was another eleven years, however, before Shannon [1959] presented the fundamental theorems which serve as the cornerstone of rate distortion theory. In the late sixties there was a renewed interest in this theory, and at that time the general information theory texts by Gallager [1968] and Jelinek [1968*a*] each contained a chapter devoted to rate distortion theory. The most complete presentation of this theory can be found in the text by Berger [1971], which is devoted primarily to this subject.

In this chapter, the presentation of rate distortion theory is different from earlier treatments in that we first emphasize the coding theorems and later discuss the rate distortion function, its properties, and its evaluation. The proofs of the coding theorems for block codes (Theorem 7.2.1) and for trellis codes (Theorem 7.4.1) are due to the authors (Omura [1973], Viterbi and Omura [1974]). They are analogous to the proofs of the corresponding channel coding theorems of Chaps. 3 and 5. The de-emphasis of techniques for the evaluation of $R(D)$ is due primarily to the fact that there now exists an efficient computational algorithm for $R(D)$ which is due to Blahut [1972] and is included here in App. 7A.

APPENDIX 7A COMPUTATIONAL ALGORITHM FOR $R(D)$ (BLAHUT [1972])

The algorithm for computing $R(D)$ is similar to the algorithm for channel capacity given in App. 3C. Recall that for a discrete memoryless source with alphabet $\mathscr{U}$, letter probability distribution $\{Q(u): u \in \mathscr{U}\}$, representation alphabet $\mathscr{V}$, and distortion $\{d(u, v): u \in \mathscr{U}, v \in \mathscr{V}\}$ the rate distortion function $R(D)$ is given by (7.2.53)

$$R(D) = \min_{\mathbf{P} \in \mathscr{P}_D} I(\mathbf{P})$$

where

$$I(\mathbf{P}) = \sum_u \sum_v Q(u)P(v \mid u) \ln \frac{P(v \mid u)}{\sum_{u'} P(v \mid u')Q(u')}$$

and

$$\mathscr{P}_D = \left\{P(v \mid u): D(\mathbf{P}) = \sum_u \sum_v Q(u)P(v \mid u)d(u, v) \le D\right\}$$

The parametric representation for $R(D)$ in terms of parameter $s \le 0$ is given by (7.6.32) and (7.6.33)

$$D_s = \sum_u \sum_v \lambda(u)Q(u)P(v)e^{sd(u, v)}d(u, v)$$

$$R(D_s) = sD_s + \sum_u Q(u) \ln \lambda(u)$$

where, by (7.6.31)

$$\lambda(u) = \left(\sum_v P(v)e^{sd(u, v)}\right)^{-1} \qquad \text{for all } u \in \mathscr{U}$$

The transition probability $\{P(v \mid u)\}$ which achieves $R(D_s)$ is given by the necessary and sufficient conditions of (7.6.19)

$$P(v \mid u) = \lambda(u)P(v)e^{sd(u, v)} \qquad \text{if } P(v) > 0$$

and

$$\sum_u \lambda(u)Q(u)e^{sd(u,\, v)} \leq 1 \qquad \text{if } P(v) = 0$$

The algorithm for computing $R(D)$ is based on the following theorem.

Theorem 7A.1 Given parameter $s \leq 0$. Let $\{P_0(v): v \in \mathscr{V}\}$ be a probability vector for which $P_0(v) > 0$ for all $v \in \mathscr{V}$. For integers $n = 0, 1, 2, \ldots$ define

$$P_{n+1}(v) = P_n(v) \sum_u \frac{Q(u)e^{sd(u,\, v)}}{\sum_{v'} P_n(v')e^{sd(u,\, v')}} \tag{7A.1}$$

and

$$P_{n+1}(v \mid u) = \frac{P_n(v)e^{sd(u,\, v)}}{\sum_{v'} P_n(v')e^{sd(u,\, v')}} \tag{7A.2}$$

Then, in the limit as $n \to \infty$, we have

$$\begin{aligned} D(\mathbf{P}_n) &\to D_s \\ I(\mathbf{P}_n) &\to R(D_s) \end{aligned} \tag{7A.3}$$

where $(D_s, R(D_s))$ is the point on the $R(D)$ versus D curve parameterized by s.

Proof Consider the ID plane shown in Fig. 7A.1. Define $V(\mathbf{P}) = I(\mathbf{P}) - sD(\mathbf{P})$ which can be interpreted as the I-axis intercept of a line of slope s which passes through the point $(I(\mathbf{P}), D(\mathbf{P}))$. Recall that the point on the $R(D)$-versus-D curve parameterized by s has a tangent that is parallel to every such line of slope s, and this point lies beneath all such lines since $R(D)$ is defined as a minimization over $I(\mathbf{P})$. We show that $V(\mathbf{P}_n)$ is strictly decreasing with n, unless $(I(\mathbf{P}_n), D(\mathbf{P}_n))$ is a point on the $R(D)$-versus-D curve.

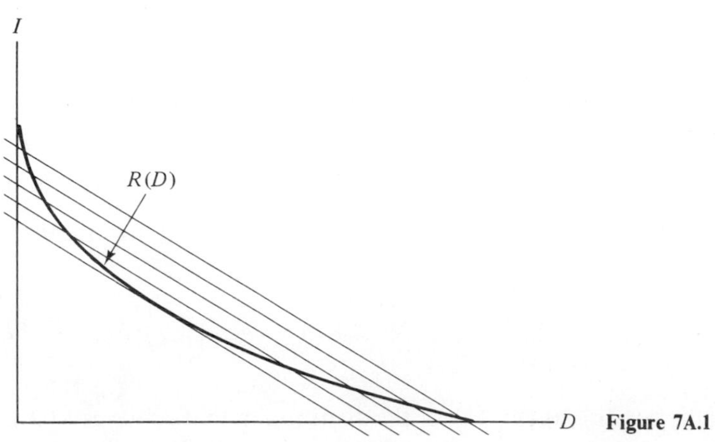

Figure 7A.1 Sketch of ID plane.

From (7A.2) we have

$$
\begin{aligned}
V(\mathbf{P}_{n+1}) &= I(\mathbf{P}_{n+1}) - sD(\mathbf{P}_{n+1}) \\
&= \sum_u \sum_v Q(u)P_{n+1}(v \mid u) \ln \left[\frac{P_{n+1}(v \mid u)}{P_{n+1}(v)} \right] - s \sum_u \sum_v Q(u)P_{n+1}(v \mid u) d(u, v) \\
&= \sum_u \sum_v Q(u)P_{n+1}(v \mid u) \ln \left[\frac{P_n(v)e^{sd(u, v)}}{P_{n+1}(v)\left(\sum_{v'} P_n(v')e^{sd(u, v')} \right)} \right] \\
&\quad - \sum_u \sum_v Q(u)P_{n+1}(v \mid u) \ln e^{sd(u, v)} \\
&= \sum_v P_{n+1}(v) \ln \left[\frac{P_n(v)}{P_{n+1}(v)} \right] - \sum_u Q(u) \ln \left(\sum_v P_n(v)e^{sd(u, v)} \right)
\end{aligned} \tag{7A.4}
$$

From this we get the difference

$$
\begin{aligned}
V(\mathbf{P}_{n+1}) - V(\mathbf{P}_n) &= \sum_v P_{n+1}(v) \ln \left[\frac{P_n(v)}{P_{n+1}(v)} \right] \\
&\quad - \sum_u \sum_v Q(u)P_n(v \mid u) \ln \left[\frac{P_{n-1}(v)\left(\sum_{v'} P_n(v')e^{sd(u, v')} \right)}{P_n(v)\left(\sum_{v'} P_{n-1}(v')e^{sd(u, v')} \right)} \right] \\
&= \sum_v P_{n+1}(v) \ln \left[\frac{P_n(v)}{P_{n+1}(v)} \right] \\
&\quad + \sum_u \sum_v Q(u)P_n(v \mid u) \ln \left[\frac{P_n(v)e^{sd(u, v)}}{P_n(v \mid u)\left(\sum_{v'} P_n(v')e^{sd(u, v')} \right)} \right] \\
&\le \sum_v P_{n+1}(v) \left[\frac{P_n(v)}{P_{n+1}(v)} - 1 \right] \\
&\quad + \sum_u \sum_v Q(u)P_n(v \mid u) \left[\frac{P_n(v)e^{sd(u, v)}}{P_n(v \mid u)\left(\sum_{v'} P_n(v')e^{sd(u, v')} \right)} - 1 \right] \\
&= 0
\end{aligned} \tag{7A.5}
$$

where again we used $\ln x \le x - 1$. We have equality in (7A.5) if and only if $P_{n+1}(v) = P_n(v)$ and

$$
P_n(v \mid u) = \frac{P_n(v)e^{sd(u, v)}}{\sum_{v'} P_n(v')e^{sd(u, v')}} \tag{7A.6}
$$

which is one of the conditions (7.6.19) for the distribution that achieves $R(D_s)$. Since $V(\mathbf{P}_n)$ is nonincreasing and is bounded below by $R(D) - sD$, it must converge to some value $V(\mathbf{P}_\infty)$ as $n \to \infty$. The sequence $\mathbf{P}_n$ must have a limit point $\mathbf{P}^*$, and by continuity of $V(\mathbf{P})$ this limit point must satisfy (7A.1)

$$P^*(v) = P^*(v) \sum_u \frac{Q(u)e^{sd(u,v)}}{\sum_{v'} P^*(v')e^{sd(u,v')}} \tag{7A.7}$$

Thus $\mathbf{P}^*$ satisfies necessary and sufficient conditions to achieve $R(D_s)$ so that $V(\mathbf{P}^*) = R(D_s) - sD_s$.

The accuracy of the computational algorithm after a finite number of steps is given by the following theorem.

Theorem 7A.2 Given any probability distribution $\{P(v): v \in \mathscr{V}\}$ let

$$C(v) = \sum_u \frac{Q(u)e^{sd(u,v)}}{\sum_{v'} P(v')e^{sd(u,v')}} \qquad \text{for all } v \in \mathscr{V} \tag{7A.8}$$

Then for $\{P(v \mid u): u \in \mathscr{U}, v \in \mathscr{V}\}$ satisfying

$$P(v \mid u) = \frac{P(v)e^{sd(u,v)}}{\sum_{v'} P(v')e^{sd(u,v')}} \tag{7A.9}$$

we have at the point

$$D = D(\mathbf{P}) = \sum_u \sum_v Q(u) \frac{P(v)e^{sd(u,v)}d(u,v)}{\sum_{v'} P(v')e^{sd(u,v')}}$$

the bounds

$$\begin{aligned} -\max_v \ln C(v) &\le R(D) - sD + \sum_u Q(u) \ln\left[\sum_v P(v)e^{sd(u,v)}\right] \\ &\le -\sum_v P(v)C(v) \ln C(v) \end{aligned} \tag{7A.10}$$

PROOF If $D(\mathbf{P}) = D$ then $\mathbf{P} \in \mathscr{P}_D$ and

$$\begin{aligned} R(D) &\le I(\mathbf{P}) \\ &= \sum_u \sum_v Q(u)P(v \mid u) \ln\left[\frac{P(v \mid u)}{\sum_{u'} Q(u')P(v \mid u')}\right] \\ &= \sum_u \sum_v Q(u)P(v \mid u) \ln\left[\frac{P(v)e^{sd(u,v)}}{\left(\sum_{v'} P(v')e^{sd(u,v')}\right)\left(\sum_{u'} Q(u')P(v \mid u')\right)}\right] \\ &= sD - \sum_u Q(u) \ln\left(\sum_v P(v)e^{sd(u,v)}\right) \\ &\quad - \sum_u \sum_v Q(u)P(v \mid u) \ln\left[\frac{\sum_{u'} Q(u')P(v \mid u')}{P(v)}\right] \end{aligned} \tag{7A.11}$$

But

$$\sum_u Q(u)P(v \mid u) = P(v)C(v) \tag{7A.12}$$

so that

$$R(D) \leq sD - \sum_u Q(u) \ln \left[\sum_v P(v) e^{sd(u, v)} \right] - \sum_v P(v)C(v) \ln C(v) \tag{7A.13}$$

From Theorem 7.6.3 we have

$$R(D) \geq sD + \sum_u Q(u) \ln \lambda(u) \tag{7A.14}$$

where $\boldsymbol{\lambda}$ is any vector such that

$$\sum_u \lambda(u)Q(u)e^{sd(u, v)} \leq 1 \qquad \text{for all } v \in \mathscr{V} \tag{7A.15}$$

Let us choose

$$\lambda(u) = \left[C_{\max} \sum_v P(v) e^{sd(u, v)} \right]^{-1} \qquad \text{for all } u \in \mathscr{U} \tag{7A.16}$$

where

$$C_{\max} = \max_v C(v)$$

Then (7A.15) is satisfied and

$$R(D) \geq sD - \sum_u Q(u) \ln \left[\sum_v P(v) e^{sd(u, v)} \right] - \max_v \ln C(v) \tag{7A.17}$$

We see that, for $\{P(v): v \in \mathscr{V}\}$ that achieves the point $R(D)$, we have

$$R(D) = sD - \sum_u Q(u) \ln \left[\sum_v P(v) e^{sd(u, v)} \right] \tag{7A.18}$$

and

$$C(v) \leq 1 \tag{7A.19}$$

with equality when $P(v) > 0$. Thus

$$\begin{aligned} -\max_v \ln C(v) &= -\sum_v P(v)C(v) \ln C(v) \\ &= 0 \end{aligned} \tag{7A.20}$$

and the bounds in (7A.10) are tight. The two theorems suggest the following algorithm for a given $\epsilon > 0$ level of desired accuracy.

Step 1: Set $n = 1$ and pick an initial probability $\mathbf{P}_0$. (The uniform distribution will do.)

Step 2: Compute[21] for the given $Q(u)$, $d(u, v)$, and for any $s < 0$

$$C_n(v) = \sum_u \frac{Q(u)e^{sd(u, v)}}{\sum_{v'} P_n(v')e^{sd(u, v')}} \tag{7A.21}$$

$$P_{n+1}(v) = P_n(v)C_n(v) \tag{7A.22}$$

$$A_n = -\sum_v P_n(v)C_n(v) \ln C_n(v) \tag{7A.23}$$

$$B_n = -\max_v \ln C_n(v) \tag{7A.24}$$

Step 3: If $A_n - B_n \le \epsilon$, compute $D(\mathbf{P}_n)$

$$R(D(\mathbf{P}_n)) = sD(\mathbf{P}_n) - \sum_u Q(u) \ln \left[\sum_v P_n(v)e^{sd(u, v)}\right] + A_n \tag{7A.25}$$

and stop.

Step 4: If $A_n - B_n > \epsilon$, change n to $n + 1$ and go to step 2.

PROBLEMS

7.1 Prove inequality (7.2.47), using a proof similar to the proof of Lemma 1.2.2 for $I(\mathscr{X}_N; \mathscr{Y}_N)$ given in Chap. 1.

7.2 For sequences of length N define

$$\mathscr{P}_{D, N} = \{P_N(\mathbf{v} \mid \mathbf{u}) \colon \sum_{\mathbf{u}} \sum_{\mathbf{v}} Q_N(\mathbf{u})P_N(\mathbf{v} \mid \mathbf{u})d_N(\mathbf{u}, \mathbf{v}) \le D\}$$

and

$$R_N(D) = \min_{\mathbf{P}_N \in \mathscr{P}_{D, N}} \frac{1}{N} I(\mathbf{P}_N)$$

For a discrete memoryless source where

$$Q_N(\mathbf{u}) = \prod_{n=1}^{N} Q(u_n)$$

show that

$$R(D) = R_N(D) \qquad N = 1, 2, \ldots$$

7.3 (Gallager [1968]) For Theorem 7.2.4 show that

$$-E_o''(\rho; \mathbf{P}) \le C_o = 2 + 16[\ln A]^2$$

for $-\frac{1}{2} \le \rho \le 0$. It is convenient to define

$$\alpha(u) = \sum_v P(v)Q(u \mid v)^{1/(1+\rho)}$$

$$\omega(u) = \frac{\alpha(u)^{1+\rho}}{\sum_z \alpha(z)^{1+\rho}}$$

$$\beta(v \mid u) = \frac{P(v)Q(u \mid v)^{1/(1+\rho)}}{\alpha(u)}$$

[21] The choice of $s = 0$ yields $R(D_{\max}) = 0$, where $D_{\max}$ is given by (7.6.7). The choice of $s < 0$ yields the point $(R(D), D)$, where the slope is s.

and show that

$$-E_o(\rho, \mathbf{P}) = \ln \sum_u \alpha(u)^{1+\rho}$$

$$-E_o'(\rho, \mathbf{P}) = \sum_u \omega(u) \sum_v \beta(v \mid u) \ln \left[\frac{\alpha(u)}{Q(u \mid v)^{1/(1+\rho)}} \right]$$

$$= \sum_u \omega(u) \sum_v \beta(v \mid u) \ln \left[\frac{P(v)}{\beta(v \mid u)} \right]$$

and

$$-E_o''(\rho, \mathbf{P}) \le \frac{1}{1+\rho} \sum_u \omega(u) \sum_v \beta(v \mid u) \left[\ln \frac{P(v)}{\beta(v \mid u)} \right]^2$$

7.4 Show that the source coding theorem given by Corollary 7.2.2 remains true when either $D + \epsilon$ is replaced by D (provided $D > D_{\min}$) or $R(D) + \epsilon$ is replaced by $R(D)$.

7.5 Prove Theorem 7.3.2 using the proof given in the converse source coding theorem (Theorem 7.2.3) and the data processing theorem (Theorem 1.2.1).

7.6 A source and channel are said to be *matched* to each other when the channel transition probabilities satisfy the conditions for achieving $R(D)$ of the source, and the source letter probabilities drive the channel at capacity. Here $R(D) = C$ where the time per source output is equal to the time per channel use. Show that when a source and channel are matched there is no need for any source and channel encoding to achieve ideal performance. Examine the equiprobable binary source with error distortion at fidelity D and the binary symmetric channel with crossover probability ϵ where $\epsilon = D$.

7.7 Consider the source encoder and decoder of Fig. 7.3. If fidelity D can be achieved with a code of rate $R > R(D)$, show that the entropy of the encoder output

$$H(\mathcal{M}) = \frac{1}{M} \sum_{m=1}^{M} P_m \ln \frac{1}{P_m}$$

where P_m is the probability of index $m \in \{1, 2, \ldots, M\}$, satisfies

$$R(D) \le H(\mathcal{U}) \le R$$

7.8 For an arbitrary DMC, show that the expurgated exponent $E_{\text{ex}}(R)$ satisfies

$$E_{\text{ex}}(R) \ge D$$

where $R = R(D)$ is given by (7.3.17). Also find the necessary and sufficient conditions for equality.

Hint: Examine Prob. 3.21 and show that

$$R(D_s) \ge R_L(D_s) = sD_s - \ln \gamma(s, \mathbf{q})$$

7.9 For a DMC, define the Bhattacharyya distance given by (7.3.16) and the natural rate distortion function given by (7.3.17). Then prove a generalized Gilbert bound for this distance measure, analogous to Theorem 7.3.3.

7.10 (Analysis of Tree Codes, Jelinek [1969]) Suppose we have a binary symmetric source with the error distortion measure. From (7.2.42), the rate distortion function is given by $R(D) = \ln 2 - \mathcal{H}(D)$ nats per source symbol where $0 \le D \le \frac{1}{2}$. We now consider encoding this source with a binary tree code of rate $R = (\ln 2)/n$ nats per source symbol where we assume $R > R(D)$. This tree code has n binary representation symbols on each branch. Let T_l be such a tree code that is terminated at l branches. Then for source sequence $\mathbf{u} \in \mathcal{U}_{nl}$, we define $d(\mathbf{u} \mid T_l)$ as the minimum normalized error distortion between $\mathbf{u}$ and paths in the terminated tree T_l. A larger terminated tree T_L where $L = ml$ can be constructed from many terminated trees of length l by attaching the base nodes of these trees to terminal nodes of other trees. We now consider an ensemble of terminated tree codes where all branch binary representation symbols are independent and equally likely to be "0" or "1".

(*a*) Taking the expectation over the tree code ensemble for any source output sequence **u**, show that

$$D^* = \lim_{l \to \infty} E\{d(\mathbf{u} \mid T_l)\}$$
$$= \lim_{m \to \infty} E\{d(\mathbf{u} \mid T_{ml})\}$$

exists and is independent of the source output sequence.

(*b*) Next, given any $\delta > 0$ and output sequence $\mathbf{u} \in \mathscr{U}_{nml}$, define $\mathbf{u} = (\mathbf{u}_1, \mathbf{u}_2, \ldots, \mathbf{u}_m)$ where $\mathbf{u}_i \in \mathscr{U}_{nl}$ for each $i = 1, 2, \ldots, m$ and variables z_0, z_1, z_2, z_m associated with code tree T_{ml} as follows:

$z_0 = 1$
$z_1 =$ number of paths with distortion $D + \delta$ or less from $\mathbf{u}_1$ over the first l branches
$z_2 =$ number of paths extending the z_1 paths above with distortion $D + \delta$ or less from $\mathbf{u}_2$ over the second l branches
$\vdots \qquad \vdots$
$z_m =$ number of paths extending the z_{m-1} paths above with distortion $D + \delta$ or less from $\mathbf{u}_m$ over the mth l branches

It follows from the branching process extinction theorem (Feller [1957]) that, over the tree code ensemble, $\Pr\{z_m > 0\}$ decreases monotonically with m and approaches a strictly positive limiting value,

$$\lim_{m \to \infty} \Pr\{z_m > 0\} > 0$$

provided $E\{z_1\} > 1$. Using Chernoff bounds (see App. 8A), show that

$$E\{z_1\} = 2^l \Pr\{d_l(\mathbf{u}, \mathbf{v}) \le D + \delta \mid \mathbf{u}\}$$
$$\ge 2^l(1 - 1/nl\delta^2)e^{-nl[R(D) - R'(D)\delta]}$$
$$= (1 - 1/l\delta^2)e^{nl[R - R(D) + R'(D)\delta]}$$

Hence for small δ such that $R > R(D) - R'(D)\delta$, we can find l large enough to have $E\{z_1\} > 1$.

(*c*) Assuming $E\{z_1\} > 1$ use the branching process extinction theorem in (*b*) to prove

$$\lim_{m \to \infty} \Pr\{d(\mathbf{u} \mid T_{ml}) \le D + \delta\} > 0$$

(*d*) From the definition of D^* given in (*a*), we can choose l large enough so that

$$D^* - \delta < E\{d(\mathbf{u} \mid T_l)\} < D^* + \delta$$

For such a choice of l show that

$$\lim_{m \to \infty} \Pr\{d(\mathbf{u} \mid T_{ml}) \le D^* - \delta\} = 0$$

Hint: For $\mathbf{u} = (\mathbf{u}_1, \mathbf{u}_2, \ldots, \mathbf{u}_m)$, note that

$$d(\mathbf{u} \mid T_{ml}) = \frac{1}{m} \sum_{i=1}^{m} d_l(\mathbf{u}_i, \mathbf{v}_i)$$

where $\mathbf{v} = (\mathbf{v}_1, \mathbf{v}_2, \ldots, \mathbf{v}_m)$ is the minimum distortion path sequence in T_{ml}. But for $i = 1, 2, \ldots, m$

$$d_l(\mathbf{u}_i, \mathbf{v}_i) \ge d(\mathbf{u}_i \mid T_l^i)$$

where T_l^i is the subtree of T_{ml} in which $\mathbf{v}_i$ belongs. Thus

$$\Pr\{d(\mathbf{u} \mid T_{ml}) \le D^* - \delta\} \le \Pr\left\{\frac{1}{m} \sum_{i=1}^{m} d_l(\mathbf{u}_i \mid T_l^i) \le D^* - \delta\right\}$$

(*e*) Note that we have from (*c*)

$$\lim_{m\to\infty} \Pr \{d(\mathbf{u} \mid T_{ml}) \leq D + \delta\} > 0$$

and from (*d*)

$$\lim_{m\to\infty} \Pr \{d(\mathbf{u} \mid T_{ml}) \leq D^* - \delta\} = 0$$

From this show that, for any $\epsilon > 0$, there exists a binary tree code of rate $R = (\ln 2)/n > R(D)$ such that the average distortion D^* satisfies

$$D^* \leq D + \epsilon$$

Here the average is taken over all source output sequences.

7.11 Consider the same source coding situation presented in Prob. 7.10 where we consider binary tree codes of rate $R = (\ln 2)/n$ nats per source symbol. For fixed source sequence $\mathbf{u} \in \mathscr{U}_{nl}$, we define over the tree code ensemble the probabilities

$$G(t \mid l) = \Pr \left\{d(\mathbf{u} \mid T_l) \geq \frac{t}{nl}\right\} \qquad \begin{array}{l} t = 0, 1, \ldots, nl \\ l = 0, 1, \ldots \end{array}$$

where

$$G(t \mid 0) = \begin{cases} 0 & t \neq 0 \\ 1 & t = 0 \end{cases}$$

Show that

$$G(t \mid l + 1) = \left[\sum_{k=0}^{n} \binom{n}{k} (\tfrac{1}{2})^n G(t - k \mid l)\right]^2$$

Numerical solutions to $G(t \mid l)$ show that for this symmetric source, tree codes also exhibit the doubly exponential behavior observed for block source coding of symmetric sources with balanced distortions (see Chap. 8).

7.12 Show that for continuous-amplitude memoryless sources if the condition on the distortion given by (7.5.1) is replaced by

$$\int_{-\infty}^{\infty} Q(u) d^\alpha(u, 0)\, du \leq d_0^\alpha \qquad \text{for } \alpha > 1$$

then the source coding theorem (Theorem 7.5.1) has the form for (7.5.24) given by

$$d(\mathscr{B}) \leq D + d_0\, e^{-[(\alpha-1)/\alpha]NE(R,\, D)}$$

7.13 Show that convexity of $R(D)$ implies that $R(D)$ is a continuous strictly decreasing function of D for $D_{\min} < D < D_{\max}$. Show that it further implies that if $\mathbf{P} \in \mathscr{P}_D$ yields $R(D) = I(\mathbf{P})$, then $D(\mathbf{P}) = D$.

7.14 Let $R(D)$ be the rate distortion function for a discrete memoryless source with distortion measure $\{d(u, v)\colon u \in \mathscr{U}, v \in \mathscr{V}\}$. Now consider another distortion measure defined as

$$\{\tilde{d}(u, v) = d(u, v) - \min_{v \in \mathscr{V}} d(u, v)\colon u \in \mathscr{U}, v \in \mathscr{V}\}$$

and let $\tilde{R}(D)$ be the corresponding rate distortion function. Show that

$$\tilde{R}(D) = R(D + D_{\min})$$

where

$$D_{\min} = \sum_u Q(u) \min_{v \in \mathscr{V}} d(u, v)$$

7.15 Consider a source alphabet $\mathcal{U} = \{0, 1\}$ with probability $Q(0) = Q(1) = \frac{1}{2}$. Let the representation alphabet be $\mathcal{V} = \{0, 1, 2\}$ and the distortion defined as

$$d(0, v) = \begin{cases} 0 & v = 0 \\ 1 & v = 1 \\ \alpha & v = 2 \end{cases}$$

$$d(1, v) = \begin{cases} 1 & v = 0 \\ 0 & v = 1 \\ \alpha & v = 2 \end{cases}$$

where $\alpha < \frac{1}{2}$. Sketch $R(D)$ for this case. For $\alpha \geq \frac{1}{2}$, show that $R(D) = \ln 2 - \mathscr{H}(D)$.

7.16 Suppose $\mathcal{U} = \mathcal{V}$ and $d(u, v) = 1 - \delta_{uv}$. For

$$0 \leq D \leq (A - 1) \min_u Q(u)$$

show that

$$R(D) = H(\mathcal{U}) - \mathscr{H}(D) - D \ln (A - 1)$$

7.17 (Gallager [1968]) Consider a discrete memoryless source with four equiprobable outputs from $\mathcal{U} = \{1, 2, 3, 4\}$. Let $\mathcal{V} = \{1, 2, 3, 4, 5, 6, 7\}$, and distortion be given by

$$d(u, v) = \begin{cases} 0 & u = v \\ 1 & u = 1 \text{ or } 2 \text{ and } v = 5 \\ 1 & u = 3 \text{ or } 4 \text{ and } v = 6 \\ 3 & v = 7 \\ \infty & \text{otherwise} \end{cases}$$

Show that the rate distortion function is given as shown:

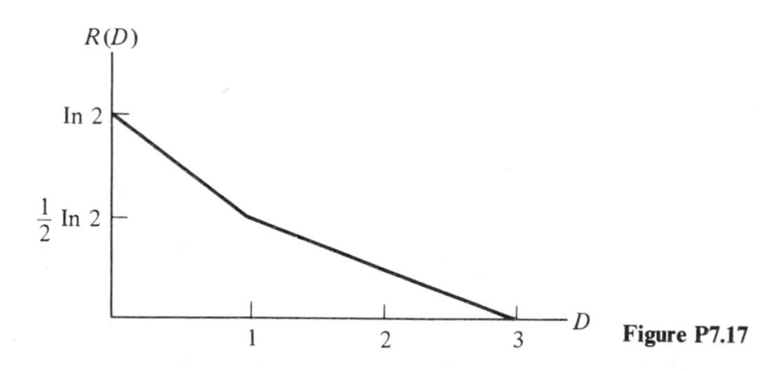

Figure P7.17

Note: With infinite distortion measure the source coding theorem still holds if there is a $v^* \in \mathcal{V}$ such that $\sum_u Q(u)\, d(u, v^*) < \infty$ ($v^* = 7$ in this example). (For further results concerning infinite distortion measures, see Gallager [1968]. Also note the discussion following Theorem 7.5.2.)

7.18 For parameter $s \leq 0$, show that if a probability density $\{P_s(v)\colon -\infty < v < \infty\}$ satisfies (7.7.46), then Shannon's lower bound is tight. That is, $R(D_s) = R_{LB}(D_s)$.

7.19 For memoryless sources the Shannon lower bound, $R_{LB}(D)$, is given by Theorem 7.7.4.

(*a*) Show that the maximizing value of $s \leq 0$ in the definition of $R_{LB}(D)$ satisfies

$$\int d(z) G_s(z)\, dz = D$$

where

$$G_s(z) = \frac{e^{sd(z)}}{\int e^{sd(\alpha)}\, d\alpha}$$

(*b*) Next let $\mathscr{G}_D$ be the set of all probability densities for which

$$\int d(z)G(z)\,dz \le D$$

and use variational calculus to show that

$$R_{LB}(D) = h(\mathscr{U}) - \max_{G \in \mathscr{G}_D} h(G)$$

7.20 (Berger [1971].) In Prob. 7.19, let $d(u, v) = |u - v|$.
(*a*) Show that

$$G_s(z) = \frac{|z|}{2} e^{s|z|}$$

$$D = \frac{1}{|s|}$$

$$R_{LB}(D) = h(\mathscr{U}) - \ln(2eD)$$

(*b*) For $R(D) = R_{LB}(D)$, $\{P(v): -\infty < v < \infty\}$ must satisfy (7.7.46) (see Prob. 7.18). Show that then $P(v)$ must satisfy

$$P(v) = Q(v) - D^2 Q''(v) \qquad -\infty < v < \infty$$

(*c*) Apply (*b*) to a source with

$$Q(u) = \frac{\alpha}{2} e^{-\alpha|u|} \qquad -\infty < u < \infty$$

and show that

$$R(D) = R_{LB}(D) = -\ln(\alpha D) \qquad 0 \le D \le \frac{1}{\alpha}$$

(*d*) Apply (*b*) to a source with

$$Q(u) = \frac{2}{\pi}(1 + u^2)^{-2} \qquad -\infty < u < \infty$$

and show that

$$R(D) = R_{LB}(D) = \ln\left(\frac{4\pi}{D}\right) - 3 \qquad 0 \le D \le \frac{1}{\sqrt{6}}$$

7.21 (Berger [1971].) For a memoryless Gaussian source and a difference distortion measure other than $d(u, v) = (u - v)^2$, show that the Shannon lower bound is never exact. That is, $R(D) > R_{LB}(D)$ for all D. Note the example of $d(u, v) = |u - v|$ in Sec. 7.7.

Hint: Use Cramer's theorem.

7.22 (Linkov [1965] and Pinkston [1966].) For a memoryless Gaussian source, find $R_{LB}(D)$ for $d(u, v) = |u - v|^\alpha$. Check your results by specializing to $\alpha = 1$ and $\alpha = 2$.

7.23 Generalize the lower bound in Lemma 7.6.4 to continuous-amplitude memoryless sources. Then show that this becomes the Shannon lower bound when $d(u, v)$ is a difference distortion measure.

7.24 Using the calculus of variations (see Courant and Hilbert [1953], chap. 4), prove Theorem 7.7.1.

7.25 (Countably Infinite Size Alphabet) Discrete memoryless sources with a countably infinite size alphabet and unbound distortion measures have coding theorems that are given by Theorem 7.5.1 and Theorem 7.5.3, where $R(D)$ is given by (7.5.23) with integrals replaced by summations.

(*a*) For a discrete memoryless source with a countably infinite alphabet of integers $\mathcal{I} = \{0, 1, 2, \dots\}$ and the magnitude distortion measure, $d(u, v) = |u - v|$, show that $R(D) \geq R_{LB}(D)$ where $R_{LB}(D)$ is given parametrically by

$$R_{LB}(D_s) = H(\mathcal{U}) + sD_s - \ln(1 + e^s) + (1 - Q(0)) \ln(1 - e^s)$$

and

$$D_s = \frac{e^s}{1 + e^s} + (1 - Q(0)) \frac{e^s}{1 - e^s}$$

for $s < 0$.

Hint: Choose $\lambda(u)$ as follows (See Tan and Yao [1975].):

$$\lambda(0) = \frac{1}{Q(0)} \left(\frac{1}{1 + e^s} \right)$$

$$\lambda(u) = \frac{1}{Q(u)} \left(\frac{1}{1 + e^s} \right) \qquad u \geq 1$$

(*b*) Show that necessary and sufficient conditions for $R(D) = R_{LB}(D)$ in (*a*) is that there exists a probability distribution $\{P(v)\}$ that satisfies

$$\sum_{v=0}^{\infty} P(v) e^{s|u-v|} = \begin{cases} (1 + e^s) Q(0) & u = 0 \\ \dfrac{1 + e^s}{1 - e^s} Q(u) & u \geq 1 \end{cases}$$

7.26 In Prob. 7.25, let the source have a Poisson distribution

$$Q(u) = \frac{\lambda^u}{u!} e^{-\lambda} \qquad \lambda > 0, \; u = 0, 1, 2, \dots$$

Show that $R(D) > R_{LB}(D)$, for all $0 < D < D_{\max}$.

7.27 In Prob. 7.25, let the source have a geometric distribution

$$Q(u) = (1 - \theta)^u \qquad 0 < \theta < 1, \; u = 0, 1, 2, \dots$$

For this case show that $R(D) = R_{LB}(D)$ for all $0 < D < D_c$ where

$$D_c = \frac{e^{s_c}}{1 + e^{s_c}} + (1 - \theta) \frac{e^{s_c}}{1 - e^{s_c}}$$

and s_c is given by

$$e^{s_c} = \begin{cases} \dfrac{1}{2 - \theta} & \text{if } \theta^4 - 4\theta^3 + 4\theta^2 + 4\theta - 4 < 0 \\ \dfrac{(1 - \theta)^2 + 1}{2(2 - \theta)} - \left\{ \left[\dfrac{(1 - \theta)^2 + 1}{2(2 - \theta)} \right]^2 - \dfrac{1 - \theta}{2 - \theta} \right\}^{1/2} & \text{otherwise.} \end{cases}$$

(See Tan and Yao [1975].)

7.28 (Shannon's First Theorem Revisited, Gallager [1976].) Consider a DMS with alphabet $\mathcal{U}$ and probability distribution $Q(u)$, $u \in \mathcal{U}$. We encode each sequence $\mathbf{u} \in \mathcal{U}_N$ of length N by an index $f(\mathbf{u}) = m \in \{1, 2, \dots, M\}$ where $M = e^{RN}$. The index m is sent over a noiseless channel to a source decoder that estimates the sequence by

$$\hat{\mathbf{u}} = \max_{f(\tilde{\mathbf{u}}) = m}^{-1} Q_N(\tilde{\mathbf{u}})$$

That is, $\hat{\mathbf{u}}$ is chosen among all $\tilde{\mathbf{u}}$ which satisfies $f(\tilde{\mathbf{u}}) = m$ and maximizes $Q_N(\tilde{\mathbf{u}})$, the probability of the sequence $\tilde{\mathbf{u}}$. We want to show that there exist encoders [described by $f(\mathbf{u}) = m$] such that

$$\lim_{N \to \infty} \Pr\{\hat{\mathbf{u}} \neq \mathbf{u}\} = 0$$

as long as $R > H(\mathscr{U})$, the entropy of the source. This system is shown below.

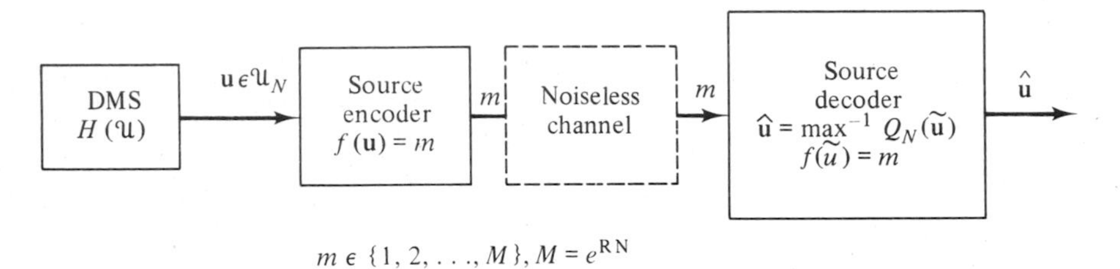

Figure P7.28

(*a*) Define the functions

$$\psi(\mathbf{u}, \tilde{\mathbf{u}} \mid \mathbf{f}) = \begin{cases} 1 & f(\mathbf{u}) = f(\tilde{\mathbf{u}}) \\ 0 & f(\mathbf{u}) \neq f(\tilde{\mathbf{u}}) \end{cases}$$

$$\Phi(\mathbf{u}, \mathbf{u} \mid \mathbf{Q}) = \begin{cases} 1 & Q_N(\tilde{\mathbf{u}}) \geq Q_N(\mathbf{u}) \\ 0 & Q_N(\tilde{\mathbf{u}}) < Q_N(\mathbf{u}) \end{cases}$$

Show that for any $0 \leq \rho \leq 1$

$$\Pr\{\hat{\mathbf{u}} \neq \mathbf{u}\} \leq \sum_{\mathbf{u}} Q_N(\mathbf{u}) \left[\sum_{\tilde{\mathbf{u}} \neq \mathbf{u}} \psi(\mathbf{u}, \tilde{\mathbf{u}} \mid \mathbf{f}) \Phi(\mathbf{u}, \tilde{\mathbf{u}} \mid \mathbf{Q}) \right]^{\rho}$$

(*b*) Next, show that for any $0 \leq \rho \leq 1$

$$\Pr\{\hat{\mathbf{u}} \neq \mathbf{u}\} \leq \sum_{\mathbf{u}} Q_N(\mathbf{u})^{1/(1+\rho)} \left[\sum_{\tilde{\mathbf{u}} \neq \mathbf{u}} \psi(\mathbf{u}, \tilde{\mathbf{u}} \mid \mathbf{f}) Q_N(\mathbf{u})^{1/(1+\rho)} \right]^{\rho}$$

(*c*) Randomly choose a source encoder function **f** such that over the ensemble of encoder functions for any $\mathbf{u} \neq \tilde{\mathbf{u}}$ and any m, $\tilde{m}$ we have

$$\Pr\{f(\mathbf{u}) = m, f(\tilde{\mathbf{u}}) = \tilde{m} \mid \mathbf{u}, \tilde{\mathbf{u}}\} = \Pr\{f(\mathbf{u}) = m \mid \mathbf{u}\} \Pr\{f(\tilde{\mathbf{u}}) = \tilde{m} \mid \tilde{\mathbf{u}}\}$$

$$= \frac{1}{M^2}$$

Averaging $\Pr\{\hat{\mathbf{u}} \neq \mathbf{u}\}$ over the ensemble of encoders, show that

$$\overline{\Pr\{\mathbf{u} \neq \mathbf{u}\}} \leq M^{-\rho} \left[\sum_{\mathbf{x}} Q_N(\mathbf{x})^{1/(1+\rho)} \right]^{1+\rho} \qquad 0 \leq \rho \leq 1$$

(*d*) Prove the source coding theorem from above by showing that for any N there exists an encoder and decoder such that

$$\Pr\{\hat{\mathbf{u}} \neq \mathbf{u}\} \leq e^{-NE_s(R)}$$

where $E_s(R) > 0$ for $R > H(\mathscr{U})$.

7.29 (Slepian and Wolf Extension to Side Information.) Suppose in Prob. 7.28 only the source decoder has additional side information $\mathbf{v} \in \mathscr{V}_N$ such that when the source sequence is $\mathbf{u} \in \mathscr{U}_N$ then the source decoder receives index m from the channel as well as $\mathbf{v}$. Here $\mathbf{u}$, $\mathbf{v}$ have joint distribution

$$Q_N(\mathbf{u}, \mathbf{v}) = \prod_{n=1}^{N} Q(u_n, v_n)$$

The source decoder chooses $\hat{\mathbf{u}}$ where

$$\hat{\mathbf{u}} = \max_{f(\tilde{\mathbf{u}})=m}{}^{-1} Q_N(\tilde{\mathbf{u}} \mid \mathbf{v})$$

Prove the generalization of Prob. 7.28 for this side information at the decoder situation, by showing that for any N there exist encoders and decoders such that

$$\Pr\{\hat{\mathbf{u}} \neq \mathbf{u}\} \leq e^{-NE_s(R)}$$

where $E_s(R) > 0$ for $R > H(\mathscr{U} \mid \mathscr{V})$.

7.30 (Joint Source and Channel Coding Theorem, Gallager [1968].)

(*a*) Let $p_N(\mathbf{v} \mid \mathbf{x})$ be the transition probability assignment for sequences of length N on a discrete channel, and consider an ensemble of codes, in which M codewords are independently chosen, each with a probability assignment $q_N(\mathbf{x})$. Let the messages encoded into these codewords have a probability assignment Q_m, $1 \leq m \leq M$, and consider a maximum a posteriori probability decoder, which, given $\mathbf{y}$, chooses the m that maximizes $Q_m p_N(\mathbf{y} \mid \mathbf{x}_m)$. Let

$$\bar{P}_e = \sum_m Q_m \bar{P}_{e,m}$$

be the average error probability over this ensemble of messages and codes, and by modifying the proof of (3.1.14) where necessary, show that

$$\bar{P}_e \leq \left[\sum_{m=1}^{M} Q_m^{1/(1+\rho)}\right]^{1+\rho} \sum_{\mathbf{y}} \left[\sum_{\mathbf{x}} q_N(\mathbf{x}) p_N(\mathbf{y} \mid \mathbf{x})^{1/(1+\rho)}\right]^{1+\rho}$$

(*b*) Let the channel be memoryless with transition probabilities $p(y \mid x)$, let the letters of the codewords be independently chosen with probability assignment $q(x)$, and let the messages be sequences of length L from a discrete memoryless source $\mathscr{U}$ with probability assignment $Q(i)$, $1 \leq i \leq A$. Show that

$$\bar{P}_e \leq e^{-NE_o(\rho, \mathbf{q}) + LE_s(\rho)}$$

$$E_s(\rho) = (1 + \rho) \ln \left[\sum_{i=1}^{A} Q(i)^{1/(1+\rho)}\right]$$

(*c*) Show that $E_s(0) = 0$, that

$$\left.\frac{\partial E_s(\rho)}{\partial \rho}\right|_{\rho=0} = H(\mathscr{U})$$

and that $E_s(\rho)$ is strictly increasing in ρ [if no $Q(i) = 1$].

(*d*) Let $\lambda = L/N$, and let $N \to \infty$ with λ fixed. Show that $\bar{P}_e \to 0$ if $\lambda H(\mathscr{U}) < C$ where C is the channel capacity.

CHAPTER

EIGHT

RATE DISTORTION THEORY: MEMORY, GAUSSIAN SOURCES, AND UNIVERSAL CODING

8.1 MEMORYLESS VECTOR SOURCES

Chapter 7 presented the rate distortion theory for memoryless sources that emit discrete or continuous random variables. For these sources, an output occurs once every T_s seconds, and the sequence of outputs are independent random variables with identical probability distributions. We can extend these results to memoryless sources with outputs that belong to more abstract alphabets. For example, the output of the memoryless source may be a random vector, a continuous-time random process, or a random field. By generalizing in this manner, we can extend the theory to more general sources with memory.

Consider a memoryless source that outputs every T_s seconds a random vector of dimension L denoted by x. Here

$$x = (u^{(1)}, u^{(2)}, \ldots, u^{(L)}) \tag{8.1.1}$$

where[1]

$$u^{(l)} \in \mathcal{U} = \{a_1, a_2, \ldots a_A\} \qquad l = 1, 2, \ldots, L$$

[1] We can equally allow each component to belong to a different alphabet. Although x is a vector, we regard it as a letter from some abstract alphabet $\mathcal{X} = \mathcal{U}_L$.

Denote the alphabet for all such vectors by $\mathscr{X} = \mathscr{U}_L$ and assume that the probability distribution for $x \in \mathscr{X}$ is given by $Q(x)$ where $x \in \mathscr{X}$. Note that the components of x are not necessarily independent. We represent the L-dimensional vector source outputs by vectors

$$y = (v^{(1)}, v^{(2)}, \ldots, v^{(L)}) \tag{8.1.2}$$

belonging to the alphabet $\mathscr{Y} = \mathscr{V}_L$ where $\mathscr{V} = \{b_1, b_2, \ldots, b_B\}$. Throughout this discussion, assume that for each source–user pair of vectors $x \in \mathscr{U}_L$ and $y \in \mathscr{V}_L$, we have a bounded distortion defined by the set of L distortion measures

$$d^{(l)}(u, v) \leq d_0^{(l)} < \infty \qquad \text{for all } u \in \mathscr{U}, v \in \mathscr{V}, l = 1, 2, \ldots, L \tag{8.1.3}$$

The memoryless source that emits a vector of dimension L every T_s seconds can be viewed as L memoryless sources with outputs every T_s seconds that are not necessarily independent of each other. This description is shown in Fig. 8.1, where we assume that only one noiseless channel is available. From this viewpoint, we have L users who seek an estimate of the corresponding L source outputs, and each source–user pair has a distortion measure given by (8.1.3).

Although a single-letter distortion measure is given for each source–user component pair, there is no overall fidelity criterion for evaluating or designing a source encoder–decoder system. A vector distortion measure consisting of the L single-letter distortion measures, for example, is inadequate because two systems yielding two average vector distortions generally cannot be compared, since vectors, unlike real numbers, cannot be completely ordered. Therefore, we require some overall real-valued distortion measure to proceed further in our analysis. Next, we consider two such distortion measures.

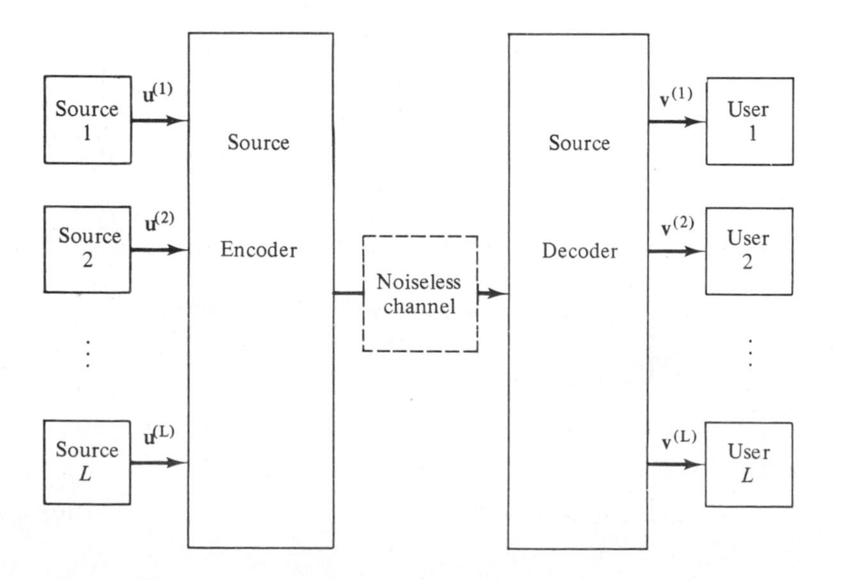

Figure 8.1 Multiple source–user system.

8.1.1 Sum Distortion Measure

A natural choice for a single real-valued distortion measure is the sum distortion measure between $x \in \mathscr{X}$ and $y \in \mathscr{Y}$ defined by

$$\gamma(x, y) = \sum_{l=1}^{L} d^{(l)}(u^{(l)}, v^{(l)}) \tag{8.1.4}$$

where

$$\begin{aligned} x &= (u^{(1)}, u^{(2)}, \ldots, u^{(L)}) \\ y &= (v^{(1)}, v^{(2)}, \ldots, v^{(L)}) \end{aligned} \tag{8.1.5}$$

For sequences of N successive terms $\mathbf{x} \in \mathscr{X}_N$ and $\mathbf{y} \in \mathscr{Y}_N$ the obvious generalization is

$$\begin{aligned} \gamma_N(\mathbf{x}, \mathbf{y}) &= \frac{1}{N} \sum_{n=1}^{N} \gamma(x_n, y_n) \\ &= \sum_{l=1}^{L} d_N^{(l)}(\mathbf{u}^{(l)}, \mathbf{v}^{(l)}) \end{aligned} \tag{8.1.6}$$

where

$$d_N^{(l)}(\mathbf{u}^{(l)}, \mathbf{v}^{(l)}) = \frac{1}{N} \sum_{n=1}^{N} d^{(l)}(u_n^{(l)}, v_n^{(l)}) \qquad l = 1, 2, \ldots, L \tag{8.1.7}$$

Since $d^{(l)}(u, v) \leq d_0^{(l)} < \infty$ for all l we have

$$\gamma(x, y) \leq \gamma_0 \equiv \sum_{l=1}^{L} d_0^{(l)} < \infty$$

Hence, for the sum distortion measure defined above, we have reduced the problem to a single discrete memoryless source with alphabet $\mathscr{X}$, probability $Q(\cdot)$, representation alphabet $\mathscr{Y}$, and a bounded single-letter distortion measure $\gamma(x, y)$. The coding theorems of Sec. 7.2 apply directly and the rate distortion function is given by [see (7.2.53)]

$$R(D) = \min_{\mathbf{P} \in \mathscr{P}_D} I(\mathbf{P}) \tag{8.1.8}$$

where

$$\mathscr{P}_D = \left\{ P(y \mid x) \colon \sum_x \sum_y Q(x) P(y \mid x) \gamma(x, y) \leq D \right\} \tag{8.1.9}$$

From Theorem 7.6.1, necessary and sufficient conditions for $\mathbf{P} \in \mathscr{P}_D$ to achieve $R(D) = I(\mathbf{P})$ are given by

$$P(y \mid x) = \lambda(x) P(y) e^{s\gamma(x, y)} \qquad \text{if } P(y) > 0 \tag{8.1.10}$$

and

$$\sum_x \lambda(x) Q(x) e^{s\gamma(x, y)} \leq 1 \qquad \text{if } P(y) = 0 \tag{8.1.11}$$

where

$$\lambda(x) = \left(\sum_y P(y)e^{s\gamma(x,\, y)}\right)^{-1} \qquad x \in \mathcal{X} \tag{8.1.12}$$

and $s \leq 0$ satisfies the parametric equations for $R(D)$

$$D = \sum_x \sum_y \lambda(x)Q(x)P(y)e^{s\gamma(x,\, y)}\gamma(x, y) \tag{8.1.13}$$

and

$$R(D) = sD + \sum_x Q(x) \ln \lambda(x) \tag{8.1.14}$$

Note that the components of each x are not necessarily independent, although the successive vectors $x_1, x_2, \ldots, x_N$ are mutually independent. A special case of interest is when the L components of the source output vectors are independent of each other, so that in the description of Fig. 8.1, we have L independent memoryless sources.

Lemma 8.1.1: Independent components—sum distortion measure For independent components and the sum distortion measure, the rate distortion function is given parametrically by

$$D_s = \sum_{l=1}^{L} D_s^{(l)} \tag{8.1.15}$$

and

$$R(D_s) = \sum_{l=1}^{L} R^{(l)}(D_s^{(l)}) \tag{8.1.16}$$

where $R^{(l)}(D_s^{(l)})$ is the rate distortion function for the lth component with the lth distortion measure, and is given parametrically by the same parameter $s \leq 0$ for all $l = 1, 2, \ldots, L$.

PROOF Let $\{Q^{(l)}(u): u \in \mathcal{U}\}$ be the lth source output component probability distribution. Recall that the distortion measure for this component is given by $d^{(l)}(u, v)$. (We can regard each component as an output of some discrete memoryless source.) Suppose the conditional probability $P^{(l)}(v \mid u)$ achieves the rate distortion function of the lth component sequence for parameter $s \leq 0$ and thus satisfies

$$P^{(l)}(v \mid u) = \lambda^{(l)}(u)P^{(l)}(v)e^{sd^{(l)}(u,\, v)} \qquad \text{if } P^{(l)}(v) > 0 \tag{8.1.17}$$

and

$$\sum_u \lambda^{(l)}(u)Q^{(l)}(u)e^{sd^{(l)}(u,\, v)} \leq 1 \qquad \text{if } P^{(l)}(v) = 0 \tag{8.1.18}$$

where

$$\lambda^{(l)}(u) = \left[\sum_v P^{(l)}(v)e^{sd^{(l)}(u,\, v)}\right]^{-1} \qquad u \in \mathcal{U} \tag{8.1.19}$$

and that it also satisfies the parametric equations

$$D_s^{(l)} = \sum_u \sum_v \lambda^{(l)}(u)Q^{(l)}(u)P^{(l)}(v)e^{sd^{(l)}(u,\,v)}d^{(l)}(u, v) \tag{8.1.20}$$

and

$$R^{(l)}(D_s^{(l)}) = sD_s^{(l)} + \sum_u Q^{(l)}(u) \ln \lambda^{(l)}(u) \tag{8.1.21}$$

Since the sources are independent, we have

$$Q(x) = \prod_{l=1}^{L} Q^{(l)}(u^{(l)}) \tag{8.1.22}$$

Defining

$$P(y \mid x) = \prod_{l=1}^{L} P^{(l)}(v^{(l)} \mid u^{(l)}) \tag{8.1.23}$$

and

$$\lambda(x) = \prod_{l=1}^{L} \lambda^{(l)}(u^{(l)}) \tag{8.1.24}$$

we see that this choice of $\{P(y|x): y \in \mathscr{Y}, x \in \mathscr{X}\}$ and $\{\lambda(x): x \in \mathscr{X}\}$ satisfy the necessary and sufficient conditions of (8.1.10) to (8.1.14), giving the desired result.

One expects that when the L source output components are not independent, then the rate distortion function is upper-bounded by the corresponding rate distortion function when we assume the components are independent. We show this next.

Theorem 8.1.1 For the sum distortion measure, the rate distortion function $R(D)$ is bounded by $\hat{R}(D)$, the rate distortion function obtained if the source output components are independent with the same marginal probability distributions. That is,

$$R(D) \le \hat{R}(D) \tag{8.1.25}$$

where $\hat{R}(D)$ is given by (8.1.15) and (8.1.16).

PROOF Recall that for any $\mathbf{P} \in \mathscr{P}_D$

$$R(D) \le I(\mathbf{P}) \tag{8.1.26}$$

But from Lemma 1.2.1

$$\begin{aligned} I(\mathbf{P}) &= \sum_x \sum_y Q(x)P(y \mid x) \ln \frac{P(y \mid x)}{P(y)} \\ &\le \sum_x \sum_y Q(x)P(y \mid x) \ln \frac{P(y \mid x)}{\hat{P}(y)} \end{aligned} \tag{8.1.27}$$

for any probability distribution $\hat{P}(y)$. Choose

$$\hat{P}(y) = \prod_{l=1}^{L} P^{(l)}(v^{(l)}) \tag{8.1.28}$$

and

$$P(y \mid x) = \prod_{l=1}^{L} P^{(l)}(v^{(l)} \mid u^{(l)}) \tag{8.1.29}$$

where $\{P^{(l)}(\,\cdot\,)\}$ and $\{P^{(l)}(\,\cdot \mid \cdot\,)\}$ correspond to $\mathbf{P} \in \mathscr{P}_{D_s^{(l)}}$ that achieves $R^{(l)}(D_s^{(l)})$ for each $l = 1, 2, \ldots, L$. Then

$$\begin{aligned} I(\mathbf{P}) &\le \sum_x \sum_y Q(x)P(y \mid x) \ln \prod_{l=1}^{L} \frac{P^{(l)}(v^{(l)} \mid u^{(l)})}{P^{(l)}(v^{(l)})} \\ &= \sum_{l=1}^{L} \sum_u \sum_v Q^{(l)}(u)P^{(l)}(v \mid u) \ln \frac{P^{(l)}(v \mid u)}{P^{(l)}(v)} \\ &= \sum_{l=1}^{L} I(\mathbf{P}^{(l)}) \\ &= \sum_{l=1}^{L} R^{(l)}(D^{(l)}) \end{aligned} \tag{8.1.30}$$

These theorems also hold for continuous-amplitude random vectors under the bounded variance condition on the distortion measures of each of the L source–user component pairs. The memoryless source with vector outputs, together with the above sum distortion measure, is a very useful model in understanding the problem of encoding sources with memory. We will return to the above results when we discuss both discrete-time and continuous-time sources with memory.

Example (Gaussian vector sources, squared error distortion) Suppose we have a memoryless source that emits every T_s seconds a vector with L independent zero-mean Gaussian components where

$$\int_{-\infty}^{\infty} u^2 Q^{(l)}(u)\, du = \sigma_l^2 \qquad l = 1, 2, \ldots, L \tag{8.1.31}$$

Also let $d^{(l)}(u, v) = (u - v)^2$ for $l = 1, 2, \ldots, L$. For the lth source–user component pair (see Sec. 7.7), we have the rate distortion function

$$R^{(l)}(D_s^{(l)}) = \begin{cases} \frac{1}{2} \ln \dfrac{\sigma_l^2}{D_s^{(l)}} & 0 \le D_s^{(l)} \le \sigma_l^2 \\ 0 & \sigma_l^2 < D_s^{(l)} \end{cases} \tag{8.1.32}$$

with slope (Lemma 7.7.1)

$$s = \frac{d}{dD_s^{(l)}} R^{(l)}(D_s^{(l)}) = \begin{cases} -\dfrac{1}{2D_s^{(l)}} & 0 \le D_s^{(l)} \le \sigma_l^2 \\ 0 & \sigma_l^2 < D_s^{(l)} \end{cases} \tag{8.1.33}$$

for $l = 1, 2, \ldots, L$. Hence for common parameter s, for each component

$$D_s^{(l)} = \begin{cases} -\dfrac{1}{2s} & -\infty < s \le -\dfrac{1}{2\sigma_l^2} \\ \sigma_l^2 & -\dfrac{1}{2\sigma_l^2} < s \le 0 \end{cases} \tag{8.1.34}$$

or

$$D_s^{(l)} = \min(\theta, \sigma_l^2) \tag{8.1.35}$$

where

$$\theta = -\frac{1}{2s} \ge 0 \tag{8.1.36}$$

For the sum distortion measure, the rate distortion function is thus given in terms of parameter θ as

$$D_\theta = \sum_{l=1}^{L} \min(\theta, \sigma_l^2) \tag{8.1.37}$$

and

$$R(D_\theta) = \sum_{l=1}^{L} \max\left(0, \tfrac{1}{2} \ln \frac{\sigma_l^2}{\theta}\right) \tag{8.1.38}$$

For small distortions $D < \min\{\sigma_1^2, \sigma_2^2, \ldots, \sigma_L^2\}$, this becomes

$$R(D) = \tfrac{1}{2} \ln\left(\prod_{l=1}^{L} \frac{\sigma_l^2}{D}\right) \tag{8.1.39}$$

8.1.2 Maximum Distortion Measure

For the memoryless source with vector outputs, where there is a set of L source–user component distortion measures (8.1.3), another natural choice for a single real-valued distortion measure for sequences of length N is to define the distortion between $\mathbf{x} \in \mathscr{X}_N$ and $\mathbf{y} \in \mathscr{Y}_N$ as

$$\begin{aligned} \gamma_N(\mathbf{x}, \mathbf{y}) &= \max_l \{d_N^{(l)}(\mathbf{u}^{(l)}, \mathbf{v}^{(l)}) - \theta_l\} \\ &= \max_l \left\{\frac{1}{N} \sum_{n=1}^{N} d^{(l)}(u_n^{(l)}, v_n^{(l)}) - \theta_l\right\} \end{aligned} \tag{8.1.40}$$

where $\theta_1, \theta_2, \ldots, \theta_L$ is a set of nonnegative real numbers. Recall that for each $n = 1, 2, \ldots, N$

$$\begin{aligned} x_n &= (u_n^{(1)}, u_n^{(2)}, \ldots, u_n^{(L)}) \\ y_n &= (v_n^{(1)}, v_n^{(2)}, \ldots, v_n^{(L)}) \end{aligned} \tag{8.1.41}$$

This distortion measure is essentially the maximum of the L distortions of the source–user pairs. The bias parameters $\{\theta_l\}$ allow for control of the amount of distortion of each source–user pair. Since we attempt to minimize distortion $\gamma_N(\mathbf{x}, \mathbf{y})$, this can be viewed as a *minimax approach.* Note that although the source is memoryless, the above distortion is no longer a single letter distortion measure.

That is

$$\gamma_N(\mathbf{x}, \mathbf{y}) \neq \frac{1}{N} \sum_{n=1}^{N} \gamma_1(x_n, y_n) \tag{8.1.42}$$

Hence it appears that the coding theorem of Sec. 7.2 will no longer apply. However, with only slight modifications, the earlier coding-theorem proofs can be applied to this maximum distortion measure.

For a code $\mathscr{B} = \{\mathbf{y}_1, \mathbf{y}_2, \ldots, \mathbf{y}_M\}$ of block length N and rate $R = (\ln M)/N$ nats per source symbol, the average distortion is

$$\begin{aligned}\gamma(\mathscr{B}) &= \sum_{\mathbf{x}} Q_N(\mathbf{x})\gamma(\mathbf{x} \mid \mathscr{B}) \\ &= \sum_{\mathbf{x}} Q_N(\mathbf{x}) \min_{\mathbf{y} \in \mathscr{B}} \gamma_N(\mathbf{x}, \mathbf{y})\end{aligned} \tag{8.1.43}$$

Now for any conditional probability distribution $\{P(y \mid x): y \in \mathscr{Y}, x \in \mathscr{X}\}$, consider a code ensemble where all codeword components are selected independently according to $\{P(y): y \in \mathscr{Y}\}$ where

$$P(y) = \sum_{x} Q(x)P(y \mid x) \qquad y \in \mathscr{Y} \tag{8.1.44}$$

Then following Sec. 7.2 leading to (7.2.30), we find that the code-ensemble average of $\gamma(\mathscr{B})$ is bounded by

$$\overline{\gamma(\mathscr{B})} \leq \gamma_N(\mathbf{P}) + \gamma_0 e^{-NE(R, \mathbf{P})} \tag{8.1.45}$$

where

$$\begin{aligned}\gamma_N(\mathbf{P}) &= \sum_{\mathbf{x}} \sum_{\mathbf{y}} Q_N(\mathbf{x})P_N(\mathbf{y} \mid \mathbf{x})\gamma_N(\mathbf{x}, \mathbf{y}) \\ &= \sum_{\mathbf{x}} \sum_{\mathbf{y}} Q_N(\mathbf{x})P_N(\mathbf{y} \mid \mathbf{x}) \max_{l} \{d_N^{(l)}(\mathbf{u}^{(l)}, \mathbf{v}^{(l)}) - \theta_l\}\end{aligned} \tag{8.1.46}$$

and where

$$\gamma_0 = \sum_{l=1}^{L} d_0^{(l)} \tag{8.1.47}$$

$$E(R, \mathbf{P}) = \max_{-1 \leq \rho \leq 0} E(R; \rho, \mathbf{P}) \tag{8.1.48}$$

$$E(R; \rho, \mathbf{P}) = -\rho R + E_o(\rho, \mathbf{P}) \tag{8.1.49}$$

$$E_o(\rho, \mathbf{P}) = -\ln \sum_{x} \left[\sum_{y} P(y)Q(x \mid y)^{1/(1+\rho)}\right]^{1+\rho} \tag{8.1.50}$$

and

$$Q(x \mid y) = \frac{P(y \mid x)Q(x)}{P(y)} \tag{8.1.51}$$

The only change from the form in (7.2.30) is the term $\gamma_N(\mathbf{P})$ which is bounded further by defining sets

$$\mathscr{A}_l = \{(\mathbf{x}, \mathbf{y}): d_N^{(l)}(\mathbf{u}^{(l)}, \mathbf{v}^{(l)}) - \theta_l > 0\} \qquad l = 1, 2, \ldots, L \tag{8.1.52}$$

and the union

$$\mathscr{A} = \bigcup_{l=1}^{L} \mathscr{A}_l = \left\{(\mathbf{x}, \mathbf{y}): \max_l \{d_N^{(l)}(\mathbf{u}^{(l)}, \mathbf{v}^{(l)}) - \theta_l\} > 0\right\} \tag{8.1.53}$$

Then, restricting the sum to $\mathscr{A}$ and using the union-of-events bound, we have

$$\begin{aligned}
\gamma_N(\mathbf{P}) &\le \sum_{(\mathbf{x},\mathbf{y}) \in \mathscr{A}}\sum Q_N(\mathbf{x})P_N(\mathbf{y}\,|\,\mathbf{x}) \max_l \{d_N^{(l)}(\mathbf{u}^{(l)}, \mathbf{v}^{(l)}) - \theta_l\} \\
&\le \max_l d_0^{(l)} \sum_{(\mathbf{x},\mathbf{y}) \in \mathscr{A}}\sum Q_N(\mathbf{x})P_N(\mathbf{y}\,|\,\mathbf{x}) \\
&\le \gamma_0 \Pr\left\{(\mathbf{x}, \mathbf{y}) \in \mathscr{A} = \bigcup_{l=1}^{L} \mathscr{A}_l \,\middle|\, \mathbf{P}\right\} \\
&\le \gamma_0 \sum_{l=1}^{L} \Pr\{(\mathbf{x}, \mathbf{y}) \in \mathscr{A}_l \,|\, \mathbf{P}\} \\
&= \gamma_0 \sum_{l=1}^{L} \Pr\{d_N^{(l)}(\mathbf{u}^{(l)}, \mathbf{v}^{(l)}) > \theta_l \,|\, \mathbf{P}\}
\end{aligned} \tag{8.1.54}$$

Using this to further bound (8.1.45) gives

$$\overline{\gamma(\mathscr{B})} \le \gamma_0 \sum_{l=1}^{L} \Pr\{d_N^{(l)}(\mathbf{u}^{(l)}, \mathbf{v}^{(l)}) > \theta_l \,|\, \mathbf{P}\} + \gamma_0 e^{-NE(R,\,\mathbf{P})} \tag{8.1.55}$$

where

$$E(R, \mathbf{P}) > 0 \qquad \text{for } R > I(\mathbf{P}) \tag{8.1.56}$$

Suppose we now wish to encode in such a way as to achieve average distortions $\{D^{(l)}: l = 1, 2, \ldots, L\}$ for each source–user pair. Let $\mathbf{D} = (D^{(1)}, D^{(2)}, \ldots, D^{(L)})$ be the desired vector distortion. Consider the average of $d^{(l)}(u^{(l)}, v^{(l)})$ over the joint distribution $Q(x)P(y\,|\,x) = Q(u^{(1)}, u^{(2)}, \ldots, u^{(L)})P(v^{(1)}, v^{(2)}, \ldots, v^{(L)}\,|\,u^{(1)}, u^{(2)}, \ldots, u^{(L)})$

$$\sum_x \sum_y Q(x)P(y\,|\,x)d^{(l)}(u^{(l)}, v^{(l)}) = \sum_u \sum_v Q^{(l)}(u)P^{(l)}(v\,|\,u)d^{(l)}(u, v) \tag{8.1.57}$$

where $Q^{(l)}(u)$ and $P^{(l)}(v\,|\,u)$ are marginal distributions of $Q(x)$ and $P(y\,|\,x)$, and define the class of conditional probability distributions

$$\mathscr{P}_{\mathbf{D}} = \left\{P(y\,|\,x): \sum_x \sum_y Q(x)P(y\,|\,x)d^{(l)}(u^{(l)}, v^{(l)}) \le D^{(l)};\ l = 1, 2, \ldots, L\right\} \tag{8.1.58}$$

We now define the vector rate distortion function as

$$R(\mathbf{D}) = \min_{\mathbf{P} \in \mathscr{P}_{\mathbf{D}}} I(\mathbf{P}) \tag{8.1.59}$$

To show that $R(\mathbf{D})$ indeed is the rate distortion function for encoding each source–user component pair with distortion $\{D^{(l)}: l = 1, \dots, L\}$, we must prove a coding theorem and its converse.

Theorem 8.1.2: Source coding theorem—vector distortion Given $\epsilon > 0$ and desired distortions $\{D^{(l)}: l = 1, 2, \dots, L\}$ for the L source–user component pairs, there exists an integer N_ϵ such that for each block length $N \geq N_\epsilon$ there exists a code $\mathscr{B} = \{\mathbf{y}_1, \mathbf{y}_2, \dots, \mathbf{y}_M\}$ of rate $R < R(\mathbf{D}) + \epsilon$ for which

$$\sum_{\mathbf{x}} Q_N(\mathbf{x}) \min_{\mathbf{y} \in \mathscr{B}} \max_{l} \left\{ \frac{1}{N} \sum_{n=1}^{N} d^{(l)}(u_n^{(l)}, v_n^{(l)}) - D^{(l)} \right\} \leq \epsilon \tag{8.1.60}$$

That is, the lth source–user pair has average distortion less than or equal to $D^{(l)} + \epsilon$ for $l = 1, 2, \dots, L$.

PROOF In equality (8.1.55), choose parameters $\theta_l = D^{(l)} + \epsilon/2$. Then for each l

$$\Pr\left\{ d_N^{(l)}(\mathbf{u}^{(l)}, \mathbf{v}^{(l)}) > D^{(l)} + \frac{\epsilon}{2} \,\middle|\, \mathbf{P} \right\} = \Pr\left\{ \frac{1}{N} \sum_{n=1}^{N} d^{(l)}(u_n^{(l)}, v_n^{(l)}) > D^{(l)} + \frac{\epsilon}{2} \,\middle|\, \mathbf{P} \right\} \tag{8.1.61}$$

For $\mathbf{P} \in \mathscr{P}_{\mathbf{D}}$ and source distribution $Q(\cdot)$, the terms $\{d^{(l)}(u_n^{(l)}, v_n^{(l)}): n = 1, 2, \dots, N\}$ are independent, identically distributed random variables with mean values less than or equal to $D^{(l)}$. Hence by the weak law of large numbers

$$\lim_{N \to \infty} \Pr\left\{ d_N^{(l)}(\mathbf{u}^{(l)}, \mathbf{v}^{(l)}) > D^{(l)} + \frac{\epsilon}{2} \,\middle|\, \mathbf{P} \right\} = 0 \tag{8.1.62}$$

for any $\mathbf{P} \in \mathscr{P}_{\mathbf{D}}$. In particular, let $\mathbf{P} \in \mathscr{P}_{\mathbf{D}}$ achieve $R(\mathbf{D}) = I(\mathbf{P})$. Then from (8.1.55) and (8.1.62), for any $R > R(\mathbf{D})$ there exists an integer N_ϵ such that, for any block length $N \geq N_\epsilon$

$$\begin{aligned} \overline{\gamma(\mathscr{B})} &\leq \gamma_0 \sum_{l=1}^{L} \Pr\left\{ d_N^{(l)}(\mathbf{u}^{(l)}, \mathbf{v}^{(l)}) > D^{(l)} + \frac{\epsilon}{2} \,\middle|\, \mathbf{P} \right\} + \gamma_0 e^{-NE(R, \mathbf{P})} \\ &\leq \frac{\epsilon}{2} \end{aligned} \tag{8.1.63}$$

Hence there exists a code $\mathscr{B}$ of rate $R < R(\mathbf{D}) + \epsilon$ and block length $N \geq N_\epsilon$ such that

$$\begin{aligned} \gamma(\mathscr{B}) &= \sum_{\mathbf{x}} Q_N(\mathbf{x}) \min_{\mathbf{y} \in \mathscr{B}} \max_{l} \left\{ d_N^{(l)}(\mathbf{u}^{(l)}, \mathbf{v}^{(l)}) - \left(D^{(l)} + \frac{\epsilon}{2} \right) \right\} \\ &\leq \frac{\epsilon}{2} \end{aligned} \tag{8.1.64}$$

or

$$\sum_{\mathbf{x}} Q_N(\mathbf{x}) \min_{\mathbf{y} \in \mathscr{B}} \max_{l} \left\{ \frac{1}{N} \sum_{n=1}^{N} d^{(l)}(u_n^{(l)}, v_n^{(l)}) - D^{(l)} \right\} \leq \epsilon \tag{8.1.65}$$

Theorem 8.1.3: Converse source coding theorem—vector distortion If a code $\mathscr{B} = \{\mathbf{y}_1, \mathbf{y}_2, \ldots, \mathbf{y}_M\}$ of block length N and rate $R = (\ln M)/N$ achieves average distortion $\{D^{(l)}: l = 1, 2, \ldots, L\}$ for each of the L source–user component pairs, then $R \geq R(\mathbf{D})$ where $\mathbf{D} = (D^{(1)}, D^{(2)}, \ldots, D^{(L)})$.

PROOF For the code $\mathscr{B} = \{\mathbf{y}_1, \mathbf{y}_2, \ldots, \mathbf{y}_M\}$, define the conditional probability

$$P_N(\mathbf{y} \mid \mathbf{x}) = \begin{cases} 1 & \mathbf{y} \in \mathscr{B} \quad \text{and} \quad \gamma_N(\mathbf{x}, \mathbf{y}) = \gamma(\mathbf{x} \mid \mathscr{B}) \\ 0 & \text{otherwise} \end{cases} \tag{8.1.66}$$

Then since code $\mathscr{B}$ achieves average distortion $D^{(l)}$ for each l, it follows that

$$\sum_{\mathbf{x}} \sum_{\mathbf{y}} Q_N(\mathbf{x}) P_N(\mathbf{y} \mid \mathbf{x}) d_N^{(l)}(\mathbf{u}^{(l)}, \mathbf{v}^{(l)}) \leq D^{(l)} \qquad l = 1, 2, \ldots, L \tag{8.1.67}$$

Let $P^{(n)}(y \mid x)$ be the nth marginal distribution of $P_N(\mathbf{y} \mid \mathbf{x})$ and define the probability distribution

$$\hat{P}(y \mid x) = \frac{1}{N} \sum_{n=1}^{N} P^{(n)}(y \mid x) \tag{8.1.68}$$

Then for each l

$$\begin{aligned} \sum_{\mathbf{x}} \sum_{\mathbf{y}} Q_N(\mathbf{x}) P_N(\mathbf{y} \mid \mathbf{x}) d_N^{(l)}(\mathbf{u}^{(l)}, \mathbf{v}^{(l)}) &= \sum_{\mathbf{x}} \sum_{\mathbf{y}} Q_N(\mathbf{x}) P_N(\mathbf{y} \mid \mathbf{x}) \frac{1}{N} \sum_{n=1}^{N} d^{(l)}(u_n^{(l)}, v_n^{(l)}) \\ &= \frac{1}{N} \sum_{n=1}^{N} \sum_{x} \sum_{y} Q(x) P^{(n)}(y \mid x) d^{(l)}(u^{(l)}, v^{(l)}) \\ &= \sum_{x} \sum_{y} Q(x) \left(\frac{1}{N} \sum_{n=1}^{N} P^{(n)}(y \mid x) \right) d^{(l)}(u^{(l)}, v^{(l)}) \\ &= \sum_{x} \sum_{y} Q(x) \hat{P}(y \mid x) d^{(l)}(u^{(l)}, v^{(l)}) \\ &\leq D^{(l)} \end{aligned} \tag{8.1.69}$$

Hence $\hat{\mathbf{P}}$ given by (8.1.68) belongs to $\mathscr{P}_{\mathbf{D}}$ and thus

$$\begin{aligned} R(\mathbf{D}) &\leq I(\hat{\mathbf{P}}) \\ &= I\left(\frac{1}{N} \sum_{n=1}^{N} \mathbf{P}^{(n)} \right) \end{aligned} \tag{8.1.70}$$

From inequalities (7.2.46) and (7.2.47), we have bounds

$$\begin{aligned} R(\mathbf{D}) &\leq \frac{1}{N} \sum_{n=1}^{N} I(\mathbf{P}^{(n)}) \\ &\leq \frac{1}{N} I(\mathbf{P}_N) \\ &\leq \frac{1}{N} \ln M \\ &= R \end{aligned} \tag{8.1.71}$$

Theorems 8.1.2 and 8.1.3 establish $R(\mathbf{D})$ as the rate distortion function for the vector source with a maximum distortion measure. For the special case where the L source components are independent, we have the following corollary.

Corollary 8.1.4: Independent components—maximum distortion When the L source components are independent so that

$$Q(x) = \prod_{l=1}^{L} Q^{(l)}(u^{(l)})$$

where $x = (u^{(1)}, u^{(2)}, \ldots, u^{(L)})$, the rate distortion function is

$$R(\mathbf{D}) = \sum_{l=1}^{L} R^{(l)}(D^{(l)}) \tag{8.1.72}$$

where $R^{(l)}(D^{(l)})$ is the rate distortion function of the lth component of the source output vector.

PROOF This follows directly from the proofs of Theorems 8.1.2 and 8.1.3 with the further independence $P(y \mid x) = \prod_{l=1}^{L} P^{(l)}(v^{(l)} \mid u^{(l)})$. Heuristically, since the sources are independent in the multiple source–user description of Fig. 8.1, the source encoder is forced to send, for each source–user pair, enough information to achieve its distortion independent of information for other source–user pairs.

8.2 SOURCES WITH MEMORY

Although many sources that arise in practice can be modeled as discrete-time sources with real-valued output symbols, they generally have memory of some sort. By taking advantage of the statistical dependence between source output symbols, for a given fidelity criterion, sources with memory can be encoded using fewer bits per source symbol than with corresponding memoryless sources. For a given average distortion level D, the rate distortion function for a source with statistical dependence between output symbols is less than for a corresponding memoryless source. Theorem 8.1.1 shows this to be true in a special case. Indeed, for memoryless sources, the data rate cannot be reduced without incurring large distortions. For this reason, source coding techniques of rate distortion theory are mainly worthwhile for sources with memory. In this section, we examine discrete-time stationary sources with memory and define the rate distortion function for discrete-time stationary ergodic sources.

Many sources, such as speech, are modeled as continuous-time sources. Continuous-time sources can be treated as discrete-time sources with source alphabets that are time functions. By considering general alphabets, we can treat a large class of sources, including picture sources such as television. Coding theorems for discrete-time stationary ergodic sources with general abstract alphabets are given in Berger [1971]. In Sec. 8.4 of this chapter, we examine a few Gaussian source examples of these more abstract alphabets.

Let us consider now a discrete-time source with statistically dependent source output symbols. For convenience, attention is restricted to a source with discrete output alphabet $\mathscr{U} = \{a_1, a_2, \ldots, a_A\}$. Let $\mathbf{u} = (\ldots, u_{-1}, u_0, u_1, \ldots)$ denote the random sequence of output letters produced by the source.[2] The source is completely described by the probabilities

$$Q_L(\alpha_1, \alpha_2, \ldots, \alpha_L; t) = \Pr\{u_{1+t} = \alpha_1, u_{2+t} = \alpha_2, \ldots, u_{L+t} = \alpha_L\}$$

for all times t and lengths L. In general, little can be said about source coding of sources which are nonstationary. Hence, we assume throughout this section that the source is stationary; that is

$$Q_L(\alpha_1, \alpha_2, \ldots, \alpha_L; t) = Q_L(\alpha_1, \alpha_2, \ldots, \alpha_L) \tag{8.2.1}$$

is independent of time t for all letter sequences $\{\alpha_1, \alpha_2, \ldots, \alpha_L\}$ and all lengths L.

In addition to assuming that the source is stationary, we temporarily require that the source also be ergodic. (Later, in Sec. 8.6, we shall relax this ergodicity assumption by examining an example of a nonergodic stationary source which we can encode efficiently.) Ergodicity is essentially equivalent to the requirement that the time averages over any sample source output sequence are equal to the ensemble averages. Specifically, let $\mathbf{u} = (\ldots, u_{-1}, u_0, u_1, \ldots)$ be a sample output sequence and let $\mathbf{u}^l$ denote the sequence $\mathbf{u}$ shifted in time by l positions. That is

$$u_t^l = u_{t+l} \qquad \text{for all } t \tag{8.2.2}$$

Also, let $f_N(\mathbf{u})$ be a function of $\mathbf{u}$ that depends only on $u_1, u_2, \ldots, u_N$. Then a stationary source is ergodic if and only if for all $N \geq 1$ and all such functions $f_N(\mathbf{u})$ for which

$$E\{|f_N(\mathbf{u})|\} < \infty \tag{8.2.3}$$

we have

$$\lim_{L \to \infty} \frac{1}{L} \sum_{l=1}^{L} f_N(\mathbf{u}^{(l)}) = E\{f_N(\mathbf{u})\} \tag{8.2.4}$$

for all source sequences $\mathbf{u}$ (except at most a set of probability zero). Here $E\{\cdot\}$ is the usual ensemble average. The ergodicity assumption will ensure that if a source code is "good" for encoding a particular sample sequence with fidelity D, then it will also be good for all sample sequences of the stationary ergodic source. This will become even more evident when we consider an example of a nonergodic stationary source.

Now suppose we have a discrete-time stationary ergodic source, as described above, with discrete source alphabet $\mathscr{U} = \{a_1, a_2, \ldots, a_A\}$, representation alphabet $\mathscr{V} = \{b_1, b_2, \ldots, b_B\}$, and a bounded single-letter distortion measure $\{d(u, v)\}$ where $0 \leq d(u, v) \leq d_0$ for all u, v. The source probabilities are given by

[2] Continuous-amplitude sources can be easily handled by replacing probability distributions with probability density functions. Coding theorems follow with an appropriate bounded moment condition similar to that imposed in Sec. 7.5.

$\{Q_L(u_1, u_2, \ldots, u_L), L \geq 1\}$. Shannon [1959] and Gallager [1968] have shown that the rate distortion function is given by

$$R(D) = \lim_{L \to \infty} R_L(D) \tag{8.2.5}$$

where

$$R_L(D) = \min_{\mathbf{P}_L \in \mathscr{P}_{D,L}} \frac{1}{L} I(\mathbf{P}_L) \tag{8.2.6}$$

$$\mathscr{P}_{D,L} = \left\{P_L(\mathbf{v} \mid \mathbf{u}) \colon \sum_{\mathbf{u}} \sum_{\mathbf{v}} Q_L(\mathbf{u}) P_L(\mathbf{v} \mid \mathbf{u}) d_L(\mathbf{u}, \mathbf{v}) \leq D\right\} \tag{8.2.7}$$

$$I(\mathbf{P}_L) = \sum_{\mathbf{u}} \sum_{\mathbf{v}} Q_L(\mathbf{u}) P_L(\mathbf{v} \mid \mathbf{u}) \ln \frac{P_L(\mathbf{v} \mid \mathbf{u})}{P_L(\mathbf{v})} \tag{8.2.8}$$

$$P_L(\mathbf{v}) = \sum_{\mathbf{u}} Q_L(\mathbf{u}) P_L(\mathbf{v} \mid \mathbf{u}) \tag{8.2.9}$$

$$d_L(\mathbf{u}, \mathbf{v}) = \frac{1}{L} \sum_{l=1}^{L} d(u_l, v_l) \tag{8.2.10}$$

The coding theorem for this case is rather difficult to prove. A direct proof will be given here only for the Gaussian source with the squared-error distortion measure. General proofs can be found in Gallager [1968] and Berger [1971].

We present instead a simple heuristic argument which requires an additional assumption that appears reasonable for many real source models. Assume that there exists a finite interval T_0 such that source outputs separated by T_0 or more units of time are statistically independent. That is, for two random source output letters u_t and $u_{t'}$ at corresponding times t and t', for which $|t - t'| \geq T_0$, we have

$$Q(u_t, u_{t'}) = Q(u_t) Q(u_{t'}) \tag{8.2.11}$$

For many real sources, a model with such a finite interval of dependence seems reasonable. From a mathematical point of view, this is a rather strong assumption which simplifies our heuristic argument that (8.2.5) is the rate distortion function.

Consider grouping together consecutive source output symbols into groups of length $L + T_0$. Out of each group we only attempt to encode the first L source output symbols and ignore the remaining T_0 symbols (i.e., we neither represent them nor send them, although the decoder knows that these last T_0 symbols are missing). Because of our assumption we then have a sequence of independent identically distributed sets of source output sequences, each consisting of L source output symbols. Defining

$$\begin{aligned} x &= (u_1, u_2, \ldots, u_L) \in \mathscr{X} = \mathscr{U}_L \\ y &= (v_1, v_2, \ldots, v_L) \in \mathscr{Y} = \mathscr{V}_L \end{aligned} \tag{8.2.12}$$

and distortion

$$d_L(x, y) = \frac{1}{L} \sum_{t=1}^{L} d(u_t, v_t) \leq d_0 \tag{8.2.13}$$

we have a new extended discrete memoryless source with source probability $Q_L(x) = Q_L(u_1, u_2, \ldots, u_L)$ for each letter $x \in \mathcal{X} = \mathcal{U}_L$ and single-letter distortion measure $d_L(x, y)$. Applying the results of Sec. 8.1 for a memoryless source with vector outputs, the rate distortion function for the extended discrete memoryless source is given by

$$R(D; L) = \min_{\mathbf{P}_L \in \mathcal{P}_{D, L}} I(\mathbf{P}_L) \qquad \text{nats/extended source symbol} \tag{8.2.14}$$

where

$$\mathcal{P}_{D, L} = \left\{ P_L(\mathbf{v} \mid \mathbf{u}) \colon \sum_{\mathbf{u}} \sum_{\mathbf{v}} Q_L(\mathbf{u}) P_L(\mathbf{v} \mid \mathbf{u}) d_L(\mathbf{u}, \mathbf{v}) \le D \right\} \tag{8.2.15}$$

Here the dimensions of $R(D; L)$ are nats per symbol of the extended source. But each extended source symbol corresponds to $L + T_0$ actual source output symbols. Hence, in terms of nats per actual source symbol, (8.2.14) becomes, using (8.2.6),

$$\frac{R(D; L)}{L + T_0} = \frac{L}{L + T_0} R_L(D) \qquad \text{nats/source symbol} \tag{8.2.16}$$

Since the T_0 unrepresented source symbols can produce upon decoding the maximum distortion d_0, this means that by using the above encoding strategy we can achieve average distortion

$$D + d_0 \left(\frac{T_0}{L + T_0} \right)$$

with a code of rate

$$\frac{L}{L + T_0} R_L(D)$$

Clearly, by letting $L \to \infty$, we can achieve average distortion D with a code rate

$$R(D) = \lim_{L \to \infty} R_L(D)$$

Hence we see that if there exists a finite interval T_0 such that source outputs separated by T_0 or more units of time are statistically independent, then the heuristic proof of the coding theorem follows directly from the coding theorem for memoryless vector sources. For general stationary ergodic sources there are similar (though more difficult to prove) coding theorems resulting in the definition of the rate distortion function given in (8.2.5).

In the above discussion we assumed that $R_L(D)$ converged for stationary ergodic sources. We can interpret $R_L(D)$ as the normalized rate distortion function of a memoryless vector source of L components as described in Sec. 8.1. By increasing L, more of the statistical dependence between source outputs can be exploited, so that we expect the required rate per source symbol to decrease with an increase in L. This is true for all stationary sources, as shown next.

Lemma 8.2.1

$$R(D) = \lim_{L \to \infty} R_L(D) = \inf_{L \geq 1} R_L(D) \tag{8.2.17}$$

PROOF Consider integers l and m and let $N = l + m$. Let $\mathbf{P}_l$ and $\mathbf{P}_m$ be conditional probabilities that achieve $R_l(D) = (1/l)I(\mathbf{P}_l)$ and $R_m(D) = (1/m)I(\mathbf{P}_m)$ and define

$$P_N(\mathbf{v} \mid \mathbf{u}) \equiv P_l(\mathbf{v}^l \mid \mathbf{u}^l)P_m(\mathbf{v}^m \mid \mathbf{u}^m) \qquad \text{where} \qquad \mathbf{v} = \mathbf{v}^l\mathbf{v}^m,\ \mathbf{u} = \mathbf{u}^l\mathbf{u}^m \tag{8.2.18}$$

Then

$$\begin{aligned}
&\sum_{\mathbf{u}} \sum_{\mathbf{v}} Q_N(\mathbf{u})P_N(\mathbf{y} \mid \mathbf{u})\, d_N(\mathbf{u}, \mathbf{y}) \\
&\quad = \sum_{\mathbf{u}} \sum_{\mathbf{v}} Q_N(\mathbf{u})P_N(\mathbf{v} \mid \mathbf{u}) \left\{ \frac{l}{N} d_l(\mathbf{u}^l, \mathbf{v}^l) + \frac{m}{N} d_m(\mathbf{u}^m, \mathbf{v}^m) \right\} \\
&\quad = \frac{l}{N} \sum_{\mathbf{u}^l} \sum_{\mathbf{v}^l} Q_l(\mathbf{u}^l)P_l(\mathbf{v}^l \mid \mathbf{u}^l)\, d_l(\mathbf{u}^l, \mathbf{v}^l) + \frac{m}{N} \sum_{\mathbf{u}^m} \sum_{\mathbf{v}^m} Q_m(\mathbf{u}^m)P_m(\mathbf{v}^m \mid \mathbf{u}^m)\, d_m(\mathbf{u}^m, \mathbf{v}^m) \\
&\quad \leq \frac{l}{N} D + \frac{m}{N} D \\
&\quad = D
\end{aligned} \tag{8.2.19}$$

Hence $P_N(\mathbf{v} \mid \mathbf{u})$ belongs to $\mathscr{P}_{D,N}$, and from Lemma 1.2.1 of Chap. 1

$$\begin{aligned}
R_N(D) &\leq \frac{1}{N} I(\mathbf{P}_N) \\
&= \frac{1}{N} \sum_{\mathbf{u}} \sum_{\mathbf{v}} Q_N(\mathbf{u})P_N(\mathbf{v} \mid \mathbf{u}) \ln \frac{P_N(\mathbf{v} \mid \mathbf{u})}{P_N(\mathbf{v})} \\
&\leq \frac{1}{N} \sum_{\mathbf{u}} \sum_{\mathbf{v}} Q_N(\mathbf{u})P_N(\mathbf{v} \mid \mathbf{u}) \ln \frac{P_N(\mathbf{v} \mid \mathbf{u})}{\hat{P}_N(\mathbf{v})}
\end{aligned} \tag{8.2.20}$$

where $\hat{P}_N(\mathbf{v})$ is any probability distribution. We choose $\hat{P}_N(\mathbf{v}) = P_l(\mathbf{v}^l)P_m(\mathbf{v}^m)$ where

$$P_l(\mathbf{v}^l) = \sum_{\mathbf{u}} Q_l(\mathbf{u})P_l(\mathbf{v}^l \mid \mathbf{u})$$

and

$$P_m(\mathbf{v}^m) = \sum_{\mathbf{u}} Q_m(\mathbf{u})P_m(\mathbf{v}^m \mid \mathbf{u}) \tag{8.2.21}$$

Hence

$$\begin{aligned}
R_N(D) &\leq \frac{1}{N} \{I(\mathbf{P}_l) + I(\mathbf{P}_m)\} \\
&= \frac{l}{N}\left[\frac{1}{l} I(\mathbf{P}_l)\right] + \frac{m}{N}\left[\frac{1}{m} I(\mathbf{P}_m)\right] \\
&= \frac{l}{N} R_l(D) + \frac{m}{N} R_m(D)
\end{aligned} \tag{8.2.22}$$

Now let $\underline{R}(D) = \inf_{L \geq 1} R_L(D)$. Then for any $\epsilon > 0$, choose N to satisfy

$$R_N(D) \leq \underline{R}(D) + \epsilon \tag{8.2.23}$$

From (8.2.22), letting $l = m = N$, we have

$$\begin{aligned} R_{2N}(D) &\leq \tfrac{1}{2}R_N(D) + \tfrac{1}{2}R_N(D) \\ &= R_N(D) \\ &\leq \underline{R}(D) + \epsilon \end{aligned} \tag{8.2.24}$$

Similarly

$$R_{kN}(D) \leq \underline{R}(D) + \epsilon \qquad \text{for all } k \geq 1 \tag{8.2.25}$$

For any integer L, we can find k and j such that $L = kN + j$ where $0 \leq j \leq N - 1$. Then

$$\begin{aligned} R_L(D) &\leq \frac{kN}{L} R_{kN}(D) + \frac{j}{L} R_j(D) \\ &\leq \frac{kN}{L} [\underline{R}(D) + \epsilon] + \frac{N}{L} R_j(D) \\ &\leq \underline{R}(D) + \epsilon + \frac{N}{L} R_j(D) \\ &\leq \underline{R}(D) + \epsilon + \frac{N}{L} \bar{R}(D) \qquad \text{where} \qquad \bar{R}(D) = \sup_{L \geq 1} R_L(D) \end{aligned} \tag{8.2.26}$$

Since $\epsilon > 0$ is arbitrary, we have

$$\lim_{L \to \infty} R_L(D) = \underline{R}(D)$$

Having given a heuristic argument to motivate the coding theorem for at least a subclass of stationary ergodic sources, we next prove the general converse coding theorem.

Theorem 8.2.1: Converse source coding theorem—stationary ergodic sources For any source encoder–decoder pair, if the average distortion is less than or equal to D, then the rate R must satisfy $R \geq R(D)$.

PROOF Any encoder–decoder pair defines a mapping from source sequences to user sequences. For any length N, consider the mapping from $\mathscr{U}_N$ to $\mathscr{V}_N$, where we let M be the number of distinct sequences in $\mathscr{V}_N$ into which sequences of $\mathscr{U}_N$ are mapped. Define

$$P_N(\mathbf{v} \mid \mathbf{u}) \equiv \begin{cases} 1 & \text{if } \mathbf{v} \text{ is the sequence into which } \mathbf{u} \text{ is mapped} \\ 0 & \text{otherwise} \end{cases} \tag{8.2.27}$$

Then if this mapping results in average distortion of D or less, we have average distortion

$$\begin{aligned} D(\mathbf{P}_N) &= \sum_{\mathbf{u}} \sum_{\mathbf{v}} Q_N(\mathbf{u}) P_N(\mathbf{v} \mid \mathbf{u}) d_N(\mathbf{u}, \mathbf{v}) \\ &\leq D \end{aligned} \tag{8.2.28}$$

and hence $\mathbf{P}_N \in \mathscr{P}_{D,N}$. Thus

$$\begin{aligned} R_N(D) &\leq \frac{1}{N} I(\mathbf{P}_N) \\ &\leq \frac{1}{N} \ln M \end{aligned} \tag{8.2.29}$$

Since

$$R(D) = \inf_{L \geq 1} R_L(D) \leq R_N(D)$$

we have $R(D) \leq (1/N) \ln M = R$.

This converse theorem together with the heuristic proof of the coding theorem completes our justification of $R(D)$ given by (8.1.5) as the rate distortion function for stationary ergodic sources.[3] This discussion easily extends to continuous amplitude stationary ergodic sources where, instead of a bounded distortion measure, we require a bounded moment condition on the distortion measure.

Another form of $R(D)$ for stationary ergodic sources can be obtained using a definition given in terms of random processes, rather than limits of minimizations involving random vectors. This definition of a rate distortion function is analogous to Khinchine's process definition of channel capacity [1957]. Again consider the stationary ergodic source described above. Next suppose there is a jointly stationary ergodic random process $\{u_n, v_n\}$ consisting of *pairs* $u_n \in \mathscr{U}$ and $v_n \in \mathscr{V}$. This implies that there is a consistent family of probability distribution functions $\{P_N(\mathbf{u}, \mathbf{v}) \colon \mathbf{u} \in \mathscr{U}_N, \mathbf{v} \in \mathscr{V}_N\}$ for all N which satisfies the condition

$$Q_N(\mathbf{u}) = \sum_{\mathbf{v}} P_N(\mathbf{u}, \mathbf{v}) \qquad \text{for all } N \tag{8.2.30}$$

Given a stationary ergodic source, there always exists a jointly ergodic pair source that satisfies this condition. Since the *pair process* is stationary, we can define the average per letter mutual information

$$I_p = \lim_{N \to \infty} \frac{1}{N} I_p(\mathscr{U}_N, \mathscr{V}_N) \tag{8.2.31}$$

[3] This converse theorem is true for nonergodic stationary sources if we interpret average distortion as an ensemble average.

where the subscript p emphasizes the dependence of the particular pair processes. In addition, we have average distortion

$$\begin{aligned} D_p &= E_p\{d_N(\mathbf{u}, \mathbf{v})\} \\ &= E_p\left\{\frac{1}{N}\sum_{n=1}^{N} d(u_n, v_n)\right\} \\ &= \sum_u \sum_v P(u, v)d(u, v) \end{aligned} \tag{8.2.32}$$

For this particular jointly ergodic process, a sequence of block codes of rates approaching I_p can be found that can achieve average distortion arbitrarily close to D_p.

Theorem 8.2.2 Given any $\epsilon > 0$ and the jointly stationary ergodic process defined above which satisfies the source condition (8.2.30), there exists a sequence of block codes $\{\mathscr{B}_N\}$ each of rate $R < I_p + \epsilon$ such that the average distortions $\{d(\mathscr{B}_N)\}$ satisfy

$$\lim_{N\to\infty} d(\mathscr{B}_N) \le D_p + \epsilon$$

PROOF For any block code[4] $\mathscr{B}_N = \{\mathbf{v}_1, \mathbf{v}_2, \ldots, \mathbf{v}_M\}$, we have average distortion

$$\begin{aligned} d(\mathscr{B}_N) &= \sum_{\mathbf{u}} Q_N(\mathbf{u})d(\mathbf{u}|\mathscr{B}_N) \\ &= \sum_{\mathbf{u}}\sum_{\mathbf{v}} P_N(\mathbf{u}, \mathbf{v})d(\mathbf{u}|\mathscr{B}_N) \end{aligned} \tag{8.2.33}$$

where

$$d(\mathbf{u}|\mathscr{B}_N) = \min_{v \in \mathscr{B}_N} d_N(\mathbf{u}, \mathbf{v}) \tag{8.2.34}$$

Let

$$\Phi(\mathbf{u}, \mathbf{v}; \mathscr{B}_N) = \begin{cases} 1 & d(\mathbf{u}|\mathscr{B}_N) > d_N(\mathbf{u}, \mathbf{v}) \\ 0 & d(\mathbf{u}|\mathscr{B}_N) \le d_N(\mathbf{u}, \mathbf{v}) \end{cases} \tag{8.2.35}$$

Then

$$\begin{aligned} d(\mathscr{B}_N) = &\sum_{\mathbf{u}}\sum_{\mathbf{v}} P_N(\mathbf{u}, \mathbf{v})\, d(\mathbf{u}|\mathscr{B}_N)[1 - \Phi(\mathbf{u}, \mathbf{v}; \mathscr{B}_N)] \\ &+ \sum_{\mathbf{u}}\sum_{\mathbf{v}} P_N(\mathbf{u}, \mathbf{v})\, d(\mathbf{u}|\mathscr{B}_N)\Phi(\mathbf{u}, \mathbf{v}; \mathscr{B}_N) \end{aligned}$$

Noting that in the first term we have

$$d(\mathbf{u}|\mathscr{B}_N)[1 - \Phi(\mathbf{u}, \mathbf{v}; \mathscr{B}_N)] \le d_N(\mathbf{u}, \mathbf{v}) \tag{8.2.36}$$

[4] Each codeword here corresponds to the choice of N random processes $\mathbf{v}_1, \mathbf{v}_2, \ldots, \mathbf{v}_N$ as a mapping for the N source processes $\mathbf{u}_1, \mathbf{u}_2, \ldots, \mathbf{u}_N$.

and in the second term we can have

$$d(\mathbf{u} \mid \mathscr{B}_N) \le d_0 \tag{8.2.37}$$

then

$$d(\mathscr{B}_N) \le D_p + d_0 \sum_{\mathbf{u}} \sum_{\mathbf{v}} P_N(\mathbf{u}, \mathbf{v})\Phi(\mathbf{u}, \mathbf{v}; \mathscr{B}_N) \tag{8.2.38}$$

Defining[5]

$$P_N(\mathbf{v}) \equiv \sum_{\mathbf{u}} P_N(\mathbf{u}, \mathbf{v}) \tag{8.2.39}$$

we bound the second term using the Hölder inequality,

$$\begin{aligned}
&\sum_{\mathbf{u}} \sum_{\mathbf{v}} P_N(\mathbf{u}, \mathbf{v})\Phi(\mathbf{u}, \mathbf{v}; \mathscr{B}_N) \\
&\quad = \sum_{\mathbf{u}} \sum_{\mathbf{v}} P_N(\mathbf{v}) \left[\frac{P_N(\mathbf{u}, \mathbf{v})}{P_N(\mathbf{v})}\right] \Phi(\mathbf{u}, \mathbf{v}; \mathscr{B}_N) \\
&\quad \le \sum_{\mathbf{u}} \left\{\sum_{\mathbf{v}} P_N(\mathbf{v}) \left[\frac{P_N(\mathbf{u}, \mathbf{v})}{P_N(\mathbf{v})}\right]^{1/(1+\rho)}\right\}^{1+\rho} \left[\sum_{\mathbf{v}} P_N(\mathbf{v})\Phi(\mathbf{u}, \mathbf{v}; \mathscr{B}_N)\right]^{-\rho}
\end{aligned} \tag{8.2.40}$$

for any $-1 \le \rho \le 0$. Averaging the bound with respect to an ensemble of codes of block length N and rate R where codewords are chosen independently with probability distribution $P_N(\mathbf{v})$, results in

$$\begin{aligned}
\overline{\left(\sum_{\mathbf{v}} P_N(\mathbf{v})\Phi(\mathbf{u}, \mathbf{v}; \mathscr{B}_N)\right)^{-\rho}} &\le \left(\sum_{\mathbf{v}} P_N(\mathbf{v})\overline{\Phi(\mathbf{u}, \mathbf{v}; \mathscr{B}_N)}\right)^{-\rho} \\
&= \left(\frac{1}{M+1}\right)^{-\rho} \\
&\le M^{\rho} \\
&= e^{N\rho R}
\end{aligned} \tag{8.2.41}$$

where the first inequality follows from the Jensen inequality and the first equality follows from the complete symmetry of $\{\mathbf{v}, \mathbf{v}_1, \mathbf{v}_2, \ldots, \mathbf{v}_M\}$. Thus,

$$\overline{d(\mathscr{B}_N)} \le D_p + d_0\, e^{N\rho R} \sum_{\mathbf{u}} \left\{\sum_{\mathbf{v}} P_N(\mathbf{v}) \left[\frac{P_N(\mathbf{u}, \mathbf{v})}{P_N(\mathbf{u})}\right]^{1/(1+\rho)}\right\}^{1+\rho} \tag{8.2.42}$$

for $-1 \le \rho \le 0$. Certainly there exists at least one code $\mathscr{B}_N$ in the ensemble which also satisfies this bound on the ensemble average.

Next, letting $\rho = -\alpha/N$ for any $\alpha > 0$, choose $N > \alpha$ so that

$$\rho = -\alpha/N \in (-1, 0)$$

[5] As in the proof of Lemma 7.2.1, $\mathbf{v}$ is a dummy vector.

Now consider the identity

$$\frac{1}{1+\rho} = 1 - \rho + \frac{\rho^2}{1+\rho}$$

$$= 1 + \frac{\alpha}{N} + \frac{(\alpha/N)^2}{1-(\alpha/N)}$$

$$= 1 + \frac{\alpha}{N} + o(N) \qquad \text{where} \qquad o(N) = (\alpha/N)^2/[1-(\alpha/N)] \tag{8.2.43}$$

and consider the inequality

$$\sum_{\mathbf{u}} \left\{ \sum_{\mathbf{v}} P_N(\mathbf{v}) \left[\frac{P_N(\mathbf{u}, \mathbf{v})}{P_N(\mathbf{v})} \right]^{1/(1+\rho)} \right\}^{1+\rho}$$

$$= \sum_{\mathbf{u}} Q_N(\mathbf{u}) \left\{ \sum_{\mathbf{v}} P_N(\mathbf{v}) \left[\frac{P_N(\mathbf{u}, \mathbf{v})}{Q_N(\mathbf{u})P_N(\mathbf{v})} \right]^{1/(1+\rho)} \right\}^{1+\rho}$$

$$\leq \left\{ \sum_{\mathbf{u}} \sum_{\mathbf{v}} Q_N(\mathbf{u})P_N(\mathbf{v}) \left[\frac{P_N(\mathbf{u}, \mathbf{v})}{Q_N(\mathbf{u})P_N(\mathbf{v})} \right]^{1/(1+\rho)} \right\}^{1+\rho}$$

$$= \left\{ \sum_{\mathbf{u}} \sum_{\mathbf{v}} P_N(\mathbf{u}, \mathbf{v}) \left[\frac{P_N(\mathbf{u}, \mathbf{v})}{Q_N(\mathbf{u})P_N(\mathbf{v})} \right]^{(\alpha/N + o(N))} \right\}^{1-\alpha/N}$$

$$= \left\{ \sum_{\mathbf{u}} \sum_{\mathbf{v}} P_N(\mathbf{u}, \mathbf{v}) \exp \left[\left(\frac{\alpha}{N} + o(N) \right) \ln \frac{P_N(\mathbf{u}, \mathbf{v})}{Q_N(\mathbf{u})P_N(\mathbf{v})} \right] \right\}^{1-\alpha/N} \tag{8.2.44}$$

Substituting this into (8.2.42) yields for some code $\mathscr{B}_N$

$$d(\mathscr{B}_N) \leq D_p + d_0 e^{-\alpha R} \left\{ \sum_{\mathbf{u}} \sum_{\mathbf{v}} P_N(\mathbf{u}, \mathbf{v}) \exp \left[\left(\frac{\alpha}{N} + o(N) \right) \ln \frac{P_N(\mathbf{u}, \mathbf{v})}{Q_N(\mathbf{u})P_N(\mathbf{v})} \right] \right\}^{1-\alpha/N} \tag{8.2.45}$$

for any $\alpha > 0$ and N large enough to guarantee $N > \alpha$. For jointly ergodic sources (McMillan [1953]) we have

$$\lim_{N\to\infty} \frac{1}{N} \ln \frac{P_N(\mathbf{u}, \mathbf{v})}{Q_N(\mathbf{u})P_N(\mathbf{v})} = I_p \tag{8.2.46}$$

where the convergence is with probability one. Hence

$$\lim_{N\to\infty} d(\mathscr{B}_N) \leq D_p + d_0 e^{-\alpha(R - I_p)} \tag{8.2.47}$$

Finally, choose $R = I_p + \epsilon/2$ and $\alpha = (2/\epsilon) \ln (d_0/\epsilon)$, where $\epsilon < d_0$, so that

$$\lim_{N\to\infty} d(\mathscr{B}_N) \leq D_p + \epsilon$$

for $R \leq I_p + \epsilon$.

According to Theorem 8.2.2, $R(D)$ is the smallest possible rate for average distortion D. Thus

$$\inf_{D_p \leq D} I_p \geq R(D) \tag{8.2.48}$$

where the minimization is taken over all stationary ergodic joint processes that satisfy $D_p \leq D$ and (8.2.30). It has been shown (Gray et al. [1975]) that the minimization can be taken with respect to all jointly stationary sources since all jointly stationary sources that satisfy the minimization can be approximated arbitrarily closely by a stationary ergodic source. In addition Gray et al. [1975] have proven a converse coding theorem analogous to Theorem 8.2.1 which establishes that

$$R(D) = \inf_{D_p \leq D} I_p \tag{8.2.49}$$

For stationary ergodic sources, there are two equivalent definitions of the rate distortion function, $R(D)$, given by (8.2.5) and (8.2.49). In (8.2.5), $R(D)$ is given as a limit of minimizations involving random vectors, whereas in (8.2.49) it is given in terms of minimizations involving random processes. In either case, $R(D)$ is generally difficult to evaluate for most stationary ergodic sources. This is one of the main weaknesses of the theory.

The most direct way to compute $R(D)$ is to first find the form of $R_L(D)$ and then take the limit as $L \to \infty$. $R_L(D)$, given by (8.2.6), can be interpreted as the rate distortion function of an L-dimensional memoryless vector source, where the vector components are not necessarily independent and the distortion between vector outputs and representation vectors is the sum distortion measure. Thus $R_L(D)$ is exactly the rate distortion function of a vector source with the sum distortion measure discussed in Sec. 8.1.1. There we found a simple expression for this rate distortion function when the component sources were independent. If by an appropriate transformation we can reduce the calculation of $R_L(D)$ to that of the independent component sources, then we can obtain an equally simple expression for $R_L(D)$ and often obtain $R(D)$. We do this in the following example.

Example (Gaussian source, squared-error distortion) Consider a discrete-time zero-mean stationary Gaussian source with output sequence $(\ldots, u_{-1}, u_0, u_1, \ldots)$ and correlation between outputs u_i and u_j denoted by

$$\phi_{ij} = \phi_{|i-j|} = E\{u_i u_j\} \qquad \text{for all } i, j \tag{8.2.50}$$

Stationarity implies that this correlation depends only on $|i - j|$ and since the source is Gaussian it also implies that it is ergodic. We wish to calculate $R(D)$ for this source with the squared-error distortion measure

$$\begin{aligned} d_L(\mathbf{u}, \mathbf{v}) &= \frac{1}{L} \sum_{l=1}^{L} (u_l - v_l)^2 \\ &= \frac{1}{L} \|\mathbf{u} - \mathbf{v}\|^2 \end{aligned} \tag{8.2.51}$$

for any $\mathbf{u}, \mathbf{v} \in \mathscr{R}_L$ where we have $\mathscr{U} = \mathscr{V} = \mathscr{R}$. We begin by calculating $R_L(D)$.

The sequence $\mathbf{u} \in \mathscr{R}_L$ has the joint density function

$$Q_L(\mathbf{u}) = \frac{1}{(2\pi)^{L/2} |\Phi|^{1/2}} e^{-(1/2)\mathbf{u}\Phi^{-1}\mathbf{u}^T} \tag{8.2.52}$$

where

$$\Phi = \begin{bmatrix} \phi_0 & \phi_1 & \cdots & \phi_{L-1} \\ \phi_1 & \phi_0 & \cdots & \cdots \\ \cdots & \cdots & \cdots & \cdots \\ \cdots & \cdots & \phi_0 & \phi_1 \\ \phi_{L-1} & \cdots & \phi_1 & \phi_0 \end{bmatrix} \tag{8.2.53}$$

is the covariance matrix. Here, assume that Φ is positive definite so that Φ^{-1} exists for any finite L. Let Γ denote the unitary modal matrix whose columns are the orthonormal eigenvectors of Φ with eigenvalues $\lambda_1, \lambda_2, \ldots, \lambda_L$. Since Φ is positive definite, the eigenvalues are positive. Letting

$$\Lambda = \begin{bmatrix} \lambda_1 & & & & \mathbf{0} \\ & \lambda_2 & & & \\ & & \cdot & & \\ & & & \cdot & \\ & & & & \cdot \\ \mathbf{0} & & & & \lambda_L \end{bmatrix} \tag{8.2.54}$$

we have

$$\Phi = \Gamma\Lambda\Gamma^T \qquad \text{and} \qquad \Phi^{-1} = \Gamma\Lambda^{-1}\Gamma^T \tag{8.2.55}$$

Define transformed source and representation vectors by $\hat{\mathbf{u}} = \mathbf{u}\Gamma$ and $\hat{\mathbf{v}} = \mathbf{v}\Gamma$, where now $\hat{\mathbf{u}}$ has covariance matrix Λ and probability density

$$Q_L(\hat{\mathbf{u}}) = \prod_{l=1}^{L} \frac{1}{\sqrt{2\pi\lambda_l}} e^{-\hat{u}_l^2/2\lambda} \tag{8.2.56}$$

Note that the components of $\hat{\mathbf{u}}$ are independent random variables. In addition, since $\Gamma\Gamma^T = I$ we have

$$\begin{aligned} d_L(\hat{\mathbf{u}}, \hat{\mathbf{v}}) &= \frac{1}{L}\|\hat{\mathbf{u}} - \hat{\mathbf{v}}\|^2 \\ &= \frac{1}{L}(\hat{\mathbf{u}} - \hat{\mathbf{v}})(\hat{\mathbf{u}} - \hat{\mathbf{v}})^T \\ &= \frac{1}{L}[(\mathbf{u} - \mathbf{v})\Gamma][\Gamma^T(\mathbf{u} - \mathbf{v})^T] \\ &= \frac{1}{L}(\mathbf{u} - \mathbf{v})(\mathbf{u} - \mathbf{v})^T \\ &= d_L(\mathbf{u}, \mathbf{v}) \end{aligned} \tag{8.2.57}$$

For any conditional probability density $P_L(\mathbf{v} \mid \mathbf{u})$, let $\hat{P}_L(\hat{\mathbf{v}} \mid \hat{\mathbf{u}})$ be the corresponding density for $\hat{\mathbf{v}}$ conditioned on $\hat{\mathbf{u}}$. Since Γ is an invertible mapping, it preserves average mutual information

$$\begin{aligned} I(\mathbf{P}_L) &= \int_{-\infty}^{\infty} \cdots \int_{-\infty}^{\infty} Q_L(\mathbf{u})P_L(\mathbf{v} \mid \mathbf{u}) \ln \frac{P_L(\mathbf{v} \mid \mathbf{u})}{P_L(\mathbf{v})}\, d\mathbf{v}\, d\mathbf{u} \\ &= \int_{-\infty}^{\infty} \cdots \int_{-\infty}^{\infty} \hat{Q}_L(\hat{\mathbf{u}})\hat{P}_L(\hat{\mathbf{v}} \mid \hat{\mathbf{u}}) \ln \frac{\hat{P}_L(\hat{\mathbf{v}} \mid \hat{\mathbf{u}})}{\hat{P}_L(\hat{\mathbf{v}})}\, d\hat{\mathbf{v}}\, d\hat{\mathbf{u}} \\ &= I(\hat{\mathbf{P}}_L) \end{aligned} \tag{8.2.58}$$

Also, $d_L(\mathbf{u}, \mathbf{v}) = d_L(\hat{\mathbf{u}}, \hat{\mathbf{v}})$ implies

$$\begin{aligned} D(\mathbf{P}_L) &= \int_{-\infty}^{\infty} \cdots \int_{-\infty}^{\infty} Q_L(\mathbf{u}) P_L(\mathbf{v} \mid \mathbf{u}) d_L(\mathbf{u}, \mathbf{v}) \, d\mathbf{v} \, d\mathbf{u} \\ &= \int_{-\infty}^{\infty} \cdots \int_{-\infty}^{\infty} \hat{Q}_L(\hat{\mathbf{u}}) \hat{P}_L(\hat{\mathbf{v}} \mid \hat{\mathbf{u}}) d_L(\hat{\mathbf{u}}, \hat{\mathbf{v}}) \, d\hat{\mathbf{v}} \, d\hat{\mathbf{u}} \\ &= D(\hat{\mathbf{P}}_L) \end{aligned} \tag{8.2.59}$$

Thus $R_L(D)$ can be expressed in terms of the transformed space

$$R_L(D) = \inf_{\hat{\mathbf{P}}_L \in \hat{\mathscr{P}}_{D, L}} \frac{1}{L} I(\hat{\mathbf{P}}_L) \tag{8.2.60}$$

where

$$\hat{\mathscr{P}}_{D, L} = \{\hat{P}_L(\hat{\mathbf{v}} \mid \hat{\mathbf{u}}) : D(\hat{\mathbf{P}}_L) \leq D\} \tag{8.2.61}$$

Since $\hat{\mathbf{u}} \in \mathscr{R}_L$ has independent components, we can regard $R_L(D)$ as the rate distortion function of a vector source with independent components where the lth component source output has density function

$$Q^{(l)}(\hat{u}_l) = \frac{1}{\sqrt{2\pi\lambda_l}} e^{-\hat{u}_l^2/2\lambda_l} \tag{8.2.62}$$

In Lemma 8.1.1, $R_L(D)$ in nats per sample is given by the parametric equations

$$D_s = \frac{1}{L} \sum_{l=1}^{L} D_s^{(l)} \tag{8.2.63}$$

and

$$R_L(D_s) = \frac{1}{L} \sum_{l=1}^{L} R^{(l)}(D_s^{(l)}) \tag{8.2.64}$$

where $R^{(l)}(D_s^{(l)})$ is the rate distortion function of the lth component source. The example in Sec. 8.1 gives for this case the parametric equations for $R_L(D)$ and for parameter $\theta = -1/2s > 0$

$$D_\theta = \frac{1}{L} \sum_{l=1}^{L} \min\,(\theta, \lambda_l) \tag{8.2.65}$$

and

$$R_L(D_\theta) = \frac{1}{L} \sum_{l=1}^{L} \max\left(0, \tfrac{1}{2} \ln \frac{\lambda_l}{\theta}\right) \tag{8.2.66}$$

We are now ready to pass to the limit $L \to \infty$. To do this we need to use the well-known limit theorem for Toeplitz matrices.

Theorem 8.2.3: Toeplitz distribution theorem Let Φ_0 be the infinite covariance matrix. The eigenvalues of Φ_0 are contained in the interval $\delta \leq \lambda \leq \Delta$, where δ and Δ denote the essential infinum and supremum, respectively, of the function

$$\Phi(\omega) = \sum_{k=-\infty}^{\infty} \phi_k \, e^{-ik\omega} \tag{8.2.67}$$

Moreover, if both δ and Δ are finite and $G(\lambda)$ is any continuous function of λ, then

$$\lim_{L\to\infty} \frac{1}{L} \sum_{l=1}^{L} G(\lambda_l^{(L)}) = \frac{1}{2\pi} \int_{-\pi}^{\pi} G[\Phi(\omega)]\, d\omega \tag{8.2.68}$$

where $\lambda_l^{(L)}$ is the lth eigenvalue of Φ, the $L \times L$ covariance matrix.

PROOF See Grenander and Szego [1958, sec. 5.2].

Applying this theorem to (8.2.65) and (8.2.66), we have the parametric equation for $R(D)$ given by

$$D_\theta = \frac{1}{2\pi} \int_{-\pi}^{\pi} \min\,[\theta, \Phi(\omega)]\, d\omega \tag{8.2.69}$$

and

$$R(D_\theta) = \frac{1}{4\pi} \int_{-\pi}^{\pi} \max\left[0, \ln \frac{\Phi(\omega)}{\theta}\right] d\omega \tag{8.2.70}$$

For this Gaussian source with the squared-error distortion measure, we now prove a coding theorem, in essentially the same way as was done earlier for memoryless sources, by encoding the transformed source output sequence $\hat{\mathbf{u}} = \mathbf{u}\Gamma \in \mathscr{R}_L$ with M codewords denoted $\mathscr{B} = \{\hat{\mathbf{v}}_1, \hat{\mathbf{v}}_2, \ldots, \hat{\mathbf{v}}_M\}$. For any conditional density function

$$P_L(\hat{\mathbf{v}} \mid \hat{\mathbf{u}}) = \prod_{l=1}^{L} P^{(l)}(\hat{v}_l \mid \hat{u}_l) \tag{8.2.71}$$

we follow the coding theorem of Sec. 7.2 to get a bound on the average distortion (over code and source ensemble)

$$\overline{d(\mathscr{B})} \le \frac{1}{L} \sum_{l=1}^{L} D^{(l)} + d_0 e^{-(L/2)E_L(R,\rho,\mathbf{P}_L)} \tag{8.2.72}$$

where

$$D^{(l)} = \int_{-\infty}^{\infty} \int_{-\infty}^{\infty} (\hat{v} - \hat{u})^2 P^{(l)}(\hat{v} \mid \hat{u}) Q^{(l)}(\hat{u})\, d\hat{v}\, d\hat{u} \tag{8.2.73}$$

$$d_0 = \sqrt{3} \max_{1 \le l \le L} \lambda_l \tag{8.2.74}$$

$$E_L(R, \rho, \mathbf{P}_L) = -\rho R - \frac{1}{L} \ln \left[\int_{-\infty}^{\infty} \cdots \int_{-\infty}^{\infty} \left(\int_{-\infty}^{\infty} \cdots \int_{-\infty}^{\infty} P_L(\hat{\mathbf{v}}) Q_L(\hat{\mathbf{u}} \mid \hat{\mathbf{v}})^{1/(1+\rho)}\, d\hat{\mathbf{v}}\right)^{1+\rho} d\hat{\mathbf{u}}\right] \tag{8.2.75}$$

$$\begin{aligned} P_L(\hat{\mathbf{v}}) &= \int_{-\infty}^{\infty} \cdots \int_{-\infty}^{\infty} P_L(\hat{\mathbf{v}} \mid \hat{\mathbf{u}}) Q_L(\hat{\mathbf{u}})\, d\hat{\mathbf{u}} \\ &= \prod_{l=1}^{L} P^{(l)}(\hat{v}_l) \end{aligned} \tag{8.2.76}$$

and

$$\begin{aligned} Q_L(\hat{\mathbf{u}} \mid \hat{\mathbf{v}}) &= \frac{P_L(\hat{\mathbf{v}} \mid \hat{\mathbf{u}}) Q_L(\hat{\mathbf{u}})}{P_L(\hat{\mathbf{v}})} \\ &= \prod_{l=1}^{L} Q^{(l)}(\hat{u}_l \mid \hat{v}_l) \end{aligned} \tag{8.2.77}$$

For a given parameter θ, choose (Tan [1975])

$$P^{(l)}(\hat{v}_l \mid \hat{u}_l) = \begin{cases} \delta(v_l) & \lambda_l \leq \theta \\ \dfrac{1}{\sqrt{2\pi\beta_l\theta}} e^{-(\hat{v}_l - \beta_l\hat{u}_l)^2/2\beta_l\theta} & \lambda_l > \theta \end{cases} \tag{8.2.78}$$

where

$$\beta_l = 1 - \frac{\theta}{\lambda_l} \tag{8.2.79}$$

This choice yields

$$D^{(l)} = \min(\theta, \lambda_l) \tag{8.2.80}$$

and

$$E_L(R, \rho, \mathbf{P}_L) = -\rho R - \frac{1}{L}\sum_{l=1}^{L} \max\left\{0, \frac{\rho}{2}\ln\left[\frac{\theta(1+\rho)}{\lambda_l + \rho\theta}\right]\right\} \tag{8.2.81}$$

Thus

$$\overline{d(\mathscr{B})} \leq \frac{1}{L}\sum_{l=1}^{L} \min(\theta, \lambda_l) + d_0 \exp\left[-\frac{L}{2}\left(-\rho R - \frac{1}{L}\sum_{l=1}^{L} \max\left\{0, \frac{\rho}{2}\ln\left[\frac{\theta(1+\rho)}{\lambda_l + \rho\theta}\right]\right\}\right)\right] \tag{8.2.82}$$

The Toeplitz distribution theorem gives

$$\lim_{L\to\infty} \frac{1}{L}\sum_{l=1}^{L} \min(\theta, \lambda_l) = D_\theta \tag{8.2.83}$$

and

$$\lim_{L\to\infty} \frac{1}{L}\sum_{l=1}^{L} \max\left\{0, \frac{\rho}{2}\ln\left[\frac{\theta(1+\rho)}{\lambda_l + \rho\theta}\right]\right\} = E_\infty(\rho, \theta) \tag{8.2.84}$$

where

$$E_\infty(\rho, \theta) = -\frac{1}{4\pi}\int_{-\pi}^{\pi} \max\left\{0, \rho\ln\left[\frac{\theta(1+\rho)}{\Phi(\omega) + \rho\theta}\right]\right\} d\omega \tag{8.2.85}$$

Here $E_\infty(\rho, \theta)$ has all the usual properties given in Lemma 7.2.2 where

$$\lim_{\rho\to 0} \frac{\partial E_\infty(\rho, \theta)}{\partial\rho} = R(D_\theta) \tag{8.2.86}$$

Defining

$$E(R, D_\theta) \equiv \max_{-1\leq\rho\leq 0} [-\rho R + E_\infty(\rho, \theta)] \tag{8.2.87}$$

we have that for each $\epsilon_1 > 0$ and $\epsilon_2 > 0$ there exists an integer $N_0(\theta, R, \epsilon_1, \epsilon_2)$ such that for each $L \geq N_0$ there exists a block code $\mathscr{B}$ of rate R and block length L such that

$$d(\mathscr{B}) \leq D_\theta + \epsilon_1 + \sqrt{3}\,\Delta e^{-(L/2)[E(R, D_\theta) - \epsilon_2]} \tag{8.2.88}$$

where $E(R, D_\theta) > 0$ for $R > R(D_\theta)$.

This bound gives the rate of convergence to the rate distortion limit $(D_\theta, R(D_\theta))$ and can be generalized to continuous-time Gaussian sources and

Gaussian image sources together with the squared-error distortion measures. Explicit evaluation of the rate distortion function

$$R(D) = \lim_{L \to \infty} R_L(D)$$

as was done in this example is generally possible only if $R_L(D)$ can be expressed as the rate distortion function of a vector source with independent components and a sum distortion measure. Otherwise we must settle for bounds on $R(D)$.

8.3 BOUNDS FOR $R(D)$

For sources with memory, $R(D)$ is known exactly only for a few cases, primarily those involving Gaussian sources with a squared-error distortion measure. Easy-to-calculate bounds to $R(D)$ are therefore very important for general stationary ergodic sources. Lower bounds particularly are useful since they represent limits below which one cannot encode within the desired fidelity.

Recall that for stationary ergodic sources

$$\begin{aligned} R(D) &= \lim_{L \to \infty} R_L(D) \\ &= \inf_L R_L(D) \\ &\le R_1(D) \end{aligned} \tag{8.3.1}$$

Hence a trivial upper bound is $R_1(D)$, which may be found analytically or by using the computational methods of App. 7A. For a squared-error distortion measure, there is a more general version of Theorem 7.7.3 which shows that the Gaussian source has the largest rate distortion function.

Theorem 8.3.1 For any zero-mean stationary ergodic source with spectral density

$$\Phi(\omega) = \sum_{k=-\infty}^{\infty} \phi_k \, e^{-ik\omega} \tag{8.3.2}$$

where $\phi_k = E\{u_t u_{t+k}\}$ and the squared-error distortion measure, the rate distortion function $R(D)$ is bounded by

$$R(D) \le \frac{1}{4\pi} \int_{-\pi}^{\pi} \max \left[0, \ln \frac{\Phi(\omega)}{\theta}\right] d\omega \tag{8.3.3}$$

where θ satisfies

$$D = \frac{1}{2\pi} \int_{-\pi}^{\pi} \min \left[\theta, \Phi(\omega)\right] d\omega \tag{8.3.4}$$

That is, for a given spectral density, the Gaussian source yields the largest rate distortion function.

PROOF Recall from (8.2.55) that $\Phi = \Gamma \Lambda \Gamma^T$, and $\Lambda = \text{diag}(\lambda_1, \ldots, \lambda_L)$ is the diagonal matrix of eigenvalues of Φ. The components of $\hat{\mathbf{u}} = \mathbf{u}\Gamma$ are uncorrelated random variables with covariance matrix Λ. The rate distortion function $R_L(D)$ can be expressed in terms of these transformed coordinates. Now recall from Theorem 8.1.1 that

$$R_L(D) \le \hat{R}_L(D) \tag{8.3.5}$$

where $\hat{R}_L(D)$ is the rate distortion function obtained if the coordinates of $\hat{\mathbf{u}} = \mathbf{u}\Gamma$ are independent. $\hat{R}_L(D)$, on the other hand, is given by the parametric equations (see Lemma 8.1.1)

$$D_s = \frac{1}{L} \sum_{l=1}^{L} D_s^{(l)} \tag{8.3.6}$$

and

$$\hat{R}_L(D_s) = \frac{1}{L} \sum_{l=1}^{L} R^{(l)}(D_s^{(l)}) \tag{8.3.7}$$

where $R^{(l)}(D_s^{(l)})$ is the rate distortion function of the lth component source with the squared-error distortion measure. From Theorem 7.7.3, there is the further bound

$$R^{(l)}(D_s^{(l)}) \le \tfrac{1}{2} \max\left(0, \ln \frac{\sigma^2}{D_s^{(l)}}\right) \tag{8.3.8}$$

Thus

$$R_L(D) \le R_L^g(D) \tag{8.3.9}$$

where $R_L^g(D)$ is the rate distortion function for the Gaussian source with the same spectral density. Taking the limit as $L \to \infty$, we get the desired result.

Thus we have shown that one general upper bound on $R(D)$ is simply $R_1(D)$, the first-order rate distortion function, while for the squared-error distortion, a bound can be obtained which is the known rate distortion function of a Gaussian source with the same covariance properties. Lower bounds can also be found by generalizing the lower bounds for memoryless sources.

Suppose we have a continuous-amplitude stationary ergodic source and some distortion measure. Let $R_L(D)$ be its Lth-order rate distortion function. The L-dimensional version of Theorem 7.6.3 is

$$R_L(D) = \sup_{s \le 0,\ \lambda_L \in \Lambda_{s,L}} \left[sD + \frac{1}{L} \int_{-\infty}^{\infty} \cdots \int_{-\infty}^{\infty} Q_L(\mathbf{u}) \ln \lambda_L(\mathbf{u})\, d\mathbf{u} \right] \tag{8.3.10}$$

where

$$\Lambda_{s,L} = \left\{ \lambda_L(\mathbf{u}) : \int_{-\infty}^{\infty} \cdots \int_{-\infty}^{\infty} \lambda_L(\mathbf{u}) Q_L(\mathbf{u}) e^{s d_L(\mathbf{u},\mathbf{v})}\, d\mathbf{u} \le 1,\ \ \mathbf{v} \in \mathscr{V}_L \right\} \tag{8.3.11}$$

Now choose

$$\lambda_L(\mathbf{u}) = \frac{1}{Q_L(\mathbf{u})} \prod_{l=1}^{L} \lambda(u_l) Q(u_l) \tag{8.3.12}$$

where $\boldsymbol{\lambda} \in \Lambda_s$. Then

$$R_L(D) \geq \frac{1}{L} h(\mathscr{U}_L) - h(\mathscr{U}) + \sup_{s \leq 0,\, \lambda \in \Lambda_s} \left(sD + \int_{-\infty}^{\infty} Q(u) \ln \lambda(u)\, du \right)$$

$$= R_1(D) + \frac{1}{L} h(\mathscr{U}_L) - h(\mathscr{U}) \tag{8.3.13}$$

where

$$h(\mathscr{U}_L) = -\int_{-\infty}^{\infty} \cdots \int_{-\infty}^{\infty} Q_L(\mathbf{u}) \ln Q_L(\mathbf{u})\, d\mathbf{u} \tag{8.3.14}$$

This results in the following theorem.

Theorem 8.3.2 For a stationary ergodic source with rate distortion function

$$R(D) = \lim_{L \to \infty} R_L(D)$$

there is the lower bound

$$R(D) \geq R_1(D) + h - h(\mathscr{U}) \tag{8.3.15}$$

where

$$h(\mathscr{U}) = -\int_{-\infty}^{\infty} Q(u) \ln Q(u)\, du \tag{8.3.16}$$

is the first-order differential entropy rate of the source and

$$h = -\lim_{L \to \infty} \frac{1}{L} \int_{-\infty}^{\infty} \cdots \int_{-\infty}^{\infty} Q_L(\mathbf{u}) \ln Q_L(\mathbf{u})\, d\mathbf{u} \tag{8.3.17}$$

is the differential entropy rate of the source.

PROOF Take the limit as $L \to \infty$ in (8.3.13). The limiting value h exists and is approached monotonically from above (see Fano [1961]).

In this general lower bound, we express the bound in terms of $R_1(D)$, which can usually be found by computational methods. Of course, further lower bounds exist for $R_1(D)$, as described in Sec. 7.7. For difference distortion measures there is also a generalized Shannon lower bound (see Prob. 8.7) given by[6]

$$R(D_s) \geq R_{LB}(D_s) = h + sD_s - \ln \left[\int_{-\infty}^{\infty} e^{sd(z)}\, dz \right] \tag{8.3.18}$$

where D_s is the distortion level associated with parameter s.

[6] We assume

$$\int_{-\infty}^{\infty} e^{sd(z)}\, dz < \infty$$

Corollary 8.3.3 For a stationary Gaussian source with spectral density function $\Phi(\omega)$ and the squared-error distortion measure, the rate distortion function, $R(D)$, is bounded from below by

$$R(D) \geq R_{LB}(D) = \tfrac{1}{2} \ln \frac{E}{D} \tag{8.3.19}$$

where

$$E = \exp \left\{ \frac{1}{2\pi} \int_{-\pi}^{\pi} \ln \Phi(\omega)\, d\omega \right\} \tag{8.3.20}$$

is both the entropy rate power and the one-step prediction error of the Gaussian source (see Grenander and Szego [1958, chap. 10]). Moreover, $R(D) = R_{LB}(D)$ for $D \leq \delta$, where δ is the essential infimum of $\Phi(\omega)$.

PROOF For the Gaussian source where

$$R_1(D) = \tfrac{1}{2} \ln \frac{\sigma^2}{D} \tag{8.3.21}$$

we have

$$h(\mathscr{U}) = \tfrac{1}{2} \ln (2\pi e \sigma^2) \tag{8.3.22}$$

and

$$h = \tfrac{1}{2} \ln (2\pi e E) \tag{8.3.23}$$

(see Prob. 8.8). Thus

$$\begin{aligned} R_{LB}(D) &= R_1(D) + h - h(\mathscr{U}) \\ &= \tfrac{1}{2} \ln \frac{\sigma^2}{D} + \tfrac{1}{2} \ln (2\pi e E) - \tfrac{1}{2} \ln (2\pi e \sigma^2) \\ &= \tfrac{1}{2} \ln \frac{E}{D} \end{aligned} \tag{8.3.24}$$

From (8.2.69) and (8.2.70), we see that if $\theta \leq \delta$ then

$$\begin{aligned} D_\theta &= \frac{1}{2\pi} \int_{-\pi}^{\pi} \min\, [\theta, \Phi(\omega)]\, d\omega \\ &= \theta \end{aligned} \tag{8.3.25}$$

and

$$\begin{aligned} R(D) &= \frac{1}{4\pi} \int_{-\pi}^{\pi} \max \left[0, \ln \frac{\Phi(\omega)}{\theta}\right] d\omega \\ &= \frac{1}{4\pi} \int_{-\pi}^{\pi} \ln \frac{\Phi(\omega)}{\theta}\, d\omega \\ &= \frac{1}{2} \left[\frac{1}{2\pi} \int_{-\pi}^{\pi} \ln \Phi(\omega)\, d\omega - \ln D \right] \\ &= \tfrac{1}{2} \ln \frac{E}{D} \end{aligned} \tag{8.3.26}$$

As just shown in the Gaussian case, the generalized Shannon lower bound given by (8.3.15) is often equal to $R(D)$ for a range of small D. The examples of Sec. 7.7 imply that in most cases the Shannon lower bound is fairly tight for all D.

8.4 GAUSSIAN SOURCES WITH SQUARED-ERROR DISTORTION

Up to this point we have always assumed that the source probability distributions and the distortion measure are given. In practice, statistical properties of real sources are not known a priori and must be determined by measurement. Typically only the mean and correlation properties of a source are available. These first- and second-order statistics of a source are sufficient to completely characterize a source if it is Gaussian, an assumption which is often made in practice. In many cases one can justify the Gaussian assumption with a central limit theorem argument. The choice of distortion measure depends on the application, and again it is usually not known a priori. In speech and picture compression applications, for example, there have been evaluations of various distortion measures based on subjective fidelity ratings of compressed speech and pictures. In practice, the most commonly used distortion measure is the squared-error distortion.

For the most part in data compression practice, the sources are assumed to be Gaussian and the distortion measure is assumed to be squared error. Theorem 8.3.1 shows that, for the squared-error distortion measure, the Gaussian assumption results in the maximum rate distortion function. Thus for a given fidelity D, the value of the rate distortion function of the Gaussian source $R(D)$ is an achievable rate regardless of whether or not the source is Gaussian. Another important point is the fact that the Gaussian source with the squared-error distortion measure is the only example where the rate distortion function is easily obtained for all sorts of generalizations. These serve as a baseline with which various compression techniques can be compared. We look first at quantization of a memoryless Gaussian source and compare the resulting averaged squared error with the corresponding distortion that is achievable according to the rate distortion function. Then we examine more general Gaussian sources with memory and find expressions for their rate distortion functions.

8.4.1 Quantization of Discrete-Time Memoryless Sources

We begin with the simplest of sources, the discrete-time memoryless Gaussian source with the squared-error distortion measure, where the rate distortion function is given by (7.7.20)

$$R(D) = \tfrac{1}{2} \ln \frac{\sigma^2}{D} \qquad 0 \leq D \leq \sigma^2$$

Here the source outputs are independent Gaussian random variables with zero mean and variance σ^2. For this example, $R(D)$ represents the minimum rate required to achieve average squared-error distortion D and, as shown by Theorem 7.7.3, even for non-Gaussian sources, $R(D)$ given above represents an achievable rate for the squared-error distortion measure.

The simplest and most common data compression technique is quantization of the real-valued outputs of the source. An m-level quantizer, for example, converts each source output $u \in \mathcal{R}$ into one of m values $q_1, q_2, \ldots, q_m$. This can best be described in terms of thresholds $T_1, T_2, \ldots, T_{m-1}$ where the source output $u \in \mathcal{R}$ is converted to $q(u) \in \{q_1, q_2, \ldots, q_m\}$ according to

$$q(u) = \begin{cases} q_1 & u \le T_1 \\ q_l & T_{l-1} < u \le T_l \qquad l = 2, 3, \ldots, m-1 \\ q_m & T_{m-1} < u \end{cases} \tag{8.4.1}$$

The m-level quantizer converts each source output independently of other outputs and yields an average distortion

$$D_m = \sum_{l=1}^{m} \int_{T_{l-1}}^{T_l} (u - q_l)^2 \frac{1}{\sqrt{2\pi\sigma^2}} e^{-u^2/2\sigma^2} \, du \tag{8.4.2}$$

where we take $T_0 = -\infty$ and $T_m = \infty$. Since there are m quantized values, this requires at most $R_m = \ln m$ nats per output of the source to send over the channel the exact quantized values. In Fig. 8.2, we plot the theoretical limit $(D, R(D))$ together with (D_m, R_m) for various values of m. Here we take the values of $\{q_1, q_2, \ldots, q_m\}$ and thresholds $\{T_1, \ldots, T_{m-1}\}$ that minimize D_m as determined by Lloyd [1959] and Max [1960].

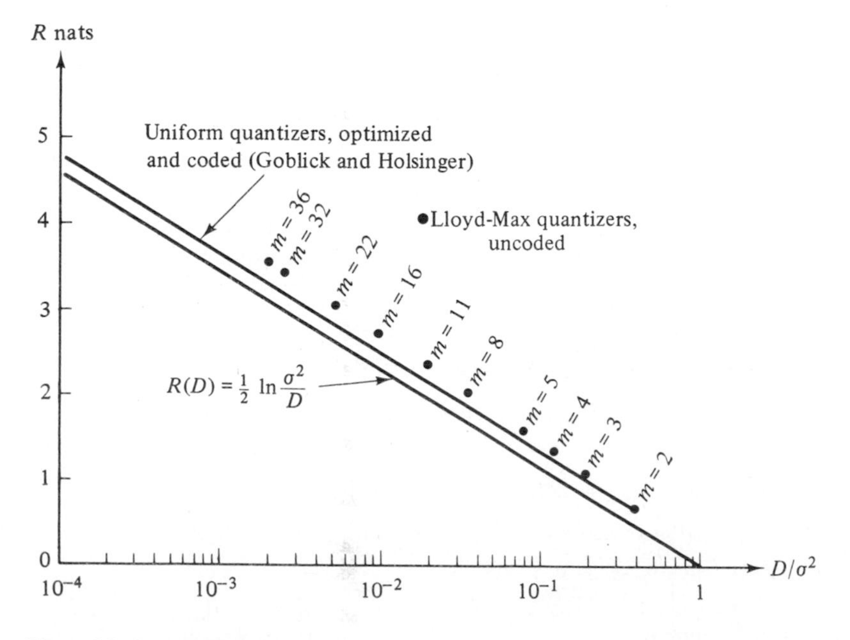

Figure 8.2 Quantization techniques.

The quantization technique can be improved by observing that quantization level q_l has probability

$$P_l = \int_{T_{l-1}}^{T_l} \frac{1}{\sqrt{2\pi\sigma^2}} e^{-u^2/2\sigma^2}\, du$$
$$= Q\left(\frac{T_{l-1}}{\sigma}\right) - Q\left(\frac{T_l}{\sigma}\right) \tag{8.4.3}$$

and the entropy of the quantized values is

$$H_m = -\sum_{l=1}^{m} P_l \ln P_l$$
$$\leq \ln m \tag{8.4.4}$$

We can encode without distortion (see Chap. 1) the quantized source outputs with rate arbitrarily close to H_m. Goblick and Holsinger [1967] investigated the minimization of H_m by varying m, $\{q_l\}$, and $\{T_l\}$, subject to the requirement that $D_m \leq D$ for uniform $T_l - T_{l-1}$. Their results consist of a family of uniform quantizers whose performance envelope is shown in Fig. 8.2. Quantization with distortionless coding of the quantized source outputs results in a required rate which is only about 0.2 nats per source output more than the theoretical limit given by the rate distortion function $R(D) = \frac{1}{2} \ln (\sigma^2/D)$. This is not too surprising since the source is memoryless. Also, the distortionless source coding of the quantized values requires both memory and the use of codewords similar to the procedure for encoding the source directly with a fidelity criterion. If distortionless coding is not used, then the performance gets worse as rate increases, as shown by the Lloyd–Max quantizers in Fig. 8.2.

Although our example is based on the Gaussian memoryless source with squared-error distortion measure, for a large class of memoryless sources and distortion measures, the simple quantization technique should result in performance close to the theoretical rate distortion limit. Quantization followed by distortionless coding of the quantized values will further improve the performance. This example points out the fact that, in practice for most memoryless sources, quantization is an efficient technique. For real-valued sources with memory and for more general sources, quantization by itself is no longer adequate.

8.4.2 Discrete-Time Stationary Sources

Consider next a discrete-time stationary (ergodic) Gaussian source with output autocorrelation

$$\phi_k = E\{u_t u_{t+k}\} \qquad \text{all } t, k \tag{8.4.5}$$

For the squared-error distortion measure, the rate distortion function is given in terms of parameter θ in (8.2.69) and (8.2.70)

$$D_\theta = \frac{1}{2\pi}\int_{-\pi}^{\pi} \min\,[\theta, \Phi(\omega)]\, d\omega \qquad \text{and} \qquad R(D_\theta) = \frac{1}{4\pi}\int_{-\pi}^{\pi} \max\left[0, \ln \frac{\Phi(\omega)}{\theta}\right] d\omega$$

where

$$\Phi(\omega) = \sum_{k=-\infty}^{\infty} \phi_k \, e^{-ik\omega} \tag{8.4.6}$$

Recall from the example in Sec. 8.2 that the above rate distortion function was derived by considering the encoding of transformed source outputs. In particular, for large integer N, let Γ be the unitary modal matrix of the correlation matrix

$$\Phi = \{\phi_{|i-j|}\}_{i,\, j=1}^{N}$$

and transform each source output sequence of length N, $\mathbf{u} \in \mathscr{R}_N$, into $\hat{\mathbf{u}} = \mathbf{u}\Gamma$. The components of $\hat{\mathbf{u}}$ are uncorrelated (also independent for this Gaussian source). The Nth-order rate distortion function can be determined by regarding each component of $\hat{\mathbf{u}}$ as an independent output of a memoryless source, where an output occurs each time N actual source outputs occur. There is no loss in encoding the transformed variables, since the transformation preserves the squared-error distortion measure. That is, for $\hat{\mathbf{u}} = \mathbf{u}\Gamma$ and $\hat{\mathbf{v}} = \mathbf{v}\Gamma$, we have

$$\begin{aligned} d_N(\hat{\mathbf{u}}, \hat{\mathbf{v}}) &= \frac{1}{N} \|\hat{\mathbf{u}} - \hat{\mathbf{v}}\|^2 \\ &= \frac{1}{N} \|\mathbf{u} - \mathbf{v}\|^2 \\ &= d_N(\mathbf{u}, \mathbf{v}) \end{aligned} \tag{8.4.7}$$

We have already shown in Sec. 8.4.1 that, for a memoryless Gaussian source, quantization of the source outputs is an efficient way to encode. For a Gaussian source with correlated outputs, this suggests that we should first transform the source output sequence into an uncorrelated sequence and then quantize. This is in fact the most common data compression procedure. We may argue intuitively that since we have an efficient and simple data compression technique for memoryless sources, we should first "whiten" the source output sequence and by so transforming it, obtain a memoryless (uncorrelated) sequence which can thus be efficiently encoded by quantization. The transformation should be chosen so as to preserve the distortion measure. For example, let T be an invertible transformation so that the output sequence $\mathbf{u}$ is transformed into the uncorrelated sequence $\hat{\mathbf{u}} = \mathbf{u}T$. Let $\hat{\mathbf{q}}$ be the quantized sequence of $\hat{\mathbf{u}}$ and assume this is sent over the noiseless channel. The decoder uses $\mathbf{q} = \hat{\mathbf{q}}T^{-1}$ as the representation of the source sequence $\mathbf{u}$.

For the squared-error distortion measure, the unitary modal matrix of the covariance matrix satisfies this requirement. Here, quantization may be slightly more general in that different quantizers may be applied to different components of the uncorrelated sequence $\hat{\mathbf{u}}$.

8.4.3 Continuous-Time Sources and Generalizations

Up to this point we have examined only discrete-time sources with source alphabets which are sets of real numbers. Many common information sources with outputs such as voice waveforms and pictures can be modeled as discrete-time real-valued sources only if the source has been sampled in an appropriate manner. In this section we take the approach of modeling all such more general sources as discrete-time sources with abstract alphabets. For continuous-time sources such as voice, for example, we consider sources that emit a continuous-time waveform each unit of time. Thus each unit of time the discrete-time model for a voice source emits an element belonging to the more abstract alphabet of continuous-time functions. Picture sources or television can similarly be modeled as a discrete-time source with the source alphabet consisting of pictures. Hence, by allowing the source alphabets to lie in more general spaces, we can model more general classes of sources.

The corresponding source coding problem for general sources modeled in this manner can be formulated conceptually in the same way as for those with real source alphabets. Defining appropriate probability measures on the abstract source and representation alphabets and defining a distortion measure between elements in these alphabets, Berger [1971] has formulated the problem in this more abstract setting. The resulting rate distortion functions are defined in terms of mutual information between source and representation alphabets in the same manner as those given earlier for stationary ergodic sources with real alphabets. The main difference lies in the more general probability measures required for the abstract alphabets.

We do not attempt to prove coding theorems for discrete-time stationary ergodic sources with abstract alphabets. Indeed, we will not even define the corresponding rate distortion function. Besides requiring some measure-theoretic definitions, generally these rate distortion functions are difficult to evaluate and are known exactly only for some special cases. In this section, we present only a few of the known cases for which the rate distortion function can be evaluated by reducing the source outputs to a countable collection of independent random variables, and where the distortion measure can be defined in terms of these representative random variables.

Before proceeding with various examples we point out that, although we can derive rate distortion functions for sources with abstract alphabets, to achieve the limiting distortions implied by these functions requires coding with codewords whose components are elements from the abstract representation alphabet. In practice this is usually too difficult to accomplish. The rate distortion function does, however, set theoretical limits on performance and often motivates the design of more practical source encoding (data compression) schemes. The Gaussian source with squared-error distortion which is presented here represents the worst case for the commonly used squared-error criterion. This and the subsequent examples are often used as standards of comparison for practical data compression schemes.

Continuous-time Gaussian process, squared-error distortion Consider a source that emits the zero-mean random process of T seconds duration, $\{u(t): 0 \le t \le T\}$. As we stated above, our approach is to model this source as a stationary ergodic discrete-time source with source alphabet consisting of time waveforms of duration T. Assume the energy of the output samples to be finite and choose the source alphabet to be

$$\mathcal{U} = \left\{u(t): \int_0^T u^2(t)\, dt < \infty\right\} \tag{8.4.9}$$

and the representation alphabet to be

$$\mathcal{V} = \left\{v(t): \int_0^T v^2(t)\, dt < \infty\right\} \tag{8.4.10}$$

That is, our abstract alphabets are $\mathcal{U} = \mathcal{V} = L_2(T)$, the space of square-integrable functions over the interval $0 \le t \le T$, and the distortion measure

$$d_T: \mathcal{U} \times \mathcal{V} \to [0, \infty) \tag{8.4.11}$$

satisfies a bounded second moment condition. The rate distortion function is defined as a limit of average mutual information defined on abstract spaces $\mathcal{U}_N$ and $\mathcal{V}_N$. For stationary ergodic discrete-time sources with these alphabets, there are coding theorems which establish that the rate distortion function does in fact represent the minimum possible rate to achieve the given distortion.

Modeling sources which generate continuous-time random processes as discrete-time sources is somewhat artificial since we do not assume continuity of the random process between successive source outputs (see Berger [1971]). Rather, we usually have a single continuous random process of long duration which we wish to encode efficiently. Still, in our discrete-time model, by letting the signal duration T get large, we can usually reduce the source to a memoryless vector source with outputs of duration T. This is analogous to the arguments in the heuristic proof of the coding theorem for stationary ergodic sources given in Sec. 8.2. When we assume the discrete-time source is memoryless, then the rate distortion function depends only on the single output probability measure, namely on the space $\mathcal{U} \times \mathcal{V}$ and the distortion $d_T: \mathcal{U} \times \mathcal{V} \to [0, \infty)$. We denote this rate distortion function as $R_T(D)$.

Even with the memoryless assumption, the rate distortion function $R_T(D)$ is difficult to evaluate. The key to its evaluation is the reduction of the problem from one involving continuous-time random processes to one involving a countable number of random variables. A natural step is to represent the output and representation waveforms[7] in terms of an orthonormal basis $\{f_k(t)\}$ for $L_2(T)$ such that

$$u(t) = \sum_{k=1}^{\infty} u^{(k)} f_k(t) \qquad 0 \leq t \leq T \tag{8.4.12}$$

and

$$v(t) = \sum_{k=1}^{\infty} v^{(k)} f_k(t) \qquad 0 \leq t \leq T \tag{8.4.13}$$

for any $u \in \mathscr{U}$ and $v \in \mathscr{V}$. If now the distortion measure $d_T: \mathscr{U} \times \mathscr{V} \to [0, \infty)$ can be expressed in terms of the coefficients $\{u^{(k)}\}$ and $\{v^{(k)}\}$, then $R_T(D)$ is the rate distortion function of a memoryless source with a real vector output. Earlier in Sec. 8.1, we examined such rate distortion functions for the sum distortion measure

$$d(u, v) \equiv \sum_{k=1}^{\infty} d^{(k)}(u^{(k)}, v^{(k)}) \tag{8.4.14}$$

All known evaluations of $R_T(D)$ involve reduction to not only a memoryless vector source with a sum or maximum distortion measure, but to one having uncorrelated vector components. This can be easily accomplished by choosing the basis $\{f_k\}$ to be the Karhunen–Loève expansion of the source output process. That is, choose the $f_k(t)$ to be the orthonormal eigenfunctions of the integral equation

$$\int_0^T \phi(t, s) f(s)\, ds = \lambda f(t) \qquad 0 \leq t \leq T \tag{8.4.15}$$

where $\phi(t, s) = E\{u(t)u(s)\}$ is assumed to be both positive definite and absolutely integrable over the rectangle[8] $0 \leq s, t \leq T$.

For each normalized eigenfunction $f_k(t)$, the corresponding constant λ_k is an eigenvalue of $\phi(t, s)$. This choice of orthonormal basis yields the representation[9]

$$u(t) = \sum_{k=1}^{\infty} u^{(k)} f_k(t) \tag{8.4.16}$$

where

$$E\{u^{(k)} u^{(j)}\} = \lambda_k \delta_{kj} \qquad \text{for } k, j = 1, 2, \ldots \tag{8.4.17}$$

The choice of distortion measure is not always clear in practice. Yet, even though we are concerned with encoding a random process, there is no reason why we cannot choose distortion measures that depend directly on the expansion

[7] For source output $\{u(t): 0 \leq t \leq T\}$, this representation holds in the mean square sense uniformly in $t \in [0, T]$.

[8] This is a sufficient condition for the eigenfunctions $\{f_k\}$ to be complete in $L_2(T)$. However, completeness is not necessary, for we can, without loss of generality, restrict our spaces to the space spanned by the eigenfunctions.

[9] Without loss of generality, we can assume $\lambda_1 \geq \lambda_2 \geq \cdots$. If $\{u^{(k)}\}$ are mutually independent, this representation holds with probability one for each $t \in [0, T]$.

coefficients of the random process with respect to some orthonormal basis. Indeed, practical data compression schemes essentially use this type of distortion measure. The squared-error distortion measure lends itself naturally to such a choice for while $d_T: u \times v \to [0, \infty)$ is given by

$$d_T(u, v) = \frac{1}{T} \int_0^T [u(t) - v(t)]^2 \, dt \tag{8.4.18}$$

it may also be expressed in terms of the Karhunen–Loève expansion coefficients

$$d_T(u, v) = \frac{1}{T} \sum_{k=1}^{\infty} (u^{(k)} - v^{(k)})^2 \tag{8.4.19}$$

The rate distortion function $R_T(D)$ is thus the rate distortion function of a memoryless vector source with uncorrelated components and a sum distortion measure. It follows from Lemma 7.7.3 and Theorem 8.1.1 that $R_T(D)$ is bounded by the corresponding rate distortion function for the Gaussian source. Thus from (8.2.65) and (8.2.66), we have

$$R_T(D) \leq \frac{1}{T} \sum_{k=1}^{\infty} \max\left(0, \tfrac{1}{2} \ln \frac{\lambda_k}{\theta}\right) \tag{8.4.20}$$

where θ satisfies

$$D = \frac{1}{T} \sum_{k=1}^{\infty} \min(\theta, \lambda_k) \tag{8.4.21}$$

Here (8.4.20) becomes an equality if and only if the continuous-time random process is Gaussian. Further, if we now let $T \to \infty$ and we assume the source output process is stationary with spectral density

$$\Phi(\omega) = \int_{-\infty}^{\infty} \phi(\tau) e^{-i\omega\tau} \, d\tau \tag{8.4.22}$$

where $\phi(\tau) = E\{u(t)u(t + \tau)\}$, then based on a continuous-time version of the Toeplitz distribution theorem (see Berger [1971], theorem 4.5.4)[10] we have

$$\lim_{T \to \infty} R_T(D) \leq \frac{1}{4\pi} \int_{-\infty}^{\infty} \max\left[0, \ln \frac{\Phi(\omega)}{\theta}\right] d\omega \tag{8.4.23}$$

where θ satisfies

$$D = \frac{1}{2\pi} \int_{-\infty}^{\infty} \min[\theta, \Phi(\omega)] \, d\omega \tag{8.4.24}$$

with equality if and only if the source output process is Gaussian.

[10] This requires finite second moment, $\phi(0) < \infty$, and finite essential supremum of $\Phi(\omega)$.

Again we see that for the squared-error distortion measure the Gaussian source statistics yield the largest rate distortion function among all stationary processes with the same spectral density $\Phi(\omega)$. The Gaussian source rate distortion function

$$R^g(D) = \frac{1}{4\pi} \int_{-\infty}^{\infty} \max \left[0, \ln \frac{\Phi(\omega)}{\theta}\right] d\omega \tag{8.4.25}$$

where θ satisfies (8.4.24) often serves as a basis for comparing various practical data compression schemes.

Example (Band-limited Gaussian source) An ideal band-limited Gaussian source with constant spectral density

$$\Phi(\omega) = \begin{cases} \dfrac{\sigma^2}{W} & |\omega| \le 2\pi W \\ 0 & |\omega| > 2\pi W \end{cases} \tag{8.4.26}$$

yields the rate distortion function

$$R^g(D) = W \ln \frac{\sigma^2}{D} \qquad 0 \le D \le \sigma^2 \tag{8.4.27}$$

This is Shannon's [1948] classical formula. It is easy to see that this is also the rate distortion function for any stationary Gaussian source of average power σ^2 whose spectral density is flat over any set of radian frequencies of total measure W.

Gaussian images, squared-error distortion Information sources that produce pictures (two-dimensional images) may be modeled as discrete-time sources with outputs that are two-dimensional random fields represented by

$$\left\{u(x, y);\ |x| \le \frac{L}{2},\ |y| \le \frac{L}{2}\right\} \tag{8.4.28}$$

Images are usually described by the nonnegative image intensity function $\{i(x, y); |x| \le L/2, |y| \le L/2\}$. We assume that the source output is $u(x, y) = \ln i(x, y)$, which is modeled here as a zero-mean Gaussian random field. In addition, if $u(x, y)$ and $v(x, y)$ are any two-dimensional functions, we define the distortion measure to be

$$d_L(u, v) = \frac{1}{L^2} \int_{-L/2}^{L/2} \int_{-L/2}^{L/2} [u(x, y) - v(x, y)]^2\, dx\, dy \tag{8.4.29}$$

The fact that we encode $u(x, y) = \ln i(x, y)$, the log of the intensity function, with a mean square criterion may appear somewhat artificial. There is, however, evidence (see Campbell and Robson [1968] and Van Ness and Bouman [1965]) that an observer's ability to determine the difference between two field intensities corresponds to the difference between corresponding transformed fields of the logarithm of the intensities.

Thus, for sources that produce two-dimensional images, we model our source as a discrete-time source that outputs a zero-mean Gaussian random field. The abstract source and representation alphabets are assumed to be

$$\mathcal{U} = \mathcal{V} = \left\{ u(x, y) \colon \int_{-L/2}^{L/2} \int_{-L/2}^{L/2} u^2(x, y)\, dx\, dy < \infty \right\} \tag{8.4.30}$$

and we choose the squared-error distortion measure given by (8.4.29). If we assume the discrete-time source is stationary and ergodic, then a rate distortion function can be defined which represents the smallest rate achievable for a given average distortion. First assume that the discrete-time source is memoryless. This means that successive output images of the source are independent and the rate distortion function $R_L(D)$ depends only on the probability measures on $\mathcal{U} \times \mathcal{V}$ and the single output distortion measure given in (8.4.29).

For the memoryless case, evaluation of $R_L(D)$ is the natural generalization of the continuous-time problem given above. We begin by defining the autocorrelation function of the zero-mean Gaussian random field as

$$\phi(x, y; x', y') = E\{u(x, y)u(x', y')\} \tag{8.4.31}$$

To be able to evaluate $R_L(D)$, we again require a representation of source outputs in terms of a countable number of independent random variables, and again we attempt to express our distortion measure in terms of these random variables. With the squared-error distortion measure, any orthonormal expansion of the source output random field will suffice. To have independent components, however, we need the Karhunen–Loève expansion. We express outputs as

$$u(x, y) = \sum_{k=1}^{\infty} u^{(k)} f_k(x, y) \qquad |x| \le \frac{L}{2},\ |y| \le \frac{L}{2} \tag{8.4.32}$$

where

$$u^{(k)} = \int_{-L/2}^{L/2} \int_{-L/2}^{L/2} u(x, y) f_k(x, y)\, dx\, dy \tag{8.4.33}$$

and $\{f_k(x, y)\}$ are orthonormal functions (eigenfunctions) that are solutions to the integral equation

$$\lambda f(x, y) = \int_{-L/2}^{L/2} \int_{-L/2}^{L/2} \phi(x, y; x', y') f(x', y')\, dx'\, dy' \tag{8.4.34}$$

For each eigenfunction $f_k(x, y)$, the corresponding eigenvalue λ_k is nonnegative and satisfies the condition[11]

$$E\{u^{(k)}u^{(j)}\} = \lambda_k \delta_{kj} \qquad \text{for } k, j = 1, 2, \ldots \tag{8.4.35}$$

[11] Again we assume $\lambda_1 \ge \lambda_2 \ge \cdots$. This representation holds with probability one for every $x, y \in [-L/2, L/2]$.

As for the one-dimensional case, we assume that the autocorrelation $\phi(x, y; x', y')$ satisfies the conditions necessary to insure that the eigenfunctions $\{f_k\}$ span the alphabet space $\mathscr{U} = \mathscr{V}$. Thus for any two functions in $\mathscr{U} = \mathscr{V}$, we have

$$u(x, y) = \sum_{k=1}^{\infty} u^{(k)} f_k(x, y) \tag{8.4.36}$$

$$v(x, y) = \sum_{k=1}^{\infty} v^{(k)} f_k(x, y) \tag{8.4.37}$$

and the distortion measure becomes

$$d_L(u, v) = \frac{1}{L^2} \sum_{k=1}^{\infty} (u^{(k)} - v^{(k)})^2 \tag{8.4.38}$$

For this sum distortion measure, $R_L(D)$ is now expressed in terms of a memoryless vector source with output $\mathbf{u} = \{u^{(1)}, u^{(2)}, \ldots\}$ whose components are independent Gaussian random variables, with the variance of $u^{(k)}$ given by λ_k, for each k. The rate distortion function of the random field normalized to unit area is thus (see Sec. 8.2)

$$R_L(D) = \frac{1}{L^2} \sum_{k=1}^{\infty} \max\left(0, \tfrac{1}{2} \ln \frac{\lambda_k}{\theta}\right) \tag{8.4.39}$$

where θ satisfies

$$D = \frac{1}{L^2} \sum_{k=1}^{\infty} \min(\theta, \lambda_k) \tag{8.4.40}$$

Here $R_L(D)$ represents the minimum rate in nats per unit area required to encode the source with average distortion D or less.

Since eigenvalues are difficult to evaluate, $R_L(D)$ given in this form is not very useful. We now take the limit as L goes to infinity. Defining

$$R^g(D) \equiv \lim_{L \to \infty} R_L(D) \tag{8.4.41}$$

we observe that $R^g(D)$ represents the minimum rate over all choices of L and thus the minimum achievable rate per unit area. In addition, since for most images L is large compared to correlation distances, letting L approach infinity is a good approximation. To evaluate this limit we must now restrict our attention to homogeneous random fields where we have

$$\phi(x, y; x', y') = \phi(x - x', y - y') \tag{8.4.42}$$

This is the two-dimensional stationarity condition and allows us to define a two-dimensional spectral density function,

$$\Phi(w_x, w_y) = \int_{-\infty}^{\infty} \int_{-\infty}^{\infty} \phi(r_x, r_y) e^{-i(w_x r_x + w_y r_y)} \, dr_x \, dr_y \tag{8.4.43}$$

Sakrison [1969] has derived a two-dimensional version of the Toeplitz distribution theorem which allows us to evaluate the asymptotic distribution of the eigenvalues of (8.4.34). This theorem shows that for any continuous function $G(\lambda)$

$$\lim_{L\to\infty} \frac{1}{L^2} \sum_{k=1}^{\infty} G(\lambda_k) = \frac{1}{(2\pi)^2} \int_{-\infty}^{\infty} \int_{-\infty}^{\infty} G[\Phi(w_x, w_y)]\, dw_x\, dw_y \tag{8.4.44}$$

Applying this theorem to (8.4.39) and (8.4.40) yields

$$\begin{aligned} R^g(D) &= \lim_{L\to\infty} R_L(D) \\ &= \frac{1}{8\pi^2} \int_{-\infty}^{\infty} \int_{-\infty}^{\infty} \max\left[0, \ln \frac{\Phi(w_x, w_y)}{\theta}\right] dw_x\, dw_y \end{aligned} \tag{8.4.45}$$

where θ satisfies

$$D = \frac{1}{4\pi^2} \int_{-\infty}^{\infty} \int_{-\infty}^{\infty} \min\,[\theta, \Phi(w_x, w_y)]\, dw_x\, dw_y \tag{8.4.46}$$

As with our one-dimensional case, $R^g(D)$ is an upper bound to all other rate distortion functions of non-Gaussian memoryless sources with the same spectral density $\Phi(w_x, w_y)$, and thus serves as a basis for comparison for various image compression schemes.

Example (Isotropic field) An isotropic field has a correlation function which depends only on the total distance between two points in the two-dimensional space. That is,

$$\phi(r_x, r_y) = \tilde{\phi}(\sqrt{r_x^2 + r_y^2}) \tag{8.4.47}$$

By defining r, θ_r, w, and θ_w as polar coordinates where

$$r_x = r \cos \theta_r \qquad r_y = r \sin \theta_r \tag{8.4.48}$$

and

$$w_x = w \cos \theta_w \qquad w_y = w \sin \theta_w \tag{8.4.49}$$

we obtain

$$\begin{aligned} \tilde{\Phi}(w, \theta_w) &\equiv \Phi(w_x, w_y) \\ &= \int_{-\infty}^{\infty} \int_{-\infty}^{\infty} \phi(r_x, r_y) e^{-iw(r_x \cos\theta_w + r_y \sin\theta_w)}\, dr_x\, dr_y \\ &= \int_0^{\infty} \int_0^{2\pi} \tilde{\phi}(r) e^{-iwr(\cos\theta_r \cos\theta_w + \sin\theta_r \sin\theta_w)} r\, dr\, d\theta_r \\ &= \int_0^{\infty} \tilde{\phi}(r) \left(\int_0^{2\pi} e^{-iwr\cos(\theta_w - \theta_r)}\, d\theta_r \right) r\, dr \\ &= 2\pi \int_0^{\infty} \tilde{\phi}(r) J_0(wr) r\, dr \end{aligned} \tag{8.4.50}$$

where $J_0(\cdot)$ is the zeroth order Bessel function of the first kind. Since there is no θ_w dependence

$$\tilde{\Phi}(w) = 2\pi \int_0^{\infty} r\tilde{\phi}(r) J_0(wr)\, dr \tag{8.4.51}$$

where

$$\tilde{\Phi}(w) = \Phi(w_x, w_y) \qquad \tilde{\phi}(r) = \phi(r_x, r_y)$$
$$w = \sqrt{w_x^2 + w_y^2} \qquad r = \sqrt{r_x^2 + r_y^2} \tag{8.4.52}$$

$\tilde{\Phi}(w)$ and $\tilde{\phi}(r)$ are related by the Hankel transform of zero order.

For television images, a reasonably satisfactory power spectral density is

$$\tilde{\Phi}(w) = \frac{2w_0}{w_0^2 + w^2} \tag{8.4.53}$$

resulting in

$$\tilde{\phi}(r) = e^{-|r|/d_c} \tag{8.4.54}$$

where $d_c = 1/w_0$ is the coherence distance of the field (Sakrison and Algazi [1971]).

For many sources successive images are often highly correlated so that the above memoryless assumption is unrealistic. We now find an upper bound to the rate distortion function of a discrete-time stationary ergodic source that emits the two-dimensional homogenous Gaussian random field described above. Let the nth output be denoted

$$\left\{u_n(x, y): |x| \le \frac{L}{2}, |y| \le \frac{L}{2}\right\} \tag{8.4.55}$$

Again use the usual Karhunen–Loève expansion

$$u_n(x, y) = \sum_{k=1}^{\infty} u_n^{(k)} f_k(x, y) \tag{8.4.56}$$

where $\{f_k(\cdot, \cdot)\}$ and $\{\lambda_k\}$ are eigenfunctions and eigenvalues which satisfy the integral equation of (8.4.34). By the assumed stationarity of the discrete-time source with memory, the autocorrelation of the random field $\phi(x, y; x', y')$ is independent of the output time index n, and hence eigenfunctions and eigenvalues are the same for each output of the discrete-time stationary ergodic source. We now have a source that outputs a vector $u_n = (u_n^{(1)}, u_n^{(2)}, \ldots)$ at the nth time.

The rate distortion function of the discrete-time stationary ergodic source is given by

$$R_L(D) = \lim_{N \to \infty} R_{L, N}(D) \tag{8.4.57}$$

where $R_{L, N}(D)$ is the Nth-order rate distortion function [i.e., which uses only the first N terms in the expansion (8.4.56)]. We can upper-bound $R_L(D)$ by the rate required with any particular encoding scheme that achieves average distortion D. Consider the following scheme:

1. Encode each Karhunen–Loève expansion coefficient independently of other coefficients.[12] That is, regard the kth coefficient sequence $\{u_1^{(k)}, u_2^{(k)}, \ldots\}$ as the

[12] This amounts to partitioning the source into its spatial spectral components and treating successive (in time) samples of a given component as a subsource which is to be encoded independent of all other component subsources.

output of a zero-mean Gaussian subsource and encode it with respect to a squared-error distortion measure with average distortion $D^{(k)}$.

2. Choose the distortions $D^{(1)}$, $D^{(2)}$, ... so as to achieve an overall average distortion D.

The required rate for the above scheme, which we now proceed to evaluate, will certainly upper-bound $R_L(D)$. Let us define correlation functions for each subsource.

$$\phi^{(k)}(r) = E\{u_n^{(k)} u_{n+r}^{(k)}\} \tag{8.4.58}$$

and corresponding spectral density functions

$$\psi^{(k)}(w) = \sum_{r=-\infty}^{\infty} \phi^{(k)}(r) e^{-irw} \tag{8.4.59}$$

Consider encoding the sequence $\{u_1^{(k)}, u_2^{(k)}, \ldots\}$ with respect to the squared-error distortion measure. From (8.2.69) and (8.2.70), we see that for distortion $D^{(k)}$ the required rate is

$$R^{(k)}(D^{(k)}) = \frac{1}{4\pi} \int_{-\pi}^{\pi} \max \left[0, \ln \frac{\psi^{(k)}(w)}{\theta}\right] dw \tag{8.4.60}$$

where θ satisfies

$$D^{(k)} = \frac{1}{2\pi} \int_{-\pi}^{\pi} \min \left[\theta, \psi^{(k)}(w)\right] dw \tag{8.4.61}$$

Here $R^{(k)}(D^{(k)})$ is in nats per output of the subsource.

Recall that the total single-output distortion measure is

$$d_L(u, v) = \frac{1}{L^2} \sum_{k=1}^{\infty} (u^{(k)} - v^{(k)})^2 \tag{8.4.62}$$

Hence, choosing $\{D^{(k)}\}$ such that

$$D = \frac{1}{L^2} \sum_{k=1}^{\infty} D^{(k)} \tag{8.4.63}$$

will achieve average distortion D. The total rate per unit area is given by

$$\frac{1}{L^2} \sum_{k=1}^{\infty} R^{(k)}(D^{(k)}) \tag{8.4.64}$$

Thus we have

$$R_L(D) \le \frac{1}{L^2} \sum_{k=1}^{\infty} \frac{1}{4\pi} \int_{-\pi}^{\pi} \max \left[0, \ln \frac{\psi^{(k)}(w)}{\theta}\right] dw \tag{8.4.65}$$

where now we choose θ to satisfy

$$D = \frac{1}{L^2} \sum_{k=1}^{\infty} \frac{1}{2\pi} \int_{-\pi}^{\pi} \min \left[\theta, \psi^{(k)}(w)\right] dw \tag{8.4.66}$$

We consider next a special case for which this upper bound is tight.

Example (Separation of correlation) Suppose the time and spatial correlation of source outputs separate as follows:

$$E\{u_n(x, y)u_{n+\tau}(x', y')\} = \hat{\varphi}(\tau)\phi(x - x', y - y') \tag{8.4.67}$$

where $\hat{\varphi}(0) = 1$.

Recall that any two Karhunen–Loève expansion coefficients $u_n^{(k)}$ and $u_{n+\tau}^{(j)}$ are given by

$$\begin{aligned} u_n^{(k)} &= \int_{-L/2}^{L/2} \int_{-L/2}^{L/2} u_n(x, y) f_k(x, y)\, dx\, dy \\ u_{n+\tau}^{(j)} &= \int_{-L/2}^{L/2} \int_{-L/2}^{L/2} u_{n+\tau}(x, y) f_j(x, y)\, dx\, dy \end{aligned} \tag{8.4.68}$$

Thus we have correlation

$$\begin{aligned} E\{u_n^{(k)} u_{n+\tau}^{(j)}\} &= \int_{-L/2}^{L/2} \cdots \int_{-L/2}^{L/2} E\{u_n(x, y)u_{n+\tau}(x', y')\} f_k(x, y) f_j(x', y')\, dx\, dy\, dx'\, dy' \\ &= \int_{-L/2}^{L/2} \cdots \int_{-L/2}^{L/2} \hat{\varphi}(\tau)\phi(x - x', y - y') f_k(x, y) f_j(x', y')\, dx\, dy\, dx'\, dy' \\ &= \hat{\varphi}(\tau)\lambda_k \int_{-L/2}^{L/2} \int_{-L/2}^{L/2} f_k(x', y') f_j(x', y')\, dx'\, dy' \\ &= \lambda_k \hat{\varphi}(\tau)\delta_{kj} \end{aligned} \tag{8.4.69}$$

Hence

$$\begin{aligned} \varphi^k(\tau) &= E\{u_n^{(k)} u_{n+\tau}^{(k)}\} \\ &= \lambda_k \hat{\varphi}(\tau) \end{aligned} \tag{8.4.70}$$

and for any $k \neq j$

$$E\{u_n^{(k)} u_{n+\tau}^{(j)}\} = 0 \qquad \text{for all } \tau \tag{8.4.71}$$

Since we have Gaussian statistics, the uncorrelated random variables are independent random variables and the different Karhunen–Loève expansion coefficient sequences can be regarded as independent subsources. Lemma 8.1.1 shows that the upper bound given in (8.4.65) is in fact exact, and we have for this case

$$R_L(D) = \frac{1}{L^2} \sum_{k=1}^{\infty} \frac{1}{4\pi} \int_{-\pi}^{\pi} \max\left[0, \ln \frac{\lambda_k \hat{\psi}(w)}{\theta}\right] dw \tag{8.4.72}$$

where θ is chosen to satisfy

$$D = \frac{1}{L^2} \sum_{k=1}^{\infty} \frac{1}{2\pi} \int_{-\pi}^{\pi} \min\left[\theta, \lambda_k \hat{\psi}(w)\right] dw \tag{8.4.73}$$

Using (8.4.44) in taking the limit as $L \to \infty$, we have the limiting rate distortion function given by

$$\begin{aligned} R(D) &= \lim_{L \to \infty} R_L(D) \\ &= \frac{1}{16\pi^3} \int_{-\pi}^{\pi} \int_{-\infty}^{\infty} \int_{-\infty}^{\infty} \max\left[0, \ln \frac{\Phi(w_x, w_y)\hat{\psi}(w)}{\theta}\right] dw_x\, dw_y\, dw \end{aligned} \tag{8.4.74}$$

where θ satisfies

$$D = \frac{1}{8\pi^3} \int_{-\pi}^{\pi} \int_{-\infty}^{\infty} \int_{-\infty}^{\infty} \min\left[\theta, \Phi(w_x, w_y)\hat{\psi}(w)\right] dw_x\, dw_y\, dw \tag{8.4.75}$$

and where $\Phi(w_x, w_y)$ is given by (8.4.43) and

$$\hat{\psi}(w) = \sum_{\tau=-\infty}^{\infty} \hat{\varphi}(\tau)e^{-i\tau w}$$

This example shows that the particular scheme of encoding expansion coefficients independently of one another is an optimum encoding scheme when the time and spatial correlations are separated as in (8.4.67). This general idea of taking a complex source and decomposing it into independent subsources, which are encoded separately, is a basic design approach for practical data compression schemes.

8.5 SYMMETRIC SOURCES WITH BALANCED DISTORTION MEASURES AND FIXED COMPOSITION SEQUENCES

In Sec. 7.6 we found that for symmetric sources with balanced distortion measures, the rate distortion functions are easily obtained in closed parametric form [see (7.6.69) and (7.6.70)]. We now show that these symmetric sources with balanced distortion measures have the property that, for fixed rate arbitrarily close to $R(D)$ and sufficiently large block lengths, there exist codes that encode *every* source output sequence with distortion D or less. This is a considerably stronger result than that stated in Theorem 7.2.1 which shows this only for the *average* distortion. A similar strong result holds for the encoding of sequences of fixed composition of an arbitrary discrete source and this will lead us in the next section to the notion of robust source coding techniques that are independent of source statistics. We begin by restating the definition of symmetric sources and balanced distortion measures.

8.5.1 Symmetric Sources with Balanced Distortion Measures

A symmetric source is a discrete memoryless source with equally likely output letters. That is,

$$\mathscr{U} = \{a_1, a_2, \ldots, a_A\} \tag{8.5.1}$$

where

$$Q(a_k) = \frac{1}{A} \qquad k = 1, 2, \ldots, A \tag{8.5.2}$$

Assuming the same number of representation letters as source letters where $\mathscr{V} = \{b_1, b_2, \ldots, b_A\}$, for a balanced distortion measure, there exist nonnegative numbers $\{d_1, d_2, \ldots, d_A\}$ such that

$$\{d(u, b_1), d(u, b_2), \ldots, d(u, b_A)\} = \{d_1, d_2, \ldots, d_A\} \qquad \text{for all } u \in \mathscr{U}$$

and (8.5.3)

$$\{d(a_1, v), d(a_2, v), \ldots, d(a_A, v)\} = \{d_1, d_2, \ldots, d_A\} \qquad \text{for all } v \in \mathscr{V}$$

The rate distortion function $R(D)$ is given parametrically by

$$D = D_s = \frac{\sum_{k=1}^{A} d_k e^{sd_k}}{\sum_{k=1}^{A} e^{sd_k}} \tag{7.6.69}$$

$$R(D_s) = sD_s + \ln A - \ln\left(\sum_{k=1}^{A} e^{sd_k}\right) \tag{7.6.70}$$

where $s \leq 0$ is the independent parameter.

Consider again the block source encoding and decoding system of Fig. 7.3. As we did earlier, we prove a coding theorem by considering an ensemble of block codes of size M and block length N. By symmetry in this ensemble, we choose code $\mathscr{B} = \{\mathbf{v}_1, \mathbf{v}_2, \ldots, \mathbf{v}_M\}$ with uniform probability distribution, that is

$$P(\mathscr{B}) = \left(\frac{1}{A}\right)^{MN} \tag{8.5.4}$$

Here each code letter is chosen independently of other code letters and with a uniform one-dimensional probability distribution. Furthermore, since the distortion matrix is balanced, for fixed $u \in \mathscr{U}$, the random variable $d(u, v)$ is independent of u. That is, for any $u \in \mathscr{U}$

$$\Pr\{d(u, v) = d_k \,|\, u\} = \frac{1}{A} \qquad k = 1, 2, \ldots, A \tag{8.5.5}$$

This means that for any fidelity criterion D and any two source sequences $\mathbf{u}, \mathbf{u}' \in \mathscr{U}_N$ we have

$$\Pr\{d_N(\mathbf{u}, \mathbf{v}) > D \,|\, \mathbf{u}\} = \Pr\{d_N(\mathbf{u}', \mathbf{v}) > D \,|\, \mathbf{u}'\} \tag{8.5.6}$$

This is the key property of symmetric sources with balanced distortion measures which we now exploit.

Lemma 8.5.1 Given block length N, distortion level $D > D_{\min}$, and any source output sequence $\mathbf{u} \in \mathscr{U}_N$, over the ensemble of codes $\mathscr{B}$ of block length N and rate $R > R(D)$

$$\begin{aligned} \Pr\{d(\mathbf{u} \,|\, \mathscr{B}) > D \,|\, \mathbf{u}\} &\leq e^{-MF_N(D)} \\ &\leq e^{-\exp N[R - R(D) + o(N)]} \end{aligned} \tag{8.5.7}$$

where

$$o(N) \to 0 \qquad \text{as } N \to \infty$$

and

$$F_N(D) = \Pr\{d_N(\mathbf{u}, \mathbf{v}) \leq D \,|\, \mathbf{u}\} \tag{8.5.8}$$

is independent of $\mathbf{u} \in \mathscr{U}_N$.

PROOF Let $\mathscr{B} = \{\mathbf{v}_1, \mathbf{v}_2, \ldots, \mathbf{v}_M\}$. Then since code words are independent and identically distributed, according to (8.5.6)

$$\begin{aligned}
\Pr\{d(\mathbf{u} \mid \mathscr{B}) > D \mid \mathbf{u}\} &= \Pr\left\{\min_{\mathbf{v} \in \mathscr{B}} d_N(\mathbf{u}, \mathbf{v}) > D \mid \mathbf{u}\right\} \\
&= \Pr\{d_N(\mathbf{u}, \mathbf{v}_m) > D \colon m = 1, 2, \ldots, M \mid \mathbf{u}\} \\
&= \prod_{m=1}^{M} \Pr\{d_N(\mathbf{u}, \mathbf{v}_m) > D \mid \mathbf{u}\} \\
&= [1 - F_N(D)]^M \\
&\leq e^{-MF_N(D)}
\end{aligned} \tag{8.5.9}$$

where the inequality follows from $\ln x \leq x - 1$.

Next note that, for fixed $\mathbf{u} \in \mathscr{U}_N$

$$d_N(\mathbf{u}, \mathbf{v}) = \frac{1}{N} \sum_{n=1}^{N} d(u_n, v_n) \tag{8.5.10}$$

is a normalized sum of independent identically distributed random variables. In App. 8A we apply the Chernoff bounding technique to obtain for any $\epsilon > 0$

$$\left(1 - \frac{d_0^2}{N\epsilon^2}\right) e^{-N[R(D) - 2s\epsilon]} \leq F_N(D) \leq e^{-NR(D)} \tag{8.5.11}$$

where s satisfies

$$D - \epsilon = \frac{\sum_{k=1}^{A} d_k e^{sd_k}}{\sum_{k=1}^{A} e^{sd_k}} \tag{8.5.12}$$

We assume $D > D_{\min}$ and choose $\epsilon > 0$ small enough so that $D - \epsilon > D_{\min}$. This guarantees that s is finite and converges to a finite limit as $\epsilon \to 0$. In particular, choosing

$$\epsilon = \sqrt{\frac{\ln N}{N}} \tag{8.5.13}$$

we have

$$-[R(D) + o(N)] \leq \frac{1}{N} \ln F_N(D) \leq -R(D) \tag{8.5.14}$$

From this lemma it follows immediately that the average distortion $\overline{d(\mathscr{B})}$ satisfies

$$\overline{d(\mathscr{B})} \leq D + d_0 e^{-\exp N[R - R(D) + o(N)]} \tag{8.5.15}$$

and hence that there exists a code $\mathscr{B}$ for which $d(\mathscr{B})$ also satisfies this bound. Comparing this with Theorem 7.2.1, we see that this lemma is a stronger result since the second term here is decreasing at a double exponential rate with block length N, compared to the single exponential rate of Theorem 7.2.1. Another observation is that Lemma 8.5.1 holds regardless of the source probability distribution and is true even for sources with memory. This happens since we have a balanced distortion matrix and assume a uniform distribution on the code ensemble. Of course, when the source output probability distribution is not uniform, we cannot say that the $R(D)$ of the symmetric source is the rate distortion function. It is clear, however, that the rate distortion function of the symmetric source, $R(D)$, is an upper bound to the rate distortion functions of all other sources with the same balanced distortion, since we can always achieve distortion arbitrarily close to D with rate arbitrarily close to $R(D)$. We consider this in greater detail when we examine the problem of encoding source sequences of fixed composition. We next prove the source coding theorem for symmetric sources with balanced distortion measures.

Theorem 8.5.1 For a symmetric source with a balanced distortion measure and any rate R where $R > R(D)$, there exists a block code $\mathscr{B}$ of sufficiently large block length N and rate R such that

$$d(\mathbf{u} \mid \mathscr{B}) \le D \qquad \text{for all } \mathbf{u} \in \mathscr{U}_N \tag{8.5.16}$$

PROOF For any code $\mathscr{B}$ of block length N and rate R, define the indicator function

$$\Phi(\mathbf{u} \mid \mathscr{B}) \equiv \begin{cases} 1 & d(\mathbf{u} \mid \mathscr{B}) > D \\ 0 & d(\mathbf{u} \mid \mathscr{B}) \le D \end{cases} \tag{8.5.17}$$

for $\mathbf{u} \in \mathscr{U}_N$. Averaging Φ over source output sequences gives

$$\sum_{\mathbf{u}} Q_N(\mathbf{u})\Phi(\mathbf{u} \mid \mathscr{B}) = \frac{1}{A^N} \sum_{\mathbf{u}} \Phi(\mathbf{u} \mid \mathscr{B}) \tag{8.5.18}$$

Averaging this over the ensemble of codes yields

$$\begin{aligned} \frac{1}{A^N} \overline{\sum_{\mathbf{u}} \Phi(\mathbf{u} \mid \mathscr{B})} &= \sum_{\mathbf{u}} \sum_{\mathscr{B}} Q_N(\mathbf{u}) P(\mathscr{B}) \Phi(\mathbf{u} \mid \mathscr{B}) \\ &= \sum_{\mathbf{u}} Q_N(\mathbf{u}) \sum_{\mathscr{B}} P(\mathscr{B}) \Phi(\mathbf{u} \mid \mathscr{B}) \\ &= \sum_{\mathbf{u}} Q_N(\mathbf{u}) \Pr\{d(\mathbf{u} \mid \mathscr{B}) > D \mid \mathbf{u}\} \\ &\le e^{-\exp N[R - R(D) + o(N)]} \end{aligned} \tag{8.5.19}$$

where the inequality follows from Lemma 8.5.1. This means there exists at least one code $\mathscr{B}$ for which

$$\begin{aligned} \frac{1}{A^N} \sum_{\mathbf{u}} \Phi(\mathbf{u} \mid \mathscr{B}) &\le \frac{1}{A^N} \overline{\sum_{\mathbf{u}} \Phi(\mathbf{u} \mid \mathscr{B})} \\ &\le e^{-\exp N[R - R(D) + o(N)]} \end{aligned}$$

or

$$\sum_{\mathbf{u}} \Phi(\mathbf{u} \mid \mathscr{B}) \leq A^N e^{-\exp N[R - R(D) + o(N)]} \tag{8.5.20}$$

The bound can be made less than 1 by choosing N large enough when $R > R(D)$. Then we have

$$\sum_{\mathbf{u}} \Phi(\mathbf{u} \mid \mathscr{B}) < 1 \tag{8.5.21}$$

But by the definition (8.5.17), for each $\mathbf{u}$, $\Phi(\mathbf{u} \mid \mathscr{B})$ can only be 0 and 1. Hence (8.5.21) implies that $\Phi(\mathbf{u} \mid \mathscr{B}) = 0$ for all $\mathbf{u} \in \mathscr{U}_N$, which requires $d(\mathbf{u} \mid \mathscr{B}) \leq D$ for all $\mathbf{u}$.

Since (8.5.16) holds for all output sequences, we see that this theorem holds for any source distribution $\{Q_N(\mathbf{u}) \colon \mathbf{u} \in \mathscr{U}_N\}$ when $R(D)$ is the symmetric source rate distortion function and $R > R(D)$. For any other source distribution, the actual rate distortion function will be less than that of the uniform distribution.

8.5.2 Fixed-Composition Sequences—Binary Alphabet Example

There is a close relationship between symmetric sources with balanced distortions and fixed-composition source output sequences of an arbitrary discrete source. For sequences of fixed composition, we can prove a theorem analogous to Theorem 8.5.1. Although this property is easily generalizable to arbitrary discrete alphabet sources with a bounded single-letter distortion measure (see Martin [1976]), we demonstrate the results for the binary source alphabet and error distortion measure.

Suppose we have a source alphabet $\mathscr{U} = \{0, 1\}$, a representation alphabet $\mathscr{V} = \{0, 1\}$, and error distortion measure

$$d(k, j) = 1 - \delta_{kj} \qquad \text{for } k, j = 0, 1 \tag{8.5.22}$$

For $\mathbf{u} \in \mathscr{U}_N$, define its weight as $w(\mathbf{u}) \equiv$ number of 1s in $\mathbf{u}$, and define the composition classes,

$$\mathscr{C}_N(l) = \{\mathbf{u} \colon \mathbf{u} \in \mathscr{U}_N,\ w(\mathbf{u}) = l\} \qquad l = 0, 1, 2, \ldots, N \tag{8.5.23}$$

with probabilities

$$Q^{(l)}(u) = \begin{cases} \dfrac{l}{N} & u = 1 \\ 1 - \dfrac{l}{N} & u = 0 \end{cases} \qquad l = 0, 1, 2, \ldots, N \tag{8.5.24}$$

and corresponding rate distortion functions [see (7.6.62)]

$$R(D; \mathbf{Q}^{(l)}) = \mathscr{H}\left(\frac{l}{N}\right) - \mathscr{H}(D) \tag{8.5.25}$$

$$0 \leq D \leq \min\left(\frac{l}{N}, 1 - \frac{l}{N}\right) \qquad l = 0, 1, 2, \ldots, N$$

Using the Chernoff bound (see Prob. 1.5) we have for the number of sequences in $\mathscr{C}_N(l)$, denoted $|\mathscr{C}_N(l)|$

$$|\mathscr{C}_N(l)| = \binom{N}{l} \leq e^{N\mathscr{H}(l/N)} \tag{8.5.26}$$

This means we can always find a code of rate

$$R > \mathscr{H}\left(\frac{l}{N}\right) \qquad \text{such that } M = e^{NR} > |\mathscr{C}_N(l)|$$

which can uniquely represent each sequence in $\mathscr{C}_N(l)$ and thus achieve zero distortion. We shall encode some composition classes with zero distortion and others with some nonzero distortion.

Let us now pick δ such that $0 < \delta < \ln 2$, pick fixed rate R in the interval $\delta < R < \ln 2$, and choose $0 < \epsilon < 0.3$ to satisfy

$$\mathscr{H}(\epsilon) < \delta \tag{8.5.27}$$

Observe that we can make ϵ and δ as small as we please and still satisfy (8.5.27). Let the binary distribution $\mathbf{Q}^*$ satisfying $Q^*(1) \leq \frac{1}{2}$ be defined parametrically in terms of the rate R, ϵ and δ, as follows:

$$\begin{aligned} R &= R(\epsilon; \mathbf{Q}^*) + \delta \\ &= \mathscr{H}(Q^*(1)) - \mathscr{H}(\epsilon) + \delta \end{aligned} \tag{8.5.28}$$

Also let l^* be the largest integer such that $l^*/N \leq Q^*(1) \leq \frac{1}{2}$. Then from Fig. 8.3 we see that for any fixed composition class $\mathscr{C}_N(l)$ where either

$$l/N \leq l^*/N \qquad \text{or} \qquad 1 - l/N \leq l^*/N \tag{8.5.29}$$

we have

$$\mathscr{H}\left(\frac{l}{N}\right) = \mathscr{H}\left(1 - \frac{l}{N}\right) \leq \mathscr{H}\left(\frac{l^*}{N}\right) \leq \mathscr{H}(Q^*(1)) \tag{8.5.30}$$

and

$$|\mathscr{C}_N(l)| = \binom{N}{l} \leq \binom{N}{l^*} \leq e^{N\mathscr{H}(l^*/N)} \tag{8.5.31}$$

Thus for any composition class $\mathscr{C}_N(l)$ for which $\mathscr{H}(l/N) \leq \mathscr{H}(Q^*(1))$, we can find a block code of rate R and block length N such that

$$\begin{aligned} R &= \mathscr{H}(Q^*(1)) - \mathscr{H}(\epsilon) + \delta \\ &> \mathscr{H}(Q^*(1)) \\ &\geq \mathscr{H}\left(\frac{l}{N}\right) \end{aligned} \tag{8.5.32}$$

and from (8.5.26)

$$M = e^{NR} \geq e^{N\mathscr{H}(l/N)} \geq |\mathscr{C}_N(l)| \tag{8.5.33}$$

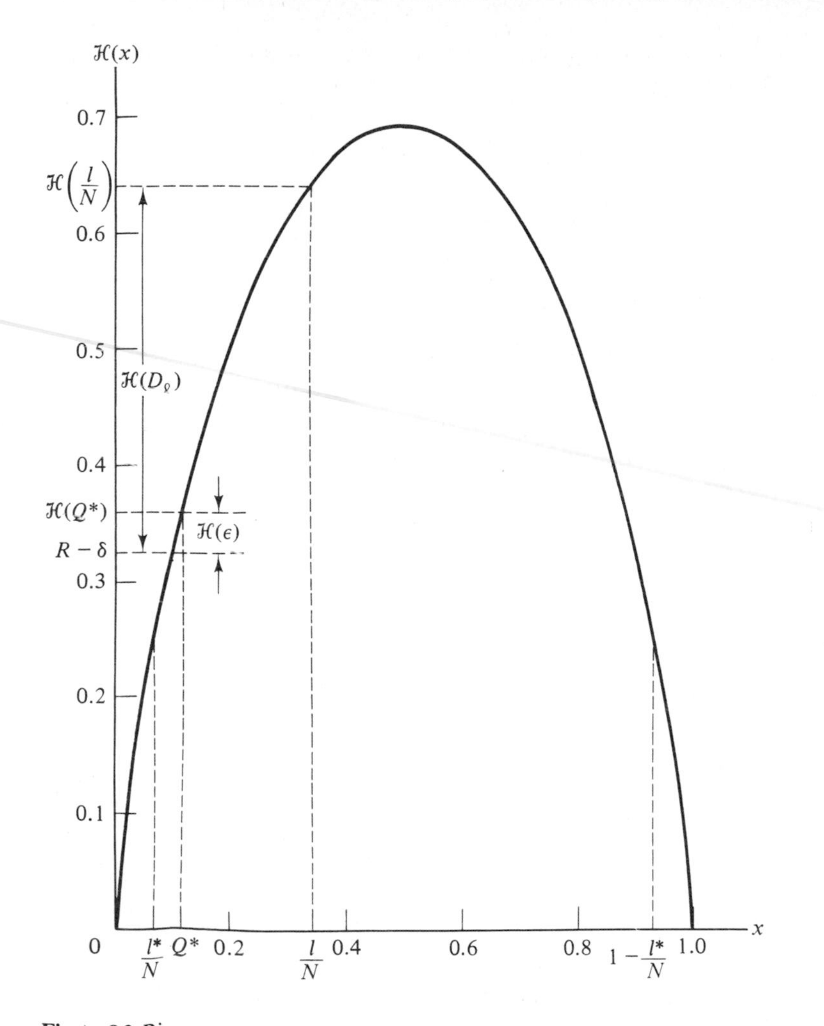

Figure 8.3 Binary entropy relationships.

Therefore, since there are more representation sequences M than sequences in the class, such a code can encode sequences from $\mathscr{C}_N(l)$ with zero distortion where l satisfies (8.5.29).

For any other fixed composition class $\mathscr{C}_N(l)$ for which instead

$$\frac{l^*}{N} < \frac{l}{N} < 1 - \frac{l^*}{N} \tag{8.5.34}$$

define $D_l \geq \epsilon$ to satisfy

$$\begin{aligned} R &= R(D_l; Q^{(l)}) + \delta \\ &= \mathscr{H}\left(\frac{l}{N}\right) - \mathscr{H}(D_l) + \delta \end{aligned} \tag{8.5.35}$$

Such a D_l can be found in the range $\epsilon \leq D_l \leq l/N$. This is illustrated in Fig. 8.3. We show next that, like our result for the symmetric source with balanced distortion measure presented in Theorem 8.5.1, we can find a code of rate R such that all sequences in $\mathscr{C}_N(l)$ can be encoded with distortion D_l or less. First we establish a lemma analogous to Lemma 8.5.1 by considering an ensemble of block codes $\mathscr{B} = \{\mathbf{v}_1, \mathbf{v}_2, \ldots, \mathbf{v}_M\}$ of block length N and rate $R = (\ln M)/N$ with probability distribution

$$P(\mathscr{B}) = \prod_{m=1}^{M} P_N(\mathbf{v}_m)$$
$$= \prod_{m=1}^{M} \prod_{n=1}^{N} P^{(l)}(v_{mn}) \tag{8.5.36}$$

where

$$P^{(l)}(v) = Q^{(l)}(0)P^{(l)}(v \mid 0) + Q^{(l)}(1)P^{(l)}(v \mid 1)$$
$$= \left(1 - \frac{l}{N}\right)P^{(l)}(v \mid 0) + \frac{l}{N}P^{(l)}(v \mid 1) \tag{8.5.37}$$

and $P^{(l)}(v \mid u)$ is the conditional probability yielding the rate distortion function $R(D_l; Q^{(l)}) = I(\mathbf{P}^{(l)})$.

Lemma 8.5.2 Let $\epsilon > 0$, $\delta > 0$ and rate $\delta < R < \ln 2$ satisfy (8.5.27) and (8.5.28). For a fixed composition class $\mathscr{C}_N(l)$ satisfying (8.5.34), D_l satisfying (8.5.35), and any $\mathbf{u} \in \mathscr{C}_N(l)$, over the ensemble of block codes with probability distribution (8.5.36)

$$\Pr\{d(\mathbf{u} \mid \mathscr{B}) > D_l \mid \mathbf{u} \in \mathscr{C}_N(l)\} \leq e^{-(1 - 4/N\epsilon^2)\exp N[\delta + \epsilon \ln(\epsilon/2)]} \tag{8.5.38}$$

PROOF

$$\Pr\{d(\mathbf{u} \mid \mathscr{B}) > D_l \mid \mathbf{u} \in \mathscr{C}_N(l)\}$$
$$= \Pr\{d_N(\mathbf{u}, \mathbf{v}_m) > D_l;\ m = 1, 2, \ldots, M \mid \mathbf{u} \in \mathscr{C}_N(l)\}$$
$$= [\Pr\{d_N(\mathbf{u}, \mathbf{v}) > D_l \mid \mathbf{u} \in \mathscr{C}_N(l)\}]^M$$
$$\leq e^{-M \Pr\{d_N(\mathbf{u}, \mathbf{v}) \leq D_l \mid \mathbf{u} \in \mathscr{C}_N(l)\}} \tag{8.5.39}$$

Here the key property we employ is that $\Pr\{d_N(\mathbf{u}, \mathbf{v}) \leq D_l \mid \mathbf{u} \in \mathscr{C}_N(l)\}$ is independent of $\mathbf{u} \in \mathscr{C}_N(l)$, since only the composition determines the probability distribution of $d_N(\mathbf{u}, \mathbf{v})$, which is a normalized sum of independent (though not identically distributed) random variables. The generalized Chernoff bounds in App. 8A again suffice for our purpose. Here we have

$$\Pr\{d_N(\mathbf{u}, \mathbf{v}) \leq D_l \mid \mathbf{u} \in \mathscr{C}_N(l)\} \geq \left(1 - \frac{4}{N\epsilon^2}\right)e^{-N[R(D_l;\, Q^{(l)}) - \epsilon \ln(\epsilon/2)]} \tag{8.5.40}$$

Substituting (8.5.35) into (8.5.40) and the result into (8.5.39) then gives us the desired result.

It is easy to see that, for $\epsilon < 0.3$, we have $\mathscr{H}(\epsilon) \geq -\epsilon \ln (\epsilon/2)$ so that $\delta > -\epsilon \ln (\epsilon/2) > 0$ (see Prob. 8.12). Hence the exponent $[\delta + \epsilon \ln (\epsilon/2)] > 0$ in (8.5.38). From this lemma follows the desired result.

Theorem 8.5.2 Let $\epsilon > 0$, $\delta > 0$ satisfy $\mathscr{H}(\epsilon) < \delta$. For sufficiently large integer N^*, for any rate R in the interval $\delta \leq R \leq \ln 2$, and any composition class $\mathscr{C}_N(l)$ where $N \geq N^*$, there exists a code $\mathscr{B}_l$ of block length N and rate R such that

$$d(\mathbf{u}|\mathscr{B}_l) \leq D_l \qquad \text{for all } \mathbf{u} \in \mathscr{C}_N(l) \tag{8.5.41}$$

where D_l satisfies

$$R = \mathscr{H}\left(\frac{l}{N}\right) - \mathscr{H}(D_l)$$

when

$$Q^*(1) \leq \frac{l}{N} \leq 1 - Q^*(1)$$

and $D_l = 0$ otherwise. Here $Q^*(1) < \frac{1}{2}$ satisfies

$$R = \mathscr{H}(Q^*(1)) - \mathscr{H}(\epsilon) + \delta$$

PROOF For $l/N \notin [Q^*(1), 1 - Q^*(1)]$, $D_l = 0$ as a result of (8.5.33). Now for any $l/N \in [Q^*(1), 1 - Q^*(1)]$, suppose we have a source that emits only sequences from $\mathscr{C}_N(l)$ with equal probabilities. For any block code $\mathscr{B}$ of block length N and rate R, define the indicator function

$$\Phi(\mathbf{u}|\mathscr{B}) = \begin{cases} 1 & d(\mathbf{u}|\mathscr{B}) > D_l \\ 0 & d(\mathbf{u}|\mathscr{B}) \leq D_l \end{cases} \qquad \text{for } \mathbf{u} \in \mathscr{C}_N(l) \tag{8.5.42}$$

Averaging Φ over output sequences, we obtain

$$\sum_{\mathbf{u} \in \mathscr{C}_N(l)} \frac{1}{|\mathscr{C}_N(l)|} \Phi(\mathbf{u}|\mathscr{B}) = \frac{1}{|\mathscr{C}_N(l)|} \sum_{\mathbf{u} \in \mathscr{C}_N(l)} \Phi(\mathbf{u}|\mathscr{B}) \tag{8.5.43}$$

Next consider an ensemble of block codes where code $\mathscr{B} = \{\mathbf{v}_1, \mathbf{v}_2, \ldots, \mathbf{v}_M\}$ is chosen according to the probability distribution (8.5.36) and (8.5.37). Averaging (8.5.43) over this code ensemble yields

$$\begin{aligned} \frac{1}{|\mathscr{C}_N(l)|} \overline{\sum_{\mathbf{u} \in \mathscr{C}_N(l)} \Phi(\mathbf{u}|\mathscr{B})} &= \sum_{\mathbf{u} \in \mathscr{C}_N(l)} \frac{1}{|\mathscr{C}_N(l)|} \sum_{\mathscr{B}} P(\mathscr{B})\Phi(\mathbf{u}|\mathscr{B}) \\ &= \sum_{\mathbf{u} \in \mathscr{C}_N(l)} \frac{1}{|\mathscr{C}_N(l)|} \Pr\{d(\mathbf{u}|\mathscr{B}) > D_l | \mathbf{u} \in \mathscr{C}_N(l)\} \\ &\leq e^{-(1 - 4/N\epsilon^2) \exp N[\delta + \epsilon \ln (\epsilon/2)]} \end{aligned} \tag{8.5.44}$$

where the inequality follows from Lemma 8.5.2. Using the bound $|\mathscr{C}_N(l)| \leq 2^N$, it follows that there exists a code $\mathscr{B}_l$ of block length N and rate R such that

$$\sum_{\mathbf{u} \in \mathscr{C}_N(l)} \Phi(\mathbf{u} \mid \mathscr{B}_l) \leq \overline{\sum_{\mathbf{u} \in \mathscr{C}_N(l)} \Phi(\mathbf{u} \mid \mathscr{B})}$$
$$\leq 2^N e^{-(1-4/N\epsilon^2)\exp N[\delta + \epsilon \ln(\epsilon/2)]} \tag{8.5.45}$$

Choosing N^* to be any integer for which the bound is less than one, it follows as in the proof of Theorem 8.5.1 that $\Phi(\mathbf{u} \mid \mathscr{B}_l) = 0$ for all $\mathbf{u} \in \mathscr{C}_N(l)$.

This theorem shows that given any $0 < \delta < \ln 2$, rate R such that $\delta \leq R \leq \ln 2$, and $0 < \epsilon < 0.3$ satisfying $\mathscr{H}(\epsilon) < \delta$, for any composition class $\mathscr{C}_N(l)$ where $N \geq N^*$, we can find a block code, $\mathscr{B}_l$, of block length N and rate R such that $d(\mathbf{u} \mid \mathscr{B}_l) = 0$ for all $\mathbf{u} \in \mathscr{C}_N(l)$ if $\mathscr{H}(l/N) \leq \mathscr{H}(Q^*(1))$, and $d(\mathbf{u} \mid \mathscr{B}_l) \leq D_l$ for all $\mathbf{u} \in \mathscr{C}_N(l)$ if $\mathscr{H}(l/N) > \mathscr{H}(Q^*(1))$ where $\mathbf{Q}^*$ satisfies (8.5.28) and $D_l \geq \epsilon$ satisfies (8.5.35) (see also Fig. 8.3).

It is natural to define the composite code

$$\mathscr{B}_C = \bigcup_{l=0}^{N} \mathscr{B}_l \tag{8.5.46}$$

which has $(N+1)e^{NR}$ elements (e^{NR} for each of the $N+1$ composite classes) and hence rate

$$R_C = R + \frac{\ln(N+1)}{N} \tag{8.5.47}$$

For the code $\mathscr{B}_C$, we have

$$d(\mathbf{u} \mid \mathscr{B}_C) \leq D_l \qquad \text{if } \mathbf{u} \in \mathscr{C}_N(l) \tag{8.5.48}$$

where we take $D_l = 0$ if $\mathscr{H}(l/N) \leq \mathscr{H}(Q^*(1))$. We see that, as $N \to \infty$, $R_C \to R$, and thus by choosing N large enough we can make the rate of the composite code $\mathscr{B}_C$ arbitrarily close to R.

Up to this point, the results depend only on the source alphabet and are independent of the source statistics. The composite code $\mathscr{B}_C$ satisfies (8.5.48) regardless of the actual source statistics. Suppose, however, that our binary source is memoryless with probability $Q(1) = q < \frac{1}{2}$ and $Q(0) = 1 - q$. Then the rate distortion function for this source is $R(D) = \mathscr{H}(q) - \mathscr{H}(D)$ for $0 \leq D \leq q$. How well does the composite code encode this source? The average distortion using the composite code is

$$\begin{aligned} d(\mathscr{B}_C) &= \sum_{\mathbf{u}} Q_N(\mathbf{u}) d(\mathbf{u} \mid \mathscr{B}_C) \\ &= \sum_{l=0}^{N} \sum_{\mathbf{u} \in \mathscr{C}_N(l)} Q_N(\mathbf{u}) d(\mathbf{u} \mid \mathscr{B}_C) \\ &\leq \sum_{l=0}^{N} \sum_{\mathbf{u} \in \mathscr{C}_N(l)} q^l (1-q)^{N-l} D_l \\ &= \sum_{l=0}^{N} \binom{N}{l} q^l (1-q)^{N-l} D_l \end{aligned} \tag{8.5.49}$$

As N increases, $\binom{N}{l}q^l(1-q)^{N-l}$ concentrates its mass around its mean Nq. This follows from the asymptotic equipartition property (McMillan [1953]) which says that, as block length increases, almost all source sequences tend to have the same composition. Thus we have (see Prob. 8.13 and Chap. 1)

$$\lim_{N\to\infty} \sum_{l=0}^{N} \binom{N}{l} q^l (1-q)^{N-l} D_l = D \tag{8.5.50}$$

where D satisfies (8.5.35) with $l = Nq$; that is

$$\begin{aligned} R &= R(D; q) + \delta \\ &= \mathscr{H}(q) - \mathscr{H}(D) + \delta \\ &= R(D) + \delta \end{aligned} \tag{8.5.51}$$

The code rate for $\mathscr{B}_C$ then becomes

$$R_C = R(D) + \delta + \frac{\ln(N+1)}{N} \tag{8.5.52}$$

Hence given any $\eta > 0$, we can find δ small enough and N large enough so that

$$d(\mathscr{B}_C) \leq D + \eta \tag{8.5.53}$$

and

$$R_C \leq R(D) + \eta \tag{8.5.54}$$

Thus the composite codes can encode any memoryless binary source with error distortion arbitrarily close to the theoretical rate distortion limit. This is a robust source encoding scheme for memoryless sources in the sense that the same composition class code is efficient (near the rate distortion limit) for all such sources and the composite code is constructed independent of actual source statistics.

The preceding example of a binary alphabet with the error distortion measure can be generalized to arbitrary discrete alphabets and arbitrary single-letter distortions (see Prob. 8.14). Further generalizations are possible by considering fixed finite sequences of source outputs as elements of a larger extended discrete alphabet. In this manner, the robust source coding technique can be applied to sources with memory (see Martin [1976]). The basic approach of considering a single source as a composite of subsources and finding codes for each subsource in constructing a total composite code is also used in encoding nonergodic stationary sources. This is referred to as *universal source coding* and is discussed in Sec. 8.6.

We have demonstrated a similarity between symmetric sources with balanced distortions and fixed composition classes. In general with any discrete alphabet, for any fixed composition class, we may define a function $R(D; \mathbf{Q})$ where $\mathbf{Q}$ is the distribution determined by the composition. We can show that if $R > R(D; \mathbf{Q})$ and the block length is large enough, we can find a code that will encode all sequences of the composition class to distortion D or less. Certainly if

$$R > \max_{\mathbf{Q}} R(D; \mathbf{Q}) \tag{8.5.55}$$

then every output sequence can be encoded with distortion D or less. Symmetric sources with balanced distortions have the property that

$$R(D) = \max_{\mathbf{Q}} R(D; \mathbf{Q}) \tag{8.5.56}$$

Thus the symmetric source coding theorem (Theorem 8.5.1) is actually a special case of the composition class source coding theorem (Theorem 8.5.2 appropriately generalized to arbitrary discrete alphabets and any single-letter distortion measures). See Probs. 8.14 and 8.15 for generalizations and further details.

8.5.3 Example of Encoding with Linear Block Codes

We conclude our discussion with a coding example for the simplest symmetric source with balanced distortion, the binary symmetric source with error distortion measure. This example, due to Goblick [1962], shows that Theorem 8.5.1 is satisfied with a linear binary code.

Let $\mathscr{U} = \mathscr{V} = \{0, 1\}$, $Q(0) = Q(1) = \frac{1}{2}$, and $d(k, j) = 1 - \delta_{kj}$. The rate distortion function is, of course, $R(D) = \ln 2 - \mathscr{H}(D)$ for $0 \le D \le \frac{1}{2}$. Now we consider linear binary (N, K) codes for source coding where the rate is $r = K/N$ bits per symbol or $R = (K/N) \ln 2$ nats per symbol. First consider K binary sequences of length N, $\{\mathbf{b}_1, \mathbf{b}_2, \ldots, \mathbf{b}_K\}$, which we call code-generator vectors. With these generator vectors we generate a sequence of codes of block length N and different rates by defining for $l = 1, 2, \ldots, K$ the subcodes

$$\mathscr{B}(l) = \{\mathbf{v}: \mathbf{v} = c_1\mathbf{b}_1 \oplus c_2\mathbf{b}_2 \oplus \cdots \oplus c_l\mathbf{b}_l\} \tag{8.5.57}$$

where the binary coefficients $c_1, c_2, \ldots, c_l$ are all possible binary sequences of length l. There are then 2^l codewords in $\mathscr{B}(l)$. By defining the set

$$\mathscr{B}(l; \mathbf{b}_{l+1}) = \{\mathbf{v}: \mathbf{v} = \mathbf{v}' \oplus \mathbf{b}_{l+1}, \mathbf{v}' \in \mathscr{B}(l)\} \tag{8.5.58}$$

we see that

$$\mathscr{B}(l+1) = \mathscr{B}(l) \cup \mathscr{B}(l; \mathbf{b}_{l+1}) \tag{8.5.59}$$

That is, code $\mathscr{B}(l+1)$, which has rate $(l+1)/N$ bits per symbol, is the union of code $\mathscr{B}(l)$, which has rate l/N bits per symbol, and a "shifted" version of this code denoted $\mathscr{B}(l; \mathbf{b}_{l+1})$.

Generate the ensemble of linear binary codes obtained by randomly selecting the generator vectors such that all components of all vectors are treated as independent equiprobable binary random variables. Since there are Nl components in the generator vectors $\mathbf{b}_1, \mathbf{b}_2, \ldots, \mathbf{b}_l$, the code $\mathscr{B}(l)$ has ensemble probability distribution given by

$$P(\mathscr{B}(l)) = (\tfrac{1}{2})^{Nl} \tag{8.5.60}$$

Recall that $\mathbf{u} \in \mathscr{U}_N$ also has a uniform probability distribution so that over the source and generator ensembles $\mathbf{u}$ and $\mathbf{u} \oplus \mathbf{b}$ are independent binary vectors. (Check this for $N = 1$ and generalize.)

The usual ensemble coding argument must be modified here to a series of average coding arguments and a sequential selection of codeword generators, Since code $\mathscr{B}(l+1)$ is constructed from code $\mathscr{B}(l)$ and another randomly selected generator vector $\mathbf{b}_{l+1}$, we have

$$\Pr\{d(\mathbf{u}\,|\,\mathscr{B}(l+1)) > D\,|\,\mathscr{B}(l)\} = \Pr\{d(\mathbf{u}\,|\,\mathscr{B}(l)) > D,\ d(\mathbf{u}\,|\,\mathscr{B}(l;\mathbf{b}_{l+1})) > D\,|\,\mathscr{B}(l)\} \tag{8.5.61}$$

where the probability is over the ensemble of $\mathbf{u} \in \mathscr{U}_N$ and $\mathbf{b}_{l+1} \in \mathscr{V}_N$. But now

$$\begin{aligned} d(\mathbf{u}\,|\,\mathscr{B}(l;\mathbf{b}_{l+1})) &= \min_{\mathbf{v}' \in \mathscr{B}(l)} d_N(\mathbf{u}, \mathbf{v}' \oplus \mathbf{b}_{l+1}) \\ &= \min_{\mathbf{v}' \in \mathscr{B}(l)} d_N(\mathbf{u} \oplus \mathbf{b}_{l+1}, \mathbf{v}') \\ &= d(\mathbf{u} \oplus \mathbf{b}_{l+1}\,|\,\mathscr{B}(l)) \end{aligned} \tag{8.5.62}$$

and, since $\mathbf{u}$ and $\mathbf{u} \oplus \mathbf{b}_{l+1}$ are independent of each other, (8.5.61) becomes

$$\begin{aligned} &\Pr\{d(\mathbf{u}\,|\,\mathscr{B}(l+1)) > D\,|\,\mathscr{B}(l)\} \\ &\quad = \Pr\{d(\mathbf{u}\,|\,\mathscr{B}(l)) > D\,|\,\mathscr{B}(l)\}\ \Pr\{d(\mathbf{u} \oplus \mathbf{b}_{l+1}\,|\,\mathscr{B}(l)) > D\,|\,\mathscr{B}(l)\} \\ &\quad = [\Pr\{d(\mathbf{u}\,|\,\mathscr{B}(l)) > D\,|\,\mathscr{B}(l)\}]^2 \end{aligned} \tag{8.5.63}$$

The left side of (8.5.63) can also be written as an average over $\mathbf{b}_{l+1}$

$$\begin{aligned} &\Pr\{d(\mathbf{u}\,|\,\mathscr{B}(l+1)) > D\,|\,\mathscr{B}(l)\} \\ &\quad = \sum_{\mathbf{b}_{l+1}} P(\mathbf{b}_{l+1}) \Pr\{d(\mathbf{u}\,|\,\mathscr{B}(l+1)) > D\,|\,\mathscr{B}(l), \mathbf{b}_{l+1}\} \\ &\quad = \sum_{\mathbf{b}_{l+1}} P(\mathbf{b}_{l+1}) \Pr\{d(\mathbf{u}\,|\,\mathscr{B}(l+1)) > D\,|\,\mathscr{B}(l+1)\} \end{aligned} \tag{8.5.64}$$

Hence given any code $\mathscr{B}(l)$, there exists a generator vector $\mathbf{b}_{l+1}$ such that

$$\begin{aligned} \Pr\{d(\mathbf{u}\,|\,\mathscr{B}(l+1)) > D\,|\,\mathscr{B}(l+1)\} &\le \Pr\{d(\mathbf{u}\,|\,\mathscr{B}(l+1)) > D\,|\,\mathscr{B}(l)\} \\ &= [\Pr\{d(\mathbf{u}\,|\,\mathscr{B}(l)) > D\,|\,\mathscr{B}(l)\}]^2 \end{aligned} \tag{8.5.65}$$

We can select a sequence of generator vectors $\mathbf{b}_1, \mathbf{b}_2, \ldots, \mathbf{b}_K$ such that for each l, (8.5.65) holds. Then for such a set of K generator vectors we have

$$\begin{aligned} \Pr\{d(\mathbf{u}\,|\,\mathscr{B}(K)) > D\,|\,\mathscr{B}(K)\} &\le [\Pr\{d(\mathbf{u}\,|\,\mathscr{B}(0)) > D\,|\,\mathscr{B}(0)\}]^{2^K} \\ &= [\Pr\{d(\mathbf{u}, \mathbf{0}) > D\}]^{2^K} \\ &= [1 - F_N(D)]^{2^K} \\ &\le e^{-2^K F_N(D)} \end{aligned} \tag{8.5.66}$$

where we have used $\ln x \le x - 1$ and defined $F_N(D) = \Pr\{d(\mathbf{u}, \mathbf{0}) \le D\}$. From App. 8A, we have

$$F_N(D) \ge e^{-N\{R(D) + o(N)\}}$$

so that there exists a code $\mathscr{B}(K)$ such that

$$\Pr\{d(\mathbf{u}\,|\,\mathscr{B}(K)) > D\,|\,\mathscr{B}(K)\} \leq e^{-\exp N[R-R(D)+o(N)]} \tag{8.5.67}$$

where $R = (K/N) \ln 2$. Following the same argument as in the proof of Theorem 8.5.1, we see that by choosing N sufficiently large, for any fixed rate

$$R = (K/N) \ln 2 > R(D) = \ln 2 - \mathscr{H}(D)$$

there exists a linear binary (N, K) code $\mathscr{B}(K)$ such that

$$d(\mathbf{u}\,|\,\mathscr{B}(K)) \leq D \qquad \text{for all } \mathbf{u} \in \mathscr{U}_N \tag{8.5.68}$$

Thus for a binary symmetric source and error distortion measure, a uniform distortion condition is met by a *linear* code.

8.6 UNIVERSAL CODING

The source coding theorems of Sec. 8.2 were restricted to stationary ergodic sources. The formal definition of $R(D)$ given by (8.2.5), however, can also be given for nonergodic stationary sources where Lemma 8.2.1 still applies. The converse coding theorem (Theorem 8.2.1) applies to nonergodic stationary sources only if we interpret average distortion as an ensemble average. The coding theorems, however, do require that the sources be ergodic. One might expect that it would be possible to prove coding theorems for arbitrary stationary sources and then show that $R(D)$ is indeed the minimum possible rate that can be achieved with ensemble average distortion of D or less. We present next, however, a counterexample which shows that $R(D)$ given by (8.2.5) does not represent the minimum possible rate necessary to achieve ensemble average distortion D for nonergodic stationary sources.

Example (Gray [1975]) Consider a memoryless Gaussian source of zero mean and variance σ^2. For the squared-error distortion measure $d(u, v) = (u - v)^2$, the rate distortion function is given by (7.7.20)

$$R^g(D) = \tfrac{1}{2} \ln \frac{\sigma^2}{D} \text{ nats/symbol} \qquad 0 \leq D \leq \sigma^2 \tag{7.7.20}$$

Next suppose we have any stationary source whose outputs are random variables (not necessarily independent) with zero mean and variance σ^2. For the squared-error distortion, we can define the function $R(D)$ as given by (8.2.5). Lemma 8.2.1 shows that

$$R(D) \leq R_1(D) \tag{8.6.1}$$

where $R_1(D)$ is the rate distortion function for the corresponding memoryless source. From Theorem 7.7.3, we have the inequality

$$R_1(D) \leq \tfrac{1}{2} \ln \frac{\sigma^2}{D} = R^g(D) \tag{8.6.2}$$

with equality if and only if the source single-letter probability density is Gaussian. Hence, for any rate R, if we pick D_1 and D_g to satisfy

$$R = R_1(D_1) = R^g(D_g) \leq R^g(D_1) \tag{8.6.3}$$

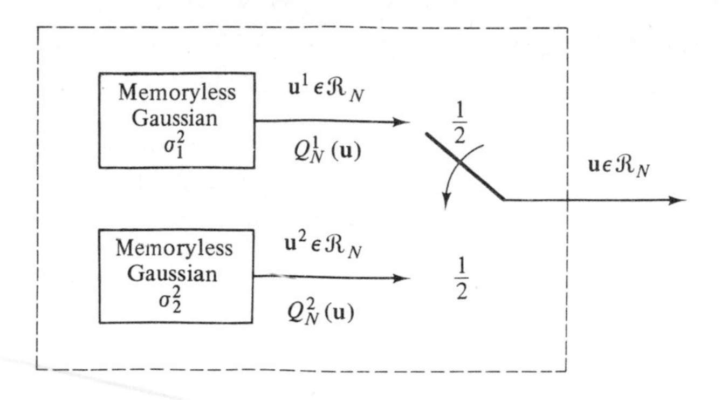

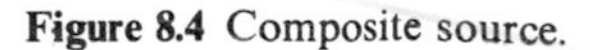
Figure 8.4 Composite source.

then we have

$$D_g = \sigma^2 e^{-2R} \geq D_1 \tag{8.6.4}$$

with equality if and only if the memoryless source is Gaussian.

Now consider a composite source consisting of two memoryless Gaussian subsources, each of zero mean. One subsource has variance σ_1^2 and the other subsource has variance $\sigma_2^2 \neq \sigma_1^2$. The composite source has the output sequence of the first subsource with probability $\frac{1}{2}$ and the output sequence of the second subsource with probability $\frac{1}{2}$. This source is sketched in Fig. 8.4. Hence $\mathbf{u} \in R_N$ has probability density

$$\begin{aligned} Q_N(\mathbf{u}) &= \frac{1}{2(2\pi\sigma_1^2)^{N/2}} e^{-\|\mathbf{u}\|^2/2\sigma_1^2} + \frac{1}{2(2\pi\sigma_2^2)^{N/2}} e^{-\|\mathbf{u}\|^2/2\sigma_2^2} \\ &\equiv \tfrac{1}{2} Q_N^{(1)}(\mathbf{u}) + \tfrac{1}{2} Q_N^{(2)}(\mathbf{u}) \end{aligned} \tag{8.6.5}$$

which is clearly non-Gaussian when $\sigma_1^2 \neq \sigma_2^2$. The composite source has memory and is stationary. It is not ergodic.[13] Its first-order density is

$$Q(u) = \tfrac{1}{2}Q^{(1)}(u) + \tfrac{1}{2}Q^{(2)}(u) \tag{8.6.6}$$

where

$$\int_{-\infty}^{\infty} uQ(u)\, du = 0$$

and

$$\begin{aligned} \int_{-\infty}^{\infty} u^2 Q(u)\, du &= \frac{1}{2}\int_{-\infty}^{\infty} u^2 Q^{(1)}(u)\, du + \frac{1}{2}\int_{-\infty}^{\infty} u^2 Q^{(2)}(u)\, du \\ &= \tfrac{1}{2}\sigma_1^2 + \tfrac{1}{2}\sigma_2^2 \\ &= \sigma^2 \end{aligned} \tag{8.6.7}$$

For the distortion $d(u, v) = (u - v)^2$, we can define $R(D)$ and $R_1(D)$. For any rate R, we have from (8.6.4) that D_1, where $R = R_1(D_1)$, satisfies

$$\sigma^2 e^{-2R} > D_1 \qquad \text{or} \qquad \sigma^2 e^{-2R} = D_1 + \delta \tag{8.6.8}$$

where $\delta > 0$, since (8.6.6) is not a Gaussian density function.

[13] The variance of any sample output sequence is either σ_1^2 or σ_2^2, while the ensemble variance is $\sigma^2 = \frac{1}{2}\sigma_1^2 + \frac{1}{2}\sigma_2^2$.

Let $\mathscr{B}$ be any block code of block length N and rate R. If this code is used to encode the composite source, the ensemble average distortion is

$$\begin{aligned} d(\mathscr{B}) &= \int_{-\infty}^{\infty} \cdots \int_{-\infty}^{\infty} Q_N(\mathbf{u})\, d(\mathbf{u} \mid \mathscr{B})\, d\mathbf{u} \\ &= \frac{1}{2} \int_{-\infty}^{\infty} \cdots \int_{-\infty}^{\infty} Q_N^{(1)}(\mathbf{u})\, d(\mathbf{u} \mid \mathscr{B})\, d\mathbf{u} + \frac{1}{2} \int_{-\infty}^{\infty} \cdots \int_{-\infty}^{\infty} Q_N^{(2)}(\mathbf{u})\, d(\mathbf{u} \mid \mathscr{B})\, d\mathbf{u} \\ &= \tfrac{1}{2} d_1(\mathscr{B}) + \tfrac{1}{2} d_2(\mathscr{B}) \end{aligned} \tag{8.6.9}$$

But

$$d_1(\mathscr{B}) = \int_{-\infty}^{\infty} \cdots \int_{-\infty}^{\infty} Q_N^{(1)}(\mathbf{u})\, d(\mathbf{u} \mid \mathscr{B})\, d\mathbf{u} \tag{8.6.10}$$

is the average distortion for the zero-mean Gaussian source with variance σ_1^2. The converse coding theorem states that

$$d_1(\mathscr{B}) \geq \sigma_1^2 e^{-2R} \tag{8.6.11}$$

and similarly

$$d_2(\mathscr{B}) \geq \sigma_2^2 e^{-2R} \tag{8.6.12}$$

yielding

$$\begin{aligned} d(\mathscr{B}) &\geq \tfrac{1}{2}\sigma_1^2 e^{-2R} + \tfrac{1}{2}\sigma_2^2 e^{-2R} \\ &= \tfrac{1}{2}(\sigma_1^2 + \sigma_2^2) e^{-2R} \\ &= \sigma^2 e^{-2R} \\ &= D_1 + \delta \end{aligned} \tag{8.6.13}$$

where $\delta > 0$, according to (8.6.8).

If $R(D)$ represents the achievable rate for which we can encode the stationary composite source with ensemble average distortion D or less, then given any $\epsilon > 0$ we can find a block code of rate[14] $R = R(D)$ such that

$$d(\mathscr{B}) \leq D + \epsilon \tag{8.6.14}$$

But from (8.6.1) and (8.6.3) we have that $R = R(D) = R_1(D_1) \leq R_1(D)$ which implies

$$D \leq D_1 \tag{8.6.15}$$

and so

$$d(\mathscr{B}) \leq D_1 + \epsilon \tag{8.6.16}$$

However, from (8.6.13),

$$D_1 + \delta \leq d(\mathscr{B}) \leq D_1 + \epsilon \tag{8.6.17}$$

which is a contradiction since we can choose $\epsilon < \delta$. Hence $R(D)$ does not represent minimum achievable rates for the stationary composite source.

The above counterexample shows us that the function $R(D)$, although definable for arbitrary stationary sources, has operational significance only for stationary ergodic sources. It turns out, however, that a stationary source in

[14] In Corollary 7.2.2 we can replace $R(D) + \epsilon$ by $R(D)$ (see Prob. 7.4).

general can always be viewed as a union of stationary ergodic subsources (Gray and Davisson [1974]). (In the above counterexample the source consisted of two subsources.) This fact has led to the development of coding theorems for general stationary sources without the ergodicity assumption. We illustrate this generalization to nonergodic stationary sources with a simple example.

Example (Stationary binary source) Suppose we have a binary source which consists of L memoryless binary subsources as shown in Fig. 8.5, where the lth subsource $\mathscr{S}_l$ outputs independent binary symbols with probability p_l of a "1" output at any given time, for $l = 1, 2, \ldots, L$. The composite binary source has as its output sequence the output sequence of one of its subsources. It has a priori probability $\pi_l (l = 1, 2, \ldots, L)$ of being connected to subsource $\mathscr{S}_l$ for all time. Hence $\mathbf{u} = (u_{t+1}, u_{t+2}, \ldots, u_{t+N})$ has probability

$$\begin{aligned} P_N(\mathbf{u}) &= \sum_{l=1}^{L} P_N(\mathbf{u} \mid \mathscr{S}_l)\pi_l \\ &= \sum_{l=1}^{L} \pi_l p_l^{w(\mathbf{u})}(1 - p_l)^{N - w(\mathbf{u})} \end{aligned} \tag{8.6.18}$$

where $w(\mathbf{u})$ is the number of "1"s in $\mathbf{u}$. Clearly this binary source is a stationary source. It is not ergodic since any sample output sequence $(\ldots, u_{-1}, u_0, u_1, \ldots)$ has time average

$$\lim_{N \to \infty} \frac{1}{N} \sum_{n=1}^{N} u_n = p_l \tag{8.6.19}$$

if it is the output of subsource $\mathscr{S}_l$, whereas the ensemble expectation is

$$E\{u_n\} = \sum_{l=1}^{L} \pi_l p_l \tag{8.6.20}$$

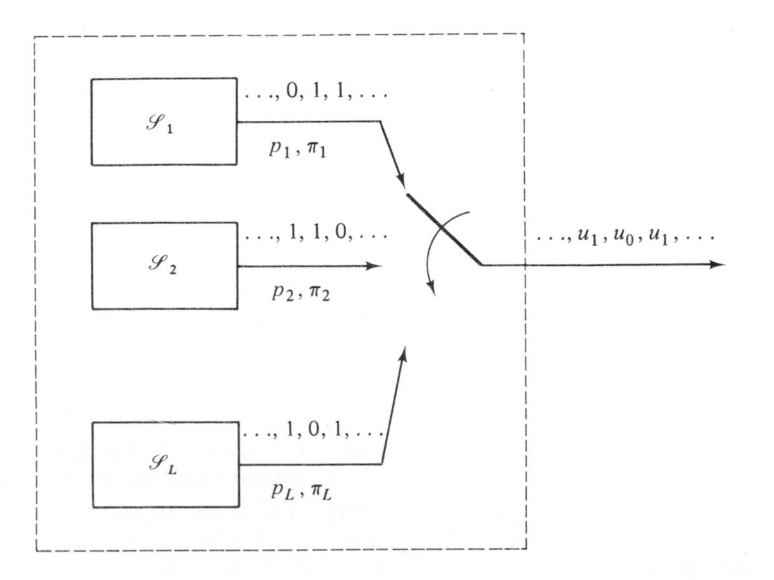

Figure 8.5 Stationary nonergodic binary source.

Suppose we have the representation alphabet $\mathscr{V} = \mathscr{U} = \{0, 1\}$, and error distortion measure $d(u, v) = 1 - \delta_{uv}$. What is the smallest average distortion we can achieve for this binary source? Although $R(D)$ can be defined in terms of (8.6.5), the previous example showed that $R(D)$ does not necessarily represent the minimum rate that can achieve average distortion D. We do know that, given $\epsilon > 0$, there exist block codes $\mathscr{B}^1, \mathscr{B}^2, \ldots, \mathscr{B}^L$ of block length N and rate R such that the first subsource can be encoded using code $\mathscr{B}^1$ with average distortion

$$d^1(\mathscr{B}^1) \leq D^1 + \epsilon \tag{8.6.21}$$

where D^1 satisfies

$$\begin{aligned} R &= R(D^1; p_1) \\ &= \mathscr{H}(p_1) - \mathscr{H}(D^1) \end{aligned} \tag{8.6.22}$$

Similarly, the lth source can be encoded using code $\mathscr{B}^l$ with average distortion

$$d^l(\mathscr{B}^l) \leq D^l + \epsilon \tag{8.6.23}$$

where D^l satisfies

$$\begin{aligned} R &= R(D^l; p_l) \\ &= \mathscr{H}(p_l) - \mathscr{H}(D^l) \end{aligned} \tag{8.6.24}$$

In other words, for a given rate R and any $\epsilon > 0$ we can find for each subsource a block code which will give average distortion within ϵ of the smallest average distortion possible for that subsource. The converse theorem applied to the lth subsource says we cannot do any better than average distortion D^l.

Suppose we construct a code for our nonergodic stationary binary source as the union of the above codes designed for each subsource and denote this composite code,

$$\mathscr{B}_C = \bigcup_{l=1}^{L} \mathscr{B}^l \tag{8.6.25}$$

This code has

$$M_C = Le^{NR} \tag{8.6.26}$$

codewords since there are e^{NR} codewords in each of the subcodes $\mathscr{B}^1, \mathscr{B}^2, \ldots, \mathscr{B}^L$. The rate of the composite code is thus

$$\begin{aligned} R_C &= (\ln M_C)/N \\ &= R + \frac{\ln L}{N} \end{aligned} \tag{8.6.27}$$

where, as N approaches infinity, $(\ln L)/N$ converges to zero. For any source sequence of length N, $\mathbf{u} = (u_1, u_2, \ldots, u_N)$, this code has distortion

$$\begin{aligned} d(\mathbf{u} \mid \mathscr{B}_C) &= \min_{\mathbf{v} \in \mathscr{B}_C} d_N(\mathbf{u}, \mathbf{v}) \\ &= \min \left\{ \min_{\mathbf{v} \in \mathscr{B}^1} d_N(\mathbf{u}, \mathbf{v}), \min_{\mathbf{v} \in \mathscr{B}^2} d_N(\mathbf{u}, \mathbf{v}), \ldots, \min_{\mathbf{v} \in \mathscr{B}^L} d_N(\mathbf{u}, \mathbf{v}) \right\} \\ &= \min \{ d(\mathbf{u} \mid \mathscr{B}^1), d(\mathbf{u} \mid \mathscr{B}^2), \ldots, d(\mathbf{u} \mid \mathscr{B}^L) \} \end{aligned} \tag{8.6.28}$$

Hence the average distortion using code $\mathscr{B}_C$ is at least as small as is achievable with the knowledge of which subsource is connected to the output and using the appropriate subcode. That is

$$d(\mathscr{B}_C) \leq D^l + \epsilon \tag{8.6.29}$$

if subsource $\mathscr{S}_l$ is connected to the output. Hence, for a fixed code rate and by choosing large enough block lengths, the code $\mathscr{B}_C$ can have average distortion arbitrarily close to the minimum possible average distortion.

In Sec. 8.2, we established the performance of the best possible encoding methods for stationary ergodic sources. Generalizing on the above example, we may show that when a source can be modeled as a finite collection of stationary ergodic subsources, then by using good codes for each of the subsources to form a composite code for the overall stationary, but not necessarily ergodic, source, we can still achieve the minimum average distortion possible for a fixed rate. This technique generalizes to a large class of nonergodic stationary sources, because nonergodic stationary sources can generally be represented as a collection of stationary ergodic subsources, characterized by an a priori probability distribution that any particular subsource output sequence is the total source output sequence. Although for many sources the number of subsources thus required is infinite, under certain topological conditions (on both the source and the distortion measure) the collection of subsources can be approximated by a finite collection of subsources. Once the finite approximation is made, we can proceed as in the above example. To illustrate this approach, we return to the binary example, but now with an uncountable number of stationary ergodic subsources.

Example (Binary source with a random parameter) Consider a memoryless binary source where the probability p of a "1" is a random variable with range between 0 and 1. We wish to encode this source using the error distortion measure $d(u, v) = 1 - \delta_{uv}$. If $p \in [0, 1]$ were known we would have a memoryless binary source which is stationary and ergodic. Because of the random parameter p, the overall source is stationary but nonergodic. In order to reduce this problem to the case of our previous example, we need to approximate the set of all possible subsources by a finite set of subsources. To do this, we define a distance between two binary memoryless sources, each with known but different parameters.

Let $\mathscr{S}$ and $\hat{\mathscr{S}}$ be two binary memoryless sources with parameters p and $\hat{p}$ respectively. Let $Q(u, \hat{u})$ be any joint distribution such that

$$p = \sum_{\hat{u}=0}^{1} Q(1, \hat{u}) = Q(1, 0) + Q(1, 1) \tag{8.6.30}$$

and

$$\hat{p} = \sum_{u=0}^{1} Q(u, 1) = Q(0, 1) + Q(1, 1) \tag{8.6.31}$$

That is, let $Q(u, \hat{u})$ be any joint distribution with marginal distributions corresponding to sources $\mathscr{S}$ and $\hat{\mathscr{S}}$. Define the distance between the two sources as

$$\bar{d}(p, \hat{p}) = \min_{Q \in \mathscr{Q}} \sum_{u} \sum_{\hat{u}} Q(u, \hat{u}) d(u, \hat{u}) \tag{8.6.32}$$

where $\mathscr{Q}$ is the collection of such joint distributions. Then

$$\sum_{u} \sum_{\hat{u}} Q(u, \hat{u}) d(u, \hat{u}) = Q(0, 1) + Q(1, 0) \tag{8.6.33}$$

since $d(u, v) = 1 - \delta_{uv}$ is the distance measure. It follows easily (see Prob. 8.17) that

$$\bar{d}(p, \hat{p}) = |p - \hat{p}| \tag{8.6.34}$$

Let $\mathscr{B}$ be any block code of length N and let $\mathbf{u} \in \mathscr{U}_N$ be an output sequence of length N from source $\mathscr{S}$ and $\hat{\mathbf{u}} \in \mathscr{U}_N$ be an output sequence from source $\hat{\mathscr{S}}$. Let $\mathbf{v}(\hat{\mathbf{u}}) \in \mathscr{B}$ satisfy

$$d_N(\hat{\mathbf{u}}, \mathbf{v}(\hat{\mathbf{u}})) = \min_{\mathbf{v} \in \mathscr{B}} d(\hat{\mathbf{u}}, \mathbf{v}).$$

Then

$$\begin{aligned} \min_{\mathbf{v} \in \mathscr{B}} d_N(\mathbf{u}, \mathbf{v}) &\le d_N(\mathbf{u}, \mathbf{v}(\hat{\mathbf{u}})) \\ &\le d_N(\mathbf{u}, \hat{\mathbf{u}}) + d_N(\hat{\mathbf{u}}, \mathbf{v}(\hat{\mathbf{u}})) \\ &= d_N(\mathbf{u}, \hat{\mathbf{u}}) + \min_{\mathbf{v} \in \mathscr{B}} d_N(\hat{\mathbf{u}}, \mathbf{v}) \end{aligned} \tag{8.6.35}$$

where the second inequality is the triangle inequality which this error distortion measure clearly satisfies. By symmetry we then have

$$\min_{\mathbf{v} \in \mathscr{B}} d_N(\hat{\mathbf{u}}, \mathbf{v}) \le d_N(\mathbf{u}, \hat{\mathbf{u}}) + \min_{\mathbf{v} \in \mathscr{B}} d_N(\mathbf{u}, \mathbf{v}) \tag{8.6.36}$$

Now averaging either (8.6.35) or (8.6.36) with respect to the joint distribution $Q(u, \hat{u})$ which satisfies (8.6.30), (8.6.31), (8.6.32), and (8.6.34), we obtain

$$|d(\mathscr{B} \,|\, p) - d(\mathscr{B} \,|\, \hat{p})| \le \bar{d}(p, \hat{p}) = |p - \hat{p}| \tag{8.6.37}$$

where $d(\mathscr{B} \,|\, p)$ and $d(\mathscr{B} \,|\, \hat{p})$ are the average distortions attained with code $\mathscr{B}$ for source $\mathscr{S}$ and $\hat{\mathscr{S}}$, respectively. This "mismatch" equation tells us the maximum average distortion loss we can have when applying a code designed for one source to another source. It allows us to make a finite approximation to the source space since, when two sources are close in source distance $\bar{d}(p, \hat{p})$, then a good code for one source is also good for the other. In addition, if $R(D; p)$ and $R(D; \hat{p})$ are the rate distortion functions for the two sources, we can easily show (see Prob. 8.18) that

$$R(D + \bar{d}(p, \hat{p}); p) \le R(D; \hat{p}) \le R(D - \bar{d}(p, \hat{p}); p) \tag{8.6.38}$$

Given any $\epsilon > 0$ let us divide the unit interval into L equally spaced intervals of length less than ϵ, which requires $L > 1/\epsilon$. Let $p_1, p_2, \ldots, p_L$ be the midpoints of the L intervals. By construction $|p_l - p_{l+1}| \le \epsilon$, and for any $p \in [0, 1]$ we have

$$\min_l |p - p_l| \le \epsilon \tag{8.6.39}$$

Hence for any subsource with parameter p there is a subsource with parameter in the finite set $\{p_1, p_2, \ldots, p_L\}$ which is within "source distance" ϵ. We now use subsources corresponding to these parameters as the finite approximation to the uncountable set of subsources. Following the results of our earlier example, we find codes $\mathscr{B}^1, \mathscr{B}^2, \ldots, \mathscr{B}^L$ satisfying (8.6.21) to (8.6.24) and define the composite code

$$\mathscr{B}_C = \bigcup_{l=1}^{L} \mathscr{B}^l \tag{8.6.40}$$

For any subsource with parameter $p \in [0, 1]$ we have from (8.6.37) that the average distortion

$$d(\mathscr{B}_C | p) \le d(\mathscr{B}_C | p^*) + \bar{d}(p, p^*) \tag{8.6.41}$$

where $p^* \in \{p_1, p_2, \ldots, p_L\}$ such that $\bar{d}(p, p^*) = |p - p^*| \le \epsilon$. Then since $d(\mathscr{B}_C | p^*) \le D^* + \epsilon$ [see (8.6.29)], we have

$$\begin{aligned} d(\mathscr{B}_C | p) &\le D^* + \epsilon + \epsilon \\ &= D^* + 2\epsilon \end{aligned} \tag{8.6.42}$$

where D^* satisfies [see (8.6.24)]

$$\begin{aligned} R &= \mathscr{H}(p^*) - \mathscr{H}(D^*) \\ &= R(D^*; p^*) \end{aligned} \tag{8.6.43}$$

For the source with parameter p, the smallest average distortion possible is D where

$$\begin{aligned} R &= R(D; p) \\ &= R(D^*; p^*) \end{aligned} \tag{8.6.44}$$

But from (8.6.38) we have

$$R(D^* + \epsilon; p) \leq R(D^*; p^*) = R(D; p) \leq R(D^* - \epsilon; p) \tag{8.6.45}$$

and so

$$D^* \leq D + \epsilon \tag{8.6.46}$$

Thus, finally substituting in (8.6.42), we obtain

$$d(\mathscr{B}_C | p) \leq D + 3\epsilon \tag{8.6.47}$$

The code rate for the composite code $\mathscr{B}_C$ is

$$R_C = R + (\ln L)/N \tag{8.6.48}$$

which approaches R as $N \to \infty$. This shows that for any fixed rate, regardless of the value of the unknown parameter, p, we can use a single code $\mathscr{B}_C$ to encode our binary source with unknown parameter with an average distortion which is asymptotically equal to the minimum achievable when the parameter is known.

The method of this example generalizes to a large class of nonergodic stationary sources and distortion measures. The basic idea is to first observe that all nonergodic stationary sources can be represented as a collection of stationary ergodic subsources (Rohlin [1967]). By defining a distance measure (see Prob. 8.18) on the subsource space, we can often "carve up" this space into a finite number of subsets with each subset of subsources approximated by a single subsource. This finite approximation then allows us to design good codes for each of the finite representative subsources and take the union of these as the code for the actual source. If there are L such subsources, then the rate of the composite code is at most $(\ln L)/N$ larger than the rate for each subcode. For sufficiently large N, this additive term is negligible.

Universal coding refers to all such techniques where the performance of the code selected without knowledge of the unknown "true" source converges to the optimum performance possible with a code specifically designed for the known true source. The technique of representing or approximating a source as a finite composite of stationary ergodic subsources and forming a union code is one of several universal coding techniques. Another closely related technique involves using a small fraction of the rate to learn and characterize the stationary source, and then using the rest of the rate in encoding the source outputs. Earlier, in Sec. 8.5, we considered a stronger robust coding technique for finite alphabet sources wherein the source outputs were classified according to a finite set of composition classes. This technique also is independent of the source statistics and is conceptually related to the approach in this section. In all cases the purpose is to encode unknown or nonergodic sources which often may be characterized as sources with unknown parameters. The main result of these two sections is that these universal coding techniques can asymptotically do as well as when we know the unknown parameter exactly. A secondary purpose of this section is to demonstrate that, unlike stationary ergodic sources, there is no single function for nonergodic stationary sources which plays the role of the rate distortion function.

8.7 BIBLIOGRAPHICAL NOTES AND REFERENCES

Sources with memory were also first treated by Shannon [1948, 1959]. The calculation of the rate distortion function for discrete-time Gaussian sources is due to Shannon [1948], and the rate distortion function for a Gaussian random process is due to Kolmogorov [1956]. Sakrison and Algazi [1971] extended this to Gaussian random fields. Except for the Gaussian sources with squared-error distortions, the evaluations of rate distortion functions are difficult, and various bounds due to several researchers, have been developed.

The robust source encoding of fixed composition sequences presented here appears in Berger [1971], while the techniques of universal coding are due to Ziv [1972], Davisson [1973], and Gray and Davisson [1974].

APPENDIX 8A CHERNOFF BOUNDS FOR DISTORTION DISTRIBUTIONS

8A.1 SYMMETRIC SOURCES

For the symmetric source defined by (8.5.1), (8.5.2), and (8.5.3) we have the rate distortion function given parametrically by (7.6.69)

$$D = D_s = \frac{\sum_{k=1}^{A} d_k e^{sd_k}}{\sum_{k=1}^{A} e^{sd_k}}$$

and (7.6.70)

$$R(D_s) = sD_s + \ln A - \ln \left(\sum_{k=1}^{A} e^{sd_k} \right)$$

where $s \le 0$. We now bound $F_N(D) = \Pr\{d_N(\mathbf{u}, \mathbf{v}) \le D \mid \mathbf{u}\}$ where $\mathbf{v}$ has uniform probability distribution $P_N(\mathbf{v}) = 1/A^N$. Using $E\{\cdot\}$ for expectation with respect to $\mathbf{v}$ for any $\alpha > 0$, we have the Chernoff bound

$$\begin{aligned} F_N(D) &= \Pr\{d_N(\mathbf{u}, \mathbf{v}) \le D \mid \mathbf{u}\} \\ &= \Pr\left\{\sum_{n=1}^{N} d(u_n, v_n) - ND \le 0 \,\middle|\, \mathbf{u}\right\} \\ &\le E\left(\exp\left\{\alpha\left[ND - \sum_{n=1}^{N} d(u_n, v_n)\right]\right\} \,\middle|\, \mathbf{u}\right\} \\ &= e^{\alpha ND} E\left(\prod_{n=1}^{N} e^{-\alpha d(u_n, v_n)} \,\middle|\, \mathbf{u}\right) \\ &= e^{\alpha ND}\left(\sum_{k=1}^{A} \frac{1}{A} e^{-\alpha d_k}\right)^N \\ &= \exp\left\{-N\left[-\alpha D + \ln A - \ln\left(\sum_{k=1}^{A} e^{-\alpha d_k}\right)\right]\right\} \end{aligned} \tag{8A.1}$$

By choosing $\alpha = -s > 0$, where s satisfies (7.6.69) and (7.6.70), we have the bound

$$F_N(D) \le e^{-NR(D)} \tag{8A.2}$$

To derive a lower bound to $F_N(D)$, define, for any $\beta \le 0$,

$$\mu(\beta) = \ln\left(\sum_{k=1}^{A} \frac{1}{A} e^{\beta d_k}\right) \tag{8A.3}$$

and note that

$$\mu'(\beta) = \frac{\sum_{k=1}^{A} d_k e^{\beta d_k}}{\sum_{k=1}^{A} e^{\beta d_k}} \tag{8A.4}$$

and

$$\begin{aligned} \mu''(\beta) &= \frac{\sum_{k=1}^{A} d_k^2 e^{\beta d_k}}{\sum_{k=1}^{A} e^{\beta d_k}} - \left(\frac{\sum_{k=1}^{A} d_l e^{\beta d_l}}{\sum_{k=1}^{A} e^{\beta d_k}}\right)^2 \\ &= \frac{1}{\sum_{k=1}^{A} e^{\beta d_k}} \sum_{k=1}^{A} e^{\beta d_k}\left(d_k - \frac{\sum_{l=1}^{A} d_l e^{\beta d_l}}{\sum_{l=1}^{A} e^{\beta d_l}}\right)^2 \end{aligned} \tag{8A.5}$$

Here since $d_k \leq d_0$ for $k = 1, 2, \ldots, A$

$$0 \leq \mu''(\beta) \leq d_0^2 \tag{8A.6}$$

For each $u \in \mathscr{U}$, define a tilted probability on $\mathscr{V}$ given by

$$\begin{aligned}\tilde{P}(v|u) &= \frac{e^{\beta d(u, v)}}{\sum_{k=1}^{A} e^{\beta d_k}} \\ &= \frac{(1/A)e^{\beta d(u, v)}}{\sum_{k=1}^{A} (1/A)e^{\beta d_k}} \\ &= P(v)e^{\beta d(u, v) - \mu(\beta)}\end{aligned} \tag{8A.7}$$

Given $\mathbf{u} \in \mathscr{U}_N$, the tilted distribution for $\mathbf{v} \in \mathscr{V}_N$ becomes

$$\tilde{P}_N(\mathbf{v}|\mathbf{u}) = P_N(\mathbf{v})e^{\beta N d_N(\mathbf{u}, \mathbf{v}) - N\mu(\beta)} \tag{8A.8}$$

Note that for this tilted distribution

$$\sum_{\mathbf{v}} \tilde{P}_N(\mathbf{v}|\mathbf{u})d_N(\mathbf{u}, \mathbf{v}) = \mu'(\beta) \tag{8A.9}$$

and

$$\begin{aligned}\sum_{\mathbf{v}} \tilde{P}_N(\mathbf{v}|\mathbf{u})(d_N(\mathbf{u}, \mathbf{v}) - \mu'(\beta))^2 &= \frac{\mu''(\beta)}{N} \\ &\leq \frac{d_0^2}{N}\end{aligned} \tag{8A.10}$$

Given any $\epsilon > 0$, we then have the bounds

$$\begin{aligned}\Pr\{d_N(\mathbf{u}, \mathbf{v}) \leq \mu'(\beta) + \epsilon \,|\, \mathbf{u}\} &= \sum_{d_N(\mathbf{u}, \mathbf{v}) \leq \mu'(\beta) + \epsilon} P_N(\mathbf{v}) \\ &\geq \sum_{|d_N(\mathbf{u}, \mathbf{v}) - \mu'(\beta)| \leq \epsilon} P_N(\mathbf{v}) \\ &= \sum_{|d_N(\mathbf{u}, \mathbf{v}) - \mu'(\beta)| \leq \epsilon} \tilde{P}_N(\mathbf{v}|\mathbf{u})e^{-\beta N d_N(\mathbf{u}, \mathbf{v}) + N\mu(\beta)} \\ &= e^{-N[\beta\mu'(\beta) - \mu(\beta)]} \sum_{|d_N(\mathbf{u}, \mathbf{v}) - \mu'(\beta)| \leq \epsilon} \tilde{P}_N(\mathbf{v}|\mathbf{u})e^{-\beta N[d_N(\mathbf{u}, \mathbf{v}) - \mu'(\beta)]} \\ &\geq e^{-N[\beta\mu'(\beta) - \mu(\beta)]}e^{\beta N\epsilon} \sum_{|d_N(\mathbf{u}, \mathbf{v}) - \mu'(\beta)| \leq \epsilon} \tilde{P}_N(\mathbf{v}|\mathbf{u})\end{aligned} \tag{8A.11}$$

The Chebychev inequality (see Prob. 1.4) gives

$$\sum_{|d_N(\mathbf{u},\,\mathbf{v})-\mu'(\beta)|\le\epsilon} \tilde{P}_N(\mathbf{v}\,|\,\mathbf{u}) \ge 1 - \frac{\mu''(\beta)}{N\epsilon^2}$$

$$\ge 1 - \frac{d_0^2}{N\epsilon^2} \tag{8A.12}$$

since $d_N(\mathbf{u}, \mathbf{v})$ has mean $\mu'(\beta)$ and variance $\mu''(\beta)/N$ over the tilted distribution. Here (8A.11) becomes

$$\Pr\,\{d_N(\mathbf{u}, \mathbf{v}) \le \mu'(\beta) + \epsilon\,|\,\mathbf{u}\} \ge \left(1 - \frac{d_0^2}{N\epsilon^2}\right) e^{-N[\beta\mu'(\beta)-\mu(\beta)]} e^{\beta N\epsilon} \tag{8A.13}$$

When $D > D_{\min}$ and $\epsilon > 0$ is small enough so that $D - \epsilon > D_{\min}$, we can choose $\beta \le 0$ to satisfy

$$D - \epsilon = \mu'(\beta)$$

$$= \frac{\sum_{k=1}^{A} d_k e^{\beta d_k}}{\sum_{k=1}^{A} e^{\beta d_k}} \tag{8A.14}$$

Let s satisfy (7.6.69) so that $\mu'(s) = D$. Then

$$\int_s^\beta \int_s^\omega \mu''(\alpha)\, d\alpha\, d\omega = \mu(\beta) - \mu(s) - (\beta - s)\mu'(s) \tag{8A.15}$$

Since $\mu''(\alpha) > 0$ we have

$$\mu(\beta) \ge \mu(s) + (\beta - s)\mu'(s) \tag{8A.16}$$

so that subtracting $\beta\mu'(\beta) = \beta D - \beta\epsilon = \beta\mu'(s) - \beta\epsilon$ from both sides gives

$$\mu(\beta) - \beta\mu'(\beta) \ge \mu(s) - s\mu'(s) + \beta\epsilon$$

$$= -sD - \ln A + \ln\left(\sum_{k=1}^{A} e^{sd_k}\right) + \beta\epsilon$$

$$= -R(D) + \beta\epsilon \tag{8A.17}$$

where we use (7.6.70). Using (8A.14) and (8A.17) in (8A.13), we get the desired result

$$F_N(D) = \Pr\,\{d_N(\mathbf{u}, \mathbf{v}) \le D\,|\,\mathbf{u}\}$$

$$\ge \left(1 - \frac{d_0^2}{N\epsilon^2}\right) e^{-NR(D)} e^{2N\beta\epsilon} \tag{8A.18}$$

8A.2 BINARY ALPHABET COMPOSITION CLASS $\mathscr{C}_N(l)$

We have a source alphabet $\mathscr{U} = \{0, 1\}$, a representation alphabet $\mathscr{V} = \{0, 1\}$, and error distortion measure $d(k, j) = 1 - \delta_{kj}$ for $k, j = 0, 1$. For fixed integers N and $l < N$, define as in (8.5.23), (8.5.24), and (8.5.25)

$$\mathscr{C}_N(l) = \{\mathbf{u}: \mathbf{u} \in \mathscr{U}_N, w(\mathbf{u}) = l\}$$

$$Q^l(u) = \begin{cases} \dfrac{l}{N} & u = 1 \\ 1 - \dfrac{l}{N} & u = 0 \end{cases}$$

$$R(D; Q^{(l)}) = \mathscr{H}\left(\frac{l}{N}\right) - \mathscr{H}(D) \qquad 0 \le D \le \min\left(\frac{l}{N}, 1 - \frac{l}{N}\right)$$

Now pick any $0 < \delta < \ln 2$, fixed rate R such that $\delta < R < \ln 2$, and choose $0 < \epsilon < 0.3$ to satisfy (8.5.27). Assume l is such that there exists a $D_l \ge \epsilon$ where from (8.5.35)

$$R = R(D_l; \mathbf{Q}^{(l)}) + \delta$$

We now find bounds as in (8.5.36) and (8.5.37) for $\Pr\{d_N(\mathbf{u}, \mathbf{v}) \le D_l \mid \mathbf{u} \in \mathscr{C}_N(l)\}$ where $\mathbf{v} \in \mathscr{V}_N$ has probability distribution

$$P_N(\mathbf{v}) = \prod_{n=1}^{N} P^{(l)}(v_n)$$

where

$$P^{(l)}(v) = \left(1 - \frac{l}{N}\right) P^{(l)}(v \mid 0) + \frac{l}{N} P^{(l)}(v \mid 1)$$

and $P^{(l)}(v \mid u)$ is the conditional probability distribution yielding the rate distortion function, $R(D_l; Q^{(l)}) = I(\mathbf{P}^{(l)})$.

Using $E\{\cdot\}$ for expectation with respect to $\mathbf{v}$, for any $s \le 0$ we have the Chernoff bound

$$\begin{aligned}
\Pr\{d_N(\mathbf{u}, \mathbf{v}) \le D_l \mid \mathbf{u} \in \mathscr{C}_N(l)\} &\le E\{e^{sN[d_N(\mathbf{u}, \mathbf{v}) - D_l]} \mid \mathbf{u} \in \mathscr{C}_N(l)\} \\
&= e^{-NsD_l} E\left\{\prod_{n=1}^{N} e^{sd(u_n, v_n)} \mid \mathbf{u} \in \mathscr{C}_N(l)\right\} \\
&= e^{-NsD_l} \prod_{n=1}^{N} E\{e^{sd(u_n, v_n)} \mid \mathbf{u} \in \mathscr{C}_N(l)\} \\
&= e^{-NsD_l}[E\{e^{sd(1, v)}\}]^l [E\{e^{sd(0, v)}\}]^{N-l} \\
&= e^{-NsD_l}[P^{(l)}(0)e^s + P^{(l)}(1)]^l [P^{(l)}(0) + P^{(l)}(1)e^s]^{N-l} \\
&= \exp\left(-N\left\{sD_l - \frac{l}{N} \ln [P^{(l)}(0)e^s + P^{(l)}(1)]\right.\right. \\
&\qquad \left.\left. - \left(1 - \frac{l}{N}\right) \ln [P^{(l)}(0) + P^{(l)}(1)e^s]\right\}\right)
\end{aligned} \tag{8A.19}$$

We choose s to satisfy the parametric equations for $D = D_s$ and $R(D_s)$. From (7.6.58), we have

$$\left(1 - \frac{l}{N}\right)(1 + e^s) = P^{(l)}(0) + P^{(l)}(1)e^s$$

$$\frac{l}{N}(1 + e^s) = P^{(l)}(0)e^s + P^{(l)}(1) \tag{8A.20}$$

and

$$s = \ln \frac{D_l}{1 - D_l} \tag{8A.21}$$

Hence

$$sD_l - \frac{l}{N} \ln [P^{(l)}(0)e^s + P^{(l)}(1)] - \left(1 - \frac{l}{N}\right) \ln [P^{(l)}(0) + P^{(l)}(1)e^s]$$

$$= D_l \ln \frac{D_l}{1 - D_l} - \frac{l}{N} \ln \left[\frac{l}{N}\left(1 + \frac{D_l}{1 - D_l}\right)\right] - \left(1 - \frac{l}{N}\right) \ln \left[\left(1 - \frac{l}{N}\right)\left(1 + \frac{D_l}{1 - D_l}\right)\right]$$

$$= -\frac{l}{N} \ln \frac{l}{N} - \left(1 - \frac{l}{N}\right) \ln \left(1 - \frac{l}{N}\right) + D_l \ln D_l + (1 - D_l) \ln (1 - D_l)$$

$$= \mathscr{H}\left(\frac{l}{N}\right) - \mathscr{H}(D_l) = R(D_l; Q^{(l)}) \tag{8A.22}$$

and

$$\Pr \{d_N(\mathbf{u}, \mathbf{v}) \leq D_l \,|\, \mathbf{u} \in \mathscr{C}_N(l)\} \leq e^{-NR(D_l;\, Q^{(l)})} \tag{8A.23}$$

To derive a lower bound, we first define, for any $\beta \leq 0$ and $\mathbf{u} \in \mathscr{C}_N(l)$

$$\mu(\beta \,|\, \mathbf{u}) \equiv \frac{1}{N} \ln [E\{e^{N\beta d_N(\mathbf{u}, \mathbf{v})} \,|\, \mathbf{u} \in \mathscr{C}_N(l)\}]$$

$$= \frac{1}{N} \ln \left[\prod_{n=1}^{N} E\{e^{\beta d(u_n, v_n)} \,|\, \mathbf{u} \in \mathscr{C}_N(l)\}\right]$$

$$= \frac{l}{N} \ln [P^{(l)}(0)e^\beta + P^{(l)}(1)] + \left(1 - \frac{l}{N}\right) \ln [P^{(l)}(0) + P^{(l)}(1)e^\beta] \tag{8A.24}$$

Derivatives with respect to β are

$$\mu'(\beta \,|\, \mathbf{u}) = \frac{l}{N}\left(\frac{P^{(l)}(0)e^\beta}{P^{(l)}(0)e^\beta + P^{(l)}(1)}\right) + \left(1 - \frac{l}{N}\right)\left(\frac{P^{(l)}(1)e^\beta}{P^{(l)}(0) + P^{(l)}(1)e^\beta}\right) \tag{8A.25}$$

and

$$\mu''(\beta \,|\, \mathbf{u}) = \frac{l}{N}\left\{\frac{P^{(l)}(0)e^\beta}{P^{(l)}(0)e^\beta + P^{(l)}(1)} - \left[\frac{P^{(l)}(0)e^\beta}{P^{(l)}(0)e^\beta + P^{(l)}(1)}\right]^2\right\}$$

$$+ \left(1 - \frac{l}{N}\right)\left\{\frac{P^{(l)}(1)e^\beta}{P^{(l)}(0) + P^{(l)}(1)e^\beta} - \left[\frac{P^{(l)}(1)e^\beta}{P^{(l)}(0) + P^{(l)}(1)e^\beta}\right]^2\right\} \tag{8A.26}$$

Here we have

$$0 \le \mu''(\beta \,|\, \mathbf{u}) \le 1 \tag{8A.27}$$

For a given $\mathbf{u} \in \mathscr{C}_N(l)$, define a tilted probability on $\mathscr{V}_N$ given by

$$\begin{aligned}\tilde{P}_N(\mathbf{v} \,|\, \mathbf{u}) &= \frac{P_N(\mathbf{v})e^{N\beta d_N(\mathbf{u},\, \mathbf{v})}}{\sum_{\mathbf{v}'} P_N(\mathbf{v}')e^{N\beta d_N(\mathbf{u},\, \mathbf{v}')}} \\ &= P_N(\mathbf{v})e^{N\beta d_N(\mathbf{u},\, \mathbf{v}) - N\mu(\beta|\mathbf{u})}\end{aligned} \tag{8A.28}$$

For this tilted distribution, we have

$$\sum_{\mathbf{v}} \tilde{P}_N(\mathbf{v} \,|\, \mathbf{u})d_N(\mathbf{u}, \mathbf{v}) = \mu'(\beta \,|\, \mathbf{u}) \tag{8A.29}$$

and

$$\sum_{\mathbf{v}} \tilde{P}_N(\mathbf{v} \,|\, \mathbf{u})(d_N(\mathbf{u}, \mathbf{v}) - \mu'(\beta \,|\, \mathbf{u}))^2 = \frac{\mu''(\beta \,|\, \mathbf{u})}{N} \le \frac{1}{N} \tag{8A.30}$$

Now following the same inequalities as in (8A.11), (8A.12), and (8A.13), we have

$$\Pr\left\{d_N(\mathbf{u}, \mathbf{v}) \le \mu'(\beta \,|\, \mathbf{u}) + \frac{\epsilon}{2} \,\middle|\, \mathbf{u} \in \mathscr{C}_N(l)\right\} \ge \left(1 - \frac{4}{N\epsilon^2}\right)e^{-N[\beta\mu'(\beta|\mathbf{u}) - \mu(\beta|\mathbf{u})]}\, e^{\beta N\epsilon/2} \tag{8A.31}$$

Since $D_l \ge \epsilon > 0$, we have $D_l - \epsilon/2 \ge \epsilon/2 > 0$, and we can choose β to satisfy the parametric equations for $D_l - \epsilon = D_\beta$ and $R(D_\beta; \mathbf{Q}^{(l)})$. Hence from (7.6.58) we have

$$\begin{aligned}\left(1 - \frac{l}{N}\right)(1 + e^\beta) &= P^{(l)}(0) + P^{(l)}(1)e^\beta \\ \frac{l}{N}(1 + e^\beta) &= P^{(l)}(0)e^\beta + P^{(l)}(1)\end{aligned} \tag{8A.32}$$

and

$$\begin{aligned}P^{(l)}(0) &= \frac{\left(1 - \frac{l}{N}\right) - \frac{l}{N}e^\beta}{1 - e^\beta} \\ P^{(l)}(1) &= \frac{\frac{l}{N} - \left(1 - \frac{l}{N}\right)e^\beta}{1 - e^\beta}\end{aligned} \tag{8A.33}$$

giving us the relationships

$$\begin{aligned}\mu'(\beta \,|\, \mathbf{u}) &= \frac{e^\beta}{1 + e^\beta} \\ &= D_l - \frac{\epsilon}{2}\end{aligned} \tag{8A.34}$$

and

$$\mu'(\beta|\mathbf{u}) - \mu(\beta|\mathbf{u}) = \mathscr{H}\left(\frac{l}{N}\right) - \mathscr{H}\left(D_l - \frac{\epsilon}{2}\right)$$

$$= R\left(D_l - \frac{\epsilon}{2}; \mathbf{Q}^{(l)}\right) \tag{8A.35}$$

Choosing the parameter s to satisfy $D_l = D_s$, we then have, as in (8A.17)

$$\mu(\beta|\mathbf{u}) - \beta\mu'(\beta|\mathbf{u}) \geq \mu(s|\mathbf{u}) - s\mu'(s|\mathbf{u}) + \frac{\beta\epsilon}{2}$$

$$= -R(D_l; \mathbf{Q}^{(l)}) + \frac{\beta\epsilon}{2} \tag{8A.36}$$

Using (8A.35) and (8A.36) in (8A.31) results in the lower bound

$$\Pr\{d_N(\mathbf{u}, \mathbf{v}) \leq D_l | \mathbf{u} \in \mathscr{C}_N(l)\} \geq \left(1 - \frac{4}{N\epsilon^2}\right) e^{-NR(D_l;\, \mathbf{Q}^{(l)})} e^{N\beta\epsilon} \tag{8A.37}$$

From (8A.34) we have

$$\beta = \ln\left[\frac{D_l - \frac{\epsilon}{2}}{1 - \left(D_l - \frac{\epsilon}{2}\right)}\right]$$

$$\geq \ln\left(D_l - \frac{\epsilon}{2}\right)$$

$$\geq \ln\frac{\epsilon}{2} \tag{8A.38}$$

since $D_l - \epsilon/2 \geq \epsilon/2 > 0$. Hence (8A.37) becomes

$$\Pr\{d_N(\mathbf{u}, \mathbf{v}) \leq D_l | \mathbf{u} \in \mathscr{C}_N(l)\} \geq \left(1 - \frac{4}{N\epsilon^2}\right) e^{-N[R(D_l;\, \mathbf{Q}^{(l)}) - \epsilon \ln(\epsilon/2)]} \tag{8A.39}$$

PROBLEMS

8.1 Consider L independent memoryless discrete-time Gaussian sources in the multiple-source–user system of Fig. 8.1. Let $\sigma_1^2, \sigma_2^2, \ldots, \sigma_L^2$ be the output variance of the sources, and for some positive weights $w_1, w_2, \ldots, w_L$ define the sum distortion measure

$$d(\mathbf{u}, \mathbf{v}) = \sum_{l=1}^{L} w_l(u^{(l)} - v^{(l)})^2$$

where $u^{(l)}$ is the lth source output symbol. Find a parametric form for the rate distortion function in terms of the variances and weights.

8.2 (*a*) In (8.2.66), for $D < \min\{\lambda_1, \lambda_2, \ldots, \lambda_L\}$, show that

$$R_L(D) = \frac{1}{2L} \ln \frac{|\Phi|}{D}$$

where Φ is the covariance matrix defined in (8.2.53) and $\lambda_1, \lambda_2, \ldots, \lambda_L$ are its eigenvalues.

(*b*) In (8.2.66), let $\theta = \max\{\lambda_1, \lambda_2, \ldots, \lambda_L\}$ and show that

$$D_\theta = D_{\max}$$

and

$$R(D_\theta) = 0$$

8.3 Verify Eq. (8.2.72) by following the proof of the source coding theorem in Sec. 7.2.

8.4 Consider a discrete-time first-order Gaussian Markov source with

$$\phi_k = E\{u_t u_{t+k}\} = \sigma^2 \rho^k \qquad 0 < \rho < 1 \qquad k = 0, 1, 2, \ldots$$

For the squared-error distortion show that

$$R(D) = \tfrac{1}{2} \ln \frac{1 - \rho^2}{D} \qquad D \le \frac{1 - \rho}{1 + \rho}$$

(For large D, see Berger [1971], example 4.5.2.2.)

8.5 For any discrete-time zero-mean stationary ergodic source with spectral density $\Phi(\omega)$ and the squared-error distortion measure, show that the rate distortion function is bounded by

$$R(D) \le \tfrac{1}{2} \ln \frac{\sigma^2}{D}$$

where

$$\sigma^2 = \frac{1}{2\pi} \int_{-\pi}^{\pi} \Phi(\omega)\, d\omega$$

Generalize this for continuous-time stationary sources where

$$\Phi(\omega) = 0 \qquad \text{for } |\omega| > \omega_0$$

8.6 Generalize the lower bound given in Theorem 8.3.2 to

$$R(D) \ge R_L(D) + h - h(\mathcal{U}_L) \qquad \text{for any integer } L$$

8.7 Prove the generalized Shannon lower bound given by (8.3.18).

8.8 For a stationary discrete-time Gaussian source with spectral density function $\Phi(\omega)$, show that the differential entropy rate is

$$h = \tfrac{1}{2} \ln (2\pi e E)$$

where

$$E = \exp \frac{1}{2\pi} \int_{-\pi}^{\pi} \ln \Phi(\omega)\, d\omega$$

8.9 Suppose we have a continuous-time Gaussian Markov source with spectral density

$$\Phi(\omega) = A\left[1 + \left(\frac{\omega}{\omega_0}\right)^2\right]^{-1}$$

where A is a normalizing constant that satisfies

$$\sigma^2 = \frac{1}{2\pi} \int_{-\infty}^{\infty} \Phi(\omega)\, d\omega$$

For this case show that for the squared-error distortion measure

$$R(D) = \frac{\omega_0}{\pi} (\beta - \tan^{-1} \beta)$$

where β satisfies

$$D = \sigma^2 \left[1 + \left(\frac{2}{\pi}\right)\left(\frac{\beta}{1 + \beta^2} - \tan^{-1} \beta\right)\right]$$

Here $1 + \beta^2 = A/\theta = 2\sigma^2/(\omega_0 \theta)$, where θ is the usual parameter (Berger [1971]).

8.10 For the continuous-time Gaussian process with the squared-error distortion measure discussed in Sec. 8.4.3, derive the source coding theorem in the same manner as shown in Sec. 8.2 for the discrete-time Gaussian process. That is, derive a bound similar to (8.2.88).

8.11 Verify that (8.5.15) follows from (8.5.7).

8.12 Show that

$$\mathscr{H}(\epsilon) = \epsilon \ln \epsilon - (1 - \epsilon) \ln (1 - \epsilon) > -\epsilon \ln \frac{\epsilon}{2} \qquad \text{for } \epsilon < 0.3$$

8.13 Prove (8.5.50) by using the converse source coding theorem (Theorem 7.2.3) and the law of large numbers in

$$\sum_{l=0}^{N} \binom{N}{l} q^l (1 - q)^{N-l} D_l = \sum_{|l - nq| \leq n\gamma} \binom{N}{l} q^l (1 - q)^{N-l} D_l + \sum_{|l - nq| > n\gamma} \binom{N}{l} q^l (1 - q)^{N-l} D_l$$

$$\leq D_{n(q+\gamma)} + \sum_{|l - nq| > n\gamma} \binom{N}{l} q^l (1 - q)^{N-l}$$

for any $\gamma > 0$.

8.14 (Generalization of Sec. 8.5.2) Consider source alphabet $\mathscr{U} = \{a_1, a_2, \ldots, a_A\}$, representation alphabet $\mathscr{V} = \{b_1, b_2, \ldots, b_B\}$, and distortion $\{d(u, v): u \in \mathscr{U}, v \in \mathscr{V}\}$ such that $D_{\min} = 0$. Next define, for any $\mathbf{u} \in \mathscr{U}_N$, the numbers

$$n(a_k | \mathbf{u}) \equiv \text{number of places where } u_n = a_k \qquad k = 1, 2, \ldots, A$$

define the composition vector

$$C(\mathbf{u}) = (n(a_1 | \mathbf{u}), n(a_2 | \mathbf{u}), \ldots, n(a_A | \mathbf{u}))$$

and define the composition classes

$$\mathscr{C}_N(l) = \{\mathbf{u}: C(\mathbf{u}) = \mathbf{C}_l\} \qquad l = 1, 2, \ldots, L_N$$

where L_N is the number of distinct compositions of output sequences of length N. For the lth composition $\mathbf{C}_l = (n_{l_1}, n_{l_2}, \ldots, n_{l_A})$, define the probability

$$Q^{(l)}(a_k) = \frac{n_{l_k}}{N} \qquad k = 1, 2, \ldots, A$$

and the rate distortion function $R(D; \mathbf{Q}^{(l)})$, which is the rate distortion function of a memoryless source with output probability distribution $\mathbf{Q}^{(l)}$.

(*a*) Show that $L_N \leq (N + 1)^{A-1}$.

(*b*) Pick $\delta > 0$, $\epsilon > 0$, and rate R such that

$$\delta < R < \max_{\mathbf{Q}} R(\epsilon; \mathbf{Q})$$

and let Q^* satisfy

$$R = R(\epsilon; \mathbf{Q}^*) + \delta$$

For a fixed composition class $\mathscr{C}_N(l)$ where $R(\epsilon; Q^*) < R(\epsilon; Q^{(l)})$, define $D_l \geq \epsilon$ such that

$$R = R(D_l; \mathbf{Q}^{(l)}) + \delta$$

Generalize Lemma 8.5.2 and Theorem 8.5.2 for this case.

(*c*) Construct composite codes and show that, if the source is memoryless, these composite codes can approach the rate distortion limit.

8.15 For a memoryless source with source alphabet $\mathscr{U}$, probability $\{Q(u): u \in \mathscr{U}\}$, representation alphabet $\mathscr{V}$, and distortion measure $\{d(u, v): u \in \mathscr{U}, v \in \mathscr{V}\}$, let $R(D)$ be the rate distortion function and define

$$P_N(R, D) \equiv \min_{\mathscr{B}} \Pr\{d(\mathbf{u} \mid \mathscr{B}) > D \mid \mathscr{B}\}$$

where the minimization is over all codes of block length N and rate $R > R(D)$. Define the exponent

$$F(R, D) = -\lim_{N \to \infty} \frac{1}{N} \ln P_N(R, D)$$

(*a*) Let $\mathbf{Q}'$ be any other source probability distribution and $R(D; \mathbf{Q}')$ the corresponding rate distortion function. Show that

$$F(R, D) = \infty \qquad \text{if } R > \max_{\mathbf{Q}'} R(D; \mathbf{Q}')$$

Note that for symmetric sources with balanced distortions

$$R(D) = \max_{\mathbf{Q}'} R(D; \mathbf{Q}')$$

and thus $F(R, D) = \infty$ for all $R > R(D)$.

Hint: Prob. 8.14 shows that, if $R > \max_{\mathbf{Q}'} R(D; \mathbf{Q}')$, then all sequences can be encoded with distortion less than or equal to D for large enough N.

(*b*) Consider the composition classes defined in Prob. 8.14. Sterling's formula gives

$$\begin{aligned}
\Pr\{\mathbf{u} \in \mathscr{C}_N(l)\} &= \sum_{\mathbf{u} \in \mathscr{C}_N(l)} Q(a_1)^{n(a_1|\mathbf{u})} Q(a_2)^{n(a_2|\mathbf{u})} \cdots Q(a_A)^{n(a_A|\mathbf{u})} \\
&= \frac{n!\, Q(a_1)^{n(a_1|\mathbf{u})} Q(a_2)^{n(a_2|\mathbf{u})} \cdots Q(a_A)^{n(a_A|\mathbf{u})}}{n(a_1|\mathbf{u})!\, n(a_2|\mathbf{u})! \cdots n(a_A|\mathbf{u})!} \\
&= e^{-N(J(\mathbf{Q}^{(l)}, \mathbf{Q}) + o(N))}
\end{aligned}$$

where

$$J(\mathbf{Q}^{(l)}, \mathbf{Q}) = \sum_u Q^{(l)}(u) \ln \frac{Q^{(l)}(u)}{Q(u)}$$

Use the results of Prob. 8.14 to show that, for

$$R(D) < R < \max_{\mathbf{Q}'} R(D; \mathbf{Q}')$$

we have

$$\begin{aligned}
P_N(R, D) &\leq \Pr\{\mathbf{u} \in \mathscr{C}_N(l): R(D) \leq R(D; Q^{(l)}), l = 1, 2, \ldots, L_N\} \\
&\leq \sum_{l:\, R(D) \leq R(D, Q^{(l)})} \Pr\{\mathbf{u} \in \mathscr{C}_N^{(l)}\} \\
&\leq \sum_{l:\, R(D) \leq R(D, Q^{(l)})} e^{-N(J(\mathbf{Q}^{(l)}, \mathbf{Q}) + o(N))}
\end{aligned}$$

Then show that for any $\delta > 0$

$$F(R, D) \geq \min_{\tilde{\mathbf{Q}}} J(\tilde{\mathbf{Q}}, \mathbf{Q})$$

where $\tilde{\mathbf{Q}}$ satisfies $R(D) = R - \delta \leq R(D; \tilde{\mathbf{Q}})$.

(*c*) For $R(D) < R < \max_{\mathbf{Q}'} R(D; \mathbf{Q}')$, let $\tilde{\mathbf{Q}}$ be any probability distribution such that

$$R < R(D; \tilde{\mathbf{Q}})$$

Use the converse source coding theorem (Theorem 7.2.3) to show that there exists an $\alpha > 0$ (independent of N) such that any code $\mathscr{B}$ of rate R satisfies

$$\widetilde{\Pr}\,\{d(\mathbf{u}\,|\,\mathscr{B}) > D\,|\,\mathscr{B}\} \geq \alpha$$

Here $\widetilde{\Pr}\,\{\cdot\}$ is the probability using distribution $\tilde{\mathbf{Q}}$.

(*d*) Next show that, for any $\gamma > 0$ and any code $\mathscr{B}$ of block length N and rate R such that $R(D) < R < R(D; \tilde{\mathbf{Q}})$, we have

$$\Pr\,\{d(u\,|\,\mathscr{B}) > D\,|\,\mathscr{B}\} \geq \left(\alpha - \frac{\sigma^2}{N\gamma^2}\right) e^{-N[J(\tilde{\mathbf{Q}}, \mathbf{Q}) + \gamma]}$$

where

$$\sigma^2 = \sum_u \left[\ln \frac{\tilde{Q}(u)}{Q(u)} - J(\tilde{\mathbf{Q}}, \mathbf{Q})\right]^2 \tilde{Q}(u)$$

Hint: Define the region

$$G_\gamma = \left\{\mathbf{u}: \left|\frac{1}{N} \ln \frac{\tilde{Q}_N(\mathbf{u})}{Q_N(\mathbf{u})} - J(\tilde{\mathbf{Q}}, \mathbf{Q})\right| < \gamma\right\}$$

and obtain the lower bound to $\Pr\,\{d(u\,|\,\mathscr{B}) > D\,|\,\mathscr{B}\}$ by restricting the summation to this subset of outputs. Then lower-bound $Q_N(u)$ by $\tilde{Q}_N(\mathbf{u}) \exp\{-N[J(\tilde{\mathbf{Q}}, \mathbf{Q}) + \gamma]\}$ and use both (*c*) above and the Chebyshev inequality.

(*e*) Combine the above upper and lower bounds to $P_N(R, D)$ to show that

$$F(R, D) = \min_{\tilde{\mathbf{Q}}} J(\tilde{\mathbf{Q}}, \mathbf{Q})$$

where $\tilde{\mathbf{Q}}$ satisfies $R \leq R(D; \tilde{\mathbf{Q}})$ and where

$$R(D) < R < \max_{\mathbf{Q}'} R(D; \mathbf{Q}')$$

8.16 In (8.5.68) we showed that, for the binary symmetric source with error distortion, linear codes can achieve the rate distortion limit. Consider using the linear (7, 4) Hamming code for encoding source sequences of block length $N = 7$. This code has rate $R = (4/7) \ln 2$ nats per source symbol. Find the average distortion using this code and compare it with the rate distortion limit.

8.17 Show that, for the set of joint distributions $Q(u, \hat{u})$ on $\{0, 1\} \times \{0, 1\}$ where

$$p = Q(1, 0) + Q(1, 1)$$

$$\hat{p} = Q(1, 1) + Q(0, 1)$$

for given p and $\hat{p}$, $\bar{d}(p, \hat{p})$ as defined in (8.6.32) becomes

$$\bar{d}(p, \hat{p}) = |p - \hat{p}|$$

8.18 Let $\mathscr{S}$ and $\hat{\mathscr{S}}$ be two memoryless sources that differ only in their source probabilities, $\{Q(u): u \in \mathscr{U}\}$ and $\{\hat{Q}(\hat{u}): \hat{u} \in \mathscr{U}\}$. Let $\mathscr{V} = \mathscr{U}$ be a common representation alphabet and suppose that the distortion measure $\{d(u, v): u \in \mathscr{U}, v \in \mathscr{V}\}$ satisfies the triangle inequality

$$d(x, y) \leq d(x, z) + d(z, y) \qquad \text{for all } x, y, z \in \mathscr{U}$$

and the symmetry condition

$$d(u, \hat{u}) = d(\hat{u}, u) \qquad \text{for all } u, \hat{u} \in \mathscr{U}$$

For all joint distributions $\{Q(u, \hat{u}): u, \hat{u} \in \mathscr{U}\}$ where

$$Q(u) = \sum_{\hat{u}} Q(u, \hat{u}) \qquad \text{for all } u \in \mathscr{U}$$

and

$$\hat{Q}(\hat{u}) = \sum_{u} Q(u, \hat{u}) \qquad \text{for all } \hat{u} \in \mathscr{U}$$

define the distance between the two sources as

$$\bar{d}(\mathscr{S}, \hat{\mathscr{S}}) = \min_{Q} \sum_{u} \sum_{\hat{u}} Q(u, \hat{u})\, d(u, \hat{u})$$

Show that (8.6.37) generalizes to

$$|d(\mathscr{B} \mid \mathscr{S}) - d(\mathscr{B} \mid \hat{\mathscr{S}})| \leq \bar{d}(\mathscr{S}, \hat{\mathscr{S}})$$

where $d(\mathscr{B} \mid \mathscr{S})$ and $d(\mathscr{B} \mid \hat{\mathscr{S}})$ are the average distortions for sources $\mathscr{S}$ and $\hat{\mathscr{S}}$ respectively when using the same block code $\mathscr{B}$. This is the general "mismatch theorem" for memoryless sources. If $R(D; Q)$ and $R(D; \hat{Q})$ are rate distortion functions of the two sources, show that

$$R(D + \bar{d}(\mathscr{S}, \hat{\mathscr{S}}); Q) \leq R(D; \hat{Q}) \leq R(D - \bar{d}(\mathscr{S}; \hat{\mathscr{S}}); Q)$$

This is the general form of (8.6.38).

BIBLIOGRAPHY

Abramson, N. (1963), *Information Theory and Coding*, McGraw-Hill, New York.

Acampora, A. S. (1976), "Maximum-Likelihood Decoding of Binary Convolutional Codes on Band-Limited Satellite Channels," *Conf. Rec.*, National Telecommunication Conference.

Anderson, J. B., and F. Jelinek (1973), "A 2-Cycle Algorithm for Source Coding with a Fidelity Criterion," *IEEE Trans. Inform. Theor.*, vol. IT-19, pp. 77–91.

Arimoto, S. (1976), "Computation of Random Coding Exponent Functions," *IEEE Trans. Inform. Theor.*, vol. IT-22, pp. 665–671.

Arimoto, S. (1973), "On the Converse to the Coding Theorem for Discrete Memoryless Channels," *IEEE Trans. Inform. Theor.*, vol. IT-19, pp. 357–359.

Arimoto, S. (1972), "An Algorithm for Computing the Capacity of Arbitrary Discrete Memoryless Channels," *IEEE Trans. Inform. Theor.*, vol. IT-18, pp. 14–20.

Arthurs, E., and H. Dym (1962), "On the Optimum Detection of Digital Signals in the Presence of White Gaussian Noise—A Geometric Interpretation and a Study of Three Basic Data Transmission Systems," *IRE Trans. Commun. Syst.*, vol. CS-10, pp. 336–372.

Ash, R. B. (1965), *Information Theory*, Interscience, New York.

Berger, T. (1971), *Rate Distortion Theory*, Prentice-Hall, Englewood Cliffs, N. J.

Berlekamp, E. R. (1968), *Algebraic Coding Theory*, McGraw-Hill, New York.

Blahut, R. E. (1974), "Hypothesis Testing and Information Theory," *IEEE Trans. Inform. Theor.*, vol. IT-20, pp. 405–417.

Blahut, R. E. (1972), "Computation of Channel Capacity and Rate-Distortion Functions," *IEEE Trans. Inform. Theor.*, vol. IT-18, pp. 460–473.

Blake, I., and R. C. Mullin (1976), *An Introduction to Algebraic and Combinatorial Coding Theory*, Academic, New York.

Bode, H. W., and C. E. Shannon (1950), "A Simplified Derivation of Linear Least-Squares Smoothing and Prediction Theory," *Proc. IRE*, vol. 38, pp. 417–425.

Brayer, K. (1971), "Error-Correcting Code Performance on HF, Troposcatter, and Satellite Channels," *IEEE Trans. Commun. Technol.*, vol. COM-19, pp. 835–848.

Bucher, E. A., and J. A. Heller (1970), "Error Probability Bounds for Systematic Convolutional Codes," *IEEE Trans. Inform. Theor.*, vol. IT-16, pp. 219–224.

Bussgang, J. J. (1965), "Some Properties of Binary Convolutional Code Generators," *IEEE Trans. Inform. Theor.*, vol. IT-11, pp. 90–100.

Campbell, F. W., and J. G. Robson (1968), "Application of Fourier Analysis to the Visibility of Gratings," *J. Physiol.*, vol. 197, pp. 551–566.

Courant, R., and D. Hilbert (1953), *Methods of Mathematical Physics*, vol. 1, Wiley-Interscience, New York.

Darlington, S. (1964), "Demodulation of Wideband, Low-Power FM Signals," *Bell Syst. Tech. J.* vol. 43, pp. 339–374.

Davisson, L. D. (1973), "Universal Noiseless Coding," *IEEE Trans. Inform. Theor.*, vol. IT-19, pp. 783–795.

Elias, P. (1960), unpublished. (See Berlekamp, E. R. [1968].)

Elias, P. (1955), "Coding for Noisy Channels," *IRE Conv. Rec.*, pt. 4, pp. 37–46.

Fano, R. M. (1963), "A Heuristic Discussion of Probabilistic Decoding," *IEEE Trans. Inform. Theor.*, vol. IT-9, pp. 64–74.

Fano, R. M. (1961), *Transmission of Information*, MIT Press, Cambridge, Mass., and Wiley, New York.

Fano, R. M. (1952), "Class Notes for Transmission of Information," Course 6.574, MIT, Cambridge, Mass.

Feinstein, A. (1958), *Foundations of Information Theory*, McGraw-Hill, New York.

Feinstein, A. (1955), "Error Bounds in Noisy Channels without Memory," *IRE Trans. Inform. Theor.*, vol. IT-1, pp. 13–14.

Feinstein, A. (1954), "A New Basic Theorem of Information Theory," *IRE Trans. Inform. Theor.*, vol. PGIT-4, pp. 2–22.

Feller, W. (1957), *An Introduction to Probability Theory and its Applications*, vol. 1, 2d ed. Wiley, New York.

Forney, G. D., Jr. (1974), "Convolutional Codes II: Maximum-Likelihood Decoding" and "Convolutional Codes III: Sequential Decoding," *Inform. Contr.*, vol. 25, pp. 222–297.

Forney, G. D., Jr. (1973), "The Viterbi Algorithm," *Proc. IEEE*, vol. 61, pp. 268–278.

Forney, G. D., Jr. (1972*a*), "Maximum-Likelihood Sequence Estimation of Digital Sequences in the Presence of Intersymbol Interference," *IEEE Trans. Inform. Theor.*, vol. IT-18, pp. 363–378.

Forney, G. D., Jr. (1972*b*). "Convolutional Codes II: Maximum Likelihood Decoding," Stanford Electronics Labs. Tech. Rep. 7004-1.

Forney, G. D., Jr. (1970), "Convolutional Codes I: Algebraic Structure," *IEEE Trans. Inform. Theor.*, vol. IT-16, pp. 720–738.

Forney, G. D., Jr., and E. K. Bower (1971), "A High-Speed Sequential Decoder: Prototype Design and Test," *IEEE Trans. Commun. Tech.*, vol. COM-19, pp. 821–835.

Gallager, R. G. (1976), private communication.

Gallager, R. G. (1974), "Tree Encoding for Symmetric Sources with a Distortion Measure," *IEEE Trans. Inform. Theor.*, vol. IT-20, pp. 65–76.

Gallager, R. G. (1968), *Information Theory and Reliable Communication*, Wiley, New York.

Gallager, R. G. (1965), "A Simple Derivation of the Coding Theorem and Some Applications," *IEEE Trans. Inform. Theor.*, vol. IT-11, pp. 3–18.

Gantmacher, F. R. (1959), *Applications of the Theory of Matrices*, Interscience, New York.

Geist, J. M. (1973), "Search Properties of Some Sequential Decoding Algorithms," *IEEE Trans. Inform. Theor.*, vol. IT-19, pp. 519–526.

Gilbert, E. N. (1952), "A Comparison of Signalling Alphabets," *Bell Syst. Tech. J.*, vol. 31, pp. 504–522.

Gilhousen, K. S., J. A. Heller, I. M. Jacobs, and A. J. Viterbi (1971), "Coding Study for High Data Rate Telemetry Links," Linkabit Corp. NASA CR-114278 Contract NAS 2-6024.

Goblick, T. J., Jr. (1962), "Coding for a Discrete Information Source with a Distortion Measure," Ph.D. Dissertation, MIT, Cambridge, Mass.

Goblick, T. J., Jr., and J. L. Holsinger (1967), "Analog Source Digitization: A Comparison of Theory and Practice," *IEEE Trans. Inform. Theor.*, vol. IT-13, pp. 323–326.

Gray, R. M. (1975), private communication.

Gray, R. M., and L. D. Davisson (1974), "Source Coding without the Ergodic Assumption," *IEEE Trans. Inform. Theor.*, vol. IT-20, pp. 502–516.

Gray, R. M., D. L. Neuhoff, and J. K. Omura (1975), "Process Definitions of Distortion-Rate Functions and Source Coding Theorems," *IEEE Trans. Inform. Theor.*, vol. IT-21, pp. 524–532.

Grenander, U., and G. Szego (1958), *Toeplitz Forms and Their Applications*, University of California Press, Berkeley.

Hardy, G. H., J. E. Littlewood, and G. Polya (1952), *Inequalities*, 2d ed., Cambridge University Press, London.

Heller, J. A. (1975), "Feedback Decoding of Convolutional Codes," in A. J. Viterbi (ed.), *Advances in Communication Systems*, vol. 4, Academic, New York, pp. 261–278.

Heller, J. A. (1968), "Short Constraint Length Convolutional Codes," Jet Propulsion Labs. Space Programs Summary 37-54, vol. III, pp. 171–177.

Heller, J. A., and I. M. Jacobs (1971), "Viterbi Decoding for Satellite and Space Communication," *IEEE Trans. Commun. Technol.*, vol. COM-19, pp. 835–848.

Helstrom, C. W. (1968), *Statistical Theory of Signal Detection*, 2d ed., Pergamon, Oxford.

Huffman, D. A. (1952), "A Method for the Construction of Minimum Redundancy Codes," *Proc. IRE*, vol. 40, pp. 1098–1101.

Jacobs, I. M. (1974), "Practical Applications of Coding," *IEEE Trans. Inform. Theor.*, vol. IT-20, pp. 305–310.

Jacobs, I. M. (1967), "Sequential Decoding for Efficient Communication from Deep Space," *IEEE Trans. Commun. Technol.*, vol. COM-15, pp. 492–501.

Jacobs, I. M., and E. R. Berlekamp (1967), "A Lower Bound to the Distribution of Computation for Sequential Decoding," *IEEE Trans. Inform. Theor.*, vol. IT-13, pp. 167–174.

Jelinek, F. (1969*a*), "A Fast Sequential Decoding Algorithm Using a Stack," *IBM J. Res. Dev.*, vol. 13, pp. 675–685.

Jelinek, F. (1969*b*), "Tree Encoding of Memoryless Time-Discrete Sources with a Fidelity Criterion," *IEEE Trans. Inform. Theor.*, vol. IT-15, pp. 584–590.

Jelinek, F. (1968*a*), *Probabilistic Information Theory*, McGraw-Hill, New York.

Jelinek, F. (1968*b*), "Evaluation of Expurgated Bound Exponents," *IEEE Trans. Inform. Theor.*, vol. IT-14, pp. 501–505.

Kennedy, R. S. (1969), *Fading Dispersive Communication Channels*, Wiley, New York.

Kohlenberg, A., and G. D. Forney, (1968), "Convolutional Coding for Channels with Memory," *IEEE Trans. Inform. Theor.*, vol. IT-14, pp. 618–626.

Kolmogorov, N. (1956), "On the Shannon Theory of Information Transmission in the Case of Continuous Signals," *IRE Trans. Inform. Theor.*, vol. IT-2, pp. 102–108.

Kraft, L. G. (1949), "A Device for Quantizing, Grouping and Coding Amplitude Modulated Pulses," M.S. Thesis, MIT, Cambridge, Mass.

Kuhn, H. W., and A. W. Tucker (1951), "Nonlinear Programming," *Proc. 2nd Berkeley Symp. Math. Stat. Prob.*, University of California Press, Berkeley, pp. 481–492.

Landau, H. J., and H. O. Pollak (1962), "Prolate Spheroidal Wave Functions, Fourier Analysis, and Uncertainty-III," *Bell System Tech. J.*, vol. 41, pp. 1295–1336.

Landau, H. J., and H. O. Pollak (1961), "Prolate Spheroidal Wave Functions, Fourier Analysis, and Uncertainty-II," *Bell System Tech. J.*, vol. 40, pp. 65–84.

Lesh, J. R. (1976), "Computational Algorithms for Coding Bound Exponents," Ph.D. Dissertation, University of California, Los Angeles.

Lin, S. (1970), *An Introduction to Error-Correcting Codes*, Prentice-Hall, Englewood Cliffs, N.J.

Linkov, Yu. N. (1965), "Evaluation of ϵ-Entropy of Random Variables for Small ϵ," *Problems of Inform. Transmission*, vol. 1, pp. 12–18. (Trans. from *Problemy Peredachi Informatsii*, vol. 1, pp. 18–26.)

Lloyd, S. P. (1959), "Least Square Quantization in PCM," unpublished Bell Telephone Lab. memo, Murray Hill, N.J.

Lucky, R. W., J. Salz, and E. J. Weldon (1968), *Principles of Data Communication*, McGraw-Hill, New York.

Mackechnie, L. K. (1973), "Maximum-Likelihood Receivers for Channels Having Memory," Ph.D. Dissertation, University of Notre Dame, Indiana.

Martin, D. R. (1976), "Robust Source Coding of Finite Alphabet Sources via Composition Classes," Ph.D. Dissertation, University of California, Los Angeles.

Massey, J. L. (1974), "Error Bounds for Tree Codes, Trellis Codes, and Convolutional Codes with Encoding and Decoding Procedures," Lectures presented at the Summer School on "Coding and Complexity," Centre International des Sciences Mechaniques, Udine, Italy. (Notes published by Springer-Verlag.)

Massey, J. L. (1973), "Coding Techniques for Digital Communications," tutorial course notes, 1973 International Conference on Communications.

Massey, J. L. (1972), "Variable-Length Codes and the Fano Metric," *IEEE Trans. Inform. Theor.*, vol. IT-18, pp. 196–198.

Massey, J. L. (1963), *Threshold Decoding*, MIT Press, Cambridge, Mass.

Massey, J. L., and M. K. Sain (1968), "Inverses of Linear Sequential Circuits," *IEEE Trans. Computers*, vol. C-17, pp. 330–337.

Max, J. (1960), "Quantizing for Minimum Distortion," *IRE Trans. Inform. Theor.*, vol. IT-6, pp. 7–12.

McEliece, R. J., and J. K. Omura, (1977), "An Improved Upper Bound on the Block Coding Error Exponent for Binary-Input Discrete Memoryless Channels," *IEEE Trans. Inform. Theor.*, vol. IT-23, pp. 611–613.

McEliece, R. J., E. R. Rodemich, H. Rumsey, and L. R. Welch (1977), "New Upper Bounds on the Rate of a Code via the Delsarte-MacWilliams Inequalities," *IEEE Trans. Inform. Theor.*, vol. IT-23, pp. 157–166.

McMillan, B. (1956), "Two Inequalities Implied by Unique Decipherability," *IRE Trans. Inform. Theor.*, vol. IT-2, pp. 115–116.

McMillan, B. (1953), "The Basic Theorems of Information Theory," *Ann. Math. Stat.*, vol. 24, pp. 196–219.

Morrissey, T. N., Jr. (1970), "Analysis of Decoders for Convolutional Codes by Stochastic Sequential Machine Methods," *IEEE Trans. Inform. Theor.*, vol. IT-16, pp. 460–469.

Neyman, J., and E. Pearson, (1928), "On the Use and Interpretation of Certain Test Criteria for Purposes of Statistical Inference," *Biometrika*, vol. 20A, pp. 175–240, 263–294.

Odenwalder, J. P. (1970), "Optimal Decoding of Convolutional Codes," Ph.D. Dissertation, University of California, Los Angeles.

Omura, J. K. (1975), "A Lower Bounding Method for Channel and Source Coding Probabilities," *Inform. Cont.*, vol. 27, pp. 148–177.

Omura, J. K. (1973), "A Coding Theorem for Discrete-Time Sources," *IEEE Trans. Inform. Theor.*, vol. IT-19, pp. 490–498.

Omura, J. K. (1971), "Optimal Receiver Design for Convolutional Codes and Channels with Memory via Control Theoretical Concepts," *Inform. Sci.*, vol. 3, pp. 243–266.

Omura, J. K. (1969), "On the Viterbi Decoding Algorithm," *IEEE Trans. Inform. Theor.*, vol. IT-15, pp. 177–179.

Oppenheim, A. V., and R. W. Schafer (1975), *Digital Signal Processing*, Prentice-Hall, Englewood Cliffs, N.J.

Peterson, W. W. (1961), *Error-Correcting Codes*, MIT Press, Cambridge, Mass.

Peterson, W. W., and E. J. Weldon (1972), *Error-Correcting Codes*, 2d ed., MIT Press, Cambridge, Mass.

Pilc, R. (1968), "The Transmission Distortion of a Source as a Function of the Encoding Block Length," *Bell Syst. Tech. J.*, vol. 47, pp. 827–885.

Pinkston, J. T. (1966), "Information Rates of Independent Sample Sources," M.S. Thesis, MIT, Cambridge, Mass.

Plotkin, M. (1960), "Binary Codes with Specified Minimum Distance," *IRE Trans. Inform. Theor.*, vol. IT-6, pp. 445–450, originally Res. Div. Rep. 51-20, Univ. of Penn. (1951).

Ramsey, J. L. (1970), "Realization of Optimum Interleavers," *IEEE Trans. Inform. Theor.*, vol. IT-16, pp. 338–345.

Reiffen, B. (1960), "Sequential Encoding and Decoding for the Discrete Memoryless Channel," MIT Research Lab. of Electronics Tech. Rept. 374.

Rohlin, V. A. (1967), "Lectures on the Entropy Theory of Measure-Preserving Transformations," *Russ. Math. Surv.*, vol. 22, no. 5, pp. 1–52.

Rosenberg, W. J. (1971), "Structural Properties of Convolutional Codes," Ph.D. Dissertation, University of California, Los Angeles.

Rubin, I. (1973), "Information Rates for Poisson Sequences," *IEEE Trans. Inform. Theor.*, vol. IT-19, pp. 283–294.

Sakrison, D. J. (1975), "Worst Sources and Robust Codes for Difference Distortion Measure," *IEEE Trans. Inform. Theor.*, vol. IT-21, pp. 301–309.

Sakrison, D. J. (1969), "An Extension of the Theorem of Kac, Murdock, and Szego to N Dimensions," *IEEE Trans. Inform. Theor.*, vol. IT-15, pp. 608–610.

Sakrison, D. J., and V. R. Algazi (1971), "Comparison of Line-by-Line and Two Dimensional Encoding of Random Images," *IEEE Trans. Inform. Theor.*, vol. IT-17, pp. 386–398.

Savage, J. E. (1966), "Sequential Decoding—the Computation Problem," *Bell Syst. Tech. J.*, vol. 45, pp. 149–176.

Shannon, C. E. (1959), "Coding Theorems for a Discrete Source with a Fidelity Criterion," *IRE Nat. Conv. Rec.*, pt. 4, pp. 142–163. Also in R. E. Machol (ed.), *Information and Decision Processes*, McGraw-Hill, New York, 1960.

Shannon, C. E. (1948), "A Mathematical Theory of Communication," *Bell System Tech. J.*, vol. 27, (pt. I), pp. 379–423 (pt. II), pp. 623–656. Reprinted in book form with postscript by W. Weaver, Univ. of Illinois Press, Urbana, 1949.

Shannon, C. E., R. G. Gallager, and E. R. Berlekamp (1967), "Lower Bounds to Error Probability for Coding on Discrete Memoryless Channels," *Inform. Contr.*, vol. 10, pt. I, pp. 65–103, pt. II, pp. 522–552.

Slepian, D., and H. O. Pollak (1961), "Prolate Spheroidal Wave Functions, Fourier Analysis, and Uncertainty-I," *Bell System Tech. J.*, vol. 40, pp. 43–64. (See Landau and Pollak [1961, 1962] for Parts II and III.)

Stiglitz, I. G. (1966), "Coding for a Class of Unknown Channels," *IEEE Trans. Inform. Theor.*, vol. IT-12, pp. 189–195.

Tan, H. (1975), "Block Coding for Stationary Gaussian Sources with Memory under a Squared-Error Fidelity Criterion," *Inform. Contr.*, vol. 29, pp. 11–28.

Tan, H., and K. Yao (1975), "Evaluation of Rate Distortion Functions for a Class of Independent Identically Distributed Sources under an Absolute Magnitude Criterion," *IEEE Trans. Inform. Theor.*, vol. IT-21, pp. 59–63.

Van Lint, J. (1971), *Coding Theory, Lecture Notes in Mathematics*, Springer-Verlag, Berlin.

Van de Meeberg, L. (1974), "A Tightened Upper Bound on the Error Probability of Binary Convolutional Codes with Viterbi Decoding," *IEEE Trans. Inform. Theor.*, vol. IT-20, pp. 389–391.

Van Ness, F. L., and M. A. Bouman (1965), "The Effects of Wavelength and Luminance on Visual Modulation Transfer," *Excerpta Medica Int. Congr.*, ser. 125, pp. 183–192.

Van Trees, H. L. (1968), *Detection, Estimation, and Modulation Theory, Part I*, Wiley, New York.

Varsharmov, R. R. (1957), "Estimate of the Number of Signals in Error Correcting Codes," *Dokl. Akad. Nauk, SSSR* 117, no. 5, pp. 739–741.

Viterbi, A. J. (1971), "Convolutional Codes and Their Performance in Communication Systems," *IEEE Trans. Commun. Tech.*, vol. COM-19, pp. 751–772.

Viterbi, A. J. (1967*a*), "Error Bounds for Convolutional Codes and an Asymptotically Optimum Decoding Algorithm," *IEEE Trans. Inform. Theor.*, vol. IT-13, pp. 260–269.

Viterbi, A. J. (1967*b*), "Orthogonal Tree Codes for Communication in the Presence of White Gaussian Noise," *IEEE Trans. Commun. Tech.*, vol. COM-15, pp. 238–242.

Viterbi, A. J. (1967*c*), "Performance of an M-ary Orthogonal Communication System Using Stationary Stochastic Signals," *IEEE Trans. Inform. Theor.*, vol. IT-13, pp. 414–422.

Viterbi, A. J. (1966), *Principles of Coherent Communication*, McGraw-Hill, New York.

Viterbi, A. J., and I. M. Jacobs (1975), "Advances in Coding and Modulation for Noncoherent Channels Affected by Fading, Partial Band, and Multiple-Access Interference," in A. J. Viterbi (ed.), *Advances in Communication Systems*, vol. 4, Academic, New York, pp. 279–308.

Viterbi, A. J., and J. P. Odenwalder (1969), "Further Results on Optimum Decoding of Convolutional Codes," *IEEE Trans. Inform. Theor.*, vol. IT-15, pp. 732–734.

Viterbi, A. J., and J. K. Omura (1974), "Trellis Encoding of Memoryless Discrete-Time Sources with a Fidelity Criterion," *IEEE Trans. Inform. Theor.*, vol. IT-20, pp. 325–331.

Wolfowitz, J. (1961), *Coding Theorems of Information Theory*, 2d ed., Springer-Verlag and Prentice-Hall, Englewood Cliffs, N.J.

Wolfowitz, J. (1957), "The Coding of Messages Subject to Chance Errors," *Ill. J. of Math.*, vol. 1, pp. 591–606.

Wozencraft, J. M. (1957), "Sequential Decoding for Reliable Communication," *IRE Nat. Conv. Rec.*, vol. 5, pt. 2, pp. 11–25.

Wozencraft, J. M., and I. M. Jacobs (1965), *Principles of Communication Engineering*, Wiley, New York.

Yudkin, H. L. (1964), "Channel State Testing in Information Decoding," Sc.D. Thesis, MIT, Cambridge, Mass.

Zigangirov, K. Sh. (1966), "Some Sequential Decoding Procedures," *Problemy Peredachi Informatsii*, vol. 2, pp. 13–25.

Ziv, J. (1972), "Coding of Sources with Unknown Statistics," *IEEE Trans. Inform. Theor.*, vol. IT-18, pp. 384–394.

INDEX